D1401346

STRUCTURE AND CHANGE

# Structure and Change

## An Introduction to the Science of Matter

G. S. CHRISTIANSEN

PAUL H. GARRETT

*Connecticut College*

Drawings by EVAN L. GILLESPIE

W. H. FREEMAN & COMPANY

*San Francisco and London   1960*

The authors gratefully acknowledge receiving, from the Carnegie Corporation of New York, a grant that assisted in the original planning of the course on which this text is based.

PREFACE

THE PURPOSE of this book is to introduce the student to the scientific view of the physical world. The subject matter includes our entire material environment. In the development of this huge subject the student will be presented with large amounts of information, much of it entirely new, almost all of it in new contexts and with new interpretations. Such accumulation of information by the student is a valuable by-product of the study of science, but it is only a by-product. The most important lesson to be derived from the study of science is an understanding of science itself—first, the realization that science is an intellectual method of prodigious power; second, so far as possible, the acquisition of ease in the use of this method.

The physical products of science are obviously dominating our social and economic culture. It is less obvious but equally true that the intellectual accomplishments of science are having profound effects on our intellectual culture. The scientific method, one of the greatest achievements and probably the most powerful intellectual tool of mankind, has proved remarkably effective in solving the problems of our physical and biological universes. Through its use we have acquired a very considerable knowledge, and through this knowledge we are now able partially to control vast parts of our environment. The extreme power of this method has begun to have its effect on the social sciences, on philosophy, and on other areas within the humanities. But that effect is still slight—man is still more at home among the atoms and the stars than among his fellow men.

Science is almost unique among the intellectual disciplines in that it is thoroughly based on experience. The information that leads us to propose generalizations and the testing of the usefulness of those generalizations both come from experiments. Science is thus a self-correcting system: though it makes mistakes, it is capable of discovering its own mistakes, correcting them, and preventing their recurrence. Because of this importance of the experimental aspect of science, the ideas included in this text are closely and directly related to laboratory experiments.

Physical science includes many separate branches: physics, chemistry, astronomy, geology, mineralogy, meteorology, and others. It would be impossible, in a single book, to convey adequately even parts of all these sciences. Even the barest simple information offered by physical science is far beyond the capacity of a single book. To avoid the common faults of the "survey" course—shallowness, triviality, and looseness—we have limited the scope of this book to a single major theme, the structure of matter. This theme, approached from "where the student now stands" (that is, from the casual, common-sense information and ideas of a partially educated non-scientist), is developed with constantly increasing completeness and complexity until we reach the modern quantum-mechanical and relativistic view of the structure of matter.

In developing our theme, we use all the ideas that contribute to it regardless of their position in the classical subdivisions of science. Although most of the ideas and information used are part of conventional elementary chemistry and physics courses, not all of either conventional course is included: much of descriptive chemistry and the parts of introductory physics that do not contribute directly to our understanding of the structure of matter have been excluded. Nevertheless, a student who masters the material of this text is prepared to continue study at more advanced levels in either chemistry or physics.

Most students will probably find that the material included in this text can be supplemented to advantage by outside reading. There is, of course, much very good material that deals with the subjects treated here, and the student is encouraged to seek it out and use it. In doing so, however, he will probably find the following comments to be useful as a guide. (1) Most textbooks of physical science are too limited in their treatment of any particular subject to be of much value. Some of them, however, as well as histories of physics and chemistry, will amplify the very brief historical comments made here and will establish individuals and developments in their historical settings. (2) Certain "science for the layman" books, in isolated passages, will supplement certain parts of this text. (3) Many textbooks of introductory chemistry and physics include detailed and rigorous treatments of most of the ideas used in this book. In the use of such books, however, the student should be particularly cautious. Since the order of presentation in them is generally quite different from that used here, there is a danger of confusion from the use of concepts not yet studied. Furthermore, many of the conventional courses in science are designed as strictly professional training, and their textbooks therefore use the categorical approach to the learning of science. Such an approach is antithetical to that of this book, and the student must be alert to recognize the unjustified assumptions and the too pat explanations. As a final caution in the use of such textbooks, the student is warned that many conventions of science, including abbreviations, symbols, terminology, units, and standards, are not universal. The conventions used in this book are widely accepted and are consistent. The student must be wary of the confusion that could arise from a misunderstood set of conventions. (4) One book that will be of inestimable value as an outside source of information is a good dictionary.

Acquiring knowledge of the structure of matter is an exciting and absorbing experience. But to find out how scientific knowledge is created is not only interesting; it is participation in one of man's greatest intellectual adventures. An open mind, some tough thinking, and a fair share of hard work are the sufficient requirements for participation in this adventure.

*January 1960*                    G. S. CHRISTIANSEN
                                  PAUL H. GARRETT

TABLE OF CONTENTS

PART TWO

*The Electrical View
of the Physical World*

CHAPTER 16

**Electricity and Magnetism:
Fundamental Effects**

CHAPTER 17

**Electric and Magnetic Fields:
Quantitative Relations**

CHAPTER 18

**Atomic Theory (II): The Electron**

CHAPTER 19

**Ionic Theory**

# LIST OF SYMBOLS AND ABBREVIATIONS

| | |
|---|---|
| $a$ | acceleration |
| A | angstrom |
| $A$ | area; isotopic mass number |
| amp | ampere |
| at wt | atomic weight |
| $B$ | magnetic induction |
| Bev | billion electron volts |
| $c$ | velocity of light; concentration |
| C | centigrade |
| $C$ | Coulomb's law constant |
| cal | calorie |
| cm | centimeter |
| coul | coulomb |
| $d$ | density |
| $e$ | electronic charge |
| $E$ | intensity of electric field |
| $\varepsilon$ | energy |
| ev | electron volt |
| $F$ | force |
| $\mathcal{F}$ | faraday |
| $g$ | acceleration due to gravity |
| $G$ | gravitational constant; conductance |
| $h$ | Planck's constant; height |
| $H$ | heat |
| $I$ | electric current |
| $J$ | mechanical equivalent of heat |
| $k$ | Boltzmann's constant; rate constant |
| $k_B$ | molal-boiling-point-elevation constant |
| $k_F$ | molal-freezing-point-depression constant |
| K | Kelvin (absolute) temperature |
| $K$ | proportionality constant |
| $K_{equ}$ | equilibrium constant |
| $K_p$ | equilibrium constant expressed in partial pressures |
| $K_{sp}$ | solubility-product constant |
| $K_w$ | ion-product constant for water |
| KE | kinetic energy |
| kgm | kilogram |
| $l$ | length; shape quantum number |
| $L$ | length; heat of fusion; heat of vaporization |

| m | meter |
| $m$ | mass |
| $m_l$ | space quantum number |
| $m_s$ | spin quantum number |
| M | molar concentration |
| $M$ | momentum |
| Mev | million electron volts |
| mol wt | molecular weight |
| $n$ | number of moles; principal quantum number |
| $n_0$ | number of molecules per $cm^3$ |
| $N$ | number of molecules in an arbitrary sample |
| $N_0$ | Avogadro's number |
| $P$ | pressure |
| PE | potential energy |
| $q$ | quantity of electric charge |
| $Q$ | quantity of electric charge; net mass-energy exchange in nuclear reactions |
| $r$ | radius |
| $R$ | universal gas constant |
| $\mathcal{R}$ | Rydberg constant |
| rms | root-mean-square |
| $s$ | distance |
| $S$ | specific heat |
| sec | second |
| $t$ | centigrade temperature; time |
| $T$ | absolute (Kelvin) temperature; period of revolution; half-life |
| $v$ | velocity |
| $V$ | electric potential difference; volume |
| $w$ | weight |
| $W$ | work; energy |
| $X$ | mole fraction |
| $Z$ | atomic number |
| $\alpha$ | degree of dissociation |
| $\Delta$ | change in |
| $\epsilon$ | energy of a photon |
| $\lambda$ | wavelength |
| $\nu$ | frequency |
| $\pi$ | osmotic pressure |

# CHAPTER 1

# Introduction: The Language and Problems of Science

NEITHER physics nor chemistry has meaning independent of the other. The development of the two sciences, now as in the past, exhibits their complete interdependence. The great theories of one are also great theories of the other; the methods of one are closely similar to the methods of the other; the informational parts of one are crucial to the development of the other; and even the practitioners of the two sciences are mostly interchangeable. The prominent figures in such current developments as atomic energy and rocket research can be classified only with the greatest difficulty. The great physicists of the nineteenth century were also the great chemists. Michael Faraday, after whom two major electrical quantities were named and who stands among the great physicists of history, was a chemist of equal note. His experimental interests ranged over the breadth of science from electricity to biochemistry.

These two classical subdivisions of science, physics and chemistry, strive for the same goal: an understanding of the substantial universe. They differ only in point of view. One of the major purposes of this book is to break down the arbitrary separation of the two sciences and to approach the understanding of matter from any points of view that contribute to our knowledge, regardless of the classical boundaries of the sciences.

In this introductory chapter we hope to forge some of the basic tools that will be used throughout the text. These tools are, of course, intellectual ones; they are methods of thinking and problem-solving, systems of special symbols, definitions, special qualities of language, mathematical operations, etc. To read a long chapter of such material, which is often difficult, uninteresting, and apparently sterile, is a task that some students will refuse to carry out. At this stage, however, some effort is necessary. The task can be compared to the dull and irritating one of learning simple vocabulary and rules of grammar as a necessary first step toward the enjoyment of the literature of a foreign language. This chapter includes only the minimum of such material, without which it is impossible to communicate. It should be read once and then used for reference as the study of the text progresses.

The student should also read Appendix I, an introduction to mathematical methods that will be used constantly in the study of this book.

Before undertaking the chore of acquiring the rudiments of the language of science, we should examine the scope of the problem before us. Toward the end of this book, the contemporary view of the structure of matter is presented. This view is magnificently complex, full of subtleties and holding the promise of continuing puzzles. But such a grand concept did not spring full-blown from the forebrain of a brilliant twentieth-century physicist. It is a laboriously constructed system, built by the painstaking work of many people on the surviving fragments of wrecks of many generations of previous theories. And the fate of this beautiful intellectual construction, with all its perfectly fitted interlocking parts, its graceful embellishments, and its pillars of empirical foundation, is already sealed: it will be destroyed. It will probably never be entirely swept aside, but it will certainly be dismantled and replaced. It will be pulled apart and shored up, modified and adapted; pieces will be re-used, and some major parts will be discarded as faulty. From the rubble will be built an even more imposing theoretical edifice—this is the nature of progress in science.

The beginning student must therefore pick around a good deal among the ruins of scientific development, occasionally rebuilding almost completely a structure that has long since been abandoned, often examining a theory that will be displaced by a more acceptable one, and certainly studying the solid experimental generalizations on which all of these theories, the fossils as well as the living theories, are based. In this way only can a student grasp the nature of the evolution of science, or judge why a theory that was effective for a hundred years may eventually be found faulty and may therefore be abandoned. This approach is necessary even for adequate understanding of the meaning and value of current theories. It is also in this way that a student grasps the meaning of the pessimistic prediction that the "modern science" we study today will be little more than a ruin of displaced and inadequate theories a few generations hence.

## 1-1. Problems of Physical Science

The science of matter is the study of our substantial environment. Earth, air, water, and the things that exist in them; the nature of these things; their relative amounts; their form and their influence on each other; all these make up the science of matter. These topics have been the subject of speculation and investigation since the earliest records. In the course of this history the questions and problems, as well as the methods of solving them, have become clearer and better defined. The methods of study have varied and evolved throughout this history, but the broad problems have remained the same. To know about the materials around us, we must know the form and composition of the various kinds of matter, their amounts, their interactions with other kinds, and their properties.

FORM AND COMPOSITION. Perhaps the most obvious necessity in the description of an object (a sample of matter in general) is a statement of its form. Is it a smooth sphere, an irregularly shaped piece, a homogeneous liquid, a red gas, a heterogeneous aggregate, a pile of heavy granules? Is it a complex sample of matter, including several different kinds, or is it a pure sample of one entity? If we recognize complex kinds of matter, what is the criterion of elemental matter (the parts that make up complex matter)? How many different forms of elemental matter are there? How can these be combined to form complex matter, and how can they be separated? Can one elemental form be changed to another? How are complex forms changed? Is there an underlying structure of matter, elemental or complex? If so, what is this structure and how is it related to the grossly observable nature of matter? These few simple questions arise immediately when one begins to consider the form and composition of matter. Such questioning can go on without limit, each question answered raising several new ones, of increasing subtlety and increasingly difficult to investigate.

AMOUNT. Any description of a sample of matter must include the notion of amount. The sample may be a large object or a small one, heavy or light, long or short, etc. Complex forms of matter may include greater or lesser relative amounts of the various components. We have here introduced the idea of quantitative measurement, an essential part of every bit of the subsequent discussion in this text. Each comparison mentioned must be treated quantitatively, and the treatment must include a **number** and a **unit.** The details of the use of quantitative statements and quantitative notation will be taken up in later chapters and in the appendixes. At this point we shall concentrate on the units of amount of matter. In the comparison "heavy or light" is included the concept of **mass.** A heavy, or *massive,* object has a large mass; a light object has a smaller mass. In our general vocabulary the term "weight" implies the same quality in a less exact way.

Another way of stating amount of matter is by **volume,** which is the space occupied by a sample of the material. These two concepts, mass and space, pervade all of physical science on several levels of abstraction. Their use in expressing amount of material is the basis of all quantitative work in science. A somewhat subtler mathematical combination of the two terms creates a new, derived quantity, which also expresses the amount of matter. The *ratio of mass to volume is called the* **density,** which is the degree of compactness of the particular type of matter—a statement of how much of it can be packed into a given space. Density is a characteristic property of each substance, and its magnitude offers much information as to how the elementary particles, the atoms, of the substance are put together.

INTERACTIONS. A still subtler examination of the relation between space and mass, and of the relation between these and the third fundamental quantity of science, *time,* poses a vast number of new problems, which can be classified loosely as *interactions* of matter. **Motion** is clearly the commonest and most readily observed of these interactions. A definition of motion would be "change in the spatial relations of two objects." The magnitude of this motion involves both the amount of mass and the amount of space. When the time element—how long this change of position takes—is included, a new set of mechanical quantities arises, including force, inertia, momentum, and energy. A careful study of these concepts in the sub-science called **mechanics** shows us, in fact, that the only way we can sense mass itself, the first fundamental quantity we considered, is by changes in its motion. And it is by just such change in motion that we detect the subtler interactions of matter in nature—those we call **gravity, electricity,** and **magnetism,** phenomena that are exhibited when two samples of matter take on a particular relation or series of relations in space and time.

We shall also see that the spectacular interactions of matter called **chemical reactions** are amenable to study in terms of the mass-space-time quantities of classical mechanics. Careful study will show, however, that a *purely* mechanical interpretation of the form and composition of matter is not enough, that this mechanical study must be expanded to include refined concepts, not only of electricity and magnetism, but of even more remarkable interactions of matter.

PROPERTIES OF MATTER. The total description of matter—or of anything else—is a statement of all of its characteristic qualities, or **properties.** These properties of matter are simply statements of what is known about the three categories outlined above: the form and composition, the amount or relative amount or some variation of this, and the characteristics of interaction in given situations. We might describe a substance by stating that it has a density of 13.6 grams per cubic centimeter (amount per volume); is a silvery liquid (form); conducts electricity but is not attracted by a magnet (interaction); will react with the oxygen of the air at high temperatures (interaction); and can be made by the decomposition of the mineral cinnabar (form and interaction). Many, many other properties might be listed, but these are more than enough to identify this substance as the element mercury. The description of matter—any sample of matter or matter in general—does require this cataloguing and classification of properties. But, obviously, if there were nothing more than a long list of characteristic qualities, the science of matter would be much less than a science; it would be a sterile and worthless thing indeed. The essence of science is not this information; it is the system that can be constructed by the proper organization of the information.

## 1-2. Structure of Scientific Knowledge

Science is a system of knowledge, the structural elements of which are the informational facts gathered by observation and experiment. The form of science is established by the organization of these facts into systems, generalizations, and theories. Without this organization the information is as low in the scale of meaning as a dictionary or a shopping list.

Probably the first step in the organization of knowledge beyond simple bare observation is the process of **classification.** Although there are limits on the usefulness of classification, the sorting of observations into categories is a necessary and often very effective first step in establishing the patterns and systems of knowledge that lead to understanding. The compiling of vast taxonomies of botany and zoology during the eighteenth and nineteenth centuries is a good example of classification in science. These taxonomic manuals are still crucial to the proper study of physiology and biochemistry; a hundred years ago they adequately summarized the knowledge of the species; but they do not contain an understanding of plants and animals—one cannot learn botany by reading Gray's manual just as one cannot learn literature by reading Webster's dictionary.

This taxonomic phase of science is essentially descriptive and qualitative. But the qualitative description of anything is quite incomplete without quantitative measurements. One does not know the quality of something when it is described as long or short, large or small, much or little; it is necessary to know *how* long, *how* large, and *how* much.

Modern physical science is characterized by its great dependence on experiments. This im-

plies a probing beyond the stage of simple, passive observation—the search for new facts by manipulation of matter and its immediate environment. Our knowledge of the interactions of matter, mentioned in the previous section of this chapter, depends almost entirely on the use of the **experimental method.** Probably the greatest single difference between ancient science and modern science (and the dividing point is really quite recent, about three hundred years ago) is our systematic use of experimental investigation of natural problems as an adjunct to observation and speculation. The tremendous advances in our understanding of the physical universe that have taken place during the last three centuries parallel almost exactly the increasing use of this investigational approach.

Still, experiments as well as passive observation supply nothing more than cold lifeless facts. It is the subsequent stages of the growth of science that make it the powerful, dynamic social force that it is in our culture. The first stage of this intellectual creation of science is the statement of experimental or factual generalizations. These generalizations are usually called **scientific laws** and take the form of succinct summaries of factual information. This evening you may make the observation that the moon and several stars rise over the eastern horizon and pass across the sky; and, if you stay up long enough, you may see these same objects disappear over the western horizon. Tomorrow you may observe the sun traveling a similar course. Many other people have made these observations, and, so far as the records show, no one has observed a reversal of or major deviation from this behavior. These many isolated observations can be summarized in an elementary "law of motion of heavenly bodies." The law would be that all such objects travel in a westerly direction across the heavens. This law, as stated, is trivial. We shall see in subsequent chapters that more careful observation gives rise to much more subtle, sophisticated, and complex generalizations—laws of planetary motion, etc. We shall also see that, in general, limitless numbers of observational and experimental facts can be summarized by such laws and generalizations, and that these generalizations serve an extremely important function by reducing the information of science to wieldy terms.

The obvious next step in system-formation is a search for an "explanation" of the generalized behavior that we have formulated into a law. This is an intellectual, non-experimental function. We advance a **postulate,** which most often takes the form of a model. And if we are scientific about this stage, we maintain an attitude of skepticism and a feeling of tentativeness about this postulate. When we are not critical about our postulates and allow them to become rigid, we have ceased to be scientists and have become dogmatic zealots. Such rigid postulates serve no purpose in our attempt to understand nature; on the contrary, they make understanding impossible.

Several postulates have been put forward to explain our simple law of motion of heavenly bodies. It has been suggested, for example, that the sun is a golden chariot driven by Apollo, one of the gods, across the highway of the sky once each day, and that the moon is a silver boat that sails across the sky. Another postulate is that these bodies, as well as the stars and planets, form a complex network of lights, which rotates round a fixed earth. A third postulate is that this network of heavenly lights is actually fixed and that the apparent motion is due to the rotation of the earth on its axis. Now, in fact, none of these postulates is entirely true in the scientific sense; that is, the predicted behavior of the model does not correspond exactly with all of the detailed observations. Some are more nearly true than others; some have been abandoned entirely because it was not possible to reconcile the postulate with new experimental and observational facts; one has survived in part and, with considerable modification and extension, has been fitted into the currently accepted (though not absolutely accepted) scientific **theory** of the structure of the astronomical universe.

The distinction between the initial, tentatively advanced postulate and the accepted, established theory is not clear-cut. It has more to do with the length of time the idea has been around, its scope or inclusiveness, and its popularity than with any criterion of truth. The important point

of this discussion is that all postulates of science, tentative as well as broad and apparently firmly established theories, are constantly evolving, suffering modifications, additions, deletions, and sometimes total destruction. The moving force of this change is the constant test of experiment. Theories must be measured against facts; when inconsistent facts arise, the theory becomes weakened or modified and is liable to displacement by theories that *are* consistent with the facts of experiment and observation.

## 1-3. *Grand Principles of Science*

Out of the collection of information and the evolution of theories have arisen several great principles that are almost articles of faith with scientists. The first and broadest of these might be called the concept of **the lawfulness of nature.** Included in this concept is the basis for the experimental approach to natural problems. Any effort to synthesize experimental facts into conceptual systems, even the simple investigation of natural problems, demands a firm belief in this notion. It is simply a statement of the faith of the scientist that an observation can be repeated by the same or a different investigator with assurance that the same results will be obtained. It is a belief that the results of experiment and observation are indeed *facts*. But there are other, more significant implications of this belief in the lawfulness of nature. One of these is the **law of causality,** which asserts that a particular situation or series of events *always* results in a unique effect, that effects are not capricious but have their source in a definable situation, which causes them. Another of the subtler implications of this concept is the belief that there is a system of orderliness in nature, and that this underlying system, which "explains" the facts of science, is characterized by simplicity and symmetry. It is this ingrained faith of scientific man that causes him to prefer a postulate of celestial mechanics to the postulate of a golden chariot as an explanation of the observed regular motion of the sun with respect to the earth. It is characteristic of all of the more effective theories of science that they are beautifully simple and uncomplicated in their essence. This is not to say that there are no complications in the study of science; science is indeed complex, and current theories are more complex than those of a century or three centuries or twenty centuries ago. But the progress has always been toward greater inclusiveness and less complexity. Modern science is a complicated study because its scope is very great; celestial mechanics is more complicated than the Apollo legend because it encompasses more. It is a cardinal tenet of modern science that, whenever there is a choice, the simpler explanation is always preferred.

A second large principle, which has powerfully affected much of scientific thinking, has to do with the dichotomy of a continuous or discontinuous quality of nature. There is a strong tendency, which increases with the evolution of the science, toward the **concept of the ultimately small unit.** In biology the ultimate unit of living material is the single cell. If a tissue is reduced to dimensions less than those of a single cell, it is no longer living. The acceptance of this concept of a discontinuous quality has evolved quite slowly in physical science, but in the three major cases where it has been accepted the effect has been a new burst of striking progress. At the beginning of the nineteenth century the atomic theory was established. In essence this theory is simply the notion of ultimately small particles of *substance* called **atoms,** which are the smallest possible subdivision of each particular type of matter. About half a century later the concept of the ultimate unit of *electricity,* the **electron,** was established. At the beginning of this century the idea emerged that *energy* also occurs not continuously but in discrete bundles. These ultimate units of energy are called **quanta** (singular, quantum), and the associated theory is called the **quantum theory.** A major part of the adventure in science presented in this text has to do with the development of the logical necessity of accepting these concepts and with the evolution of the ideas that emerged from them.

A third major principle of physical science is the concept of **conservation.** As the title of this book implies, the study of *change* is at the heart of the study of matter. But it is characteristic of all such change that it takes place without the gain or loss of any of the quantities being changed. Chemicals neutralize each other, but no substance is destroyed. Positive charges neutralize negative ones but never with the *destruction* or *creation* of charges. Forces may cancel each other, but there is always conservation of energy. Motion may be changed, but momentum is conserved. Each of these has been stated as a law of science, and the group is known as the conservation laws. Again, these concepts were not apparent in the beginning of science but evolved only slowly. When they were finally established, in each case a great new sweep of understanding resulted. These conservation laws are still evolving, and new vistas of science are being opened up by this evolution. The whole development of atomic energy hinges on the merging of the law of conservation of mass and the law of conservation of energy into a new conservation law—that of the **conservation of mass-energy.**

The last of the great principles of science to be presented in this introductory chapter is the concept of **equilibrium.** Throughout the study of matter and its interaction runs a thread of checks and balances. A process or reaction takes place, an influence is exerted, or a transformation begins. But usually these events are not free and uncontrolled. Often the process, influence, or transformation itself sets in motion counteracting effects that tend to reverse the initial change or produce its opposite. These situations are described by the term *equilibrium,* which means simply "equal balance." The study of equilibrium offers an excellent example of the great power of the scientific method, in which a starkly simple concept becomes a most powerful analytical tool for the solving of many types of problems, not only in science but in any situation involving dynamic interactions.

## 1-4. Background of Modern Science

We have taken several paragraphs to sketch very briefly and in general terms the problems that must be faced by a student of the science of matter, and we have commented on some of the broad concepts through which we approach these problems. We have also taken a very brief look at the form that scientific knowledge has taken. Throughout this discussion, the evolutionary nature of the problems and concepts and form has been emphasized. Science has a most interesting and exciting history, the story of the evolution of a remarkable intellectual system. This text makes no attempt to present this history or to relate the development of science to political or other cultural developments. Most of its subject matter, moreover, is quite modern in its origins. But it would probably serve a useful purpose to outline the historical evolution of the generalities that are the subject of this introductory chapter.

The origins of science, as of most other parts of our Western culture, are found in the civilization of Greece. The Greeks considered most of the broad problems outlined above, but they put much more emphasis on the question of form than on interactions. Several theories of the elementary nature of substance were advanced, all postulating a few elements, such as earth, air, fire, and water, plus something called the "quintessence." The Greeks also proposed a rudimentary theory of atoms, the ultimately small particles of substance. Their view of the mechanics of motion was largely governed by the concept of "natural motions": heavy objects move downward, air moves upward, circular motion is more fitting than linear, etc. But most of these ideas of the Greeks were not truly scientific by the standards of science as we know it today. These concepts were entirely the result of speculation; observation and experiment were invoked only casually and were rarely used to test a postulate. The Greek test of theories was based on purely intellectual considerations, which generally involved intensely egocentric notions of *purpose*. The purpose of nature was Man, and all theories were measured by this concept. The experimental method, most of the underlying principles of modern science, and the self-critical approach were lacking.

During the Middle Ages the ideas of the Greeks were in part preserved (but usually in a rigid form that discouraged development), in part perverted, and in large part lost or ignored. An activity called *alchemy* originated in north-ern Africa and spread through Europe. The alchemists were not true scientists but were primarily magicians or mystics. They did, however, perform the useful function of collecting information, and they did experiments. Their great lack was a synthesis of experimental information into unifying concepts. They were further hampered, even in the records of their experiments, by a prevailing tendency toward secrecy and obscurantism. In the fifteenth century, however, the alchemists were strongly influenced by the practitioners of the "useful arts" of healing and metallurgy. Alchemy thus became the forerunner of modern medicine and chemistry.

The beginning of modern science dates from the tremendous scientific revolution that took place between the middle of the sixteenth and the middle of the seventeenth century. The two major figures of this revolution were Galileo and Newton. Since the work of these two great men takes up a large part of the early chapters of this text, it is unnecessary to consider it in detail here.

The scientific revolution reached chemistry somewhat later. Newton had proposed an atomic theory as the explanation of chemical interactions, but it required another century, during which information was accumulated and an effective experimental approach was devised, to establish the study of chemical interaction on a rational basis. The man most instrumental in this development was a Frenchman, Antoine Laurent Lavoisier. Lavoisier established the necessity of precise quantitative measurements of the masses of substances involved in chemical reactions. From his work and from his influence on the experimentation of others, the laws of mass relations in chemical reactions were established about the end of the eighteenth century, and on those laws Dalton constructed the first experimentally based and comprehensive atomic theory of matter.

The theories established by Galileo, Newton, Lavoisier, and Dalton are the basis of almost all the development in physical science up to the beginning of the present century. We are right now in the midst—or perhaps only in the beginning—of a new scientific revolution at least as great as that of the sixteenth and seventeenth centuries. The theories of Newton and Dalton and their subsequent variations have been tested and examined by more and more searching experiments for many decades. And it has developed that these theories are lacking, that they are not entirely consistent with facts. It is not easy to decide who all the great revolutionaries of the current upheaval are, but certainly Albert Einstein, Max Planck, Ernest Rutherford, and Niels Bohr are among them. Part Three of this text is a discussion of this great modern scientific revolution, in which the hallowed theories of several centuries' standing are being undermined by exciting new experimental developments and displaced by even more exciting new theories. Now is indeed a wonderful time to be a student of physical science.

## 1-5. *Language of Science*

To begin our study of the science of matter, we must first consider some qualities of the language of science. We shall continue to use English in this text, but a rather peculiar kind of English. We will strive for a precision that is rarely achieved in ordinary usage but is necessary for the unambiguous communication of the facts and concepts of science. We will attempt to define carefully, in the language of ordinary usage, the new terms with which we are not already familiar. It is not always profitable, however, or even possible, to accomplish this definition in a single simple statement. Many of the terms we shall encounter represent concepts of considerable extent and require many paragraphs for a full explanation; others represent concepts so broad that they can be fully understood only after years of study. Still other terms are fundamental in the sense that it is not possible to define them in simpler terms. The word "matter" itself is one of these fundamental terms from which the meaning of other terms is derived.

Beginning with what we already know about matter, and without attempting a succinct, precise definition, we can state that matter is represented by the things around us: the material of the floor, chairs, tables, walls; water, earth,

air; plants, animals, our own bodies. Matter, in short, is the stuff of which all things are composed—our physical environment. This is, of course, a very vague and scientifically unsatisfactory statement of the meaning of this very important term. The unlimited variety of the material of our environment can be reduced to an understandable level only by being summarized in a scheme of classification. The central quality of the classification used in modern science is found in its hierarchy of complexity. Most of the examples of matter mentioned above are obviously complex: the grain structure of wood can easily be seen; concrete is clearly an aggregate of several types of matter; soil may easily be separated into components. Other types of matter are not so obviously heterogeneous.† Milk appears homogeneous‡ at first observation; but microscopic examination shows very fine fat droplets dispersed in a watery medium, and it is possible to separate these two constituents. A sample of sea water is homogeneous by any method of observation; it appears to contain *only one* substantial entity however closely it is scrutinized. The complexity of sea water is easily demonstrated, however, if we allow the water to evaporate: it leaves a crystalline residue of salt. The water evaporated or distilled from sea water may be condensed to a homogeneous liquid, which resembles the original sea water in its homogeneity but differs in other respects. The important difference is that it cannot be further separated into components by ordinary means. At first sight this seems to be a limit on the complexity of matter. By more drastic means, however, it is possible to separate water into two constituents. This separation of water into two gases, hydrogen and oxygen, is accomplished by *electrolysis,* a demonstration that is often seen in general-science courses. Not only is this separation more drastic than the separation of sea water into water and salt, but the original complex material cannot be reconstituted by the simple mixing of the two con-

---

† A heterogeneous material is composed of separate parts that show differences from one part to another.

‡ A homogeneous material is continuous throughout and shows no discontinuity of properties from one area to another.

stituents. A still more drastic process is involved in the recombination of hydrogen and oxygen to form water. We must therefore draw a distinction between the two types of complex matter characterized by these two types of separation.

Efforts to continue this subdivision of matter were totally unsuccessful for several centuries; only recently has the subdivision been carried further, and then only by extraordinarily drastic treatment. Furthermore, the products of this separation are made only in minute amounts; they exist separately only for exceedingly short periods of time; and they are not a usual part of our ordinary environment. In our classification of matter according to complexity we stop, then, at the level of separability exemplified by the separation of water into hydrogen and oxygen, and we say that these are *elemental substances* from which more complex forms of matter are constituted.

## 1-6. *Classification of Matter*

The first definition of elements in terms of separability was phrased by Robert Boyle in the middle of the seventeenth century. His definition is essentially similar to the modern meaning of this term: **An element is a substance that**

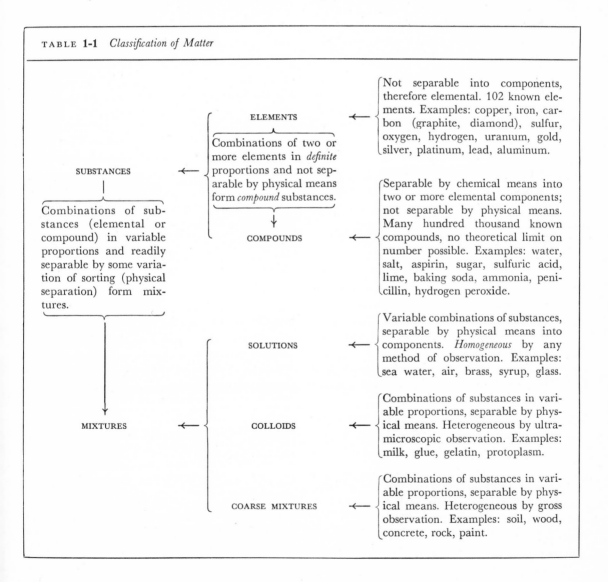

TABLE **1-1**  *Classification of Matter*

| | | |
|---|---|---|
| **ELEMENTS** | | Not separable into components, therefore elemental. 102 known elements. Examples: copper, iron, carbon (graphite, diamond), sulfur, oxygen, hydrogen, uranium, gold, silver, platinum, lead, aluminum. |
| **SUBSTANCES** Combinations of two or more elements in *definite* proportions and not separable by physical means form *compound* substances. | | |
| **COMPOUNDS** | | Separable by chemical means into two or more elemental components; not separable by physical means. Many hundred thousand known compounds, no theoretical limit on number possible. Examples: water, salt, aspirin, sugar, sulfuric acid, lime, baking soda, ammonia, penicillin, hydrogen peroxide. |
| Combinations of substances (elemental or compound) in variable proportions and readily separable by some variation of sorting (physical separation) form mixtures. | **SOLUTIONS** | Variable combinations of substances, separable by physical means into components. *Homogeneous* by any method of observation. Examples: sea water, air, brass, syrup, glass. |
| **MIXTURES** | **COLLOIDS** | Combinations of substances in variable proportions, separable by physical means. Heterogeneous by ultramicroscopic observation. Examples: milk, glue, gelatin, protoplasm. |
| | **COARSE MIXTURES** | Combinations of substances in variable proportions, separable by physical means. Heterogeneous by gross observation. Examples: soil, wood, concrete, rock, paint. |

**cannot be decomposed into simpler substances.** There are now (1959) 102 known elements, from which all the matter of our environment is constituted by various combination. The next higher order of complexity is a combination of two or more elements into a *compound substance,* or, simply, a *compound.* **A compound is a substance that has a fixed composition and is separable by chemical means into two or more elements.** More than half a million different compounds have now been isolated, characterized, and named, and all of these are made up of various combinations of two or more of the 102 elements. In this paragraph and in Table 1-1 the definition of the word "substance" has been made by implication. **A substance is a specific form of matter that is homogeneous and has a fixed composition.** Elements and compounds are included within this definition.

The criterion "separable by chemical means" is the distinction referred to earlier between the separation of the compound water into the elements hydrogen and oxygen and the separation of sea water into the two compounds salt and water. This distinction is between a *chemical separation,* which requires drastic treatment and changes one substance into other substances, and a *physical separation,* which is some variation of sorting, such as evaporation, sifting, or filtering. Sea water, which is made up of substances that are separable by physical means, is a *mixture.* **A mixture is a material that does not have a fixed composition and is separable by physical means into two or more substances.** This definition includes grossly heterogeneous mixtures as well as **homogeneous mixtures; the latter are called solutions.** Sea water is a solution; it is homogeneous but has a variable composition, and its constituents are separable by physical means.

With these categories—element, compound, mixture, solution—we are able to set up the classification of matter outlined in Table 1-1, which summarizes the definitions of categories and the relations among the forms of matter.

Of the three criteria that we have used in establishing this classification—homogeneity, separability, and composition—only the last is unambiguous. A material may appear homogeneous

under one type of observation, but on closer scrutiny it may show discontinuities of structure. Coarse mixtures are obviously heterogeneous; true solutions are homogeneous by any means of observation (and are therefore indistinguishable from substances by this criterion). Between these extremes are materials whose heterogeneity is not visible but is detectable by special optical means. These intermediate materials are called *colloids.*

A classification of matter based on the separability of material can never be perfect. The failure of many attempts at separation can never categorically prove that a substance is an element; perhaps the next attempt will be successful. Several compounds were once thought to be elements because attempts at separation had failed. Independent methods, established a few decades ago, have now proved with certainty that the distinction between elements and compounds on the basis of chemical separability is accurate. It should be emphasized that this criterion of separability, though logically imperfect, was used successfully in the actual classification of substances as elements and compounds.

The distinction between a physical process of separation and a chemical one is even more ambiguous. We are left, therefore, with composition as the significant distinction between solutions and compounds. Experimentally, this is a problem for *analysis,* the determination of the relative amounts of elemental substances in complex matter. Analysis of compounds always shows the same relative amounts of the constituent elements. The ratio of the amount of hydrogen to the amount of oxygen in water is *constant* regardless of the amount of water analyzed, the method of analysis, the source of the sample, or any other factor. Similarly, the ratio of the amount of sodium to the amount of chlorine in common table salt is constant. These materials are therefore compounds. On the other hand, the amount of salt in sea water varies from less than 3 percent to more than 4 percent; a very strong brine may have nearly 40 percent salt dissolved in the water; and another salt solution may contain only a fraction of 1 percent salt. All of these are solutions of salt in water; all are homogeneous; and the group is distinguished from compounds because the composition is variable.

## 1-7. Terminology and Symbols

Each special area of knowledge has its own jargon of special meanings, its own set of symbols that stand for rather complicated ideas. We shall encounter many a quantity or concept that is given a special symbol. But there is one whole system of symbols that should be considered here. Probably the fact about chemistry that is best known to people who are not trained in chemistry is that chemists use symbols. Instead of writing the word "water" chemists often use the symbol $H_2O$. Water is a compound, and its symbol is therefore complex, a combination of the symbols for hydrogen and oxygen, H and O. Often the symbol for an element is simply the first letter of the name of that element, H for hydrogen, O for oxygen, I for iodine, etc. But two or more elements may have the same initial letter—for example, argon and aluminum. Two letters of the name are then used: argon is Ar, and aluminum is Al. The symbol never includes more than two letters; the first is always capitalized, and the second is always lower-case. There is one further complication. Some of the elements have Latin or German names, not used by English-speaking scientists, and the symbols are abbreviations of these names. Iron, for example, is Fe, copper is Cu, mercury is Hg, and potassium is K because the Latin names of these elements are *ferrum, cuprum, hydrargyrum,* and *kalium;* the symbol of tungsten is W because its German name is *wolfram.*

The next stage of complexity in the system has already been mentioned: the symbols for compound substances, or *formulas.* Water is a compound substance made of hydrogen and oxygen; its symbol reflects this fact by combining the symbols of hydrogen and oxygen in $H_2O$. The subscript "2" in this formula implies that there are twice as many hydrogen as oxygen in water. Note, twice as *many,* not twice as much. The significance of this subtlety will appear in later chapters. Another well-known formula is that for sulfuric acid, $H_2SO_4$. This formula states

that sulfuric acid is a compound made up of hydrogen, sulfur, and oxygen, and that there are twice as many hydrogens and four times as many oxygens as there are sulfur in all samples of sulfuric acid. The symbol $H_2SO_4$ implies the substance, its compound nature, its composition, and many other facts about it that will be learned as we progress through this text.

The third stage of complexity in the system of symbols is the use of several formulas in a chemical equation. For example, water is formed by the burning of hydrogen in oxygen. Hydrogen has the formula $H_2$, oxygen is $O_2$, and water, as we have already observed, is $H_2O$. The reaction of burning hydrogen can be most succinctly stated in terms of these symbols by the equation

$$2H_2 + O_2 \longrightarrow 2H_2O$$

Equations of this type convey much information in a very compact statement. The complete usefulness of this extension of the system of chemical symbols can be appreciated only after we have studied the quantitative details of chemical reactions in later chapters.

Another series of terms needed in the description of matter can be illustrated by a further consideration of the substance water. We are all familiar with water in three different states. The commonest is liquid water, the stuff that comes out of taps and fills ponds. We are also familiar with this same substance as a solid called ice. Ice is the same matter as water, differing only in its physical state; it is a solid instead of the more familiar liquid. We also may be familiar with a third state of water—steam. Steam is gaseous water. Here a new term, "state," has been introduced. At this point in the discussion the reader very likely has a pretty good idea of what is meant by **state.** It can be defined as **the condition of a substance, gaseous, liquid, or solid, at a particular temperature.** The important aspect of the definition of the term "state" is the definition of the three states; that is, what is meant by "solid," "liquid," and "gas"? A **solid** is a sample of matter that has a fixed volume, or size, and a fixed shape. A **liquid** is a sample of matter that has a fixed volume but assumes the shape of the container it occupies. A quart of milk may have the shape of a milk bottle, of a rectangular paper carton, or of the four cylindrical glasses into which it is poured, or it may be a thin flat layer of irregular outline on the kitchen floor. In each case, though, its volume is the same. A **gas** is a sample of matter that has neither fixed volume nor fixed shape. Any sample of gas will assume the shape and *size* of the container it occupies. A small volume of compressed air, for example, assumes the large spherical shape of a toy balloon when it is used to fill the balloon. Or it may assume the volume and shape of an automobile tire.

Finally, the interconvertibility of these three states must be emphasized. The same sample of a substance may assume any of the three states under various conditions, in particular as the temperature changes. If water remains at or near room temperature, it remains liquid. If it is heated above a certain temperature, its **boiling point,** it assumes the gaseous state; if cooled below a certain temperature, its **melting** or **freezing point,** it becomes solid. This interconvertibility of states is a property of most substances. A few substances that are gaseous at normal room temperature have not yet been solidified, and some compounds decompose when heated instead of melting or vaporizing; but in general the interconvertibility is complete, and it must be remembered that we are dealing with the *same* substance in all three states.

For the time being we may use, without further question, these rather common-sense definitions of the three states. In subsequent chapters we shall see that a knowledge of the intimate microscopic structure of a substance is necessary to a proper understanding of the states of that substance.

Another term that we must use and must therefore define is "system." When we speak of a substance such as water or copper or iron, we are often referring to these substances in general —that is, to all the water or copper or iron in the universe. But on many occasions—for example, in laboratory operations—we must deal with something less than all the matter in the universe; we must limit ourselves to a particular sample of matter, isolated from the rest of the universe. This is what we call a **system—a particular sample of matter isolated from its environment.** Generally a beaker or a test-tube is a sufficient barrier to the environment. In some special cases, better isolation is needed, as in a Thermos bottle, to prevent the passage of heat between the system and its environment.

Another word that needs a specialized definition is "phase." A short, succinct definition is: **A phase is a homogeneous part of a system separated from other parts of the system by physical boundaries.** For example, a beaker of water plus a cube of ice is a system. Here we clearly have two phases in the beaker, the liquid water and the solid ice, separated by a physical boundary, the surface of the ice cube. To be complete, our account of the phases of this system should include the air in the beaker, a third phase separated from the water phase by a physical boundary, the surface of the water. We have, then, a total of three phases, made up, in this case, of two components. The gaseous phase, air, is separated by the surface of the water from the other phases; the liquid phase, water, is separated by its surface from the gaseous phase; and the solid phase, also water (ice), is separated by its surface from the liquid phase.

Now suppose that we pour some oil (which does not dissolve in water) into the beaker. We now have another liquid phase, for this newly added material forms a physical boundary that separates it from the water. We could go on and include a second solid phase by dropping a piece of chalk into our system, which would then include two solid phases, two liquid phases, and a gaseous phase. Note that two pieces of chalk or two ice cubes do not constitute separate phases; there are only one chalk phase and one ice phase even if we break the original pieces in two. Here, then, by an explanation of a rather simple demonstration, we have defined, in the sense of establishing a mutual understanding, the terms "phase" and "system."

The next term we must deal with is "property" in the sense we have already used—that is, "properties of matter." We have defined properties as the **characteristic qualities of a substance,** and we have observed that the sum of the properties of a substance amounts to a definition of the substance. These characteristic qualities, or properties, are observable and in many cases are quantitatively measurable. Color helps us, for example (if we are not color-blind), to characterize objects or substances even though it is not ordinarily measured quantitatively; weight, which is observed quantitatively, also helps us to characterize objects.

Properties can be classified by division into *physical properties* and *chemical properties*. This division, like all divisions of physics and chemistry, is not clear-cut. In general, the difference is based on change or lack of change in the material during observation of the property. Since no change is brought about by our observation of color, mass, hardness, size, etc., those properties are physical properties. On the other hand, measuring such a property as the ignition temperature of gasoline does cause a change in the substance; this is therefore classed as a chemical property.

The study of our physical environment has begun with the introduction of some terminology and symbolism, a part of the language of science. We have also introduced a few of the conceptual tools that aid in the organization of physical and chemical facts into a theory of the structure of matter. We have begun a critical study of matter by a general consideration of properties, the characteristics that identify and distinguish substances. In the next chapters we shall examine three properties that are common to all matter, properties that are so ubiquitous and constant as to be general properties of the physical universe. On these properties, and on an understanding of them, the development of much of physics and chemistry and all of the subsequent parts of this book rest. These properties are motion, inertia, and gravitation.

## Concepts and Terms

| | | | |
|---|---|---|---|
| Scientific Knowledge | Classification of Matter | Properties | Heterogeneous |
| structure | substance | physical | Composition |
| types | element | chemical | physical separation |
| evolution | compound | Density | chemical separation |
| problems of science | mixture | Postulates | State |
| principles of science | solution | Scientific Laws | gas |
| experimental method | Terminology | Theories | liquid |
| classical science | symbols | Law of Causality | solid |
| alchemy | formulas | Conservation | Phase |
| scientific revolution | chemical equations | Equilibrium | System |
| modern science | | Homogeneous | |

## Problems

**1-1.** The following materials are probably in daily use in your home:

| | |
|---|---|
| salt | starch |
| flour | syrup |
| sterling silver | pepper |
| china | aluminum |
| water | ice |
| sugar | milk |
| vanilla extract | aspirin |
| butter | |

Classify these materials as elements, compounds, or mixtures; distinguish solutions from other mixtures; justify your classification.

**1-2.** List properties that distinguish each of the materials listed in Prob. 1-1 from all others in the list.

**1-3.** Describe the components and phases of a glass of iced tea in which the sugar has not yet entirely dissolved. Consider the soluble extract of tea as one component.

**1-4.** Suppose that you wish to carry out an experiment designed to measure the effect of room temperature on the perception of weak red light by human beings. Describe the system you would set up and the way it would be isolated from environmental factors that would influence the experiment.

**1-5.** The property *density* was defined on page 3. Write an equation that expresses this relation mathematically.

**1-6.** The density of mercury is 13.6 grams/cm³. What is the mass of 254 cm³ of mercury?

**1-7.** A pound is 454 grams. What is the volume of one pound of mercury?

*Ans.* 33.4 cm³

**1-8.** One pint contains 473 cm³. What is the mass in grams of one pint of mercury? How many pounds in a pint of mercury?

**1-9.** The density of benzene is 0.89 gram/cm³. Calculate the volume occupied by 100 grams of benzene.

**1-10.** What is the mass of 50 cm³ of benzene?

**1-11.** A sample of glycerine was observed to have a mass of 100 grams and a volume of 79.4 cm³. Calculate the density of glycerine.

*Ans.* 1.26 grams/cm³

**1-12.** A colorless liquid was suspected of being benzene. To test this possibility, you determine the density by weighing an empty graduated cylinder (mass = 114.6 grams), filling the cylinder to the 30 cm³ mark with the liquid, weighing again (mass of cylinder plus liquid = 151.2 grams), and calculating the density of the liquid. Could this liquid be benzene? Why?

*Ans.* density = 1.22 grams/cm³

## Suggested Readings

1. G. Holton, *Principles of Physical Science* (Addison-Wesley, 1953). Part D, which consists of Chaps. 12, 13, and 14, is an excellent treatment of the intellectual qualities of physical science.
2. H. Shapley, Helen Wright, and S. Rapport, *Readings in the Physical Sciences* (Appleton-Century-Crofts, 1948). Part 1 is a series of essays on the methods of science and the place of science in our culture.
3. J. H. Hildebrand and R. E. Powell, *Principles of Chemistry*, 6th edition (Macmillan, 1952). Chap. 1 considers the basic terminology and symbolism.
4. L. Pauling, *College Chemistry*, 2nd edition (W. H. Freeman and Company, 1955), Chap. 1.

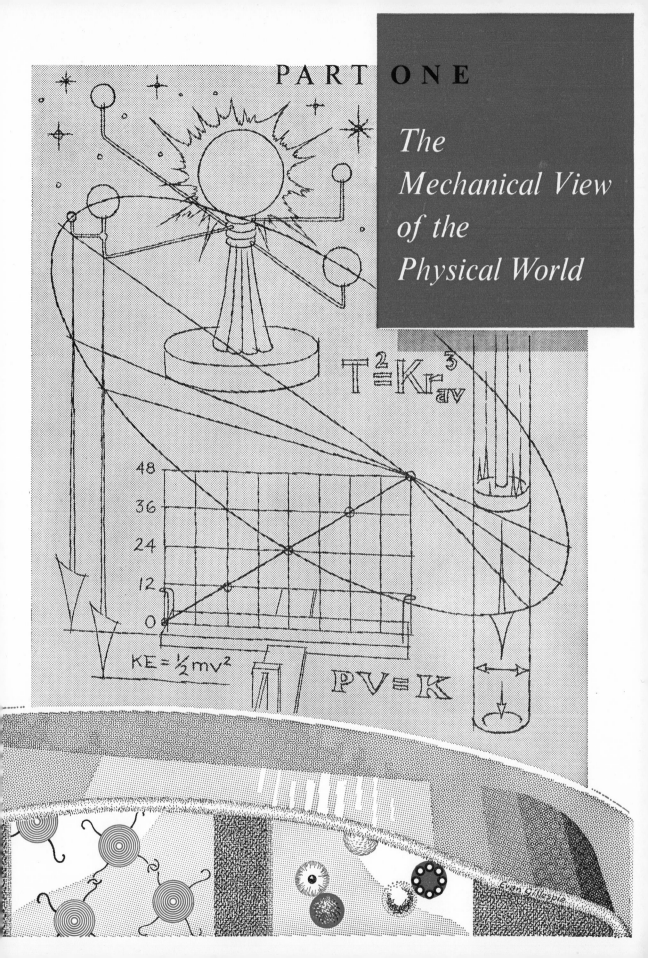

PART ONE

*The Mechanical View of the Physical World*

BOTH HISTORICALLY and logically the science of mechanics, which is the study of the motions of material bodies, is fundamental to the development of physical science. There is, however, an added reason for starting a systematic study of the physical world with mechanics. Since motion is the most obvious aspect of the world around us, an intuitive understanding of mechanical phenomena is one of our first experiences in learning. Everyone senses the essence of Newton's laws of motion sufficiently to control his motions and to live in an environment pervaded by motions, even though most of us do not comprehend these laws.

The beginning of modern science is customarily placed at the time of Galileo Galilei (1564–1642). In his study of falling bodies, Galileo emphasized the expression of concepts in mathematical form and the experimental method of investigating problems. This method, which was the prototype of all modern scientific study, based theories on experiment and verified or modified them by further experiment. Two generations later Isaac Newton (1642–1727) synthesized all problems of motion, both celestial and terrestrial, through his laws of motion and gravitation; he thus set a pattern for the mechanical view of the physical world that dominated scientific thought for over two hundred years. By the latter half of the nineteenth century the mechanical view had been so successful in relating so many widely different facts of experience that it was generally believed that *all* problems could be solved by the laws of mechanics. The fact that this solution has never been completely realized does not detract from the fundamental character of the science of mechanics.

The concepts of mechanics pervade all of physical science. The laws of electricity and magnetism are formulated in terms of interacting forces; the mechanical concepts of momentum and energy play a fundamental role in the formulation of contemporary atomic theory. Thus the concepts of mechanics appear again and again throughout the study of the physical world.

CHAPTER

2

The Motions
of the Planets

OF ALL the motions in our immediate experience, those of the heavenly bodies across the sky are apparently the simplest. Here events follow one another in precise and orderly cycles. Some of the earliest records of civilization show that man had already been studying these motions and had related them to his economy and his religions. And as early as several centuries before Christ the construction of a world system to explain these motions was an important problem of philosophy. What, then, are the motions that can be observed by the unaided eye?

## 2-1. Motions of the Heavens

The most obvious motion is the daily rising and setting of the sun and moon. They appear above the eastern horizon, sweep across the sky along the arc of a circle, and disappear below the western horizon, only to reappear again in the east and repeat the cycle. It takes little imagination to assume that these observed paths are parts of complete circles about the earth and that the settings and risings are the result of the fact that the rest of the circles is hidden from our view by the earth itself. A little observation of the night sky will reveal that the stars also show a **diurnal** revolution. If a camera is mounted rigidly and left pointing at the northern sky with the shutter open for several hours, each star, as it moves across the sky, will leave a trail on the photographic plate. These trails are found to be circular, and all the circles have a common center. Very near the common center, so that it appears hardly to move at all, is the star **Polaris,** or the **North Star.** Stars not too far removed from Polaris describe complete circles about it and never set. They travel from east to west above Polaris and from west to east below it. As stars farther from Polaris are observed, their diurnal circles become larger until they dip below the horizon. Such are the circles described by the sun and moon and the stars of the southern sky. Thus the heavens seem to revolve daily about a north-south axis through the earth.

We know now, of course, that these diurnal motions are merely apparent: that they are due to the daily eastward rotation of the earth on its axis, and that Polaris happens to be the star directly over the North Pole. Most of us, however, know this because we have been told so and are brought up to believe it.† This belief is only a few centuries old and was come by with great difficulty at a time when it was considered dangerously radical to contemplate a moving earth. For more than two thousand years the more "obvious" and satisfying geocentric‡ view was maintained, with man on an immovable earth at the middle of things. Let us continue to consider the motions of heavenly bodies in more detail and see why the earth was finally displaced from this central position and made not only to rotate on an axis but also to revolve round the sun.

Except for their diurnal motions, the stars do not appear to move; that is, their positions relative to one another remain the same. The random distribution of the stars in the sky has remained virtually unchanged for thousands of years. The ancients saw the images of their gods in certain groups of stars and named these groups accordingly. These groups are the **constellations.** Most of the groups bear little resemblance to their mystical namesakes. On the other hand, each constellation is an easily recognized arrangement of stars. The Big Dipper and its neighbor the Little Dipper, with Polaris at the end of the handle, are familiar groups in the northern sky. The V-shaped group of stars forming the face and horn tips of Taurus, and the great rectangle of the legendary hunter Orion, with three bright stars for his belt, are prominent constellations of the winter sky. With the aid of a star map anyone can readily learn to recognize most of the constellations. In the second century before Christ, the Greek astronomer Hipparchus compiled the earliest known list of stars. He recognized and listed more than half of the eighty-eight constellations recognized today. He listed those he could see in the northern hemisphere. After the great explorations, which ranged over the sky as well as the earth, the remaining constellations of the southern hemisphere were observed and added to the list during the sixteenth and seventeenth centuries. The eighty-eight constellations arbitrarily divide the whole sky into areas of varying shape and size, which are used by the modern astronomer in much the same way as a geographer uses the map of the world. The general location of a celestial object is given by the statement that it is in Orion, just as Paris is located by the statement that it is in France. Because of their apparently unchanged positions over the centuries, the stars of the constellations are called "fixed" stars. The quotation marks are used because we know now that even these stars are moving. But the changes are exceedingly slow and require the sensitive instruments of modern astronomy for their detection.

The moon and the sun, on the other hand, show a definite motion against the background of the fixed stars. In their diurnal revolutions the moon and the sun move more slowly than the stars and therefore display a steady *eastward* drift among the constellations. This motion of the moon, more rapid than that of the sun, is easily observed. If the moon is located with reference to a bright star near it, and then observed at the same time the following night, it will be found a considerable distance—more than twenty times its own diameter—to the east. This eastward drift of the moon may be observed, in fact, within a few hours, for it moves approximately its own diameter every hour. The sun's eastward motion is not so easily observed, since it moves only about twice its diameter per day; but if, over a period of several days, the constellations that appear just after sundown are observed, the sun's movement across the constellations may be noticed: because of the sun's eastward drift, the constellations rise a few minutes earlier each night.

## 2-2. *The Zodiac*

The line along which the sun travels round the sky is called the **ecliptic.** The path of the moon through the constellations lies near the ecliptic but is inclined to it by a little more than 5°. The moon therefore crosses the ecliptic twice

---

† It is questionable whether many readers could present evidence for the earth's rotation. Certainly the rising and setting of the sun is not.

‡ "Earth-centered," from the Greek word *ge*, for earth.

during each circuit of the heavens. If, during one of these crossings, the sun is also at that point of the ecliptic, the moon passes across the face of the sun, and we have a total eclipse of the sun. The moon just covers the sun since each has an angular size of about half a degree.† Eclipses happen infrequently because the moon is usually either above or below the ecliptic when in the same direction as the sun. In this position we have the "dark of the moon" or the new moon. As the moon (with its more rapid eastward motion) moves away from the sun, it increases from crescent through quarter and gibbous phases to full moon, which it attains when it arrives at the opposite part of the sky from the sun. It then repeats these phases in reverse as it completes its path round the sky and arrives in conjunction with the sun again. This cycle, from new moon to new moon (one lunar month), requires almost thirty days. Hence there are slightly more than twelve lunar months in a year, the time during which the sun swings once round the sky along the ecliptic.

A belt round the sky 18° wide and with the ecliptic as a central line is called the **zodiac.** This belt is divided into twelve parts each 30° long, and each part has a constellation. From the earliest recorded times, these constellations (with the exception of Libra) were given names of living creatures; hence the name "zodiac," derived from the Greek word *zōon,* meaning living things. The sun and the moon, clearly, are always to be found in the zodiac. Five "stars" also appear to wander among the zodiacal constellations. These are the **planets,** so named from a Greek word meaning wanderer. The five planets observable by the unaided eye are Mercury, Venus, Mars, Jupiter, and Saturn. In ancient times it was firmly believed that the positions of the planets, sun, and moon in the various constellations of the zodiac controlled and foretold the course of human events (a belief not com-

† Sight along the edge of a straight stick at one edge of the moon, and then swing the stick round to point at the opposite edge; it is found that the stick has swung through half a degree. The same is found for the sun. We know that the sun is much larger than the moon, but, since it is also much farther away, its angular size is the same. Both sun and moon can be "eclipsed" by a penny held at arm's length.

pletely without followers even today). Hence the ancient astrologers made and recorded careful observations of the motions of these celestial objects for thousands of years. These motions have also been subjected to intense study by astronomers ever since the time of the classical Greek scholars. By this time many cycles of the motions have been recorded even though some of the cycles require many years for completion. These astronomical observations constitute the hugest accumulation of data in any of the sciences.

## 2-3. Retrograde Motion of the Planets

The wanderings of the planets, although irregular, are by no means random. They were soon found to be definite and predictable. At a certain time, Venus appears in the western sky shortly after sunset as the brilliant and beautiful "evening star." She gradually moves eastward in the zodiac, little by little each day, until about 48° east of the sun. She then *turns round* and moves *westward,* toward the sun, disappears into the sunset, and reappears as the "morning star." She continues westward (thus rising earlier each day) until about 48° west of the sun. She then turns eastward, disappears into the sunrise, reappears in the western sky, and repeats the cycle. Thus Venus seems to oscillate along the zodiac, never getting more than 48° away from the sun. She is never seen overhead at night. When she is overhead during the diurnal revolution, the sun is also up and obliterates her light. Mercury executes a similar pattern but is more difficult to observe. Mercury is less brilliant, never gets more than 28° away from the sun, and therefore must usually be observed close to the horizon in either a sunset or a sunrise glow. Both Venus and Mercury participate in the general eastward motion of the sun through the constellations of the zodiac, but combine with it a periodic westward motion that results in the observations described above. This westward motion is called **retrograde** (that is, backward compared with that of the sun).

Mars, Jupiter, and Saturn also show a retrograde motion but are not bound to the sun as Mercury and Venus are. They display, generally, an eastward drift through the zodiac, but they periodically reverse their motion, travel westward (retrograde) for some weeks, then continue eastward, and then repeat the retrograde motion. Thus they travel eastward round the zodiac in a series of loops as seen against the fixed stars. Jupiter requires about twelve years for a complete circuit of the sky and describes eleven loops in this time. Mars completes his circuit in about two years with one loop. Saturn requires twenty-nine years and makes twenty-eight loops. At various times, depending on their distance from the sun, these three planets may be seen in all parts of the zodiac.

These, then, are the motions of the heavenly objects that may be discerned by careful and patient observation of the sky. To summarize: all objects in the sky seem to revolve daily round a line from Polaris to the earth; the sun, moon, and planets also drift steadily eastward through the constellations of the zodiac except that the planets periodically turn westward for a time before continuing their eastward journeys.

## 2-4. Precession of the Equinoxes

There is one other motion that must be described. It is an apparent westward (backward) motion of the sun, so slow that it becomes obvious only after centuries of observation and with careful observation shows less than 1° during a lifetime. Everyone is familiar with the varying lengths of day and night as the year progresses. Twice a year, however (about March 22 and September 22), the day and the night are equal. These times are called *equinoxes*. Many ancient cultures reckoned the year from the vernal (spring) equinox; the position of the sun at that time was therefore important. Late in the second century before Christ the great observer Hipparchus noticed that the sun did not return to the same point in the sky at successive vernal equinoxes. By comparing his observations with those of earlier observers, he discovered that the position of the sun at vernal equinox was moving *westward* at a very low speed, which he

determined, his value being in surprisingly good agreement with the present value. In Hipparchus' time, the sun was in Aries (the Ram) at vernal equinox. Today, two thousand years later, it is in Pisces (the Fish), the next zodiacal constellation to the west of Aries. Very early writings from the Euphratean civilizations indicate that two thousand years before Hipparchus the sun at vernal equinox was in Taurus (the Bull), which is the next zodiacal constellation to the east of Aries. This gradual shifting of the constellations with respect to the seasons is called the *precession of the equinoxes*.

## 2-5. Ptolemaic System

One of the earliest, most persistent, and most revealing problems of mankind has been the construction of a conceptual model to account for the observed motions of the heavens. As already mentioned, a common-sense structure of the universe would be one in which all the heavenly bodies revolved in circular paths round a stationary earth. A casual observation of the heavens shows this picture to be "obviously" true—and "obviously" the earth is stationary. Such a picture was accepted by the ancient Greek astronomers. To be sure, not all of the Greeks held this view. Aristarchus (third century before Christ) proposed a heliocentric† universe in which the fixed stars were stationary and the earth and planets revolved about a fixed sun at the center. His proposal had little influence on Greek thought, but it strongly influenced Copernicus eighteen centuries later.

The reigning theories of Greek astronomy were based on a set of principles (derived mostly from the metaphysics of the time) that went somewhat like this: The natural place of the earth is at the center of the universe and immovable. By their nature the heavenly bodies must be "perfect" in form (that is, spherical and unblemished) and must move round the

---

† "Sun-centered" from the Greek *helios*, sun. If the earth revolved round the sun, the fixed stars should *appear* to move in much the same way as the landscape viewed from a moving train appears to move (§ 5-9). Since this movement was not observed, Hipparchus rejected Aristarchus' proposal.

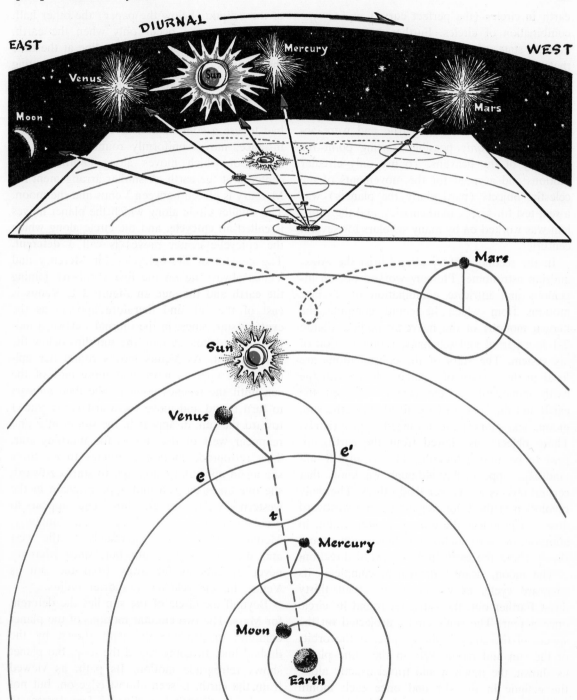

FIGURE **2-1** *Schematic and partial diagram of the Ptolemaic system of planetary motions. As viewed from a stationary earth, the planets would appear to move among the stars in accordance with observations.*

earth in circles (the perfect curve) or in some combination of circles. Furthermore, since the natural state of earthly matter is rest, while that of the heavenly bodies is continuous motion, the heavenly bodies must be composed of a weightless ethereal substance completely different from earthly matter. These principles were regarded as obviously true and were accepted as the *only* possible starting point for a theory of the heavens. To use only circular motions and account for the movements of the celestial objects (particularly the planets) was a real test for Greek mathematics, and the problem was worked on by many scholars for several centuries.

In the second century after Christ the Alexandrian astronomer Ptolemy worked out an ingenious and intricate combination of circular motions from which he could compute the known motions of the heavenly bodies. Figure 2-1 is a partial and schematic representation of his system. The stars of the constellations are fixed in the surface of a large sphere, with the earth immovable at the center. Between the earth and the sphere of the fixed stars, the sun, moon, and planets are arranged appropriately. These objects, as viewed from the earth, appear to be among the stars just as any distant landscape appears flat although we know that certain objects are nearer than others. The daily revolution of the whole apparatus in a westward direction produces the diurnal motions; and, in addition, the sun, moon, and planets move more slowly about the earth in an eastward direction.

The moon, nearest the earth, completes its eastward cycle, as we know, in about thirty days. Farther out, the sun goes round its circle once a year. The sun's circle, projected on the sphere of the stars, is the ecliptic. If the orbits of the sun and moon were in the same plane, as shown, the moon would travel exactly along the ecliptic in the sky and once each month would be between the earth and sun and produce an eclipse. But the moon is on the ecliptic only twice each month, and eclipses occur infrequently. To take care of this, the moon's orbit is tilted a few degrees about a diameter of the orbit. The moon is therefore north of the ecliptic (above the paper) half of the month and south

of the ecliptic (below the paper) the other half. And eclipses can occur only when the earth, moon, and sun happen to be in line at the time the moon is crossing the ecliptic (that is, cutting through the plane of the paper).

Since a steady eastward cycle of the planets would never show retrograde motion, Ptolemy had to use a combination of circles. Venus, for instance, moves uniformly round a circle, the center of which moves along another circle centered at the earth. A similar arrangement for Mercury is placed between Venus and the moon. The smaller circle along which the planet moves is called an **epicycle,** and the circle along which the epicyclic center moves is call a **deferent.** The centers of the epicycles for Mercury and Venus always lie on the line (broken) joining the earth and the sun. In Figure 2-1, Venus is east of the sun and therefore appears as the evening star, since, in the diurnal westward motion of the whole system, the sun dips below the horizon first. As Venus moves round her epicycle, she appears more and more east of the sun until she reaches point e. She then *appears* to turn round and move westward (retrograde) toward the sun, disappear in the sunset at *t,* and reappear west of the sun as the morning star. This retrograde motion continues to *e′;* there she again appears to stop and to start eastward; she overtakes the sun and appears again in the western sky after sunset. Thus Venus appears to oscillate about the sun in the zodiac. Similarly, Mercury also appears alternately to the west and the east of the sun; but, since Mercury never appears as far away from the sun as Venus, his epicycle has a shorter radius.

Beyond the circle of the sun lies the deferent for Mars. The two circular motions of the planet combine to produce the path shown by the dashed line. In going round the loop, the planet shows retrograde motion. Its path, as viewed from the earth, is seen almost edge on, but not exactly so, since it is inclined a few degrees to the plane of the ecliptic. Thus the apparent path through the constellations of the zodiac contains flattened loops in accordance with observation. Not shown are similar cycles for Jupiter and Saturn. Saturn is the farthest from the earth, and Jupiter is between Mars and Saturn.

Although the system we have been describing accounted for the major aspects of the heavenly motions, the results of careful calculations were not exactly consistent with the long series of observations available to Ptolemy. He was therefore forced to employ more epicycles and to invent other devices. One such was the eccentric. The motions were still circular, but the earth had to be displaced somewhat from the center. Other compromises were also necessary, but each component motion remained circular. Ptolemy finally modified the system so that calculated positions and observations agreed. It was intricate and unwieldy, but he was able to compute positions that agreed well with the records of several centuries and with observations made in succeeding years.

Soon after the time of Ptolemy, learning declined in Europe. Ptolemy's system was preserved by the Arabs, however, and seemed to be adequate for their limited observations for over a thousand years. With the revival of learning, the Ptolemaic system and Aristotelian science were incorporated into the Scholastic dogma of the time, primarily by the authority of Saint Thomas Aquinas. The view of the heavens that was held by an educated man of the fourteenth century is given in Dante's *Paradiso,* in which he takes a journey through a heaven that is definitely Ptolemaic.

## 2-6. *Copernican System*

By the sixteenth century, however, it had become obvious that the Ptolemaic system was not quite right. Small but easily observed discrepancies between predicted and observed positions were evident. Hence a further modification of the system was necessary. But already more than seventy simultaneous motions were required for the observed paths of the seven celestial bodies. Perhaps the time had come to question the principles underlying the geocentric

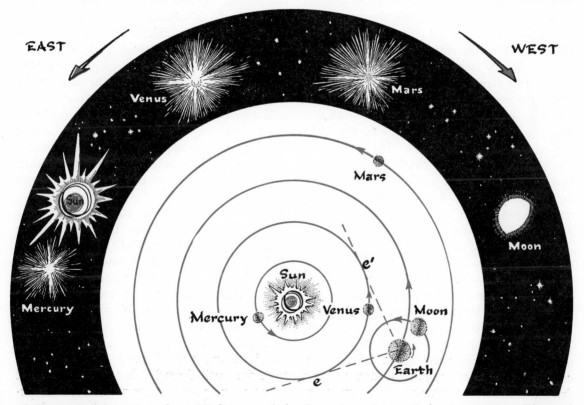

FIGURE **2-2** *Schematic and partial diagram of the Copernican system of planetary motions. The earth rotates daily on its axis and revolves yearly in a circle round a stationary sun.*

model and to search for new hypotheses that might lead to a simpler structure. This was politically dangerous thinking for the sixteenth century. To question part was to question all of the Scholastic dogma of the churchmen who were the temporal as well as the spiritual rulers of the time.

Nikolaus Copernicus (1473–1543) was the first to depart from doctrine and consider a new hypothesis for the structure of the world. A well-educated and able scholar in many fields, he devoted much of his effort to astronomy and to working out his system of the heavens. What he discovered was that by *interchanging* the sun and the earth in the Ptolemaic system he was able to reduce the number of required motions to less than half (about thirty-four). The sun was stationary at the center of the universe, and revolving round it in circular paths were the five planets *and the earth.* In addition to revolving about the sun, the earth also rotated once a day on a north-south axis. Thus it was no longer necessary to require the entire heavens to revolve daily about the earth, since the rising and setting of the celestial objects were apparent motions due to the rotation of the earth. The stars could now stand still. The moon, as in the Ptolemaic system, made a monthly revolution about the earth. Figure 2-2 is a partial and schematic representation of the Copernican system. Not shown are the orbits for Jupiter (next out from Mars) and Saturn. The fixed stars (considered to be at relatively great distance by Copernicus) formed a stationary sphere with the *sun* at its center. As in the Ptolemaic system, the sun, moon, and planets were seen as projected on the background of the stars.

All motions are *eastward,* including the rotation of the earth on its axis. From any point on the surface of the earth, of course, only half of the sky can be seen at one time. The horizon, which is a plane tangent to the earth at the point of observation, rotates eastward with the earth. Thus the celestial objects *appear* to rise over the eastern horizon, swing across the sky, and disappear below the western horizon in their diurnal motion. The periods of revolution of the planets increase with the radius of their orbits, being least for Mercury and greatest for

Saturn. As the earth moves round its orbit, the sun appears to drift eastward among the constellations. Thus the period of revolution of the earth is one year, and the projection of its orbit on the sky is the ecliptic.

In Figure 2-2, Venus is seen in the sky west of the sun and thus is the morning star, rising ahead of the sun. Venus, traveling more rapidly, runs away from the earth and therefore appears farther west of the sun on succeeding nights. This continues until she reaches $e'$, which is the point of tangency to the orbit of the sight line from the earth (broken line). Continuing on her orbit, Venus appears to move eastward toward the sun, disappearing in the sunrise when she is on the opposite side of the sun from the earth. A few nights later she appears east of the sun (as the evening star) and continues to drift eastward until she reaches the point $e$, where she is seen at her greatest eastward distance from the sun. She then appears to turn round and move westward (retrograde) through the zodiac, and she disappears into the setting sun when she is between the sun and the earth. Thus the apparent oscillation of Venus about the sun in the zodiac is explained. Since Venus does not move exactly along the ecliptic, her orbit must be tilted a few degrees to the plane of the earth's orbit. The angle sun–earth–$e'$ (determined by the relative sizes of the two orbits) is the greatest angular distance from the sun at which Venus can appear. A similar explanation applies to Mercury, but, since his orbit is smaller, his maximum apparent distance from the sun is smaller.

The retrograde motion of the planets lying farther from the sun than the earth can be understood from Figure 2-3. Here the earth, with its shorter period of revolution, catches up with and passes the other planet. Nine equally spaced (in time), simultaneous positions of the earth and Mars are shown. At positions 1–4 the earth is behind Mars. At position 5 the earth passes Mars and continues getting farther ahead of him from 5 to 9. The sight lines from the earth through Mars for each pair of simultaneous positions show the apparent position of Mars among the constellations. Thus, as the earth passes Mars (between 4 and 6), he *appears* to move westward in the zodiac. A similar explanation applies to Jupiter and Saturn. Since both the earth and the planet move eastward, the retrograde loops occur at intervals of something more than a year. The periods of revolution for Mars, Jupiter, and Saturn are approximately two years, twelve years, and twenty-nine years respectively. The retrograde loops for these planets therefore occur at intervals of (approximately) two years, thirteen months, and 377 days.

As in the Ptolemaic system, the orbits of the planets and the moon must be tilted somewhat to the plane of the ecliptic (that is, the plane of the earth's orbit). This is due to the fact that none of these objects is observed to move along the ecliptic, each being sometimes north and sometimes south of it. The tilt, however (different for each object), is only a few degrees, since all of them move well within the zodiac, which, as we have seen, extends only nine degrees on each side of the ecliptic. Thus the system of sun, earth, moon, and planets is nearly flat.

This system also failed to yield results that agreed with observation as long as circles exactly centered on the sun were used. So Copernicus also used eccentrics, placing the circular orbits so that the sun was slightly off their centers. But he had dispensed with the large epicycles and other devices of the Ptolemaic system, and thus had greatly reduced the number of required motions. With this heliocentric system, tables of planetary motions could be computed with much greater ease than with the geocentric system of Ptolemy; and this greater simplicity of his system led Copernicus to hope that it would be accepted despite current prejudices. But he had rejected the doctrine of a central stationary earth (although he had retained that of circular motion) and thus had demoted the earth (and with it man) from its central place of importance to the status of merely one of several planets. To most people of the sixteenth century, simplicity of calculation was small reward for abandoning the satisfying, common-sense view of man at the center of the universe. According to modern criteria, the comparative simplicity of the Copernican system would argue strongly for its acceptance. On the other hand, the planetary positions predicted by the new system were no more accurate than those computed by the Ptolemaic system. What was needed was new, unanswerable evidence to support the superiority of one system over the other. Such evidence was not produced until seventy years after the death of Copernicus. As so often happens in science, the determining evidence was a result of the more extensive and precise information made possible by the invention of new methods of observation. We shall see many examples of sudden development of new theories or destruction or corroboration of old ones following immediately the development of new experimental techniques.

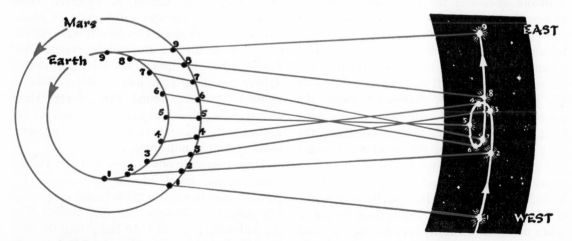

FIGURE **2-3** *Retrograde motion of Mars. Nine simultaneous positions of the earth and Mars are shown. As the earth passes Mars (4, 5, and 6), Mars appears to move backwards among the stars.*

## 2-7. Galileo's Telescopic Observations

Galileo Galilei (1564–1642) has been called the father of modern science. This remarkable Florentine was active in many areas of investigation. His quantitative studies of the laws of falling bodies not only laid the empirical foundation for Newton's general laws of motion a generation later, but also were the prototype of the experimental method that characterized the vigorous revolution in scientific thought of the seventeenth century. Galileo was one of the scientists of his time who believed in the Copernican system. In 1609 he constructed a telescope, which to his friends seemed a wondrous toy. But for Galileo it was an excellent instrument with which to extend the range of astronomical observation. Through his telescope he observed the surface of the moon to be scarred with craters and jagged mountains. The surface of the sun was blemished with black spots, which moved as though the sun were rotating. Saturn showed definite bulges around its equator as though this planet were "not a single star but three together which, as it were, touch each other." These were obviously not the perfect spheres of Scholastic doctrine. But the most convincing evidence for the Copernican system was Galileo's observation of the phases of Venus and his discovery of four of Jupiter's moons.

Before discussing the phases of Venus, let us consider the phases of the moon. The moon and planets shine by reflected sunlight and not by any luminescence of their own. For that reason only the half of the sphere that is facing the sun is illuminated. If we are to see the moon (or planet) as a fully illuminated circle, the moon (or planet), the earth, and the sun must be in a line, with the illuminated half facing the earth. The situation for the moon is illustrated in Figure 2-4. As the moon revolves eastward round the earth, the half facing the sun is illuminated (inner ring). But usually only a part of this illuminated half is visible from the earth. When the moon is directly between the earth and the sun, none of the illuminated half is seen, and we have the new moon. A few days later a portion of the illuminated face is visible from the earth, and a crescent moon is seen in the sky east of the sun (outer ring). As the moon continues round its orbit, more and more of the illuminated half becomes visible from the earth until the moon is on the opposite side of the earth from the sun. The whole illuminated half is then visible, and a full moon rises in the east as the sun sets in the west. The phase then decreases through gibbous phase and last quarter to new moon, and the cycle starts again. This will work in either a Ptolemaic or a Copernican system, since the moon revolves about the earth in each.

But not so with Venus (or Mercury). As can be seen from Figure 2-1, Venus, in a Ptolemaic system, would always be seen either in new or in crescent phase, since she could never turn as much as half of the illuminated surface toward the earth. In a Copernican system, however, Venus, like the moon, would show a full cycle of phases. At $e$ and $e'$ (Fig. 2-2) she would be seen in quarter phases. From $e$ to $e'$, as she moves past the earth, she would go from crescent through new to crescent. From $e'$ she would go through gibbous to full (when on the opposite side of the sun from the earth) and then decrease through gibbous to quarter again at $e$. Copernicus was aware of this and was confident that, if the eye were powerful enough, this full cycle of phases would be observed. The telescope made Galileo's eye "powerful" enough, and, much to his delight, he observed Venus gradually move through a full cycle of phases like that of the moon. This indeed was convincing evidence for the Copernican system. And finally, when he turned his telescope toward Jupiter, he discovered four satellites (that is, moons) revolving round that planet. Here, clearly, were celestial objects that did not revolve about the earth, that presented, indeed, a Copernican system in miniature.

These telescopic observations were for Galileo unanswerable proof of the heliocentric hypothesis, and he said so publicly and eloquently. His statements brought him into conflict with the authorities, who in 1616 had placed the writings of Copernicus on the prohibited list. In 1633 Galileo was summoned by the Inquisition and offered the alternative of renouncing his Copernican views or suffering torture. He wisely chose to recite the formal renunciation. He retired to his home on the outskirts of Florence and continued his scientific studies, but he did no more work in astronomy.

## 2-8. Kepler's Laws of Planetary Motion

Galileo's investigations in astronomy were descriptive. However, excellent quantitative work had been going on in Denmark. At the royal observatory of Uraniborg the astronomer Tycho Brahe (1546–1601) had spent more than twenty years observing the planets and recording very accurate data on their positions. Since he had made distinct improvements in the methods of measurement, his recorded positions were over twenty times more precise than the data available to Copernicus.

In 1599 Tycho undertook to establish for the German emperor a new observatory at Prague, where one of his assistants was a brilliant young mathematician named Johannes Kepler (1571–

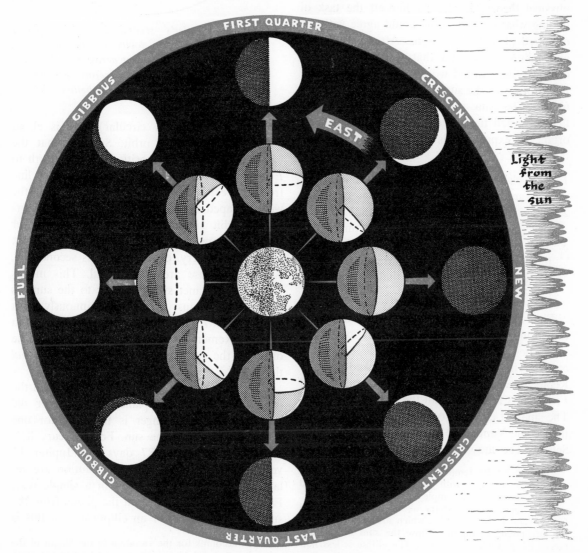

FIGURE **2-4** *Phases of the moon. The portion of the illuminated half of the moon visible from the earth appears as shown (white) in the outer circle.*

1630). When Tycho died suddenly in 1601, Kepler succeeded him as principal mathematician to the emperor. Kepler, like Galileo, was a firm believer in the Copernican system. His first task was to assign the proper circular orbits to the planets so that computed positions would agree with Tycho's voluminous data. But after four years of arduous calculations he was forced to admit that he could not do it. No combination of uniform circular motions could be made to fit Tycho's precise measurements.†

In accordance with the new idea that precise, quantitative observation is the final arbiter of physical theory, Kepler set himself the task of finding what form of orbit would agree with the observed planetary positions. After many trials and failures he found that Copernicus' heliocentric system would work if the planets *moved in ellipses* with the sun *not at the center* but at a focus.‡ The data, furthermore, yielded relations that governed the speeds of the planets in their orbits. He expressed his findings in the following three laws:

1. The planets move round the sun in orbits that are ellipses, with the sun at one focus.
2. The line joining the planet and the sun sweeps over equal areas in equal times.
3. The squares of the periods of revolution of the planets round the sun are directly proportional to the cubes of their average distances from the sun.

Figure 2-5 shows the orbit of the earth. It is drawn more flattened than it really is so that the properties of the motion may be seen more easily. The actual orbits, as worked out by Kepler, are more nearly circular. The sun is at *F*, which is a focus for all the planetary ellipses. The smallest ellipse is occupied by Mercury, and then come Venus, the earth, Mars, Jupiter, and Saturn. The moon revolves about the earth in

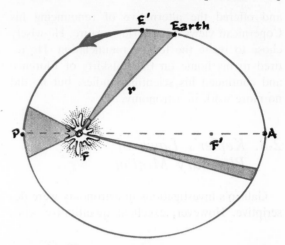

FIGURE **2-5** *Kepler's second law. The planet changes its orbital velocity so that equal areas (shaded areas) are swept across by* r *in equal times. The velocity is therefore greatest at perihelion* (P) *and least at aphelion* (A).

an orbit (very nearly circular) that is about 1/400 of the earth's orbit. Suppose that the earth moves from the position labeled Earth to *E'* while rotating once on its axis. Then the line from the earth to the sun will sweep over the wedge-shaped area Earth–*F*–*E'*. At other parts of the orbit similar areas will be swept over during the same time of one rotation of the earth. Kepler's discovery, expressed in his second law, is that all these areas are equal. This means that, as the planet swings nearer to the sun, its orbital speed must increase continuously to a maximum at *P* and then decrease to a minimum at *A*.† (Remember that the distances along the orbit for the areas shown are traversed in *equal* times.)

The third law states another regularity in the orbital speeds of the planets. The larger the planet's orbit, the longer is the time for one complete circuit of the sun. For Mercury it is 88 days, for Mars 687 days, for Jupiter 12 years, etc. These periods of revolution are related to the size of the orbit in a simple way. First the average distance of the planet from the sun is determined. For an elliptical path this is

---

† One might be tempted to return to a geocentric system. But, to agree with the facts, the system would have to be incredibly complex.

‡ An ellipse has symmetry about two points called foci (*F* and *F'* in Fig. 2-5), which are so located that for any point, *E*, on the ellipse the sum of the distances *FE* and *F'E* is constant. The ellipse is less flattened if *F* and *F'* are closer together, and it becomes a circle if *F* and *F'* coincide. The ancient Greek geometers had worked out the properties of the ellipse.

---

† This accounts for the variation in the length of the solar day (see § 3-1), which is longest when the earth is at *P* (December 22) and shortest when it is at *A* (June 22).

half of the distance *PA*. When this average radius is cubed and divided into the square of the period of revolution, the *same* value is obtained for *any* planet. This direct proportion is expressed algebraically by the equation

$$T^2 = Kr^3_{av} \tag{2-1}$$

in which $T$ is the period of revolution and $K$ is a proportionality constant.

Thus, finally, the heavenly motions were described as simple motions—one for each planet. (Remember the more than seventy required by the Ptolemaic system.) Furthermore, the speed of a planet in different parts of its orbit and the relative speeds of different planets are governed by simple rules. And the rules work, not only for Tycho's data but for observations made thousands of years earlier.† Surely here is the true

scheme of the heavens even if the doctrines of a stationary earth and "perfect" circular motions have to be abandoned. But the work of Galileo and Kepler did not immediately displace the Ptolemaic system. Rarely is a well-established theory displaced by new facts alone. What is needed is a better theory. For such a theory the world had to await the development of terrestrial mechanics and the genius of Newton, who related all observable motions, both terrestrial and celestial, in one monumental synthesis. In order to trace this development, we next consider the general laws of motion derived from terrestrial observations. This will be the subject of the next two chapters.

---

† Three centuries of precise telescopic observations since Kepler's time have shown his laws to hold within small and well-understood deviations.

## Concepts and Terms

Diurnal Revolutions
   diurnal circles
   North Star, Polaris
Constellations
Zodiac
   eastward motion of sun and moon
   ecliptic
   divisions of zodiac
Planets
   retrograde motions

Ptolemaic System
   deferent and epicycle
Copernican System
Galileo's Observations
   phases of the moon
   phases of Venus
   moons of Jupiter
Keplerian System
   Kepler's three laws

## Problems

**2-1.** Observe the northern sky, and locate the Big Dipper. Make a freehand sketch of this portion of the sky, showing the Big Dipper and two or three other groups of stars.

**2-2.** Repeat Prob. 2-1 several times at intervals of an hour. Make observations from the same place, and sketch the same star groups each time. After studying your diagrams, locate approximately the point about which the stars appear to revolve. In what direction do they move?

**2-3.** Locate the North Star (Polaris). Notice that the two stars forming the outer side of the Dipper bowl form a line pointing at Polaris.

**2-4.** Locate the moon with reference to a recognizable group of stars in its vicinity. Repeat at

the same time the following evening. How has the moon moved through the sky (background of stars)? How far did it move during 24 hours?

*Ans.* About 24 moon diameters

**2-5.** Compare the Ptolemaic and Copernican systems of the universe. What are the advantages and disadvantages of each? Did they relate the observations equally well? Discuss the observed retrograde motion of the planets from each point of view.

**2-6.** The average distance of Venus from the sun is 0.72 of the average distance of the earth from the sun. Assuming circular orbits, determine, from a scaled diagram, the maximum angle at which Venus can appear either east or west of the sun (see Fig. 2-2).          *Ans.* 46°

On p. 19 the maximum angle observed is given as 48°. Why the discrepancy?

**2-7.**
(A) Make a diagram to show that, in a Ptolemaic system, Venus, under telescopic observation, would never show more than a crescent phase.
(B) On the diagram of Prob. 2-6, mark the positions of Venus, as viewed from the earth, for new, crescent, quarter, and full phases.

**2-8.** Sketch the appearance of Venus that you would expect to observe through a telescope at thin crescent, quarter, and full phases. (Note: As an object recedes from an observer, it appears to be smaller.)

**2-9.** The average distance of Mars from the sun is 1.52 times the average distance of the earth

from the sun. Diagram these orbits, and convince yourself that Mars should never show less than a gibbous phase.

**2-10.** Show, with the aid of a diagram, why, according to Kepler's laws, the solar day is longest when the earth is nearest the sun and shortest six months later.

**2-11.** The periods of revolution of Venus, the earth, and Mars are 0.615 year, 1.0 year, and 1.88 years respectively. Let the average distance from the sun to the earth be one unit. Then $K$ (equation 2-1) is equal to 1 for the earth. Calculate the value of $K$ for the other two planets. See Probs. 2-6 and 2-9 for further data.

**2-12.** The average distance of Jupiter from the sun is 5.20 times that of the earth. What is the period of revolution of Jupiter?
          *Ans.* About 12 years

## Suggested Readings

1. R. H. Baker, *An Introduction to Astronomy,* 5th edition (D. Van Nostrand, 1957), Chap. 11. Descriptions of constellations, including star maps.
2. W. T. Skilling and R. S. Richardson, *A Brief Text in Astronomy* (Henry Holt, 1954), Chap. 1. Also see p. 160 for photographs of various phases of Venus and pp. 303 ff. for monthly star maps.
3. Cecilia Payne-Gaposchkin, *Introduction to Astronomy* (Prentice-Hall, 1954), Chap. 1 and pp. 149–168.
4. G. Holton and D. H. D. Roller, *Foundations of Modern Physical Science* (Addison-Wesley, 1958). Excellent discussions of Ptolemaic system (Chap. 6), Copernican system (Chap. 7), Kepler's laws (Chap. 9), and Galileo's contribution to astronomy (Chap. 10).
5. H. Shapley and H. E. Howarth, *A Source Book in Astronomy* (McGraw-Hill, 1929). Excerpts from original works; see especially Copernicus (pp. 1–12), Kepler (pp. 29–40), and Galileo (pp. 41–57).

CHAPTER

3

Force and
the Production
of Motion

AT ABOUT the same time that Kepler was discovering and formulating the laws of planetary motion, Galileo was studying the very familiar terrestrial motion of a falling body. This problem had received considerable attention before Galileo's study, but ideas concerning terrestrial motion were muddled by Aristotelian doctrine, which stated that a body fell *because* it was seeking out its "natural place"—that is, the earth. This quite reasonable a-priori assumption as to *why* a body falls led logically to the conclusion that a body a hundred times as heavy as another would seek out its natural place a hundred times as vigorously and thus fall to the ground a hundred times as quickly. There is a story that Galileo dropped a heavy cannon ball and a small shot from the top of the Leaning Tower at Pisa to show that they reach the ground together. It is doubtful if Galileo ever performed this experiment. He must have known, however, that similar experiments had previously been performed and reported on; and in his writings he vigorously supported the expected result of simultaneous arrival as a necessary consequence of his theory of falling bodies. To be sure, in such an experiment the cannon ball actually reaches the ground slightly before the shot. Galileo argues, however, that one must not reject his theory because of this small discrepancy while overlooking the *large* discrepancies predicted by Aristotelian theory. He rightly ascribed the small discrepancy to the friction of the air† and regarded the failure of exactly simultaneous arrival as an experimental circumstance rather than a fundamental truth. Since a vacuum was not known in his time (many even believed the Aristotelian doctrine that a vacuum was impossible; see § 9-4), he

---

† The frictional resistance of the air is proportional to the area of the falling body, but the weight of the body is proportional to its volume. For spheres of same density (such as the cannon ball and the shot) the area increases as the square of the radius but the weight increases as the cube of the radius. Thus the air resistance increases less rapidly than the weight as the sphere becomes larger. Hence the air resistance is a *smaller fraction* of the weight for the cannon ball than for the shot. As a result, the cannon ball is less affected by the air than the shot. As an extreme example, a large raindrop falls to the ground quite rapidly while the small drops of water sprayed from an atomizer fall quite slowly.

could not test directly the effect of air on free fall. By "thinking away" the air he arrived at a deeper understanding of the phenomenon.

The constancy of the rate of fall of *all* freely falling bodies is an important discovery (see § 5-3). Even more important to the development of science was Galileo's method in studying this motion. He considered the question *why* a body fell to be premature before it was determined *how* it fell. Kepler had shown that the planets move in accordance with simple mathematical laws, and Galileo was convinced that mathematical laws could be found for the motions of terrestrial bodies also. In order to achieve this result, he had first to abstract the essential concepts that would lend themselves to mathematical treatment. These were the concepts of space and time, which had played an unimportant role in Aristotelian thought, since there the major emphasis was on why and not on how a body moved. Galileo gave the concepts of space and time the primary and fundamental character they have held in physical science ever since. He then made clear and unambiguous definitions of velocity and acceleration as useful quantities in the description of motion. His next step was to form hypotheses as to how a falling body moves. His first hypothesis, that the velocity of a falling body increases uniformly with the distance fallen, was soon found to involve a contradiction. Next he considered the hypothesis that the velocity increases with the time of fall. Since this involved no apparent contradictions, he then formulated the mathematical laws for this type of motion; and from those laws he deduced results that were amenable to experimental test. The results of the tests were in agreement with the predictions of the theory and thus confirmed the fundamental hypothesis that a freely falling body moves with a constant acceleration. This method, which was first outlined and applied by Galileo, and which involves the interplay of hypothesis, mathematical theory, and experimental test of predictions, is the foundation of modern scientific thought. History has shown that Galileo was indeed right when he remarked that his method in "the hands of other investigators will continually lead to wonderful new knowledge. It is conceivable that

in such a manner a worthy treatment may be gradually extended to all the realms of nature."

In this chapter we shall also develop a quantitative description of motion and discover the laws that apply to a freely falling body. We shall, however, use more modern techniques than were available to Galileo. Since the time of fall through convenient distances is much too short to be measured accurately by the methods of his time, he had to extend these times to convenient values by allowing his experimental bodies to fall down inclined planes. With modern clocks, the times of free fall may be easily measured, and thus this motion may be directly observed. Furthermore, we shall use more highly developed (and thus more powerful) mathematical tools than were available to Galileo. The ordinary high-school algebra of today is a much more convenient mode of quantitative statement than the analysis of Galileo's day. And, finally, we shall also use the graphical representation of algebraic relations. This device, invented by Descartes a generation after Galileo, is one of the most useful and powerful tools for analyzing experimental data.

## 3-1. *Length and Time*

Among the multitude of impressions obtained from observations of the many and varied motions in the world about us, two stand out as common to all kinds of motion. In every situation the body is changing its position in space as time passes. These fundamental concepts, space and time, are, at best, intuitive and are not capable of definition in simpler terms. On the other hand, with some mutual understanding, we can easily determine *how much* space or time we are talking about. All we need to do is to select, in a quite arbitrary way, a certain amount of extension in space and a certain interval of time and have everyone agree that these amounts shall each be one unit. Such an agreed-upon unit is called a **standard.** The number of times the standard is contained in any other length or interval gives a measure of that quantity.

Many standards of length have been set up in times past. The most familiar one is the yard.

It is the standard used in the civil life of English-speaking countries. Just how it originated is not known; perhaps the distance from a man's nose to the fingertips of his outstretched arm suggested the unit. At any rate, the yard is now accepted as the distance between two grooves of a metal bar maintained by the government. Since it is often inconvenient to measure a length in terms of the standard, multiples and sub-multiples of the standard are desirable. In the English system these were defined as needed and grew into a system with very awkward relations. You probably learned in elementary school that a yard contains three feet, that a foot contains twelve inches, and that inches are fractionated by successive halving; that five and a half yards equal a rod, and that 320 rods equal one mile. Since these numbers are in no way related to the *decimal* nature of our number system, conversions are very awkward: to change 1.63 miles into inches, for instance, would require considerable arithmetic.

Another set of units, called the metric system, has been universally adopted by scientists. In this system we obtain the multiples by either multiplying or dividing the standard by 10, 100, 1,000, etc. This is the system we shall use in this book. The standard length is called the **meter** (abbreviation, m). When the standard was defined, an attempt was made to set it at one ten-millionth of the distance from the equator of the earth to one of the poles. Subsequent measurements of the earth showed, however, that these distances are not quite equal. This is unimportant if everyone agrees that the meter is the distance between two grooves on a metal bar known as the international **standard meter.** The bar is made of a stable alloy of platinum and iridium and is in the custody of the French government. When used to calibrate secondary standards, the bar is held at the temperature of melting ice. The meter is approximately forty inches long, a little more than a yard. A convenient submultiple is the centimeter (cm), which is one hundredth of a meter; 1 m = 100 cm. This conversion is, of course, very simple; for instance, 1.63 m = 163 cm. For large distances, the multiple, kilometer (1,000 m), is equally convenient.

For a standard of time, what is needed is some definite, reproducible amount of time, and any cyclic phenomenon would serve this purpose. The cycle that has been used since early times is the apparent revolution of the sun round the heavens. In its diurnal motion the sun reaches a highest point in the sky about twelve o'clock and approximately twenty-four hours later is again highest in the sky. The time for this cycle is called a solar day. Unfortunately, this is a slightly different amount of time each day. The length of the solar day gradually increases until just before Christmas; then it starts decreasing, and it reaches a minimum toward the end of June, whereupon the cycle starts again. The average value, called the mean solar day, determines the time kept by clocks in all countries. This day is subdivided into hours, minutes, and seconds. For scientific purposes the **second** is the most convenient unit of time. It is defined as 1/86,400 of the mean solar day. Awkward as this standard may seem, it is quite constant and is capable of precise observation. Governments maintain observatories where standard clocks are constantly checked against the motion of the sun and from which time signals are broadcast so that all clocks may be calibrated to keep the same time.

The variation in the solar day can be understood by reference to Figure 2-5 (p. 28). Consider the earth at any point in its orbit. The sun, located at $F$, will appear overhead to an appropriate observer on the earth. If the earth remained in the same position, the sun, after one complete rotation of the earth, would again appear to be overhead. But, while rotating once on its axis, the earth also moves along its orbit to $E'$. Hence, to bring the observer round to the line $E'F$ (and thus have the sun again appear overhead), the earth will have to turn somewhat more than one rotation after leaving the position we started with. A little consideration of the geometry of Figure 2-5 will show that this extra rotation is equal to the angle Earth–$F$–$E'$. According to Kepler's second law, this angle is a maximum when the earth is at $P$ (December 22) and a minimum when the earth is at $A$ (June 22). Thus the solar day, as defined, is constantly changing as stated in the previous paragraph.

## 3-2. Constant Velocity

We are now prepared to formulate a quantitative description of motion in terms of distance and time. We shall formulate the definitions for **rectilinear motion**—that is, for the motion of an object along a straight line. If you wish to be specific, you may think of an automobile moving along a level, straight stretch of road. But note that what we have to say is true for any body as long as the motion is rectilinear. The body is already in motion when we begin to observe it. As it passes some arbitrarily chosen point (*O*), we start a clock and measure the time the body takes to travel to other points (*A, B,* etc.) at measured distances from *O* along the line. Thus we might arrive at a series of measurements such as those in Table 3-1.

An inspection of these data will immediately reveal a relation. The distance from *O* to *B* is just twice that from *O* to *A*. But the time of travel from *O* to *B* is also twice that from *O* to *A*. This suggests a constant ratio of distance to time, which the data will confirm. For instance, for point *B* we have $\dfrac{24 \text{ meters}}{4 \text{ seconds}} = 6\,\dfrac{\text{m}}{\text{sec}}$. It can easily be verified that the same value is obtained from the data of all the points. Furthermore, we need not consider only distances from *O*. Between *A* and *C* the body moved 18 meters and took 3 seconds to do it. We see that the ratio of the change in the position of the body to the time required for the change is again $6\,\dfrac{\text{m}}{\text{sec}}$. Other pairs of points lead to the same result. We can summarize all these results by using *s* to represent the position of the body, as measured from some arbi-

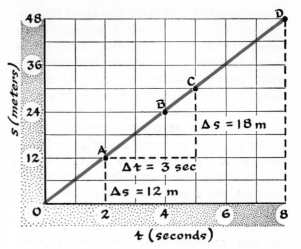

FIGURE **3-1** *Distance-time graph for constant velocity of 6 m/sec.*

trarily chosen point (*O* in this case), and by using Δ to stand for the phrase "the change in." Then the symbols Δ*s* would read "the change in position." (Note that this does *not* mean Δ multiplied by *s*, as is usual in algebraic notation.) Similarly, Δ*t* would stand for the corresponding change in time. Then all the above results are included in the equation

$$\frac{\Delta s}{\Delta t} = 6\,\frac{\text{m}}{\text{sec}}$$

This ratio is, *by definition,* the **velocity** of the body. (More critically, it is the speed. The distinction between velocity and speed will be made in § 5-1.) When this ratio remains constant throughout a particular motion, the body is said to have a **constant velocity.** A little thought will show, furthermore, that any other case of constant velocity can be described by this same statement, the only difference being in the numerical value of the ratio. Another body might be moving so as to cover—for example— 8.3 meters every second.

Although the situation that led to the data of Table 3-1 is possible, most observations do not yield such convenient numbers, and the quantitative analysis of the data is not usually so simple. A much more useful and powerful method of analyzing data is derived from a graphical representation of the observations. The method is very general

|  | TABLE | **3-1** | *Motion with Constant Velocity* |
|---|---|---|---|

| POINT | DISTANCE FROM *O* IN METERS | TIME OF TRAVEL FROM *O* IN SEC |
|---|---|---|
| *O* | 0 | 0 |
| *A* | 12 | 2 |
| *B* | 24 | 4 |
| *C* | 30 | 5 |
| *D* | 48 | 8 |

and is applicable to a series of observations of any pair of related quantities. Certain technical aspects of graphing data are discussed in Appendix I and should be studied at this time. The graph of the data of Table 3-1 is shown in Figure 3-1. Distances are plotted as ordinates, with one space representing 6 meters, and times as abscissae, with one space representing one second. Each pair of measurements of Table 3-1 is represented by a point (labeled here but not usually labeled). The curve joining the experimental points—that is, the graph—is, in this case, a straight line through the origin. The velocity ratios discussed above are ratios of quantities represented by line segments. For instance, the 48 meters to $D$ is represented by the perpendicular dropped from point $D$ to the time axis, and the 8 seconds travel time is represented by the line from $O$ to 8 along the time axis. The ratio of these two is, of course, 6 $\frac{m}{sec}$. Similarly for other points. Furthermore, $\Delta s$ and $\Delta t$ between any two points can be found (as shown) by appropriate differences of the coordinates.

*So long as the graph is a straight line through the origin,* the ratios of ordinate to abscissa, or of change in ordinate to corresponding change

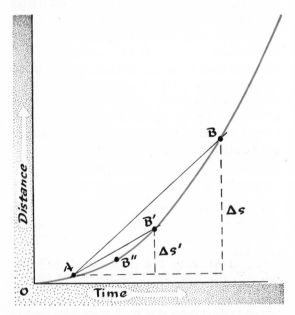

FIGURE **3-2** *Distance-time graph for rectilinear motion with constantly increasing velocity.*

in abscissa, have a constant value, since they are ratios of corresponding sides of similar right triangles. Two general statements can now be made. The first is that, if a distance-time graph is a straight line, the body is moving with constant velocity. The second is still more general. A careful consideration of the discussion of a straight-line graph will show that there is nothing in the method that limits it to distance-time measurements. We can therefore say that, if the graph of a series of measurements of two related quantities is a straight line through the origin, the ratio of the two quantities is a constant. This constant, called the slope, gives a measure of how steeply the graph is rising. The value of the slope can be determined from the graph. This is a very useful technique, which we shall use frequently.

## 3-3. Average and Instantaneous Velocity

Only infrequently does the rectilinear motion of a body proceed with constant velocity. Usually the velocity is changing. To deal with this situation, we shall need to develop the concepts of *average velocity* and *instantaneous velocity*. Suppose that a series of distance-time measurements of a rectilinear motion yields the graph shown in Figure 3-2. Here the graph joining the experimental points is no longer straight but curves upward. Intuitively we see that this represents the motion of a body that is moving at a constantly increasing velocity since during successive equal intervals of time successively larger intervals of distance are traversed. Consider any two points along the path of travel, such as $A$ and $B$. We can, from the graph, easily evaluate $\Delta s$ and $\Delta t$ between these points. Their ratio gives the constant velocity represented by the straight line $AB$. The actual motion, of course, is represented by the *curved* line $AB$. However, if, when the body reached point $A$, it began to move with this fictitious constant velocity and maintained it for the time $\Delta t$, it would cover the same distance, $\Delta s$, as that covered by the actual motion during the same time interval. This constant velocity that would carry the body, during a given time, the same distance as the actual motion is called the **average velocity** between the two points in question. If we let the symbol $v_{av}$ represent average velocity, then, by definition,

$$v_{av} = \frac{\Delta s}{\Delta t}$$

Note that this statement will hold for *any* portion of a rectilinear motion. You can think of many examples. You might, for instance, get into an automobile, start slowly, increase your velocity, and then level off at some suitable speed. Sixty seconds after starting you might have traveled 120 meters. Your average velocity over this course would then be 2 m/sec. During the first 30 seconds of the trip, however, you might have traveled only 45 meters; for this part of the run you traveled at an ·average rate of 1.5 m/sec.

The concept of instantaneous velocity is implicit in much of the preceding discussion and certainly would be very useful in discussions of non-uniform motion. How can we talk about the velocity of a body at any given instant? Suppose that we wish to know the velocity of the body at the instant when it is at $A$ in Figure 3-2. We have already seen how to determine the average velocity between $A$ and some later point, $B$. Now let us repeat this calculation but use some point nearer $A$, such as $B'$. The average velocity over this smaller interval of time is less than that from $A$ to $B$. This is readily shown by the fact that the straight line $AB'$ does not rise as sharply as the straight line $AB$ and thus represents a smaller velocity. (A comparison of the $\Delta s$'s and $\Delta t$'s will lead to the same conclusion.) Furthermore, the straight line $AB'$ is more nearly coincident with the curved line $AB'$ than the straight line $AB$ is with the curved line $AB$. That is, the average velocity for the interval $AB'$ represents a motion more nearly identical with the observed motion. We now repeat the calculation for a point still nearer to $A$, such as $B''$. (We have not drawn in the straight line $AB''$, for it would be difficult to distinguish from the actual graph.) Over this small interval the motion represented by the average velocity is very nearly the observed one. It is also clear from

the graph that the slope of $AB''$ is not as much less than $AB'$ as $AB'$ is less than $AB$ although $\Delta t$ has been approximately halved in each case. This shows that, as we compute the average velocity over successively smaller intervals of time from $A$, the value changes by smaller and smaller amounts and gets closer and closer to some particular value. This value is called the *limit* of the series of computations and is, by definition, the instantaneous velocity at $A$. With this idea of a limit we can now make a succinct definition of *instantaneous velocity* as the *limit that the average velocity approaches as the time interval is made successively smaller.*† Arduous as the process may seem, it gives an unambiguous and meaningful definition in terms of operations with measurable quantities. This concept of a limit is an extremely powerful method for dealing with continuously changing quantities. We shall have occasion to use it again.

## 3-4. Acceleration

When we describe a motion whose velocity is changing, a useful concept is **acceleration.** We *define* acceleration as the *ratio of the change in velocity to the corresponding change in time.* Once the distance-time graph is determined from experiment, the instantaneous velocities at various times can be determined as outlined above. The velocities are then plotted against time, and we get a velocity-time graph for the motion being considered. This graph may be a straight line or may be curved. In either case it can be treated exactly as the distance-time graphs are treated above. If we let $v$ symbolize instantaneous velocity, the average acceleration is

$$a_{av} = \frac{\Delta v}{\Delta t}$$

and the **instantaneous acceleration** $(a)$ is *the limit that the average acceleration approaches as the time interval is made successively smaller.* These

---

† Notice that, as the limit is approached, the secants $AB$, $AB'$, etc. approach the tangent to the curve at point $A$. One can therefore obtain reasonably accurate values of the instantaneous velocity by constructing the tangent to the distance-time graph at the point required and computing the constant velocity represented by this straight line.

definitions are quite general. The unit of acceleration, a derived one, is meters per second per second. Algebraically this is $\dfrac{m/sec}{sec}$, which reduces to m/sec².

## 3-5. *Rectilinear Motion with Constant Acceleration*

One of the most important motions for our purposes is one in which the body starts from rest and moves along a straight line with constant acceleration. The distance-time graph for such a motion is similar to that shown in Figure 3-2. The instantaneous velocity at the origin is zero and, as can be seen, gets greater as time progresses. By determining $v$ at a number of points and plotting these against the time, we obtain the velocity-time graph shown in Figure 3-3. The linearity of this graph shows that the acceleration is constant. At the start of this motion, $v$, $s$, and $t$ are all zero; so, if we consider changes *from the starting point*, $\Delta v$, $\Delta s$, and $\Delta t$ become the instantaneous values of these quantities. For this motion, therefore, the definition of acceleration becomes

$$a = \frac{v}{t} \qquad (3\text{-}1)$$

Another useful aspect of graphs is illustrated in Figure 3-4. This is a velocity-time graph of

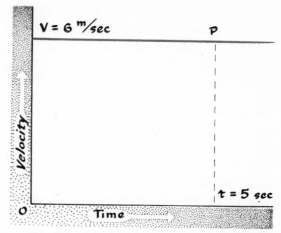

FIGURE **3-4** *Velocity-time graph for constant velocity.*

the simple situation of a constant velocity of 6 m/sec. Obviously the distance traveled in any time, $t$, such as 5 seconds, is $vt$, or 6 m/sec × 5 sec = 30 m. But note that this distance is represented by the *area OvPt*; the area under a velocity-time graph represents the distance moved. (This is a general aspect of graphs: the area under the graph represents the product of the two variables.) Now refer again to Figure 3-3. The distance traveled in any time, $t$, is given by the area of the triangle $OPt$. But the average velocity during this same time is the constant velocity that would carry the body the same distance. From the geometry of the straight-line graph of Figure 3-3 it is clear that, for the motion we are considering, the average velocity ($v_{av}$) is half of the final instantaneous velocity (that is, $v/2$) since the shaded triangular areas must be equal. But from our general definition of average velocity we have $v_{av} = s/t$ if $s$ is the total distance traveled in time $t$. Hence we have two ways of expressing the average velocity, and the two expressions must, of course, be equal. Therefore

$$\frac{s}{t} = \frac{v}{2} \qquad (3\text{-}2)$$

Equations 3-1 and 3-2 completely describe the motions under consideration and give us quantitative relations for dealing with such motions. Notice that four quantities are involved —$a$, $v$, $t$, and $s$—and that both equations involve both $v$ and $t$. Two very convenient relations can

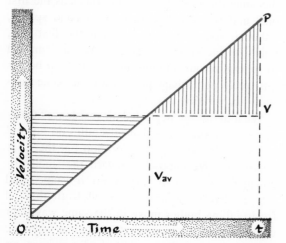

FIGURE **3-3** *Velocity-time graph for rectilinear motion starting from rest and with constant acceleration.*

be found in which either $v$ or $t$ is not explicit. Solve equation 3-1 for $v$, substitute this value in equation 3-2, and you have

$$s = \tfrac{1}{2}at^2 \qquad (3\text{-}3)$$

You can also find this formula by determining the area under the graph of Figure 3-3. Try it. If we eliminate $t$, we have

$$v^2 = 2as \qquad (3\text{-}4)$$

These equations are consistent in units, and, since they follow by the logic of mathematics from equations 3-1 and 3-2, we must have confidence in their ability to describe the motion just as accurately.

A rote memorizing of equations 3-1–3-4 would not be very effective. If the story behind them is understood, they become meaningful and express useful relations. Finally, we must remember that they apply only to rectilinear motion that starts from rest and proceeds with constant acceleration.

## 3-6. Free Fall

We now have the tools for investigating linear motions. An important case is that of a freely falling body.† Unless supported in some manner, any material body will move toward the center of the earth with increasing velocity. What is the nature of this acceleration produced by the pull of gravity? Let us assume that the acceleration is constant and perform an experiment to test the correctness of our hypothesis.

To be sure that we are studying only the effect of gravity, we must arrange our experiment so that other agencies that might affect the motion are eliminated. Such agencies, except the resistance of the air, are easily eliminated. To minimize the effect of the air, we shall use steel spheres as the moving bodies in our experiment. By using such a dense material, bounded by a smooth and relatively small surface, we may assume that the air resistance, compared with the weight, is negligible. Thus we assume

that the spheres are free of all influences except the pull of gravity—that is, that they are freely falling. A large electric stop clock, which measures time to hundredths of a second, measures the time of fall. A steel sphere is held by an electromagnet. The magnet and the clock are connected in such a way that the sphere is released by the pushing of a button and the clock is started at the same instant. After falling a measured distance, the sphere strikes a switch and stops the clock. Thus a series of direct measurements of distance and time are made.

To test our hypothesis, we must determine whether the observed motion is in accord with the theoretical predictions for constantly accelerated motion that we developed in the previous section. Equation 3-3 says that the ratio of the distance to the time squared is a constant. Furthermore, this constant is equal to half of the acceleration—that is, $s/t^2 = a/2$. To test our data, we construct a graph with distances as ordinates and times squared as abscissae. This graph turns out to be linear and thus establishes that the acceleration due to gravity is constant. Also, two times the slope of our graph of $s$ vs. $t^2$ is equal to the acceleration of the freely falling sphere.

We now repeat our experiment with a sphere of very different weight from the first one. It soon becomes apparent that, within the precision of our experiment, this sphere falls through the same distances in the same times as the first one, and we conclude that this second sphere, although somewhat heavier than the first one, falls with the same acceleration. We are tempted to generalize our findings and say that *all* bodies fall freely at a given place with the same constant acceleration.

What about the neglected air resistance? Careful observation shows that all bodies do not fall with *exactly* the same acceleration but that they *almost* do. We choose to regard the small discrepancies as due to varying air resistance and thus as irrelevant to the central truth that all freely falling bodies move in the same way. Our confidence in this view is strengthened when we repeat our experiment with bodies whose air resistance is lessened (such as those with more polished and streamlined surfaces) and find that

† This was Galileo's problem.

the actual motion more nearly agrees with the "idealized" statements of equations 3-1–3-4, which are the laws for this type of motion. And finally, when we are able to remove the air from a glass tube by means of a vacuum pump and observe the truly simultaneous fall of a light feather and a heavy coin, our hypothesis is completely confirmed.

The acceleration due to gravity is usually represented by the letter $g$. Although $g$ is constant for all bodies at a particular place, careful experiments show that it changes both with latitude and with altitude. Some values at sea level are: at New York, 9.80 m/sec²; at the equator, 9.78 m/sec²; at the North Pole, 9.83 m/sec². On top of Pikes Peak (approximately at the same latitude as New York) $g = 9.79$ m/sec². Since these vary by less than 1 percent, we may generally use the convenient value $g = 9.8$ m/sec².

## Concepts and Terms

Length and Time
  standard meter
  standard second
Graphical Representation of Data
Velocity
  constant velocity
  average velocity
  instantaneous velocity
Concept of a Limit

Acceleration
    constant Acceleration
  average acceleration
  instantaneous acceleration
Rectilinear Motion Starting from Rest and with Constant Acceleration
  formulas for this motion
Freely Falling Bodies
  experimental test for constant acceleration
  values of $g$

## Problems

**3-1.** Consider the following two propositions:
  (A) From the center of a room, step halfway to a wall. Then step half the remaining distance, and so go on, always halving the remaining distance to the wall. Will you ever reach the wall?
  (B) Achilles and the tortoise are to run a 200 meter race. Since Achilles can run 100 times as fast as the tortoise, the tortoise is given a 100 meter head start. Achilles runs the first 100 meters while the tortoise runs 1 meter. While Achilles runs the next meter, the tortoise runs 1/100 meter and is still ahead. And so on. Does Achilles win the race? (Note: If Achilles can pass the tortoise, then, by the same argument, he wins easily.)

According to the classical Greek mathematics (which dominates your high-school geometry), the answer to both questions is "no." According to modern mathematics, the answer is "yes." Discuss.

**3-2.** A body starts from rest and is observed to travel the distances shown in the table during the given times. Calculate the average velocity be-

| $s$ (m) | $t$ (sec) |
|---|---|
| 0 | 0 |
| 1.00 | 1.0 |
| 4.00 | 2.0 |
| 4.41 | 2.1 |
| 4.84 | 2.2 |
| 6.25 | 2.5 |
| 9.00 | 3.0 |
| 16.0 | 4.0 |

tween $t = 2$ and $t = 4$ sec. Repeat for $2 \rightarrow 3$ sec and so on for the other times greater than 2 sec, always starting at $t = 2$ sec. What is the approximate instantaneous velocity at $t = 2$ sec?

*Ans.* 4.0 m/sec

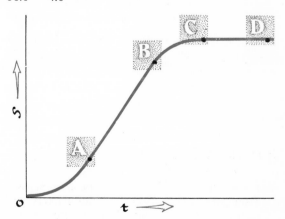

FIGURE **P3-3**

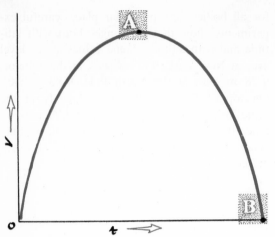

FIGURE **P3-4**

**3-3.** Fig. P3-3 shows the graph of distance against time for the motion of a certain object. Describe the motion from $O$ to $A$; from $A$ to $B$; from $B$ to $C$; from $C$ to $D$.

**3-4.** Fig. P3-4 shows the graph of velocity against time for one swing of the end of a pendulum, from an extreme position ($O$) through the center ($A$) to the other extreme position ($B$). Is the graph a reasonable representation of observation?
(A) Compare the instantaneous accelerations at $O$, $A$, and $B$.
(B) If the axes showed numerical scales for $v$ and $t$, how could you determine from the graph the distance the end of the pendulum moved during the time from $O$ to $B$?

**3-5.** Derive equations 3-3 and 3-4.

**3-6.** A body starts from rest and 8 sec later is moving with a velocity of 6 m/sec. What is the acceleration, and how far did it move?
*Ans.* $a = 0.75$ m/sec$^2$; $s = 24$ m

**3-7.** A body starts from rest and after traveling 300 m is moving at the rate of 35 m/sec. What is the acceleration?
*Ans.* 2.04 m/sec$^2$

**3-8.** An object dropped from a bridge over a river is observed to strike the water 5 sec later. How high is the bridge above the water?
*Ans.* 123 m

**3-9.** A bullet is fired vertically up with a velocity of 294 m/sec. How long and how high will it rise? (Remember that the acceleration due to gravity produces a 9.8 m/sec *change* of velocity *downward* each second.)
*Ans.* 30 sec; $4.41 \times 10^3$ m

**3-10.** In the free-fall experiment, calculate the velocity of the ball after 0.5 sec; after 0.75 sec; after 1.0 sec.
*Ans.* 4.9; 7.4; 9.8 m/sec

**3-11.** Plot a velocity-time graph of the answers of Prob. 3-10. From this graph determine the distance fallen in 0.6 sec. Verify by use of equation 3-3.

**3-12.** Show by graphical analysis that the data of the table in Prob. 3-2 represent a motion of constant acceleration equal to 2 m/sec$^2$.

**3-13.** An automobile, when first observed, is moving at the rate of 5 m/sec; in other words, the starting velocity is *not* zero but is 5 m/sec when $t = 0$. Subsequently, the velocity is observed to be as shown in the table.

| $v$ m/sec | $t$ sec |
|-----------|---------|
| 5 | 0 |
| 8 | 1 |
| 11 | 2 |
| 14 | 3 |
| 17 | 4 |

(A) Plot the data, and show that the motion is uniformly accelerated at the rate of 3 m/sec$^2$.
(B) Show that the velocity at any time is $v = 5$ m/sec $+ 3tm/$sec$^2$ (see Prob. I-10).
(C) From the graph of A find the distance traveled during the first 4 sec.
*Ans.* 44 m

**3-14.** Generalize the situation of Prob. 3-13, and show that, if a constantly accelerated body has velocity $v_0$ when $t = 0$, at any time ($t$) later $v = v_0 + at$ and $s = v_0 t + at^2/2$. (Note: For the case where $v_0 = 0$—that is, starting from rest—these relations reduce to equations 3-1 and 3-3.)

## Suggested Readings

1. L. W. Taylor, *Physics the Pioneer Science* (Houghton Mifflin, 1941). An introductory text including interesting historical background (see pp. 1–30).

2. H. Semat, *Fundamentals of Physics*, 3rd edition (Rinehart, 1957), pp. 42–61. Formulation of rectilinear motion with initial velocity not zero.

3. L. Hogben, *Mathematics for the Million* (W. W. Norton, 1937), pp. 507–520. A discussion of slopes.

4. G. Holton and D. H. D. Roller, *Foundations of Modern Physical Science* (Addison-Wesley, 1958), Chap. 1 (formulation of rectilinear motion) and Chap. 2 (discussion of Galileo's study of freely falling bodies).

5. W. F. Magie, *A Source Book in Physics* (McGraw-Hill, 1935). Valuable short biographies and excerpts from original works. See pp. 1–17, on Galileo's study of freely falling bodies.

6. Galileo Galilei, *Dialogues Concerning Two New Sciences,* translated by H. Crew and A. DeSalvio (Macmillan, 1914), pp. 61–67 of the "First Day," pp. 153–187 and 215–218 of the "Third Day."

7. A. N. Whitehead, *Essays in Science and Philosophy* (Philosophical Library, 1947), pp. 227–242.

IN THIS chapter we shall develop the concepts of inertia and force and discuss their relation as this was stated by Sir Isaac Newton in his famous three laws of motion.

## 4-1. Concepts of Inertia and Force

The inertia of matter is one of its familiar properties. It is common experience that a passenger in an automobile is "thrown forward" when the brakes are applied and, indeed, if no counterbalancing effect were present (such as pressure of the floor boards), would hit the windshield. In the absence of any external agency acting on him, the passenger would maintain his uniform forward motion and would thus catch up with the windshield, which would be slowing down under the action of the brakes. The reverse is true in starting. The passenger is disturbed from his state of rest by the push of the seat on his back while the automobile is being accelerated. As soon as a constant velocity is acquired, the push disappears. Many other examples will come to mind.

Consider a ball at rest on a long horizontal table. The pull of gravity is counterbalanced by the table, and the ball will remain at rest until some other agency acts upon it. A slight push will start it rolling, and it will continue to roll in a straight line. Eventually it will stop; for it is not, after all, entirely free of external effects: there is friction between the two surfaces. As the friction is reduced (the ball and the table may be made of harder materials, or the surfaces polished, or both), the ball is observed to roll greater distances as a result of the same starting push. We conclude that in the *ideal* situation of no friction the ball would roll indefinitely. It was experiments of this kind that led Galileo, early in the seventeenth century, to reject the currently accepted idea that some agency outside a body was necessary to maintain its motion. This argument of the Aristotelian scholars of Galileo's time is not far from contemporary common-sense opinion. Since, in ordinary experience, friction is always present (often to a great extent), bodies come to rest *apparently* on their own account. Rest was therefore

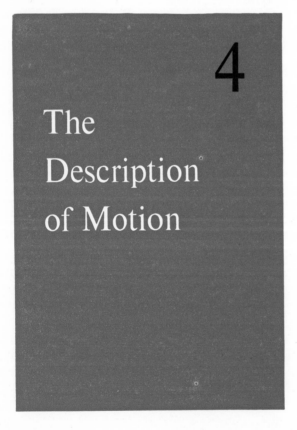

CHAPTER

4

The
Description
of Motion

considered the natural state of all terrestrial bodies, and some cause was deemed necessary just to keep a moving body going. On the other hand, Galileo realized that friction is merely one of many agencies that may change the motion of a body. By "thinking away" the friction he arrived at a deeper understanding of the nature of physical bodies. He concluded that all bodies *naturally* maintain their instantaneous motion, and that an agency is required *only to change* the motion. In this view "rest" is merely the special case of zero velocity and is no more a natural state than constant velocity along a straight line. This fundamental property of all matter—resistance to a change of motion—is called *inertia*. We cannot explain this observed property in other terms. We simply accept the fact that physical bodies are characterized by inertia.

The concept of force is implied in the preceding discussion. The word "force," which in everyday language may mean many things, is used in science to mean the agency that overcomes inertia and changes the motion of a body. In other words, **force** *is that which accelerates a body.*† Note the generality of the concept. We need not know the nature or origin of forces although we shall categorize them as gravitational force, electric force, etc. All we need in order to recognize that a force is present is to observe the changing motion of a body. Notice also that a force is not directly observable. It is known only by its observable effects.

The discussion so far has been qualitative, and we shall, of course, need a quantitative way of dealing with these concepts. The concept of inertia, like the concepts of length and time (§ 3-1), is fundamentally undefinable. We may, however, choose an arbitrary amount of inertia as a standard unit and measure the inertia of other bodies by this unit. A body's inertia, measured by the standard unit, is called its **mass.** *Inertia* is a qualitative word describing a fundamental property of all material bodies; *mass* is a quantitative word referring to the amount of inertia, measured by an arbitrary unit, that

---

† A change in motion may be either a change (increase or decrease) in speed or a change in direction. We shall see in the next chapter that in *either* case the body experiences an acceleration. The definition of force is therefore completely general.

a particular body has. Force, then, can be defined in terms of mass and the acceleration that the force produces. Acceleration, however, is defined in terms of length and time (§ 3-4). Force is therefore defined in terms of the three fundamental undefined concepts of mass, length, and time.

## 4-2. *Mass*

The standard unit of mass is the kilogram (kgm). This unit, like that of length, is necessarily quite arbitrary. At Sèvres, France (along with the standard meter), there is a cylinder of platinum-iridium alloy. The amount of inertia displayed by this cylinder is, by international agreement, the **standard kilogram.** Accurate replicas of this standard are kept at the bureaus of standards of governments throughout the world. Secondary standards are made from these and distributed to laboratories, manufacturers, etc.

It may seem strange that the standard mass has a name implying that it is 1,000 times a smaller mass. The reasons for this are mostly historical. Late in the eighteenth century a standard of mass, called the gram, was defined as the amount of inertia offered by 1 cm³ of water at 4°C. This had the advantage that water is readily and inexpensively available everywhere. It had the very great disadvantages of inaccuracy of measurement, due to the small amount, the rapid evaporation of water, and the difficulty of precise determinations of volume. An attempt was made to have the present standard equal to 1,000 times the original gram. The fact that this is not quite so is no more important than that the meter is not exactly equal to 1/10,000,000 of a quadrant of the earth. The difference between the masses of 1/1,000 of the standard kilogram and 1 cm³ of water is less than 0.01 percent.

There are several methods of comparing an unknown mass with the standard—that is, of measuring mass. The method that is most direct and most free of logical flaws involves the interaction of two masses. From the discussion so far it is clear that, if the *same* force acts on each of two bodies, the body with the smaller mass

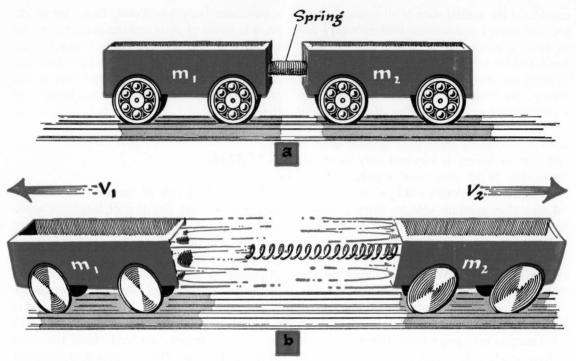

FIGURE 4-1 *Inertia cars for determining mass.*

will receive the larger acceleration, and vice versa. The force may be a magnetic or gravitational attraction, or a mechanical or electrical repulsion between the two bodies. The nature and amount of the force are irrelevant so long as the bodies are accelerated by the same interaction. The method can be understood and the meaning of mass clarified by a consideration of the "inertia car" experiment. The apparatus is shown schematically in Figure 4-1. The wheels of the cars turn on carefully machined bearings, which reduce friction to a negligible minimum. The wheels roll on a horizontal steel track. Since the track is horizontal, the pull of gravity is balanced out and does not enter into the experiment. When the cars are pushed together, the spring attached to $m_2$ is compressed. The cars are then released. The expanding spring pushes *equally* on both cars and accelerates them until they are separated. Not only is the force on each body the same at any instant, but it acts for the *same time*—from the moment of release until the spring becomes disengaged. An inspection of equation 3-1 shows that for equal times accelerations are proportional to final velocities.

We have already indicated that mass is inversely proportional to acceleration if the same force is acting. Therefore

$$\frac{m_1}{m_2} = \frac{v_2}{v_1}$$

and

$$m_1 = m_2 \frac{v_2}{v_1}$$

Since the velocities are measurable, $m_1$ is measured in terms of $m_2$. If $m_2$ is the arbitrarily defined standard, we now have a method of measuring other masses in terms of it. For example, if the standard moves off with a velocity of 4 m/sec ($= v_2$) and the unknown moves off with a velocity of 2 m/sec ($= v_1$), the unknown ($m_1$) has a mass of 2 kgm. Note that the method involves *no measurement* of force. The method assumes only that the interaction of the two bodies is the *same* in both directions—an assumption amply verified by experience. The method thus avoids the circularity of defining force in terms of mass and mass in terms of force.

## 4-3. Newton's Laws of Motion

The concepts of mass and force were not as readily accepted and clarified as might be indicated by the brief discussion above. The whole development occupied two generations, starting with Galileo and ending with Newton. Although much of modern mechanics is implicit in the work of Galileo, his great contribution was the effect his work had on the thinking of his contemporaries and immediate successors. It is difficult for us to appreciate Galileo's battle. He had to combat the strongly entrenched science of the Scholastics, which was primarily one of purpose and was not much concerned with quantitative discrepancies between predictions and observations. Galileo in his work took the opposite view. For him the task of science was the formulation of unambiguous definitions and the development of concepts and hypotheses that would lead to quantitative agreement with observation. He has rightly been called the father of modern science. By the time Newton arrived on the scene, however, the battle had been mostly won, and he could direct his brilliant energies to problems *in* science rather than to establishing new attitudes and methods *for* science. Newton was born the same year Galileo died (1642). He attended Cambridge University, where at the age of twenty-seven he was appointed professor of mathematics, a post he held for the next twenty-six years. During this time he conducted investigations in many fields, the most important of which were in mechanics.

In 1687 Newton published the *Principia*† —probably the greatest single book in the literature of science. In the *Principia* Newton formulated three laws governing the motion of all material bodies, which laws are still the basis of the science of mechanics. He also stated his law of gravitation and showed that it governs the motions of falling bodies on the earth and the motions of the planets in their orbits. He thus brought together under one interconnected set of laws all the various, and apparently different, problems of motion; and he established a mechanical view of the world that dominated the thinking of scientists for two hundred years.

To attain a full appreciation of the magnitude of Newton's scientific achievement, we should have to make a more extensive study of the period than is consistent with the purposes of this text. It was a period of great intellectual activity. After Galileo, more and more able scientists (and there were many able ones) were accepting the "New Philosophy"—the quantitative, experimental study of nature. New and powerful mathematical techniques were invented to implement this study. Scientific societies were founded, and their members vigorously defended and criticized one another's work. Through these societies and through the young art of printing, men of different countries who were working on related problems were able to communicate more freely with one another. Science had become international. It was the genius of Newton to see the relations among the many excellent researches in mechanics and to synthesize them all in his laws of motion and of gravitation. He modestly acknowledges his debt to others, however, by saying that if he had seen further "it is by standing on the shoulders of giants." Among these giants Whitehead singles out Descartes and Huygens in addition to the great terminal figures (Galileo and Newton) and remarks that the results of the work of these four men (which culminated in the formulation of the laws of motion and gravitation) "has some right to be considered as the greatest single intellectual success which mankind has achieved."†

We now turn to a brief discussion of the laws of motion. The three laws may be stated as follows:

1. Every material body maintains its state of rest or of uniform motion in a straight line unless compelled to change that state by external forces.
2. The acceleration produced by a force is directly proportional to the magnitude of the force and inversely proportional to the mass of the accelerated body; and the acceleration is in the direction of the force.

---

† *Naturalis Philosophiae Principia Mathematica* (Mathematical Principles of Natural Philosophy).

† A. N. Whitehead, *Science and the Modern World*.

3. For every force there is always an equal and opposite force; or the actions of two bodies on each other are always equal in magnitude and oppositely directed.

The first aspect of these laws to be noticed is that they are not of the type of physical law that states empirically discovered relations between varying quantities. Rather they constitute a set of definitions of the fundamental concepts of dynamics and state the quantitative relations between them. The evolution of these key concepts is a major accomplishment, but the fame of the three laws rests equally upon their great practical success in the treatment of moving bodies.

The first law states the principle of inertia and gives a qualitative definition of force. This law —sometimes called the law of inertia—is a direct denial of the Aristotelian dogma of rest as the "natural" state of bodies. The discussion earlier in this chapter was directed toward an understanding of these ideas.

The second law is a quantitative definition of force. The definition is given in the form of a proportion and may be symbolized as

$$a \propto \frac{F}{m}$$

It is clear that this expresses the ideas of force and mass as we have developed them, with the acceleration giving a measure of the change of motion. If we wish, for instance, to produce the same acceleration on a body of twice the mass of another, we must apply a force that is twice as large. On the other hand, the same force will produce an acceleration three times as great for a body whose mass is one-third that of another; and so on. Stated in this form, the law will hold for *any* set of units of the three quantities. Since it is more fruitful to work with equations, we rewrite the law as

$$a = K \frac{F}{m} \tag{4-1}$$

in which $K$ is a constant determined by the *particular* set of units employed. The units for $a$ and $m$ are already defined in terms of the arbitrary standards of length, time, and mass, which leave $K$ and $F$ for further definition. One unit of force might be taken (quite arbitrarily)

as the gravitational pull of the earth on the standard mass at some specified place such as the Bureau of Standards at Washington, D. C. The constant $K$ would then have to be assigned a value (both magnitude and units) that would make equation 4-1 consistent with the other units and with experience. This is done, in fact, in engineering practice, and the unit is called the pound of force. (The standard of mass used is, of course, the pound mass.†) This unit, like the other English units, has the advantage of historical familiarity and thus seems to have a convenient size, but a unit of force so defined is really both awkward and provincial—awkward since the value of $K$ must appear in all calculations, provincial since the value depends on the gravitational pull at a particular point in the universe.

A universal (and therefore a scientifically more useful) unit of force may be defined in terms of the fundamental units of length, mass, and time. Let us say (again quite arbitrarily) that the numerical value of $K$ is 1 and that it has no units—that is, is a pure number. Equation 4-1 then becomes

$$F = ma \tag{4-2}$$

The unit of force, then, is the force that will give a mass of 1 kgm an acceleration of 1 m/sec². This amount of force is called one **newton.** In the fundamental units of mass, length, and time, 1 newton is 1 kgm m/sec².

The deceptively simple relation expressed in equation 4-2 is fundamental to all problems of moving bodies. As a simple example consider again the inertia-car experiment. Suppose that the time required for the cars to spring apart is measured as 0.5 second. If the acceleration is constant, the 2 kgm mass is accelerated at the rate of 4 m/sec², and the spring is therefore pushing on it with a force of

$$F = 2 \text{ kgm } 4 \text{ m/sec}^2 = 8 \text{ kgm m/sec}^2 = 8 \text{ newtons}$$

A similar calculation for the standard mass shows that the spring also pushes on it with a force of 8 newtons. In this situation the only

---

† The standard of mass in the English system is the pound avoirdupois (lb) and is very nearly equal to 0.454 kgm, or 1 kgm is very nearly equal to 2.2 lb. It will be convenient to remember this conversion.

force acting in the direction of motion is the push of the spring.

Not all situations are so simple. Suppose that two persons push with equal amounts of force on a block but push in opposite directions. The block, of course, will not move. If one person now pushes with a greater amount of force than the other person, the block will move in the direction of the larger force. The acceleration, however, is proportional to the excess of the larger force over the smaller one. As a more specific example, suppose that the drive wheels of a 1,000 kgm automobile push it forward with a force of 2,500 newtons but that wind resistance, friction in the mechanism, etc. set up a retarding force of 500 newtons. In this situation, 500 newtons are required just to balance out the frictional effect; 2,000 newtons are left to overcome the inertia of the automobile. Hence, from equation 4-2, the acceleration is

$$a = \frac{F}{m} = \frac{(2,500 - 500) \text{ newtons}}{1,000 \text{ kgm}}$$

$$= \frac{2,000 \text{ kgm m/sec}^2}{1,000 \text{ kgm}} = 2 \text{ m/sec}^2$$

The point of this simple example is that the $F$ of equation 4-2 represents the net *unbalanced* force acting on the body. The same kind of analysis would hold for *any number* of forces acting on a body; the computation would merely be more tedious. As a last example suppose that by using some previously calibrated device (such as a spring balance) we observe that 15 newtons will pull a body along a frictionless surface with an acceleration of 2 m/sec². We should then be able to determine the mass of the body from equation 4-2 as

$$m = \frac{F}{a} = \frac{15 \text{ kgm m/sec}^2}{2 \text{ m/sec}^2} = 7.5 \text{ kgm}$$

We shall see later that this use of the second law is very effective when we determine the masses of electrons and other atomic particles by observing the accelerations produced by known electric and magnetic forces.

In the third law Newton states a further general, but not immediately obvious, characteristic of the concept of force. Forces always occur in pairs, never singly. Forces appear only as the interaction of *two* entities; a completely isolated object could neither exert nor experience force. If you push on the wall, the wall pushes equally back on you. A book is pulled down toward the earth by the force of gravity, and the earth is pulled up toward the book by the same amount of force. If the book is lying on a table, elastic forces come into play, and the table pushes up on the book with the same amount of force. (This follows from the second law since the book is not being accelerated.) The table pushes on the floor, which pushes back on the table, and so on down through the building to the earth. Thus a state of static equilibrium is maintained. On the other hand, if the table and the building do not intervene, the book accelerates toward the earth and the earth accelerates toward the book. This motion of the earth, to be sure, is imperceptibly small because of the relatively enormous mass of the earth, and in such situations it is neglected; that is, the earth is considered as a stationary reference. In the similar situation of the acceleration of the moon toward the earth, the earth's acceleration toward the moon is not at all imperceptible but is precisely observed.

## 4-4. Weight

Among the many forces that may act on an object the commonest, and perhaps the most remarkable, is the gravitational pull of the earth. The object needs no previous preparation to experience this force. Furthermore, the force is undiminished by any material that may be between the object and the earth.† All that is necessary for the object to experience this force is that the object be near the earth. This downward pull of gravity on an object is called its **weight.** If a body is free of all other forces, it falls freely, as we have seen, with a constant acceleration, $g$. Although we may have no idea how or why the force of gravity is applied to an object, the amount of this force is immediately given by the second law of motion. If we let $w$ represent

---

† This is not so for other forces. Steel, for instance, must first be magnetized to attract a piece of iron; and an object may be shielded from an electric force by a surrounding metallic screen.

FIGURE **4-2** *Equal-arm balance for determining mass.*

venient and very precise method of measuring their masses. The method is the familiar one of weighing† an object on an equal-arm balance. Such a balance is shown schematically in Figure 4-2. A rigid bar is delicately pivoted at its midpoint, $P$. Pans are suspended near the ends of the bar so that the distance $AP$ is very accurately equal to $BP$. The whole apparatus is adjusted so that when the pans are empty the system comes into equilibrium with the bar in a horizontal position. If the unknown mass, $m_x$, is placed on the left-hand pan, the system will rotate to the left. If a sufficient number of marked auxiliary standard masses are placed on the right-hand pan, the system will come back to the original equilibrium position. When this is accomplished, the *weight* of the object being weighed is equal to the sum of the weights of the standard masses. Thus $m_xg = m_sg$ if $m_s$ is the sum of the standard masses. But, *experimentally, g* is the same for all objects at a particular place; it therefore cancels out, and $m_x = m_s$.

We have presented in this chapter two very different methods of comparing the masses of bodies with arbitrary standards. The first is a dynamic method whereby the masses are compared in terms of the motions produced by their interaction. Gravitational forces do not necessarily enter into the method, and it would work equally well in a region completely free of gravitational effects. The second method is a static one and depends upon balancing the gravitational pull on the object by that on the standard. Very careful determinations of the mass of the same object by both methods give the same value. At first this result might seem obvious. But some thought will show that this experimental fact is in no way foreseeable. Not only are the methods very different operationally, but also they depend upon very different properties of matter—the first upon the property of inertia and the second upon the property of gravitation. The gravitational property of matter will be the topic of the next chapter.

the weight of an object whose mass is $m$, then $w = mg$. Furthermore, since at a particular location all objects fall with the *same* acceleration, the weights of different objects are directly proportional to their masses. That is, as required by the second law, an object whose mass is three times that of another object would require a gravitational pull three times as large in order to be given the same acceleration. *This does not mean that mass and weight are the same thing.* It was pointed out at the end of Chapter 3 that the value of $g$ is different at various locations and becomes smaller as the distance from the earth becomes greater. The weight of an object therefore changes with location, becoming less as it is moved farther from the earth. At some isolated point far out in space an object would have no weight at all. But it would still have its mass! The inertia-car experiment would give the same results far out in space as on the laboratory table.

The weights of objects make possible a con-

---

† A more critical term would be "massing."

## Concepts and Terms

Inertia
Force
Mass
    standard kilogram
    comparison of masses

Newton's Three Laws of Motion
    definition of the newton
    forces occur in pairs
Weight
    distinction from mass
    equal-arm balance

## Problems

**4-1.** A familiar parlor trick is this: Place a playing card on top of an empty milk bottle, and place a nickel on the card so that it is directly over the mouth of the bottle. With a quick snap of your finger move the card horizontally, and the nickel falls into the bottle. Repeat, but this time push the card slowly, and the nickel goes along with the card. Discuss in detail.

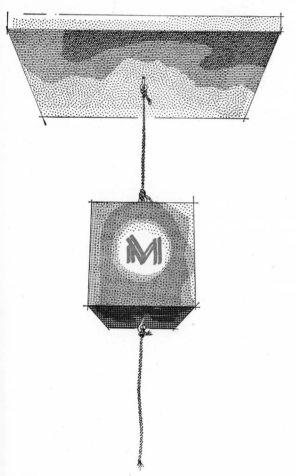

FIGURE **P4-2**

**4-2.** $M$ is a 1 kgm mass suspended by a light string and with a piece of similar string attached below. If you pull down on the lower string with gradually increasing force, the string will break above $M$. If you pull down with a sudden jerk, the string will break below $M$. Discuss in detail.

**4-3.** In the next chapter we shall see that the earth and the moon are accelerating toward each other under the interaction of gravitational attraction. The accelerations are approximately $a_E = 3.4 \times 10^{-5}$ m/sec$^2$ and $a_M = 2.8 \times 10^{-3}$ m/sec$^2$. What are the relative masses of earth and moon?     *Ans.* $m_E \approx 82\ m_M$

**4-4.** A 1,500 kgm car is accelerated at the rate of 1.7 m/sec$^2$. What is the net force acting on the car?     *Ans.* $2.6 \times 10^3$ newtons

**4-5.** A force of 12 newtons acts steadily on a body and moves it from rest a distance of 150 m during 10 sec. What is the mass of the body?     *Ans.* 4 kgm

**4-6.** A body starts from rest and after 5 sec is observed to have a velocity of 20 m/sec. If the mass of the body is 7 kgm, what net force was acting?     *Ans.* 28 newtons

**4-7.** A 1,500 kgm automobile traveling at 27 m/sec (about 60 miles/hour) crashes into a stone wall and is brought to rest in 0.1 sec. What was the stopping force? Compare this with the weight of the car.
    *Ans.* $4.05 \times 10^5$ newtons; 27.6 times as large

**4-8.**
  (A) Calculate your weight (see the footnote on p. 46).
  (B) A common unit of force is the pound force. This is defined as the weight of a 1 lb mass. How many newtons is it?
  (C) If you are concerned about being overweight, is it really your weight or your mass that worries you?
    *Ans.* (A) 450–900 newtons
          (B) 4.45 newtons

**4.9.** To stop a car most rapidly, the brakes must be applied so that the wheels lock and the tires skid along the pavement. Under these conditions, on a dry concrete road, experiment shows that the frictional force is 0.7 as large as the weight of the car. How far will a 2,000 kgm car travel while being brought to rest from a speed of 30 m/sec (something less than 70 miles/hour)? How far will a lighter car, of 1,000 kgm, go? How far will a motorcycle of only 100 kgm go?

*Ans.* 65.5 m ($\approx$215 feet) in all cases!

**4-10.** An 80 kgm man standing in an elevator is acted upon by two forces. One is his weight, and the other is the upward push ($P$) of the floor on his feet. Calculate the force $P$ if the elevator is (A) standing still; (B) rising with acceleration of 2.8 m/sec$^2$; (C) falling with 2.8 m/sec$^2$ acceleration; (D) rising with constant velocity of 7.0 m/sec; (E) falling freely, as it would be if the cables were to break.

*Ans.* (A) 784 newtons; (B) 1,008 newtons; (C) 560 newtons; (D) 784 newtons; (E) zero

**4-11.** A 100 kgm man slides down a rope that can support no more than 800 newtons. Can the man slide with constant velocity, or must he accelerate? Give a quantitative answer.

**4-12.** In a certain system of units, the force unit is *arbitrarily* defined as the weight of the standard kilogram and is called the kilogram force (kgf). In such a system, what would be the value and units of the $K$ of equation 4-1, § 4-3?

**4-13.** The acceleration due to gravity on the surface of Mars (see p. 61) is about one-third what it is on the surface of the earth. Give a quantitative comparison of the forces at the surface of the earth and at the surface of Mars required (A) to lift a 0.5 kgm mass; (B) to throw a 0.5 kgm mass horizontally with a speed of 2 m/sec if the accelerating time is 0.25 sec.

FIGURE **P4-14**

**4-14.** A monkey clings to a rope that passes over a pulley and supports a weight. The masses of the monkey and the weight are equal, and the system is in equilibrium. The monkey starts climbing up the rope. Describe the subsequent motion of the system. (Neglect the mass and friction of the pulley.)

**4-15.** "You can't lift yourself by your bootstraps." Analyze this statement in terms of Newton's laws.

**4-16.** Suppose you were becalmed in a sailboat but had a powerful blower aboard. Could you propel the boat by blowing against the sails? Could you propel the boat by pointing the blower over the stern? Explain.

## Suggested Readings

1. L. W. Taylor, *Physics the Pioneer Science* (Houghton Mifflin, 1941), pp. 112–145.
2. H. Semat, *Fundamentals of Physics,* 3rd edition (Rinehart, 1957), pp. 70–83 and 95–96.
3. G. Holton and D. H. D. Roller, *Foundations of Modern Physical Science* (Addison-Wesley, 1958), Chap. 4.
4. W. F. Magie, *A Source Book in Physics* (McGraw-Hill, 1935), pp. 30–46. Excerpts from the *Principia.*
5. Isaac Newton, *Mathematical Principles of Natural Philosophy,* translated by A. Motte and revised by F. Cajori (University of California Press, 1934), all of the prefaces and pp. 1–28.

IN FORMULATING his laws of motion, Newton laid the foundations for the general theory of dynamics. The way was now clear to reconsider the motions of the planets in the light of this theory. The substance of the planets was assumed to have the same mechanical properties as terrestrial matter and not to be composed of some ethereal quintessence. Then, by the law of inertia, an external agency was needed only to change the planets' motions, and no external agency (such as Aristotle's Unmoved Mover) was needed to maintain the motions. The problem could now be correctly stated. What is the nature of the force that *changes* the motion of the planets in their curving paths about the sun? Newton set himself this problem and found the answer. Before we can follow Newton's development, however, we need to learn how to add directed quantities and how to apply our general definitions of velocity and acceleration to the important situation of uniform circular motion.

## 5-1. Vectors

Many quantities encountered in science require for their complete description a statement of direction as well as a magnitude and a unit. The statement that a person walked 200 meters is incomplete, for he might have walked in any one of a number of directions. To say that he walked north 200 meters completely specifies the situation. To be told that an airplane passed overhead at 150 miles per hour would be of little use in locating it thirty minutes later. But it could easily be located with the added information that it was moving in a direction 30° east of north. Such quantities, which have a direction in space, are called **vector quantities.** Displacement, velocity, acceleration, and force are vector quantities. In our previous discussion of force and motion the vector nature of these quantities could be overlooked because the discussion was limited to motion along a straight line. In a more general situation both the magnitude and the direction would have to be considered.†

---

† The term *speed* refers to the magnitude of the vector velocity; for example, 30 m/sec is a speed, but 30 m/sec northwest is a velocity.

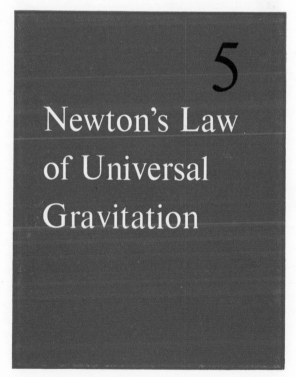

CHAPTER

5

Newton's Law
of Universal
Gravitation

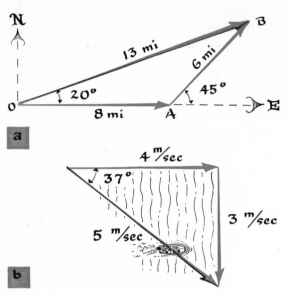

FIGURE **5-1** *Vector addition. Sum of* (a) *two displacements and* (b) *two velocities.*

Starting at *A,* the vector *AB* is drawn to represent the northeasterly displacement of 6 miles. Its length is 3 cm, and it is drawn with the aid of a protractor at an angle of 45° with the easterly direction. The vector *OB* represents the resultant displacement. By *measurement OB* is found to be 6.5 cm, and the angle *BOA* is 20°. Thus the man arrives at a point 13 miles from his starting point in a direction 20° north of east.

As another example suppose a boat that can travel through motionless water at the rate of 4 m/sec heads straight across a river that has a current of 3 m/sec. As the boat moves across the river, it is also carried downstream. What is the resultant velocity of the boat? Here the two vectors to be added are at right angles to each other. The construction is shown in Figure 5-1b, where 1 cm = 1 m/sec. The boat moves with a speed of 5 m/sec in a direction 37° downstream with respect to its heading.

Notice that the method is geometric and involves the solution of triangles—that is, determining the remaining parts of a triangle if certain parts are given. Any mathematics for the

There are quantities, however, that require only a magnitude and a unit for their description. One such quantity is mass; a 5 kgm body displays the same inertia whatever the direction in which it is accelerated. Another is volume; the angle at which a flask is held has no effect upon the number of cubic centimeters it contains. Such quantities, which are independent of direction, are called **scalar quantities.** In addition to mass and volume, time and speed are also scalars.

The familiar rules of arithmetic and algebra are for *scalar quantities only*. To combine vector quantities, we need a new mathematics. Here, however, we shall need to learn only how to add vectors. The method can best be understood if we consider specific examples. Suppose that a man walks 8 miles east and then walks 6 miles northeast. What is his resultant displacement; that is, how many miles and in what direction is he displaced from his starting point? First we choose some convenient scale to represent the magnitudes (Fig. 5-1a). In this case let 1 cm = 2 miles. Then an arrow (*OA*) 4 cm long and pointed to the right will represent the easterly displacement of 8 miles. Such a scaled arrow representing the magnitude and direction of a vector quantity is called a **vector.**

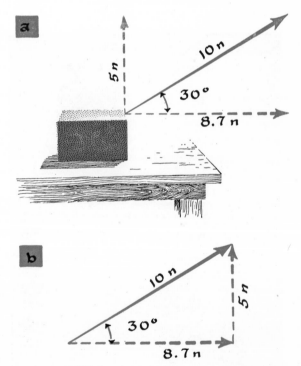

FIGURE **5-2** *Vector resolution into rectangular components.*

solution of triangles that the reader may know (such as trigonometry) can be used for vector addition. The construction method outlined above, however, will always work.

It is often convenient to determine two vectors at right angles to each other, which, acting simultaneously, would produce the same result as a given vector.

Suppose that a force of 10 newtons acts at 30° to the horizontal while sliding a block across a horizontal table, as shown in Figure 5-2a. What horizontal and vertical forces acting simultaneously will produce the same motion? The given force is drawn to scale in the proper direction in Figure 5-2b. Here 1 cm = 2 newtons. With this force as the hypotenuse a right triangle is constructed. By measurement the required forces (the horizontal and the vertical side) are 8.7 newtons and 5 newtons. These forces (shown by broken lines in Fig. 5-2a) may *replace* the given force since their sum is 10 newtons in a direction of 30° with the horizontal. (Note that in this situation the force accelerating the block is the 8.7 newtons; the 5 newtons merely helps

the table support the weight of the block.) The process just described is called the **resolution** of a vector into **rectangular components.**

## 5-2. *Centripetal Force*

The general definitions of velocity and acceleration developed in Chapter 3 are applicable to any motion if the vector nature of the quantities involved is taken into consideration. When, for example, we apply the definition of average acceleration (§ 3-4), the $\Delta v$ may be due to a change in the magnitude (speed) or a change in the direction of the vector velocity, or to both. In Chapter 3 the definitions were applied to a situation in which the direction was held constant and the speed was changed uniformly. Let us now consider the reverse situation: the speed is held constant and the direction is changed uniformly. Motion with constant speed along the circumference of a circle is such a motion.

An object moving along a circle is being accelerated. This follows from the definition of

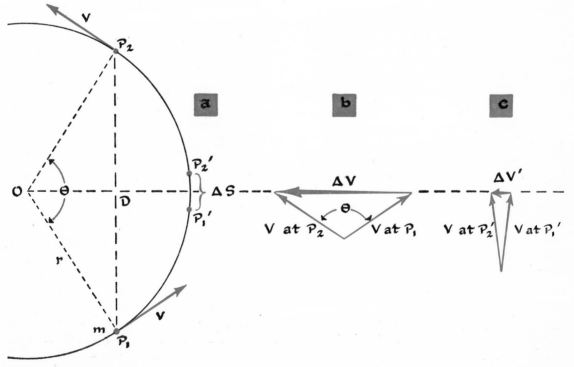

FIGURE **5-3** *Centripetal acceleration. $\Delta v$ is directed toward the center of the circle. If $\theta$ is very small (c), $\Delta v$ is nearly perpendicular to v.*

acceleration since the direction of the motion is constantly changing. The second law of motion also requires the motion to be accelerated, for experiment shows that a force is necessary to hold a moving object in a circular path. If an object on the end of a string is whirled in a circle, the string is under tension. If the string is released (or if it breaks), the object moves off along a tangent to the circle just as water flies off a spinning bicycle wheel. The problem now is to determine the magnitude and direction of the acceleration.†

Figure 5-3a shows part of the circular path of a particle of mass $m$. The circle has radius $r$ and is centered at $O$. From any point, $P_1$, the particle will move with a constant speed, $v$, to some other point, $P_2$, in time $\Delta t$, and will move distance $\Delta s$ along the circumference of the circle. The velocities at $P_1$ and $P_2$ are represented by vectors of the same length, $v$ (since the speed is constant), and drawn along the tangents to the circle at the points (since that is the instantaneous direction of motion at the points). To find the average acceleration during $\Delta t$, we must determine the change in velocity, $\Delta v$. We ask what velocity, added to the velocity at $P_1$, will give the velocity at $P_2$. This must be a vector addition and is shown in Figure 5-3b. It may at first be surprising that a sizable $\Delta v$ is required merely to change the direction of $v$. Without the change, however, $v$ would remain fixed in direction, and the particle would move off in a straight line. Now note that the vector triangle and triangle $P_1OP_2$ are similar isosceles triangles since the angles $\theta$ are equal (their sides are mutually perpendicular). Therefore

$$\frac{\Delta v}{v} = \frac{D}{r} \quad \text{or} \quad \Delta v = \frac{vD}{r}$$

if $D$ is the length of the chord $P_1P_2$. Then the average acceleration while the particle is moving from $P_1$ to $P_2$ is

$$a_{av} = \frac{\Delta v}{\Delta t} = \frac{vD}{r(\Delta t)}$$

The instantaneous acceleration is the value that

$a_{av}$ approaches when $\Delta t$ is made smaller and smaller (§ 3-4). For some smaller $\Delta t$, such as that from $P_1'$ to $P_2'$, the angle $\theta$ is smaller, and the vector diagram would be that shown in Figure 5-3c. As $\Delta t$ (and $\theta$ along with it) gets smaller and smaller, the chord $D$ becomes more and more nearly equal to the distance $\Delta s$ along the circle. Hence *in the limit* we may write $D = \Delta s$. But $\Delta s = v(\Delta t)$ since the speed is constant. The instantaneous acceleration is therefore

$$a = \frac{v\,v(\Delta t)}{r(\Delta t)} = \frac{v^2}{r}$$

By definition the acceleration is in the direction of the *change* in velocity, $\Delta v$. From the figure, $\Delta v$ is seen to be always at right angles to the chord $D$ and thus, in the limit, to be pointing along the radius toward the center of the circle. For this reason it is called *centripetal* (center-seeking) acceleration and is indicated by the subscript "c":

$$a_c = \frac{v^2}{r} \tag{5-1}$$

A convenient form of equation 5-1 expresses $a_c$ in terms of the period, $T$, which is the time in which the particle makes one revolution of the circle. Since the speed is constant, $v = 2\pi r/T$. Squaring this and substituting in equation 5-1, we get

$$a_c = \frac{4\pi^2 r}{T^2} \tag{5-2}$$

Each of these equations yields the proper unit for acceleration.

According to the second law of motion, a force is necessary to produce the centripetal acceleration. This centripetal force is given by the equation $F_c = ma_c$ (in which $a_c$ may be expressed by either 5-1 or 5-2) and acts along the radius toward the center of the circle. If an object on the end of a string is whirled in a circle, $F_c$ is the tension in the string. For an automobile rounding a curve, $F_c$ is supplied by the friction between the road and the tires. Whenever a body is observed moving in a circle, we can be sure that a centripetal force is acting on it even though the origin of the force may not be immediately apparent. This force (which is always at a right angle to the instantaneous velocity) does not increase the speed of the body

---

† The solution of this problem was first published by Huygens in 1673. There is evidence that Newton had the solution some years earlier, but he published it later (1687) in the *Principia*.

but overcomes the inertia and keeps the body from moving off along a straight line. In a sense the body is constantly "falling" toward the center of the circle, and its forward motion is just sufficient to keep it in the circular path.

## 5-3. *Newton's Law of Gravitation*

An outbreak of the plague at Cambridge during 1665 and 1666 forced Newton to return to his family home in Woolsthorpe and to continue his studies in isolation. From his notes it appears that he had already (at the age of twenty-four!) formed a clear idea of the laws of motion and developed the formula for centripetal acceleration; and "the same year I began to think of gravity extending to the orb of the moon and . . . from Kepler's Rule . . . I deduced the forces which keep the planets in their orbs." There is a story (first told by Voltaire) that the casual observation of a falling apple from a tree in his garden set Newton to speculating on the nature of the force that accelerated the apple to the earth. Since this attraction is felt in the deepest mines and on the highest mountains, might it not extend (if somewhat diminished) as far as the moon and thus explain that object's continuous fall toward the earth in its monthly revolution? And, if so, should not a similar attraction between the sun and the planets account for Kepler's laws of planetary motions about the sun? What, then, are the factors that determine such a gravitational force?

According to Kepler's first law the planets move in ellipses round the sun. But the ellipses, as worked out by Kepler, are very nearly circles. As a first approximation, then, we may treat a planet's motion *as though* it were along a circle with a radius equal to the planet's average distance, $r_{av}$, from the sun (see p. 28). The mechanics of this *approximate* situation, then, would be a simple centripetal acceleration of the planet toward the sun. The gravitational attraction would be a centripetal force given by the equation (derived from equation 5-2)

$$F = m\frac{4\pi^2 r_{av}}{T^2}$$

in which $m$ is the mass of the planet and $T$ its period of revolution. From Kepler's third law (§ 2-8) we substitute for $T^2$ and get

$$F = m\frac{4\pi^2 r_{av}}{K(r_{av})^3} = \left[\frac{m4\pi^2}{K}\right]\frac{1}{(r_{av})^2}$$

This says that the gravitational force would be inversely proportional to the square of the distance between the sun and the planet, since the quantity in the brackets is a constant involving the constant mass of the planet and Kepler's empirical constant $K$. If the planet and the sun were twice as far apart, the force would be one-fourth as much; if they were three times as far apart, the force would be one-ninth as much; etc.†

Another clue to the nature of the gravitational force is found in the constancy, at a given place, of the acceleration due to gravity. By the second law of motion this means that the gravitational attraction on a body grows directly with its mass. But if the attraction between two bodies grows with the mass of one, ought it not equally to grow with the mass of the other? Newton generalized these ideas and stated as a hypothesis that any two *particles* in the universe attract each other with a force that is directly proportional to their masses and inversely proportional to the square of the distance between them. Stated algebraically, this is

$$F = G\frac{m_1 m_2}{s^2} \qquad (5\text{-}3)$$

in which $G$ is a constant of proportionality.

Before he was able to test this hypothesis, Newton had to prove that a sphere attracts as though its mass were *concentrated at its center*. In other words, when equation 5-3 is applied to the case of a falling body (such as the apple), the distance to be used must be to the center of the earth and not to its surface. Then the weight of the apple or any mass $m$ at the surface of the earth is given by equation 5-3. But it is also equal to $mg$. Equating these two expressions for the weight, we get

$$mg = G\frac{mE}{r_E^2}$$

† By the use of mathematics beyond the scope of this book, Newton was able to show that a force of attraction varying inversely with the square of the distance from the sun would, in general, produce an elliptical path. A circle is the special case of an ellipse when the two foci coincide, which they almost do for the planetary ellipses.

in which $E$ is the mass of the earth and $r_E$ is the radius of the earth. The mass of the body divides out and gives

$$g = G\frac{E}{r_E^2} \qquad (5\text{-}4)$$

This says that for any given location on the surface of the earth the acceleration due to gravity is the same for all bodies since the mass of the body does not appear on the right side. But, as the distance from the center of the earth increases, the value of $g$ decreases. Both these predictions agree with experimental fact. The slight variation in $g$ from sea level to mountain tops is understood, for such changes in altitude produce only slight changes in $r_E$.

If the gravitational pull of the earth extends to the moon, the moon should be falling toward the earth with an acceleration also given by equation 5-4. The distance from the center of the earth to the center of the moon is 60 times the radius of the earth. Then, according to equation 5-4, the acceleration of the moon toward the earth should be 1/3,600 of $g$. But the moon's acceleration toward the earth is its centripetal acceleration in its circular revolution about the earth. This can be easily computed by the use of equation 5-2 since the radius of its orbit and

its period of revolution are both known. (See Appendix I.) This acceleration comes out to be $2.74 \times 10^{-3}$ m/sec², which is just 1/3,600 of 9.8 m/sec², the measured value of $g$ on the surface of the earth.

Newton then proceeded to show that Kepler's laws of planetary motion are necessary consequences of his law of gravitation. We cannot follow the general mathematical development, but Figure 5-4 will indicate how theory and experiment agreed. As the planet, $P$, revolves about the sun, the gravitational pull, $F$, on the planet is always along the line from $P$ to the sun. As the planet moves nearer the sun (top of diagram), $F$ resolves into the rectangular components $N$, perpendicular to the path, and $f$, along the path. $N$ supplies the centripetal force to hold the planet in its curving path while $f$ increases the speed of the planet along the path. Later, when the planet is moving farther from the sun, $N$ still supplies the necessary centripetal force, but $f$ now opposes the motion and slows the planet down. These varying speeds are precisely those required by Kepler's second law, and the quantitative agreement is exact. And finally, if we again consider the planet's orbit as approximately circular, with a radius equal to the average distance from the sun, the centripetal force would be the gravitational attraction, and we may write (by using equations 5-3 and 5-2)

$$G\frac{SP}{(r_{av})^2} = P\frac{4\pi^2 r_{av}}{T^2}$$

in which $S$ and $P$ are the masses of the sun and the planet respectively. $P$ divides out, and solving for $T^2$ gives

$$T^2 = \left[\frac{4\pi^2}{GS}\right](r_{av})^3 \qquad (5\text{-}5)$$

which is Kepler's third law since the term in the brackets is constant. It is the same for all the planets since it involves only the mass of the sun and the proportionality constant of the law of gravity.

Newton's hypothesis, as stated by equation 5-3, seems to be amply verified. So far, however, the arguments have assumed that the proportionality constant, $G$, has the same value in all circumstances. To test this assumption, New-

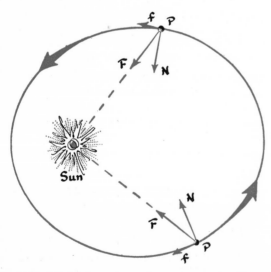

FIGURE 5-4 *The rectangular components, N and f, of the gravitational attraction, F, affect a planet's motion in accordance with Kepler's laws.*

ton measured the acceleration due to gravity ($g$) on all the different kinds of substance he could obtain and found the value to be always the same.† Then (by equation 5-4), since $E$ and $r_E$ are certainly constant for any given location (such as his laboratory), $G$ must be constant and independent of the composition of the gravitating bodies. Thus $G$ acquired the status of a *universal* constant (one of the few of nature) and the hypothesis of equation 5-3 the status of a *universal* law of nature. No longer were the celestial bodies composed of some unearthly essence; rather, through the sweeping law of gravitation, they were seen to move in accordance with the laws of earthly motion. Thus did Newton synthesize all the problems of motion and give to science a tool for reaching far out into space.

## 5-4. *Gravitational Constant*

Newton's experiments established the constancy of $G$ but did not yield a numerical value for it. Such a determination would have two important consequences. First, if the value of $G$ were found to be the same for all available kinds of material, Newton's conclusion would be further verified. We could then assume with greater confidence that gravitation is indeed a universal property of *all* matter and apply the law of gravitation (5-3) on a cosmic scale. Second, once the value of $G$ is known, the mass of the earth and other celestial bodies can be determined. Newton knew how to proceed in measuring $G$ but did not have the necessary delicate instruments. More than a hundred years went by, in fact, before a sufficiently sensitive device was developed. The problem is to measure the force of attraction between two masses that can be independently measured and placed a measured distance apart. Then, in equation 5-3, $F$, $m_1$, $m_2$, and $s$ are all known, and $G$ is determined. But such a force must be exceed-

ingly small. This is clear when we realize that the gravitational attraction between the earth and some mass in the laboratory (that is, its weight) is only moderately large even though one of the $m$'s of equation 5-3 is the enormous (if unknown) mass of the earth. It was a real achievement when, in 1798, Henry Cavendish succeeded in measuring the value of $G$. He used a very delicate torsion balance (see Fig. 16-1). One of the masses was attached to the end of a horizontal rod that was suspended at its midpoint by a very fine wire. When a second mass was placed near the suspended one, the gravitational attraction produced a small but measurable twist in the wire suspension. The angle of twist, combined with the known mechanical properties of the wire, gave the amount of force between the two masses. The Cavendish experiment has been repeated many times with improved (but in principle the same) apparatus. In these experiments the masses were composed of a wide variety of materials, including meteoritic material from outer space. *Always* the same value for $G$ was found. The accepted value today is

$$G = 6.67 \times 10^{-11} \text{ newton m}^2/\text{kgm}^2 \qquad (5-6)$$

Once the numerical value of $G$ had been determined, it was easy to compute the mass of the earth, and Cavendish proceeded to do so. In equation 5-4 the only quantity not known is $E$. The computation gives $6 \times 10^{24}$ kgm as the approximate mass of the earth. This enormous number is difficult to relate to our experience in a meaningful way. However, if we divide the mass of the earth by its volume, we get the *average* density of the earth. This comes out to be about 5.5 grams/cm³. This is the value that we should obtain if we determined the density of all the various homogeneous substances of the earth and then averaged these densities, taking into consideration the relative amount of each substance. This has not been done, of course, for the *whole* earth, but it has been done for the earth's crust. As a result of extensive geologic surveys, the average density of the earth's crust is believed to be about 2.7 grams/cm³. We must conclude that the interior of the earth is composed of materials of con-

---

† Newton was aware of Galileo's work on the constancy of $g$, but Newton's exhaustive experiments investigated a wide variety of substances and were more precise. His method involved the timing of the swing of a pendulum, which could be measured much more precisely than the time of fall of a body.

siderable density to make the over-all average as high as 5.5 grams/cm³. Thus, by measuring the minute gravitational attraction between two masses in his laboratory, Cavendish obtained evidence of the nature of the core of the earth!

After Newton's time, the improvement in telescopic observations and other experimental techniques made possible more and more precise measurements of both celestial and terrestrial motions. These observations further verified the validity of Newtonian mechanics and made many ancient problems understandable. We can consider only some of these successes, which illustrate the great power and usefulness of the laws of motion and gravitation. These examples will also illustrate how astronomers, armed with Newton's laws and increasingly precise observations, are able to deduce a great deal of information about the heavenly bodies without actually performing experiments on their surfaces.

## 5-5. Size of the Solar System

One consequence of the increased precision of telescopic measurements was the accurate determination of the size of the solar system. The reader may be surprised that this is mentioned now, for we have already been talking about the size of orbits. A careful consideration of the arguments presented so far will show, however, that the distances involved were relative distances. (The one exception was the distance

to the moon.) Kepler did not need to know the absolute distance of any of the planets from the sun. He was, however, able to determine from Tycho's data the *relative* distances of the planets. He knew quite accurately, for instance, that the mean distance from the sun for Mars is 1.524 times that for the earth, that Venus is only 0.723 as far from the sun as the earth, etc. Thus he was able to construct an accurate scale model of the solar system although he did not know accurately the *size* of the scale. For convenience of comparison, the mean distance of the earth from the sun may be taken as one unit of distance. This distance is called an **astronomical unit** (A.U.). Mars is 1.524 A.U. from the sun, Venus 0.723 A.U., and so on for the rest of the planets (see Table 5-1). Without knowing the size of the astronomical unit, Kepler was able to discover his laws from Tycho's data. The third law, for instance (§ 2-8), will work as well with $r_{av}$ in A.U. as in meters, as the reader can readily verify from the data of Table 5-1. If the mean distance from the earth to the sun (the A.U.) could be determined in meters, the mean distances to the other planets could be found by simple multiplication, and the size of the solar system would be determined.

The measurement of astronomical distances is very simple in principle but somewhat difficult in practice. Consider Figure 5-5. Imagine that $A$ and $B$ are two observing stations on the earth and that $P$ is some object in the sky whose distance is to be determined. Now, if $P$ is observed from $A$ and $B$ at the same time, it will be seen

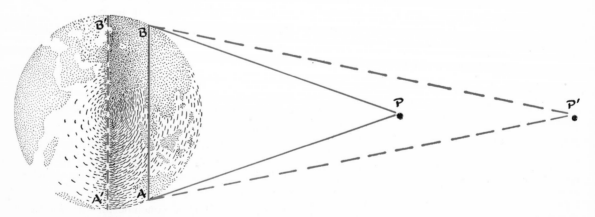

FIGURE **5-5** *Determination of astronomical distances from the earth.*

in a different direction from each station. These measured directions give the angles at $A$ and $B$ in the triangle $APB$; and, since the distance $AB$ is known, the triangle is determined. Then the distance to $P$ (that is, $AP$ or $BP$) is computed by simple trigonometry. The distance $AB$ is called the **base line,** and the angle at $P$ is called the **parallax** of the base line. Clearly the parallax is the *difference* in the direction of $P$ as viewed from $A$ and $B$. For some more distant object, such as $P'$, the parallax is smaller and thus more difficult to determine. And for some very distant object the parallax becomes immeasurably small. Such an object appears to be in the *same* direction from *both* $A$ and $B$, and the method breaks down. A longer base line would, of course, increase the parallax. On the earth, however, the longest base line possible is its diameter, when the stations are on opposite sides of the earth ($A'B'$ in Fig. 5-5). Thus there is a practical limit on the distance that can be measured by this method.

With the diameter of the earth as a base line the parallax of the moon is just a little under $2°$. Since this parallax is large enough to be easily measured, a reliable value for the distance to the moon was available to Newton. Today the moon's distance is known very precisely as $3.84 \times 10^8$ meters (about 240,000 miles). But the sun is much farther away, and its parallax is proportionately smaller. With the same base line ($A'B'$) the sun's parallax is only about 18 seconds of arc, or about 0.005 degree. This angle is so small that early attempts to measure it met with little success. Although reasonably correct values were known in the seventeenth century, it was not until the nineteenth century that precise values of the sun's parallax began to be determined. Even today, since the direct measurement of this angle is not very precise, the value is arrived at indirectly. The method depends on measuring the distance from the earth to some member of the solar system which is nearer than the sun and whose orbit has been accurately placed in the scaled model of the solar system. This was first done with Mars. As the earth swings past Mars, the distance between these two planets is, on the average, about half of the distance of the earth from the sun. Thus

the parallax of Mars in this position is about twice the sun's and can be measured with good precision. This gives the distance to Mars as about $7.5 \times 10^{10}$ meters. This is also the *difference* of the distances of Mars and the earth from the sun. But from the scale model (Kepler) we know that the distance of Mars from the sun is approximately 1.5 times the earth's distance from the sun. Hence we know both the difference and the quotient of these distances and can compute both by simple algebra. The reader can easily show that these approximate values yield $15.0 \times 10^{10}$ meters for the earth's distance from the sun. Many careful measurements of this kind, made during the last half of the nineteenth and in the twentieth century, have led to an average value of the sun's parallax that is reliable to almost 0.01 percent. This gives $14.945 \times 10^{10}$ meters as the size of the astronomical unit of distance. This is almost 93 *million* miles! As pointed out in a previous paragraph, once the A.U. is known, the distances to the other planets are also known. Vast as these distances are, however, they become quite small, as we shall see, when compared with the distances to the stars.

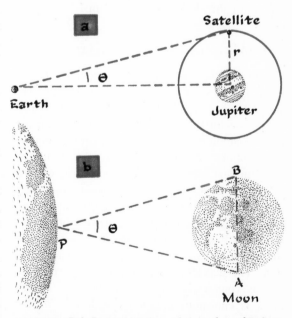

FIGURE **5-6** *Determination of* (a) *the orbital radius of a satellite and* (b) *the diameter of the moon.*

Once the distances to the planets are known, other dimensions in the solar system may be determined. For example, the radius of the orbit of a satellite (that is, a moon) about a planet may be measured. Consider Figure 5-6a, which shows the earth, Jupiter, and one of Jupiter's twelve satellites. As viewed from the earth, the difference in the directions of Jupiter and the satellite is the angle $\theta$, and this is measurable. Then, since the distance to Jupiter is known, the radius $r$ may be calculated. Similarly, the diameters of members of the solar system may be measured. Figure 5-6b shows the situation for the moon. By sighting the opposite edges of the moon ($A$ and $B$) we measure the angle $\theta$, and this, combined with the known distance $PA$, gives the diameter $AB$. The angular sizes of the moon ($\theta$) and the sun are the same, each being about 0.5 degree. But the sun is approximately 400 times as far away and so is 400 times as large. The moon's diameter is 2,160 miles (a little more than one-quarter the diameter of the earth), and the sun's diameter is over eight hundred thousand miles, or about 110 times the diameter of the earth. Compared with the sun, the planets are small indeed, the largest planet, Jupiter, having a diameter only one-tenth the diameter of the sun.

## 5-6. Mass of the Solar System

The observed motions of the members of the solar system and the measured distances between them make possible the determination of the masses of the system. As we have seen, the determination of mass depends upon the relative accelerations of two bodies as the result of some mutual interaction (the inertia-car experiment, Chap. 4). For two bodies in the solar system the interaction is their mutual attraction as given by Newton's law of gravitation. If we release a ball near the earth, it moves toward the center of the earth with a definite acceleration. The acceleration of the *earth toward the ball* is completely negligible, since the earth's mass is enormous compared with that of the ball. In other words, the ball does all the moving. Then, as we have seen earlier in this chapter, the measured acceleration of the ball toward the

earth permits the calculation of the earth's mass. By exactly the same method we could determine the mass of another member of the solar system if we could get there and observe the fall of a ball toward its surface. But Newton showed that a revolving satellite is just as useful as a falling ball in determining the mass of a planet. The acceleration of the falling ball is rectilinear, and that of the satellite is centripetal; but in each case the acceleration is toward the center of the planet. Just as the acceleration of the earth toward a falling ball is negligible, so the acceleration of a planet toward its satellite is negligible if the planet's mass is much larger than that of the satellite. In other words, the satellite would do all the revolving and would move in an orbit round the planet. Such is the behavior of all observed satellites in the solar system except our moon. These satellites revolve round the planets in elliptical orbits in accordance with Kepler's laws.† But a satellite's orbit round its planet, like the orbit of a planet round the sun, may be considered as an approximate circle whose radius is the mean distance, $r_{av}$, of the satellite from the center of the planet. The mechanics of this situation is, then, a simple centripetal acceleration of the satellite toward the center of the planet. The centripetal force is the gravitational attraction, but, by Newton's second law of motion, it is also equal to the mass of the satellite times the centripetal acceleration (equation 5-2). Equating these two expressions for the force, we have

$$G \frac{Pm}{(r_{av})^2} = m \frac{4\pi^2}{T^2} r_{av}$$

in which $P$ and $m$ are the masses of the planet and satellite respectively, $T$ is the period of revolution of the satellite, and $r_{av}$ is its mean distance from the center of the planet. The mass of the satellite ($m$) divides out, and everything else except the planet's mass ($P$) is measurable. Solving for $P$, we have

$$P = \frac{4\pi^2}{G} \frac{(r_{av})^3}{T^2} \tag{5-7}$$

(Note that this is Kepler's third law for the planet-satellite system.)

---

† Galileo was right in considering Jupiter and his moons as a solar system in miniature (§ 2-7).

TABLE 5-1  *Mechanical Data for the Solar System*

| NAME | SUN | MER-CURY | VENUS | EARTH | MARS | JU-PITER | SAT-URN | URA-NUS | NEP-TUNE | PLUTO |
|---|---|---|---|---|---|---|---|---|---|---|
| Period, $T$ | | 88 days | 225 days | 365 days | 687 days | 11.9 years | 29.5 years | 84.0 years | 165 years | 248 years |
| Mean distance, $r_{av}$ (A.U.) † | | 0.39 | 0.72 | 1.00 | 1.52 | 5.20 | 9.54 | 19.2 | 30.1 | 39.5 |
| Orbital inclination (deg) | | 7° 0′ | 3° 24′ | 0° | 1° 51″ | 1° 18″ | 2° 29′ | 0° 46′ | 1° 47′ | 17° 19′ |
| Diameter (Earth = 1) | $1.1 \times 10^2$ | 0.39 | 0.97 | 1.0 | 0.53 | 11.0 | 9.03 | 4.00 | 3.90 | 0.46 |
| Mass (Earth = 1) | $3.32 \times 10^5$ | 0.04 | 0.82 | 1.0 | 0.11 | 318 | 95.3 | 14.7 | 17.3 | ? |
| Density (grams/cm³) | 1.41 | 5.46 | 5.06 | 5.52 | 4.12 | 1.35 | 0.71 | 1.56 | 2.47 | ? |
| Surface gravity (m/sec²) | 270 | 2.65 | 8.45 | 9.80 | 3.62 | 25.8 | 11.5 | 9.02 | 14.1 | ? |

† A.U. = $1.4945 \times 10^{11}$ m.

Satellites have been observed for all of the planets except Mercury, Venus, and Pluto. The earth is unique in having only one. Jupiter, with the most, has twelve, four of which (the ones discovered by Galileo) are large enough to be seen through a good pair of binoculars. The observed orbital radius and period of revolution substituted in equation 5-7 will give the mass of the satellite's planet. For convenience of comparison, these masses are listed in Table 5-1 in terms of the earth's mass (that is, the mass of the earth is one unit). Table 5-2 lists data for two of the bright satellites of Jupiter and for the two satellites of Mars.

As might be expected, the four largest planets (the *major* planets) are also the most massive, ranging from about 17 to over 300 times the mass of the earth. Of the others (the *terrestrial* planets), the earth is the most massive, although Venus and Pluto have nearly the same mass as the earth. On the other hand, Mars is little more than one-tenth as massive as the earth, and tiny Mercury has but 4 percent of the earth's mass.

In view of the enormous mass of the earth, compared with that of ordinary objects about us, the total mass of all the planets in kilograms becomes a meaninglessly large number; but even this tremendous sum becomes almost negligible when compared with the mass of the sun. Since all the planets are clearly satellites of the sun, equation 5-7 will also give the mass of the sun if values for $r_{av}$ and $T$ for a planet are inserted. The reader can easily show that this yields a mass for the sun that is more than three hundred thousand times that of the earth (see Table 5-1). Thus all the planets together account for only about 0.1 percent of the total mass of the solar system, the other 99.9 percent being concentrated in the sun. The planets are but small chips of matter circulating round the massive sun under the action of his gravitational attraction. We can now more easily understand why the sun plays such a dominant role at the center of the whole system.

The preceding discussion was based on the assumption that the mass of the satellite is negligible compared with that of the planet. If this is not so, we have a different situation, though the fundamental principles are the same. It is a familiar fact that, if two equal masses on the ends of a light rod are twirled into the air, the masses will revolve round a common center, C,

TABLE 5-2  *Periods and Orbital Radii of Satellites*

| | | $r_{av}$ (10⁹ m) | $T$ |
|---|---|---|---|
| Jupiter | Europa | 0.671 | 3 days, 13 hours |
| | Callisto | 1.88 | 16 days, 17 hours |
| | | $r_{av}$ (10⁶ m) | $T$ |
| Mars | Phoebus | 9.37 | 7 hours, 39 min |
| | Deimos | 23.5 | 30 hours, 18 min |

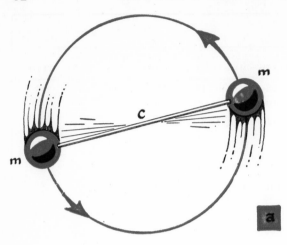

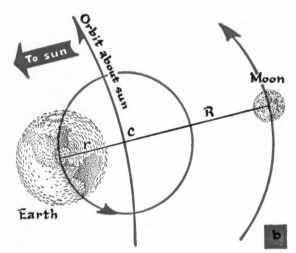

FIGURE 5-7 *Common center of rotation, C, of two masses:* (a) *C is midway between two equal masses;* (b) *C is nearer the larger of two unequal masses.*

at the middle of the rod (Fig. 5-7a). If one of the masses is larger than the other (such as earth and moon in Fig. 5-7b), they still revolve about a common center, but that center is nearer the larger mass. The larger mass goes round a smaller circle of radius r, and the smaller mass moves in a larger circle of radius R. The period of revolution, of course, is the same for both. Such is the situation of the earth and the moon, those bodies being held in their circular motions by the gravitational attraction between them rather than by the tension in a connecting rod. Not only is the moon falling toward the

earth, but the *earth is falling toward the moon* also, and by an appreciable amount. Just as in the inertia-car experiment, the masses of the two bodies may be compared by the *inverse* ratio of accelerations that are due to a mutual interaction. For the inertia cars the accelerations were *rectilinear* and *away* from a common center as the result of the expansion of the compressed spring. For the earth and moon the accelerations are *centripetal* and *toward* a common center as the result of their mutual attraction. With the aid of equation 5-2 we may therefore write

$$\frac{M}{E} = \frac{a_c \text{ of } E}{a_c \text{ of } M} = \frac{\dfrac{4\pi^2}{T^2} r}{\dfrac{4\pi^2}{T^2} R}$$

and, since the period of revolution about $C$ is the same for both, we have

$$M = E\frac{r}{R} \tag{5-8}$$

Since the mass of the earth $(E)$ is known, the mass of the moon $(M)$ is determined if the ratio $r/R$ can be measured.

As Newton pointed out, it is not the center of the earth but the common center $C$ of the earth-moon system that moves along a smooth elliptic orbit about the sun. Thus, as can be seen from Figure 5-7b, for the two weeks from full moon to new moon the earth falls *behind C*. During the next two weeks (new to full moon) the earth runs *ahead* of $C$, and then the cycle starts again. This periodic *actual* retardation and advancement of the earth in its motion about the sun will make the sun *appear* to be periodically retarded and advanced in its apparent motion along the ecliptic. These monthly variations in the apparent motion of the sun are very small but are measurable with precise telescopic observations. And, since the distance from the sun to the earth is known, it is a matter of simple geometry to determine the actual displacement of the earth from $C$—that is, the length of the radius $r$. This comes out to be $4.65 \times 10^6$ meters.† The measured distance from earth to moon $(r + R)$ is $348 \times 10^6$ meters, and $R$ is

---

† Since this is only about three-quarters of the radius of the earth $(6.37 \times 10^6$ m$)$, $C$ is actually below the surface of the earth and not as shown in Fig. 5-7b.

therefore $379 \times 10^6$ meters. By equation 5-8 the mass of the moon is $E/81.5$, or a little over 1 percent of the mass of the earth. From the measured diameter of the moon its volume is found to be 1/49 of the volume of the earth. The moon's density is therefore $49/81.5 = 0.6$ as great as the earth's. This gives the moon an average density of about 3.3 grams/cm³, which is about the same as the density of the basic rock just below the surface layer of the earth. It has been suggested that the moon was once part of the earth (§ 15-6). One of the major facts supporting the theory of the earthly origin of the moon is this close correspondence between the density of the moon and that of the surface rock of the earth.

So far we have considered each situation as a "two-body" problem; that is, we neglected the gravitational attraction of the other planets on the moon, for instance, and considered the earth-moon system as though it were isolated in space. This is very nearly so. The great separation of the members of the solar system makes their mutual gravitational effects small compared with the pull of the enormous mass of the sun. The planets do affect each other's motion to a slight degree, however, particularly neighboring planets when they are near each other in their orbits. In other words, the planets do not move precisely in ellipses about the sun but suffer small variations from the elliptical paths. Such variations are called *perturbations*. It is fortunate that the perturbations are small; otherwise Kepler might not have discovered the wonderful regularities of the solar system, and the whole development of our knowledge of that system would have been delayed. The amount of a perturbation may be calculated from Newton's law of gravity. The mathematics is involved; in fact, the "many-body" problem can be solved only by successive approximations. Nevertheless, it was solved, and these slight irregular motions also were found to be in accord with Newton's laws.†

---

† Perturbations may be used to determine the mass of a planet that has no satellites. For instance, the observed perturbations of the orbit of Venus produced by the gravitational attractions of the earth and Mars, whose masses are known, yield a good value for the mass of Venus.

## 5-7. Discovery of Neptune

Perturbations played a dramatic role in the discovery of Neptune, the eighth planet out from the sun. In 1781 Uranus (the seventh planet) had been discovered quite by accident. It was found to be a hundred times larger than the earth and nearly twice as far from the sun as Saturn (till then the outermost planet known). The motion of Uranus was observed for several years, and from these observations astronomers were able to work out the details of its orbit and predict its future positions in the sky. In these calculations not only the gravitational pull of the sun was considered but also the small effects of the attraction of the neighboring planets, Saturn and Jupiter. For about the next forty years all went well—observation and prediction agreed. Then, little by little, Uranus moved away from its predicted path. The calculations were rechecked for errors, but none was found. Perhaps, it was thought, the law of gravitation did not hold strictly at such great distances from the sun. An alternative explanation, however, was that some unknown planet still farther out than Uranus was attracting it from its calculated path. Two young men, Urbain Leverrier in France and John Couch Adams in England, independently undertook to calculate the position of an unknown planet whose gravitational pull would produce the observed discrepancies in Uranus's positions. Adams finished his computations first and sent them to the Astronomer Royal, who, being busy with other things, set them aside for future checking. Meanwhile Leverrier sent his completed calculations to the German astronomer Johann Gottfried Galle, who, on the very evening of the day he received them, turned his telescope in the predicted direction. And there very near to the predicted position, Galle found a faint object, which proved to be the eighth member of the solar system. Thus did Neptune furnish one more triumph for the law of universal gravitation. A similar calculation, based on the variations of Neptune's orbit, led in 1930 to the discovery of Pluto, the ninth and farthest known planet.

## 5-8. *Mechanical Aspects of the Solar System*

Measurements and calculations of the kind we have been discussing have resulted in detailed knowledge of the mechanical properties of the solar system. Some of these results—among them a few unexpected ones—are shown in Table 5-1. Jupiter, the largest both in diameter and in mass, is only about one-quarter as dense as the earth, which is, in fact, the densest of all the planets. The largest planets all have surprisingly low densities—so low that they must, it seems, have a large fraction of their matter in the gaseous state. The principal constituent of Jupiter's atmosphere is elemental hydrogen. Spectroscopic analysis (Chap. 25) of the light from Jupiter also reveals large amounts of ammonia and methane in its atmosphere. These gases form a layer that is about one-fifth of Jupiter's radius thick. Under that is a thick layer of ice (the surface temperature of Jupiter is −130°C), and the rocky core has a diameter that is only about half of the diameter of the planet. Saturn appears to have a similar structure.

Surface gravity (that is, the acceleration of a freely falling body at the surface of the planet) is another interesting property. On Mars, objects would have only about one-third of the *weight* that they have on the earth. An object moving fast enough can escape from the gravitational pull of a planet. The necessary velocity increases with surface gravity. We shall see (Chap. 12) that gaseous molecules move with great speeds, which increase with the temperature and decrease with increasing mass of the molecule. At the high temperature of Mercury (near the sun) atmospheric gases would have tremendous velocities. Hence any atmosphere that Mercury may have had has escaped and fallen into the sun. Similarly, the earth has stolen the moon's atmosphere if it ever had one. On the other hand, the low temperature and high surface gravity of the major planets permit them to keep their gaseous atmospheres, even including hydrogen, which is the lightest gas. Many other detailed features of the solar system are known, but we cannot include them. The reader is referred to one of the many excellent introductory texts on astronomy for further details.

The dimensions of the solar system are such that scale diagrams on a sheet of paper are practically impossible. If, for instance, the astronomical unit, our mean distance from the sun (≈93 million miles), is represented by 1 cm, the earth's orbit would have a diameter of 2 cm. But Pluto's orbit would be 80 cm wide. On such a scale even the enormous sun would be about a tenth as big as the period at the end of this sentence. Hence to show the planets and sun so that their relative sizes were clear, the orbital sizes would run to miles. Suppose, for instance, that we let one meter represent a million miles. The sun would be a ball about 80 cm in diameter; the earth would be a pea more than a city block away; Saturn, an orange, would be more than half a mile away; and Pluto, a small-sized pea, would be over two miles from the sun. This model could be laid out on a prairie but not in a book.

The solar system is practically flat. The plane of the earth's orbit is used as reference. This plane, extended, intersects the celestial sphere of the stars in a circle, the ecliptic. As the earth moves round its orbit, the sun appears to move across the heavens along the ecliptic. The planes of the orbits of the other planets, except Pluto, are inclined to the ecliptic plane by no more than 7°. Thus, as viewed from the earth, all the planets but one are seen in a band that is 16° wide with the ecliptic running along the center. This, as we have seen (§ 2-2), is the zodiac.

## 5-9. *Motions of the Earth*

One of the objections to a heliocentric solar system, both in ancient times and in the times of Copernicus and Kepler, was that the stars did not show any displacement. As the earth moves along its orbit, the stars, apparently near, ought to appear to move just as the fields and houses along a railroad do when seen from a moving train. The answer given was that perhaps the stars are very distant and that the effect is therefore unobservable, just as a distant mountain

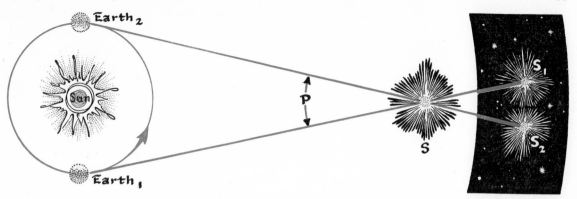

FIGURE **5-8** *Because of the revolution of the earth, a star appears to change its position. (The angle* p *is greatly exaggerated.)*

does not appear to move when seen from a moving train. This turned out to be so. Consider Figure 5-8. A star, S, viewed from the earth at position 1, would be seen, against the background of greatly distant stars, at $S_1$. Six months later, when viewed from position 2, the star would be seen at $S_2$, and then the cycle would repeat itself. The reference stars are at such a great distance that they show very little if any motion. The star S, however, as the earth revolves, should appear to oscillate back and forth in a tiny orbit among the distant stars. After Kepler and Newton this effect was searched for diligently. But it was not until 1832 that observational technique developed sufficient precision to detect the motion. For even the nearest stars, the angle $p$ is not as great as one second of arc; so the guess that the stars are very distant is indeed true. Thus these measurements not only establish the revolution of the earth but furnish a determination of stellar distance. Enormous as the solar system is, it shrinks to a mere point when compared with the distance of our nearest stellar neighbor.

The rising and setting of the sun, although required by a heliocentric system, do not establish the rotation of the earth. A simple experiment that did prove the rotation of the earth was performed by J. B. L. Foucault in 1851. He suspended a long, massive pendulum (one that would oscillate for a long time) from the dome of the Pantheon in Paris. The pendulum hung from a pivot resting on a support fastened

to the ceiling. There is so little friction in such a pivoted suspension that, if the earth was rotating and turning the building, no twist would be transmitted to the suspension by the turning support. Then, by Newton's first law of motion, the pendulum would continue to oscillate in a fixed direction since there was no external force to change its motion. This is exactly what happened. To a person watching the pendulum, of course, it would *seem* to change its direction of swing as he rotated with the earth. What happens is that the direction of motion of the pendulum remains *fixed in space* and the observer rotates round it with the earth. The rate of apparent change in direction is precisely what would be produced by a daily rotation of the earth.

We have traced some of the successes that Newton's laws of motion and law of gravity had in correlating the observations of the solar system. There are many others, and we shall mention some in later chapters. The ordering of celestial as well as terrestrial motions established great confidence in the generality of these laws and in the universal aspect of the law of gravity. One final word on gravitation. The law does not explain the gravitational force; it just describes it. There is no model or mechanism to account for the origin of the force. The law merely states that every particle in the universe acts as if this force existed and thus reveals another fundamental property of all matter—gravitation.

## Concepts and Terms

Vector Quantities
representation of vector quantities—vectors
vector addition
Circular Motion with Constant Speed
centripetal acceleration
centripetal force
Newton's Law of Gravitation
Cavendish Experiment
gravitational constant
mass and density of the earth
Distances in the Solar System
astronomical unit

parallax
angular size
Masses in the Solar System
Perturbations
Densities of the Planets
Surface Gravity and Velocity of Escape
Dimensions and Form of the Solar System
Revolution of the Earth
apparent motion of stars
Rotation of the Earth
Foucault pendulum

## Problems

**5-1.** Characterize vector and scalar quantities, and list several examples of each.

**5-2.** What is a vector? Outline the method of adding vectors.

**5-3.** Vector A is 7 units in the positive $x$-direction, and vector B is 5 units in a direction 40° above the $x$-axis.
(A) What is the sum of A and B?
(B) What is the result of subtracting B from A? (Hint: Remember that subtracting any quantity, $x$, is the same as adding $-x$.)
>    *Ans.* (A) 11.4 units 17° above $x$-axis
>            (B) 4.5 units 45° below $x$-axis

**5-4.** An airplane maintains an air speed (speed relative to the air) of 50 m/sec due north. There is a 20 m/sec wind blowing toward the west. What is the plane's velocity relative to the ground?
>    *Ans.* 54 m/sec 22° west of north

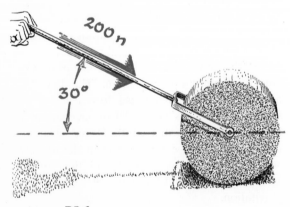

FIGURE **P5-6**

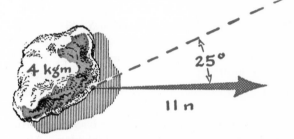

FIGURE **P5-8**

**5-5.** A boat sails 6.5 km due east. How far and in what direction must it then sail in order to reach an island 10 km in a direction 20° north of east from the original starting point?
>    *Ans.* 4.5 km 50° north of east

**5-6.** A man pushes with 200 newtons on the handle of a 100 kgm lawn roller as shown.
(A) How much force pushes the roller forward?
(B) With how much force is the roller pressed against the lawn?
>    *Ans.* (A) 173 newtons
>            (B) 1,080 newtons

**5-7.** A 2 kgm mass is dragged across a "frictionless" table by a 10 newton force acting at 37° above the horizontal.
(A) What is the acceleration of the mass?
(B) What is the force on the table?
>    *Ans.* (A) 4 m/sec²
>            (B) 13.6 newtons

**5-8.** A 4 kgm mass has *two* forces acting on it at the same point, one of which is 11 newtons as shown. The mass is observed to accelerate from rest along the broken line. After a distance of 2.25 m the mass is moving with a speed of 3.0 m/sec. What is the second force?

*Ans.* 5.0 newtons at 113° above line of motion

**5-9.** Draw, with a compass, something more than one quarter of a circle with a radius of 15 cm. Start at a point near one end of this arc and lay off (with the aid of a protractor) points that are 5°, 10°, 20°, 60°, and 90° from the starting point. Draw a straight line from the starting point to the 90° point. Measure the length of this chord, and compare it with the length of the 90° arc. (Note: The arc for angle $\theta$ is $\theta\pi r/180°$.) Repeat for the other points, and make a table listing angle, arc, and chord. In view of the idea of limits, are the chord and the arc ever equal? For what approximate angle do they differ by no more than 5 percent? For very small angles ($<1°$) is it valid to consider chord equal to arc? (Note the use of this geometric fact in the derivation of centripetal acceleration.)

**5-10.** A 1,500 kgm car travels with a constant speed of 25 m/sec round a circular curve of radius 500 m. What is the frictional force of the road on the tires?

*Ans.* $1.9\times10^3$ newtons

What is the force if the speed is doubled?

**5-11.** A centrifuge rotates liquid mixtures at high speed in order to hasten sedimentation. A certain centrifuge turns at the rate of 100 revolutions per second. What is the acceleration of that part of the liquid which is 8 cm from the axis of rotation? How many times $g$ is this?

*Ans.* $3.16\times10^4$ m/sec$^2$; $a = 3,220$ $g$

**5-12.** Compute the acceleration with which the moon is "falling" toward the earth. (See App. I for pertinent information.) Compare with the value of $g$ at New York.

*Ans.* $a = 2.75\times10^{-3}$ m/sec$^2$

**5-13.** You can swing a pail of water in a vertical circle without spilling the water at the top of the circle. Explain. If the radius of the circle is 1 m, what is the minimum speed of the water that will prevent spilling? (Hint: At the top of the circle what supplies the centripetal force for the limiting case?)

*Ans.* 3.13 m/sec

**5-14.** A fighter pilot pulls out of a dive along the arc of a vertical circle. If he is traveling at too great a speed, or if he pulls out too "sharply" (that is, moves along a circle of too small a radius), the blood leaves his head and he goes unconscious. Explain. If the plane is going 250

m/sec and the pilot can withstand no more than 7 $g$ centripetal acceleration, what is the minimum allowable radius of the pull-out path?

*Ans.* 910 m

**5-15.** Compute the mass of the earth. Use $6.45\times10^6$ m as the radius of the earth. Compute the density of the earth. (The volume of a sphere is $V = \frac{4}{3}\pi r^3$.)

*Ans.* $6.11\times10^{24}$ kgm; $d = 5.45$ grams/cm$^3$

**5-16.** What would be the value of $g$ at a height of $6.45\times10^6$ m?

*Ans.* 2.45 m/sec$^2$

**5-17.** Calculate the attraction between two lead spheres whose centers are 0.5 m apart and whose masses are 125 kgm and 25 kgm respectively. Could this force be detected by an arm balance that will just register 0.01 gram imbalance? Support your answer quantitatively.

*Ans.* $8.35\times10^{-7}$ newton; about 100 times too small

**5-18.**
(A) The mean angular size of the moon as viewed from the earth (the angle $\theta$, Fig. 5-6b) is 0.52°. The distance to the moon is $3.84\times10^8$ m. What is the diameter of the moon? (Remember the result of Prob. 5-9.)
(B) The mass of the moon is 1/81.5 that of the earth. What is the density of the moon?
(C) What is the acceleration of gravity at the surface of the moon?

*Ans.* (A) $3.48\times10^6$ m
(B) 3.4 grams/cm$^3$
(C) 1.66 m/sec$^2$

**5-19.** Calculate the masses of Mars, Jupiter, and the sun. Compare with the values given in Table 5-1. (See Table 5-2 for appropriate data.)

**5-20.**
(A) On a large sheet of wrapping paper (about 1 m square) draw the *orbits* of the solar system, using the scale suggested in § 5-5. For the larger circles make a "compass" by tying a string to a pencil.
(B) If viewed edgewise from a distance (for example, along the plane of the paper of the diagram of part A), each orbit would appear as a straight line. Draw a line for the earth's orbit, and put a dot at the center to represent the center of the sun. (Use the sheet of paper used in part A.) This is the plane of the ecliptic. Draw lines through the sun for the orbits of the other planets. Use a protractor to lay off the angles. See Table 5-1 for data. The solar system is indeed flat!

**5-21.**

(A) Consider Fig. 5-8. The distance between $Earth_1$ and $Earth_2$ is 2 A.U. For the star (S) *nearest* the solar system, the angle $p$ is observed to be $4.14 \times 10^{-4}$ degree. How far is this closest stellar neighbor?

(B) Light travels at a finite velocity such that it takes only 8 minutes to come from the sun to us. How long does it take the light from the nearest star to reach us?

(C) Suppose that the angle $p$ is observed from Pluto instead of from the earth. What would its value be?

(D) If the planets could be seen from S, how much of the sky, as compared with the moon as seen from the earth, would the whole solar system cover?

*Ans.* (A) $2.76 \times 10^5$ A.U.

(B) 4.2 years

(C) $1.64 \times 10^{-2}$ degree

(D) Only about 0.03 as much!

## Suggested Readings

1. H. Semat, *Fundamentals of Physics,* 3rd edition (Rinehart, 1957), pp. 14–24 (vectors) and 128–135 (centripetal acceleration and force). (Note: Before reading this reference, see App. I for the definitions of sine, cosine, and tangent of an angle.)

2. L. W. Taylor, *Physics the Pioneer Science* (Houghton Mifflin, 1941), Chap. 13 (law of gravitation).

3. G. Holton and D. H. D. Roller, *Foundations of Modern Physical Science* (Addison-Wesley, 1958), pp. 164–197.

4. L. Hogben, *Science for the Citizen* (Knopf, 1938), Chap. V. A rather discursive account of mechanics, with many interesting sections and clear diagrams.

5. W. F. Magie, *A Source Book in Physics* (McGraw-Hill, 1935), pp. 27–30 (Huygens' theorems on centrifugal force; compare theorems I–IV with the equations derived in § 5-2) and 105–111 (the Cavendish experiment).

6. H. Shapley and H. E. Howarth, *A Source Book in Astronomy* (McGraw-Hill, 1929), pp. 74–79 (Newton on rules of reasoning and on gravitation) and 245–254 (Adams and Leverrier on the discovery of Neptune).

7. Sir W. C. Dampier, *A History of Science,* 4th edition (Cambridge University Press, 1949), Chaps. III (The Renaissance) and IV (The Newtonian Epoch).

8. A. N. Whitehead, *Science and the Modern World* (Macmillan, 1925), pp. 1–82.

9. W. T. Skilling and R. S. Richardson, *A Brief Text in Astronomy* (Henry Holt, 1954), Chap. 3 (the scale of the solar system and tables of data on the planets and their satellites).

10. R. H. Baker, *An Introduction to Astronomy,* 5th edition (D. Van Nostrand, 1957), pp. 20–47 (the motions of the earth).

11. Cecilia Payne-Gaposchkin, *Introduction to Astronomy* (Prentice-Hall, 1954), pp. 172–174 (the scale of the solar system) and Chap. VIII (descriptions of the planets).

THE ATOMIC theory is one of Man's oldest intellectual constructs. Paradoxically, the atomic theory is also one of the newest products of modern science. As in most paradoxes, the apparent inconsistency exists because we are talking about two different things in our two statements. The Greeks had an atomic theory, and modern physicists and chemists have a quite different one. Both theories postulate a *particulate* structure of matter; they suggest that all matter is made up of small discrete particles that cannot be subdivided without profound alteration of the substance. In this, the ancient and modern theories are similar, but the dissimilarities are much more important than this trivial likeness—particularly in two respects. First, modern scientists have concerned themselves very much with the nature of the ultimate particles, or *atoms,* but the Greeks did not. Second, the methods by which the two theories were arrived at are vastly different.

## 6-1. Classical Atomic Theory

If you or an ancient Greek or a modern physicist had no information and no preconceived notions about the ultimate structure of matter and simply thought about the problem, each would have exactly a 50 percent chance of inventing an atomic theory of matter. Let one of these thinkers contemplate a piece of coal. Then let him break the piece of coal, actually or figuratively; the fragments are still coal. Let him again break the fragments, and the small pieces are still coal with all its properties. Even when ground to a fine dust, the particles are still particles of coal. Now imagine that this subdivision of the particles continues without limit: however finely they have been divided already, divide them again. Here a question arises. Is there a limit beyond which further subdivision is impossible without destroying the properties of the coal? Or can these particles be divided endlessly and always retain their properties as fragments of coal? If we answer "yes" to the first question, we have postulated an *atomic* theory of matter; if we answer "yes" to the second question, we believe that matter has a *continuous* structure.

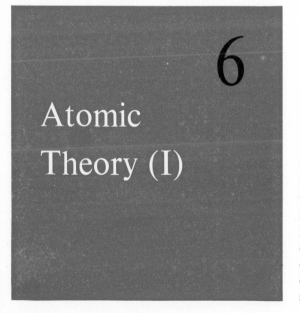

CHAPTER

6

Atomic
Theory (I)

One school of ancients chose the first of the two possibilities and has been credited ever since with inventing the atomic theory; but just as many ancient thinkers believed just as strongly that matter was continuous. And the two groups had equally good reasons for their choice, for neither had any reason at all. Until 150 years ago the choice between these two views was made on esthetic, moral, theological, or similar grounds. Even to a neophyte scientist these bases for a choice between two theories are clearly "unscientific" and probably seem quite inadequate. It is worth while, in the process of learning science, to examine briefly the reasons why these are inadequate bases for determining a scientific theory.

## 6-2. Nature of Scientific Theories

A scientific theory is a step—in both senses of the word—toward understanding. A useful theory is in itself an *advancement* of our knowledge, and it is also a firm *base* for further advancement. Scientific theories are intellectual constructs that relate broad collections of experimentally observed facts. The advancement of knowledge inherent in a theory is in this relating or "explaining" of otherwise isolated and trivial sets of facts. The base for further advancement is in prediction, guidance of new experiments, and extension to new and broader theories. The basis, existence, and function of a scientific theory are pervaded by experimental observation.

Here, then, is why the atomic theory of the ancients cannot be considered a scientific theory in the modern sense of the word "science." It was not a step toward understanding matter, for it was in no way related to experience. It was not based on observation, nor did it lead to experiments or further theories. Indeed, the notion of "ultimate particle" discouraged both experiment and speculation beyond this point. As long as the existence of atoms was postulated only because it seemed fitting, beautiful, moral, or God's will that there be atoms, no science had been created, nor had understanding been ap-

proached. But when John Dalton,† in 1804, postulated an atomic structure because matter behaves in such a way that it *must* be particulate, our understanding took a long and bold step forward. The atomic theory became a scientific theory.

## 6-3. Laws of Chemical Combination

The few decades immediately preceding Dalton's first statement of the atomic theory were marked by many discoveries and the accumulation of much experimental information in the science of chemistry. Hitherto unknown elements and compounds were discovered, but of even more importance was the *quantitative* examination of chemical reactions. Investigators had caused elements to combine into compounds, and compounds to decompose into their elemental constituents, and had weighed the reactants and products. The important point is that the *masses* of the substances were carefully observed. The results of large numbers of such experiments, done over a long period of time by many different investigators, were generalized into *laws*.

A scientific law is a limited concept that summarizes and generalizes a large mass of experimental facts without attempting to state an underlying principle or explanation. It is simply a concise statement of many experimental facts. One other characteristic of laws is that they are extrapolations. Though based on *many* individual cases, they make a statement about *all* cases.

---

† Dalton was an elementary-school teacher in England and was somewhat of a contrast to most of the eighteenth- and early nineteenth-century scientists, who were almost invariably men of considerable wealth. But, like the others, he was a curious amateur who practiced science as an avocation. Some historians have said that Dalton was a dull fellow and have doubted whether he was original in his proposal of his theory. Whether or not he was dull, the theory he proposed was a strong and successful effort to remove some of the abstraction from the description of chemical reactions. His statement of the theory was essentially a diagraming of reactions. He developed a rather involved and complicated system of symbols, partly carried over from the alchemists. We shall use, not his symbols, but the currently used ones.

One of the generalizations based on the experiments described above—and one that Dalton considered in the development of his theory—is called **the law of conservation of mass.** This law states that, in all chemical reactions, matter (that is, mass) is neither created nor destroyed. Chemists had measured the masses of the products and reactants of many, many reactions. In every experiment that was done carefully, it was found that the sum of the masses of the products was equal to the sum of the masses of the reactants. Even though we can never study all reactions, it is valid to extend our generalization from the *many* that have been studied to *all* reactions.

In one sense this law is self-evident to us now. If one starts with so much stuff and doesn't spill any of it, he has neither more nor less after a reaction has taken place, however much it has been changed around. In the past, however, and in our own uncritical thinking, the conservation of mass is by no means a self-evident notion. We think of fuel as being "consumed" in the reaction of combustion. A burning candle disappears, and there is an apparent loss of mass. Conversely, the chemists of the seventeenth and eighteenth centuries were baffled by the apparent *gain* in mass when metals were burned (or more slowly oxidized) in air. The ash weighed more than the metal. Here was an apparent creation of matter. A rather strange theory of combustion, in repute for almost a hundred years, tried to explain this fact. The theory depended on a hypothetical principle called "phlogiston," which had, among other remarkable properties, a negative mass. The source of confusion, both for the eighteenth-century scientists and for modern non-scientists, is the fact that in these reactions one or more of the participants are gaseous and therefore not

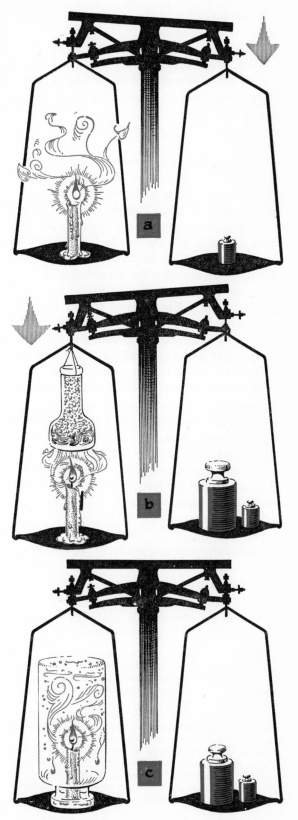

FIGURE **6-1** *Conservation of mass: (a) the candle appears to lose mass because products of the reaction escape into the surrounding atmosphere; (b) the candle and the absorber appear to gain mass because one reactant is taken from the surrounding atmosphere and all products are absorbed; (c) the balance is not deflected, for no products are lost and no unaccounted-for reactants enter the system.*

easily accounted for by the usual uncritical techniques. When a candle burns, the products of combustion are carbon dioxide and steam, both of which escape into the atmosphere and hence give the impression of an over-all loss of mass. When metals (and the candle) burn, one of the reactants is oxygen from the air, which, unless accounted for, will give the impression of a gain in mass.†

The classical demonstration of a candle burning on a balance illustrates this point. A candle is burned under three sets of conditions, which are progressively more complete in accounting for all the components of the reaction. In condition a, Figure 6-1, the candle burns freely in air. As it burns, the products of the reaction are allowed to escape into the surrounding atmosphere, and there is an apparent loss of mass, indicated by the balance tipping toward the side opposite the candle. In condition b the candle burns freely in air, but the products of the reaction are kept in the system by a device that absorbs carbon dioxide and water. There is an apparent increase in mass under these conditions because oxygen taken from the air is one of the reactants. In condition c the candle is burned inside a closed container so that the gaseous components of the reaction can neither enter nor escape from the system. Under these conditions, all reactants and products being included in the mass balance sheet, there is no change in mass, and the balance remains steady.

This concept of the conservation of mass, which required many centuries of struggle to establish among scientists, and which is still not completely a part of our non-scientific culture, is the basis for all quantitative chemistry and is implicit in the use of any chemical equation. The formation of magnesium oxide, for example, can be described by the following word equation:

$$\text{magnesium} + \text{oxygen} \longrightarrow \text{magnesium oxide}$$

This equation states the bare fact that the two elements unite to form the compound, but it also states (if the law of conservation of mass is accepted) that the mass of the magnesium oxide formed is *just equal to* the sum of the masses of the oxygen and magnesium that reacted. The burning of a candle can also be stated in a word equation:

$$\text{candle} + \text{oxygen} \longrightarrow \text{carbon dioxide} + \text{water}$$

Again the law of conservation of mass states that the loss in mass of the candle (the amount of the candle that participates in the reaction) plus the mass of the oxygen taken from the air is equal to the sum of the masses of the carbon dioxide and water produced.

The second generalization that Dalton considered is called **the law of definite proportions.** This law, which is implicit in the definition of a substance (§ 1-5), states that the elemental composition of any substance is always the same. Clearly the composition of any *elemental* substance is constant at 100 percent that element. If the substance is a compound (for example, copper sulfide), the ratio of the masses of the elements in the compound (copper and sulfur in this example)—or the percentage of each of the elements—is always the same, whatever the source, method of formation, or method of analysis. This is, again, an extrapolation of *many* experimental facts to a generalization that covers *all* similar cases. Many experiments of both synthesis and decomposition between compounds and elements had been done by Dalton, his contemporaries, and his predecessors, and the results substantiated this generalized law.

The third generalization used by Dalton is called **the law of multiple proportions.** This law states that, when two elements unite to form two or more different compounds, the ratios of the mass of one element to the mass of the other element in the several compounds stand to each other as the ratio of small whole numbers. For example, there are two oxides of copper—compounds composed only of copper and oxygen. The ratio of the mass of copper to the mass of

---

† For discussions of the extremely important experimental and theoretical developments that immediately preceded Dalton and were essential as a groundwork for his theory, the student is referred to treatments of the work of Lavoisier and Priestley and discussions of the phlogiston theory. One excellent source is a paper-bound book, *On Understanding Science,* by J. B. Conant.

All of this work, though of the greatest importance in the development of modern chemistry and illustrative of a good deal of science, is not taken up in detail in this book, for it is not logically required in this non-historical treatment.

oxygen in one of these oxides is always found to be 8/1 (an illustration of the law of definite proportions). The ratio in the other compound is always 4/1. These two ratios differ from each other by a factor of 2; that is, they stand to each other as the ratio 2/1, two small whole numbers. There are also two oxides of iron, in one of which the ratio of mass of iron to mass of oxygen is 7/2 and in the other is 7/3. These two ratios stand to each other as the ratio of the small whole numbers 2/3.

Both the law of definite proportions and the law of multiple proportions were established by experiments that might be done by elementary students. The two mercury oxides, for example, can be decomposed by heat, which drives off the oxygen and leaves a residue of elemental mercury. The nature of the experiment is such that the direct weighing of the oxygen removed is extremely difficult. We therefore calculate the mass of the oxygen removed by difference, using the law of conservation of mass. A typical experiment might be as follows: 26 grams of one oxide of mercury was decomposed by heat and left a residue of 25 grams of mercury. The difference must have been oxygen; therefore the mass of oxygen originally combined with the 25 grams of mercury must have been 1 gram. The ratio of masses is, then, 25/1. A sample of 27 grams of the other mercury oxide, when decomposed, left a residue of 25 grams of mercury by losing 2 grams of oxygen. The ratio of masses for this compound is therefore 25/2.

Equations can be written for these reactions, and they may point out more clearly the mass calculations:

$$26 \text{ grams mercury}^I \text{ oxide} \longrightarrow$$
$$25 \text{ grams mercury} + x \text{ grams oxygen}$$

By the law of conservation of mass, the components of each side of the equation must have equal mass:

$$26 \text{ grams} = 25 \text{ grams} + x$$
$$x = 26 \text{ grams} - 25 \text{ grams} = 1 \text{ gram oxygen}$$

And for the other oxide:

$$27 \text{ grams mercury}^{II} \text{ oxide} \longrightarrow$$
$$25 \text{ grams mercury} + y \text{ grams oxygen}$$
$$27 \text{ grams} = 25 \text{ grams} + y$$
$$y = 2 \text{ grams oxygen}$$

Many repetitions of these experiments show the *same* two ratios for the two oxides. The fact that for oxide$^I$ the ratio is always 25/1 supports our faith in the law of definite proportions, as does the fact that the ratio for oxide$^{II}$ is always 25/2. The fact that the two ratios are to each other as the ratio of the small whole numbers 2/1 supports the law of multiple proportions.

## 6-4. *Dalton's Atomic Theory*

Now let us return to the question raised by the hypothetical subdividing of the lump of coal: "Is the structure of substances continuous or particulate?" But this time approach the problem, not without information, but keeping in mind the three laws that describe the mass relations in chemical reactions. Guided by this information, Dalton attempted to answer the question: "What characteristic of matter would be consistent with these facts or would 'explain' these observations?" His answer was that an atomic structure of matter is required. He became convinced that there *is* a limit beyond which the coal cannot be divided. This limit is the ultimate particle of coal, a carbon atom. All carbon atoms are identical, are indestructible, and are different from the atoms of any other substance. These postulates, here applied specifically to carbon atoms, were applied to atoms of all of the fifty-odd elements known to Dalton. There are now more than a hundred known elements, and Dalton's theory is still applicable to all of them. Some of Dalton's postulates were unnecessary, and others were quite untrue; yet, despite several notable modifications and extensions, the essence of the original theory remains valid. For the most part we shall concern ourselves only with the parts of the theory that are now known to be valid and necessary.

## 6-5. *Postulates of the Atomic Theory*

(1) *All elements are composed of very small, discrete, indivisible particles called atoms.* Dalton had no clear idea how small atoms are; they

are, in fact, several orders of magnitude smaller than he imagined. At this stage of our development of the theory of the structure of matter it is not necessary to specify how small they are except by saying that they are small enough so that any sensible sample of matter contains extremely large numbers of atoms.

(2) *All atoms of any one element are identical.* Modern experiments have proved that this statement is not true, but the exceptions to it involve subtle characteristics of the structure of matter and at this point need not concern the student. At this stage of our development we shall assume that the masses of all atoms of any element are identical, whether they are uncombined or are a part of a compound molecule. We must, however, admit at least minor differences among the atoms of a particular element —differences that depend on the type of combination in which the atoms are involved.

(3) *The atoms of no two elements are alike.* This postulate of Dalton's is now known to be perfectly true.

(4) *The atoms are indestructible and suffer no changes in chemical reactions.* This postulate is not quite true; in some reactions atoms are destroyed, and in all reactions there are subtle changes in atoms. The understanding of these exceptions must be deferred until more background has been established. At this stage it will be most useful to assume with Dalton that the atoms are unchanging.

(5) *Compounds are formed when atoms of two or more different elements combine to form a molecule of the compound.* Molecules, which are the ultimate particles of compound substances, are also exceedingly small; any sensible sample of matter contains vast numbers of molecules. It is important that we include this notion that very large numbers of particles are present in any experimentally usable sample of matter. The term "molecule," used strictly, means the ultimate particle of any substance. In many elemental substances the ultimate particle (molecule) is, in fact, a single atom, but some elements exist only as aggregates of particles made of two or more atoms, and the ultimate particle is therefore a di-atomic or tri-atomic, etc. molecule; all compounds are made up of two or more

different atoms, and the ultimate particle of these substances is the compound molecule made up of several atoms.

(6) *In general, atoms combine in simple ratios.* Dalton's original assumption was that the combination is always 1/1 or, if two compounds of the same two elements exist, 1/2. He further assumed that all elemental substances had monatomic molecules—that is, that the ultimate particle was always a single atom. These rigid assumptions had the advantage of simplicity, but they proved to be untenable. Dalton's insistence on the simplest possible combinations prevented his acceptance of an extremely useful modification and extension of the theory suggested by experiments of Gay-Lussac. The combinations of atoms to form molecules are usually quite simple, but by no means are they always the simplest possible.

The view that we will take of atoms at this time is quite close to the view taken by Dalton. They are small, indestructible spheres, rather like billiard balls but *very* much smaller; the atoms of any element are alike in most properties, including mass; the atoms of different elements differ in ways as yet unspecified—but at least in mass; in forming compounds, they become quite firmly attached to each other by attachments that are still unspecified; when compounds decompose, these attachments are broken. Almost all of the parts of this picture of atoms will be modified as the subject is developed in this text, but for the present the picture is adequate. And it will be seen that all the modifications that do come about will be consistent with, and will be an extension of, this simplified picture.

## 6-6. *Relation of the Laws of Combination to the Atomic Theory*

We can best establish the relation of this series of hypotheses to the experimental laws of chemical combination by interpreting examples of reactions in terms of these postulates, using the symbols described in Chapter 1 and indicating the atoms as small rectangles.

Magnesium is a silvery-white metallic element that will readily burn in air. This reaction is the combination of magnesium with oxygen to produce magnesium oxide, a soft, white, powdery ash. Using the postulates of the atomic theory, including the one that the combination is the simplest possible, we represent the reaction by the following equation:

$$\boxed{\text{Mg}} \;+\; \boxed{\text{O}} \;\longrightarrow\; \boxed{\text{Mg}\,|\,\text{O}}$$

1 atom    1 atom     1 molecule

The decomposition of mercury oxide, as another example, is represented by:

$$\boxed{\text{Hg}\,|\,\text{O}} \;\longrightarrow\; \boxed{\text{Hg}} \;+\; \boxed{\text{O}}$$

1 molecule     1 atom    1 atom

In both these equations we have spoken of single atoms or molecules. Obviously, because of the extremely small size, it would be impossible to sense in any way the reaction of only one atom of oxygen with one atom of magnesium. In order to have a sensible sample of the materials, we have to start with some very large number of atoms. But the equation states that exactly the *same number* of atoms of oxygen and of magnesium react and produce the same number of molecules of magnesium oxide. Similarly, if $N$ molecules of mercury oxide are decomposed, $N$ atoms of mercury and $N$ atoms of oxygen are produced. These numbers are the same *only* if our assumptions as to the formulas of the oxides are correct. At this stage we have no reason for knowing that they are correct; we have only followed the postulate and assumed the simplest possible formulas.

The law of conservation of mass is related to our theory by simple logical consideration of the postulates: The mass of all magnesium atoms is the same and is constant whether the atoms are uncombined or are a part of a compound. The mass of all the oxygen atoms is also the same and constant whether they are free or combined. Exactly the same number of magnesium atoms are on each side of our equation—that is, in the products and in the reactants. The same number of oxygen atoms also appear on both sides. The total masses on the two sides of the equation must therefore be equal. Similar reasoning would be applied to the other example or to any chemical equation.

The law of definite proportions is similarly related to the atomic theory by simple logic. The ratio of the mass of magnesium to the mass of oxygen in a single molecule of magnesium oxide must be the ratio of the mass of the magnesium atom to the mass of the oxygen atom. Since the two atomic masses are constant, the ratio must be the same for *any* molecule of magnesium oxide. And, since all molecules of magnesium oxide have this same ratio, any bulk sample of molecules of the compound must have the same ratio.

In order to relate the law of multiple proportions, we must consider sets of equations in which two (or more) compounds are formed by the same two elements, such as the two mercury oxides or the two copper oxides. In both of these pairs the ratio of the mass of the metal to the mass of oxygen in one of the oxides is just twice the ratio for the other oxide. We have postulated that the mass of all mercury atoms is the same, the mass of all copper atoms is the same, and the mass of all oxygen atoms is the same. The only logical explanation of the factor 2 between the ratios for the pairs of compounds is that there are twice as *many* atoms of metal per atom of oxygen in one member of each pair as in the other. Our postulate of simplicity would direct that the formulas of the two oxides of mercury be $HgO$ and $Hg_2O$ *or* $HgO_2$ and $HgO$.[†] Both of these pairs of formulas have ratios of atoms of mercury to atoms of oxygen that differ by the factor 2, and at this stage the choice between them is entirely arbitrary. To avoid confusion, we will choose the pair that will later prove to be correct. If we assume, then, that the first pair is correct, the equations for decomposition of the oxides are

$$\boxed{\text{Hg}\,|\,\text{O}} \;\longrightarrow\; \boxed{\text{Hg}} \;+\; \boxed{\text{O}}$$

1 molecule     1 atom    1 atom

$$\boxed{\text{Hg}\,|\,\text{O}\,|\,\text{Hg}} \;\longrightarrow\; \boxed{\text{Hg}} \;+\; \boxed{\text{Hg}} \;+\; \boxed{\text{O}}$$

1 molecule      2 atoms     1 atom

If, as we consider these equations, we keep in mind the postulates of the atomic theory, we shall clearly see that the factor 2, which relates

---

[†] The formulas could also be multiples of these, such as $Hg_4O_2$ and $Hg_2O_2$ or $Cu_4O_2$ and $Cu_2O_2$, etc. But these are ruled out by the postulate of simplicity.

the two ratios of masses for the two oxides, is a manifestation of (or, from the opposite point of view, a proof of) the fact that there are two atoms of mercury to one atom of oxygen in one compound and only one atom of mercury to one atom of oxygen in the other.

The decomposition of the two copper oxides can be represented by a similar pair of equations: †

$$\boxed{Cu \mid O} \longrightarrow \boxed{Cu} + \boxed{O}$$
1 molecule        1 atom    1 atom

$$\boxed{Cu \mid O \mid Cu} \longrightarrow \boxed{Cu} + \boxed{Cu} + \boxed{O}$$
1 molecule              2 atoms         1 atom

Again, the atomic theory's explanation of the factor 2 between the ratios of the mass of copper to the mass of oxygen in the two oxides is that there are twice as many atoms of copper per oxygen atom in one oxide as in the other.

The case of the two iron oxides is a little more complex but is also explained directly by the atomic theory. The two oxides show mass ratios that stand to each other as the ratio 3/2. That means that there must be $3/2 = 1.5$ times as many iron atoms in one of the oxides as in the other. Now, clearly, we cannot have a fraction of an atom in either molecule and therefore must have some even multiple of 1.5. The various pairs of formulas that could represent these compounds are $Fe_2O$ and $Fe_3O$, $Fe_2O_2$ and $Fe_2O_3$, $FeO$ and $Fe_2O_3$, $FeO_2$ and $FeO_3$, or any multiple of these pairs. The multiples and probably the second pair would be rejected because they are unnecessarily complex. The choice between the other pairs is arbitrary. We shall see later that the formulas must be the third pair:

$$\boxed{Fe \mid O} \quad \text{and} \quad \boxed{O \mid Fe \mid O \mid Fe \mid O}$$

The atomic theory we have proposed is consistent with these three generalizations of experimental facts, the mass relations of chemical reaction. Furthermore, it integrates these three laws, which otherwise were isolated collections of information. It is now apparent that the three laws are simply various gross manifestations of the underlying structure of matter and are almost self-evident consequences of its particulate na-

† See the footnote on p. 75.

ture. The theory has met, then, the first requirement of a useful scientific concept. We shall see in the subsequent sections of this chapter and in later chapters that the atomic theory has also been eminently useful in the extension of our knowledge of the structure of matter and therefore has the second characteristic of a good theory.

## 6-7. Combining Weights

The obvious next step in expanding the atomic theory is to establish the relative masses of the various atoms. Ultimately we shall be interested in the absolute masses of the atoms. But, in order to deal with such small quantities of mass, we must first build up a background of information and experience. Only near the end of this book can the question of absolute masses be faced. In the meantime it would be extremely helpful to know even relative masses of the atoms. Even this, however, must be attained by a two-stage process. We must consider **combining weights** before we are able to approach atomic weights.

The experiments in which we have indicated quantitative data can serve as the basis for establishing the relative masses of the various elements that combine with or replace each other in chemical reactions; that is, all of these experiments show the ratio of the mass of one element that is *chemically equivalent* to a given mass of the other element. Such experiments do *not* show the relative masses of the *atoms,* for we have, up to this point, no experimental basis for knowing the relative *numbers* of the atoms that combine.

We can illustrate this point by considering again the formation of magnesium oxide. A typical experimental result would be the observation that 3 grams of magnesium, burned in air, produced 5 grams of magnesium oxide. Clearly this was accomplished by a reaction with 2 grams of oxygen:

3 grams magnesium + 2 grams oxygen $\longrightarrow$
5 grams magnesium oxide

In this reaction, 3 grams of Mg is chemically equivalent to 2 grams of O, or the ratio of their combining weights is 3/2 or 1.5. Now, *if* we knew for certain that one atom of Mg combines with one atom of O, we should know from this experiment that the Mg atom has just 1.5 times the mass of the oxygen atom. But, since we do not *know* the relative numbers of the two atoms that combine, we cannot say anything about the relative masses of the atoms (the atomic weights) and must limit ourselves to saying that the *combining weight* of magnesium is 1.5 times the combining weight of oxygen.

The experiments on the two copper oxides showed ratios of Cu to O of 8/1 for copper$^I$ oxide and 4/1 for copper$^{II}$ oxide. These ratios are the same as saying that 8 grams of Cu$^I$ or 4 grams of Cu$^{II}$ is chemically equivalent to 1 gram of O, for, in the experiments described, these relative masses were combined. Now, if 1.5 grams of Mg is chemically equivalent to 1 gram of O and 4 grams of Cu$^{II}$ is also chemically equivalent to 1 gram of O, then 1.5 grams of Mg should be chemically equivalent to 4 grams of Cu$^{II}$. Such a statement means that 1.5 grams of Mg could replace 4 grams of Cu$^{II}$ in a compound. It should also be noted that 8 grams of Cu$^I$ is chemically equivalent to 4 grams of Cu$^{II}$ or to 1.5 grams of Mg as well as to 1 gram of O.†

It is already obvious that these ratios, which are *direct experimental observations,* are too cumbersome for our description of the mass relations of these atoms, even though we are talking about only three different elements. To try to extend the terminology to all 102 elements would be impossible. For this reason we introduce the idea of combining weights. These are masses (of the various elements) that are chemically equivalent to each other—that is, will react with each other or replace each other.

| TABLE 6-1 *Combining Weights* |
| :--- |
| O = 1 (standard) |
| Mg = 1.5 |
| Cu$^{II}$ = 4 |
| Cu$^I$ = 8 |

Such quantities are *relative*. They have no absolute significance and depend on some *arbitrarily* defined standard. Table 6-1 is the beginning of a table of combining weights based on a defined standard of O = 1. (Note that we might make O = 10 or 100, in which case all the values in the table would be multiplied by 10 or 100. Or we could use *any* other number for our standard if we just relate all the other values to the standard by the experimentally observed ratios.) In such a table the combining weight assigned to each element is determined by the ratio of the mass of that element to the mass of oxygen with which it combines.

By considering the ratios of combining masses we can extend this table to include all the other elements we have talked about. The two mercury oxides were shown to have ratios of Hg to O of 25/1 for Hg$^I$ and 25/2 (= 12.5/1) for Hg$^{II}$. One of the iron oxides (Fe$^{III}$) had an Fe/O ratio of 7/3, which is 2.33/1; the other (Fe$^{II}$) had a ratio of 7/2 = 3.5/1. Copper$^I$ sulfide has a Cu/S ratio of 4/1. In order to include S in our table, we must observe that 8 grams of Cu$^I$ is equivalent to 1 gram of O and, since the ratio of Cu$^I$ to S is 4/1, that 8 grams of Cu$^I$ would be equivalent to 2 grams of S. Therefore 2 grams of S is equivalent to 1 gram of O. All of these combining weights can now be included in our table. And by exactly the same type of experiments and calculations we could, in principle, include all the 102 known elements.

It will be instructive to describe a few more hypothetical experiments so that we may include a few other elements in the table. We can decompose water into its elements, H and O, or can synthesize it by burning hydrogen in oxygen. If such a reaction is done quantitatively, the ratio of the mass of hydrogen to the mass of oxygen with which it combines is observed to be 1/8. A typical experiment might provide data

---

† We stated earlier in this chapter that we would assume, with Dalton, that all atoms of an element are identical in mass but vary in other properties, which depend on the type of combination they are involved in. Here we point out two types of copper atoms. The difference between them, which is in their combining weights, is actually a manifestation of a difference in combining power (see Chap. 7). But, as we shall observe in later chapters, this is an extremely subtle difference, which, when understood, helps to establish the atomic theory as a useful explanation of the structure of matter.

TABLE 6-2   *Combining Weights*

| O = 1 | | H = 1 | |
|---|---|---|---|
| H | 1/8 | H | 1 |
| O | 1 | O | 8 |
| Mg | 1.5 | Mg | 12 |
| S | 2 | S | 16 |
| $Fe^{III}$ | 2.33 | $Fe^{III}$ | 18.7 |
| $Fe^{II}$ | 3.5 | $Fe^{II}$ | 28 |
| $Cu^{II}$ | 4 | $Cu^{II}$ | 32 |
| Cl | 4.5 | Cl | 36 |
| $Cu^{I}$ | 8 | $Cu^{I}$ | 64 |
| Br | 10 | Br | 80 |
| $Hg^{II}$ | 12.5 | $Hg^{II}$ | 100 |
| $Hg^{I}$ | 25 | $Hg^{I}$ | 200 |

such as the following: 0.5 gram of H combines with 4.0 grams of O to produce 4.5 grams of water. The mass of hydrogen that is equivalent to 1 gram of oxygen is, then, 1/8 gram. Hydrogen also forms compounds with both chlorine and bromine.† Experiments show that the mass ratio of H to Cl in hydrogen chloride is 1/36 and that the mass ratio of H to Br in hydrogen bromide is 1/80. If we go through the same calculations as for the other elements, we obtain ratios of the combining weights of Cl and Br to the combining weight of O of 4.5 and 10. Table 6-2 includes these combining weights on the basis of O = 1 in the left-hand column.

Now that H is included in the list, a difficulty arises. The combining weight of H is only 1/8 on the basis of O = 1. It would be convenient if all the combining weights were greater than 1. The original choice of O as a standard equal to 1 was entirely arbitrary, and, since all the values are only relative, there is no reason at all why we cannot now change the basis so that all the

combining weights will be greater than 1. Extensive experimentation has shown that hydrogen has the smallest combining weight of all the elements. It is therefore logical as well as convenient to assign a value of 1 to the combining weight of hydrogen and then calculate all the others to this base. We accomplish this, of course, simply by multiplying each number under O by 8 to get the numbers under H. There is another advantage in using this base: most of the combining weights in the fourth column are whole numbers.

This table does *not* show the relative masses of the atoms. It shows only the masses that are chemically equivalent to each other. If all the combinations were 1 atom to 1 atom, these would indeed be the relative masses of the atoms. We know, however, that some of them, at least, cannot be the relative masses. And we have no reason, except Dalton's postulate of simplicity, to guide us in deciding how many of each of the atoms combine with an atom of any other element. To answer this question, we need more information. The relative masses of the atoms, the atomic weights, can be established only when we know the combining powers of the elements in the compounds we have examined. And in order to establish these combining powers, we must consider a very important experimental generalization and an equally important theoretical postulate, both of which have to do with gases and gas reactions. In Chapter 7 we shall continue our study of quantitative relations in chemical reactions, but our interest will be in the *volumes* of gases that are chemically equivalent to each other rather than the *masses* of the reacting substances.

This apparent impasse that we have come to was of considerable importance historically. It was extremely difficult to establish atomic weights during most of the nineteenth century. The combining weights were well known and extensively used, but they did not depend on, nor did they support, the atomic theory. For this reason many chemists were extremely skeptical of the existence of atoms and the usefulness of the atomic theory. As late as 1890 a very prominent chemist announced publicly that he did not believe in the existence of atoms.

† The combining weight of hydrogen is so much smaller than that of the other elements that it is impossible for elementary students to do quantitative mass experiments involving hydrogen. A 1 percent error in weighing, for example, would entirely obscure the mass relation between hydrogen and bromine in hydrogen bromide. The apparatus available and the technical abilities of the students would eliminate the possibility of doing this experiment. Furthermore, the reactions involved in these experiments are dangerous because of the likelihood of explosion.

## Concepts and Terms

Greek Atomic Theory
  nature of Greek science
Experimental Basis of Atomic Theory
  law of conservation of mass
  law of definite proportions
  law of multiple proportions

Dalton's Atomic Theory
  postulates of the atomic theory
  relation to laws of chemical combination
Combining Weights

## Problems

**6-1.** Discuss the fundamental differences between the classical (Greek) atomic theory and the modern atomic theory.

**6-2.** When a piece of iron rusts, it gains in mass. Explain.

**6-3.** A 20 lb log of wood burned in your fireplace would be consumed and leave only a pound or so of ashes. Does this fact controvert the law of conservation of mass? Explain.

**6-4.** One of the classical experiments of plant physiology, probably the first and certainly one of the best, was interpreted as proving that a living plant can create matter. This experiment was long attributed to J. B. van Helmont, who reported it as original in 1683 after copying it almost word for word from writings of Nicholas of Cusa published in 1450. The experiment was later repeated by Sir Robert Boyle (see Chaps. 9 and 10). It consisted of planting a 5 lb willow in a tub containing just 200 lb of dry earth. The sapling was watered with rain water or distilled water and was protected from dust so that nothing was added except pure water. After five years the willow, now a tree, weighed 169 lb; yet the earth still weighed just 200 lb. Discuss this experiment and its relation to the law of conservation of mass. What is the source of the gain in mass? Wood contains about 40 percent carbon and 60 percent hydrogen and oxygen. Water contains *only* hydrogen and oxygen. Did the plant transmute other elements to carbon? What is the source of the carbon in the grown tree?

**6-5.** Two copper oxides (compounds containing only copper and oxygen) were decomposed in the laboratory to elemental copper and other products. The results of these experiments were reported as ratios of mass of copper to mass of oxygen in the compounds. In one laboratory section, several students reported ratios that varied

from 3.9 to 4.3 and averaged 4.1; several other students reported ratios that varied from 7.9 to 8.5 and averaged 8.3. One student reported the ratio of mass of copper to mass of oxygen as 28.9. Discuss the significance of all these data to the quantitative relations that govern chemical combination. Consider also the question of experimental error.

**6-6.** Phrase in your own words the postulates of the atomic theory stated in this chapter. Pay close attention to the qualifications of these postulates and the points at which they differ from the postulates of Dalton.

**6-7.** Relate these postulates of the atomic theory to the empirical laws of chemical combination: conservation of mass, definite proportions, multiple proportions.

**6-8.** Discuss the concept of simplicity in scientific theories, paying attention to the important qualification that Dalton ignored. Discuss the theories of heavenly motions mentioned on pp. 22 and 24 in relation to this concept of simplicity.

**6-9.** Compare the Greek theory that five elements make up all matter (page 7) with the modern theory, which requires over 100 elements, especially in relation to the concept of simplicity in theories. Do not be deceived by apparent simplicity.

**6-10.** The ratio of the mass of calcium to the mass of oxygen in calcium oxide was determined in experiments similar in principle to those cited in this chapter. A sample of 1.55 grams of calcium, when combined with the chemically equivalent amount of oxygen, produced 2.17 grams of calcium oxide.
(A) Calculate the ratio of the mass of calcium to the mass of oxygen in calcium oxide.
(B) Calculate the combining weight of calcium on the basis of $O = 8$.

*Ans.* (B) 20

**6-11.** The ratio of the mass of calcium to the mass of bromine in calcium bromide is 0.25. Are these data consistent with the data of Prob. 6-10 and Table 6-2? Explain your answer.

**6-12.** What mass of calcium would replace 6 grams of magnesium in a compound? What mass of copper[II] would replace this mass of calcium?

## Suggested Readings

1. H. M. Leicester and H. S. Klickstein, *A Source Book in Chemistry* (McGraw-Hill, 1952). The short biographies and statements of the work of Dalton, his contemporaries, and immediate predecessors are contained in pp. 33–231. Of particular interest are the sections on Boyle (definition of element), pp. 33–47; Becker and Stahl (phlogiston theory), pp. 55–63; Scheele and Priestley (discovery of oxygen), pp. 101–125; Lavoisier, pp. 154–180; and Dalton, pp. 208–221.

2. W. F. Ehret, *Smith's Introductory College Chemistry* (Appleton-Century-Crofts, 1950), Chaps. 3 and 4.

3. D. C. Gregg, *Principles of Chemistry* (Allyn and Bacon, 1958), Chap. 2.

4. F. T. Bonner and Melba Phillips, *Principles of Physical Science* (Addison-Wesley, 1957), Chaps. 6 and 7.

THE ATOMIC theory of Dalton and the experiments that support the theory do not give us any information about the relative masses of the various atoms. The information that is necessary, in addition to what we already have, if we are to ascribe relative masses to the atoms, is a statement of the combining power of the various atoms; that is, we need to know how many atoms of one element are combined with how many atoms of another element in compounds. Our theory and the experiments we have considered so far do not give us this information.

## 7-1. *Law of Combining Volumes*

The answer to this question came from a study of gaseous reactions and from a famous postulate advanced just a few years after Dalton's first statement of the atomic theory. A French chemist, J. L. Gay-Lussac, made a series of observations on the volumes of gases that combine, or are chemically equivalent to each other. These observations were summarized in the law of Gay-Lussac, or the **law of combining volumes.** This law states that in gaseous reactions the volumes of two gases that combine stand to each other as the ratio of small whole numbers. This generalization, which was based, of course, on many experiments, can be illustrated by a few examples. It is known that water is composed of hydrogen and oxygen; if one measures the volume of oxygen that will just combine with a given volume of hydrogen (for example, 100 cm³), it is found that just half of the volume of oxygen (50 cm³ in this case) is needed. The ratio of the volumes that combine is 2/1. The same data can be obtained by the classical demonstration experiment of decomposing water by an electric current. In this experiment (Fig. 7-1) the two evolved gases are collected in measuring tubes, and it is always observed that the volume of hydrogen is just twice the volume of oxygen. The combination of hydrogen with chlorine gas can also be studied quantitatively. (The experiment is, however, rather dangerous, for the combination of the two gases is explosive; that is, the reaction takes place with explosive violence.) It is observed that exactly equal volumes of hy-

CHAPTER

7

Valence (I):
Combining
Power,
Atomic Weights,
and Formulas

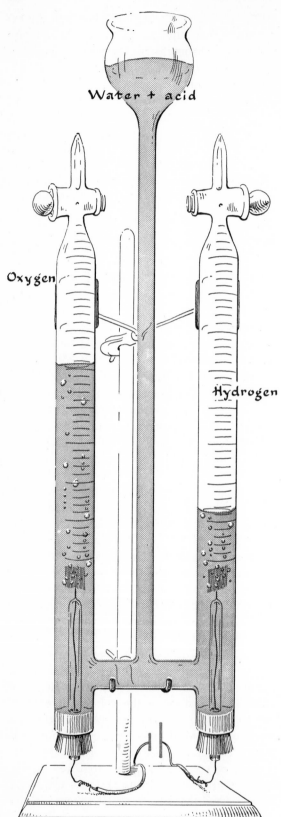

Water + acid

Oxygen

Hydrogen

drogen and chlorine combine to produce just twice that volume of hydrogen chloride gas; that is, the volume ratio of H to Cl is 1/1, and the ratio of H to HCl is 1/2 (and the ratio of Cl to HCl is also 1/2, of course). A final example is the reaction of nitric oxide with oxygen to produce the brown gas nitrogen dioxide. In this reaction, two volumes of nitric oxide react with one volume of oxygen to produce two volumes of nitrogen dioxide. Here the ratios of the three gas volumes are 2/1 and 1/1. By considering a large number of gas reactions of this type, in all of which the ratios of the combining volumes were simple ratios, usually 1/1 or 1/2 and rarely as complex as 1/3 or 2/3, Gay-Lussac made the generalization we stated above.†

Here, in the law of combining volumes, is another simple relation governing chemical reactions—one that is comparable to the simple relation described by the laws of combining masses. The question immediately arises: "Can the atomic theory explain this simple law of gas reactions as it did the simple mass laws of chemical reactions?" Dalton felt that it could not; he rejected all efforts to relate the law of combining volumes to the atomic theory and even rejected the experimental basis of the law. Chemists in general refused for half a century to accept a brilliant hypothesis that incorporated Gay-Lussac's law into the atomic theory and at the same time greatly strengthened and extended that theory.

## 7-2. Avogadro's Hypothesis

In 1810, just a few years after Dalton first proposed his theory and almost immediately after Gay-Lussac made his generalization, an Italian chemist-physicist named Amedeo Avogadro examined Gay-Lussac's law in relation to

† It was experimental results of this type that Dalton questioned. He felt that the atomic theory could not help us to understand these gaseous reactions, and he accused Gay-Lussac of reporting unreliable experimental results. In fact, however, Dalton was the inaccurate experimentalist; Gay-Lussac did the experiments properly, and his results were reliable.

FIGURE **7-1** *Volume relations in electrolysis of water.*

the atomic theory and made a very shrewd guess. He postulated that equal volumes of gases contain equal numbers of molecules. As we shall discover in a later chapter, the volume of any gas varies greatly with changes in temperature and pressure. It is therefore necessary to specify that these conditions must be the same when volumes of gases are compared. We should therefore state Avogadro's hypothesis in this way: **Equal volumes of all gases at a fixed temperature and pressure contain equal numbers of molecules.**

Clearly there can be no simple direct proof of Avogadro's hypothesis. Its proof lies in its consistency with a large mass of experimental information and in the whole structure of understanding it added to the atomic theory. Unfortunately, these proofs were not understood when the postulate was first stated. It was not until the middle of the nineteenth century that the hypothesis was revived by Avogadro's countryman, Stanislao Cannizzaro, and was generally accepted by chemists.

In the interpretation of Gay-Lussac's law we must keep in mind two facts. First, in the experiments described in illustration of the law it was implicit that the volumes of the gases involved in the reactions were measured under the same set of conditions of temperature and pressure. Second, if Avogadro's hypothesis is true, equal numbers of molecules react when equal volumes react; when reacting volumes are multiples of each other, the numbers of reacting molecules are the same multiples.

In addition to advancing his hypothesis, Avogadro also rejected one of Dalton's postulates. Avogadro suggested that some elemental molecules may be diatomic or even more complex rather than always the single atoms that Dalton insisted on. It was because of this point that Dalton refused to accept these new ideas; he was carried away by a good scientific dictum—"Always prefer the simplest theory"—and forgot the qualification—"unless experimental facts require the more complicated." Dalton chose to reject the facts in order to preserve the simplicity of the theory. By following Dalton in this error, chemists delayed by half a century the advent of rationality in chemical formulas.

## 7-3. *Analysis of Gaseous Reactions*

By considering in detail the reactions we have cited, we can indicate the reasoning that led Avogadro from the experiments of Gay-Lussac to this very important extension of the atomic theory. Consider first the reaction of hydrogen with chlorine to produce hydrogen chloride. The facts are very simple: the ratios of the volumes of H and Cl and HCl are 1/1/2. Avogadro decided that these facts are simply and logically understood if it is assumed that the *equality* of reacting *volumes* of H and Cl is a manifestation of *equal numbers* of reacting molecules of H and Cl; that is, he assumed that the reaction of H with Cl takes place by the combination of *one* molecule of hydrogen with *one* molecule of chlorine. To be consistent with his first postulate, however, he then had to assume that, for each molecule of hydrogen and for each molecule of chlorine, *two* molecules of hydrogen chloride are formed, for the volume of hydrogen chloride produced is twice that of the hydrogen and twice that of the chlorine. Now, since we accept the idea that a single atom of any element is the least amount that can be combined in any compound, we must also accept the idea that each of the two hydrogen chloride molecules contains at least one H atom and one Cl atom. In order for this to be true, the molecules of hydrogen and of chlorine must each contain *two* atoms. This single-molecule reaction could be represented diagrammatically as

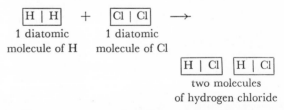

But, obviously, Avogadro could not (nor could anyone) have considered experimental results of a reaction involving only single molecules. Any sensible volumes of gases contain *vast* numbers of molecules,† and a diagram-

† Avogadro's hypothesis implies a *particular* number of molecules in a standard volume of gas. Avogadro made no assumption as to what this number is

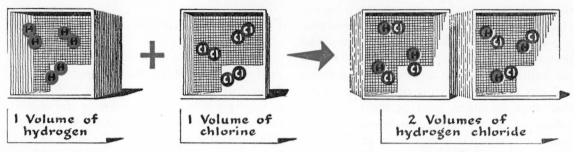

| 1 Volume of hydrogen | 1 Volume of chlorine | 2 Volumes of hydrogen chloride |

FIGURE **7-2** *Volume relations in the reaction of hydrogen and chlorine to produce hydrogen chloride.*

matic representation of the reaction should imply this fact. It is only necessary to multiply the diagrammatic equation above by Avogadro's number, $N_0$, if we wish to consider the standard volume (or double the standard volume) of the three gases. If we were to multiply this equation by some other number almost as large as $N_0$, we should be considering some other experimentally realizable volume and multiples of that volume. If we can make the mental broad jump of thinking of 3 as a vast number, we can diagram the reaction as in Figure 7-2, in which each of the diagramed spaces (volumes) contains three molecules. Obviously, a realistic diagram would be entirely impossible; but the principle is exactly the same whether we show $N_0$ or 3 or any

except that it must be very large for any experimentally realizable standard volume. The number has become identified with the hypothesis and is called Avogadro's number even though he made neither experiments nor postulates concerning its value. The determination of this number, which is now known to a precision of one part in 60,000, is an intriguing story within our science. The value was not established until fairly recently, and we shall not state it until we have prepared the student to understand its determination. We shall continue to discuss the number, however, and to use it as a quite definite quantity. It will be defined at this time as the number of molecules of any gas in a standard volume at standard temperature and pressure. It has the symbol $N_0$.

other huge number of molecules in each of the equal volumes. $N_0$ molecules of $H_2$ (we can now write formulas for these elemental gases) react with $N_0$ molecules of $Cl_2$ to give $2N_0$ molecules of HCl. The same information is conveyed in equation form as

$$N_0H_2 + N_0Cl_2 \longrightarrow 2N_0HCl$$

for standard volumes of the reacting gases. In practice, however, the $N_0$'s are left out, for the equation is equally true on a single-molecule basis and on a many-molecule basis. The equation of ordinary usage is, then,

$$H_2 + Cl_2 \longrightarrow 2HCl$$

Let us now consider, in terms of Avogadro's concept and in the diagrammatic sense used for the HCl reaction, the reaction of hydrogen and oxygen to produce water. The experimental facts can be simply stated: Two volumes of hydrogen react with one volume of oxygen. If the experiment is carried out under the proper conditions (rather high temperature), the water produced will be in the gaseous state, and its gas volume can be measured. Under these conditions the volume of the gaseous water is found to be equal to the volume of the hydrogen and twice the volume of the oxygen. By the same type of

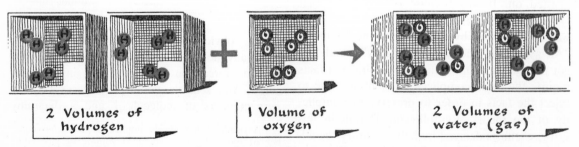

| 2 Volumes of hydrogen | 1 Volume of oxygen | 2 Volumes of water (gas) |

FIGURE **7-3** *Volume relations in the reaction of hydrogen and oxygen to produce water.*

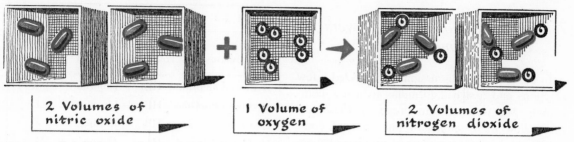

2 Volumes of
nitric oxide

1 Volume of
oxygen

2 Volumes of
nitrogen dioxide

FIGURE **7-4** *Volume relations in the reaction of nitric oxide and oxygen to produce nitrogen dioxide.*

analysis that we used before, several facts become clear: (1) The oxygen molecule must also be diatomic ($O_2$), for *one* volume of oxygen requires *two* volumes of hydrogen and *one* volume of oxygen produces *two* volumes of water. (2) The molecule of water must contain *two* atoms of hydrogen, for the volumes of $H_2$ used and water produced are equal. (3) The molecule of water must contain *one* atom of oxygen, for *one* volume of $O_2$ produces *two* volumes of water. These facts are summarized and their logical necessity is shown in Figure 7-3 and in the equations

$$2N_0H_2 + N_0O_2 \longrightarrow 2N_0H_2O \text{ (gas)}$$
$$2H_2 \;\;\; + O_2 \;\;\; \longrightarrow 2H_2O \;\;\; \text{(gas)}$$

We can similarly analyze the reaction of nitric oxide and oxygen without specifying the formula of nitric oxide (Fig. 7-4). This experiment, in which two volumes of nitric oxide react with one of oxygen to produce two of nitrogen dioxide, gives further proof that the molecule of oxygen must be diatomic. These relative volumes can be observed *only* if oxygen has the diatomic structure $O_2$.

Further analysis of gas reactions by this detailed method would be needless repetition. It should be kept in mind, though, that *many* reactions of this type were originally considered by Avogadro and that thousands have been considered since. Avogadro advanced his idea as a mere hypothesis—that is, a theory recognized as so tentative that it might be abandoned. The subsequent developments of science have completely justified the theory, and it is now a firmly established part of our knowledge of the structure of matter.

By a similar analysis of other gas reactions it

has been established that most elemental gases have diatomic molecules at ordinary temperatures. [The only exceptions are the inert gases, helium (He), neon (Ne), argon (Ar), etc., which are all monatomic.] In addition to $H_2$, $O_2$, and $Cl_2$ there are nitrogen ($N_2$), fluorine ($F_2$), bromine ($Br_2$), and iodine ($I_2$). The evidence we have just cited, however, does *not* prove categorically that these molecules are diatomic. It proves only that an *even* number of atoms must make up the molecules, which could have formulas such as $H_4$ and $O_6$. By our rule of simplicity we chose the *simplest* even number, which is 2. Recently developed physical methods have proven without doubt that the choice was correct—that these molecules are indeed diatomic.

Here, then, by the two new ideas of Avogadro —his hypothesis of equal numbers of molecules in equal volumes of gases, and his rejection of the assumption of monatomic molecules for the elemental gases—we have achieved a simple, logically acceptable explanation of gas reactions, have included a whole set of new experimental facts (Gay-Lussac's law of combining volumes) within the conceptual framework of the atomic theory, and have further strengthened this theory by broadening its experimental basis. And—most important of all to the immediate development of our science of matter—we now have a basis for assigning unquestioned formulas to several compounds and thereby for determining the combining powers of atoms. From a comparison of combining powers and combining weights we shall be able to assign relative masses to the various atoms—that is, to establish a table of atomic weights. Our ultimate goal is to determine the absolute masses of atoms, but the first step must be this relative scale of masses.

## 7-4. *Relative Combining Powers of the Elements*

In the preceding discussion we analyzed a few reactions and assigned formulas to a few compounds. We were able to prove, in these few cases, how *many* atoms of one element combined with how *many* atoms of another element (or, in the oxygen–nitric-oxide reaction, with how *many* more complex particles). We observed in one case that each atom of hydrogen combined with a single atom of chlorine; the combining powers of chlorine and hydrogen must, then, be equal in magnitude. In another case we observed that each oxygen atom combined with *two* hydrogen atoms; the combining power of oxygen must, then, be *twice* that of hydrogen and also twice that of chlorine. Analysis of many thousands of reactions and compounds has shown that one atom of hydrogen *never* combines with more than one atom of another element. Often two or more atoms of hydrogen combine with a single atom of another element, as in water, but never does more than one atom of another element combine with a single hydrogen atom. From such evidence as this it is entirely reasonable to assume that the combining power of hydrogen can never be greater than one. If we make this assumption and then consider the reaction for the formation of hydrogen chloride, we must also assign a relative combining power of one to the chlorine atom in this compound, since the combining power of each chlorine atom just satisfies the combining power of one hydrogen atom. Similarly, the combining power of oxygen must be two in water, for the formula $H_2O$ shows that the combining power of each oxygen atom is just equal to the combining power of *two* hydrogen atoms. We can now set up a table of relative combining powers of the three elements we have been considering (Table 7-1). Note that this, like our table of combining

TABLE **7-1**  *Relative Combining Powers*

| |
| --- |
| H = 1 |
| Cl = 1 |
| O = 2 |

TABLE **7-2**  *Formulas and Combining Powers*

| COMPOUND | FORMULA | ELEMENT | COMBINING POWER |
| --- | --- | --- | --- |
| Hydrogen chloride | HCl | Chlorine | 1 |
| Hydrogen fluoride | HF | Fluorine | 1 |
| Hydrogen bromide | HBr | Bromine | 1 |
| Hydrogen iodide | HI | Iodine | 1 |
| Water | $H_2O$ | Oxygen | 2 |
| Hydrogen sulfide | $H_2S$ | Sulfur | 2 |
| Ammonia | $NH_3$ | Nitrogen | 3 |
| Methane | $CH_4$ | Carbon | 4 |
| Sulfur trioxide | $SO_3$ | Sulfur | 6 |

weights, is an arbitrarily defined set of *relative* values. We could just as well (except for the general principle of preferring the simplest possible alternative) express the combining power of hydrogen by some other number—for example, 2. The others would then each be twice as great, maintaining the same *relative* combining power. Starting with this arbitrary standard of combining power, a value of 1 for hydrogen, we can now, by means of simple logical relations, and reasoning from the experimental information we have collected, assign combining powers to the atoms of all the elements we have been dealing with up to this point. And having done this, we can, in principle, extend this line of reasoning to *all* the elements.

By reasoning of this sort formulas have been established for a number of gaseous compounds involving elements that have already been, or soon will be, of interest to us. A partial list of these formulas is given in Table 7-2.

The proof of the formulas of compounds that are not gases themselves and do not involve gaseous elements is a good deal more complicated and involves more experimental information than the proofs of the formulas of the gaseous compounds of Table 7-2. The categorical proof of such formulas depends, in fact, on a new type of experimental information, the "molecular weight" of compounds—a new concept that will be taken up in a later chapter. It is possible, however, to be reasonably certain of the formulas of the other compounds we have dealt with and thereby to know the combining powers of the other elements. We need only apply our principle of accepting the simpler of two alternatives to a consideration of the quantitative mass and volume relations first considered in Chapter 6.

## 7-5. *Analysis of Non-gaseous Reactions*

Let us first consider the two oxides of copper. In § 6-6 we reasoned that the formulas of the two oxides must be one or the other of two pairs, $CuO$ and $Cu_2O$ or $CuO_2$ and $CuO$. We have now established that the combining power of oxygen is 2. In the first of these two pairs, then, the combining power of copper would have to be 2 for the copper in $CuO$ and 1 for the copper in $Cu_2O$. (The total combining power of the copper atoms in the compound must just equal the total combining power of the oxygen atoms.) In the other pair of formulas the combining power of copper would again be 2 for the copper in $CuO$ but would be 4 for the copper in $CuO_2$. The combining powers of the two forms of copper must be related by the factor 2 and must, in fact, be either 1 and 2 or 2 and 4. The first alternative is clearly the simpler. Since it has never proven necessary to ascribe a combining power greater than 2 to the copper atom in any of the copper compounds that have been studied, and since all of the information collected on copper compounds is consistent with combining powers of 1 and 2 for the two forms of copper, the simpler alternative has been accepted.

A similar consideration of the two mercury oxides (p. 75) shows that, of the two pairs of formulas, the correct ones are $HgO$ and $Hg_2O$, and that the combining powers of the two forms of mercury are 1 and 2. The other pair is eliminated because in the formulas $HgO$ and $HgO_2$ mercury would have combining powers of 2 and 4—an unnecessarily complicated assumption.

The two oxides of iron (p. 76) were shown to have three possible pairs of formulas: $Fe_2O$ and $Fe_3O$, $FeO_2$ and $FeO_3$, and $FeO$ and $Fe_2O_3$. At first glance the third pair of formulas looks more complex, but actually the other pairs require more complex assumptions as to combining powers. The first pair of formulas requires that iron have combining powers of 1 and 2/3 respectively (since oxygen has a combining power of 2), the second pair that it have powers of 4 and 6, and the third pair powers of 2 and 3. By our principle of simplicity, the first and second alternatives are rejected and the third pair accepted, establishing combining powers of 2 and 3 for iron. The proof of the combining power of magnesium (and of other elements having only a *single* combining power) is even more difficult and more uncertain. If the combining power of magnesium is 1, the formula of the oxide is $Mg_2O$; if the combining power is 2, the formula is $MgO$; other assumptions are unnecessarily complicated. The choice between the two formulas offers no advantage either way. The formula has been proven, however, to be $MgO$, giving a combining power of 2 to magnesium. We shall therefore make this choice and wait until a subsequent chapter to offer firm proof of the validity of the assumption.

We can now extend the list of elements of known combining power to include those in Table 7-3.

The scheme outlined here is entirely self-consistent. There is a good deal of cross reference among various compounds of the elements listed in Tables 7-2 and 7-3, and all of it is entirely consistent with the scheme. If, for example, the two copper bromides were ana-

TABLE **7-3** *Formulas and Combining Powers*

| COMPOUND† | FORMULA | ELEMENT | COMBINING POWER |
|---|---|---|---|
| Cuprous oxide | $Cu_2O$ | Copper[I] | 1 |
| Cupric oxide | $CuO$ | Copper[II] | 2 |
| Mercurous oxide | $Hg_2O$ | Mercury[I] | 1 |
| Mercuric oxide | $HgO$ | Mercury[II] | 2 |
| Ferrous oxide | $FeO$ | Iron[II] | 2 |
| Ferric oxide | $Fe_2O_3$ | Iron[III] | 3 |
| Magnesium oxide | $MgO$ | Magnesium | 2 |

†These compounds are named here according to the system developed in §7-13.

lyzed, the experimental results would be consistent with our assumption (not categorically proven) of combining powers of 1 and 2 for the two forms of copper. The formulas of the copper bromides would then be CuBr and $CuBr_2$. Similarly, the two copper chlorides would be CuCl and $CuCl_2$; the two iron chlorides would be $FeCl_2$ and $FeCl_3$; etc. The compound magnesium chloride is known, and all experimental information about it is consistent with the formula $MgCl_2$. These facts do not prove that our assumptions were correct, but they do increase our confidence in them and allow us to use the ideas described here even before we have met the categorical proof that they are indeed correct.

The difficulties we are having were exactly paralleled in the historical development of the science. Through most of the nineteenth century atomic weights and combining powers of the atoms were known with very little certainty. The accepted values often turned out to be multiples of the actual values. It was not until the beginning of this century that all of the erroneous atomic weights (and combining powers) were corrected and that the values could be relied upon.

## 7-6. Atomic Weights

In Chapter 6 the data from several experiments on the decomposition and synthesis of compounds were quoted. In the analysis of those data we arrived at a table of chemically equivalent masses of various elements—that is, a table of **combining weights** (Table 6-2). Combining weights have a limited usefulness for our understanding of the quantitative mass and volume relations of chemical reactions and have no fundamental theoretical significance. In Chapter 6 we remarked that a much more useful type of information would be the relative masses of the atoms of various elements—that is, a table of **atomic weights.** We now have at hand, in the combining powers of elements and the formulas of compounds, the information that we need in order to establish atomic weights.

Once again we are dealing with *relative* quantities. We have no idea, at this point in our study

of matter, what the actual mass of any single atom is—except that it must be very small. We can, however, establish that the mass of one atom is exactly so many times as great as the mass of some other atom; that is, we must decide on some arbitrary standard value for *one* of the atoms and then express the values for the other atoms in terms of that standard. This process is the same as for the combining weights. Since, as we pointed out in Chapter 6, the hydrogen atom has the smallest combining weight, we could assume that it has the smallest actual mass. It would be logical, then, to assign a value of 1 to hydrogen in the table of atomic weights and thereby to ensure that all others will have values greater than 1. Our standard of atomic weights, then, shall be hydrogen with a value of 1, and our problem is to determine the ratios of the masses of all other atoms to that of the hydrogen atom. Note that we are *not* making any statement about the absolute masses of the atoms. The atomic weights are pure numbers (that is, have no units); each is the ratio of two masses, and the units cancel out in the division.

As an example, consider the proof of the atomic weight of oxygen. We have established (p. 85) that the formula of water is $H_2O$. From the experimental data summarized in Chapter 6 we know that the ratio of the mass of hydrogen to the mass of oxygen in water is 1/8. The formula tells us that there are two atoms of hydrogen for every oxygen atom in any sample of water. The ratio of the mass of two hydrogen atoms to one oxygen atom must therefore be 1/8; or the ratio of twice the atomic weight of hydrogen to the atomic weight of oxygen must be 1/8:

$$\frac{2 \times \text{atomic weight of H}}{\text{atomic weight of O}} = \frac{1}{8}$$

We can now substitute our accepted (defined standard) value for the atomic weight of H (that is, 1) into this equation and solve the equation for the atomic weight of oxygen. This value comes out to be 16.

As another example we can consider the compound hydrogen chloride to determine the atomic weight of chlorine. The formula is HCl, and the ratio of masses is 1 of hydrogen to 36 of chlorine. Now, since the formula shows that a single atom of each element makes up the compound, this ratio of combining weights is also the ratio of the two atomic weights, and the atomic weight of chlorine must be 36.

The determination of the atomic weight of iron from the experimental mass relations and formulas of the two oxides will be described as a final example. The formulas of the two oxides are FeO and $Fe_2O_3$; the ratios of the mass of iron to the mass of oxygen in these two compounds are 3.5 and 2.33 respectively. From the formula of the first oxide we see that one atom of iron and one atom of oxygen are combined in the compound. The ratio of the masses that combine (combining weights) is, then, the same as the ratio of the atomic weights:

$$\frac{\text{atomic weight of Fe}}{\text{atomic weight of O}} = \frac{3.5}{1}$$

Now substitute the value of 16 for the atomic weight of oxygen in this equation:

$$\text{atomic weight of Fe} = 3.5 \times 16 = 56$$

The atomic weight of iron is, then, 56. But this value should be checked with the results of the experiments on the other oxide. The second formula above tells us that there are three atoms of oxygen and two of iron in each molecule of this iron oxide; the ratio of the combining weights is the ratio of the mass of two Fe atoms to the mass of three O atoms. But this is also equal to the ratio of two times the atomic weight of iron to three times the atomic weight of oxygen:

$$\frac{2 \times \text{mass of Fe atom}}{3 \times \text{mass of O atom}} = \frac{2 \times \text{atomic weight of Fe}}{3 \times \text{atomic weight of O}}$$
$$= \frac{2.33}{1}$$

We again substitute the value 16 as the atomic weight of O:

$$2 \times \text{atomic weight of Fe} = 3 \times 16 \times 2.33$$

$$\text{atomic weight of Fe} = \frac{48 \times 2.33}{2} = 24 \times 2.33 = 56$$

Consideration of both compounds gives the same value for the atomic weight of iron, which, of course, it *must* if the concept is to be of any value.

We could repeat such calculations with the

| TABLE **7-4** Atomic Weights from Combining Weights | | | |
|---|---|---|---|
| ELEMENT | COMBINING WEIGHT | COMBINING POWER | ATOMIC WEIGHT |
| H | 1 | 1 | 1 |
| O | 8 | 2 | 16 |
| Cl | 36 | 1 | 36 |
| $Fe^{II}$† | 28 | 2 | 56 |
| $Fe^{III}$† | 18.7 | 3 | 56 |

† The use of the Roman numerals in this and the preceding chapter to distinguish the pairs of compounds is entirely artificial and in no way implies a difference between the atoms except the difference in combining power. The atom of iron$^{II}$ is identical with the atom of iron$^{III}$ except that the first has a combining power of 2 and the second a combining power of 3. The same statement is true of $Cu^I$ and $Cu^{II}$ and of $Hg^I$ and $Hg^{II}$.

other relations that have been established. But if we now examine Tables 6-2, 7-2, and 7-3, which show combining weights and combining powers, and consider the atomic weights we have already calculated, we shall be able to discover a relation among these three quantities. Table 7-4 lists the three quantities for the elements we have considered in this section. For each element the atomic weight is the product of the combining weight and the combining power. This fact is a logical necessity from our definitions of the three quantities involved, and applies equally well, of course, to the other elements in the tables. We can now extend our short table of atomic weights, by use of this relation, to include all the elements so far considered.

## 7-7. *Table of Atomic Weights*

The atomic weights of all the elements so far considered are listed in Table 7-5. These values are based on H = 1 as a standard and are calculated from the experimental data quoted in this and the preceding chapter. The student should confirm the calculations by taking the combining powers from Tables 7-2 and 7-3 and the combining weights from Table 6-2 and doing calculations of the type indicated in Table 7-4 for the elements not included in that table.

| TABLE 7-5 *Atomic Weights* | | |
|---|---|---|
| ELEMENT | SYMBOL | ATOMIC WEIGHT |
| Hydrogen | H | 1 (Standard) |
| Oxygen | O | 16 |
| Magnesium | Mg | 24 |
| Sulfur | S | 32 |
| Chlorine | Cl | 36 |
| Iron | Fe | 56 |
| Copper | Cu | 64 |
| Bromine | Br | 80 |
| Mercury | Hg | 200 |

Having calculated the atomic weights of the few elements listed in Table 7-5, we have established the principle. It would be possible, without the introduction of any new ideas, to obtain the necessary experimental information and repeat such calculations for all 102 elements. The atomic weights of all the elements have been established by experiments and calculations that are, in principle, identical with those we have used for these few elements; it obviously would serve no useful purpose to repeat the same type of calculation many times in this text. Table 7-6 is a list of all the elements with their symbols and atomic weights. This table will be used constantly during the rest of the course, and all atomic weights used in calculations should be taken from this table. The weights given in Table 7-5 and in previous tables are not so precise and should therefore be ignored.

## 7-8. Standards for Atomic Weights

The atomic weights of Table 7-5 are based on the defined standard of hydrogen as exactly 1. This was the first of several standards of atomic-weight systems. But the early chemists using hydrogen as a standard encountered a difficulty that is apparent in the discussion and calculations we have gone through in the preceding pages. Since hydrogen does not form compounds with many other elements, it was necessary to use secondary standards to establish the atomic

weight of all the metallic elements in Table 7-5. It would be reasonable, then, to avoid this difficulty by using as our *primary* standard some element that forms compounds with most of the other elements. Oxygen is such an element and has been used as the basis for several different standards of atomic-weight systems.

In Table 7-5, where hydrogen = 1 is the standard, oxygen has a value of 16 (to two significant figures). It was therefore proposed some years ago that the atomic-weight system should be established on a basis of *oxygen defined as exactly 16*. It appeared that hydrogen would still remain unity in such a system and that all the other values of Table 7-5 would be the same. However, more precise determinations of the atomic weights showed that this is not quite so. If O = 16, hydrogen has an atomic weight of 1.0080. Even so, the use of O = 16 as the standard has persisted and is the basis of the atomic weights now used by chemists. There was a brief period during which a table of atomic weights based on the standard O = 100 was used; on this basis the atomic weight of hydrogen was 6.25, and all the other values of Table 7-6 would be correspondingly greater. The system survived only long enough to create a deep pit of confusion in the quantitative chemical literature of the later nineteenth century. Modern chemists who study the reports of the experiments of that time must be careful to transpose the atomic weights to the modern system in order to make sense of the results presented.

Still another system of atomic weights, other than that of Table 7-6, is based on O = 16. This is the "physicists' scale" of atomic weights. It has been introduced only recently and is used only for certain rather specialized purposes. Quantitatively, it differs very slightly from the system we are using, but the difference is based on a very interesting subtlety of the structure of matter, which will be considered in later chapters. For almost all scientific work and for most of the work in this course the atomic weights of Table 7-6 will be used. The values in Table 7-6 are the most precise attainable. For most uses, even in much advanced research and certainly in the problem work of this course, it is not necessary to use all the significant figures given.

TABLE 7-6 *International Atomic Weights*

| NAME | SYMBOL | Z | ATOMIC WEIGHT† | NAME | SYMBOL | Z | ATOMIC WEIGHT† |
|------|--------|---|----------------|------|--------|---|----------------|
| Actinium | Ac | 89 | 227 | Mercury | Hg | 80 | 200.61 |
| Aluminum | Al | 13 | 26.98 | Molybdenum | Mo | 42 | 95.95 |
| Americium | Am | 95 | (243) | Neodymium | Nd | 60 | 144.27 |
| Antimony | Sb | 51 | 121.76 | Neon | Ne | 10 | 20.183 |
| Argon | Ar | 18 | 39.944 | Neptunium | Np | 93 | (237) |
| Arsenic | As | 33 | 74.91 | Nickel | Ni | 28 | 58.71 |
| Astatine | At | 85 | (210) | Niobium | Nb | 41 | 92.91 |
| Barium | Ba | 56 | 137.36 | Nitrogen | N | 7 | 14.008 |
| Berkelium | Bk | 97 | (249) | Nobelium | No | 102 | (253) |
| Beryllium | Be | 4 | 9.013 | Osmium | Os | 76 | 190.2 |
| Bismuth | Bi | 83 | 209.00 | Oxygen | O | 8 | 16.0000 |
| Boron | B | 5 | 10.82 | Palladium | Pd | 46 | 106.4 |
| Bromine | Br | 35 | 79.916 | Phosphorus | P | 15 | 30.975 |
| Cadmium | Cd | 48 | 112.41 | Platinum | Pt | 78 | 195.09 |
| Calcium | Ca | 20 | 40.08 | Plutonium | Pu | 94 | (242) |
| Californium | Cf | 98 | (249) | Polonium | Po | 84 | 210 |
| Carbon | C | 6 | 12.011 | Potassium | K | 19 | 39.100 |
| Cerium | Ce | 58 | 140.13 | Praseodymium | Pr | 59 | 140.92 |
| Cesium | Cs | 55 | 132.91 | Promethium | Pm | 61 | (145) |
| Chlorine | Cl | 17 | 35.457 | Protactinium | Pa | 91 | 231 |
| Chromium | Cr | 24 | 52.01 | Radium | Ra | 88 | 226.05 |
| Cobalt | Co | 27 | 58.94 | Radon | Rn | 86 | 222 |
| Copper | Cu | 29 | 63.54 | Rhenium | Re | 75 | 186.22 |
| Curium | Cm | 96 | (245) | Rhodium | Rh | 45 | 102.91 |
| Dysprosium | Dy | 66 | 162.51 | Rubidium | Rb | 37 | 85.48 |
| Einsteinium | Es | 99 | (254) | Ruthenium | Ru | 44 | 101.1 |
| Erbium | Er | 68 | 167.21 | Samarium | Sm | 62 | 150.35 |
| Europium | Eu | 63 | 152.0 | Scandium | Sc | 21 | 44.96 |
| Fermium | Fm | 100 | (255) | Selenium | Se | 34 | 78.96 |
| Fluorine | F | 9 | 19.00 | Silicon | Si | 14 | 28.09 |
| Francium | Fr | 87 | (223) | Silver | Ag | 47 | 107.880 |
| Gadolinium | Gd | 64 | 157.26 | Sodium | Na | 11 | 22.991 |
| Gallium | Ga | 31 | 69.72 | Strontium | Sr | 38 | 87.63 |
| Germanium | Ge | 32 | 72.60 | Sulfur | S | 16 | 32.066 |
| Gold | Au | 79 | 197.20 | Tantalum | Ta | 73 | 180.95 |
| Hafnium | Hf | 72 | 178.50 | Technetium | Tc | 43 | (99) |
| Helium | He | 2 | 4.003 | Tellurium | Te | 52 | 127.61 |
| Holmium | Ho | 67 | 164.94 | Terbium | Tb | 65 | 158.93 |
| Hydrogen | H | 1 | 1.008 | Thallium | Tl | 81 | 204.39 |
| Indium | In | 49 | 114.82 | Thorium | Th | 90 | 232.05 |
| Iodine | I | 53 | 126.91 | Thulium | Tm | 69 | 168.94 |
| Iridium | Ir | 77 | 192.2 | Tin | Sn | 50 | 118.70 |
| Iron | Fe | 26 | 55.85 | Titanium | Ti | 22 | 47.90 |
| Krypton | Kr | 36 | 83.80 | Tungsten | W | 74 | 183.86 |
| Lanthanum | La | 57 | 138.92 | Uranium | U | 92 | 238.07 |
| Lead | Pb | 82 | 207.21 | Vanadium | V | 23 | 50.95 |
| Lithium | Li | 3 | 6.940 | Xenon | Xe | 54 | 131.30 |
| Lutetium | Lu | 71 | 174.99 | Ytterbium | Yb | 70 | 173.04 |
| Magnesium | Mg | 12 | 24.32 | Yttrium | Y | 39 | 88.92 |
| Manganese | Mn | 25 | 54.94 | Zinc | Zn | 30 | 65.38 |
| Mendelevium | Md | 101 | (256) | Zirconium | Zr | 40 | 91.22 |

† A value in parentheses is the mass number of the isotope of longest known half-life.

## 7-9. Molecular Weights

The extremely useful concept of atomic weights as the relative masses of atoms can be extended to the relative masses of molecules. If the hydrogen atom, H, has a relative mass of 1.01 on our scale, clearly the hydrogen molecule, $H_2$, which consists of two hydrogen atoms, should have a mass of twice 1.01, or 2.02, on the same scale. To include such an idea in our concept of atomic weights we must introduce a new term, **molecular weight.** "Molecular weight" means the relative mass of the molecule, on the same scale as the atomic weights, and is obviously the sum of the atomic weights of all the atoms in the molecule. The oxygen molecule, $O_2$, is made up of two oxygen atoms; its molecular weight is the sum of the atomic weights of the two oxygen atoms, $16.0 + 16.0 = 32.0$. Sulfuric acid, whose formula is $H_2SO_4$, is made up of two hydrogen atoms, one sulfur atom, and four oxygen atoms; its molecular weight is the sum of the atomic weights of these seven atoms:

$$2 \times 1.0 + 32.0 + 4 \times 16.0 = 2.0 + 32.0 + 64.0$$
$$= 98.0$$

The system of atomic and molecular weights greatly simplifies the quantitative aspect of the equations describing reactions. Consider, for example, the equation for the formation of HCl (see p. 84):

$$H_2 + Cl_2 \longrightarrow 2HCl$$

The molecular weights of these three substances are $2 \times 1.0 = 2.0$, $2 \times 35.5 = 71.0$, and $1.0 + 35.5 = 36.5$. The equation states that one molecule of hydrogen of 2.0 mass units reacts with one molecule of chlorine of 71.0 mass units to produce two molecules of hydrogen chloride each of 36.5 mass units. This equation and these quantitative relations have no conceivable practical usefulness on a single-molecule basis; but, if we multiply the whole equation by some very large number, $N_0$, so that $N_0$ mass units equal 1 gram, the same *relative* masses of the substances are involved, and the equation now tells us that 2.0 *grams* of hydrogen react with 71.0 *grams* of chlorine to produce $2 \times 36.5 = 73.0$

*grams* of hydrogen chloride. These, of course, are sensible amounts, which can be readily realized in practice. These quantities are called **gram molecular weights,** or **moles,** of the substances. A **mole of a substance is the molecular weight of the substance in grams.** A mole of hydrogen is 2.0 grams, of oxygen is 32.0 grams, of chlorine is 71.0 grams, of hydrogen chloride is 36.5 grams, and of $H_2SO_4$ is 98.0 grams.

It is clear that a mole of any substance contains the same number of molecules as a mole of any other substance, and that a gram atomic weight of any element contains that same number of atoms. In our discussion of Avogadro's number (§ 7-3) we stated that this number, $N_0$, is the number of molecules of any gas in a "standard volume" without specifying what that standard volume should be. It would enhance the logical consistency and simplicity of our series of concepts if we defined that standard volume as the volume (at standard pressure and temperature) of *one mole* of gas, a *molar volume.* Avogadro's number is, then, the number of molecules of gas in one molar volume. But, since one mole of *any* substance, gaseous or solid or liquid, contains the same number of molecules as one mole of any other substance, Avogadro's number is also the number of molecules in one mole of any substance.

## 7-10. Valence

In this and the preceding chapter we have used the term "combining power" to describe the capacity of an element to combine with other elements. We have established a quantitative character for this term, but we have used it with only a partial definition. The term itself is cumbersome, and scientists have therefore introduced a new, more concise term, which includes in its meaning the idea we have been expressing by "combining power." This term is **valence** (from the Latin *valentia*, strength). "Valence" means, in brief, the same as combining power: the number of other atoms with which any single atom will unite chemically. But, as will become evident in this and following chapters, valence signifies much more about the structure of matter than this simple statement, and an understanding of the concept requires vast amplification. The science of chemistry, in fact, is largely a detailed study of valence.

We have already observed, in the examples we have discussed in this and the previous chapter, that the valences are small numbers. Hydrogen, copper, and mercury, as well as chlorine, bromine, and iodine, have a valence of 1; magnesium, copper, and mercury, as well as sulfur and oxygen, have a valence of 2. We have mentioned nitrogen and iron with a valence of 3, carbon with a valence of 4, and sulfur with a valence of 6. From these observations we can abstract a few generalizations about valence.

First, the range of valence, among the elements we have considered, appears to be from 1 to 6. If we consider *all* elements, the range is, in fact, a little greater than this—from 0 to 8. A group of elements called the inert gases do not combine at all with other elements and therefore have a valence of 0. It has also been found that a few elements have a valence of 7 in some compounds and that two elements show a valence of 8 in some compounds. We must therefore accept a numerical range of valence from 0 to 8.

Second, many elements have multiple valence. Several of the elements we have considered form different types of compounds in which the valence of the element is different. Copper has valences of both 1 and 2; mercury has 1 and 2; sulfur has 2 and 6. This phenomenon is quite common; a single valence for an element is less common than multiple valence.

Third, in considering the compounds formed by the elements mentioned above, we observe that there is a strong tendency for hydrogen, copper, mercury, and magnesium to form compounds with chlorine, bromine, sulfur, and oxygen, but that there is *much less* tendency for the elements to form compounds with other elements within the same group. This suggests that there must be a "directional" quality about valence as well as its quantitative characteristic. This quality is included in our concept of valence by the use of plus and minus signs, an element having a plus valence always combining with an element having a minus valence.

TABLE 7-7 *Valences of Common Elements*

| NAME | SYMBOL | VALENCES† |
|------|--------|-----------|
| Aluminum | Al | $+3$ |
| Bromine | Br | $-1\ (+1,\ +5)$ |
| Calcium | Ca | $+2$ |
| Carbon | C | $-4,\ +4$ |
| Chlorine | Cl | $-1\ (+1,\ +3,\ +5,\ +7)$ |
| Copper | Cu | $+1,\ +2$ |
| Hydrogen | H | $+1\ (-1)$ |
| Iodine | I | $-1\ (+1,\ +5,\ +7)$ |
| Iron | Fe | $+2,\ +3$ |
| Lead | Pb | $+2,\ +4$ |
| Magnesium | Mg | $+2$ |
| Mercury | Hg | $+1,\ +2$ |
| Nitrogen | N | $-3,\ +5\ (-2,\ -1,\ +2,\ +3,\ +4)$ |
| Oxygen | O | $-2\ (-1)$ |
| Phosphorus | P | $-3,\ +5$ |
| Potassium | K | $+1$ |
| Silver | Ag | $+1$ |
| Sodium | Na | $+1$ |
| Sulfur | S | $-2,\ +4,\ +6$ |
| Zinc | Zn | $+2$ |

† Valences in parentheses are less common than those listed first.

## 7-11. *Table of Valences*

To set up a carefully specified and unambiguous system of valence, we must once again make use of an arbitrary standard. Valence is a relative quantity having significance only as a comparison of one element with another. The standard of valence is oxygen, which by definition has a valence of $-2$. Hydrogen is a secondary standard, with a valence of $+1$. In *all* compounds except one (hydrogen peroxide)† oxygen may

† There are many peroxides, all of which can be considered related to hydrogen peroxide. The valence of oxygen in peroxides is $-1$. This is illustrated by the formula of hydrogen peroxide, $H_2O_2$. The chemistry of the peroxides, other than hydrogen peroxide, is properly a part of more advanced courses. For the purposes of this course we may consider the valence of oxygen as constant at $-2$.

be considered as having a valence of $-2$. In all compounds involving hydrogen, except a few metallic hydrides, hydrogen has a valence of $+1$. Using these two standards of valence and the general rule that has become apparent in the discussion up to this point (that the algebraic sum of valences in any compound must be zero), we can assign valences to all the elements. (In some cases, however, it is necessary to use the established valence of other elements as secondary standards.) For example, the formula of the compound sulfur trioxide is $SO_3$. To calculate the valence of sulfur in this compound, we use the rule that the valence must add up to zero and the standard value of $-2$ for the valence of oxygen. Three atoms of oxygen, each with a valence of $-2$, supply six minus valences; these must be balanced by six plus valences, which

can be supplied only by the one sulfur atom. The valence of sulfur must, then, be $+6$ in sulfur trioxide. The valence of carbon in carbon dioxide, $CO_2$, is $+4$ by similar reasoning, but in methane, $CH_4$, the valence of carbon must be $-4$, for each hydrogen atom has a valence of $+1$. Table 7-7 lists the valences of a few common elements that will be met quite often in this course.

## 7-12. Radicals

Often a group of atoms behaves as an entity in chemical reactions. Such a group of atoms, called a **radical,** is *not* a compound, for it has no separate existence. It is always in combination with another atom or radical to form a

TABLE **7-8**    *Common Radicals, with Valences and Compounds*

| NAME | FORMULA | VALENCE | ACID | | SODIUM SALT | CALCIUM SALT |
|---|---|---|---|---|---|---|
| Nitrate | $NO_3$ | $-1$ | Nitric | $HNO_3$ | $NaNO_3$ | $Ca(NO_3)_2$ |
| Nitrite | $NO_2$ | $-1$ | Nitrous | $HNO_2$ | $NaNO_2$ | $Ca(NO_2)_2$ |
| Sulfate | $SO_4$ | $-2$ | Sulfuric | $H_2SO_4$ | $Na_2SO_4$ | $CaSO_4$ |
| Sulfite† | $SO_3$ | $-2$ | Sulfurous | $H_2SO_3$ | $Na_2SO_3$ | $CaSO_3$ |
| Carbonate | $CO_3$ | $-2$ | Carbonic | $H_2CO_3$ | $Na_2CO_3$ | $CaCO_3$ |
| Oxalate | $C_2O_4$ | $-2$ | Oxalic | $H_2C_2O_4$ | $Na_2C_2O_4$ | $CaC_2O_4$ |
| Phosphate | $PO_4$ | $-3$ | Phosphoric | $H_3PO_4$ | $Na_3PO_4$ | $Ca_3(PO_4)_2$ |
| Chlorate | $ClO_3$ | $-1$ | Chloric | $HClO_3$ | $NaClO_3$ | $Ca(ClO_3)_2$ |
| Perchlorate | $ClO_4$ | $-1$ | Perchloric | $HClO_4$ | $NaClO_4$ | $Ca(ClO_4)_2$ |
| Bromate | $BrO_3$ | $-1$ | Bromic | $HBrO_4$ | $NaBrO_3$ | $Ca(BrO_3)_2$ |
| Iodate | $IO_3$ | $-1$ | Iodic | $HIO_3$ | $NaIO_3$ | $Ca(IO_3)_2$ |
| Hydroxide‡ | $OH$ | $-1$ | Water | $HOH$ $(H_2O)$ | $NaOH$ | $Ca(OH)_2$ |
| Ammonium§ | $NH_4$ | $+1$ | Ammonium nitrate ($NH_4NO_3$), ammonium sulfate [($NH_4)_2SO_4$], ammonium phosphate [($NH_4)_3PO_4$] | | | |

† The sulfite radical, $SO_3$, with a valence of $-2$, should not be confused with sulfur trioxide, a compound with the formula $SO_3$. The radical is *never* encountered alone but is *always* in combination with some positive element or radical to form a compound.

‡ Hydroxide does not fit neatly into the classification implicit in this table. The reason for this is the special significance of the compound of this negative radical with hydrogen—that is, the compound water. We shall see in a later chapter that water has a special place in the comparison of acids, bases, and salts. In the system used in this book water is not considered an acid, and the compounds of the hydroxide radical with the metals are called, not salts, but *bases*.

§ Ammonium is the only common radical having a positive valence. It naturally does not form compounds with positive elements, but it does with negative elements and radicals, as indicated by the formulas in this table.

compound. The only reason for setting up a special category of classification for radicals is this tendency for the groups of atoms to remain together through some reactions and to behave as entities. One radical of this kind is the nitrate group, which has the formula $NO_3$. This group of atoms does not exist alone, separate from other atoms or radicals, but does recur in many compounds, in which it is always combined with atoms or other radicals that furnish a single positive valence for each nitrate radical. Such compounds are sodium nitrate ($NaNO_3$), potassium nitrate ($KNO_3$), silver nitrate ($AgNO_3$), nitric acid (hydrogen nitrate, $HNO_3$), and calcium nitrate [$Ca(NO_3)_2$]. In this last formula the whole nitrate radical must be doubled because the valence of calcium is +2. This emphasizes the radical's characteristic behavior as an entity in reactions, and the parentheses indicate that the whole group, consisting of one nitrogen atom and three oxygen atoms, remains together as the nitrate radical. This behavior of the radical as an entity can be illustrated by the equation for the dissolving of magnesium oxide in nitric acid:

$$MgO + 2HNO_3 \longrightarrow H_2O + Mg(NO_3)_2$$

Table 7-8 lists the common radicals, their valences, and the formulas of characteristic compounds containing them.

## 7-13. Formulas and Names of Compounds

In this chapter we have already used the formulas of a number of compounds. We have written the formulas and have stated and explained most of the rules and reasons for writing them. It will be worth while now to collect and summarize these rules and reasons, for this is an important and effective part of scientific terminology and symbolism.

The system of assigning valences to the various elements has been described in detail already. The range of possible valences is from 0 to 8. Some valences are positive (+) and some are negative (−), the sign signifying the type of reactivity the element shows. The metal-

lic elements usually show positive valence and the non-metallic elements negative. In general, elements whose valences are opposite in sign will react; elements whose valences are alike in sign will not react. The algebraic sum of the valences of the component atoms of any compound is zero; the positive and negative valences cancel out. Certain groups of atoms behave in compounds and in many reactions as entities (called radicals), remaining together through the reactions as units. Such a radical can be considered to have a valence as a unit. Its valence is the algebraic sum of the valences of the constituent atoms. In the ammonium radical, for example, the one nitrogen atom has a valence of −3 and the four hydrogen atoms contribute four positive valences; the net valence of +1 is the valence of the radical.

The convention in writing formulas and in naming compounds is to place the element or radical with the positive valence first. The few exceptions to this rule have already been mentioned. The formulas of compounds should, of course, indicate the actual molecular structure if it is known. The structure of hydrogen peroxide, for example, is known to be two atoms of hydrogen and two atoms of oxygen, *not* one of each. The formula of this compound is therefore $H_2O_2$ (not HO). The valences, the composition, and the atomic weights alone do not tell us which of these two formulas is correct; they tell us only that the ratio of atoms is 1/1. The formula HO for hydrogen peroxide is an **empirical formula**—one that indicates the *relative* numbers of atoms in a compound but not the absolute numbers. The true formula is always a multiple of (or the same as) the empirical formula. The evidence that decides which multiple of the empirical formula is the true one is usually an experimental determination of the molecular weight.

The empirical formulas of compounds can be written by use of the valences (Tables 7-7 and 7-8 and Fig. 8-1) and the rules of valence given above. A number of examples are included in Appendix II.

The naming of substances is partly systematic and partly "trivial." The trivial names of substances are those that were introduced and established before systematic naming was begun. The names of the elements are the basis for the names of all the compounds and must therefore be unique. There is, however, some system in the naming of the elements. The suffix -ium indicates metallic character. All elements, with one exception, whose names end in -ium (sometimes -um for euphonic reasons) are metals showing the properties associated with metals, including positive valence in many compounds. The exception to this convention, helium, was first discovered on the sun (Greek helios = sun) and was thought to be a metal. Its name and its symbol, He, were a part of chemical lore for some years before it was isolated and observed on the earth. It turned out to be, not a metal, but a gas, one of the inert gases that do not react at all and therefore have a valence of zero.

Many of the common English names of the elements do not follow this use of the suffix -ium, but most of the international names (usually Latin) do. Examples are iron (ferrum, Fe), lead (plumbum, Pb), gold (aurum, Au), silver (argentum, Ag), tin (stannum, Sn), and copper (cuprum, Cu). Even the international names of several metals are outside the system: zinc, nickel, and cobalt are entirely trivial.

Except for this single generalized suffix, the names of the elements are almost entirely trivial. Their etymology is frequently quite interesting but is hardly significant to the central purpose of this book. It is a convenience to the student as well as the practicing scientist that some of the ancient trivial names have been abandoned, such as brimstone for sulfur, quicksilver for mercury (hydrargyrum, Hg), and dephlogisticated air for oxygen. The student must memorize the names and symbols of the elements encountered frequently—but by no means all 102 of them.

Most compound substances have compound names made up of the names of the elements. There are several conventions to be followed in the use of this system. The first has already been mentioned: the positive element comes first. In **binary compounds**—compounds made up of only *two* different elements—the name of the positive element is followed by the *stem* of the name of the negative element and then by the suffix -ide. For example, the name of the compound of sodium and chlorine, NaCl, is sodium chloride; $K_2S$ is potassium sulfide; MgO is magnesium oxide. Sometimes the same two elements form two different binary compounds. Since in such cases the usual nomenclature would be ambiguous, it must be modified by prefixes or suffixes that indicate the *number* of one or the other kind of atoms involved. There are two oxides of carbon, CO and $CO_2$; these are named carbon *mon*oxide and carbon *di*oxide respectively. For some compounds, even though there is no possibility of ambiguity, the prefix is used. $CS_2$, for example, is carbon disulfide even though no other binary compound of sulfur and carbon exists. Another prefix used in this way is *per-*, which implies the maximum possible. The commonest example of the use of this prefix is hydrogen peroxide, implying the maximum possible number of oxygen atoms per hydrogen atom.

Another method of implying the same type of information in the name of binary and other compounds is the use of a suffix on the stem of the positive element's name. The suffix -ous implies the *lower* of two possible valences; the suffix -ic implies the higher of the two. For example, the two oxides of copper are CuO (copper valence +2), called *cupric* oxide, and $Cu_2O$, called *cuprous* oxide; the copper sulfide we have dealt with, $Cu_2S$, is cuprous sulfide. Similarly the two oxides of mercury are HgO, mercuric oxide, and $Hg_2O$, mercurous oxide; the iron oxide $Fe_2O_3$ is ferric oxide, and FeO is ferrous oxide. Other prefixes and suffixes are used in combination with these to name all possible such compounds, including some in which more than two valences are possible. These become rather complicated and are not necessary for the degree of complexity we shall attempt in this book.

The names of the oxygen-containing radicals (and of the compounds derived from them) employ a set of prefixes and suffixes in a similar manner. The suffixes -ite and -ate indicate relative amounts of oxygen, -ite indicating the lesser amount and -ate the greater amount. If three radicals are possible, *per-* . . . . *-ate* indicates the most oxygen. If a fourth radical exists, the one with the *least* oxygen (and the least valence for the atom other than oxygen) is named *hypo- . . . -ite*. The chlorine-oxygen radicals (all of which have a valence of $-1$) exemplify this nomenclature: $ClO$ is the *hypochlorite* radical, $ClO_2$ is chlor*ite*, $ClO_3$ is chlor*ate*, and $ClO_4$ is *perchlorate*. Consideration of the names and formulas of the compounds and radicals in Table 7-8 will make the use of this system clear. The naming of the compounds of the negative radicals with hydrogen, which are all **acids,** follows closely the naming of binary compounds; the same prefixes and suffixes are used with the stem of the name of the radical.

The system of nomenclature is by no means perfect or complete. There are many exceptions to the rules and many complexities and subtleties that have not been considered here. We have introduced the system here so that the student may begin to use it. Many more details will be introduced from time to time in the text as the need arises.

## Concepts and Terms

Law of Gay-Lussac
  = law of combining volumes
Avogadro's Hypothesis
  Avogadro's number
Combining Power
  = valence
Atomic Weights
  = relative masses of atoms
  arbitrary standards of atomic weight
  table of international atomic weights

Molecular Weights
Valence
  arbitrary standards of valence
  range of valence
  positive and negative valence
Radicals
Formulas

## Problems

**7-1.** Relate the atomic theory to the law of combining volumes in a manner similar to that of Prob. 6-7. State what assumptions are necessary in addition to the postulates of the atomic theory.

**7-2.** State all the necessary experimental data and all the assumptions and postulates used, and go through, in your own style, the reasoning that proves the formulas of water, hydrogen chloride, elemental hydrogen, elemental oxygen, and elemental chlorine to be $H_2O$, $HCl$, $H_2$, $O_2$, and $Cl_2$ respectively.

**7-3.** In the synthesis of ammonia from nitrogen and hydrogen, it is observed that the ratio of *reacting masses* of nitrogen to hydrogen is 4.67. The volumes of nitrogen and hydrogen that react and the volume of ammonia produced are in the ratios 1/3/2; that is, 1 volume of nitrogen and 3 volumes of hydrogen produce 2 volumes of ammonia.
(A) What is the combining weight of nitrogen?
(B) Prove that the formula of nitrogen gas is $N_2$ and that the formula of ammonia is $NH_3$.

(C) What is the valence of nitrogen in this compound?
(D) What is the atomic weight of nitrogen?

**7-4.** Name the following compounds, and indicate the valence of each element and radical in each compound.

(A) $CBr_4$          (K) $KOH$
(B) $P_2O_3$          (L) $Be(NO_2)_2$
(C) $P_2O_5$          (M) $CaH_2$
(D) $Al_2S_3$          (N) $Mg_3N_2$
(E) $SF_6$          (O) $HClO_3$
(F) $Al_2(CO_3)_3$          (P) $SiO_2$
(G) $CaC_2O_4$          (Q) $Na_2SO_3$
(H) $Hg(IO_4)_2$          (R) $FeS$
(I) $Cr_3(PO_4)_2$          (S) $Fe_2S_3$
(J) $NaBrO_3$          (T) $Ca(ClO)_2$

**7-5.** Write formulas for the following compounds.

(A) Zinc sulfide          (E) Stannic oxide
(B) Cupric chloride          (F) Ferric oxalate
(C) Mercuric nitrate          (G) Calcium
(D) Aluminum                  phosphate
    perchlorate          (H) Ferrous sulfate

(I) Ammonium sulfate
(J) Iodine pentoxide
(K) Boron nitride
(L) Sodium hydroxide
(M) Plumbic oxide
(N) Magnesium iodide

(O) Periodic acid
(P) Plumbous carbonate
(Q) Nitrogen tri-iodide
(R) Silver sulfide
(S) Calcium chlorite
(T) Ferric hydroxide

**7-6.** Calculate the molecular weight of each of the compounds listed in Prob. 7-4.

*Ans.* (A) 331.69; (H) 582.43

**7-7.** Calculate the number of moles in 100 grams of each compound listed in Prob. 7-4.

*Ans.* (A) 0.30; (P) 1.66

**7-8.** Below, following eleven numbered statements, are eleven lettered descriptions, each of which applies to one or more of the statements. Indicate, for each statement, which descriptions are applicable.

(1) The valence of oxygen is −2.
(2) In gaseous reactions, the volumes of the reactants and products stand to each other as the ratios of simple whole numbers.
(3) Equal volumes of different gases contain equal numbers of molecules.
(4) In the electrolytic decomposition of water, the volume of hydrogen produced is twice the volume of oxygen produced.
(5) The atoms of different elements have different properties.
(6) Hydrogen, oxygen, chlorine, and some other elemental gases have diatomic molecules.
(7) The atomic weight of oxygen is 16.
(8) The combining weight of magnesium is 1.5 times the combining weight of oxygen.
(9) The mass of the hydrogen atom is 1.008 grams.
(10) When two elements form two different compounds, the ratios of the mass of one element to the mass of the other element in the two compounds stand to each other as the ratio of small whole numbers.
(11) All elemental molecules are monatomic (single atoms).

(A) Avogadro's hypothesis.
(B) An assumption made by Dalton and now known to be true.
(C) An assumption made by Dalton and now known to be untrue.
(D) Gay-Lussac's law.
(E) An arbitrarily defined standard.
(F) A fact directly proved by a laboratory experiment.
(G) A generalized law of chemical combination.
(H) A fact logically derived from experimental information and theoretical considerations.
(I) A statement that cannot be true.
(J) The law of multiple proportions.
(K) A postulate rejected by Dalton and later accepted and used effectively by chemists.

## Suggested Readings

1. H. M. Leicester and H. S. Klickstein, *A Source Book in Chemistry* (McGraw-Hill, 1952). Biographical sketches and brief histories of the contributions of Gay-Lussac (pp. 292–301), Avogadro (pp. 231–238), and Cannizzaro (pp. 406–417).
2. L. K. Nash, *The Atomic-Molecular Theory* (Harvard University Press, 1950), No. 4 of the Harvard Case Histories in Experimental Science. An excellent historical and conceptual development of the atomic theory.
3. F. T. Bonner and Melba Phillips, *Principles of Physical Science* (Addison-Wesley, 1957). Chap. 7 is an elementary historical and conceptual treatment of atomic theory.
4. W. F. Ehret, *Smith's Introductory College Chemistry* (Appleton-Century-Crofts, 1950). Chap. 5 treats symbols and formulas and problems based on formulas; Chap. 9 discusses valence.
5. D. C. Gregg, *Principles of Chemistry* (Allyn and Bacon, 1958). Chap. 3 is a discussion of nomenclature, symbols, and formulas, with example problems.

THE STUDENT who has been carefully following the development of the science of matter, as it is presented in this text, cannot have failed to notice that our knowledge has advanced stepwise, and that the steps take the form of broad generalizations that relate isolated, trivial facts. The collection of the facts is crucial, but the spectacular advances of science are the theories "explaining" these facts. One of the most striking of such advances, which followed much speculation, much experimenting, and many fruitless efforts, was the bold innovation that culminated in the periodic classification of the elements. This generalization is one of the most daring and most beautiful intellectual constructs of science. It adds immeasurably to the strength of the atomic theory by correcting many errors in it, extending it to new sets of facts, and preparing the basis for a whole new level of generalization within it. Finally, and perhaps of most immediate importance to the student of science, this generalization serves as an easily learned summary of almost limitless information about the chemical nature of the elements.

CHAPTER

8

# The Periodic Classification of the Elements (I)

## 8-1. Döbereiner's Triads

Almost immediately after the statement of the atomic theory by Dalton and the introduction of the concept of combining weights, scientists began efforts to classify the elements on the basis of combining weights. These efforts attempted to relate the properties of the elements to the magnitude of the combining weights and to classify the elements into groups showing similar properties. Such groups had long been recognized. But, until quantitative laws of mass relations in chemical reactions had been established, these classifications had no rational basis.

In 1817 a German chemist, J. W. Döbereiner, observed a relation between the combining weights of the three elements in each of several groups and certain properties of the three elements. If the three elements in each of the groups were listed in the order of increasing combining weights, the element in the middle of the list had a combining weight that was close to the average of the combining weights of the

| TABLE 8-1 | *Properties of a Triad* | | |
|-----------|----------|---------|--------|
| PROPERTY | CHLORINE | BROMINE | IODINE |
| Combining weight | 35.5 | 79.9 | 126.9 |
| Melting point | −102° | −7° | 113° |
| Boiling point | −35° | 58° | 183° |
| Color | light green | dark red | violet to black |
| Physical state | gas | liquid | solid |
| Reaction with $H_2$ | explosive | slow | very slow |

first and last elements and *also* had properties that were close to the average of the properties of the first and last elements. These groups were called Döbereiner's **triads.** The idea is illustrated by calcium, strontium, and barium, which made up one of the triads. The combining weights of the three elements are Ca = 20, Sr = 44, and Ba = 69. The average of 20 and 69 is 44.5, which is very close to the combining weight of strontium, 44. The densities of the three elements are Ca = 1.6 grams/cm³, Sr = 2.6, Ba = 3.7; the melting points are Ca = 851°C, Sr = 771°, Ba =717°. Ba reacts rapidly with water; Sr reacts slowly with water; Ca reacts extremely slowly with water. In each of these properties, as in many others, strontium has very nearly the average of the values of the property for calcium and barium. Another triad includes the elements chlorine, bromine, and iodine. Their combining weights and a few properties are listed in Table 8-1. It is evident that this group of three elements shows the same average behavior for the middle member. Although several other such groups were observed by Döbereiner and some attention was given to his observation, his concept failed to have any striking or lasting effect on the development of our knowledge of the elements, largely because it presented neither an "explanation" nor an all-inclusive generalization. No new information could be obtained from the use of the concept, and many elements were in no way included or considered by this scheme of classification. The significance of Döbereiner's triads is that they represent the first, limited attempt to classify the elements on the basis of combining weights.

## 8-2. Newlands' Octaves

No other notable efforts at classification on the basis of combining weights were made until 1863, when J. A. R. Newlands, an English chemist, proposed what he called the **law of octaves.** Newlands listed the sixty-two elements that were known at that time in the order of increasing atomic weights. He then noted that there were often marked similarities between elements that were just eight places removed from each other. Newlands was particularly impressed with the significance of the number eight and its relation to the musical scale. His scientific contemporaries, however, much less impressed, discredited his efforts. The element of mysticism was entirely unacceptable, and there were serious flaws in the classification. At that time atomic weights were just beginning to be used, and many of them were known with very little certainty and much serious error.

## 8-3. Lothar Meyer's Table

In 1864 Lothar Meyer published a table that included only twenty-eight elements and arranged these in vertical groups according to their valence. The elements fell into six horizontal groups, each group differing from the next higher group by a constant increment of atomic weight. This table avoided the mysticism of Newlands but was incomplete.

This series of efforts, and many of lesser importance, culminated in the publication in 1869 of the first version of a periodic classification of the elements by D. I. Mendeleev, a Russian chemist. Several points in this version were criticized severely by Meyer and were corrected in versions that appeared in 1870 and 1872. The version of 1872 was essentially the same as the modern periodic table except that only about two-thirds of the elements now known were known at that time. Mendeleev's proposal was quickly accepted by the scientists of his time and immediately became a well-established part of the conceptual structure of the science of matter. A comment of Meyer's summarizes the feeling of almost all chemists of the late nineteenth century: "The properties of the elements are closely related to the atomic weight; they are functions, and periodic functions at that, of the magnitude of the atomic weight."

## 8-4. Acceptance of Mendeleev's Table

It will tell us something about the nature of science to ask why Mendeleev's proposal was accepted almost instantly after previous efforts, some of which were closely related to that of Mendeleev, had been rejected. Newlands' idea was scorned by scientists even though it was quite similar to the concept that was readily accepted only five years later. One reason for this reaction was the mystical quality that Newlands attached to the number eight in his system. Scientists detected a throwback to the irrationality of the alchemists, who were primarily magicians and only secondarily concerned with the science of matter. But even more important was the fact that Newlands offered little that was really new in his scheme. There were gaps and flaws in his table, and he had no explanation for them; there was no new, grand concept such as the atomic theory offered; and, finally, his scheme offered no apparent means of extending the knowledge of the elements.

Mendeleev's proposal, on the other hand, offered all of these and had the further advantage of being backed by a bold and brilliant supporter—its author, Mendeleev himself. The periodic classification advanced by Mendeleev was not a new theoretical explanation, but it was such a far-reaching extension and strengthening of the atomic theory as to be of almost equal status among the concepts of the science of matter. By use of this concept it was possible to

correct many erroneous atomic weights; it was possible to choose the correct multiple of the combining weight for many an atomic weight; it was possible to predict the existence of several yet undiscovered elements and even to indicate where to find them and how to obtain them; it summarized in an extremely concise and convenient form a tremendous collection of otherwise isolated factual material; and it pointed the way to profound extensions of the atomic theory. The reason why scientists rejected previous similar proposals but decided that Mendeleev's proposal was acceptable (or true) was simply that this one was *effective*.

## 8-5. Mendeleev's Proposal

There is a story, probably apocryphal, that Mendeleev dreamed the periodic classification. He did first publish the table in a handbook of chemistry, and the story suggests that he was spending a restless night worrying over a succinct and all-inclusive way of presenting the properties of the chemical elements. The table is simply a list of the elements in the order of increasing atomic weights, with one slight modification. Such a list (excluding elements not known to Mendeleev) of the first seventeen elements is presented in Table 8-2. Above each symbol is the atomic weight, and below is the common valence of the element.

In this table we have included only one property of each element, its valence. The **periodic** recurrence of even this one property is immediately apparent. If we pick any valence, say +2, we observe that every seventh element has the same valence; that is, if we start with beryllium and count over seven elements, we arrive at Mg, which also has a valence of +2; then, counting seven more elements, we arrive

TABLE **8-2** *Atomic Weights and Valences of the First Seventeen Elements*

| 1 | 7 | 9 | 11 | 12 | 14 | 16 | 19 | 23 | 24 | 27 | 28 | 31 | 32 | 35 | 39 | 40 | 48 |
|---|---|---|----|----|----|----|----|----|----|----|----|----|----|----|----|----|----|
| H | Li | Be | B | C | N | O | F | Na | Mg | Al | Si | P | S | Cl | K | Ca | Ti |
| +1 | +1 | +2 | +3 | −4 | −3 | −2 | −1 | +1 | +2 | +3 | −4 | −3 | −2 | −1 | +1 | +2 | −4 |
| | | | | +4 | +5 | | | | | | +4 | +5 | +6 | +7 | | | +4 |

TABLE 8-3    *Periodic Arrangement of the First Seventeen Elements*

| PERIOD | I | II | III | IV | V | VI | VII |
|---|---|---|---|---|---|---|---|
| 1 | 1<br>H | | | | | | |
| 2 | 7<br>Li | 9<br>Be | 11<br>B | 12<br>C | 14<br>N | 16<br>O | 19<br>F |
| 3 | 23<br>Na | 24<br>Mg | 27<br>Al | 28<br>Si | 31<br>P | 32<br>S | 35<br>Cl |
| 4 | 39<br>K | 40<br>Ca | | 48<br>Ti | | | |
| | +1 | +2 | +3 | +4, −4 | +5, −3 | +6, −2 | +7, −1 |
| Group ⟶ | I | II | III | IV | V | VI | VII |

at Ca, which also has a valence of +2. These relations become much more obvious if the information of Table 8-2 is rearranged (the slight modification mentioned above) so that the elements of similar properties fall in vertical columns, as in Table 8-3. Again the atomic weight of each element is indicated above the symbol, but in this table it is necessary to indicate the valence only once for each of the vertical groups. Also included in this table is a convenient symbol that not only designates the particular group but also indicates the positive valence a member of the group is most likely to have. The horizontal rows are called **periods,** a term that emphasizes the periodic repetition of similar properties in this tabulation of the elements according to increasing atomic weight. Hydrogen occupies a special position in this table (its position is not quite so special as indicated in Table 8-3, as we shall see presently)—a position that indicates its special relation to the structure of the other elements.

Mendeleev's tables of 1869–70 were very similar in form to Table 8-3 (with a somewhat more complicated structure in the periods beyond the third) and included the sixty-odd elements known at that time. Now a table of this sort is a convenient, concise summary of information about the elements, particularly if it is remembered that *many* physical and chemical properties show the periodic similarity within the groups that has been exemplified by valence. But it by no means appears as the grand con-

cept described in the introductory paragraphs of this chapter, nor would it be likely to fire the imagination of skeptical chemists and win their immediate and unanimous approval. The quality of Mendeleev's contribution lay in the conviction and boldness with which he used the concept to establish with certainty some questionable facts, to correct erroneous information, and to predict totally new information.

## 8-6. *Correction of Erroneous Atomic Weights*

We can illustrate each of these types of advance in knowledge of the elements by an example. In Chapter 7 we were unable to cite any experimental reason for a choice between two possible atomic weights of magnesium. It could have either an atomic weight of 12 and a valence of +1 or an atomic weight of 24 and a valence of +2. If one accepts the periodic classification, an atomic weight of 12 would put magnesium in a group with either silicon or phosphorus. But magnesium in no way resembles these two elements; it is, on the contrary, very similar in most of its properties to calcium and beryllium. Here, then, is evidence by which we *know* the atomic weight and valence of magnesium.†

One erroneous atomic weight that was ac-

† Methods developed in the last few decades have supplied independent experimental verification of the atomic weight.

cepted in Mendeleev's time but was corrected by him to the now accepted value is that of indium (see No. 49 in Table 8-5). It had been established experimentally that the combining weight of In was 38.2, and it was assumed that its valence was +2. This combination would give indium an atomic weight of 76.4 and would place it in Group VI with typical non-metals, oxygen and sulfur, which have a characteristic valence of −2. The properties of indium, a metal with strong resemblances to aluminum, make it impossible to classify it in Group VI. Mendeleev then suggested that the valence must be, not +2, but +3, which gives it an atomic weight of 114.6 and places it in Group III between cadmium and tin, where it logically belongs. A total of seventeen elements had their atomic weights corrected in this manner by Mendeleev; some of the errors were small, but others, as in the case of indium, were errors in the multiple.

## 8-7. Prediction of New Elements

The predictions of new elements by Mendeleev illustrated the most striking advantage of his periodic classification and contributed the most to its acceptance. There were notable gaps in Mendeleev's periodic tables. One of them can be seen in Table 8-3. The element titanium, Ti, came next after calcium in the order of increasing atomic weights of known elements. But its properties place it in Group IV, not in Group III; it closely resembles silicon and is rather unlike aluminum. Mendeleev had deep faith in the new system he proposed and the boldness to speak out for it. Rather than abandon or modify his scheme or force an inconsistency into it, he took the position that an element between Ca and Ti actually exists but had not yet been found. He set up his table with this space blank and suggested that chemists might start looking for the missing element, to which he gave the tentative name "eka-boron" (Sanskrit, *eka* = first). There were six such gaps in the first periodic tables of Mendeleev, in the positions of elements 21, 31, 32, 43, 75, and 84 in Table 8-5. For each gap Mendeleev predicted a still

undiscovered element. But he went much further than this: he not only predicted the existence, in these positions, of the six elements, which he named provisionally eka-boron, eka-aluminum, eka-silicon, eka-manganese, dvi-manganese (*dvi* = second), and eka-tantalum, but also predicted their chemical and physical properties, several characteristic compounds of each, the types of minerals in which they would be found, the experimental approach that would discover their existence, and the means of preparing them from their minerals (naturally occurring compounds of the elements). His predictions (a few of them modified by corrections offered by Lothar Meyer) were all borne out in a most striking manner. Three of the elements were discovered within fifteen years, and the remaining three have since been isolated or produced artificially. An element corresponding to eka-aluminum, named gallium (it was isolated in France), was discovered in 1875; scandium (eka-boron) was discovered in Sweden in 1879; and germanium (eka-silicon) was discovered in Germany in 1886. Particularly striking is the almost perfect correspondence between the properties predicted by Mendeleev and those found experimentally. Table 8-4 compares a few of the predicted and observed properties of the first three elements. The remarkable accuracy of these extremely bold predictions established the periodic table as a powerful extension of the atomic theory. That the concept was quickly accepted by the more conservative scientists is demonstrated by the fact that the Royal Society of London awarded the Davy Medal jointly to Mendeleev and Meyer in 1882 and even got around five years later to awarding the same honor to Newlands for his contribution to periodic classification.

## 8-8. Evolution of Mendeleev's Table

Mendeleev's tables of the 1870's were a good deal more complete and complex than the oversimplified Table 8-3. Period 4 and alternate periods beyond it included an extra vertical group called **transition elements.** This group, numbered VIII, had three members in each alternate pe-

TABLE 8-4  *Mendeleev's Prediction of New Elements*

| PROPERTIES PREDICTED IN 1871 BY MENDELEEV | PROPERTIES EXPERIMENTALLY OBSERVED |
|---|---|
| *Eka-aluminum* | *Gallium* (Lecoq de Boisbaudran, France, 1875) |
| Atomic weight, 68. | Atomic weight, 69.72. |
| Density, 5.9. | Density, 5.94. |
| Melting point, very low. | Melting point, 30.2°C. |
| Boiling point, very high. | Boiling point, 1,700°C. |
| Should dissolve slowly in acids and alkalies. | Dissolves slowly in acids and alkalies. |
| Oxide: formula $Ea_2O_3$. | Oxide: formula $Ga_2O_3$. |
| Should dissolve in HCl. | Dissolves in HCl to form a salt, $GaCl_3$. |
| The element will probably be discovered by spectroscopic analysis. | Gallium was first observed by spectroscopic analysis; the spectroscope aided greatly in the isolation. |
| *Eka-boron* | *Scandium* (Nilson, Sweden, 1879) |
| Atomic weight, 44. | Atomic weight, 44.96. |
| Density, 3.5. | Density, 3.86. |
| Oxide: $Eb_2O_3$. | Oxide: $Sc_2O_3$. |
| More basic than aluminum oxide; less basic than magnesium oxide. | More basic than aluminum oxide; less basic than magnesium oxide. |
| Talts colorless and difficult to crystallize. | All scandium salts are colorless; scandium sulfate can be crystallized, but with difficulty. |
| She chloride, $EbCl_3$, should be less volatile than aluminum chloride. | $ScCl_3$ vaporizes at 850°, aluminum chloride at 100°. |
| Will not be discovered by spectroscopic analysis. | Scandium was not observed spectroscopically. |
| *Eka-silicon* | *Germanium* (Winkler, Germany, 1886) |
| Atomic weight, 72. | Atomic weight, 72.6. |
| Density, 5.5. | Density, 5.47. |
| Melting point, very high. | Melting point, 958°. |
| Density of oxide, $EsO_2$, 4.7. | Density of oxide, $GeO_2$, 4.703. |
| Density of chloride, $EsCl_4$, 1.9. | Density of chloride, $GeCl_4$, 1.887. |
| Boiling point of chloride, under 100°. | Boiling point of $GeCl_4$, 86°. |
| The element should be a gray metal, stable toward acids and bases; should react with oxygen to produce the oxide, $EsO_2$, which should have a very high melting point. It will probably occur as either $EsO_2$ or $K_2EsF_6$, from which the metal can be produced by heating with metallic sodium. | Germanium is a gray metal, impervious to all acids except nitric, which attacks it slowly; impervious to all bases. It reacts with oxygen of the air to form $GeO_2$, whose melting point is 1,100°C. It can be produced from the mineral $K_2GeF_6$ by heating with metallic sodium. |

riod. It was also observed that the alternate periods showed an alternation in the closeness of their relation to elements higher in the groups. Mendeleev reduced the complexity somewhat in his later tables by combining the 4th and 5th periods, the 6th and 7th, and so on to make fewer but longer periods. The periods below the 4th then had seventeen elements each: seven closely related elements called Subgroup a, the three transition elements of Group VIII, and the seven less closely related elements called Subgroup b.

In the late nineteenth and the early twentieth century a whole new group of elements was discovered. These are the inert gases, which do not form compounds at all, have a valence of zero, and are therefore called Group 0. All of these changes and, of course, recently discovered elements have been added to the tables of Mendeleev to form the modern periodic table. But *all* these additions fit neatly into the table without any modification in principle. A modern version of the periodic table is presented as Table 8-5. The subsequent discussion will be concerned with this table, which will be used extensively throughout the remainder of this course.

## 8-9. *Description of the Modern Periodic Table*

The wealth of information contained in the periodic table and its wonderful usefulness for our understanding the chemistry of the 102 elements can be realized only after much experience in its use. By thoroughly understanding the structure of the table and the significance of its arrangement the student can get a good start toward realizing its value.

The horizontal rows of the table are called **periods;** the vertical rows are called **groups.** A very short period of two elements, hydrogen and helium, is at the head of the table. These two elements exemplify the two extremes, Group I and Group 0. There are then two short periods of eight elements each, beginning with a Group I element, progressing through the numbered groups, I–VII, and ending with a Group 0 ele-

ment. Next follow two long periods of eighteen elements each. The long periods start with elements of Groups Ia, IIa, and IIIa (indicating a *close* relation to the elements of Groups I, II, and III of the two short periods) and continue with four elements that are less closely related to the elements above. This less close relation is indicated by the suffix b attached to the group numbers V–VII. Next come the three elements of Group VIII, which cannot be related to elements of the short periods. The similarity of the Group VIII elements extends down through the group, but there is also an extremely close similarity among the three VIII elements in each period. After the Group VIII elements the similarity to the short periods begins again, less close in Ib–IIIb and quite close in Va–VIIa. Finally, a Group 0 element, closely related to helium and the other inert gases of the short periods, ends each long period. The long sixth period, with thirty-two elements, starts with two close relatives, Ia and IIa, but then follows the **lanthanide series,** a group of fifteen elements that are *very* closely related to each other and to the higher members of Group IIIa. These rare-earth elements, as they are sometimes called, were extremely difficult to separate; several were isolated only in the last few years. After the lanthanide series, which is set apart in Table 8-5, the remainder of Period 6 is entirely analogous to the long Period 5. Period 7 is incomplete but starts in the same way as Period 6; members of Groups Ia and IIa are followed by the beginning of a transition series, similar to the rare-earth elements, called the **actinide series.**

## 8-10. *Atomic Numbers*

The large numbers before the symbols of the elements in Table 8-5 are called the **atomic numbers.** These are simply the ordinal numbers of the elements arranged in the order of increasing atomic weight—with an important qualification. When Mendeleev originally formulated the periodic classification, he found that many elements were "out of order"—that is, fell into the wrong group if placed according to the

TABLE **8-5** *Periodic Classification of the Elements*

**Period 1**

| | I | O |
|---|---|---|
| | Hydrogen 1 H 1.008 | Helium 2 He 4.003 |

**Periods 2–3 (main groups)**

| | I | III | IV | V | VI | VII | O |
|---|---|---|---|---|---|---|---|
| 2 | Lithium 3 Li 6.940 | Beryllium 4 Be 9.013 | Boron 5 B 10.82 | Carbon 6 C 12.011 | Nitrogen 7 N 14.008 | Oxygen 8 O 16.000 | Fluorine 9 F 19.00 | Neon 10 Ne 20.183 |
| 3 | Sodium 11 Na 22.991 | Magnesium 12 Mg 24.32 | Aluminum 13 Al 26.98 | Silicon 14 Si 28.09 | Phosphorus 15 P 30.975 | Sulfur 16 S 32.066 | Chlorine 17 Cl 35.475 | Argon 18 Ar 39.944 |

**Periods 4–7**

| | Ia | IIa | IIIa | IV | Vb | VIb | VIIb | VIII | | | Ib | IIb | IIIb | IV | Va | VIa | VIIa | O |
|---|---|---|---|---|---|---|---|---|---|---|---|---|---|---|---|---|---|---|
| 4 | Potassium 19 K 39.100 | Calcium 20 Ca 40.08 | Scandium 21 Sc 44.96 | Titanium 22 Ti 47.90 | Vanadium 23 V 50.95 | Chromium 24 Cr 52.01 | Manganese 25 Mn 54.94 | Iron 26 Fe 55.85 | Cobalt 27 Co 58.94 | Nickel 28 Ni 58.71 | Copper 29 Cu 63.54 | Zinc 30 Zn 65.38 | Gallium 31 Ga 69.72 | Germanium 32 Ge 72.60 | Arsenic 33 As 74.91 | Selenium 34 Se 78.96 | Bromine 35 Br 79.916 | Krypton 36 Kr 83.80 |
| 5 | Rubidium 37 Rb 85.48 | Strontium 38 Sr 87.63 | Yttrium 39 Y 88.92 | Zirconium 40 Zr 91.22 | Niobium 41 Nb 92.91 | Molybdenum 42 Mo 95.95 | Technetium 43 Tc [99] | Ruthenium 44 Ru 101.1 | Rhodium 45 Rh 102.91 | Palladium 46 Pd 106.4 | Silver 47 Ag 107.880 | Cadmium 48 Cd 112.41 | Indium 49 In 114.82 | Tin 50 Sn 118.70 | Antimony 51 Sb 121.76 | Tellurium 52 Te 127.61 | Iodine 53 I 126.91 | Xenon 54 Xe 131.30 |
| 6 | Cesium 55 Cs 132.91 | Barium 56 Ba 137.36 | Lanthanide Series 57–71 | Hafnium 72 Hf 178.50 | Tantalum 73 Ta 180.95 | Tungsten 74 W 183.86 | Rhenium 75 Re 186.22 | Osmium 76 Os 190.2 | Iridium 77 Ir 192.2 | Platinum 78 Pt 195.09 | Gold 79 Au 197.0 | Mercury 80 Hg 200.61 | Thallium 81 Tl 204.39 | Lead 82 Pb 207.21 | Bismuth 83 Bi 209.00 | Polonium 84 Po 210 | Astatine 85 At [210] | Radon 86 Rn 222 |
| 7 | Francium 87 Fr [223] | Radium 88 Ra 226.05 | Actinide Series 89–102 | | | | | | | | | | | | | | | |

**Lanthanide Series**

| Lanthanum 57 La 138.92 | Cerium 58 Ce 140.13 | Praseodymium 59 Pr 140.92 | Neodymium 60 Nd 144.27 | Promethium 61 Pm [145] | Samarium 62 Sm 150.43 | Europium 63 Eu 152.35 | Gadolinium 64 Gd 157.26 | Terbium 65 Tb 158.93 | Dysprosium 66 Dy 162.51 | Holmium 67 Ho 164.94 | Erbium 68 Er 167.2 | Thulium 69 Tm 168.94 | Ytterbium 70 Yb 173.04 | Lutetium 71 Lu 174.99 |
|---|---|---|---|---|---|---|---|---|---|---|---|---|---|---|

**Actinide Series**

| Actinium 89 Ac 227 | Thorium 90 Th 232.05 | Protactinium 91 Pa 231 | Uranium 92 U 238.07 | Neptunium 93 Np [237] | Plutonium 94 Pu [242] | Americium 95 Am [243] | Curium 96 Cm [245] | Berkelium 97 Bk [249] | Californium 98 Cf [249] | Einsteinium 99 Es [254] | Fermium 100 Fm [255] | Mendelevium 101 Md [256] | Nobelium 102 No [253] |
|---|---|---|---|---|---|---|---|---|---|---|---|---|---|

atomic weight. In seventeen such cases the atomic weights were found to be in error, and the new, correct atomic weights placed the elements in the right positions—that is, in the groups to which they obviously belonged. But there are still four pairs of elements that do *not* fit the scheme when placed according to their atomic weights. These atomic weights have been the object of most intensive study by chemists for many years, and there is now no doubt whatsoever that the presently recorded atomic weights are correct. But they still do not fit a periodic scheme based on the order of increasing atomic weight. The four pairs are elements 18 and 19 (argon and potassium), 27 and 28 (cobalt and nickel), 52 and 53 (tellurium and iodine), and 90 and 91 (thorium and protactinium). Argon has an atomic weight of 39.9, and potassium has an atomic weight of 39.1. The order of increasing atomic weight is Cl, K, Ar, Ca, placing potassium with the inert gases in Group 0 and argon with the alkali metals (Group I). But the properties of these elements are such that this classification would be absurd; argon is an inert gas resembling neon and krypton, and potassium is a reactive metal resembling sodium and rubidium. Similarly, iodine *must* be placed in Group VII with chlorine and bromine, and tellurium *must* be placed in Group VI with sulfur and selenium, if the classification is to avoid absurdity. Physical evidence to be described later also requires that cobalt have atomic number 27, nickel number 28, thorium number 90, and protactinium number 91, even though their atomic weights indicate the reverse.

The difficulty presented by these anomalous pairs is a real dilemma. If the system remains consistent, it becomes absurd. Since the absurdity cannot be accepted, a choice is presented: either allow this inconsistency or abandon the whole scheme. The choice was made to keep the inconsistency because the scheme had worked beautifully and effectively for a long time. Here is an excellent example of a theory surviving several bits of seriously adverse experimental evidence. No alternative offered could approach the effectiveness of the periodic table. In such a situation theories are not abandoned to leave an intellectual vacuum.

It turned out that the choice to ignore the inconsistencies and keep the scheme was a very wise one. As we shall see in Part Two of this book, this anomaly in the classification is readily explained. The atomic numbers (symbol $Z$) have been shown to have very profound fundamental significance, much greater than that of atomic weights. This great theoretical value of atomic numbers has recently led to the development of methods of determining $Z$ to a high degree of certainty. Such determinations show that the anomalous pairs of elements *were* placed correctly in the table. In fact, the difficulty of these anomalies and the solution to the difficulty greatly strengthened the whole atomic theory. The details of the solution of this problem, which is the extension of the atomic theory to the completely new level of generalization referred to earlier, will be considered in Part Two.

## 8-11. Variation of Properties Within Groups and Periods

The similarity of the elements within a group should not be taken as implying identity. There is a gradual, usually quite regular change in most of the properties of the elements as you read down a group. This idea is well illustrated by the triads of Döbereiner, referred to earlier in this chapter. Each triad consisted of three elements of the same group from three consecutive periods. A change in properties was noted from the first to the last element of the triad, the properties of the middle element being averages of those of the extreme elements.

The change in properties going along a period is greater than that going down a group. The changes are still fairly steady, but the change from Group I to Group VII within a period is a change from one type to the *opposite* type. There is, moreover, a very abrupt change at the inert gases: Group VII is a group of very reactive elements of one type; Group 0 (the next following) contains elements that are completely inert; Group I (again the next following) contains elements of still another type, violently reactive, but with a type of reactivity that is exactly the opposite of that of Group VII.

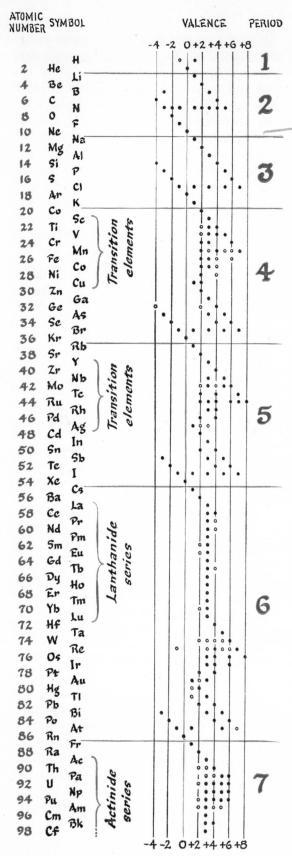

These changes in properties, gradual and within a type down the groups, less gradual and from one type to the opposite across the periods; the close similarities through the transition elements; the discontinuity and abrupt reversal at Group 0; all these are very clearly shown when a property is plotted against the atomic number. One striking demonstration of this periodicity is shown in Figure 8-1, in which valence is plotted on the horizontal axis against atomic number on the vertical axis. The solid circles in this figure represent the stable and common valences; less common or unstable valences are indicated by open circles. The stepwise diagonal increase in valence from −4 to +7 (+8 in two cases) is very apparent, even to casual observation. There is first one partial diagonal row of dots. Then there are two complete diagonal rows, separated by eight atomic numbers. Next comes a space of eighteen atomic numbers in which the dots form a more or less vertical line, representing the similarity in character of the transition elements. After the space of eighteen atomic numbers another diagonal line begins, increases to +3, goes down vertically (constant valence) through the lanthanide series, then continues its increase. The beginning of the last diagonal starts at element 83 and continues steadily to 89. Beyond 89 the elements have multiple valence, but the progression resembles that of the lanthanide series.

Other properties can be plotted similarly against atomic number. In Figures 8-2 and 8-3 the density and the ionization potential are so plotted. You are familiar with the first of these quantities, and it does not matter, for the present discussion, what the particular significance of the second may be; the important thing is that here are two more of the properties that determine the physical and chemical behavior of the elements, and that both show this remarkable periodicity when plotted against atomic number —the order in the periodic table.

## 8-12. Metallic Character and Position in the Periodic Table

Before we consider the details of each group, we shall point out certain general positional

FIGURE **8-1** *Periodicity of valence.*

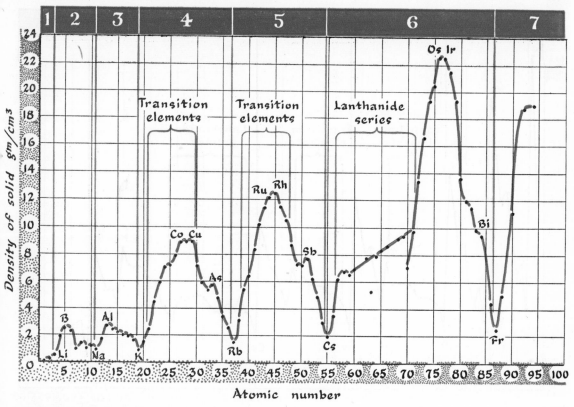

FIGURE **8-2** *Periodic plot of density of solid elements against atomic number.*

qualities of the periodic table. The elements at the left and the lower center of the table are all **metals;** those at the upper right are **non-metals.** (The meaning of these terms will be taken up below.) Metallic character is greatest for the elements at the lower left side of the table and decreases as we go up and to the right. Conversely, non-metallic character is shown most strongly by fluorine, at the upper right of the table, and decreases as we go down and to the left. The inert gases, in relation to metallic and non-metallic character, are in a group apart.

The **metallic properties** by which elements are classified into metals and non-metals include those usually associated with metals—metallic luster, ductility, malleability, high thermal conductivity, high electrical conductivity, etc. But they also include several chemical properties—strong tendency to form a positive valence, high reactivity toward negative elements, formation of alkaline compounds with oxygen, formation of salts with negative elements and radicals, etc.

The opposite of these characteristics are non-metallic properties. Most metals are solids (mercury is a liquid at room temperature, and gallium is liquefied a few degrees above room temperature, but both are metals); several non-metals are gases, and one, bromine, is a liquid. This transition from metallic to non-metallic character as we go across and up the periodic table is a reflection of changes in several fundamental structural qualities of the atoms themselves. The net result of these fundamental changes is effectively presented in the summary form of the periodic table shown as Table 8-5.

## 8-13. Description of Groups of Elements

The element hydrogen has had a unique place, up to this point, in the development of our ideas about matter. It had a similarly unique place in the historical development of our science, and it

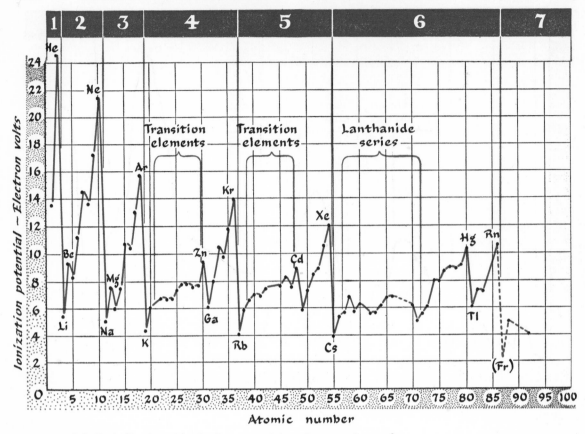

FIGURE 8-3 *Periodic plot of ionization potential against atomic number.*

will continue to be a special case in the further development of the ideas of this book. This unique position of hydrogen in the theory of matter is manifested by its position in the periodic table. It is related to the metals of Group I-Ia, for its principal valence is +1 and it has a strong tendency to form compounds with negative elements. But it is also related to the extreme non-metals of Group VII-VIIa, for all its other properties are non-metallic. It is a gas, as are most of the strong non-metals, and it even forms a series of compounds (metal hydrides) in which its valence is −1 (for example, sodium hydride, NaH). We shall see in Parts Two and Three that this rather strange behavior and the special character of hydrogen in general are direct manifestations of the unique structure of the atom of hydrogen.

**Group I-Ia, the alkali metals.** The elements of Group I-Ia, lithium, sodium, potassium, rubidium, cesium, and francium, are called the alkali metals. All are exceedingly reactive. The name *alkali metal* comes from the fact that these metals react (usually quite violently) with water to produce hydroxides that are very strong bases, and these strong bases are called *alkalies*. Sodium *hydroxide,* NaOH, is the substance called lye and is typical of the hydroxides of these metals. The elements themselves are soft, silvery metals of very low melting point, high conductivity (thermal and electrical), and very low density (near 1). Their valence in all compounds is +1. The degree of metallic character—that is, the strength of their tendency to react and form positive valence—increases as we go *down* the group from lithium to francium. All of the elements of this group except francium are fairly abundant. They occur naturally *always* in combination and can be kept in the uncombined state only with difficulty. Francium, a highly radioactive element, was discovered only recently.

**Group II-IIa, the alkaline-earth metals.** The

elements of Group II-IIa, beryllium, magnesium, calcium, strontium, barium, and radium, are all metals that have a valence of +2 in all their compounds. Most of their properties are similar, with some moderation, to those of the alkali metals. They are not quite so soft or reactive; their densities are a little greater (not quite so light); their hydroxides are alkaline but not so strongly; they are very positive but not quite so positive as the alkali metals. Most of the members of this group occur naturally rather commonly but always in combination. Radium is exceedingly rare and is very radioactive.

**The transition elements.** The elements of the "b" subgroups and Group VIII, and the lower members of Groups IIIa, IV, Va, and VIa, are all metals (a few have diminished metallic character and are sometimes called *metalloids*) and represent a *transition* from the extreme metallic character on the left of the table to the extreme non-metallic character on the right of the table. Reference to the valence chart of Figure 8-1 shows that these elements have a strong tendency to multiplicity of valence. All form binary compounds with the most negative elements, Group VII and oxygen and sulfur; but they also form many compounds in which they are part of a negative radical. The chemistry of most of these elements is quite complex and is properly part of more advanced chemistry courses.

**Group III.** The first member of this group, boron, is a metalloid; aluminum and the lower members are all metals. In some respects boron resembles the lower members, but the degree of resemblance is much greater from aluminum on down. These elements form compounds in which the valence is +3, as expected from the position in the table, but also show more complicated combining capabilities.

**Group IV.** The chemistry of compounds of carbon constitutes a whole major branch of physical science called **organic chemistry.** There are many more compounds of carbon known than all other compounds put together. This fact is the result of the ability of carbon to form four valences with either positive or negative elements and of several other unique qualities of the structure of the carbon atom. Silicon also is versatile in combination but much less so than

carbon. The other elements in this group are much more closely related to the transition metals and metalloids than to the first two members of the group.

**Group V-Va.** Nitrogen and phosphorus are non-metals, forming series of compounds in which their valence is −3, other series in which their valence is +5, and less important series arising from intermediate valence states. It is characteristic of almost all of the non-metals to show a great multiplicity of valence; nitrogen, for example, exhibits *all* valences between +5 and −3. The lower members of Group Va, arsenic, antimony, and bismuth, are metalloids, showing resemblance to the upper two members but also having a good deal of similarity to neighboring transition elements.

**Group VI-VIa.** Oxygen is the second most negative (non-metallic) element, being exceeded in this property only by fluorine. It is a powerfully reactive substance and *always* shows a negative valence. In all compounds except the peroxides the valence is −2. Sulfur is a non-metal but much less powerful than oxygen. The lower three members are metalloids and show considerable resemblance to sulfur.

**Group VII-VIIa, the halogens.** The generic name applied to these elements, *halogen,* means "salt-former." All are powerful non-metals and characteristically form binary compounds, called salts, with the positive elements. The most familiar of such compounds is sodium chloride, NaCl, which is common table salt. All of these elements have the characteristic valence of −1; all but fluorine show various positive valences up to +7 in other series of compounds. Fluorine is violently reactive and forms compounds with all other elements except the inert gases. Wood, rubber, even steel and asbestos, react with fluorine so violently as to become incandescent. Chlorine is an extremely reactive substance but not quite so reactive as fluorine. Mixtures of hydrogen and chlorine gases are detonated by light. Bromine and iodine are still less reactive but form compounds, in which they have a valence of −1, with *many* other elements.

**Group O, the inert gases.** The six elements at the extreme right of the periodic table are all gases and are all totally inert to chemical combination. This group is sometimes called the "noble gases" or "rare gases." The term "noble," sometimes applied also to the metals near platinum, implies an inertness or "aloofness" toward chemical reactivity. The term "rare" indicates that these gases occur in very minute quantities (mostly in the atmosphere). Since they have no reactivity, their chemistry is totally without interest. Some, however, have a great theoretical interest in certain radioactive decompositions and nuclear reactions (considered in Part Three). The whole group also has a considerable theoretical interest in the next great extension of the atomic theory, to be considered in Part Two.

**The lanthanide series.** This group of elements, sometimes called the rare-earth metals, acts as a transition group in the extension of the very long sixth period. As indicated by the valence chart, all have almost identical valences and therefore almost identical chemical characteristics. The two higher elements of Group IIIa, scandium and yttrium, also are almost indistinguishable from the members of this series. All these elements occur naturally together in the same ores and are exceedingly difficult to separate. The last of them was isolated only a few years ago, and for many years mixtures of several were thought to be single elements.

**The actinide series.** The elements starting with polonium, including astatine, radon, francium, and radium, and all of the actinide series are radioactive. Most of them through uranium (92) occur in small quantities naturally. All the elements above uranium, as well as several others through the periodic table (including technetium, 43, and promethium, 61) are synthetic (man-made). Elements 93 and 94, neptunium and plutonium, were synthesized on a large scale during World War II and since for military purposes. Elements 95–102 have all been synthesized since the war. As some of their names suggest, their synthesis and discovery took place at the University of California in Berkeley, California, America. The chemistry of the transuranium elements is little known for several reasons: most have been prepared only in minute traces; most are quite unstable and, once prepared, exist only briefly; and much of the information about them is classified as a defense secret.

## 8-14. Writing Chemical Equations

With the accumulation of the information contained in Table 8-5, we now have all the information we need for writing the formulas of compounds and for calculating molecular weights. With the addition of one other item, this will also be the information we need for writing equations and for making quantitative calculations based on chemical equations. The additional item is the answer to the question whether a particular reaction will actually happen as written. Some general ideas on the probability of reactions can be obtained from the reactivities (metallic and non-metallic character) of the various elements, indicated by their positions in the periodic table, but precise information on this question can come only from experience and from certain more complex ideas, some of which will be considered later in this book.

If we know that two substances *do* react, we can, by use of valences and symbols, write the formulas of the reactants and the products. Then, by using the law of conservation of mass, we can write an equation that describes this reaction. The equation so written is the next level of symbolism beyond those complex symbols, the formulas of compounds (see pp. 95–97). Silver nitrate and calcium chloride, for example, react to produce silver chloride and calcium nitrate. This information can be most readily conveyed by the equation for this reaction:

$$AgNO_3 + CaCl_2 \longrightarrow AgCl + Ca(NO_3)_2$$

The valence and symbol for silver are found in the tables; the valence of the nitrate radical is obtained from Table 7-8, or it could be calculated from the valences of oxygen and nitrogen. The formulas of the three other components of this reaction are determined in the same way. The unbalanced equation above states succinctly, then, the fact that the reaction takes place. This equation is, however, incomplete; it does not tell us how many moles of the various compounds are involved, and it cannot do so until we write it in such a way that the law of conservation of mass is satisfied—until we balance the equation. We note that there are two chlorine atoms on the left but only one on the right, and that there are two nitrate radicals on the right and only one on the left. The balancing of the equation consists of writing it in such a way that the numbers of *all* the atoms are the same on both sides of the equation. In doing this we *must not* alter the formulas of the compounds; presumably we have determined them correctly by the valences of the various atoms and radicals; if we changed a formula it would represent a quite different substance. But we need to double the number of nitrate radicals on the left. We may do this *only* by doubling the *whole compound,* silver nitrate. We then have two atoms of silver among the reactants (on the left) and therefore must double the silver-containing compound that appears among the products (on the right), silver chloride. In doing this we have doubled the number of chlorine atoms on the right, which is just what is needed to take care of the two chlorine atoms among the reactants. The balanced equation is, then,

$$2AgNO_3 + CaCl_2 \longrightarrow 2AgCl + Ca(NO_3)_2$$

As a second example let us consider the reaction for the formation of oxygen from potassium chlorate. The other product of this reaction is potassium chloride. Using the rules of nomenclature and valence that we have already considered, we can write the formulas of the three components of this reaction and can state the fact of reaction in the unbalanced equation

$$KClO_3 \longrightarrow O_2 + KCl$$

Here again the atoms on the two sides of the arrow do not balance. We must double the number of molecules of potassium chlorate in order to have an *even* number of oxygen atoms; and to accommodate this change we must then triple the number of oxygen molecules to account for the six oxygen atoms and must double the number of potassium chloride molecules so that the potassium and chlorine atoms balance. The result of these changes is the balanced equation

$$2KClO_3 \longrightarrow 3O_2 + 2KCl$$

As a final example we shall balance the equation for the reaction of oxygen with nitric oxide (NO) to produce nitrogen dioxide ($NO_2$). The unbalanced statement of the reaction is

$$O_2 + NO \longrightarrow NO_2$$

Of the two oxygen atoms in $NO_2$, one comes from the reactant NO and the other from the $O_2$. Since the oxygen atoms come *only* in pairs in molecular oxygen, the number of molecules of $NO_2$ must be doubled; this also requires the doubling of NO to supply the requisite number of nitrogen atoms. These changes give us the balanced equation

$$O_2 + 2NO \longrightarrow 2NO_2$$

To be a complete and adequate statement of a reaction, any equation must be balanced; the very term "equation," in fact, implies balance or equality between the two sides. An "unbalanced equation" is not an equation at all but is only a statement that the reaction does take place. A balanced equation conveys a good deal of extremely useful information. First, it states that the reaction takes place. Second, it conveys all the information implicit in the formulas of the various components of the reaction—the qualitative and quantitative composition and the molecular weights of the components. Finally, it states the *relative amounts* of the various substances involved in the reaction. It is important to realize that all of this information is conveyed on two different levels; on one level an equation can be considered as describing the reaction of the single particles (atoms or molecules); on the other level an equation states that a certain number of *moles* of reactants produce a certain number of moles of product(s). For example, the last equation considered tells us first that a single molecule of oxygen, made up of two atoms of oxygen, reacts with two molecules of nitric oxide (an atom of nitrogen plus an atom of oxygen) to produce two molecules of nitrogen dioxide. But the equation also states—and this information is of much greater practical usefulness in chemical calculations—that *one mole* of oxygen reacts with *two moles* of nitric oxide to produce *two moles* of nitrogen dioxide.

## 8-15. *Chemical Calculations*

Equations *always* state the amounts of reacting substances in *moles;* but it is a simple and direct mathematical operation to calculate the relative reacting quantities in grams (or any other unit of mass) by considering the molecular weight—the mass of one mole—and the number of moles. For example, in the reaction of oxygen with nitric oxide, one might wish to know how many grams of nitric oxide would react with 40 grams of oxygen. The equation states that 1 mole of oxygen and 2 moles of nitric oxide react. Since the molecular weight of oxygen ($O_2$) is 32, the 40 grams of oxygen represent $\dfrac{40 \text{ grams}}{32 \text{ grams/mole}} = 40/32$ moles $= 1.25$ moles of oxygen. Now, if 1 mole of oxygen reacts with 2 moles of NO, *any* number of moles of oxygen would react with twice that number of moles of NO. The 1.25 moles of oxygen would therefore react with $2 \times 1.25$ moles $= 2.50$ moles of NO. The molecular weight of NO is $14 + 16 = 30$; the mass of NO that reacts with this quantity of oxygen is therefore 2.50 moles $\times 30$ grams/mole $= 75$ grams. The mass of nitrogen dioxide, $NO_2$, produced from these quantities of $O_2$ and NO could also be calculated from the information given and the molecular weight of $NO_2$, which is $14 + 2 \times 16 = 46$. The equation tells us that the number of moles of $NO_2$ produced is the same as the number of moles of NO that react; that is, 2.50 moles are produced. The mass of $NO_2$ is therefore $2.50 \times 46 = 115$ grams. As a check on these calculations, this last quantity can be calculated by use of the law of conservation of mass: the mass of $NO_2$ produced must be equal to the sum of the reacting masses of $O_2$ and NO. The mass of $NO_2$ is equal to the sum of 40 grams $+$ 75 grams $= 115$ grams. All of this information is summarized thus:

| 2NO | + | $O_2$ | $\longrightarrow$ | 2NO$_2$ |
|---|---|---|---|---|
| 2 moles | | 1 mole | | 2 moles |
| 2.50 moles | | 1.25 moles | | 2.50 moles |
| 75 grams | | 40 grams | | 115 grams |

As a second example we shall calculate the mass of $KClO_3$ that will produce 8 grams of oxygen in the reaction depicted by the equation

$$2KClO_3 \longrightarrow 3O_2 + 2KCl$$

Again the equation states the relative number of *moles* of reactants. The mass of a mole of each

substance (the molecular weight) must be considered in calculations of reacting masses. The molecular weight of $O_2$ is 32; there is, then, $\frac{8}{32}$ or $\frac{1}{4}$ mole of $O_2$ produced in this reaction. The equation states that 2 moles of $KClO_3$ produce 3 moles of $O_2$; the ratio of moles of $KClO_3$ to moles of $O_2$ is, then, $\frac{2}{3}$. One mole of $O_2$ would be produced by $\frac{2}{3}$ mole of $KClO_3$, or *any number* of moles of $O_2$ would be produced by $\frac{2}{3}$ of that number of moles of $KClO_3$. In this example $\frac{1}{4}$ mole (8 grams) of $O_2$ would be produced by $\frac{2}{3} \times \frac{1}{4} = \frac{1}{6}$ mole of $KClO_3$. The molecular weight of $KClO_3$ is $39 + 35.5 + 3 \times 16 = 39 + 35.5 + 48 = 122.5$. One mole of $KClO_3$ has, then, a mass of 122.5 grams, and $\frac{1}{6}$ mole (needed to produce 8 grams of $O_2$) has a mass of $\frac{1}{6} \times 122.5 = 20.4$ grams.

One other type of calculation is now possible with the information contained in the valence table and the table of atomic weights: the calculation of percentage compositions of compounds from their formulas. We get the molecular weight of a compound by totaling the atomic weights of all the atoms composing it. The proportion of the whole (by mass) of each of the elements in the compound is indicated by the ratio of the atomic weight of the element (multiplied by any subscript) to the molecular weight of the compound. For example, the molecular weight of water, $H_2O$, is 18; a mole of water is therefore 18 grams. Of this 18 grams, 2 grams is hydrogen (atomic weight is 1, subscript is 2) and 16 grams is oxygen. The proportions of the two elements are, then, 2 parts in 18 for hydrogen and 16 parts in 18 for oxygen. The percentage composition is therefore $2/18 \times 100\% = 11.1\%$ hydrogen and $16/18 \times 100\% = 88.9\%$ oxygen.

As a second example, the percentage composition of sulfuric acid, $H_2SO_4$, is calculated as follows:

$$\text{Molecular weight: } \begin{aligned} H_2 &= 2 \times 1 = 2 \\ S & \phantom{= 2 \times 1} = 32 \\ O_4 &= 4 \times 16 = \underline{64} \\ & \phantom{= 4 \times 16 =} 98 \end{aligned}$$

Percentage of H $= 2/98 \times 100\% = 2.04\%$
Percentage of S $= 32/98 \times 100\% = 32.62\%$
Percentage of O $= 64/98 \times 100\% = 65.24\%$

Related conversely to this calculation is the

determination of the *empirical formula* from data on the composition of compounds. The empirical formula is the simplest possible formula—the one Dalton always assumed; the true formula is either the empirical formula or a multiple of it. The elemental composition of a compound states the fraction of the mass of the whole compound that is represented by each element. The composition may be expressed as percentage (parts per hundred parts) or by any other method of expressing compositions.

## EXAMPLE 1

The composition of calcium chloride is 36 percent calcium and 64 percent chlorine. The empirical formula of this compound could be calculated as follows:

The 36% Ca represents 36 parts per hundred; if we imagine a sample of the compound of 100 grams, this would contains 36 grams of Ca. The atomic weight of Ca is 40; this sample therefore contains $36/40 = 0.9$ mole of Ca. The atomic weight of chlorine is 35.5; the *same* sample (100 grams) would contain 64 grams of Cl, which is $64/35.5 = 1.8$ moles of Cl. The ratio of 0.9 to 1.8 is obviously 1/2; there are therefore just twice as many moles of Cl as of Ca in this sample of the compound and therefore just twice as many atoms of Cl as of Ca in the molecule. The empirical (simplest possible) formula is therefore $CaCl_2$, and the true formula must be this or some multiple such as $Ca_2Cl_4$ or $Ca_3Cl_6$.

The choice among multiples of the empirical formula requires some information about the molecular weight of the compound. There are several ways of determining this quantity experimentally. These methods will be taken up in later sections of this text.

## EXAMPLE 2

Calculate the formula of phosphoric acid from the composition: 3.06% H, 31.61% P, and 65.33% O.

| PARTS PER HUNDRED | ATOMIC WEIGHT | MOLES PER 100 GRAMS | LEAST COMMON MULTIPLE |
|---|---|---|---|
| H 3.06 | 1 | $3.06/1 = 3.06$ | $3.06/1.02 = 3$ |
| P 31.61 | 31 | $31.61/31 = 1.02$ | $1.02/1.02 = 1$ |
| O 65.33 | 16 | $65.33/16 = 4.08$ | $4.08/1.02 = 4$ |

The ratio of atoms of the three elements that make up phosphoric acid must, then, be 3 H to 1 P to 4 O, and the empirical formula must be $H_3PO_4$. Again, the true formula may be a multiple of this simplest possible formula.

## EXAMPLE 3

Calculate the empirical formula of the compound methane from the composition data expressed as 1 part hydrogen to 3 parts carbon.

With this composition a sample of 4 grams (or any other mass unit) would contain 1 gram (or the same mass unit) of hydrogen and 3 grams of carbon. The atomic weights (from the table) are $H = 1$ and $C = 12$. We calculate the ratio of the numbers of atoms of the two elements in the compound by dividing the grams of each element in the sample by the atomic weight of that element: $H = 1/1 = 1$; $C = 3/12 = 1/4$. The ratio of atoms of H to atoms of C is, then, $1/\frac{1}{4} = 4/1$. There must be four times as many H atoms as C atoms in methane, and its empirical formula must be $CH_4$. Its true formula must be this or some multiple such as $C_2H_8$ or $C_3H_{12}$.

# 8-16. *Significance of the Periodic Classification*

Much of this chapter has been concerned with the practical usefulness of the periodic table in summarizing and succinctly presenting a very large amount of chemical information. Its usefulness as a source of information for several types of chemical calculations has also been demonstrated. But two points of caution should be raised.

First, this table does not contain *all* the information of the science of chemistry; it serves mainly to present generalizations. The complete realization and appreciation of the periodic table as a source of information can come only after considerable practice and experience, and much of the experience must be with specific information rather than with the large generalizations contained in the table. The learning of the periodic table does not end the useful study of chemistry.

The second point of caution is that, though the usefulness of the periodic table is very great indeed, the extreme importance of its conceptual scheme lies in the theoretical implications of the remarkable periodicity of elemental properties. Little has been said in this chapter about this theoretical significance, for we have not yet laid the informational and conceptual background for it. In Parts Two and Three, returning to this scheme of classification, we shall examine closely some of its subtleties and even some of its anomalies, and from this study will come new extensions of our understanding of the structure of matter.

## Concepts and Terms

Periodic Classification
Periodic Law
Early Attempts at Classification
Mendeleev's Table
Modern Periodic Table
    anomalies
Displacement of Old Theories by New Ones
Atomic Number
Chemical Equations
Chemical Calculations
Triad
Group
Period

Metal
Non-metal
Metalloid
Halogen
Alkali Metal
Alkaline-earth Metal
Rare-earth Metal
Inert Gas
Periodicity
Transition Element
Lanthanide
Actinide

## Problems

**8-1.** Discuss the reasons why the periodic classification of the elements could not have been accomplished in 1810 but was accomplished in 1870.

**8-2.** Define the following terms with respect to the periodic classification of the elements: (A) period, (B) group, (C) atomic weight, (D) symbol, (E) atomic number, (F) halogen, (G) transition element, (H) alkali metal, (I) periodicity of properties.

**8-3.** Describe several of the striking successes of the periodic table that convinced Mendeleev's contemporaries of the usefulness of this classification.

**8-4.** Describe in your own words the reasoning that establishes the atomic weight of magnesium (or any other non-volatile element) with certainty.

**8-5.** Describe the differences between metals and non-metals, and state the areas of the periodic table in which each type of element is found.

**8-6.** Describe in your own words the general way in which properties of elements vary as you go through the periodic table (A) vertically downward, (B) horizontally across from left to right.

**8-7.** Describe in a general way the properties of each group of the periodic table.

**8-8.** Each of the following is a statement of all the reactants and products of a chemical reaction. Express these as balanced chemical equations without changing any formulas or supplying any other reactants or products.

(A) $Zn + HCl \longrightarrow ZnCl_2 + H_2$
(B) $O_2 \longrightarrow O_3$
(C) $NH_4NO_2 \longrightarrow N_2 + H_2O$
(D) $CO_2 + NaOH \longrightarrow NaHCO_3$
(E) $MnO_2 + HCl \longrightarrow MnCl_2 + Cl_2 + H_2O$
(F) $Na + H_2O \longrightarrow NaOH + H_2$
(G) $KNO_3 \longrightarrow KNO_2 + O_2$
(H) $ZnS + O_2 \longrightarrow ZnO + SO_2$
(I) $NaOH + CO_2 \longrightarrow Na_2CO_3 + H_2O$
(J) $PCl_5 + H_2O \longrightarrow H_3PO_4 + HCl$

**8-9.** Calculate the percentage composition of each of the following compounds.

(A) $H_2O$           (F) $MnO_2$
(B) $KCl$            (G) $K_2Cr_2O_7$
(C) $H_2C_2O_4$      (H) $C_6H_6$
(D) $Na_2S_2O_3$     (I) $N_2O$
(E) $Al_2S_3$        (J) $CaHPO_4$

*Ans.* (A) 11.1% H, 88.9% O
        (D) 29.1% Na, 40.5% S, 30.4% O

**8-10.** From the following percentage compositions calculate the empirical (simplest possible) formulas for the compounds.

(A) 21.8% Mg
27.9% P
50.3% O
(B) 75% C
25% H
(C) 70.0% Fe
30.0% O
(D) 77.7% Fe
22.3% O

(E) 36.0% Ca
64.0% Cl
(F) 91.2% P
8.8% H
(G) 43.4% Na
11.3% C
45.3% O
(H) 2 parts Cu
1 part S
2 parts O

*Ans.* (A) $Mg_2P_2O_7$
(G) $Na_2CO_3$

**8-11.** Calculate the mass of metal that can be obtained from 100 grams of each of the following compounds.

(A) Fe from FeO
(B) Fe from $Fe_2O_3$
(C) Li from LiH
(D) Na from $Na_2CO_3$
(E) Ra from $RaSO_4$

(F) Mg from $MgCl_2$
(G) Cu from $Cu(NO_3)_2$
(H) $H_2$ from $H_2O$
(I) Cr from $K_2CrO_4$
(J) Zn from ZnS

*Ans.* (A) 77.75 grams
(E) 70.18 grams

**8-12.** Calculate the mass of each compound that could be made from 50 grams of the metal.

(A) $K_2O$ from K
(B) CuO from Cu
(C) MgO from Mg
(D) $Hg(NO_3)_2$ from Hg

(E) ZnO from Zn
(F) $MnCl_2$ from Mn
(G) $Cr_2O_3$ from Cr
(H) $BaSO_4$ from Ba
(I) $CaF_2$ from Ca

(J) $AlPO_4$ from Al
(K) AgCl from Ag
(L) $BeCO_3$ from Be

*Ans.* (A) 60.2 grams
(E) 62.2 grams

**8-13.** Water is electrolytically decomposed into its elements according to the equation

$$2H_2O \longrightarrow 2H_2 + O_2$$

(A) What mass of water must be decomposed to produce 27.3 grams of hydrogen?
(B) What mass of oxygen would be produced as a by-product?

*Ans.* (B) 218 grams

**8-14.** In the industrial production of steel, the iron oxide $Fe_2O_3$ is decomposed to elemental iron, Fe.

(A) How many grams of $Fe_2O_3$ is needed to produce 111.7 grams of Fe?
(B) How many kilograms of the iron oxide is needed to produce 1.117 kilograms of iron?
(C) How many tons of iron oxide would be needed to produce 1,117 tons of steel (assume that steel is pure Fe)?

*Ans.* (C) 1,597 tons

**8-15.** Ammonia is synthesized from its elements according to the reaction

$$3H_2 + N_2 \longrightarrow 2NH_3$$

(A) How many grams of hydrogen is needed to make 500 grams of ammonia?
(B) What mass of nitrogen would be consumed?
(C) If air is 80% $N_2$, what mass of air would be needed to furnish the nitrogen of this reaction?

*Ans.* (B) 412 grams

# Suggested Readings

1. M. E. Weeks, *The Discovery of the Elements,* 5th edition (Journal of Chemical Education, 1945). An extensive historical background—the men and discoveries that led to the periodic classification of the elements. Many articles about the periodic classification can be found in the *Journal of Chemical Education.*

2. H. M. Leicester and H. S. Klickstein, *A Source Book in Chemistry* (McGraw-Hill, 1952). Biographical sketches and brief histories of the contributions of Döbereiner (pp. 268–272), Prout (pp. 275–279), Lothar Meyer (pp. 434–438), and Mendeleev (pp. 438–444).

3. F. T. Bonner and Melba Phillips, *Principles of Physical Science* (Addison-Wesley, 1957). Chap. 7 is an elementary historical and conceptual treatment of the periodic law.

4. G. Gamow, *Matter, Earth and Sky* (Prentice-Hall, 1958). Chaps. 9 and 10 are a brief, elementary treatment of the periodic law and related ideas, written in a rather light vein.

5. W. F. Ehret, *Smith's Introductory College Chemistry* (Appleton-Century-Crofts, 1950). Chap. 17 is an elementary but complete discussion of the periodic classification.

6. D. C. Gregg, *Principles of Chemistry* (Allyn and Bacon, 1958). Chap. 4 is a discussion of chemical equations and problems based on equations.

# CHAPTER

# 9

# Gases (I):
# Two Measurable
# Properties

THE GASEOUS state was defined in Chapter 1 as the condition in which matter assumes the shape and volume of its container; that is, any particular sample of gaseous matter, large or small in mass, occupies entirely any vessel that encloses it. This is one way of stating the most obvious property of gases—their compressibility.

## 9-1. Analogy of a Confined Gas and a Spring

If a large mass of gas occupies a small volume, the gas is said to be highly compressed; if we increase the volume occupied by the gas—for example, by raising a piston in a cylinder (Fig. 9-1b→c)—the gas expands to occupy entirely the new space within the container. Also, if force is applied to the piston (Fig. 9-1b→a), the gas becomes further compressed and still just occupies the total enclosed space. Force must be exerted on the piston to make the gas go from volume $V_2$ to $V_1$; that is, work must be done to compress the gas. Similarly, work (force acting through a displacement) is done *by* the gas in expanding from volume $V_2$ to $V_3$. The enclosed gas behaves, then, in a manner very similar to that of a simple spring (Fig. 9-2), which is compressed when force is applied (work done *on* the spring) and expands and *does* work when released.

## 9-2. Definition of Pressure

In this situation—the compression and expansion of gases—we are dealing with a force

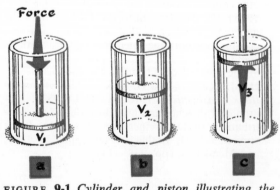

FIGURE **9-1** *Cylinder and piston illustrating the compressibility of a confined gas.*

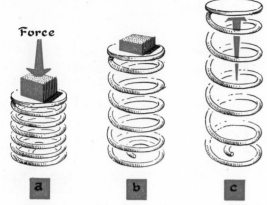

FIGURE **9-2** *Analogy of a spring and a confined gas.*

acting over an area. In the examples of Fig. 9-1 the force is the resistance of the gas to compression (or the tendency to expand), and the area over which the force acts is the area of the piston. We could continue to discuss the behavior of gases in terms of these two quantities, force and area. It is much more convenient, however, both in discussion and, as we shall see below, in experimental measurement, to use a new derived quantity called **pressure.** Pressure is defined as a force that acts divided by the area over which it acts:

$$P = \frac{F}{A} \qquad (9\text{-}1)$$

The units of pressure would, of course, be the units of force, newtons, divided by the units of area, square meters. The great convenience and usefulness of this derived quantity for describing the behavior of gases will become apparent in the following discussion and particularly in experimental work with gases.

From equation 9-1 it is clear that we could measure a pressure by observing a force and an area. A much more convenient and direct method will become obvious after some mathematical manipulation of that equation. Furthermore, the description of this method will aid materially in the understanding of pressure. Consider a column of any fluid (Fig. 9-3) having cross-sectional area $A$ and height $h$. (Note that the size and shape of the cross-sectional area do not enter the following discussion.) This column of fluid is a sample of matter that has mass, and

in a gravitational field it will exert a force downward—its weight. The magnitude of the weight is determined by the mass of the sample of matter and the gravitational acceleration, this force being the product of the two,

$$w = mg$$

in which $g$ is the acceleration due to gravity. Our equation for pressure becomes, by substitution of this value for $F$,

$$P = \frac{mg}{A} \qquad (9\text{-}2)$$

We can further manipulate this equation by substituting a value for the mass of the column of fluid in terms of the dimensions of the column and the density of the fluid. Density was defined in Chapter 1 as the ratio of the mass to the volume:

$$d = \frac{m}{V}$$

But we can express the volume, $V$, of the column of fluid as the product of the cross-sectional area, $A$, and the height, $h$: $V = hA$; and this value for $V$ can then be substituted in the equation above: $d = m/hA$. This equation is solved for the mass of the column of fluid: $m = dhA$; and this value for $m$ is then substituted in equation 9-2:

$$P = \frac{dhAg}{A} = dhg \qquad (9\text{-}3)$$

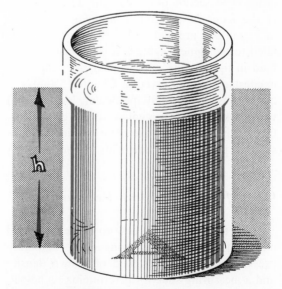

FIGURE **9-3** *Column of fluid.*

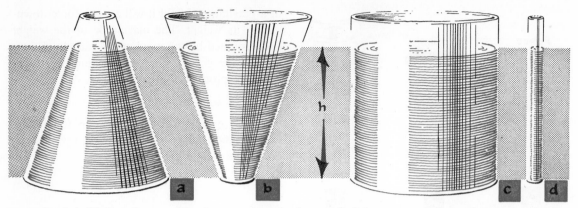

FIGURE **9-4** *Fluid columns with the same height but with different cross-sectional areas.*

Equation 9-3 relates pressure to three easily determined quantities, the density of the fluid, the height of the column, and the acceleration of gravity. This equation is derived by simple mathematical operations from our definitions of pressure, volume (in linear dimensions), and weight. It has just the same validity as equation 9-1, our original definition of pressure, and further has the great advantage of providing an easy, direct measurement of pressures.

The first characteristic of equation 9-3 to be noted is that the cross-sectional area, $A$, of our hypothetical column of fluid of Figure 9-3 has disappeared (been canceled) from the equation. The pressure at the base of such a column is, then, entirely independent of the size or shape of the cross section of the column. The pressures at the bases of the four containers diagrammed in Figure 9-4 are identical if the containers are filled to the same height, $h$, if the density of the fluid in them is the same, and if the value of $g$ is constant. We observed in Chapter 5 that $g$ is quite constant for any particular locality and varies less than 1 percent over the entire surface of the earth; it is therefore considered constant in pressure measurements in any locality.

## 9-3. Measurement of Pressure

Here, then, we have a very convenient method and apparatus for measuring and comparing pressures—a column of fluid of known density and a measuring stick for determining its height. If we wished to measure low pressures, we should, of course, use a short tube of a fluid of small density, such as water (density = 1.00 gram/cm³); if we were dealing with high pressures, we should use a long tube of a fluid of high density, such as mercury (density = 13.6 grams/cm³). Consideration of equation 9-3 shows that we should need a column of water 13.6 times as long as a column of mercury to measure the same pressure. Obviously, for reasons of economy as well as portability, a column having the shape of Figure 9-4d would be used as the pressure-measuring device.

So far in our discussion of the pressures due to the weight of fluids we have considered only the force downward. The existence of this force is one of our most casual everyday observations. But it is also part of our experience that pressures exerted by confined fluids operate in *all* directions. If, for example, the vessel of Figure 9-4c were punctured on the side near the bottom, fluid would run out with considerable speed in a *horizontal* direction. The speed of this horizontal movement of the fluid is, of course, an indication of a *force* acting horizontally against the area of the side of the container. A quantitative treatment would show that the magnitude of the pressure is the same in *all* directions, including vertically *upward,* at any point within the fluid. We shall see in a subsequent chapter that this characteristic of fluids—their transmission of forces in all directions—is a manifestation of their microscopic structure; for the time being it is only necessary to call attention to the characteristic.

It is this omnidirectional quality of the pressure of confined fluids that allows a tube of a fluid of known density to be used as a pressure-measuring instrument. Each of the arrangements diagramed in Figure 9-5, for example, could be attached at point $x$ to any vessel (the direction of attachment is immaterial) to measure the pressure inside the vessel. Variations of each of these are, in fact, used in laboratory work with gases.

## 9-4. Historical Background

Let us return now to the compressibility of gases, with which this chapter began. The two descriptions of this general property of gases—the tendency to occupy entirely all space and the analogy in behavior to a spring—gave rise to two very famous phrases that were once offered as explanations of the behavior of gases. This property of gases was known to the ancients and was first described by Aristotle as a law of nature: "Nature abhors a vacuum." This Aristotelian concept was the only basis for an understanding of the behavior of gases until the great scientific revolution of the seventeenth century. In 1660 Robert Boyle, one of the important participants in this revolution, used the phrase "the spring of the air" in describing this property of gases. Boyle's idea, with important modifications and extensions, is the basis for the modern view of this phenomenon.

This scientific revolution of the seventeenth century, which was mentioned in Chapter 4, included as one facet the development of what was called the science of "pneumatics." The development of this new subscience took place extremely suddenly (in the fifteen years from about 1645 to about 1660) but had far-reaching consequences in the further development of physics and chemistry.

The problem (and its solution) began, like many grand problems of science, as an extremely simple, almost trivial problem. Galileo, who precipitated the development of pneumatics as well as most of the other branches of the scientific revolution, considered a water pump that was perfectly sound mechanically but failed to operate as its owner expected it to: it would not raise water more than thirty-four feet. This failure was at first thought to be peculiar to this one pump although it was well known to artisans that *all* water suction pumps had this failing. For centuries engineers had removed water from deep mines by placing separate pumps at vertical intervals of thirty feet or less and pumping the water in stages. It was this *general* characteristic of water pumps and the current explanation, based on the Aristotelian concept, that concerned Galileo.

The mechanical operation of a water pump is described by the diagrams of Figure 9-6, the four stages being continually repeated by the

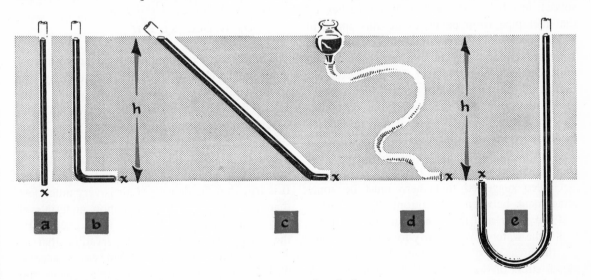

FIGURE **9-5** *Columns of mercury as pressure-measuring devices.*

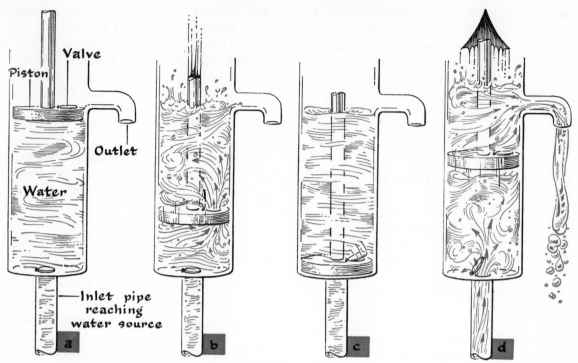

FIGURE **9-6** *Operation of a water suction pump.*

raising and lowering of the piston in the cylinder. The Aristotelian explanation of the working of this device was that the valve closes after the downward stroke of the piston (c) and the water cannot pass the piston downward as the piston is raised (c→d and d→a). Therefore, to prevent the incipient formation of a vacuum (empty space) just below the piston, water rushes up the inlet pipe from below to fill this space in accordance with the natural abhorrence (and therefore impossibility of existence) of a vacuum. Galileo recognized that this is no explanation at all, only the replacement of one mystery by another. He also recognized the particular flaw in this explanation when it was applied to the limit of lift of water pumps: why should a vacuum be abhorred up to thirty-four feet but be tolerated beyond this distance?

Galileo suggested that there must be some attachment between the bottom of the piston and the water and that the failure of the pump to lift the water beyond thirty-four feet was simply the breaking of the column of water by tensional stress of the weight of the "hanging" column. He reasoned by analogy from the breaking of a long hanging wire when the weight of the wire becomes too great to be supported by the wire. This explanation happened to be wrong. It was one mistake of science that was very quickly corrected.

## 9-5. Torricelli's Postulate of a Sea of Air

The correct explanation was advanced almost immediately (but after Galileo's death) by two young students of Galileo. These young men, Evangelista Torricelli and Vincenzo Viviani (the observation is primarily associated with Torricelli), started from an experimental fact established by Galileo. This fact, apparently totally unrelated to pumping water, is that air has mass. It is true that the density of air is very much less than the density of most common materials of our environment and that the force exerted by the air (its weight) is so all-pervading that its detection and isolation are not easily accomplished. But Galileo did accomplish them and demonstrate a measurable mass for air. Torri-

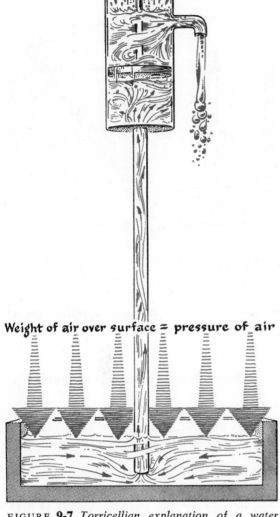

Weight of air over surface = pressure of air

FIGURE **9-7** *Torricellian explanation of a water suction pump.*

the air that *forces* the water up the pipe into the cylinder of a water pump.

The Torricellian explanation of the operation (and of the limit of lift) of a water suction pump is indicated in Figure 9-7. The weight of air exerts a force on the entire surface of the lower water level. In the absence of the piston this same pressure would be exerted down through the cylinder and the inlet pipe, and there would therefore be no tendency for the water to rise in the pipe. But with the rigid, tightly fitting piston in place over a column of water in the pipe and cylinder, there is no pressure of air downward on the column of water. As the piston is raised, the pressure of the air on the lower level of the water is transmitted up the pipe and drives the water up to the cylinder of the pump. The failure of the pump to lift water more than thirty-four feet indicates that the pressure of a column of water of that height is just equal to the pressure of the atmospheric air on the surface of the water.

## 9-6. *Confirming Experiments*

Having made this postulate of "a sea of air" that has weight and exerts a pressure on all surfaces, Torricelli set out to test his hypothesis. He reasoned that a column of fluid of very high density, such as mercury, would be supported by the air pressure to a correspondingly shorter height. The density of mercury is 13.6 times as great as that of water. Consideration of equation 9-3 shows us that, if $P$ and $g$ are constant, $d$ and $h$ must vary inversely. One would expect, then, if Torricelli's explanation is correct, that the pressure of the air that supports a column of water 34 feet high would support a column of mercury with a height of $34/13.6$ feet = 2.5 feet. Torricelli then did the experiment diagramed in Figure 9-8. A long glass tube (about 1 meter long) is sealed at one end and then filled completely with mercury. The tube is inverted (without spilling any mercury) into a large open dish of mercury so that the open end is under the surface of the mercury in the dish. The mercury in the tube immediately falls to a level just 2.5 feet (in metric units of length, 76.0 cm)

celli postulated that we are living at the bottom of "a sea of air." He then reasoned that this air has mass and exerts the force of its weight on the surface of all objects, just as pressures are exerted at the bottom of the columns of fluid diagramed and discussed in § 9-2.† Finally, he suggested that it is the weight (or pressure) of

---

† The derivation in § 9-2 of the pressure at the bottom of a column of fluid clearly applies to the pressure at the bottom of Torricelli's "sea of air." The term *fluid* includes both liquids and gases, and, although the fluid of Fig. 9-3 is implicitly a liquid, the derivation is quite rigorously applicable to a column of gas.

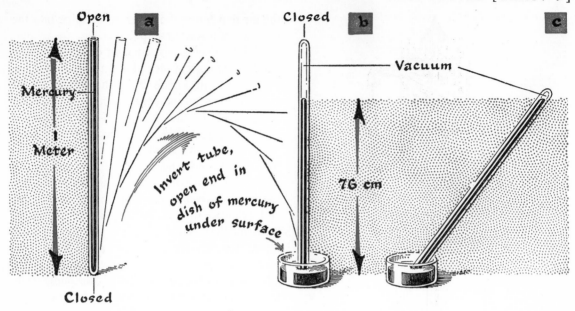

FIGURE **9-8** *Torricelli's experiment; the barometer; Torricellian vacuum.*

above the surface of mercury in the dish. It makes no difference how long the tube is (provided it is greater than 76 cm), nor does it matter if the tube is tilted; the vertical height of the column of mercury that is supported is always the same under the same conditions of *P* and *g*.

The results of this experiment are entirely consistent with Torricelli's hypothesis and therefore offer considerable confirmatory evidence to support it. Since his time vast numbers of experiments have invariably supported the theory, which is therefore now accepted as fact. One of the first and most important of these confirmatory experiments was conceived by Blaise Pascal, a young French mathematician and philosopher. He reasoned that, if Torricelli's concept of "a sea of air" is correct, then, if the depth (or height) of that sea of air is less, the pressure should be less, and therefore the height of the column of mercury in Torricelli's barometer (Fig. 9-8b) should be less. He therefore had such a barometer carried up a mountain and the height of the column of mercury read at various levels. As he had predicted, the height of the column fell steadily as the altitude increased.† This observation was accepted by the scientists of the time as very powerful confirmation of the notion that the weight of the air

around us exerts a ubiquitous pressure on all objects at the surface of the earth.

## 9-7. Barometers and Manometers

Torricelli's experiment, diagramed in Figure 9-8, was of great importance in establishing the idea of air pressure—and even in placing the theory of water pumps on a rational basis. But of even greater importance were two other aspects of this experiment. The first has already been referred to. The apparatus of Figure 9-8b is called a **barometer** and is extremely useful for measuring the pressure of the atmosphere. Modern barometers are identical in principle and differ only slightly in detail from this device. By this experiment, then, Torricelli invented a method and apparatus for the measurement of atmospheric pressure. *Pressure is usually expressed in terms of the height of the column of mercury that is supported by the pressure,* and

---

† On p. 39 we observed that the acceleration of gravity, *g*, varies with altitude. This effect is of the order of only 0.1 percent, but the change in pressure due to decreasing height of the sea of air above the surface of the mercury in the dish of the barometer is *of the order of 10* percent for a change of a few thousand feet in altitude.

the *units* are **centimeters of mercury (cm Hg).** This is, however, an artificial unit; pressure is a force per area, and the true units of pressure are newtons per square meter. This fact must always be kept in mind in any dimensional analysis even though the ease and convenience and universality of the above method of pressure measurement have established cm Hg as the usual way of expressing pressures. An atmospheric pressure of 76 cm Hg is the mean pressure at sea level and has been defined as the standard of pressure. Thereby another unit of pressure has been introduced, one used particularly in describing high pressures. This unit is the **atmosphere** of pressure and is defined as equal to 76 cm Hg pressure. Ten atmospheres would be 760 cm Hg, and 1/2 atmosphere 38 cm Hg.

A slight mechanical variation of the same basic pressure-measuring device is called a **manometer.** In this instrument a column (usually a U tube for mechanical convenience) of mercury is connected to the enclosed space whose pressure is to be determined. Manometers are generally used to measure pressure differences. Two kinds of manometer are indicated in the diagrams of Fig. 9-9. Diagram "a" shows a manometer in which one end is open to the atmosphere and the other end is connected to the closed container. In this case $h$ indicates the *difference* in pressure between the inside of the container and the atmosphere. Diagram "b" shows a manometer in which one end is closed, the space above the mercury in this column being a Torricellian vacuum and having a pressure of zero. In this case $h$ indicates the total pressure inside the enclosed space (difference from zero pressure).

## 9-8. *Torricellian Vacuum*

The other aspect of Torricelli's experiment had far-reaching effects on all three facets of science—experimental developments, theoretical developments, and philosophy. This is the question of the space above the mercury in the tube of Figure 9-8b. The question occurs immediately: "What is in this space?" The Torricellian theory says that *nothing* is in this space, that

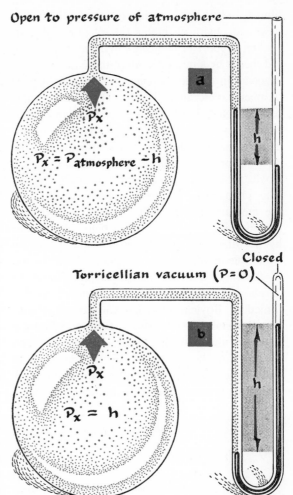

FIGURE **9-9** *Manometers:* (a) *with open arm;* (b) *with closed arm.*

here has been created the Aristotelian impossibility, **a vacuum.** The classical philosophers abhorred this idea and waged a vigorous battle against it. For them this was a time of crisis; the experiments and concepts of the "new science" were striking powerful blows from many directions and in rapid sequence at the concepts of traditional philosophy. These concepts had been working adequately for a long time as bases for understanding the world, and traditions are never given up easily. A few unpleasantly inexplicable facts or a new and unsupported theory is never sufficient reason for abandoning a well-established concept that has had a career of usefulness. It takes a powerful, concerted assault, combining a solid basis of experimental evidence, a new and obviously better theory, and the outspoken support of dedicated men, to displace an old theory by a new one. All of these factors were involved in the development of the new science of pneumatics, and all played prominent interrelated roles. Even the polemics of the traditionalists served as a powerful stimulus to new experimentation. The last-ditch effort to save the Aristotelian exclusion of the vacuum moved Boyle, for example, to do some new experiments. The philosopher Thomas Hobbes argued that the mercury in Torricelli's barometer was supported, not by the air pressure below, but rather by a "funiculus," a sort of invisible thread by which the mercury hung suspended from the top of the tube; and he and Boyle engaged in an acrimonious dispute over the existence of this funiculus. Boyle's approach was to argue with experimental facts; he successfully scotched the notion of the funiculus by his experiments, and in doing so he accomplished the much more valuable result of determining the relation between the pressure and the volume of a confined gas—a relation that is stated in Boyle's law.

## 9-9. Air Pumps

The experimental development of the new science of pneumatics was strongly influenced, as we have pointed out already, by Torricelli's first experimental production of a vacuum, by the intriguing theory he advanced, and by the philosophic controversy that raged around the theory. But it was also powerfully influenced by a much more prosaic, practical development that occurred about the same time. This was the considerable technical improvement of water suction pumps and finally their use as air pumps. The beginning of this development is attributed to a young German civil administrator, Otto von Guericke, whose interest in water pumps arose from his efforts to provide German cities with water supplies as aids in resisting sieges during the Thirty Years' War. Guericke was mayor of Magdeburg when he used his rudimentary air pump to evacuate a pair of hemispheres (which could then not be pulled apart by eight horses),

thereby adding further evidence for Torricelli's theory of air pressure.

Pascal also was doing some experimental work with air pumps at about the same time as Guericke, but it was Boyle that made Guericke's pump a useful tool. He improved the mechanical design of the pump and incorporated into the mechanism a large glass vessel into which objects and apparatus could be put for observation of their behavior in a vacuum. The importance of this new experimental tool in the development of the science of gases cannot be overemphasized. The availability of the adequate experimental technique, in this case as in most sudden, radical developments in science, was at least as great a factor as the theoretical and philosophic aspects.

To conclude this short history of the developments in one minor branch of the great seventeenth-century scientific revolution, we return to Boyle's explanation of his experimental observations. He summarized them by stating, "There is a spring or elastical power in the air we live in." This is simply a qualitative way of stating his experimental results. He then went on to offer two very tentative proposals for a more fundamental explanation of this fact. He was extremely careful, however, to point out that these were pure speculation and should be considered only as such. His experiments could not help in a choice between them, nor were they exclusive of other, unrelated possibilities. At this stage of development in this branch of science, furthermore, it was neither necessary nor helpful to choose a more fundamental explanation. "This notion may perhaps be somewhat further explained by conceiving the air near the earth to be such a heap of little bodies, lying one upon another, as may be resembled to a fleece of wool." His other suggestion was that we might suppose, ". . . with that most ingenious gentleman, Monsieur Des Cartes, that the air is nothing but a congeries or heap of small and (for the most part) of flexible particles; . . . and by the restless agitation of that celestial matter, wherein those particles swim, are so whirled round, that each corpuscle endeavours to beat off all others from coming within the little sphere requisite to its motion about its own center.

. . . But I am not willing to declare peremptorily for either of them against the other. . . . I shall decline meddling with a subject, which is more hard to be explicated than necessary to be so by him, whose business it is not to assign the adequate cause of the spring of the air, but only to manifest that the air hath a spring and to relate some of its effects." †

As we shall see in a subsequent chapter, Descartes' hypothesis (it is really so tenuous as hardly to deserve being called a hypothesis) was much closer to modern notions than Boyle's analogy to small springs. The important point of this quotation is the remarkable restraint shown by Boyle in resisting the impulse to speculate too far beyond his experimental data.

## 9-10. Temperature

The concept of temperature is one of the most difficult notions to transform from the common-sense, casually observed, intuitive level to the precisely defined, theoretically integrated state that is necessary for scientific usefulness. We all have an intuitive idea of "hot" and "cold" and of the use of the term "temperature" as a measure of these relative qualities. We can sense temperature physiologically; under ordinary circumstances we can correctly sense differences in temperature and can even make an approximate quantitative estimate of such differences. But we all know that our physiologic sense of temperature can give very erratic information. The same room would feel hot to a person who had just entered it from a cold room but cool to a person who had just entered it from a hot room. Any rational study of temperature must obviously be placed on a more consistent and reliable basis of measurement than this.

When we say that one object is hot and another cold, we are saying that heat will pass from the hot object to the cold object if they are in contact. To say that the temperature of one object is higher than that of another object conveys the same information. The notion of temperature, in this empirical sense, has meaning

† Robert Boyle, *Collected Works* (London, 1772), Vol. 1, Experiment I (pp. 100–101).

*only* as a comparison: a single temperature value has meaning only when compared with another temperature value. Experimentally, we can measure, and are interested in, temperature *differences* only. All this implies that we can set a value or a number on this quantity temperature —that "temperature" is indeed a *quantity*. An empirical definition of temperature difference would be a measure of the tendency for heat to flow from the higher to the lower temperature (from the hotter to the colder object). But, as we shall see later, the unit of heat has been defined in terms of temperature (and other quantities). This, of course, offers an opportunity for circular definitions, in which heat is defined in terms of temperature and temperature in terms of heat, neither being established. Temperature is a characteristically experimental or empirical quantity. We observe experimentally that various properties of substances change in a way that parallels this tendency to give up heat. Scales of temperature have been defined, therefore, in terms of these properties of substances (measuring devices) that change with changing temperature. There are many such **thermometric properties,** the most familiar being the length of liquid in a slender glass tube called a **thermometer.**

## 9-11. Thermometers; Standards of Temperature

Most substances expand (increase in volume) when they are heated. Volume is therefore a thermometric property. For use as a temperature-measuring instrument, the expansion of the object should be easily measurable and capable of magnification. These requirements explain the characteristic construction of the usual thermometer—a relatively large bulb of liquid connected to a tube of very fine bore. Slight expansion of the liquid causes a large change in the *length* of the liquid in the fine tube. The liquids used most commonly in thermometers are mercury and alcohol colored with a bit of dye.

Two standard units of temperature measurement have been arbitrarily defined and are in common use. The Fahrenheit degree was defined

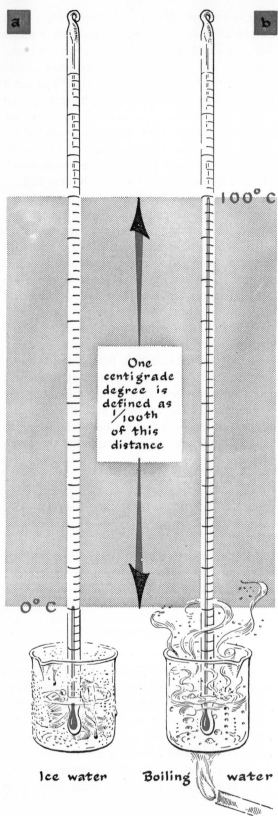

as 1/100 of the difference in temperature between the lowest temperature obtainable by mixing ice, salt, and water (defined as 0°F) and body temperature (100°F).† The Fahrenheit scale is used only for non-scientific work in English-speaking countries. All scientific work and common usage in other countries are based on the **centigrade scale of temperature.** The standard reference temperatures for this scale are the freezing point of water and the boiling point of water, both at a pressure of 1 atmosphere (76.0 cm Hg). Figure 9-10 diagrams the definition of the centigrade temperature scale.

The bulb of an uncalibrated thermometer is placed first in a mixture of ice and water, which has a constant temperature defined as the zero of centigrade temperature. The position of the mercury thread in the long thin tube is marked as 0°. The bulb is then placed in boiling water that is in contact with steam (held at 76 cm Hg pressure) and the position of the mercury thread marked again. This temperature is defined as 100°C. The distance between the two marks is then divided into a hundred equal divisions, each of which is then one degree centigrade (1°C).

Many other thermometric properties have been used experimentally as temperature-measuring devices, and there are many systems of constant temperature by which they can be calibrated. But in all cases the principle is the same: a property that changes with temperature is measured first at one fixed and known temperature and then at another, and the *difference* between the two measurements is related to the difference between the two temperatures. The thermometer in use then compares the measured temperature with one of the standards.

Gases follow the generalization stated above: they increase in volume as the temperature rises.

---

† As everyone knows, body temperature, taken by mouth in the afternoon, is usually about 98.6° on the Fahrenheit scale. Body temperature is a rather unreliable standard, and it can be presumed that G. D. Fahrenheit was feverish the day he established his temperature scale. Modern thermometers are calibrated against very precise standards, just as length-measuring devices are calibrated against the international meter as a universally accepted precise standard.

---

FIGURE **9-10** *Centigrade temperature scale; calibration of a thermometer.*

An enclosed sample of gas could be used as a thermometer; the first thermometers, in fact, were made in this way. But from the previous section it is apparent that a gas thermometer would have to be kept at constant pressure in order that volume changes should represent temperature changes rather than changes in pressure. The first systematic investigation of the relation between the volume of a confined gas and its temperature was carried out in the early nineteenth century by J. A. C. Charles and Gay-Lussac. The statement of the empirical relation between these two variables is called Charles' law.

## Concepts and Terms

Pressure
History of Pneumatics
"Sea of Air"
Barometers
Manometers
Torricellian Vacuum

Impact of Experiments on Philosophy
Temperature
   physiological sense
   thermometric properties
   standards of temperature
   temperature scales

## Problems

**9-1.** Derive the equation for the pressure at the bottom of a column of fluid.

**9-2.** What is the common unit of pressure in scientific work? Why is this unit used? How is this unit related to the fundamental units of measurement, kilogram, meter, and second?

**9-3.** Express a pressure of 2.3 atmospheres in (A) cm Hg and (B) newtons per m². 
*Ans.* (B) $2.38 \times 10^5$ newtons/m²

**9-4.** The common unit of pressure in industrial work is pounds per square inch. Show that one atmosphere of pressure is about 15 pounds per square inch. See Prob. 4-8 for the definition of the pound of force, and use the conversion 2.54 cm = 1 inch.

**9-5.** In Fig. 9-9, if $h$ is 23.6 cm Hg in each of the two diagrams and atmospheric pressure is 74.9 cm Hg, calculate the pressure, $P_x$, in each of the two vessels.

**9-6.** Calculate the pressure in cm Hg and newtons per m² at a depth of 20 meters below the surface of the ocean. Assume that the atmospheric pressure at the surface is 76 cm Hg and that the density of sea water is 1.1 grams/cm³.

**9-7.** Define *thermometric property*. List several such properties.

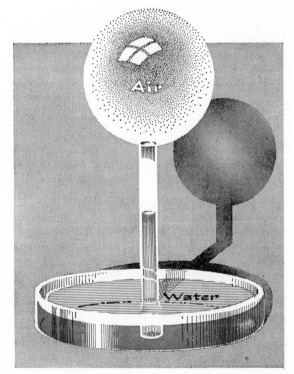

FIGURE **P9-8**

**9-8.** The first useful thermometer was developed by Galileo. The device consisted of a glass bulb filled with air and sealed to a glass tube containing some water and communicating with an open dish of water. As the temperature of the air in the bulb rises, water is forced out of the tube; as the temperature falls, water is drawn up into the tube.

(A) What thermometric property, of what material, is used in this device?

(B) There is obviously one major source of error in this device. Discuss this error. How might the design be changed to avoid the error? Consider the isolation of the system from environmental influences that can affect the experiment.

## Suggested Readings

1. W. F. Magie, *A Source Book in Physics* (Mc-Graw-Hill, 1935). Pages 69–92 contain biographical sketches and brief histories of the contributions to pneumatics of Galileo, Torricelli, Pascal, Guericke, Boyle, and Mariotte; pages 131–133 describe Fahrenheit's invention of the mercury thermometer and his statement of the temperature scale.

2. J. B. Conant, *Robert Boyle's Experiments in Pneumatics* (Harvard University Press, 1950), No. 1 of the Harvard Case Histories in Experimental Science. A critical historical discussion of Boyle's experiments and contributions to the understanding of gaseous behavior.

3. J. B. Conant, *Science and Common Sense* (Yale University Press, 1951). Chap. 4 is a historical conceptual treatment of the concept of atmospheric pressure and related ideas.

4. J. B. Conant, *On Understanding Science* (Yale University Press, 1947). Chap. 2 is a reprint of a lecture on seventeenth-century contributions in pneumatics.

5. F. T. Bonner and Melba Phillips, *Principles of Physical Science* (Addison-Wesley, 1957). The first part of Chap. 12 (pp. 241–248) is an alternative discussion of the material of this chapter.

THE DESCRIPTION of the behavior of gases is a characteristically experimental problem. The theoretical explanation of this behavior is contained in a very elegant, useful, and broadly applicable theory, which will be considered in a subsequent chapter. But the basis of this theory is the complete description of the experimental behavior of confined gases. In the experiments the variation of one property of a confined gas is measured while a second is manipulated, all other variables being held constant. With a fixed quantity of one kind of gas and at constant temperature, the variation of volume with changing pressure is measured. In other experiments, these observations are made with different quantities of different gases. In still other experiments, the variation of pressure with changing temperature is observed for fixed quantities of gas held at constant volume. Out of these observations come several experimental generalizations, which can be combined into one extremely general equation that describes completely the behavior of gases. This equation is called the **general ideal-gas law.**

## CHAPTER

# 10

# Gases (II): The General Gas Law; Absolute Temperature

## 10-1. Dependence of Volume on Pressure

The relation of the volume to the pressure of a confined gas held at constant temperature was first observed by Robert Boyle in 1662, and the statement of it is called **Boyle's law.** It can be observed in the laboratory, with the apparatus diagramed in Figure 10-1, that the pressure and volume of a sample of gas vary *inversely,* that, whatever the nature or amount of gas in the sample, the volume is inversely proportional to the pressure exerted on the gas. This is a quantitative statement of Boyle's qualitative statement that "the air hath spring." Boyle's law is commonly expressed in either of two ways that are mathematically identical:

$$P = (1/V) \text{ constant} \qquad (10\text{-}1)$$

$$PV = \text{constant} \qquad (10\text{-}2)$$

In both of these equations it is implied that the amount of gas in the sample and the temperature of the sample are constant.

Equation 10-2 results directly from the fact that the product of the two experimentally observed quantities $P$ and $V$ (the $P$-$V$ product) is a constant for any set of conditions of kind, amount, and temperature of the sample of gas. This relation is indicated in Table 10-1, which shows a hypothetical set of data for this experiment and the corresponding $P$-$V$ product for each experimental point. Note that the value of this product and the value of the constant in equation 10-2 are dependent on the amount of gas and the temperature.

We can obtain equation 10-1 from 10-2 by solving for $P$. But we can also obtain it, and thereby point out more clearly the inverse relation between $P$ and $V$, by graphing the data of Table 10-1. Such a graph, plotting $P$ against $V$, is shown in Figure 10-2. The graph is seen to be a curve, which apparently will not intersect either axis. An experienced mathematician, observing the shape of this graph, could probably tell us that it is a hyperbola and that its equation is therefore equation 10-1. Without mathematical training we must transform this graph into one whose properties we know. We do know (see Appendix I) that any straight-line graph that passes through the origin describes a *direct* relation between the two variables and that the mathematical statement of such a relation is that the one variable is equal to a constant times the other variable. We can transform the curve of Figure 10-2 into such a straight-line graph by plotting the pressure against the reciprocal of the volume $(1/V)$, as in Figure 10-3. This change in the method of graphing the data of

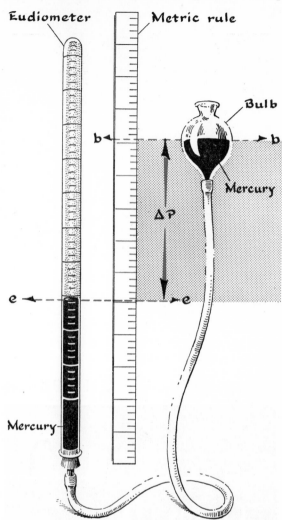

FIGURE **10-1** *Measurement of the variation of the volume of a confined gas with changing pressure.*

Table 10-1 does *not in any way* change the experimental relation; this process is nothing more than a tautology, a different way of expressing *exactly* the same thing. The only purpose of this transformation is to express the experimental relation in such a way that the equation describing it becomes readily apparent even to non-mathematicians. In Figure 10-3 the volumes from which the reciprocals were calculated are indicated in parentheses in order to emphasize this fact that the tautology of changing the graph does not change the experimental data.

Figure 10-3 is clearly a straight line passing

| TABLE **10-1** | *Boyle's Law Experiment* | |
|---|---|---|
| $P$ (cm Hg) | $V$ (cm³) | $PV$ (cm⁴) |
| 122.0 | 8.0 | 976 |
| 101.3 | 9.6 | 973 |
| 82.4 | 11.8 | 971 |
| 67.5 | 14.7 | 977 |
| 49.9 | 19.6 | 979 |
| 35.3 | 27.6 | 974 |
| 25.2 | 38.9 | 980 |
| 19.5 | 50.0 | 975 |

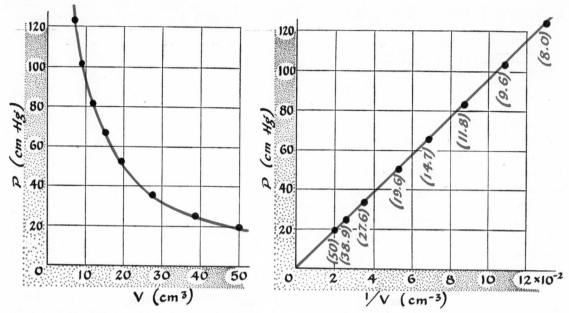

FIGURE **10-2** *Graph of pressure against volume of a confined gas at constant temperature.*

FIGURE **10-3** *Graph of pressure against reciprocal volume.*

through the origin. This graph is a plot of $P$ against $1/V$. We can therefore state that the relation between the pressure and the *reciprocal* of the *volume* ($P$ and $1/V$) is a *direct* relation, and that the equation relating these two variables is

$$P = (1/V) \text{ constant} \tag{10-1}$$

## 10-2. Pressure-volume Product

In preparation for our later theoretical consideration of the behavior of gases, we shall examine more closely the *P-V* product (Table 10-1), particularly the units of this quantity. Clearly the unit cm⁴ is an artificial one and does not describe any real physical situation. We shall understand the nature of this quantity if we recall the nature of the operation of compressing a gas in a cylinder with a piston. It takes work to do this. If we restate the *P-V* product with correct units of pressure rather than the artificial unit (cm Hg), this relation becomes apparent.

Pressures are expressed as centimeters of mercury because the height of a column of mercury is a convenient way of measuring pressures.

But according to the definition of pressure (equation 9-1 or its modified form, equation 9-3) the units of pressure must be the units of force divided by the units of area. This is immediately apparent from equation 9-1 and can be proved for equation 9-3, $P = hdg$. The unit of $h$ is length, cm; density is defined as mass per volume and its unit is therefore mass divided by length cubed, grams/cm³; $g$ is the acceleration of gravity and must have the unit characteristic of acceleration, m/sec². If all these units are combined according to equation 9-3—

$$P = h \text{ cm} \times d \frac{\text{grams}}{\text{cm}^3} \times g \frac{\text{m}}{\text{sec}^2} = hdg \frac{\text{grams} \frac{\text{m}}{\text{sec}^2}}{\text{cm}^2}$$

—it is seen that the units of pressure become mass times acceleration divided by area, or *force per area*. The units above are not the usual absolute units of force and area; we must therefore introduce conversion factors from grams to kilograms and from square centimeters to square meters in order to express a pressure measured in centimeters of mercury in absolute units of force and area. Atmospheric pressure, for example, is 76 cm of mercury; in absolute units this pressure would be

$$P = 76 \text{ cm} \times 13.6 \frac{\text{grams}}{\text{cm}^3} \times 9.8 \frac{\text{m}}{\text{sec}^2} \times \frac{10^4 \text{ cm}^2}{\text{m}^2}$$

$$\times \frac{10^{-3} \text{ kgm}}{\text{grams}} = 1.01 \times 10^5 \frac{\text{kgm} \frac{\text{m}}{\text{sec}^2}}{\text{m}^2}$$

$$= 1.01 \times 10^5 \frac{\text{newtons}}{\text{m}^2}$$

| TABLE 10-2 *Variation of Pressure with Temperature* | |
| --- | --- |
| TEMPERATURE (°C) | PRESSURE (cm Hg) |
| 2 | 69.4 |
| 15 | 72.9 |
| 32 | 76.9 |
| 44 | 80.0 |
| 58 | 83.6 |
| 73 | 87.2 |
| 88 | 91.0 |
| 100 | 94.2 |

Returning now to the *P-V* product, we see that the units of this quantity must have the units of pressure times the units of volume. The preceding discussion shows that the units of pressure are those of force over area; the units of volume are, of course, length cubed. When these are combined by multiplication, as in the *P-V* product, and the units of length are converted to meters—

$$PV = \frac{\text{newtons}}{\text{m}^2} \times \text{m}^3 = \text{newtons} \times \text{meters}$$

—the $\text{m}^2$ cancels out, leaving the units of force times distance. These are the units of **energy,** a new mechanical quantity that will be considered in the next chapter.

## 10-3. Pressure-temperature Variation

More than a century elapsed after Boyle's investigations before the influence of temperature on the behavior of gases was studied. The approach was to measure the variation of *volume* with changes in the *temperature* at constant pressure. In 1787 Charles made a qualitative study of this relation; in 1802 Gay-Lussac made a quantitative study and stated the relation in what is known as the law of Charles and Gay-Lussac or as **Charles' law.** We shall refer again to Charles' law later in this chapter but shall make use of the relation between *pressure* and *temperature* at constant volume in deriving the gas law. The experimental observation is the measurement of the variation in pressure caused by the changing temperature of a sample of gas held at constant volume (Fig. 10-4). The result is as useful as Charles' law and is experimentally much easier to accomplish.

Such experiments show that the pressure exerted by a sample of gas increases as the temperature rises if the volume, the amount, and the type of gas are held constant. It is not apparent, however, whether this variation is direct or whether one variable changes faster than the other. We can find this out only by plotting a set of experimental points. Table 10-2 presents a set of hypothetical data that might have been obtained by a student in an elementary laboratory experiment. The two observations were of the temperature of the gas and the pressure exerted by the gas.

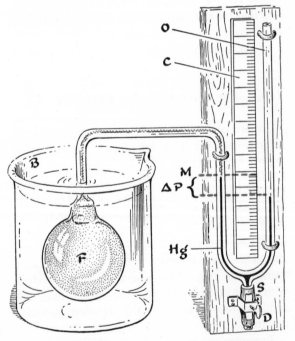

FIGURE 10-4 *Measurement of the variation of the pressure of a confined gas with changing temperature.*

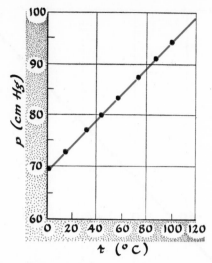

FIGURE **10-5** *Graph of pressure against centigrade temperature of a confined gas at constant volume.*

If these data are plotted (pressures against temperatures) as in Figure 10-5, it is apparent that a straight-line relation exists between these two variables. The points all neatly fit a straight line. But the line does *not* go through the origin. It does intersect the axis of zero temperature— that is, the line representing the zero on the centigrade temperature scale. But, if we recall the way this zero point was established (§ 9-11), we immediately realize that this is *not* a zero value of temperature in the sense of the *lowest* possible limit of temperature. It is, rather, nothing more than the *arbitrarily* chosen point at which we begin marking the calibrations on a thermometer. And we are quite familiar with the fact that temperatures below zero are possible —are, indeed, quite common. The temperature scale must, then, extend some distance below this arbitrarily chosen point that is called "zero" on the centigrade scale. It will be extremely instructive to use the pressure-temperature experiment, the data of which are presented in Figure 10-5 and Table 10-2, to determine *how far* the scale of temperature extends below the centigrade zero. The method we use is to shift the origin so that the graph does pass through it and thus to obtain a modified equation relating the variables. This useful mathematical operation will be used again in later chapters.

## 10-4. Absolute Temperature

In order to accomplish this extension of the temperature scale downward, we must first consider the relation of the line of Figure 10-5 to the pressure axis. That line certainly does not appear to pass throught the point of zero pressure, for such a point does not even appear

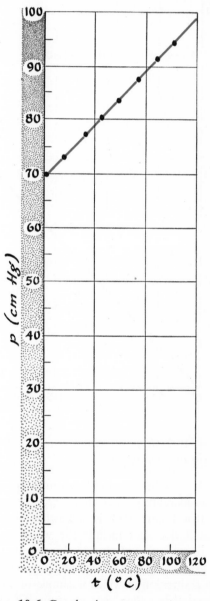

FIGURE **10-6** *Graph of pressure against temperature with the pressure scale extended to the absolute zero of pressure.*

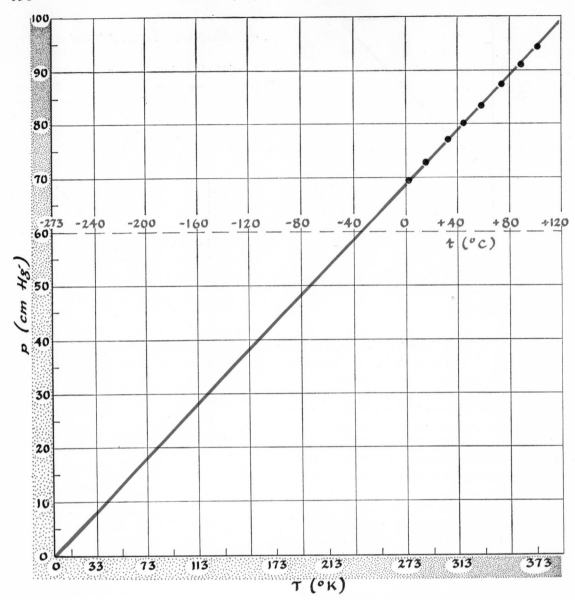

FIGURE **10-7** *Graph of pressure against absolute temperature with the scale extended to the absolute zero of temperature.*

on this graph; all the measured pressures are considerably greater than zero. It appears, then, that Figure 10-5 is somewhat unrealistic in that it does not include the whole possible scale of pressures. It would be extremely difficult to visualize or to attach any physical meaning to a situation in which a sample of confined gas exerted *less* than zero pressure. The lowest possible pressure in any physically meaningful situation is, therefore, a pressure of zero. This

extension of the pressure scale to the lowest possible limit (or absolute zero of pressure) is indicated in Figure 10-6, which is a graph of the same data (Table 10-2) as in Figure 10-5, with one difference: instead of setting the pressure axis at the arbitrarily chosen value of 60 cm Hg, as in Figure 10-5, we have included the whole range of possible pressures.

This extension of the pressure scale beyond the arbitrarily chosen point of Figure 10-5 includes the whole range of pressures and establishes on the graph the axis of absolute zero of pressure. This seems to be a rather hollow accomplishment in that the only difference between Figures 10-6 and 10-5 is a large amount of empty space below the plotted points. If we now extend the graph to the left, however, to temperatures below the arbitrary limit set in Figure 10-5, and at the same time extrapolate the plotted line beyond the experimentally observed points, as in Figure 10-7, the reason for the extension of the pressure axis to the absolute zero of pressure becomes apparent. The extrapolated line *does* now intersect the zero-pressure axis—at a temperature of $-273°$ on the centigrade scale. Now, since we have established that this is the point of absolute zero of pressure, any extension of the graph beyond this point would be totally meaningless. And the temperature corresponding to this absolute zero of pressure must be the lowest realizable temperature and is therefore the **absolute zero of temperature.** The absolute zero of temperature is defined, then, as the temperature at which any sample of enclosed gas would exert *no* pressure. This temperature, though not realizable in actual practice, has been determined by extrapolation to be $273.13°$ below the centigrade zero.

Having established the absolute zero of temperature, we could, logically, redefine the temperature scale in such a way that this point would be *marked* zero on thermometers. For practical reasons the marking of thermometers has not been changed. Most temperatures that are ordinarily measured are near the range of 0–100° centigrade, and long years of custom have established the centigrade scale with this rather illogically placed zero. But a scale of temperature in which the lowest possible temperature is called zero has been established and is in use. This scale is called the **Kelvin temperature** scale or the **absolute temperature** scale. The degrees of the Kelvin scale are identical with those of the centigrade scale; the only difference is the displacement of the zero to a point 273 of these degrees lower. It is therefore unnecessary to have thermometers marked with the Kelvin scale, for it is a simple operation to convert a centigrade reading to a Kelvin reading by

adding 273°. The two scales are indicated in Figure 10-7.

Another way of establishing the absolute zero of temperature is to approach the same data (Table 10-2 and Fig. 10-5) from the analytical rather than the graphical point of view. The slope (see pp. 35 and 578–579) of a straight-line graph is determined by the ratio of the difference of any pair of ordinates to the difference of the corresponding pair of abscissae. The slope of the graph of the data of Table 10-2 can be determined, for example, from the data of the first and last points. The difference of the two ordinates is $94.2 - 69.4 = 24.8$ cm Hg; the difference of the abscissae is $100 - 2 = 98°C$. The ratio of these two differences is $\dfrac{24.8 \text{ cm}}{98°} = 0.252$ cm/°. This quantity, called the slope, represents the rate of change in pressure per degree of change in temperature. (Note that we could have used *any* pair of points from Table 10-2 to calculate the slope. If the data truly represent a straight line, the slope calculated from different sets of points would be the same. Since these are experimental points and very likely would vary somewhat from a perfect straight line, the slope should be calculated from several points and the values averaged.)

Having determined the amount of decrease in pressure for each degree of fall in temperature, we can visualize the situation in which the pressure continues to decrease by this amount for each degree the temperature is lowered until the pressure finally reaches zero. Then, since we cannot conceive of a pressure lower than zero (a negative pressure), we must assume that the corresponding temperature is the lowest possible and is therefore the absolute zero of temperature. The extent by which the pressure must be lowered from any one of the experimental points to reach zero pressure is, of course, the pressure at that point. The extent by which the temperature must be lowered to *cause* this decrease in pressure can be calculated by use of the slope that has just been determined. The decrease in the pressure divided by the slope is equal to the fall in the temperature. We could use any set of observations in Table 10-2, but as an example we consider the third set. At a temperature of

32°C the pressure of the gas was 76.9 cm. The pressure decrease necessary to reach zero pressure is 76.9 cm, and the rate of change of pressure with temperature is 0.252 cm/°. We must now divide the pressure change by the rate of change to obtain the temperature change necessary to lower the pressure by this amount:

$$\frac{76.9 \text{ cm}}{.252 \text{ cm}/°} = \frac{76.9°}{.252} = 305°$$

The absolute zero of temperature is therefore 305° *below* the starting temperature of 32°C; that is, $0°K = 32°C - 305°C = -273°C$, which is, as expected, the value determined from the graphical analysis of the data.

## 10-5. Ideal and Real Gases

In our derivation of the absolute temperature scale and our determination of the absolute zero of temperature we have used several simplifying assumptions that cannot be entirely justified. The pressure-temperature variation of the gas in the temperature range 0–100°C clearly follows a straight-line relation; but there is no way of knowing that this relation will hold exactly over the great length of extrapolation from 0° to −273°. Actually all real gases deviate to some extent from this idealized behavior as the temperature is lowered. Some gases deviate quite markedly even at temperatures in the range from 0° to 100°C. An even greater deviation from ideality is the fact that all gases, when cooled, ultimately reach a temperature at which they condense to form a liquid, and then, of course, they no longer show a behavior even remotely resembling that of Figure 10-7.

In spite of these considerations, the derivation of absolute temperature described above and the general equation describing gas behavior (§ 10-7) are of great value. The treatment in this chapter applies to **ideal gases,** and the equation derived is called the **ideal-gas equation.** Though none of this applies exactly to any real gas, it does offer a coherent and understandable approximate description of most real gases—a description that is sufficiently accurate under most circumstances. The deviations from ideality are

of great theoretical interest. Some of them are considered in Chapter 12, but a complete study of them is a part of more advanced science courses.

## 10-6. Relation of Pressure to Temperature

Now that an absolute origin of both temperature and pressure has been established, it is apparent that the graph of pressure against temperature in Figure 10-5 is a straight line that *does* pass through the origin if we consider temperature on the *absolute* scale. If we let $T°K$ signify temperature on the absolute scale (in contrast to $t°C$ for centigrade temperatures), we can write the equation for the relation represented by the straight line of Figure 10-7:

$$P = T \times \text{constant} \tag{10-3}$$

Equation 10-3 describes the relation of the two variables, pressure and absolute temperature, when the mass and volume of the gas are held constant. Since the same relation and the same value for absolute zero are obtained for *any* kind of gas, we assume that this relation, as well as equation 10-2, is valid whatever the nature of the gas, and that the nature of the gas will not effect the more general relation that results from combining these two equations.

## 10-7. General Gas Equation

The obvious next step in an effort to phrase a general gas law would be to combine these two equations into one that describes a relation of all three of these variables, $P$, $V$, and $T$. We can combine the two separate equations by carrying out a "word experiment" in which we take note of relations that *must* exist because of the existence of equations 10-2 and 10-3. First, imagine a $P$-$V$ experiment (Boyle's law experiment) in which some arbitrary amount of gas is confined at 0°C. If the pressure is now adjusted to 76 cm, which we designate as $P_0$, the gas will occupy a volume, $v_0$, that will depend on the *amount* of gas we arbitrarily selected at the start. From equation 10-2 we know that any variation of pressure and volume in this sample of gas is described by the equation

$$PV = K \qquad (10\text{-}2)$$

in which $K$ is a constant determined by *any pair* of *corresponding* values of $P$ and $V$. It is convenient for us to let $K$ be determined by the pair of corresponding values we have defined, $P_0$ and $v_0$. $K$, then, is equal to the product of these, $P_0v_0$, and equation 10-2 becomes

$$PV = P_0v_0 \qquad (10\text{-}4)$$

which describes the variation of $V$ with $P$ for any change of pressure so long as the temperature remains at 0°C, which we shall designate as an absolute temperature, $T_0$ (which, of course, is 273°K).

Now imagine that this same sample of gas is used in a *P-T* experiment starting with the fixed volume $v_0$ at pressure $P_0$ and temperature $T_0$. If the volume is held constant and the temperature changed to some temperature, $T$, other than $T_0$, there will be a corresponding change in the pressure to $P_T$. The change in pressure with temperature is described by equation 10-3.

$$\frac{P_T}{T} = K' \qquad (10\text{-}3)$$

Again the value of $K'$ can be determined by *any* pair of experimental values of $P$ and $T$, and again it is convenient to let it be determined by the pair we have defined, $P_0$ and $T_0$, which obtained at the start of the *P-T* part of the experiment. $K'$ is, then, the ratio of $P_0$ to $T_0$: $K' = P_0/T_0$, and equation 10-3 becomes

$$\frac{P_T}{T} = \frac{P_0}{T_0}$$

If this equation is solved for $P_T$, we obtain a value for this new pressure:

$$P_T = \frac{P_0}{T_0} T \qquad (10\text{-}5)$$

The next step of this analysis is to imagine another Boyle's law experiment at this temperature $T$°K (other than $T_0$). Again the constant of equation 10-2 is determined by any pair of corresponding values of $P$ and $V$, such as $P_T$

and $v_0$ (the volume remained constant at $v_0$ during the *P-T* part of the experiment). The equation that relates $P$ and $V$ in the Boyle's law experiment at $T$°K then becomes

$$PV = P_Tv_0 \qquad (10\text{-}6)$$

which describes the variation of $P$ with $V$ at the new temperature $T$. But now we have a value for $P_T$ in terms of this new temperature, $T$, and the known quantities, $P_0$ and $T_0$, from equation 10-5. If this value for $P_T$ is substituted in equation 10-6, the resulting equation,

$$PV = \frac{P_0v_0}{T_0} T \qquad (10\text{-}7)$$

describes the relation among $P$, $V$, and $T$ for the arbitrary amount of gas that was enclosed at the beginning of the hypothetical experiment. In this equation all the subscript quantities are constant: $P_0$ is 76 cm Hg, $T_0$ is 273°K, and $v_0$ is the volume occupied by the *arbitrarily* chosen mass of gas at this temperature and pressure.

The form of this equation, $PV = K''T$, in which $K'' = P_0T_0/v_0$, all of which are constants, is quite useful in that here in a single equation three of the variables that describe gas behavior are related. But the usefulness is limited by the fact that the constant $K''$ is dependent on the amount of the gas being considered. It is therefore necessary to determine the value of $K''$ for *each* experimental situation. We evaluate $K''$ by measuring any corresponding set of $P_0$, $T_0$, and $v_0$. If we could establish some statement of the quantity of gas, which would have a *standard* volume rather than the arbitrary volume $v_0$ corresponding to the arbitrary amount used in the hypothetical experiment, the equation would have a completely general form and we should avoid this limitation on its usefulness. Avogadro's hypothesis offers a way of expressing this *standard* volume of any gas in terms of the quantity of gas. This hypothesis states that equal numbers of molecules of any gases, held at the same temperature and pressure, occupy equal volumes. From the discussion of molecular weights and moles (§ 7-9) we know that one mole of any substance contains the same number (Avogadro's number, $N_0$) of molecules as one mole of any other substance. According to Avogadro's hypothesis, one mole of any gas must have the *same* volume as one mole of any other gas. This standard volume is defined as the **molar volume:** the volume occupied by one mole of any gas at $P_0$ and $T_0$ (76 cm Hg pressure and 273°K temperature). The molar volume is a quantity that can be readily determined experimentally. It is only necessary to take exactly *one mole* of a gas rather than an arbitrary quantity—that is, to take, for example, 2 grams of $H_2$, 71 grams of $Cl_2$, 28 grams of $N_2$, or 32 grams of $O_2$, each of which quantities is one gram-molecular weight. The pressure of this quantity is then adjusted to 76 cm Hg and the temperature adjusted to 273°K, and the volume is measured under these conditions. This volume comes out to be the same, **2.24×10⁴ cm³**, for *all* gases. This identical **molar volume** for all gases is a striking corroboration of Avogadro's hypothesis. However, in including this expression of the amount of gas in the general equation it is not necessary to specify *what* this standard volume is; it is only necessary to know that such a specific volume exists and to use the symbol $V_0$ to signify it. (Note the *capital V* to distinguish this volume from the arbitrary volume $v_0$ of the previous equations.)

Returning now to equation 10-7 and the original hypothetical experiment, we can specify the arbitrary quantity of gas as *n moles* of gas. This quantity of gas would have a volume of $nV_0$ at $P_0$ and $T_0$; so we can now specify the volume that was indicated earlier by $v_0$, a definite but at that time unstated volume. This quantity can now be substituted into equation 10-7 for its equality, $v_0$, to give

$$PV = \frac{P_0 nV_0}{T_0} T = n \frac{P_0 V_0}{T_0} T \qquad (10\text{-}8)$$

But, again, all the subscript quantities are constant: $P_0$ is 76 cm Hg, $T_0$ is 273°K, and $V_0$ is the molar volume at standard conditions of temperature and pressure ($P_0$ and $T_0$). These three constant quantities in this combination are, then, equal to some other constant, which will be designated $R$, the **universal gas constant:**

$$\frac{P_0 V_0}{T_0} = R \qquad (10\text{-}9)$$

Equation 10-8 then takes the form

$$PV = nRT \qquad (10\text{-}10)$$

when $R$ replaces its equality as indicated in equation 10-9. Equation 10-10 is the **general gas-law equation** and describes the behavior of any gas under varying conditions of temperature, pressure, and volume and for any mass expressed as *n* moles.

## 10-8. Determination of the Gas Constant

For actual use of the gas-law equation the value of $R$, the universal gas constant, must be determined. This is done by experimental observation. Either equation 10-9 or equation 10-10 can be used to determine $R$. If equation 10-9 is used, the *molar volume* at standard conditions must be determined. If equation 10-10 is used, any corresponding set of $P$, $V$, $n$, and $T$ values can be used, as indicated by this equation solved for $R$:

$$R = \frac{PV}{nT} \qquad (10\text{-}11)$$

The most direct way of determining $R$, and the way in which we can use the information obtained in the laboratory, is to substitute for $n$, in equation 10-11, an expression for the number of moles of gas used in terms of the mass of the gas and the molecular weight of the gas.

A mole of any substance is defined as the molecular weight in grams of that substance. For example, the molecular weight of oxygen is 32; one mole of oxygen is therefore 32 grams of oxygen. If the sample we happen to choose has a mass of 64 grams, then, clearly, it contains 2 moles; if the sample has a mass of 16 grams, it contains 1/2 mole. In general, the number of moles, *n,* of any sample of any substance is the mass of the sample divided by the molecular weight of the substance:

$$n = \frac{\text{mass}}{\text{molecular weight}}$$

If we now make this substitution for *n,* equation 10-11 takes the form

$$R = \frac{PV}{\frac{\text{mass}}{\text{mol wt}} T} = \frac{\text{mol wt} \times PV}{\text{mass} \times T} \qquad (10\text{-}12)$$

To determine the gas constant, *R,* we now have to measure the volume, pressure, and temperature of a sample of known mass of a gas of known molecular weight.

## 10-9. Partial Pressure

In order to evaluate the gas constant, we must introduce one more experimental relation that has to do with gases. This generalization was first stated by Dalton in 1801 and is called the law of **partial pressures.** It is observed that, if two samples of gas at the same pressure and temperature are mixed, there is no change in total volume. This experimental law can be illustrated by the hypothetical experiment diagramed in Figure 10-8. Imagine, as in "a," a container divided into two equal volumes by a removable partition. Now place two different gases, A and B, in these spaces at temperature *T* and pressure *P*. If the partition is removed and the two gases are allowed to mix, as in "b," no change in pressure or temperature is observed. The volume occupied by the mixture of the gases is now $2V$, but the total pressure exerted by the mixture of A and B remains *P*. Since the volume each gas now occupies is double

ble the original volume (Boyle's law), it would be reasonable to assume that each gas exerts a pressure of $\frac{1}{2}P$. Each of the gases behaves, then, as if it occupied the new volume alone. From this experiment we can phrase the law of partial pressures in its most useful form: *In a mixture of gases each gas exerts the same pressure it would exert if it occupied the entire volume alone, and the total pressure exerted by the mixture is the sum of the partial pressures of the component gases.* This experimental law is one of the many generalized observations of gases that can be explained by the kinetic theory. Its theoretical rationale will be considered in Chapter 12. At this stage it must be considered only as an experimental fact.

The reason why this law must be used in the evaluation of the gas constant from the volume of a sample of gas observed in elementary experiments is that this volume is usually determined by its displacement of water. The gas bubbles through water into a measuring tube and therefore is saturated with water vapor by the time it is collected. Thus the sample of gas is not pure, but is rather a mixture of the collected gas and gaseous water. The *total* pressure of this mixture is measured, but in our calculations we must use the pressure exerted by the pure gas only. The total pressure must therefore be "corrected" by the amount of the pressure of the water vapor. The vapor pressure of water depends on the temperature, but near room temperature (about 25°C) it can be taken as 2.2 cm Hg. The pressure exerted by any gas collected over water is about 2.2 cm Hg *less* than the observed total pressure.

## 10-10. Evaluation of the Gas Constant

In a typical experiment of this type it was observed that 8 grams of oxygen collected over water at a temperature of 24°C and a total pressure of 72.5 cm Hg had a volume of $6.6 \times 10^3$ cm³. These data, plus the vapor pressure of water at 24°C, suffice for the calculation of the gas constant, *R*. A table of the observed data,

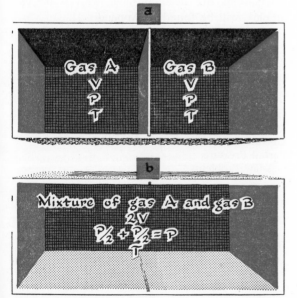

FIGURE **10-8** *Partial pressures.*

with the necessary corrections, helps to illustrate the calculation:

$V = 6.6 \times 10^3$ cm$^3$
$P = 72.5$ cm $- 2.2$ cm $= 70.3$ cm (pressure of O$_2$)
$T = 24°C + 273° = 297°K$
mass $= 8$ grams
mol wt $= 32$ grams/mole

These data are now substituted in equation 10-12:

$$R = \frac{\text{mol wt} \times PV}{\text{mass} \times T}$$

$$= \frac{32 \text{ grams/mole} \times 70.3 \text{ cm} \times 6.6 \times 10^3 \text{ cm}^3}{8 \text{ grams} \times 297°}$$

$$= \frac{32 \times 70.3 \times 6.6 \times 10^3}{8 \times 297} \frac{\text{cm}^4}{\text{mole degree}}$$

$$= 6.25 \times 10^3 \frac{\text{cm}^4}{\text{mole degree}}$$

The accepted experimental value of the gas constant, the value that will be used in all calculations involving the gas law, is

$$R = 6.23 \times 10^3 \frac{\text{cm}^4}{\text{mole}°}$$

## 10-11. *Use of the Gas Equation*

Three further comments about the gas law should be made at this time. The first has to do with the units of the gas constant $R$. The units and the value quoted above are based on the artificial unit of pressure, centimeters of mercury. If pressure is expressed in the units of force per area (see p. 119), the units of $R$ become the units of energy (or work) per mole per degree. We shall see later that several different units of energy have been set up for convenience in dealing with the various types of energy, mechanical, electrical, heat, etc. The gas constant enters the calculations that apply to some of these different forms of energy; when it does, the units and numerical value of $R$ are expressed appropriately. All of these are interconvertible by the conversion factors that relate the various units, just as lengths expressed in centimeters can be converted to lengths expressed in meters by use of the conversion factor.

The second comment has to do with the use of the gas equation in calculations. These calculations are of three main types: (1) the calculation of the volume a sample of gas would occupy at some conditions of pressure and temperature other than those at which the volume was measured; (2) the calculation of the volume occupied at some $P$ and $T$ of a known mass or known number of moles of a gas; (3) the number of moles of gas contained in a measured volume at a measured $P$ and $T$. The third type of calculation arises frequently in the determination of molecular weights by measurement of gas volumes. A discussion of the way these calculations are accomplished, with some examples, will be found in Appendix II.

## Concepts and Terms

Variation of Volume with Pressure
  Boyle's law
Variation of Volume with Temperature
  Charles' law
Variation of Pressure with Temperature
Absolute Zero of Temperature
Kelvin Temperature Scale

Ideal and Real Gases
General Gas Equation
Molar Volume
Universal Gas Constant
Partial Pressure
Gas-law Problems

## Problems

**10-1.** Calculate the *P-V* product for two of the sets of data for $P$ and $V$ in Table 10-1 in terms of the fundamental units of pressure (force per area). What physical quantity is represented by this product?

**10-2.** From the empirically observed variation of volume with pressure at constant temperature and of pressure with temperature at constant volume, derive the general gas equation.

**10-3.** Using the value of $R$ given on page 142, calculate the molar volume at 0°C and 76 cm pressure.

*Ans.* $2.24 \times 10^4$ cm³

**10-4.** The volume of a sample of gas is 200 cm³ at 250°C. What is its volume at 150°C and the same pressure?

*Ans.* 162 cm³

**10-5.** The density of helium, He, is $1.785 \times 10^{-4}$ gram/cm³ at 0°C and 76 cm pressure. What is its density at 100°C and 7,600 cm pressure?

*Ans.* $1.308 \times 10^{-2}$ gram/cm³

**10-6.** A sample of gas occupies 500 cm³ at 150°C and 82 cm pressure. Calculate its volume at standard temperature and pressure (0°C and 76 cm pressure).

*Ans.* 348 cm³

**10-7.** Calculate the volume occupied at 20°C and 74 cm pressure by the $CO_2$ gas evolved from 10 cm³ of Dry Ice (solid carbon dioxide, $CO_2$). The density of Dry Ice is 1.53 grams/cm³. Calculate also the density of the $CO_2$ gas at this temperature and pressure.

*Ans.* $V = 8.60 \times 10^3$ cm³;
$d = 1.78 \times 10^{-3}$ gram/cm³

**10-8.** Calculate the pressure that would develop if the 10 cm³ piece of Dry Ice of Prob. 10-7 were confined to a volume 10 times as great (100 cm³) at the temperature of Prob. 10-7.

*Ans.* $6.35 \times 10^3$ cm Hg = 83.6 atmospheres
Would it be sensible to keep Dry Ice in a refrigerator?

**10-9.** Analysis of the gas methane shows that it contains 1 part of hydrogen to 3 parts of carbon.
(A) Calculate the empirical formula of methane.
(B) If the density of methane at −136.5°C and 152 cm pressure is $2.86 \times 10^{-3}$ gram/cm³, what is the molecular weight of methane?
(C) What is the true formula of methane?

*Ans.* (B) 16

**10-10.** Analysis of the gas ethane shows it to be 80% C and 20% H. A sample of ethane having a mass of 3.0 grams occupies a volume of $2.53 \times 10^3$ cm³ at 27°C and 74.0 cm pressure.
(A) What is the empirical formula of ethane?
(B) What is its molecular weight?

(C) What is the true formula of ethane?

*Ans.* (B) 30

**10-11.** What pressure would be exerted by 100 grams of hydrogen gas, $H_2$, confined to a volume of $10^4$ cm³ at 25°C?

*Ans.* $9.28 \times 10^3$ cm

**10-12.** What would be the density of oxygen gas, $O_2$, compressed to a pressure of 3,000 lb per square inch at room temperature (27°C)? Assume that a pressure of 15 lb per square inch is equal to 76 cm pressure.

*Ans.* $2.6 \times 10^{-1}$ gram/cm³

**10-13.** It is found that 0.42 gram of oxygen gas collected over water at 24°C and 75.7 cm total pressure occupies 331 cm³. We know that the atomic weight of oxygen is 16, the formula of oxygen is $O_2$, and the vapor pressure of water at 24°C is 2.2 cm. Calculate the gas constant $R$ from this information.

**10-14.** If a sample of benzene occupies 252 cm³ at 100°C and 77.0 cm pressure and has a mass of 0.65 gram, (A) what is the molecular weight of benzene, and (B) what is the true formula of benzene if analysis shows it to contain 92.3% C and 7.7% H?

*Ans.* (A) 78; (B) $C_6H_6$

**10-15.** When zinc and hydrochloric acid, HCl, react, the products are $H_2$ gas and zinc chloride, $ZnCl_2$.
(A) Write a balanced equation for this reaction.
(B) Calculate the mass of $ZnCl_2$ that would be produced from 100 grams of zinc in this reaction.
(C) Calculate the mass of HCl that would be consumed.
(D) Calculate the volume of $H_2$ at 22°C and 73.8 cm pressure that would be produced by the reaction of these amounts of zinc and HCl.

*Ans.* (B) 209 grams
(D) $3.81 \times 10^4$ cm³

**10-16.** A sample of gas that has a mass of 1.25 grams has a volume of 250 cm³ when collected over water at 28°C and 73.5 cm pressure. The vapor pressure of water at 28°C is 2.8 cm. Calculate the molecular weight of this gas.

*Ans.* 133

## Suggested Readings

1. F. T. Bonner and Melba Phillips, *Principles of Physical Science* (Addison-Wesley, 1957). The last part of Chap. 12 (pp. 248–258) is a brief conceptual treatment of the gas laws.

Most elementary chemistry texts discuss the gas laws and problems based on the general gas equation. The following four references are representative of the better ones.

2. L. Pauling, *College Chemistry,* second edition (W. H. Freeman and Company, 1955), Chap. 9.
3. D. C. Gregg, *Principles of Chemistry* (Allyn and Bacon, 1958), Chap. 6.
4. L. E. Steiner and J. A. Campbell, *General Chemistry* (Macmillan, 1955), Chap. 9.
5. M. J. Sienko and R. A. Plane, *Chemistry* (McGraw-Hill, 1957), pp. 124–140.

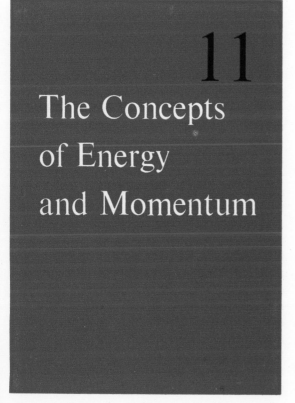

CHAPTER

11

The Concepts
of Energy
and Momentum

IT IS the purpose of this chapter to trace some of the important developments that culminated in the enunciation of the general law of conservation of energy. Those developments, which occurred mainly during the seventy years preceding 1850, included an extension of the concepts of mechanics, a study of the phenomena of heat, and the formulation of the atomic-molecular view of the structure of matter. To treat these topics in historical sequence is very difficult. The various fields progressed simultaneously, with little apparent interdependence and certainly with no conscious search for a unifying theme. The topics of this chapter may therefore at first seem unrelated. As we progress, however, we shall see that the concept of energy, first developed for strictly mechanical systems, was extended to include heat, and that with the assignment of motion to the molecules of matter (Chap. 12) a mechanical theory of heat phenomena was developed.

The atomic theory, as developed up to this point, including all the refinements and extensions implicit in the periodic law, has been remarkably effective in interpreting a vast number of facts about the behavior of matter. This particulate view of matter includes the whole array of substances of the physical world and describes logically and consistently a large part of the science of matter. The changes in matter —combination of elements to form compounds, decomposition of compounds into several elements, and changes from one compound to others—are all interpreted neatly by our theory that matter exists as aggregates of atomic or molecular particles.

It is characteristic of these changes from one substance to others that radical changes in properties are involved and that the types of change are extremely variable. On the other hand, certain effects are common to *all* substances involved in slight changes, and these changes are readily reversible. We have encountered the changes in volume of gases—the same for *all* gases—that accompany changes in temperature and pressure. Other changes also accompany the process that we call "adding heat" to a substance. All of these changes are less radical than the chemical changes and are readily reversible.

The volume of a gas increases as the pressure is decreased or the temperature raised, but it is immediately restored when the other variables are changed back. As heat is added to a substance, the temperature rises with very little change in any other property; and, if the heat is removed, the temperature falls. Another effect of adding heat to substances is a change of state, from solid to liquid or from liquid to gas. These also are easily reversible changes and take place with almost no change in other properties. In general, there is a slight increase in volume as the solid changes to the liquid state† and an almost unlimited increase as the liquid changes to the gaseous state.

These few examples of the behavior of matter are clearly quite different from the "chemical" changes with which we have been concerned in earlier chapters and on which the atomic-molecular theory was based. The logical next step in the development of our science of matter is to relate this new set of phenomena to the particulate theory that has been so effective up to this point. Most of the new class of changes are associated with the abstract notion of *heat* and with the quantity most closely related to it, *temperature*. In order to discuss these changes, however, we need to consider a method of measuring the *amounts* of heat involved.

## 11-1. Calorimetry

In Chapters 9 and 10 we established an empirical and quantitative definition of temperature. This definition, which required no understanding of the nature of temperature, was based on changes in some observable property that are associated with arbitrarily chosen degrees of hotness. Similarly, the amount of heat added to a sample of matter may be defined in terms of the associated and observable rise in temperature produced. But rise in temperature is not the only factor that defines the amount of heat

---

† It is unfortunate that the most talked-about substance, water, is an exception to this generalization. Water is one of *very* few substances that contract in going from the solid to the liquid state.

added to a sample of matter. A little consideration of ordinary experience will indicate what other factors must be included in our definition.

Whatever the nature of heat, it is certainly plausible to assume that a definite source, such as one of the "burners" on an electric stove, will give off heat at a constant rate. Now, if a large pot of water is placed on the burner, it may take ten minutes to raise the temperature of the water from 20°C to 40°C. But a small saucepan of water may require only two minutes for the same rise in temperature when placed on the same burner and after four minutes will have a temperature of 60°C. Clearly, the saucepan, even at the higher temperature of 60°C, contains less heat than the pot of water at 40°C because it was receiving heat from the burner for a shorter time. Nevertheless, as everyone knows, if the saucepan is brought in contact with the pot, heat will flow from the saucepan to the pot; that is, the water in the saucepan will cool off while that in the pot will warm up. This simple example illustrates two general facts. First: heat *always* flows from bodies of higher temperature to those of lower temperature even if the former contain a smaller amount of heat than the latter. This seeming contradiction may appear more plausible when we consider that, because there is less water in the saucepan, the heat in it is more "concentrated" than in the pot. But this has little meaning unless we know what heat is and form some picture of how it might be concentrated. The second general fact is that rise in temperature alone does not give a measure of the amount of heat added to a sample of matter. The mass of the sample must also be taken into account. In addition to this, there is one other factor that determines the amount of heat added to a sample of matter: the kind of material being heated. Anyone who has placed an empty pan on a stove knows that the pan heats up quickly. Suppose that the mass of the pan is 2 kgm and that the stove heats it from room temperature to 80°C in two minutes. If the pan contains 2 kgm of water, one may expect the stove to heat this combination to 80° in four minutes. But it does not. It takes from twelve to twenty-two minutes, depending on the kind of metal in the pan. In other words, it takes much less heat to raise the temperature of the metal pan than to raise the temperature of an equal mass of water through the same interval.

Thus we see that, to specify a definite amount of heat (that is, to define a unit), we must use a fixed mass of a particular substance and a definite temperature interval. The choice may be quite arbitrary so long as all three are specified. The unit used in scientific work is the calorie, which is defined in terms of one gram of water and one degree centigrade. By definition *one* **calorie** *is the amount of heat that will change the temperature of one gram of water by one degree centigrade.* If a calorie of heat is added to one gram of water, the temperature rises one degree. If, in the example above, the room temperature was 20°C, the temperature of the water in the pan rose 60°C. Each gram of water would require 60 calories for this temperature rise, and, since there were $2 \times 10^3$ grams of water, the stove had to give $1.2 \times 10^5$ calories to the water.

As indicated above, equal masses of different substances require different amounts of heat for equal temperature changes. Consider the following experiment. Take 1 gram of iron, observe its temperature, and place it in contact with 1 gram of water at some higher temperature. Leave the two in contact until the temperature of the water has dropped 1°C, and observe the temperature of the iron again. One calorie has been transferred from the water to the iron, and the temperature of the iron is observed to rise 8.3°C. Clearly it requires less than 1 calorie to raise the temperature of the 1 gram of iron by 1°C. From the measurements we conclude that $1/8.3 = .12$ calorie is the amount of heat that changes the temperature of 1 gram of iron 1°C. This characteristic property of iron is called its specific heat. By definition *the* **specific heat** *of a substance is the number of calories that will change the temperature of 1 gram of the substance by 1°C.* Some representative specific heats are: iron, 0.11; silver, 0.056; magnesium, 0.25; mercury, 0.033; sodium, 0.30; sulfur, 0.18; soil and rocks, variable around 0.20; glass, 0.16. The units of specific heat come from the definition as calories per gram degree centi-

grade (abbreviated as cal/gram°C). By definition of the calorie the specific heat of water is 1 cal/gram°C.† Notice that this is much larger than the other specific heats listed. Very few substances, in fact, have specific heats as large as that of water.

If the specific heat is known, the quantity of heat that will change the temperature of a sample of matter may be easily computed. For instance, if the pan in our previous example was made of iron, the heat supplied by the stove to raise its temperature was

$$.12 \, \frac{\text{cal}}{\text{gram}°\text{C}} \, 2 \times 10^3 \, \text{gram} \, 60°\text{C} = 1.44 \times 10^4 \, \text{cal}$$

Or, in general, for a sample of any substance, we may write

$$Sm \, \Delta t = \Delta H \tag{11-1}$$

in which $\Delta H$ is the amount of heat that produces change in temperature $\Delta t$ in $m$ grams of a sample of substance of specific heat $S$. If $\Delta t$ is a rise in temperature, $\Delta H$ has been added to the substance; if $\Delta t$ is a fall in temperature, $\Delta H$ has been given up by the substance.

Although the experiment described above, for the specific heat of iron, is possible in principle, it would be very difficult in practice. The measurement of $\Delta t$ while the temperature is changing is subject to large experimental errors. Furthermore, precautions would have to be taken to prevent heat exchanges with the surrounding air, the laboratory table, etc. These exchanges may be quite large, for, as we have seen, heat will always flow away from hotter bodies toward colder ones. To prevent these exchanges, we perform the experiment with a *calorimeter,* a device that includes a container so constructed that the flow of heat through the walls is greatly reduced (ideally, eliminated). Such a container, shown in Figure 11-1, is a

† Experimentally it is found that it takes a slightly different amount of heat to raise the temperature of 1 gram of water from 61°C to 62°, say, than from 11°C to 12°C. The definition of the calorie should therefore specify a particular degree. The degree from 14.5° to 15.5° is chosen. Similarly, the specific heats of other substances vary with temperature. Above room temperature, however, these variations are small and may be neglected.

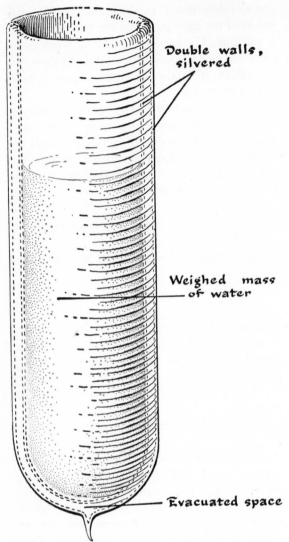

Double walls, silvered

Weighed mass of water

Evacuated space

FIGURE **11-1** *A simple calorimeter.*

for keeping liquids hot or cold is such a container.)

Heat measurements may be made conveniently and precisely by the *method of mixtures.* The substances under investigation (let us suppose there are two), after being heated (or cooled) to different temperatures, are mixed in a calorimeter. Their temperatures then change until they attain the same final temperature, for the heat given off by the hotter substance as it cools is absorbed by the cooler substance as it warms up. From the initial temperatures and the final temperature and the masses of the substances we can compute the heat exchanges. An example will help us to understand the method.

Suppose that 300 grams of water at 20°C is placed in a calorimeter. In a separate container 200 grams of magnesium is heated to 90°C. The magnesium is then put into the calorimeter, and the mixture is stirred until it reaches a final temperature of 30°C. Here the magnesium gives off heat as it cools, which heat is absorbed by the water. Since the mixture is isolated thermally, these two amounts of heat are equal. Then, with the aid of equation 11-1, we see that

heat given by Mg = heat absorbed by $H_2O$

$$S \text{ 200 grams } 60°C = 1 \frac{\text{cal}}{\text{gram } °C} \text{ 300 grams } 10°C$$

$$S = \frac{3 \times 10^3 \text{ cal}}{12 \times 10^3 \text{ grams } °C} = .25 \frac{\text{cal}}{\text{gram } °C}.$$

The method of mixtures will also yield a measurement of the heat exchanges involved in change of state. We have already noted (§ 9-11) that a mixture of ice and water will stabilize at a constant temperature so long as both phases are present. If heat is added to the mixture, some of the ice will melt, but the temperature will not change until all of the ice is gone. The addition of more heat will then raise the temperature of the water until (at the boiling point) it will again stabilize at a constant value. So long as both liquid and vapor phases are present, the temperature will not change with further addition of heat.† More of the water, however, will va-

double-walled glass vessel with a highly evacuated space between the walls. This vacuum prevents heat from being conducted out of or into the container, since heat can be *conducted* only through a material medium. Heat can be *radiated,* however, through a vacuum. (The heat that warms the earth, for instance, is radiated from the sun through millions of miles of empty space.) In order to minimize heat exchanges by radiation between the inside of the container and the environment, we silver the walls of the container so that such radiation is reflected back into the container rather than transmitted through the walls. (The familiar vacuum bottle

† This phenomenon is made use of in boiling vegetables. The flame under the pan is at a much higher temperature than the boiling water. But, since the temperature of the water and vegetables remains fixed, the vegetables "cook" and don't burn—unless the pan boils dry.

porize. (We used this phenomenon of fixed temperature during change of state for water in § 9-11 to define the centigrade scale of temperature.) Clearly, a sizable amount of heat is necessary just to change the state. Since this amount of heat produces no change in temperature, it appears to be rendered latent and is thus named. The amount of heat required depends, of course, on the mass of the substance changing state. By definition, then, *the* **latent heat** *of a substance is the number of calories required to change the state of one gram of the substance.* If the change of state is between the solid and liquid phases, the heat exchanged is called the **heat of fusion;** if the change is between the liquid and vapor states, the heat is called the **heat of vaporization.** During changes of state from solid to liquid and from liquid to vapor the latent heats are absorbed; during changes in the reverse order the latent heats are given up by the substance.

The following example will illustrate how a latent heat may be measured by the method of mixtures. Suppose that there is 220 grams of water in a calorimeter at an initial temperature of 40°C. Then 20 grams of ice is dropped into the calorimeter. It is observed that all the ice melts and that the mixture comes to a final temperature of 30°C. As the ice melts, it absorbs its heat of fusion. But the ice changes to 20 grams of water at 0°C. This water then absorbs more heat as it warms up to the final temperature of the mixture. The heat, of course, is supplied by the warm water cooling down to the final temperature. If $L$ represents the heat of fusion, we may write

heat absorbed by ice and ice water

$$= \text{heat given by warm water}$$

$$L\ 20 \text{ grams} + 1\ \frac{\text{cal}}{\text{gram °C}}\ 20 \text{ grams } 30°C$$

$$= 1\ \frac{\text{cal}}{\text{gram °C}}\ 220 \text{ grams } 10°C$$

$$L\ 20 \text{ grams} = 2{,}200 \text{ cal} - 600 \text{ cal}$$

$$L = \frac{1{,}600 \text{ cal}}{20 \text{ grams}} = 80\ \frac{\text{cal}}{\text{gram}}$$

It will be left as an exercise for the reader to

show that, if $m_s$ grams of steam is condensed in $m_w$ grams of water at $t_i°C$ and the mixture comes to a final temperature of $t_f°C$, then

$$m_s L + m_s(100°C - t_f) = m_w(t_f - t_i)$$

if $L$ is now the heat of vaporization. Since all other quantities are observable, $L$ is determined.

The exchange of latent heats with change of state is displayed by all substances. The amounts of latent heat are different and are characteristic properties of the different substances. The latent heats of a few familiar substances are listed in Table 11-1. Water's latent heats, like its specific heat, are relatively large. Very few substances have latent heats as large as those of water. Another general rule for all substances is illustrated by the data of Table 11-1. The heat of vaporization of a substance is always much larger than its heat of fusion. This fact will be of interest when we develop a dynamical theory of heat (Chap. 12).

The facts of specific and latent heats were discovered, and methods of measuring them were developed, during the latter half of the eighteenth century. The pioneer in this development (Joseph Black, 1728–1799) and his successors formulated their ideas on the basis of a theory (to be discussed in the next section) that heat is a substance. It should be clear, however, that the definitions and methods presented in this section (essentially identical with those of Black) are fundamentally empirical and do not depend on any concepts of the nature of heat. These definitions and methods still form the basis of modern calorimetry even though the modern concept of heat is radically different from that of the early experimenters in this field.

| TABLE **11-1** *Latent Heats* | | |
|---|---|---|
| SUBSTANCE | HEAT OF FUSION | HEAT OF VAPORIZATION |
| Water | 80 | 540 |
| Carbon tetra-chloride | 4 | 46 |
| Alcohol | 25 | 204 |
| Mercury | 3 | 71 |

## 11-2. Theory of Heat as a Substance

Many theories of heat and temperature have been proposed and have been part of physical science at various times. The nature of these quantities has been a matter of speculation throughout the whole history of science, with two opposing ideas dominating the thought. One was that heat is a *substance* that could diffuse quickly throughout any sample of matter. Although the hypothetical heat substance was not directly observable, it could explain most of the casual observations of heat phenomena. On the other hand, many scientists were skeptical of this somewhat mysterious fluid and tended to the opposite view that heat is an aspect of *motion*. This vibration or other small motion was attributed to the "corpuscles" of matter.† The arguments were speculative at best, and they remained so until a quantitative study of heat and temperature had been developed.

We have already seen that the concepts of heat and temperature are inextricably related. We have also seen that it is possible to construct a quantitative scale for the measurement of temperature differences and in terms of this to define a unit for the measurement of quantity of heat. These measures are arbitrarily defined in terms of empirical relations and are not dependent on any conceptual model. Such was the state of affairs just after the middle of the eighteenth century. Accurate thermometers had been made, heat and temperature had been differentiated, and reliable methods of calorimetry had been developed. Specific heats and latent heats had been discovered and their values measured. In all this experimental work it became increasingly clear that, whatever the nature of heat, the total amount in any isolated system remained constant, and that the heat merely flowed from one component to another until final temperature equilibrium was achieved.

This principle of the conservation of heat was probably the main reason for a swing of opinion toward the substance theory. And, although the modern scientific theory of heat rejects the notion of heat as a substance in favor of the opposite view of molecular motion, it will be worth while to consider in some detail the substance (or caloric) theory of heat. Most of the modern terminology of the subject is carried over from the time of the outmoded theory and would seem illogical without some knowledge of that theory. It is also of interest to trace this further aspect of the triumph of the mechanical view of the world.

The heat substance (named *caloric* by Lavoisier) was considered to be a fluid that could pass easily through all matter. It was also assumed that the particles of caloric *repelled each other* but were *attracted* by, and could attach themselves to, the corpuscles of ordinary matter.† Thus, when a sample of matter was heated, the added caloric quickly spread throughout the body and attached itself to the corpuscles of the matter, forming minute atmospheres of caloric around each corpuscle. The mutual repulsion of these caloric atmospheres partially overcame the attractive forces between the corpuscles of the matter and produced the well-known slight expansion of bodies with heating. The temperature (or "intensity" of heat) depended upon the amount of free (and thus "sensible") caloric; so, if two unequally heated bodies were brought into contact, heat flowed from the hotter to the colder until equilibrium was established. The total amount did not change—it was merely redistributed. The facts of specific heats fit into the theory by assigning to different substances different "capacities" for holding caloric. Lead, with a smaller capacity, would show a greater rise in temperature for a given amount of caloric than an equal mass of aluminum, which was assigned a greater capacity for holding the caloric fluid.

Since all substances show definite changes in their properties as a result of both physical and

---

† Although an atomic theory founded on experiment, as proposed by Dalton and as outlined in previous chapters, was not marked out until the nineteenth century, the idea of small particles of matter that might be moving appeared frequently in the scientific thought of the seventeenth and eighteenth centuries.

† This attachment was considered to be a quasi-chemical binding. The "capacity" to hold caloric (analogous to combining power) was assumed to be different for different substances and also to change, even for the same substance, with change of state, mechanical treatment, and chemical combination.

chemical changes, it was plausible to assume that such changes would cause the corpuscles of matter to exhibit marked changes in their capacities to combine caloric. When a solid substance was melted, for example, the corpuscles of the liquid, having a greater capacity for caloric than those of the solid, combined with sizable amounts of caloric and rendered it "latent." This *latent heat* would, then, have no effect on the temperature. These enlarged caloric "atmospheres" pushed the corpuscles apart and thus accounted for the expansion of the substance during its change of state. Again, when a chemical reaction gave off heat, it was plausible to assume that the products had had their capacities for holding caloric reduced by the reaction. The exactly opposite interpretation, that the products had *greater* capacities for holding caloric than the reactants, explained the dissociation reactions caused by adding heat. Examples of such reactions are the decomposition of mercuric oxide and of potassium chlorate (pp. 73 and 113). It was equally plausible to assume that mechanical stress would reduce the capacity of a substance for holding caloric. Thus the rise in temperature produced by compressing a gas or pounding a bar of metal or rubbing two surfaces together was simply evidence of the freeing of caloric as a result of the *reduction* of the capacity of the substance to hold it.

In this manner (and in much more detail) the caloric theory was expanded and developed to explain the known experimental facts, and after the 1780's it was generally accepted. But the concept of heat as a substance raised the question whether caloric possessed that most general property of all substances, *mass*. One of the ablest experimenters who investigated this question was the amateur scientist Count Rumford.† After many careful experiments, using the best balances available, he came to the conclusion in 1799 that all attempts to discover any effect of heat on the mass of bodies "will be fruitless." ‡ Rumford conducted many other experiments, the most important of which had to do with the generation of heat (the freeing of caloric) by friction. When, as part of his duties in Bavaria, he supervised the boring of cannon at the military arsenal in Munich, he was greatly impressed by the high temperature produced in the cannon and the still higher temperature of the metal chips cut out by the boring tool. According to the caloric theory, the mechanical treatment of the metal in boring *reduced* its capacity for holding caloric and thus yielded sizable amounts as free, "sensible" heat. If so, the chips should show a marked reduction in heat capacity—that is, in specific heat. Rumford tested this by careful measurements and found no appreciable difference between the specific heat of the chips and that of the bulk metal of the cannon. He then devised an experiment to test a necessary consequence of a substance theory of heat, that consequence being that any finite sample of matter must contain a limited amount of caloric. In this experiment he used a blunt, unsharpened tool and immersed the system in a large amount of water, the temperature rise of which would indicate the amount of caloric squeezed out of the metal by the grinding of the tool. The expectation, according to the caloric theory, was that after a sufficient number of rotations of the tool the temperature of the water would cease to rise, indicating that all of the caloric had been removed from the metal. But the experiment showed that there is *no limit* to the amount of caloric obtainable in this way. The water continued to get hotter and finally boiled. Numerous experiments of this kind led Rumford to the conclusion that the source of the heat so released must be inexhaustible. His interpretation was based on a *motion* of the corpuscles of matter. He found it "difficult, if not quite impossible, to form a distinct idea of anything capable of being so excited and communicated except it be MOTION" (the capitals are Rumford's).

---

† Benjamin Thompson (1753–1814), born in New England, at the time of the American Revolution went to England and subsequently to Germany, where he was employed by the reigning family of Bavaria and given the title of Count Rumford.

‡ This aspect of caloric as an imponderable fluid, though troublesome, was not decisive in the abandonment of the theory. The scientific world of the eighteenth and nineteenth centuries generally accepted a number of imponderable fluids as aids in explaining the facts of electricity and magnetism, propagation of light, etc. One such fluid (phlogiston, § 6-3) has already been mentioned, and we shall have occasion to refer to others later.

By the first decade of the nineteenth century, the experiments of Rumford and others raised serious doubts as to the validity of the caloric theory and appeared as convincing evidence for a kinetic view. Decisive as these experiments seemed to be, however, the caloric theory was not abandond at once, for there was no clearly constructed conceptual scheme to replace it. In spite of the discrepancies pointed out by Rumford, the caloric theory presented a common-sense, intuitively clear model for understanding most of the phenomena of heat. Although Rumford showed that a kinetic model would explain qualitatively such phenomena as heat conduction, thermal expansion, and change of state, such a model could not present at that time a satisfactory explanation of the well-established law of conservation of heat in mixtures. The caloric theory, on the other hand, made this law practically self-evident. We have here another example of a generally useful theory being retained in the face of serious inconsistencies because there was no better theory to replace it. The decision to accept the inconsistent order of several atomic weights in the periodic system of the elements (Chap. 8) was justified by later developments. The caloric theory, however, was finally abandoned—but only after almost fifty years.

The idea that heat is an aspect of motion was, as we have seen, by no means new at the time of Rumford's experiments. For over a hundred years, some of the most acute scientists (such as Newton, Boyle, and Cavendish) were inclined to consider heat as due to small vibrations of the "corpuscles" of matter. But they, as well as Rumford and others of the early nineteenth century, were unable to develop this idea into useful, quantitative working hypotheses. Such a development was delayed for two reasons.

First, the idea of small corpuscles, provocative as it may be, was at best vague and speculative. To attempt to apply the laws of motion to such a model would be rather fruitless. What was needed was a conceptually clear model for the structure of matter, firmly based on experimental evidence. Such a model was established, as we have seen, by Dalton and Avogadro, but it was not sufficiently developed to be generally accepted until after the middle of the nineteenth century. Cannizzaro's revival of Avogadro's hypothesis in 1858 and the successes of the periodic table in the 1870's were the determining factors.

The second reason for the delay in formulating a dynamical theory of heat was the lack of useful dynamical concepts for this kind of problem. In Chapters 3–5 the problems of motion were analyzed in terms of the concepts of force and inertia and the observed accelerations of bodies. Newton's precise statement of the relation between force and motion was extremely useful, not only in dealing with celestial motions, but also in dealing with the motions encountered in everyday life. There is much everyday experience, however, that cannot be accounted for, in a mechanical view of the world, by the simple application of a force. Such events as the boiling of a liquid, the pressure exerted by a gas, and the flow of electricity along a wire might conceivably be analyzed in terms of the actions of minute forces. But the forces are far from obvious. What was needed for these investigations was an extension of mechanics and the development of new and useful fundamental concepts. The development began in the years after Newton, but the new concepts—those of momentum and energy—were slow in coming. A clear understanding of the concept of energy and an appreciation of its universality were not achieved, in fact, until the middle of the nineteenth century, at about the same time that the existence of atoms and molecules began to be generally accepted.

This coincidental emergence of the atomic-molecular theory of the structure of matter and the dynamical concepts requisite for including this theory in a mechanical view of the world is an interesting historical fact. It does not mean, however, that the two developments were, at the time, seen to be related. The former emerged from the laws of chemical combination and the latter from a study of the motion of perceptible bodies. Before we can develop Rumford's suggestion that heat is an aspect of motion (presumably of sub-perceptible particles), we must therefore see how the study of the motion of gross matter gave rise to the concepts of momentum and energy.

## 11-3. A Famous Controversy on the "Quantity of Motion"

Some consideration of the ordinary motions encountered in the world around us would probably show that we all have an intuitive (if vague) notion that, in setting a body in motion, we give to the body something that, for the lack of a better name, we might call an "amount of motion." In getting an automobile up to 30 miles per hour, for instance, we give some motion to it. We must, obviously, add more motion to increase the speed to 50 miles per hour. We should all probably agree, on the other hand, that we must give much more motion to bring an express train to a certain velocity than to bring the automobile to the same velocity. This idea of motion as a physical entity has appeared in various forms throughout the history of science, and at one time it was endowed with the concreteness of matter. The work of Galileo and Newton removed this concreteness, and motion was thought of in abstract terms subject to precise mathematical description. The notion persisted, however, that the "quantity of motion" was a measurable, if abstract, entity. It was generally agreed that the measurement would involve both the mass and the velocity of the body; but toward the end of the seventeenth century a violent argument arose among scientists as to what combination of mass and velocity gave the proper measure for the quantity of motion.

René Descartes (1596–1650), the most active proponent of one view, held that the quantity of motion is the product of the mass and the velocity of the moving body. His argument ran somewhat like this: If a constant force were to act for equal times on two different bodies, it would impart the same amount of motion to each. In setting the first body, of mass $m$, in motion, the force would increase its velocity to some value $v$, and the product would be $mv$. If the same force now acted for the same time on a second body of twice the mass, it could increase the velocity of this body to only half as much as that of the first one. The product now would be $2m \times v/2 = mv$, which is the same as in the first case. Since the amount of motion imparted by the force is the same in both cases, mass times velocity must give the proper measure for it.

The most active opponent of this view was G. W. von Leibnitz (1646–1716) of Germany. He based his arguments on the observation that it requires the *same* "force" (as he called it) to raise a smaller and a larger mass through vertical distances that are inversely proportional to the masses. We see now that the word "force," as Leibnitz used it, had a very different meaning from that of Descartes (and Newton), since the larger mass required a larger force to counterbalance its weight. We would rephrase Leibnitz's observation (for a specific case) and say it requires the *same effort* to raise a 1 kgm mass 3 meters as to raise a 3 kgm mass 1 meter. The argument then proceeds by saying that, since the same effort was expended in raising the two masses, they would both acquire the same quantity of motion if released and allowed to fall freely back to the starting point. In such a situation, it is not the velocity but the velocity *squared* that is proportional to the distance fallen (equation 3-4); $v^2$ for the 3 kgm mass is one third that for the 1 kgm mass, and the product of the mass times the velocity squared is the *same* for both. Thus Leibnitz argued that the product $mv^2$ is the proper measure for the quantity of motion.

Several aspects of this controversy are of interest. First, it offers an excellent example of the importance in scientific thought of the precise use of language that was emphasized in the first chapter of this book. Clearly, Descartes and Leibnitz implied very different meanings by the use of the word "force"; as often happens in arguments, the confusion was one of terms. But, of more importance, the argument places historically the beginning of a new insight into dynamics. It gradually became evident, in the analysis of motion, not only that force was important but that the *cumulative* effect of force was even more important. Descartes was talking about the cumulative effect of a force acting for a *time;* Leibnitz was talking about the cumulative effect of a force acting through a *distance*. When it finally became clear that these two cumulative effects produced different entities, both were incorporated into the structure of dynamics, and both supplied simple and powerful methods of solving dynamical problems. We cannot trace this development through all the complex details—it lasted 150 years from the beginning of the eighteenth century—but we shall derive the essential arguments from the laws of motion known to us so far.

## 11-4. Momentum

On the first page of the *Principia,* Newton defines the "quantity of motion" as the product of the mass times the instantaneous velocity of a moving body. This quantity, so vigorously defended by Descartes, is called **momentum** in modern terminology. The algebraic statement of the definition of this concept is $M = mv$, in which $M$ represents the instantaneous value of the momentum. Momentum is a *vector quantity* since it is the product of a scalar (mass) and a vector (velocity). It may therefore be represented by a vector pointing in the direction of the instantaneous velocity and having a magnitude equal to $mv$. The units of momentum are mass times velocity, or kgm m/sec.

If we apply this concept to rectilinear motion, the equations of § 3-5 are valid, and we may express Newton's second law in terms of momentum. Since $a = v/t$, we may write $F = ma = mv/t$. The numerator on the right side is the momentum of the moving body at some instant $t$ seconds after the body started moving from rest. But since, in starting from rest, the initial momentum was zero, $mv$ is equal to the *change* of momentum during time $t$. Thus we may restate Newton's second law of motion: *The net force acting on a body is equal to the change in momentum per second;* or

$$F = \frac{\Delta M}{t} \qquad (11\text{-}2)$$

As an example, suppose that a 2 gram bullet is fired into a block of wood with a speed of 300 m/sec. As the bullet penetrates the block, it is brought to rest in $3 \times 10^{-4}$ sec as a result of the friction between the bullet and the wood. What is the average force acting on the bullet?

The bullet enters the block with momentum $M = 2 \times 10^{-3}$ kgm $\times 3 \times 10^2$ m/sec $= 0.6$ kgm m/sec, and ends up with zero momentum; $\Delta M$ is therefore $-0.6$ kgm m/sec. The minus sign signifies that the *change* in momentum is in the opposite direction to the velocity. Thus the force on the bullet is

$$F = \frac{-0.6 \text{ kgm m/sec}}{3 \times 10^{-4} \text{ sec}} = -2 \times 10^3 \text{ kgm m/sec}^2$$
$$= -2{,}000 \text{ newtons}$$

The minus sign indicates that the force is opposing the motion; that is, the bullet is slowing down.

We could have solved this problem equally well, of course, by first calculating the acceleration and then substituting in $F = ma$. But now consider this situation. Suppose that the block, instead of being rigidly supported, is mounted on the end of a spring so that it is free to move horizontally. A bullet entering the block exerts a force on it for the very short time required to stop the bullet. This force causes the block to move back and compress the spring momentarily. The spring then expands and returns the block to its initial position. If a succession of bullets is fired into the block, this process is repeated for each bullet provided the frequency of fire is not too great. If, on the other hand, the bullets are fired in rapid succession (as from a machine gun), a different effect is observed. The block moves back and compresses the spring a certain amount and remains in this position as long as the rate of fire is maintained; in other words, a stream of bullets entering the block in rapid succession produces the same effect as a *steady* force pushing on the block. We can determine this force experimentally by measuring the steady force that compresses the spring by the same amount as the bullets. We can also calculate it by using the momentum concept. Let us consider a specific example. Suppose that a stream of bullets, each with the same mass and velocity as in the previous example, enter the block at the rate of 15 bullets per second. According to Newton's third law, the force exerted by the bullets on the block is equal and opposite to the force exerted by the block on the bullets. This latter force changes the momenta of the bullets as they enter the block and is equal to the total change in momentum produced each second. As before, each bullet suffers a change of momentum of $-0.6$ kgm m/sec. Since the bullets are entering the block at the rate of 15 per second, the total change in momentum per second, and thus the force, is

$$F = -0.6 \text{ kgm m/sec } 15/\text{sec}$$
$$= -9 \text{ newtons}$$

and the force exerted on the block by the stream of bullets is 9 newtons. This result is found to be correct when tested experimentally. This problem, solved quite simply by the use of the momentum concept, would be very difficult by other methods. We shall see in the next chapter that a similar analysis permits the calculation of the pressure of a gas due to the incessant bombardment of the walls of the container by the rapidly moving molecules of the gas.

We have analyzed the problems of moving bodies by considering the effect of a single external force acting on a body. The first example above considered the force exerted *on the bullet* by the block, and the second considered the force exerted *on the block* by the bullet. But *both* forces are acting simultaneously, and the choice of one or the other of the pair is determined by convenience in analysis. This pairing is a general characteristic of the concept of force. We have already pointed out (§ 4-3) that forces *never* appear singly but always as interactions between *two* bodies. The forces may be elastic forces, frictional forces, gravitational attractions, electric or magnetic attractions or repulsions, or still other types of interactions. Always the forces appear in pairs; and the third law of motion tells us that at every instant one force of the pair is exactly equal, but oppositely directed, to the other one. Now consider two interacting bodies that are acted upon by no other forces than those of their interaction. The bodies may be moving in any manner whatever, and the forces may be due to any cause. The acting forces are, then, $F$ and $-F$. From equation 11-2 we have for one of the bodies $Ft = \Delta M$ and for the other $-Ft = \Delta M$ or $Ft = -\Delta M$; that is, for each body the cumulative effect of the force during time $t$ is equal to the change in momentum. But the forces are those of an interaction and therefore are exactly equal in *magnitude* and act for identical times. Thus the left sides of the equations above are equal, and consequently the *magnitudes* of the changes in momentum of the bodies are equal. But, remembering the vector character of momentum, we see that while one body *gains* momentum ($\Delta M$) the other *loses* an identical amount ($-\Delta M$). Thus the *sum* of the momenta of the two bodies *does not change* during the interaction. In other words, if we were to measure the momenta of the two bodies at the same instant and add them (vector addition), then measure them at some later instant and add them again, we should find that the two sums are equal. During the interaction the *total momentum remains constant*.

These arguments may be applied to any number of bodies if the only forces acting are interactions. Such a group of bodies is called an *isolated system*. The system may contain only two bodies (such as two billiard balls during impact) or an enormous number of bodies (such as the gas molecules in a closed container). In any case, if the only motion-producing forces are the interactions between components of the system, the total momentum of the system remains constant. No matter how many or how complicated the interactions are, each will produce equal and opposite changes of momentum in the interacting pair of bodies, and thus no change in the total momentum of the system will occur. This general principle, which was gradually becoming apparent in the seventeenth century, was stated succinctly by Newton: "the quantity of motion [that is, the total momentum] is not changed by the action of bodies among themselves." This extremely useful and still generally valid principle is now called the **law of conservation of momentum.** The law applies, it must be remembered, only to an isolated system of bodies. Only by considering a large number of specific examples can one appreciate fully the power and general usefulness of this law. We shall consider a few examples now, and others will appear later in this book.

First we consider an example with which we are already familiar, the inertia-car experiment (§ 4-2), in which the relative masses of two bodies were measured by their observed velocities. Here the system was composed of two bodies, the inertia cars. Since the cars could move only along the *horizontal* track, the force of gravity had no effect on the motion. Furthermore, the forces of friction had been reduced to a negligible amount. We thus had an isolated system, for the only forces affecting the motion were those of the interaction between the cars that was produced by the elasticity of the spring. At first the momentum of the system was zero, both cars being at rest. After the expansion of the spring, one car moved to the right with momentum $m_2v_2$ (see Fig. 4-1), and the other moved to the left with momentum $-m_1v_1$. (The minus sign tells us that this momentum is oppositely directed to the first one.) But the vector sum (in this case algebraic since the velocities are along the same straight line) of these momenta must still be zero. Thus $m_2v_2 - m_1v_1 = 0$; or $m_2v_2 = m_1v_1$, from which we see that $m_1/m_2 = v_2/v_1$, as we found on page 44.

As another example, consider the following situation. A loaded rifle is laid on a horizontal frictionless surface. When the powder explodes, the bullet leaves the rifle with a high velocity, and the rifle recoils in the opposite direction with a lower velocity. The system of rifle and bullet is isolated since the horizontal surface counterbalances the force of gravity. The forces of interaction (much more complex than those of the compressed spring in the preceding example) are due to the pressure of the gas generated by the explosion and to the great friction between the bullet and the rifle barrel. But, since these forces are not external to the system, we need not be concerned with their complexities. Suppose that the masses of the rifle and the bullet are 3 kgm and 4 grams respectively, and that the rifle is observed to recoil with a velocity of 0.48 m/sec. What is the muzzle velocity ($v$) of the bullet? Since the system was at rest before the explosion, the total momentum must remain zero, and we may write

$$4 \times 10^{-3} \text{ kgm } v - 3 \text{ kgm } 0.48 \text{ m/sec} = 0$$

from which we see that

$$v = \frac{1.44 \text{ kgm m/sec}}{4 \times 10^{-3} \text{ kgm}} = 360 \text{ m/sec}$$

The problem could be varied in the following way. Suppose that we know the mass of neither the gun nor the bullet but can measure the muzzle velocity independently. We know the total mass of gun plus bullet, however, by weighing the loaded gun before firing: $m_g + m_b = 3.004$ kgm. From the observed velocities we see that $m_b/m_g = 0.48/360$. With both the sum and the ratio of the masses known, a simple calculation will give the mass of each. This, of course, would be a roundabout way of determining the masses of the gun and the bullet. But there are almost exactly analogous situations in modern atomic science, where the method is very useful.

In Part Three we shall see that under certain circumstances an atom will break up explosively and the fragments will fly off with high velocities. Neither the atom nor the fragments, to be sure, can be seen directly; but, if the event occurs in a gas that is saturated with water vapor, the high-speed particles leave a thin trail of condensed vapor along their paths, and these "cloud" trails are easily photographed. The explosion of a uranium atom is shown schematically in Figure 11-2: when an atom in the foil explodes, two high-speed fragments move off to right and left. As the fragments move through the gas, they are slowed and finally brought to

FIGURE **11-2** *Cloud trails produced by fragments of an exploded uranium atom.*

rest. From the length and "density" of the trails the starting velocities of the fragments can be determined. The problem, then, dynamically, is the same as in the previous paragraph. The ratio of the masses of the fragments is given by the measured velocities, and the sum of their masses is (on the atomic-weight scale) the atomic weight of uranium.† The masses, thus determined, furnish an important aid to identifying the fragments.

Many similar examples may be cited. The simple process of walking is one. Initially, a person and the earth are at rest, but as soon as he begins to walk the friction between his feet and the earth comes into play as an interaction. He moves forward with a certain momentum, and the earth recoils with the same momentum. (The enormous mass of the earth, to be sure, makes the recoil velocity imperceptibly small.) On the other hand, if the person walks along some surface not rigidly attached to the earth (such as the floor of a rowboat), the recoil velocity (of the boat) is quite perceptible. In either case, the friction is the force that supplies the interaction, and without it walking would be impossible—as it almost is when one tries to walk on smooth ice.

Another familiar example is rocket flight. A rocket, by the combustion of its fuel, ejects a high-speed jet of gas. The mass of the gas is relatively small, but because of its great velocity it has a sizable momentum, and the rocket therefore "recoils" with appreciable velocity. As the gas continues to stream out, the momentum of the rocket increases, and a large final velocity is attained. The calculation is somewhat complicated by the fact that, as the fuel is consumed, the mass of the rocket decreases. But the principle is the same as in the previous examples. This recoil velocity, unlike the flight of an air-

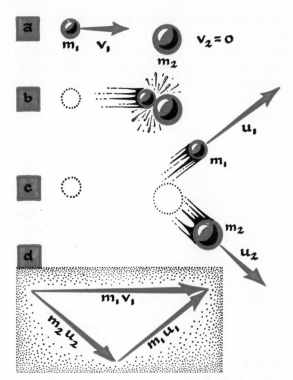

FIGURE **11-3** *Conservation of momentum during impact.*

plane, is not dependent on the presence of the atmosphere. Rockets operate more efficiently, in fact, at high altitudes, where the air resistance is greatly reduced, and in a vacuum they would operate still more efficiently. This takes interplanetary flight out of the realm of fictional fantasy and places it in the realm of real possibility.†

Another set of problems in which the law of conservation of momentum is very useful has to do with collisions. Here, since the forces during impact are internal in the system of colliding bodies, no change in total momentum occurs even though large changes in the momenta of individual components may occur, and the sum of the momenta of the colliding bodies before impact equals the sum after impact. If the collision is "head on," the changes in the momenta of the components are along the same straight line. This situation will be considered in more

† We have simplified this account somewhat. As we shall see, there are several smaller fragments in addition to the two large ones. The conservation of momentum still applies, however; the calculations are just more complicated. As an example of the principle involved, the reader should solve the following simplified problem. The velocities of separation of the fragments are $1.0 \times 10^5$ m/sec and $1.63 \times 10^5$ m/sec. Use 221 as the atomic weight of uranium (adjusted to take into account the neglected smaller fragments and other factors). Identify the two large fragments. (The more complex and detailed analysis yields the same result: Ba and Kr.)

† In the projected flight to the moon, how would the crew prevent the rocket from "crash-landing"? Remember that the moon has no atmosphere; parachutes or similar devices would therefore be useless.

detail later in this chapter. If the collision is not head on, the colliding bodies rebound in different directions. The analysis is unchanged in principle, however, if the vector nature of momentum is considered. Take the situation shown in Figure 11-3. Here (a) a body of mass $m_1$ approaches with velocity $v_1$ a body of mass $m_2$, which is at rest ($v_2 = 0$). After a glancing collision (b), the bodies move in different directions (c) with velocities $u_1$ and $u_2$ respectively. Before impact the total momentum of the system was equal to $m_1v_1 + 0$. This total momentum remains unchanged after impact. The *vector* sum of $m_2u_2$ and $m_1u_1$ therefore (d) equals $m_1v_1$. The composition of the colliding bodies and the nature of the forces during impact do not change the solution of this problem at all. For instance, $m_1$ and $m_2$ may be a golf ball and a billiard ball, or they may be atomic particles whose paths have been recorded by a cloud-track photograph. In the latter case the angle between $u_1$ and $u_2$ can be measured on the photograph and the vector diagram constructed. From this diagram one may obtain information about the nature of the recoil particle ($m_2$) when the nature of the first particle ($m_1$) is known from other experiments. Many modern atomic experiments are of this kind, and we shall refer to some of them later.

We have seen in this section that a consideration of the cumulative effect of a force acting for a certain time gives rise to a new dynamical concept, momentum. The solutions of many problems are simplified by this concept. We also found that a law of conservation of momentum is applicable to any system of interacting bodies. And from the few examples considered we perceive that the great power and usefulness of this law lie in its generality. It does not exclude any type of force, and it does not require a detailed understanding of the nature and origin of the forces. This general law, understood and formulated by Newton, attained its full development in the eighteenth century.

## 11-5. Work and Energy

The concepts involved in the cumulative effect of a force acting through a certain distance, on the other hand, were not clearly understood until the nineteenth century. This effect, which was the basis of Leibnitz's arguments about the quantity of motion, we now call **work**. The scientific meaning of the term "work" is much more specific than the ordinary usage. We might say, for instance, that a person is working while pushing hard against a wall or while sitting at a desk and figuring out a problem in mathematics. Each of these may be an arduous task, but in the scientific sense neither is work. Work, in science, is the production of motion against some opposing force. To slide a trunk across a room requires some expenditure of work to overcome the retarding force of friction. To lift a box from the floor to a table, an upward force must work to overcome the pull of gravity. It is in this sense of a force acting through a distance that the word "work" is used in science. Without motion no amount of force would do work. Standing and holding a heavy suitcase while waiting for a train is certainly fatiguing, but in the scientific sense it is not work. The amount of work must, then, involve both the force and the distance moved and increases with either (or both); it is, in fact, the product of force and distance. If we let $W$ represent work, we have, *by definition*,

$$W = Fs \qquad (11\text{-}3)$$

We obtain the unit of work by multiplying the force and distance units. Any consistent combination is possible. In the system of units used in this book, work equals newtons times meters. This unit is called a **joule** in honor of J. P. Joule, a British scientist of the nineteenth century. The newton, however, is expressed in terms of mass, length, and time; so work also may be expressed in these terms. To summarize:

$$\text{work} = \text{joule} = \text{newton meter} = \frac{\text{kgm m}^2}{\text{sec}^2}$$

Work is a scalar quantity. This may seem strange at first since it is the product of the vectors force and displacement; but the directions of $F$ and $s$ play an important role in the definition of work. Equation 11-3 will give the work accomplished *only if* F *and* s *are in the same direction.* For instance, *no* work is done, in the scientific sense, in carrying a suitcase across a room (if the air resistance is neglected), for the force is vertical and the displacement horizontal, and therefore no force is acting in the direction of motion. The centripetal force acting on a body in circular motion (§ 5-2) does no work, since at every instant the force acts along the radius of the circle, and the instantaneous motion (along the tangent to the circle) is at right angles to the force. In general, if the force is acting at some angle other than 90° to the direction of motion, only the component (see p. 53) that is parallel to the displacement is accomplishing work, and that is the force to be used in equation 11-3. In sliding the block of Figure 5-2a along the table, only the 8.7 newtons is doing work. If the block is slid 2 meters, 17.4 joules of work is done, *not* 20 joules.

Work may be done in many ways and against many kinds of forces. We have already mentioned the work we do against the force of gravity in lifting a body. We must also do work to compress a spring or, more generally, to deform any elastic body. A third kind of work is that required to overcome inertia. We know that a net unbalanced force is required to accelerate a mass (Newton's second law). If the acceleration is linear, the accelerating force moves a distance in the direction of the acceleration and thus does work. In all these situations the work done on the body may be recovered. Once a weight has been lifted, for instance, it will fall, if released, under the action of the pull of gravity. This falling weight will lift a second weight if attached to it by a cord passed over a pulley. Or, again, water falling over a mill wheel from behind a dam will do the work of turning the machinery of the mill. A compressed spring, when released, will expand and do work on some attached mechanism, such as the wheels of a watch. And, finally, a moving mass will do work on any agency that stops it. A rapidly moving hammer will, upon impact, deliver the work necessary to drive a nail into resisting wood. To drive the nail by a steady push would require a force many times the weight of the hammer. (Just laying the hammer on the nail head will not move the nail into the wood at all.)

From these examples we see that by having work done on them bodies acquire a new property, a capacity for doing work. The lifted weight, the compressed spring, and the moving mass all seem to have "stored up" the work that was done on them and under the proper conditions will give it back. This *capacity to do work* is called **energy.** Here again is a word that has many, often vague, meanings in our everyday language but only one specific meaning in scientific usage. Even so, we sense a generality in the definition and suspect that the concept of energy encompasses many more situations than the simple mechanical ones mentioned so far. This indeed is so. As we continue our study, we shall encounter chemical energy, electrical energy, thermal energy, radiant energy, and finally "atomic" energy. Much of the study of our physical environment consists, in fact, of investigations of these various forms of energy. The concept of energy was first formulated quantitatively, however, for mechanical problems.

In the examples we have been discussing, the bodies were endowed with energy because forces acting on them were doing work. The amount of energy given to a body is, then, just equal to the work done by the moving force. But this is not usually the *total* energy of the body, for it may already have acquired some energy from previous actions. A book lifted from a chair to a table, for example, has more energy than when resting on the chair. But it had energy on the chair, since it could do work while falling to the floor, and could do still more work in falling from the floor to the ground. But even on the ground the energy of the book is not zero, for it could do still more work in falling down a well, and so on (at least in principle) to the center of the earth. Thus we see that in this case (and generally also) it would be more useful to calculate the *change* of energy rather than the total energy. One further general comment: the units of energy are those of work; and energy also is a scalar quantity.

## 11-6. *Gravitational Potential Energy*

Let us now consider in more detail the energy changes involved in lifting masses against the force of gravity. Suppose (Fig. 11-4a) that we lift a mass from some level, *A*, to a higher one,

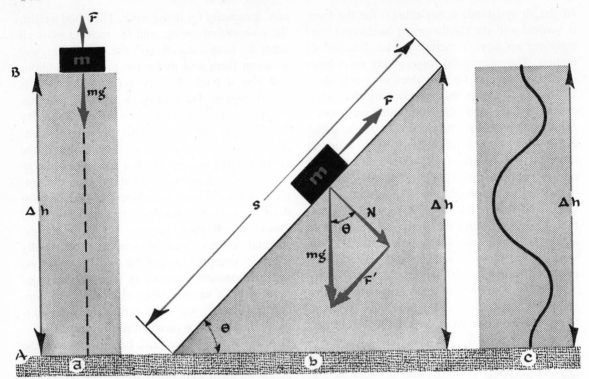

**FIGURE 11-4** *The increase in potential energy is independent of the path along which the weight is lifted from level A to level B.*

*B*, which is a vertical height, $\Delta h$, above *A*. We lift the mass straight up and move it with a small uniform speed so that the work done to overcome inertia is negligible. Under these conditions, the resistance of the air is also imperceptibly small. The amount of force required, then, is equal to the weight of the body, and the work done is $F(\Delta h) = mg(\Delta h)$. Now suppose that, instead of lifting the mass vertically, we slide it up an inclined plane from *A* to *B* (Fig. 11-4b) and specify that the plane is *frictionless*. The required amount of force is now something less than the weight $mg$. We may resolve $mg$ into rectangular components, $N$ perpendicular to the plane and $F'$ parallel to the plane. In sliding the mass, we must do work against $F'$ only, since $N$ is at right angles to the motion. Since the angles $\theta$ are equal (sides mutually perpendicular), we have, from similar right triangles, $F'/mg = \Delta h/s$ or $F' = mg(\Delta h)/s$, in which $s$ is the length of the plane from *A* to *B*. Since we move the mass with no acceleration, and since there is no retarding frictional force, the magnitude of the

moving force, $F$, is equal to $F'$. The work done is therefore $Fs = \dfrac{mg(\Delta h)}{s} s = mg(\Delta h)$; that is, the work done in sliding the mass up the plane is exactly the same as the work done in lifting it vertically. If we now carry the mass from *A* to *B* along *any* other frictionless path, such as the curved one (Fig. 11-4c), we obtain the same result. This can be understood if we remember that a small enough length, $\Delta s$, of the path is a straight line. Thus the whole path is a series of minute inclined planes, and the sum of the amounts of work needed to move the mass successively up these planes comes out to be $mg(\Delta h)$.† We conclude that the increase in the energy of a body as a result of being raised against the force of gravity depends only on the weight of the body and the *vertical* distance between the initial and final positions, and is independent of the path taken between these posi-

† Construct a path from *A* to *B* consisting of three straight-line sections of different inclination, and show that the work over this path is $mg(\Delta h)$.

tions. This kind of energy, which a body has by virtue of its position, is called *potential energy* (abbreviated as PE). Our conclusion may be summarized algebraically:†

$$\Delta(PE) = mg(\Delta h) \qquad (11\text{-}4)$$

A gradual and circuitous route up a mountain may be less fatiguing but produces no more increase in PE than a vertical climb up a precipitous face. Or, more specifically, suppose that an 80 kgm man goes from one floor of a building to a floor 27 meters higher. He may go up by elevator, or he may climb the stairs. In either case his PE is increased by

$$\Delta(PE) = 80 \text{ kgm } 9.8 \frac{m}{sec^2} 27 \text{ m}$$

$$= 2.11 \times 10^4 \text{ kgm } \frac{m^2}{sec^2} = 2.11 \times 10^4 \text{ joules}$$

After he arrives at the higher floor, he may go from room to room, but his PE will not change a bit.‡ (Consider the moon's orbit about the earth to be circular. Does its PE change during the monthly cycle?)

## 11-7. *Kinetic Energy*

We have already seen that a moving mass has a capacity to do work. The energy that a body has by virtue of its motion is called *kinetic energy* (abbreviated as KE). The energy is derived from the work done by the accelerating force to overcome inertia while setting the body in motion. But this is precisely the force that appears in Newton's second law of motion. If the body is moved through distance $s$ while be-

---

† The validity of equation 11-4 is limited by our tacit assumption that $g$ is a constant. It certainly is the same for all masses at a given position, but it decreases with increased elevation. This change in $g$ is very slight for moderate values of $\Delta h$, and equation 11-4 therefore has many applications. For large values of $\Delta h$ (such as those achieved by high-altitude rockets) the varying value of $g$ must be taken into consideration.

‡ There are other forms of PE than that due to gravitational forces. A compressed spring has PE as a result of the work done against elastic forces. Later, in our study of electricity, we shall find that charged particles exert forces on each other; as these particles approach or recede, changes in electrical PE occur as a result of the changing positions.

ing accelerated, the work done against inertia, and therefore the gain in KE, is $\Delta(KE) = Fs = mas$. Now suppose that the body started from rest and acquired final instantaneous speed $v$. Since the body had zero KE initially, $\Delta(KE)$ would be equal to the instantaneous final KE. We have, then, $KE = mas = m\frac{v^2}{2s}s$, since for this situation $a = v^2/2s$ (by equation 3-4), or

$$KE = \tfrac{1}{2}mv^2 \qquad (11\text{-}5)$$

In words this says that any moving body has a capacity to do work in an amount equal to half the product of its mass and the square of its instantaneous speed. The units of this product are kgm m²/sec², which are joules. This energy becomes available for doing work whenever the body is stopped; part of it becomes available if the speed of the body is reduced.

Let us now return to the hammer and nail. These would be reasonable data: mass of hammer, 0.6 kgm; speed of hammer, 4 m/sec; distance nail is driven into wood, 2 cm. Question: what is the average force of resistance bringing the hammer to rest (and thus, by reaction, the force on the nail)? The KE of the hammer at the instant of impact is KE = ½ 0.6 kgm 16 m²/sec² = 4.8 newton meters. As the hammer comes to rest, it does this amount of work moving the nail 2 cm into the wood. If the average force moving the nail is $F$, then $F$ 0.02 m = 4.8 newton m, and $F = 240$ newtons. This force is more than forty times as great as the weight of the hammer. We can now understand the enormous and often destructive forces that come into play when large masses moving at high speed are brought to rest abruptly. The reader can show, for instance, that over three million newtons come into play if a $2 \times 10^3$ kgm car traveling at 30 m/sec (approximately 70 miles an hour) runs into a tree (assume an effective stopping distance of 25 cm).

In modern research, atomic particles with high (and controlled) speeds are fired into samples of matter, and the results of these bombardments yield information on the nature of the bombarded atoms. If the bombarding particle is charged electrically, it can be made to travel in a circle, in one portion of which electrical forces do work on the particle. Thus, as the particle goes round inside the apparatus, it gains KE in each lap and increases its speed. One such particle (a proton), which has a mass of $1.67 \times 10^{-27}$ kgm, can be injected into the accelerator with a speed of $1.88 \times 10^7$ m/sec. If the accelerator does $1.15 \times 10^{-15}$ joule of work on the particle each time round, how many revolutions does the particle make to attain a speed of $3.00 \times 10^7$ m/sec? Initially, the particle has KE $= \frac{1}{2}$ $1.67 \times 10^{-27}$ kgm $3.53 \times 10^{14}$ m²/sec² $= 2.96 \times 10^{-13}$ joule; at a speed of $3 \times 10^7$ m/sec it has KE $= 7.56 \times 10^{-13}$ joule. Hence the gain in KE is $\Delta(\text{KE}) = (7.56 - 2.96) \times 10^{-13}$ joule $= 4.60 \times 10^{-13}$ joule. This, divided by the work done per revolution, gives as the number of revolutions $\dfrac{4.60 \times 10^{-13} \text{ joule}}{1.15 \times 10^{-15} \text{ joule/rev}}$ $= 400$ rev. This important type of problem and other, related ones could, in principle, be solved in terms of force, distance, and time. But in many such problems the magnitude and even the nature of the force are not known; and in all cases the calculation would be much more complex than this solution in terms of KE. Furthermore, measurements of KE often provide information on the nature of the forces involved.

## 11-8. Conservation of Mechanical Energy

Let us now consider a simple mechanical situation in which both PE and KE are changing simultaneously. Suppose (Fig. 11-5a) that a mass, $m$, is initially at rest at some level, $B$. It then has, with reference to lower level $A$, PE equal to $mg(\Delta h)$, and it has zero KE. It is now released and allowed to fall freely. The only force acting, then, is the force of gravity, which accelerates $m$ vertically toward $A$. When $m$ arrives at $A$, it has *lost* PE by the amount $\Delta(\text{PE}) = -mg(\Delta h)$. (The minus sign indicates that the PE has decreased.) At level $A$, however, $m$ is moving with speed $v$ and thus has a KE that is the *gain* in KE from $B$ to $A$ since $m$ was initially at rest. Thus $\Delta(\text{KE}) = \frac{1}{2}mv^2$. But this was a constantly accelerated motion from rest through distance $\Delta h$. Hence $v^2 = 2g(\Delta h)$, and $\Delta(\text{KE}) = \frac{1}{2}m2g(\Delta h) = mg(\Delta h)$. Thus we see that, as $m$ fell from $B$ to $A$, it lost PE but gained an exactly equal amount of KE.

Now suppose that, instead of letting $m$ fall freely, we let it slide down a *frictionless* inclined plane (Fig. 11-5b). Again $\Delta(\text{PE}) = -mg(\Delta h)$

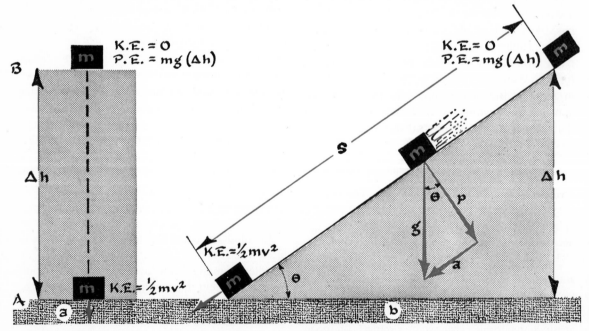

FIGURE **11-5** *Transformation of potential energy into kinetic energy.*

(same difference in levels). In this case, however, the acceleration is only a part of the gravitational acceleration. The component of $g$ perpendicular to the plane $(p)$ produces no change in motion since it is counterbalanced by the push of the plane;† the component parallel to the plane $(a)$ increases the speed of $m$ to some value $v$ at the bottom of the plane. Hence $v^2 = 2as$ if $s$ is the length of the plane. But (from similar right triangles) $a/g = \Delta h/s$. We may write, then, $\Delta(\text{KE})$

$$= \tfrac{1}{2}mv^2 = \tfrac{1}{2}m2as = \frac{mg(\Delta h)}{s}s = mg(\Delta h).$$

Although $m$ will take longer coming down the plane than falling freely, we find that it gains the same amount of KE in each case. If we now let $m$ come down along *any* frictionless path, we arrive at the same result, for we have already seen that a curved path may be treated as a series of minute inclined planes. This conclusion can be tested experimentally. A steel sphere rolling on a hard surface is very nearly frictionless. If two identical spheres roll down from the same vertical height above a table, one along a straight board and the other along a curved one (similar to a playground slide), they arrive at the table at different times but roll across the table at the same speed, neither one gaining on the other.

We see here another conservation principle emerging. For each case we found that $\Delta(\text{PE}) + \Delta(\text{KE}) = 0$ since the first was $-mg(\Delta h)$ and the second was $+mg(\Delta h)$. In other words, the PE that disappeared as $m$ moved down reappeared as KE of the same amount. Each situation, furthermore, was an isolated system. In the first the system was the falling mass and the earth, the gravitational interaction being the only forces involved. In the second the system was composed of $m$, the plane, and the earth; and the forces again were internal—namely, the gravitational interaction and the perpendicular interaction between $m$ and the plane. Thus, for at least these two systems, we may say that the *total mechanical energy* (potential and kinetic) remains unchanged; or the energy *is conserved*.

If other forces are acting, we may expand the

system to include them, and then we find that mechanical energy is still conserved. We may, for instance, instead of letting $m$ fall freely, attach it to a smaller mass, $m_2$, by a light cord passed over a frictionless pulley. Now the system consists of the two masses, the pulley, and the earth. The larger mass, $m$, as it moves down through $\Delta h$, loses PE but, being retarded by the smaller mass, does not attain as high a speed as when falling freely and thus gains less KE. The smaller mass, on the other hand, moves up with increasing speed and thus gains both PE and KE. The rotating pulley also acquires some KE. If these energy changes are computed, it is found again that mechanical energy is conserved. For more complicated systems, involving elastic and electrical forces of interaction as well as gravitational forces, the calculations become complex, but again the total mechanical energy remains unchanged. Individual components of the system, as they move about, may experience large energy changes, but in such a way that the energy lost by one part is gained by another and the *sum* of all the potential and kinetic energies remains unchanged.

So far, in our discussion of mechanical energy, one very common force has been conspicuously excluded. This is the force of friction. Friction, unlike other forces, cannot be included in the system and still leave mechanical energy conserved. Consider the simple situation of sliding a box across the floor of a room. Work certainly is being done, but little is accomplished besides changing the position of the box on the floor and a slight warming up of the surfaces rubbed together. Suppose that we slide the box up an inclined plane (Fig. 11-4b) but do not exclude friction at the surface. The force required is now greater than $F$ by an amount equal to the retarding force of friction, and the work expended in getting the box up to $B$ is therefore *greater* than $mg(\Delta h)$. But the PE at $B$ is still only $mg(\Delta h)$ since the box will arrive at $A$ with only that amount of KE if allowed to fall *freely*. But suppose that we let the block slide back down the inclined plane. Now the force of friction reverses and still retards the motion, so that the box moves down the plane with an acceleration *less* than $a$ (Fig. 11-5b).

---

† A frictionless surface can push at right angles to itself. You can easily stand still on a horizontal sheet of smooth ice; walking is what is difficult.

Hence the box arrives at $A$ with KE less than $mg(\Delta h)$. In this cycle, then, only a fraction of the work expended in sliding the box to level $B$ is stored as PE, and only a fraction of this appears as KE when the box slides back to $A$. In this isolated system (as in others including frictional forces) mechanical energy is continuously decreasing or being *dissipated*. Such a system is called a *dissipative system*, and friction is called a *dissipative force*.

We see, then, that we must put a limitation on our conservation law for mechanical energy: we can apply it only to systems that have no (or negligible) dissipative forces. We now see that, with respect to energy, Leibnitz's argument was correct. We can rephrase the argument (§ 11-3) in this way: A 3 kgm mass raised 1 meter has received the same PE as a 1 kgm mass raised 3 meters. If allowed to fall freely to the original level, each will acquire the *same* KE = $\frac{1}{2}mv^2$. This is just half of Leibnitz's "quantity of motion." The argument took place near the end of the seventeenth century, and it was not until the latter part of the eighteenth century that the law of conservation of mechanical energy evolved into a clear and generally useful form.

## 11-9. Conservative Systems

Systems of bodies with no dissipative forces are called *conservative systems;* and to these the conservation of PE + KE may be applied. A pendulum, for example, offers a very close approximation to a conservative system. If the pendulum bob is pulled to one side ($B$ of Fig. 11-6a) and released, it swings down through $A$, up to $C$, and then reverses and repeats the cycle. As it moves down toward $A$, it loses PE; this appears as KE, and the bob speeds up. At $A$ it has a maximum KE (and speed) and a minimum PE. As it moves toward $B$ (or $C$), it climbs through a vertical distance $\Delta h$, increases its PE to a maximum, and loses KE in order to supply this increase of PE. Thus, as the pendulum swings, PE is constantly being converted into KE, and vice versa. If, during a swing, a peg is placed at $P$ as the bob leaves $B$, then after

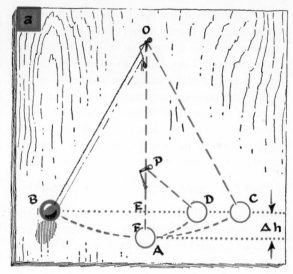

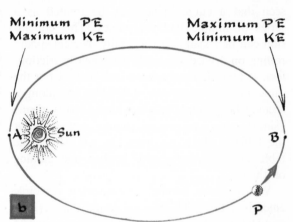

FIGURE **11-6** *Conservation of mechanical energy for* (a) *a simple pendulum and* (b) *a planet.*

$A$ the bob moves along a circle of shorter radius and climbs more steeply to $D$. But $D$ is observed to be on the horizontal line $BC$; that is, the gain in PE is the *same* as before. (If the peg is placed at $F$, where the distance $EF$ is more than half of $\Delta h$, what will happen?)

The speed of the bob at $A$ is easily calculated. Since the bob is momentarily at rest at $B$ (or $C$ or $D$), the KE at $A$ is the *gain* in KE. Hence, since $\Delta(\text{KE}) + \Delta(\text{PE}) = 0$, we have $\frac{1}{2}mv^2 - mg(\Delta h) = 0$ or $v^2 = 2g(\Delta h)$ or $v = \sqrt{2g(\Delta h)}$; that is, the speed at $A$ is the same as though the bob had fallen freely through the distance $\Delta h$. But the velocities are *not* equal; in the former case the velocity is horizontal, and in the latter it is vertical. In the pendulum system there is, in addition to the force of gravity, the action of the tension in the string. This supplies the centripetal force to keep the bob moving along a circle; but, as noted previously, this force does no work and thus does not affect the energy balance.

A situation similar to that of the pendulum is shown in Figure 11-6b. As the planet $P$ moves toward $B$, it is constantly getting farther from the sun. But, to accomplish this separation, work must be done against the interacting force of gravity between the planet and the sun. (In effect, the planet is moving to a "higher" level "above" the sun.) Hence the planet gains PE as it approaches $B$ and, since there is no other source of energy, also loses KE and thus slows down. As the planet moves from $B$ to $A$, the reverse takes place; PE constantly decreases and KE increases; and then the cycle starts again. Here, once more, we have a continuous conversion of mechanical energy from one form to the other as the planet swings round the sun in its orbit. The change in speed is more tedious to compute than for the pendulum, for in this case the force of gravity is continuously changing in magnitude, but it is in complete agreement with Kepler's second law.

Let us now reconsider the situation of colliding bodies (§ 11-4). We add the limitation that the collision be *perfectly elastic*. A perfectly elastic collision, *by definition*, is one in which no mechanical energy is dissipated during impact; that is, the system is conservative. For gross matter, however, this condition is never realized exactly. A ball dropped on a horizontal surface, for instance, will not rebound to the same height. Suppose that a golf ball is dropped from a height of 1 m onto a very hard, massive object such as a steel anvil. If the mass of the ball is 0.1 kgm, it has approximately 1 joule PE

($g \approx 10$ m/sec$^2$) with reference to the surface of the anvil. But the ball is observed to rebound to a height of only 0.6 m; during impact 0.4 joule, or 40 percent, of the mechanical energy has been dissipated. High-speed photographs show that during impact the ball is compressed and momentarily flattens. Thus, during impact, KE is changed to elastic PE and back to KE as the ball expands. During the compression and expansion some mechanical energy is dissipated by internal friction, and the ball rebounds with less KE than it had at the moment of impact. Other substances behave similarly but to a different degree. A soft rubber ball will rebound to only 0.3 m, and a ball of soft lead or one of putty will not rebound at all. A glass ball or a hard steel ball, on the other hand, will rebound to a height of more than 0.9 m—that is, almost back to the original height. Substances like glass and steel are called highly elastic, and substances like putty are completely inelastic.

Unlike the collisions of gross matter, however, many types of collisions between atomic and sub-atomic particles are perfectly elastic. In such collisions *both* momentum and mechanical energy are conserved during impact. Consider the situation shown in Figure 11-7. A particle of mass $m_1$, moving horizontally with velocity $v_1$, approaches a second particle, of mass $m_2$, which is at rest (a). The collision is "head on" (b); so after impact the particles move (c) with velocities $u_1$ and $u_2$ respectively, which are along the same straight line as $v_1$. Since the particles are moving along a horizontal line, there is no change in PE. We see, then, that the total momentum and the total KE of the system remain unchanged during impact. Hence

$$m_1v_1 = m_1u_1 + m_2u_2$$
$$\tfrac{1}{2}m_1v_1^2 = \tfrac{1}{2}m_1u_1^2 + \tfrac{1}{2}m_2u_2^2$$

These equations may be combined to yield

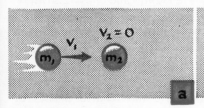

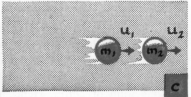

FIGURE **11-7** *Elastic impact.*

two useful relations between the velocities and the masses. (The algebra is tedious but straightforward.) The relations are

$$u_1 = u_2 \frac{m_1 - m_2}{2m_1} \qquad (11\text{-}6)$$

$$v_1 = u_2 \frac{m_1 + m_2}{2m_1} \qquad (11\text{-}7)$$

We have already seen that steel and glass are almost perfectly elastic. Hence, to a very good approximation, equations 11-6 and 11-7 can be verified by observation of the impacts of steel and glass spheres rolling on a hard and smooth surface. There are several interesting cases.

Suppose that $m_1 = m_2 = m$ (that is, we have two identical steel spheres); then $m_1 - m_2 = 0$ and $u_1 = 0$. That is, the first sphere comes to rest, and the second moves off with the same momentum and energy. This is consistent with equation 11-7 since $v_1 = u_2 \dfrac{m + m}{2m}$ or $u_2 = v_1$. The velocity of the second particle after impact ($u_2$) must always be positive; that is, it must always move off to the right in Figure 11-7. But the first particle after impact may have a velocity ($u_1$) that is either positive or negative.

Suppose, now, that $m_1$ is greater than $m_2$ (a steel sphere rolling against a glass one); then, in equation 11-6, $m_1 - m_2$ is positive, and so is $u_1$. That is, the steel sphere rolls along after the glass one but with reduced velocity. On the other hand, if $m_1$ is less than $m_2$ (a glass sphere rolling against a steel one), then, in equation 11-6, $m_1 - m_2$ is negative, and so is $u_1$. That is, the glass sphere rebounds to the left as the steel one moves off to the right. In later chapters we shall encounter similar situations involving impacts between sub-atomic particles.

If $m_2$ is very large, compared with $m_1$, then, in the numerator of equation 11-7, $m_1$ may be neglected, and $u_2 = 2m_1v_1/m_2$. Put this in equation 11-6, where $m_1$ may again be neglected in the numerator, and we have $u_1 = 2m_1v_1/m_2$ $(-m_2/2m_1)$ or $u_1 = -v_1$. That is, $m_1$ rebounds to the left with the same *speed* as before impact and thus with the same KE. But the *velocity* has been reversed, and thus $m_1$ experiences a *change* in momentum of $2m_1v_1$. Hence this amount of momentum is transferred to $m_2$. This can be

seen from equation 11-6. For this case of very large $m_2$, we have $2m_1u_1 = -m_2u_2$. But $u_1 = -v_1$; hence $m_2u_2 = 2m_1v_1$. Examples of this case are a steel ball bouncing off the surface of the earth and a gas molecule rebounding from the wall of a container. Neither the earth nor the wall shows an appreciable velocity after impact ($u_2$) because of their relatively enormous mass; but the transfer of momentum ($2m_1v_1$) is proportional to the force on each during impact. We shall consider the case of the gas molecule again in the next chapter.

The reverse of the last situation offers another interesting case—an $m_1$ very large compared with $m_2$. We could approximate this by rolling a large steel ball against a small glass marble. The steel ball is observed to continue moving with practically no decrease in velocity, and the marble rebounds with a velocity twice that of the ball. This result is consistent with equations 11-6 and 11-7. By setting $m_2$ equal to 0 (negligibly small) the reader can easily show that $u_1 = v_1$ and that $u_2 = 2u_1 = 2v_1$. The impact of an $\alpha$-particle with an electron is another example of this situation and one that much more nearly approximates the assumption that $m_2 = 0$ (here $m_1/m_2 \approx 8,000/1$).

As a final example of elastic collisions, consider the following. Suppose that a particle can be projected repeatedly with the same velocity each time but that neither the value of this velocity ($v_1$) nor the mass of the particle ($m_1$) can be observed directly. When this unknown particle collides with another particle of 2 units mass and initially at rest, this known particle is observed to move off with a velocity of 5 m/sec. The unknown is then made to collide with a particle of 6 units mass, which is observed to move off with a velocity of 2.5 m/sec. What are the mass and the velocity of the unknown? To each collision we apply equation 11-7 and get $v_1 = 5(m_1 + 2)/2m_1$ and $v_1 = 2.5(m_1 + 6)/2m_1$. But $v_1$ is the same in both collisions; hence $5m_1 + 10 = 2.5m_1 + 15$, from which $m_1 = 2$ units of mass. Then, with this, equation 11-7 gives $v_1 = 5$ m/sec. In this example we used "units of mass" for the $m$'s to emphasize that the relations give the relative masses of the colliding particles. For gross matter we generally use the arbitrary unit kgm. In a later chapter we shall see that a similar computation played a significant role in the discovery of the neutron—an important atomic particle. The known recoil particles were then hydrogen and nitrogen atoms, and the masses were expressed in the arbitrary units of the atomic-weight scale.

We have seen in this section and the four preceding sections that consideration of the cumulative effect of a force acting through a distance gave rise to the concept of work and, in terms of the capacity for doing work, to the concept of energy. We also saw that in an isolated system the total mechanical energy is conserved provided there are no dissipative forces acting. Although very useful in many problems, the conservation of energy, at this stage of our development, is a restricted principle and is not as generally valid as the conservation of momentum.

## 11-10. *General Law of Conservation of Energy*

The most prevalent dissipative force is the force due to friction. As we have seen, the work done against the force of friction produces no increase in either PE or KE. It does produce heat. If it could be established that heat and mechanical energy are equivalent, the principle of the conservation of energy could be extended to include dissipative systems as well as conservative ones. In a much less specific way this was Rumford's idea when he stated that heat must be motion (§ 11-2). He did not develop the idea, however, but was content to demonstrate the large quantities of heat that could be produced by friction. This was not merely neglect on Rumford's part. The ideas about energy were just beginning to emerge; in fact, the word "energy" in its specific sense came into use only after the first decade of the nineteenth century. And "force" was still used with many meanings in addition to its specific mechanical meaning.

The first half of the nineteenth century was a period of many discoveries and developments. As we have seen in previous chapters, this was

the period when the foundations of chemistry were laid, primarily by Dalton and Avogadro. Many chemical reactions produced heat in amounts proportional to the number of moles of the reacting chemicals. As early as the late eighteenth century an interesting relation of chemical heat was found: Lavoisier and P. S. de Laplace found by experiment that a guinea pig developed as much heat as the chemical reaction of burning its food intake. A reaction between zinc and copper produces about $5 \times 10^4$ cal per mole of zinc. It was found early in the nineteenth century, however, that these metals, when arranged properly, would react and cause an electric current to flow instead of producing heat. The properties of such currents were studied, and new discoveries about them were made, primarily by Michael Faraday, a great British experimentalist. As we shall see in Part Two, two wires carrying electric currents exert on each other forces that can move the wires and do work. In certain circumstances, however, electric currents produce sizable amounts of heat in the wires, the amount depending on the amount of current. Another effect of electric currents was the dissociation of certain compounds, a process that had previously been caused by the addition of heat. It was also discovered that one could produce electric currents by *moving* a magnet near a conducting circuit; that is, by doing mechanical work to move the magnet, one could cause currents to flow—which currents, as stated above, could do work or generate heat. The study of gases, given great impetus by the invention of the steam engine, led to the discovery of further close relations between heat and work. It was found that the temperature of a gas rose in proportion to the work done in compressing it. Conversely, if a gas expanded against the atmospheric pressure and thus did work, heat had to be supplied to keep its temperature constant.

These relations, and others, led increasingly to the belief that all the activities of nature are in some way connected—are, ultimately, all parts of a unified theme. The research was not, it is true, directed toward establishing this idea. Each development was carried on independently of the others. But in retrospect one senses a gradual emergence of a general law of conservation of energy, coming from many sides as the various branches of science developed. And, as pointed out above, heat played a central role.

The first to pull together these various ideas on the interchangeability of heat and work was J. R. von Mayer (1814–1878), a young German physician. He began to speculate on the relation of animal heat and chemical reaction and went on from that to the interchangeability of all energies in nature.† In 1842 he published an essay in which he enunciated the principle that we now call the general law of conservation of energy. His highly imaginative arguments were mostly unsupported generalization. He came to the conclusion that energies are "indestructible, convertible entities." This was the first general statement of the principle of the conservation and equivalence of all energies. His writings were not well received, however, and it was not until toward the end of his life that he received honor for his prophetic insight. Toward the end of his essay, Mayer raised the question: "How great is the quantity of heat that corresponds to a given quantity of kinetic or potential energy?" With great sagacity he chose from among available data the one from which he could calculate the answer. It was known that a gas has two specific heats depending on the condition of measurement. If the gas is confined so that it cannot expand while being heated, it has a certain specific heat; if it is allowed to expand while being heated so that the pressure remains constant, it has larger specific heat. Mayer assumed that this *extra* heat was equivalent to the work done by the gas in expanding against the constant pressure of the atmosphere. On this basis he calculated a numerical equivalence between heat and work, which, in view of the inaccuracies in the available data, is in surprisingly good agreement with our present value.

This, of course, was the crucial point. If heat and dynamical energy are the same entity, there must be a constant ratio between the two; that is, there must be a constant rate of exchange, so that any amount of work (measured in joules) will always bear the same ratio to an equivalent amount of heat (measured in calories). Since both joules and calories are defined in perfectly arbitrary ways, the ratio need not be unity any more than the ratio of the length of a table measured in meters to its length measured in feet is unity. In 1840 Joule† started a series of experiments to prove that, whenever mechanical work is turned into heat, whatever the circumstances, the ratio of work done to heat evolved is constant. Experiments of this kind are difficult to perform with precision, primarily because of the inevitable leakage of heat. The variety of experiments and the refinement of his techniques forced Joule to continue his studies for ten years before he obtained consistent and convincing results. He studied, among other processes, the following: (1) the work done against the friction of sliding metal surfaces; (2) the work done in rotating a paddle wheel in an enclosed vessel of liquid (friction developed between the paddle wheel and the liquid); (3) the work done in forcing liquids through small tubes (sliding friction between the liquid and the inside surface of the tubes); (4) the heat developed by an electric current compared with the work required to rotate the electric generator; (5) the work done in compressing a gas compared with the amount of heat developed.

In finally summarizing all his work, Joule gave the equivalent of 4.15 joules per calorie as his best value for the **mechanical equivalent of heat.** This is surprisingly good when we consider that, after a hundred years of increasingly precise measurements of this important constant, the accepted value today is

$$J = 4.185 \text{ joule/cal} \qquad (11\text{-}8)$$

That is, whenever about 4.2 joules of work (or energy) is expended in any way so as to generate heat, 1 calorie is produced. The symbol $J$ and the name of the unit of energy both honor Joule for his important work.

---

† It is interesting that in his writings he used the German word *Kraft* (force) for expressing the concept of energy.

† James Prescott Joule (1818–1889) was the son of a successful brewer in Manchester, England, whose business he inherited. At an early age he became interested in science, was a pupil of Dalton, began his experiments at the age of twenty-two, and became another important "amateur" scientist.

About 1850, primarily as a result of Joule's work, the general principle of the conservation and interconvertibility of all forms of energy began to be generally accepted. This principle, which is now called the **general law of the conservation of energy,** is (like the conservation of momentum, p. 155) a powerful tool of analysis by virtue of its generality. Many problems may be analyzed by consideration of energy exchanges without specific reference to the number or nature of the forces involved. To say that *all* forms of energy in a system are conserved is, of course, an extension of experimental results, for we have no way of knowing that *all* forms of energy have been encountered. As new situations have been analyzed, however, the principle has always been found to be valid; and it has, as we shall see, become one of the most powerful guides in the exploration of new fields. This aspect of the principle prompted a contemporary historian of science (W. C. Dampier) to say, "Because of its practical use, and for its own intrinsic interest, the principle of the conservation of energy may be regarded as one of the great achievements of the human mind."

## 11-11. Tides and the Rotation of the Earth

An interesting example of the conservation principles is furnished by the effect of the tides on the motions of the earth and the moon. The periodic rise and fall of the oceans of the earth had been a major mystery from ancient times. After his discovery of the law of universal gravitation, Newton showed that the tides are the result of the gravitational pull of (primarily) the moon. This gravitational attraction produces a bulge in the ocean toward the moon on the side nearest the moon and a bulge *away* from the moon on the opposite side of the earth. This is shown very schematically in Figure 11-8, where for simplicity the oceans are shown covering the whole earth. The calculation is very complicated, but in a crude way we can understand the effect. On the near side, the moon attracts the water and causes it to bulge toward the moon. But the moon also attracts the solid

earth and pulls it away from the water on the far side, producing there a bulge of water *away* from the moon. As the earth rotates, a shoreline passing a bulge will have a high tide and approximately six hours later (a quarter turn) will have a low tide. Thus the level of the oceans appears to rise and fall at any point of the earth. There is, however, something more than six hours between successive extremes of the tide. This is due to the fact that, as the earth rotates, the moon also moves eastward along its orbit, carrying the line of bulges with it. After one rotation of the earth (one day), therefore, a spot has not arrived again at a maximum tide but must move eastward some more in order to catch up. It is easy to compute from the periods of motion of the earth and moon that the tides are approximately fifty minutes later each day.

We have discussed only the tide-raising effect of the moon, but the sun also raises tides. Although the sun is much more massive than the moon, it is so far away that the sun tides are only about a third as high as the moon tides. When the moon is either full or new, the earth, moon, and sun are in line, and the sun tides are added to the moon tides, the result being a large net tide. Such tides are called *spring* tides. When the moon is in quarter phase (either first or third), the lines from earth to moon and from earth to sun are at right angles. The sun tides therefore partially neutralize the moon tides, the result being a small net tide. Such tides are called *neap* tides.

Local conditions, particularly the contours of

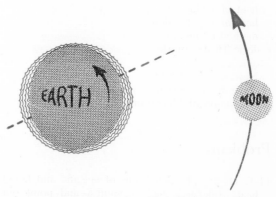

FIGURE **11-8** *Diagram of the tide-raising effect of the moon.*

the shore line, produce wide variations in the tides. But the general effects are as outlined above, with one exception. According to Figure 11-8, we should expect a high tide when the moon is overhead; but since, in its *daily* rotation, the earth must slide under the tidal bulges, there is a frictional drag. This tends to rotate the line passing through the high tides eastward with the earth; but the moon, of course, tends to hold the bulges as shown. The result is that the line through the two tidal bulges stabilizes somewhat east of the moon (broken line, Fig. 11-8). Thus high tide occurs some time after the moon has crossed its highest point in the sky.

Let us now consider this situation in the light of the conservation principles developed in this chapter. The earth-moon system may be considered an almost isolated system. Since friction, as we have seen, is a dissipative force, tidal friction is gradually converting the kinetic energy of rotation of the earth into heat. The total energy is conserved, but the kinetic energy of rotation is being reduced. The rate of dissipation is some $10^{19}$ joules per year. This is an extremely small fraction of the earth's store of kinetic energy; nevertheless, as the earth loses kinetic energy of rotation, it gradually slows down, and thus the day is gradually becoming longer. The effect is only about one-thousandth of a second per century, but it accounts for the slight discrepancies found in the recorded times of ancient eclipses when they are calculated from present-day data. Other methods also yield the same result.

As the earth slows down, it loses momentum. But in an isolated system, as we have seen, momentum is conserved no matter what type of internal force is acting. Hence, as the earth gradually loses momentum, the moon gains an equal amount. We have formalized the momentum concept for only rectilinear motion. We shall not write the equations for rotational motion but simply state that for circular motion the momentum increases as the square root of the radius. Thus, as the moon gains momentum, it moves farther from the earth. (This is taking place at the rate of about five feet per century.) As the moon spirals out into a larger orbit, the month becomes gradually longer. Astronomers have calculated that about four billion years ago (about the age of the earth) the moon was only 8,000 miles away. The day was about four hours long, and the month was not much longer. Tidal action has gradually lengthened the day and separated the earth and the moon to their present distance.

## Concepts and Terms

Distinction Between Heat and Temperature
Calorimetry
   calorie
   specific heat
   heat of fusion
   heat of vaporization
   method of mixtures
Caloric Theory of Heat
Momentum
   Newton's second law
   force due to repeated impacts
Conservation of Momentum

Work
Energy
   gravitational potential energy
   kinetic energy
Conservation of Mechanical Energy
   friction—a dissipative force
Elastic Collisions
   perfect elasticity
General Law of Conservation of Energy
   mechanical equivalent of heat
Tides

## Problems

**11-1.** Discuss the definitions of specific and latent heats. Interpret their meanings, and point out why the various quantities involved in the definitions must be included.

**11-2.** A 100 gram copper cup (specific heat = 0.093 cal/gram°C) contains 100 grams of water. The temperature is raised from 20°C to 50°C.

(A) Which (water or cup) absorbs more heat? How many times as much?

(B) What is the total heat absorbed?

*Ans.* (A) the water, 10.8 times as much

(B) $3.28 \times 10^3$ cal

**11-3.** How much more heat is required to vaporize a pound of water than to melt a pound of ice?

*Ans.* almost 7 times as much

**11-4.** 200 grams of gold at 100°C is placed in a calorimeter containing 300 grams of water at 20°C. The final temperature of the mixture is 21.6°C. What is the specific heat of gold?

*Ans.* 0.0306 cal/gram °C

**11-5.** 27.6 grams of steam is added to a calorimeter containing 400 grams of water at 20°C. The final temperature is 60°C. What is the heat of vaporization of water?

**11-6.** A 2 kgm hammer moving at 3 m/sec strikes the head of a large nail, drives it into a piece of hard wood, and comes to rest in 0.01 sec.

(A) What was the average force on the hammer?

(B) How far did the nail enter the wood?

(C) Why is the *average* force asked for in A?

*Ans.* (A) $6 \times 10^2$ newtons

(B) 1.5 cm

**11-7.** A fire hose ejects 3 kgm of water per second at a velocity of 7 m/sec. The stream is directed against a board 25 cm × 30 cm. Assume that the water is stopped by the board.

(A) What is the force on the board?

(B) What is the pressure on the board?

*Ans.* (A) 21 newtons

(B) 280 newtons/m²

**11-8.** Suppose that a group of people throw golf balls with a velocity of 7 m/sec at the board of Prob. 11-7 so that 30 balls per second hit and rebound from the board. Assume that each ball rebounds with undiminished speed. If each ball has a mass of 100 grams, what are the force and pressure on the board?

*Ans.* 42 newtons; 560 newtons/m²

**11-9.** Calculate the recoil velocity of a 3 kgm rifle that fires a 15 gram bullet with a velocity of 500 m/sec.

*Ans.* 2.5 m/sec

**11-10.** Imagine yourself in the middle of a lake that is covered with "super-smooth" ice—that is, ice with no frictional force at its surface. How would you get off the lake if left to your own devices? How could you have got there?

**11-11.** The total mass of a person and a canoe is 125 kgm. The person leaps from the canoe to a dock with a speed of 6 m/sec, and the canoe moves in the opposite direction with a speed of 4 m/sec. What are the masses of the person and the canoe?

*Ans.* person, 50 kgm; canoe, 75 kgm

**11-12.** Solve the problem stated in the first footnote on page 157.

**11-13.** Discuss the situation posed in the second footnote on page 157.

**11-14.** A 300 gram billiard ball moving at 2 m/sec collides with a 100 gram golf ball that is at rest. The golf ball after impact moves at 4 m/sec in a direction making 30° with the original line of motion of the billiard ball. With what velocity does the billiard ball rebound?

*Ans.* 1.08 m/sec at 68° with the direction of the golf ball

**11-15.** If it requires a horizontal pull of 50 newtons to slide a suitcase across the floor, how much work is done in moving it 3 m?

*Ans.* 150 joules

**11-16.** In Prob. 5-6, how much work does the man do in pushing the roller 9 m across a level lawn?

*Ans.* $1.56 \times 10^3$ joules

**11-17.**

(A) Calculate the increase in PE of a 50 kgm person who walks from the ground floor to the third floor, which is 6 m above.

(B) If this person fell out a third-floor window, with what speed would he hit the ground?

(C) Suppose that he slid down a frictionless chute. With what speed would he reach the ground?

(D) If half his energy were dissipated by friction, with what speed would he reach the ground?

*Ans.* (A) $2.94 \times 10^3$ joules

(B) 10.9 m/sec

(C) same as B

(D) 0.71 as much as B

**11-18.** A 300 gram mass swings as a pendulum on the end of a string. It is observed to be 15 cm higher at the ends of the swing than at the middle. What is its PE at the end of a swing? What is its speed at the bottom of a swing?

*Ans.* 0.442 joule; 1.72 m/sec

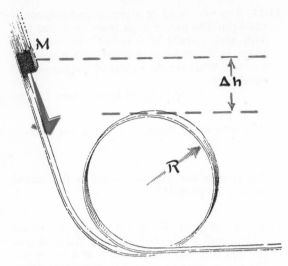

FIGURE **P11-19**

**11-19.** Consider the mechanics of the simplified "loop the loop" shown. A mass, *M*, slides down an inclined plane, round the inside of a vertical loop, and out on a horizontal plane. Assume the ideal case of no friction.

(A) Show that $\Delta h = R/2$ is the smallest value $\Delta h$ can have if the mass is to go round the loop. (Hint: For the mass to just make the loop, the centripetal force at the top of the loop must be equal to the weight.)

(B) Show that the mass will come out on the horizontal plane with speed $v = \sqrt{5gR}$.

**11-20.** A steel ball is three times as massive as a glass ball. The steel ball collides head-on with the glass ball, which was initially at rest. After impact the glass ball moves off with a velocity of 9 m/sec. What were the initial and final velocities of the steel ball?

*Ans.* 6 m/sec and 3 m/sec

**11-21.** Consider a series of identical steel balls on a smooth horizontal plane. If one ball is rolled

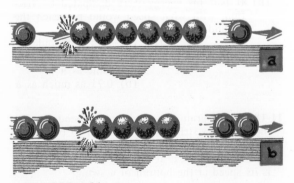

FIGURE **P11-21**

head-on into the string, one ball moves off with the same velocity from the other end (a). If two balls are rolled into the string, *two* move off with the same velocity (b), and so on for larger numbers. Although momentum could be conserved in "b" if *one* ball rebounded with *twice* the velocity, this never happens. Explain.

**11-22.** Joule, in one of his experiments, rotated a paddle wheel in a container of water and observed the rise in temperature. The paddle wheel was rotated by a mass on one end of a cord, the other end of which was wound round a pulley. Assume that the mass, *M*, falls with a low constant speed. Consider the following data. The

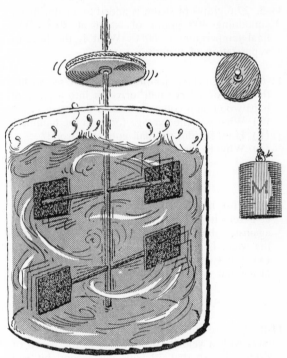

FIGURE **P11-22**

mass and specific heat of the paddle wheel and container were 2.0 kgm and 0.1 cal/gram °C. The mass of the water was 4.0 kgm, and a temperature rise of 2.0°C was produced. To accomplish this, a mass (*M*) of 9.0 kgm was allowed to fall 4.0 m, and this process was carried out 100 times. Calculate the mechanical equivalent of heat.

*Ans. J* = 4.2 joules/cal

**11-23.** A $3.0 \times 10^3$ kgm airplane lands on a level runway at 40 m/sec.

(A) If the plane then rolls up a hill, how high does it rise before coming to rest?

(B) Actually, the plane is stopped on the level runway by the brakes. If it stops in $1.0 \times 10^3$ m, what is the average stopping force of the brakes?

(c) If the brakes have a mass of 50 kgm and a specific heat of 0.2 cal/gram °C, what is the maximum increase in temperature of the brakes?

*Ans.* (A) 81.7 m
(B) $2.4 \times 10^3$ newtons
(c) 57.4°C

**11-24.** A method of determining the velocity ($v$) of a rifle bullet ($m$) is to fire it into a massive block ($M$) suspended as a pendulum and observe the height ($\Delta h$) to which the block swings. The following is a reasonable set of laboratory data: $m = 0.02$ kgm; $M = 8.0$ kgm; $\Delta h = 8$ cm.

(A) What is the velocity ($v$) of the bullet? (Hint: The impact is certainly *not* elastic, but momentum is nevertheless conserved. After impact the block and the bullet together move off with velocity $V$, which is small enough so that air friction is negligible. Start here and work backwards.)

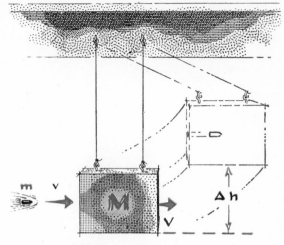

FIGURE **P11-24**

(B) How much heat is generated as the bullet enters the block?

*Ans.* (A) 507 m/sec
(B) 613 cal

## Suggested Readings

1. L. W. Taylor, *Physics the Pioneer Science* (Houghton Mifflin, 1941), pp. 200–212 and 217–224 (on momentum and mechanical energy) and 264–303 (on heat and the conservation of energy).
2. R. T. Beyer and A. O. Williams, *College Physics* (Prentice-Hall, 1957), Chaps. 5 (on momentum and energy) and 9 (on heat and the conservation of energy).
3. D. Roller, *The Early Development of the Concepts of Temperature and Heat* (Harvard University Press, 1950). One of the Harvard case histories in experimental science. An excellent account of the early development of calorimetry and of the rise and decline of the caloric theory.
4. L. Hogben, *Science for the Citizen* (Knopf, 1938). Chap. XII, on heat and energy, gives an interesting historical background and emphasizes the relation of economics to scientific developments.
5. W. F. Magie, *A Source Book in Physics* (McGraw-Hill, 1935), pp. 50–58 (Descartes, Leibnitz, and D'Alembert on the quantity of motion), 59–60 (Young on the introduction of the word "energy" for Leibnitz's quantity of motion), 134–165 (Black on specific and latent heats, Rumford and Davy on heat produced by friction), and 196–218 (Joule on the mechanical equivalent of heat, Mayer and Helmholtz on the conservation of energy).
6. W. T. Skilling and R. S. Richardson, *A Brief Text in Astronomy* (Henry Holt, 1954), Chap. 9 (on tides and the rotation of the earth).
7. Cecilia Payne-Gaposchkin, *Introduction to Astronomy* (Prentice-Hall, 1954), pp. 145–148 (on tides and the rotation of the earth).
8. H. Shapley and H. E. Howarth, *A Source Book in Astronomy* (McGraw-Hill, 1929), pp. 397–405 (Darwin on the origin of the moon).

BY THE middle of the nineteenth century, the stage was set for a combination of the concepts and theories of mechanics with the atomic-molecular theory of the structure of matter, in a mechanical theory of heat phenomena. Once Joule had established the quantitative equivalence of heat and mechanical energy, the conservation of heat in mixtures—that mainstay of the caloric theory—was clearly but one example of the more *general* law of the conservation of energy. Hence, if the property of motion was assigned to the atoms and molecules of matter, the imponderable caloric was no longer a necessary or useful concept. This extension of the atomic theory, first made by Joule and then by others, was rapidly and extensively developed into the kinetic-molecular theory of matter.

## 12-1. Some Qualitative Aspects

According to the kinetic-molecular theory, any sensible sample of matter is composed of a large number of molecules that are constantly moving. The temperature of the sample, which is assumed to be a measure of the molecular motions, rises as the motions become more violent. The molecules themselves are considered to be hard, sub-microscopic spheres that obey the same laws of Newtonian mechanics as large-scale objects. The fact of cohesion† requires the further assumption that the molecules attract each other, the attraction being appreciably great when the molecules are near to each other. Heat, then, as mechanical energy, may take the form of kinetic energy of motion of the molecules or potential energy due to the separation of the molecules against the forces of mutual attraction. We thus have the conceptual model of a sample of matter as a swarm of particles in dynamic equilibrium between two opposing tendencies: the tendency for the particles to fly apart because of thermal agitation, and the tendency for the particles to condense because of their mutual attraction. The relative dominance of one or the other of these tendencies would, then, determine the physical state of the sample.

CHAPTER

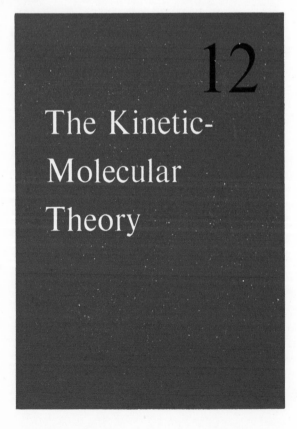

12

# The Kinetic-Molecular Theory

† Cohesion is the resistance to being separated into parts and is displayed by all substances in the solid or liquid state.

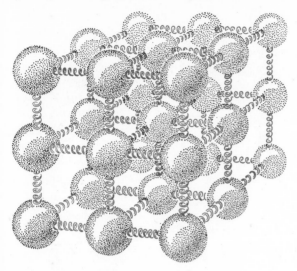

FIGURE **12-1** *Diagram of a cubic crystal.*

One of the characteristic properties of most substances is the crystalline form into which they solidify. Some substances form cubes, others rhombohedrons, others hexagonally shaped solids, etc. The point for this discussion is that the molecules of a solid substance occupy fixed positions and form a definite lattice. We conclude that in the solid state the intermolecular forces play the dominant role and hold the molecules rigidly in the crystal lattice. The thermal agitations are thus restricted to small vibrations of the molecules about their positions in the lattice. The arrangement of the molecules in a *cubic* crystal is shown in Figure 12-1. In even the tiniest observable crystal this pattern of the cubes, with a molecule at each corner, must be considered to be repeated a very large number of times. To help visualize the intermolecular forces, the molecules may be thought of as joined by tiny coiled springs along the edges of the cubes.† (The springs are, of course, merely a device of visualization; the forces, like the force of gravity between masses, act through space with no observable intervening agency.)

Under the action of these forces the molecules do not have much freedom of motion, but they can vibrate as a result of their thermal energy.

As the temperature rises, these vibrations become more energetic. At a high enough temperature (the melting point) the motion is violent enough to overcome the forces of attraction to such an extent that the molecules move somewhat farther apart and acquire a greater freedom of motion. When this happens, the substance loses its solid shape and takes on the fluidity of liquids. This pulling apart of the molecules against the forces of attraction requires energy to do the work of expansion. This work is stored as potential energy and does not affect the thermal motion. Such a picture of a melting solid is completely consistent with the facts of change of state. Most solids do expand upon melting, and the heat of fusion, which changes the state without any rise in temperature, is a measure of the increased potential energy of the molecules in the liquid state. The fact that some substances melt at higher temperatures than others is merely an indication that the forces holding their molecules in the crystal lattice are greater.

A similar analysis is consistent with the facts of vaporization. Although the intermolecular forces are not so dominant in the liquid as in the solid state, they are still effective enough to constrain the molecules to move about in such a way that their average distance apart remains unchanged. This is indicated by the fact that any liquid sample will maintain a constant volume although it may assume a variety of shapes determined by its container. At a certain temperature (the boiling point), however, the thermal motions become so violent that the intermolecular forces can no longer hold the molecules close together, and they fly apart, completely free of mutual attractions. This is consistent with the great expansion (several thousand times) that accompanies a change from the liquid to the gaseous state and with the characteristic property of gases of expanding and filling any container. Work must be done to separate the molecules, just as in fusion, and to set them free in the gaseous state. The increased potential energy of the molecules is represented by the heat of vaporization. The greater expansion from liquid to gas, compared with that from solid to liquid, indicates that the increase in potential energy during vaporization should be much greater than

---

† The fact that all solids and liquids offer very great resistance to compression indicates that forces of repulsion between the molecules come into play at *small* intermolecular distances.

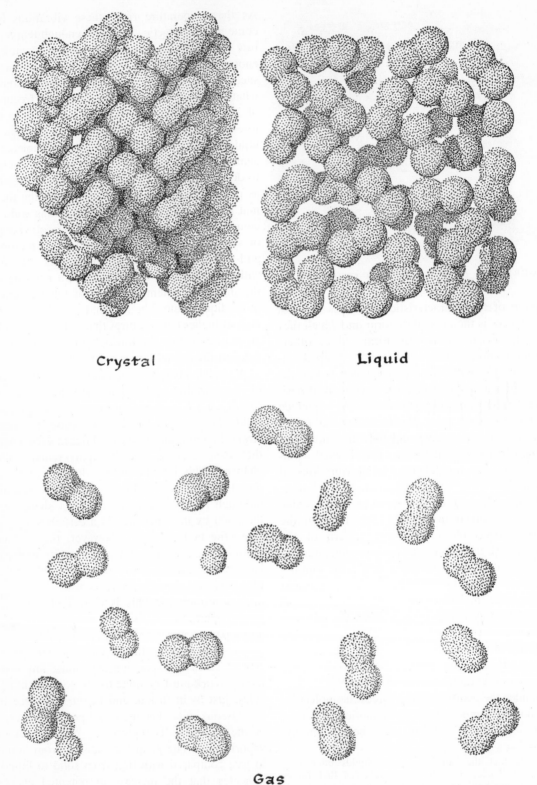

Crystal            Liquid

Gas

FIGURE **12-2** *Crystalline, liquid, and gaseous states of iodine. (Drawing by Roger Hayward.)*

the increase during fusion. This prediction is also consistent with experience. The heats of vaporization are generally larger than those of fusion (§ 11-1).

Molecules of iodine, in the crystalline, liquid, and gaseous states, are arranged as in Figure 12-2. The atoms are shown paired because iodine forms a diatomic molecule. The forces acting between the atoms within a molecule are much greater than those acting between molecules. During changes of state, therefore, the size of the molecules remains unchanged. In the crystal the molecules are closely packed in the orderly array that is characteristic of crystalline structure. In the liquid the molecules are somewhat farther apart and have enough freedom of motion to move past one another in a random grouping that changes continually. In the gas the molecules are widely separated; at atmospheric pressure the average distance between a molecule and its nearest neighbors is about ten times the molecular diameter.

Not only the phenomena of change of state but other behavior of gases is easily explained by the kinetic model of matter and the concept of heat as mechanical energy of the molecules. The pressure of a gas on the walls of a container is readily understood as the result of numerous and frequent impacts of the rapidly moving molecules. (This is analogous to the *steady* force exerted on a surface by a stream of bullets from a rapidly firing machine gun.) If the volume of the gas were reduced, the molecules, with less space in which to move about, would strike the walls more frequently and exert a greater pressure. If the volume of the gas were held constant and the temperature raised, the molecules would move more rapidly, strike the walls more frequently and with greater impact, and again exert a greater pressure. But these effects of changes in volume and temperature on the pressure of a gas are precisely those that would be observed in a laboratory study of gases (Chap. 10).

The familiar heating or cooling of a gas by compression or expansion is completely consistent with the mechanical view of the kinetic theory. Imagine the cylinder of Figure 9-1 to be filled with a large number of rapidly moving molecules that make many impacts with each other and with the walls of the cylinder. As the piston is forced down, the molecules rebound from it with increased speed in much the same way as a tennis ball speeds up when struck by a racket. Thus the work of compressing the gas appears as greater energy of motion of the molecules, and the temperature of the gas rises. If the piston is released, the molecules striking it will force it to move up. The molecules in this case will rebound with reduced speed, just as a tennis ball will rebound with reduced speed from a loosely held racket. Thus the work done by the expanding gas is achieved at the expense of the energy of motion of the molecules, and the temperature of the gas goes down.

These and many other qualitative successes of the kinetic theory give us confidence in the correctness of its fundamental assumptions. Even more convincing, however, and also productive of greater understanding, would be quantitative predictions of observed phenomena. The next step in the development of the theory, then, is to apply Newton's laws of motion to our kinetic model of a gas and see whether we can deduce observable quantitative results.

## 12-2. *Ideal-gas Law; Absolute Temperature*

The first quantitative achievement of the kinetic theory was the calculation of the pressure of a gas. The result of this calculation is in agreement with the known behavior of gases and also suggests further verifiable effects. We have already considered the pressure of a gas as due to the impact of molecules against the walls of the container. During impact a molecule experiences a change in momentum, and this, by Newton's second law, requires the application of a force. Our problem, then, is to find an expression for the total change in momentum per second of all the molecules hitting a wall. This gives the force exerted by the wall on the gas and also, by the third law of motion, the force exerted by the gas on the wall. The ratio of this force to the area of the wall would be the required expression for the pressure.

The necessary assumptions on which to base

the calculation are implicit in our previous discussion of the kinetic theory. It will be helpful, however, to state them explicitly and consider their plausibility in the light of known facts.

1. *The molecules are in random motion.* This means that all possible molecular velocities must be considered. Different molecules may be moving at widely different speeds and in many directions. Between impacts each molecule moves in straight lines at constant speed, as required by Newton's first law of motion. During impact, however, the direction and speed of a molecule change sharply. Since these changes are random, being greater for some and less for other molecules, we expect at any instant to find molecules moving at all possible speeds and in all directions. There are two reasons for this assumption. First, no property of gases suggests a preferential motion of the molecules. Second, no sample of a gas is ever observed to move (as a whole) in any direction of its own accord. A gas will expand, to be sure, but *equally* in *all* directions. On an average, therefore, the molecules must be moving just as much in one direction as in any other, and the net motion of the aggregate is zero. Note that this says nothing as to how the molecular velocities are distributed (that is, how many molecules have a particular velocity); it merely states that the motion is completely chaotic.

2. *The molecules are "point" masses.* This means that the average distance between molecules is very great compared with their diameters. The great ease with which gases are compressed indicates that there must be large spaces between the molecules, and the great expansion accompanying a change from the liquid to the gaseous state is further evidence that the gaseous molecules are relatively far apart. This assumption permits us to neglect the volumes of the molecules themselves and consider the whole volume of the container as available for the molecules to move in.

3. *The intermolecular attractions are negligible.* Since all known types of attraction (gravitational, electrical, magnetic) decrease with increasing distance, the great separation of gaseous molecules (assumption 2) makes this assumption plausible; and an experiment first performed by Gay-Lussac and later repeated by Joule lends it strong support. The experiment has to do with the change of temperature of gases as they expand. If a gas is released from a container, it does work expanding against the atmospheric pressure and thus cools itself. If, on the other hand, the gas is allowed to expand into a large evacuated vessel, it does no work against an external pressure, and we should therefore expect no change in temperature *if* there were no mutual attraction of the molecules. If the molecules *were* attracting each other, the work done to separate them against this attraction as the gas expanded into a vacuum would be done at the expense of their thermal energy, and the gas would cool itself. Both Gay-Lussac and Joule found very little change in temperature as a gas expanded into a vacuum. We conclude that intermolecular attractions are negligible in a gas, and that the only forces, which last only the brief time of impact, are those of repulsion.

4. *Kinetic energy is conserved during impact.* This is a more precise statement of the concept of molecules as tiny hard spheres. According to this assumption, a gas molecule would rebound from the walls of its container with undiminished speed. Strange as this assumption of perfect elasticity may seem,† the reasons for it are clear. If this assumption were not true, the molecules of a gas in a perfectly insulated container would gradually slow down as they kept rebounding off each other and the walls of the container. The pressure would diminish; the gas would cool and eventually liquefy. Nothing like this is ever observed.

A gas for which these assumptions are strictly true is called an **ideal gas** (§ 10-5). We shall now calculate the pressure exerted by an ideal gas on the walls of a container. To simplify the calculation, let us consider a cubic container‡

---

† No large-scale body displays this property. Glass or hard steel balls almost do, but even these substances lose some mechanical energy during impact. The loss of energy is due to the work needed to overcome internal friction and appears as increased thermal agitation of the molecules of the balls. But this argument is difficult to apply to a single molecule. Where would the loss of kinetic energy go in this situation?

‡ This is not a restrictive assumption, for *any* volume may be represented as the sum of small cubes.

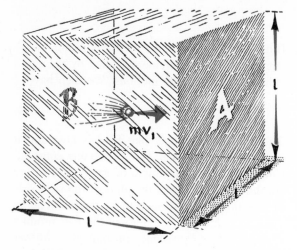

FIGURE **12-3** *Cubical box containing one molecule moving perpendicularly toward wall* A.

with sides of length $l$ and containing a large number, $N$, of molecules of a certain gas. Then, in accordance with the postulates of the atomic theory, each molecule has the same mass, $m$.

First, imagine that our box contains only one molecule and that it is moving toward wall $A$ (Fig. 12-3) with speed $v_1$ and in a direction perpendicular to $A$. The molecule has a momentum, $mv_1$, to the right, which remains unchanged until it strikes $A$. In accordance with assumption 4, the molecule rebounds with undiminished speed and thus, during impact, suffers a *change* of momentum to the left equal to $2mv_1$. (There is a change of momentum, $\Delta M$, of $mv_1$ *to the left* when the molecule is stopped by wall $A$ and *another* $\Delta M$ of $mv_1$ to the left when the molecule springs away from $A$.) After impact at $A$ the molecule moves across the box, rebounds from $B$, and returns to $A$. The time required for the round trip $A \rightarrow B \rightarrow A$ is $2l/v_1$, and the reciprocal of this ($v_1/2l$) is the number of round trips per second. Thus, for one molecule at wall $A$,

$$\frac{\Delta M}{\text{impact}} \times \frac{\text{impacts}}{\text{sec}} = \frac{\Delta M}{\text{sec}}$$

That is, the change in momentum per second is

$$2mv_1 \times \frac{v_1}{2l} = \frac{mv_1^2}{l}$$

Now imagine all $N$ molecules bouncing back and forth between $A$ and $B$ along parallel lines,

but each traveling with a different speed. Then the $\Delta M/\text{sec}$ at A due to all the molecules would be

$$\frac{mv_1^2}{l} + \frac{mv_2^2}{l} + \cdots + \frac{mv_N^2}{l}$$

in which $v_1$ is the speed of the first molecule, $v_2$ is the speed of the second molecule, and so on for all the molecules up to $v_N$ for the $N$th one. Since $m$ and $l$ are the same for each molecule, they may be factored out of this sum. We may also multiply and divide this sum by $N$ without changing its value. Thus we get

$$\frac{Nm}{l} \left( \frac{v_1^2 + v_2^2 + \cdots + v_N^2}{N} \right) \tag{12-1}$$

The term in the parentheses is the *mean* (average) of the squares of the speeds of *all* the molecules. It is called the mean-square speed:

$$(v^2)_{\text{av}} = \frac{v_1^2 + v_2^2 + \cdots + v_N^2}{N} \tag{12-2}$$

The square root of the mean-square speed is called the root-mean-square (abbreviated rms) speed:

$$\text{rms speed} = \sqrt{(v^2)_{\text{av}}}\dagger$$

Quantity 12-1 then becomes

$$\frac{Nm(v^2)_{\text{av}}}{l} \tag{12-3}$$

and expresses the total $\Delta M/\text{sec}$ produced at wall $A$ *provided all* the molecules are bouncing back and forth between $A$ and $B$. But this is a highly ordered arrangement and a definite contradiction of assumption 1, which postulates completely *random* motion. If the motion *is* random, there is as much chance of finding a molecule rebounding from *any one* of the other five walls as from $A$; but, if the number of molecules is only, let us say, twelve, the probability of finding two rebounding from each wall is very small indeed. If there are 1,200 molecules, however, the probability of finding 200 rebounding from

† Note that the rms speed is *not* the same as the average of the speeds but is somewhat larger. Imagine only three molecules with speeds of 3, 4, and 5 units. The average speed is $\frac{3+4+5}{3} = 4$. The rms speed is $\sqrt{\frac{9+16+25}{3}} = \sqrt{16.7} = 4.09$ or, in this case, approximately 2.5% larger.

each wall of the cube is much greater; and, if the number of molecules is *very* large (and we know it must be in even a small sample of gas), the probability of finding the same number rebounding from each wall becomes so great that it may be considered as certain.† Since the molecules, as they move about, rebound off one another, a molecule heading toward wall *A* may be deviated from its path. When the number of molecules is large enough, however, a molecule will always be deviated toward *A* for every one deviated away from *A*. Thus we have an equilibrium that *produces the same effect* as having one third of the molecules moving in straight lines back and forth between *A* and *B,* another third up and down between the top and bottom of the cube, and the last third forward and back between the remaining two walls of the cube. This result, which we arrived at somewhat intuitively, can be rigorously established from the mathematical laws of probability.

The total $\Delta M$/sec produced at wall *A* (and also at any other wall) is, then, just one-third of expression 12-3. But by Newton's second law of motion (§ 11-4) $\Delta M$/sec is equal to the force producing the $\Delta M$. Thus each wall of our cubic container is exerting an inward force on the gas, and according to the third law of motion the gas is exerting an equal but outward force on the wall. The magnitude of this force is

$$F = \frac{Nm\,(v^2)_{av}}{3l}$$

But this force is distributed evenly over the whole area of the wall. Since the area of the wall is $l^2$, we have, from the definition of pressure,

_____

† This idea of a probability becoming a certainty as the number of occurrences becomes large was first introduced into scientific thinking in the development of the kinetic theory and has become increasingly important from that time to the present. A simple experiment might make this idea more acceptable. In tossing a penny the chances for "heads" and "tails" are equal. In ten tosses, however, there is small chance of getting five each. But a record of several hundred tosses will show that the number of heads and the number of tails become more nearly equal as the total number of trials increases. This idea is common to all statistical problems. The *average* death rate, for instance, has little meaning for a particular person, but for an insurance company, with millions of policyholders, it is of great practical importance.

$$P = \frac{F}{l^2} = \frac{Nm(v^2)_{av}}{3l^3}$$

But $l^3$ is the volume, *V*, of the box and by assumption 2 is the volume occupied by the molecules in their random motions. We then have

$$PV = \frac{Nm(v^2)_{av}}{3} \tag{12-4}$$

This looks surprisingly like Boyle's law; and it is, in fact, that law if $(v^2)_{av}$ remains constant, since for any given sample of gas *N* and *m* are constant. Furthermore, the units of the right side of equation 12-4 are seen to be those of energy (joules), which are the units of the *P-V* product (§ 10-2). This consistency of units gives further confidence in the statement of equation 12-4.

If the factor 1/2 were in the numerator of the right side of equation 12-4, an expression for kinetic energy would appear. We can easily achieve this by multiplying and dividing by 2, which does not change the value of the term at all. Doing this and rearranging, we get

$$PV = \tfrac{2}{3}N(\tfrac{1}{2}mv^2)_{av} \tag{12-5}$$

The quantity in parentheses is the *average* KE per molecule, and that times the number of molecules, *N*, gives the total kinetic energy of all the molecules of the gas. Therefore

$$PV = \tfrac{2}{3} \text{ (total KE of the gas)}† \tag{12-6}$$

This is an unexpected consequence of our kinetic model of a gas. To be sure, we have all along considered the pressure of a gas to be due to the continuous bombardment of the rapidly moving molecules. But such a beautifully simple relation between the pressure and the kinetic energy of the molecules is completely unexpected.

Statement 12-6 can be subjected to experimental verification. Consider a mixture of two different gases‡ that exerts a pressure, *P*, on the walls of a container of volume *V*. The KE of one of the gases is $N_1(\tfrac{1}{2}m_1v_1^2)_{av}$ and of the other gas is $N_2(\tfrac{1}{2}m_2v_2^2)_{av}$, the *N*'s, *m*'s, and $(v^2)_{av}$'s having different values. Then by equation 12-6

_____

† We can easily show statement 12-6 to be *exactly* true by substituting in equation 12-5 the definition of $(v^2)_{av}$ from equation 12-2 and expanding.

‡ The argument would work equally well for any number of component gases.

$$PV = \tfrac{2}{3}N_1(\tfrac{1}{2}m_1v_1^2)_{av} + \tfrac{2}{3}N_2(\tfrac{1}{2}m_2v_2^2)_{av} \qquad (12\text{-}7)$$

But in accordance with assumption 2 *each* gas is free to move about in the total volume of the container ($V$); that is, each gas will act as though the other one were not there. If only gas No. 1 were present, it would exert pressure $P_1$, and by equation 12-5 we have $P_1V = \tfrac{2}{3}N_1(\tfrac{1}{2}m_1v_1^2)_{av}$. A similar expression applies for gas No. 2. Equation 12-7 then becomes

$$PV = P_1V + P_2V$$

and, dividing out $V$, we get

$$P = P_1 + P_2$$

But this is precisely Dalton's law of partial pressures, which he discovered experimentally early in the nineteenth century.

Equation 12-4 permits the calculation of the rms speed for gases. The product $Nm$ is clearly the total mass of the gas, and therefore

$$P = \frac{(\text{mass of gas})}{V}\frac{(v^2)_{av}}{3} = \frac{d(v^2)_{av}}{3}$$

or

$$\text{rms speed} = \sqrt{\frac{3P}{d}} \qquad (12\text{-}8)$$

if $d$ is the density of the gas. If we use the experimental values of the densities at standard temperature and pressure, the rms speeds of several gases come out to be those shown in Table 12-1. Our first interest in these speeds is the order of magnitude; the rms speed for $N_2$, for instance, is something more than 1,000 miles per hour. The second point of interest is the inverse relation between the rms speed and the molecular weight. As the molecular weight (and thus the mass of the molecule) increases, the rms speed decreases. We shall refer to these

TABLE **12-1** *Molecular Speeds*

| GAS | RMS SPEED (M/SEC) |
|-----|-------------------|
| $H_2$ | $1.84 \times 10^3$ |
| He | $1.31 \times 10^3$ |
| $H_2O$ | $.615 \times 10^3$ |
| $N_2$ | $.493 \times 10^3$ |
| $O_2$ | $.461 \times 10^3$ |

speeds again later in this chapter and cite experimental evidence for the accuracy of the values. Indirect evidence is derived from a study of the transmission of sound. Great as these molecular speeds are compared with the speeds of ordinary objects, the speed of propagation of sound through a gas is comparable. According to the theory of sound propagation, a sound wave should travel through a gas with a predictably smaller speed than the rms speed of the gas molecules. Experimental determinations of the speeds of sound in gases are consistent with the rms speeds of Table 12-1. For instance, the speed of sound in air (a mixture of $N_2$ and $O_2$) is $.332 \times 10^3$ m/sec at 0°C, and the speed in $H_2$ is $1.27 \times 10^3$ m/sec. Each of these speeds of propagation is approximately 70 percent of the corresponding rms speed of the gas molecules.

The pressure formula for an ideal gas (equation 12-5) is not precisely the empirically discovered gas equation (10-10) but it is very similar, and it suggests further relations and interpretations. First, *if* the average kinetic energy per molecule depends upon the temperature and therefore is constant at constant temperature, equation 12-5 becomes Boyle's law (equation 10-2). Second, it has been pointed out that the $P$-$V$ product represents an energy and is experimentally directly proportional to the absolute temperature of the gas. Our theory says, on the other hand, that the $P$-$V$ product is proportional to the total KE of all the gas molecules. It seems fruitful, then, to *assume* that these two expressions of the $P$-$V$ product are equivalent and to investigate the consequences of this assumption. We express the assumption algebraically by equating the right-hand sides of equations 12-5 and 10-10:

$$\tfrac{2}{3}N(\tfrac{1}{2}mv^2)_{av} = nRT$$

This may be solved for the average *KE per molecule*:

$$(\tfrac{1}{2}mv^2)_{av} = \frac{3}{2}\frac{n}{N}RT$$

The ratio $n/N$ is the reciprocal of $N/n$. But $N/n$ is the number of molecules in the sample of gas divided by the number of moles in the sample, or the number of molecules per mole. This, of course, is Avogadro's number, $N_0$. Hence

$$(\tfrac{1}{2}mv^2)_{av} = \frac{3}{2}\frac{R}{N_0}T \qquad (12\text{-}9)$$

or

$$(\tfrac{1}{2}mv^2)_{av} = \frac{3}{2}kT \qquad (12\text{-}10)$$

in which $k = R/N_0$.

We have already seen that experimentally both $R$ and $N_0$ are universal constants, and so it is convenient to express their ratio as $k$.[†] The gas constant $R$ may be expressed in several sets of units. If the $P$-$V$ product is expressed in mechanical units, equation 10-10 shows that $R$ is joules per degree per mole. Boltzmann's constant is then joules per degree per *molecule,* and equation 12-10 is seen to be consistent in units.

The importance of equation 12-10 is that it gives physical meaning to the concept of absolute temperature. It says, in words, that *the absolute temperature is directly proportional to the average kinetic energy of the molecules.* Since $k$ is a truly universal constant, this statement should hold for *any* substance. As the temperature (°K) falls, the kinetic energy per molecule decreases in direct proportion until, at absolute zero, the random thermal motion of the molecules ceases. This interpretation of absolute zero has greater physical significance than the empirical interpretation of zero pressure of a gas, since all gases liquefy before reaching 0°K. A further implication is that, at the *same temperature,* molecules of different gases move at different speeds. If we solve equation 12-9 for $\sqrt{(v^2)_{av}}$ (remembering that $mN_0$ is the molecular weight of the gas), we see that the rms speed is inversely proportional to the square root of the molecular weight for constant $T$. This result is consistent with the data of Table 12-1. For instance, $O_2$, with a molecular weight sixteen times that of $H_2$, has an rms speed one quarter as great. This is not proof of the correctness of

equation 12-9, but it is a gratifying indication of the internal consistency of the theory. What we must do is to deduce experimentally verifiable consequences from equation 12-10. There are many such consequences, but we shall consider only a few.

Consider any two gases to be at the same temperature. Then, since the right-hand side of equation 12-10 is the same for both, we have

$$(\tfrac{1}{2}m_1v_1^2)_{av} = (\tfrac{1}{2}m_2v_2^2)_{av} \quad \text{or} \quad \frac{\sqrt{(v_1^2)_{av}}}{\sqrt{(v_2^2)_{av}}} = \frac{\sqrt{m_2}}{\sqrt{m_1}}$$
$$(12\text{-}11)$$

This is the inverse proportion mentioned in the last paragraph, since the ratio of the masses of the two different molecules is the same as the ratio of the molecular weights of the gases. Now imagine the container of the gases to have a small hole opening into an evacuated space. The gases will escape through the opening—that is, diffuse into the vacuum. The less massive molecules should diffuse more rapidly because, with their greater rms speed, they have a greater chance, during their random motions, of arriving at the hole and escaping. According to our model, therefore, the rate of diffusion ($r$) of a gas should be directly proportional to the rms speed of its molecules. For any two gases at the same temperature, then, we have

$$\frac{r_1}{r_2} = \frac{\sqrt{m_2}}{\sqrt{m_1}} \qquad (12\text{-}12)$$

in accordance with equation 12-11. This relation, when tested experimentally, is found to be true.[†] $H_2O$, for instance, with nine times the molecular weight of $H_2$, diffuses only one-third as rapidly. By the same argument equation 12-12 should (and does) give the relative rates of diffusion of gases through a porous wall (such as unglazed porcelain) and through the intermolecular spaces of another gas (such as air).

Another verifiable consequence of equation 12-10 is this: Consider samples of two different gases contained in equal volumes at the same pressure and temperature. Let $N_1$ be the number of molecules in one container and $N_2$ the number in the other container. Since the volumes are

---

[†] The universal constant $k$ plays an important role in many branches of physical science. It is called Boltzmann's constant in honor of an important contributor to the development of the kinetic theory.

[†] It was established empirically in 1829 by Thomas Graham and is known as Graham's law.

equal and the gases are at the same pressure, we know, by equation 12-5, that

$$\tfrac{2}{3}N_1(\tfrac{1}{2}m_1v_1^2)_{\text{av}} = \tfrac{2}{3}N_2(\tfrac{1}{2}m_2v_2^2)_{\text{av}}$$

But, if the gases are at the same temperature, we know, by equation 12-10, that

$$(\tfrac{1}{2}m_1v_1^2)_{\text{av}} = (\tfrac{1}{2}m_2v_2^2)_{\text{av}}$$

and therefore that

$$N_1 = N_2$$

But this is Avogadro's law, which, by the time the kinetic theory was developed, had had ample verification in the field of chemistry.

## 12-3. *Equipartition of Energy*

The fact that the molecules of different gases at the same temperature have the same average kinetic energy is a special case of a very general and important principle of the kinetic theory. This principle, known as the **equipartition of energy,** is a necessary consequence of the application of statistical mechanics to the kinetic model of matter. Although the derivation of the principle is a topic for advanced courses in physical science, a brief discussion here will lead to some understanding of the meaning of this very useful theorem.

Suppose that a certain amount of mercury vapor at some fairly high temperature such as 127°C is introduced into some oxygen at 27°C. It is well known that the Hg will cool down and the $O_2$ warm up until temperature equilibrium is established. This means that, as the molecules rebound off each other, the Hg ones will slow down and the $O_2$ ones will speed up until the average kinetic energy of all the molecules is the same. But a simple calculation will show that even at 127°C the Hg molecules have an rms speed somewhat less than half that of the $O_2$ molecules at 27°C, and that the greater average kinetic energy of the Hg molecules is due to their greater mass. We see that the molecules, in their random impacts, do not equalize their speeds but *do* equalize their *average kinetic energies.* The explanation applies to other situations also; it explains, for example, why heat always flows from a body of higher to one of lower

temperature even if the former has a smaller *total* heat content than the latter. The molecules seem to act upon a "share-and-share-alike" basis and to hand the energy around until all have equal shares. We have considered only kinetic energy, but the general principle states that the same is true for *all* forms of molecular energy. If, by virtue of the molecular structure or the physical state of the substance, it is possible to absorb energy in other ways than as kinetic energy, the general principle requires that any energy added to a sample of matter be *divided equally* among all the possible ways of absorbing energy.

Consider now a sample of matter in the solid state. The situation may be that shown in Figure 12-1, and the average kinetic energy of the molecules is due to their vibratory motion about their average positions. To raise the temperature of a molecule one degree, we must increase its average kinetic energy by $\tfrac{3}{2}k$, as required by equation 12-10. But such an oscillating molecule also has a mean potential energy that is due to its average displacement against the intermolecular forces of the crystal lattice. Hence, to get the temperature of the molecule up one degree, we must also add $\tfrac{3}{2}k$ of energy to the potential energy, as required by the equipartition principle. Thus, to have its temperature raised one degree, each molecule must absorb $\tfrac{3}{2}k + \tfrac{3}{2}k = 3k$ units of energy. If the temperature of one gram of the substance is to be raised one degree, $3k$ must be multiplied by the number of molecules in one gram. Since there is Avogadro's number of molecules in one gram-molecular weight, the number of molecules per gram is $N_0/(\text{mol wt})$. And $3k$ times this number gives the specific heat of the substance. Thus we have

$$(\text{specific heat}) \times (\text{mol wt}) = \text{constant}$$

$$\left(3k\,\frac{N_0}{\text{mol wt}}\right) \times (\text{mol wt}) = 3kN_0$$

The first statement is the **law of Dulong and Petit,** which was discovered experimentally early in the nineteenth century. Furthermore, since $k = R/N_0$, the constant is equal to $3(R/N_0)N_0 = 3R$. But the gas constant, expressed in calories of energy, is 2 cal/mole °K, and the Dulong and Petit constant should therefore be 6 cal/mole °K.

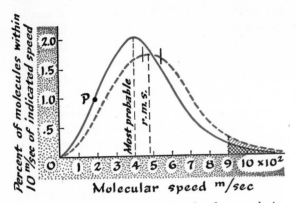

FIGURE **12-4** *Distribution of molecular speeds for nitrogen.*

This is close to the value determined experimentally.†

## 12-4. *Distribution of Molecular Speeds*

Thus far in our discussion we have considered only the rms speed of the molecules and have not been concerned with the distribution of the molecular speeds about this value. The distribution is calculated from the laws of probability as applied to the kinetic theory. The calculation is mathematically too complex for this book, but some discussion of the result will contribute to our understanding of the kinetic theory of matter. The distribution is most easily represented by a graph such as that in Figure 12-4, which shows the calculated speeds of nitrogen molecules at 0°C (solid line). The height of the graph at any point gives the percentage of all the molecules moving very near the indicated speed. Point P, for instance, shows that approximately 1 percent of the molecules are moving with speeds that differ by no more than 10 m/sec from $2 \times 10^2$ m/sec. The peak of the graph represents the *most probable* speed, which in this case is $4 \times 10^2$ m/sec. The rms speed is

1.224 times as great as the most probable speed and in this case is $4.9 \times 10^2$ m/sec. If the temperature is raised, the most probable and rms speeds move toward larger values (short lines), and the curve spreads out, as shown by the broken line. The area under any portion of the curve gives the fraction of the molecules traveling within the indicated range of speeds. (At 0°C, for instance, the fraction of the $N_2$ molecules that is moving faster than $9 \times 10^2$ m/sec is represented by the cross-hatched area in Fig. 12-4.) Thus it is seen that most of the molecules travel at speeds that lie between about 0.33 and 1.5 times the rms speed. But there is a definite, if small, fraction that moves with many times the rms speed. This does not mean that any individual molecule *always* travels at the same speed. The molecules change speed frequently as a result of their random impacts. But for any number that are speeded up a corresponding number will be slowed down, so that at any instant the distribution of speeds is as shown in Figure 12-4. Similar distribution curves have been worked out for the thermal speeds of molecules in the liquid and solid states. Many phenomena can be understood in terms of the distribution of molecular speeds. Let us now consider a few.

The evaporation of a liquid into the air above it is a familiar phenomenon. In the liquid, most of the molecules traveling at speeds near to the rms speed do not have sufficient energy to overcome the forces of cohesion and escape. A certain fraction of the molecules, however (such as those represented by the shaded area of Fig. 12-4), do have sufficient speed, at any temperature, to break away from the cohesive forces. If they are near the surface, they fly off into the space above the liquid and set up a vapor pressure in that space. If the temperature of the liquid is raised, the distribution curve shifts toward higher speeds, and a larger fraction of the molecules have the necessary energy to escape. Thus the vapor pressure of a liquid increases with a rise in temperature—a well-known experimental fact. Since the escaping molecules are those of greatest kinetic energy, the *average* KE of the remaining molecules is reduced. Hence, as a liquid evaporates, it cools

---

† The fact that the experimental value is not exactly 6 cal/mole °K, and is quite different for some substances, is an indication that the processes of absorbing energy are more complex than those considered in this elementary treatment. On the other hand, the very good agreement for a wide variety of substances is striking evidence of the validity of the theory.

itself unless additional heat is supplied from the environment. This familiar effect is very noticeable in the case of highly volatile liquids such as alcohol and ether.

A similar explanation accounts for the almost complete absence of light gases from the earth's atmosphere. As the height above the surface of the earth increases, the atmospheric pressure decreases. Thus the number of molecules per cubic meter decreases, and the average distance between molecules becomes greater. This distance may be as much as several miles in the very tenuous regions of the upper atmosphere. At these heights the intense radiation of the sun produces temperatures of about 1,000°C. Hence there is a good chance for high-speed molecules to shoot straight out into space away from the earth. Mostly, however, the gravitational pull of the earth slows them down, and they fall back into the atmosphere just as a ball thrown into the air returns to the surface of the earth. If, however, the molecule is moving faster than a certain speed (about $10^4$ m/sec), it will escape from the pull of the earth and fly off into space. At any temperature there are always some molecules with speeds greater than this "speed of escape." But, even at 1,000°C, $N_2$ and $O_2$ show an extremely small fraction of molecules with such speeds, and the rate of escape of these gases from the atmosphere is therefore negligibly small. Molecules of $H_2$ and He, however, because of their small mass, have a much higher rms speed; a sizable fraction of them are moving faster than the speed of escape, and their rate

of escape is by no means negligible. These gases disappear from the atmosphere, in fact, shortly after their liberation at the surface of the earth. For other bodies of the solar system the speed of escape is higher or lower than for the earth, and the observed compositions of their atmospheres are accordingly different. An extreme example is our moon. Because of the moon's small surface gravity, the speed of escape is so low that there is a good chance for all atmospheric gases to escape its gravitational pull. The moon has therefore long since lost any atmosphere that it may once have had.

Another effect that is consistent with the distribution of molecular speeds is the rate of chemical reactions. It is found experimentally that a rise of 10° in the temperature of the reactants will, in general, double the rate at which a reaction goes forward. For the reaction to take place at all, the reacting molecules must approach each other closely enough for the relatively short-range forces of chemical binding to take effect; but, as they do approach each other in their random motion, repulsive forces come into play and tend to make them bounce apart. Hence the only molecules that have a chance of reacting are those with high enough kinetic energy to overcome the forces of repulsion. For the sake of concreteness suppose that the broken curve of Figure 12-4 represents the distribution for a temperature 10°C higher than that represented by the solid curve. Suppose also that, to react, a molecule must have a speed greater than $9 \times 10^2$ m/sec. The cross-

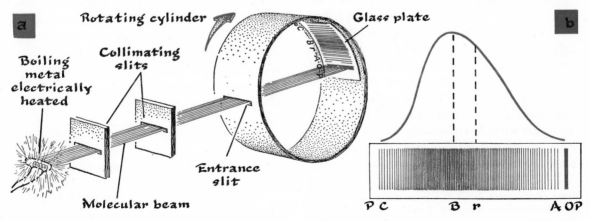

FIGURE **12-5** *Diagram of apparatus for measuring molecular speeds.*

hatched area gives the fraction of the molecules that can react at the lower temperature. At the higher temperature, even though the rms speed has increased only slightly, the fraction of the molecules with sufficient energy to react has doubled; that is, the area under the dotted curve from $9 \times 10^2$ m/sec on is twice that under the solid curve. With twice as many molecules that can react, the reaction goes forward at twice the rate.

The distribution law that we have been discussing has been verified by direct experimental measurements of molecular speeds. The technical difficulties inherent in the measurement of the great speeds of invisible molecules delayed such verification for sixty years from the time of the first calculation of the distribution (Maxwell, 1860). In the 1920's, however, several ingenious experiments were devised for measurement of the speeds of vaporized metallic molecules. An experimental arrangement for such measurements is shown schematically in Figure 12-5a. A metal filament is heated electrically to a known temperature, sufficiently high to vaporize metallic molecules. The whole apparatus is highly evacuated so that the vaporized molecules fly off along straight lines in all directions from the filament. By means of two collimating† slits a well-defined beam of molecules is directed at the side of a cylinder that carries an entrance slit. A thin glass plate is mounted on the inner surface of the cylinder opposite the entrance slit. If the cylinder is stationary, with the entrance slit in line with the collimating slits, a thin beam of the molecules will strike the cool glass plate, condense, and form a line at $O$. If the cylinder is rotated rapidly, molecules can enter it only during the brief time when the entrance slit is in line with the collimating slits. Thus a succession of groups of molecules will spurt into the cylinder as the entrance slit successively passes the point of alignment with the collimating slits. If the molecules are moving with different speeds, the fast ones will outstrip the slower ones and arrive at

the plate first. But, while the molecules are moving across the cylinder, the plate is being carried along by the rotation of the cylinder. A rapidly moving molecule will therefore condense at point $A$, since during its time of flight across the cylinder $A$ will have moved to the point formerly occupied by $O$. A less rapidly moving molecule will condense at $B$, and the slowest ones will not arrive at the plate until $C$ has moved to the original position of $O$. Thus the molecules are distributed along the plate according to their speeds, with the fastest ones near $O$ and the slowest ones near $C$. After many revolutions of the cylinder (and thus the condensation of many "spurts" of molecules) a metallic film of measurable thickness is deposited on the plate, somewhat in the manner shown in Figure 12-5b. A direct count of the molecules is, of course, impossible, but the thickness of the film at any point will give the fraction of the molecules that traveled to the plate at the corresponding speed. Thus a graph of film thickness against position on the plate is the *experimentally* determined distribution curve for the vaporized metallic molecules. Such curves are found to have the same form as the *theoretically* calculated ones (Fig. 12-4). Furthermore, the experiment yields a measurement of the rms speed, as indicated by point $r$. The known rate of rotation of the cylinder and the measured distance $O$–$r$ gives the time of flight of the molecules. This time, divided into the diameter of the cylinder, gives the rms speed. The experimental and theoretical values of the rms speed agree well within the precision of the measurements. Various metals have been used, and complete agreement between theory and experiment has always been found.

## 12-5. Mass and Size of Molecules

The vacuum-furnace experiments we have just described had been preceded by other direct evidence of molecular motions. In 1827 the English botanist Robert Brown, observing under a powerful microscope some tiny grains of plant pollen floating on water, noticed that they were in constant agitation. This phenomenon (called

---

† To collimate is to make parallel. The molecules leave the filament in all directions. Only those moving in one direction will pass through both collimating slits. Thus a narrow beam of molecules moving parallel to one another arrives at the cylinder.

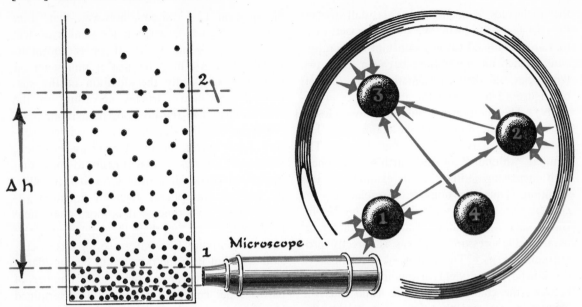

FIGURE **12-6** *Diagram of Brownian movement and Perrin's method of determining Avogadro's number.*

**Brownian movement**) was not well understood at the time. It was considered evidence of the "vitality" of the living plant pollen; but small dust or smoke particles suspended in air and finely ground inanimate substances suspended in liquids also display Brownian movements. With the development of the kinetic theory these movements were easily understood as due to the unbalanced bombardment of the particles by the highly agitated (but invisible) molecules of the gas or the liquid. Large particles do not show the effect, for the chance at any instant of finding appreciably more molecules striking such a particle in one direction than in the opposite direction is negligibly small. The chance that this situation will occur increases as the particle size decreases and is decidedly appreciable for the very small (but still visible) Brownian particles. The situation may be illustrated schematically as in the right half of Figure 12-6, which represents a small particle suspended in a liquid. The little arrows represent the impact forces of the molecules, and the imbalance is arbitrarily shown as three to two. At some instant the suspended particle, at position 1, experiences a net force that drives it to position 2. But the molecules are in random motion; the imbalance at 2 would, in general, be in a dif-

ferent direction and drive the particle to 3, where a still differently directed imbalance would drive it to 4, and so on. Thus the particle moves in random motion and participates in the thermal agitation of the molecules. Now nothing in the mechanical view of the kinetic theory says that the moving particle *must* be a chemical molecule. All that is necessary is that the particle be small and in random motion. Hence it is consistent with the kinetic theory to regard suspended Brownian particles as a gas of enormous molecular weight, which, by the principle of equipartition of energy, is at the temperature of the suspending liquid.† This view can be subjected to experimental verification, and the experiment yields the numerical value of Avogadro's number. Before discussing the experiment, however, we must consider the effect of the pull of gravity on a vertical column of gas.

Because of the thermal motion of its molecules, a gas tends to expand indefinitely. But the gravitational pull of the earth tends to make

† According to equation 12-10 the rms speed at a constant temperature is inversely proportional to the square root of the particle mass. The liquid molecules are moving at very high speeds; the Brownian particle, because of its relatively enormous mass, moves at a very low speed, which is easily observed under a microscope.

the molecules condense—that is, fall toward the surface of the earth. We should expect, then, that an unconfined gas at a constant temperature would reach an equilibrium between these two tendencies, as shown schematically at the left of Figure 12-6 (ignore the microscope temporarily). The molecules would be more closely packed near the bottom of the column and less densely spaced with increasing height. The familiar "thinning" of the earth's atmosphere with increasing altitude is an example of this situation. Thus the number of molecules per cm³ ($n_0$) should *decrease* with *increasing* height. But equation 12-5 shows that at constant temperature the pressure of a gas is directly proportional to $n_0$.† The statistical mechanics of the kinetic theory yields a quantitative relation between the change in pressure (and thus the change in $n_0$) and the change in height. We cannot derive this relation here, but we can write it out and discuss some consequences. The relation is

$$\frac{\Delta P}{P} = \frac{\Delta n_0}{n_0} = \frac{mN_0 g}{RT} \Delta h \qquad (12\text{-}13)$$

in which $g$ is the acceleration due to gravity, $\Delta h$ is the increase in height that produces a decrease in pressure, $\Delta P$, or a decrease in the number of molecules per cm³, $\Delta n_0$, and the other symbols are the same as elsewhere in this chapter. In the case of the atmosphere neither $m$ nor $N_0$ is known, but the product $mN_0$ is the molecular weight and thus is known. The validity of equation 12-13 can, then, be tested. The pressure, $P$, of the gas is measured at some level (such as 1 in Fig. 12-6) and again at some higher level (2), which is $\Delta h$ above level 1. Since the difference between the two pressures gives $\Delta P$, numerical values for all the quantities in equation 12-13 are known, and it is found to be an accurate description of the situation. Since the molecular mass is very small for ordinary gases, $\Delta h$ must be very large for sizable changes in pressure. In order to reduce the pressure of air, for instance, to half (that is, $\Delta P/P = \frac{1}{2}$), $\Delta h$ must be approximately 3.5 miles. An inspection

of equation 12-13 shows, however, that, if $m$ is proportionately larger, a much smaller $\Delta h$ will produce the same $\Delta P/P$. If $m$ is enormous (relatively), $\Delta h$ may be just a millimeter or two. This is exactly the situation of the suspended Brownian particles according to the view discussed in the previous paragraph.

During the first decade of the twentieth century Jean Perrin, at the University of Paris, performed a series of experiments to show that suspended Brownian particles do in fact follow the law of atmospheres given by equation 12-13. In these experiments it is more convenient to determine $\Delta n_0/n_0$ than the equivalent pressure ratio. Figure 12-6 will serve for this discussion also, but now the dots are to be considered suspended Brownian particles. The number of particles per cm³ ($n_0$) at level 1 is determined by direct count through the microscope. The microscope is now raised a distance $\Delta h$ (only a few millimeters) to level 2, and $n_0$ is counted again. The result of many such observations showed that $\Delta n_0/n_0$ is directly proportional to $\Delta h$, as required by equation 12-13. Thus Perrin established that the Brownian particles do, in fact, share *equally* in the thermal kinetic energy of the suspending liquid and have the mechanical properties of a gas. With this established he was able, tedious though this task turned out to be, to measure the particle mass, $m$, and thereby to determine $N_0$. He prepared a suspension of particles of uniform size and with a calibrated microscope determined the average diameter of a large number of them. This diameter, combined with the measured density of the suspended substance, gave the mass of one particle, $m$. Thus he measured all factors of equation 12-13 except $N_0$ and determined Avogadro's number. As might be expected, the experimental errors were rather high (approximately 5–10 percent), but within this precision the number of molecules per mole is, as reported by Perrin,

$$N_0 = 6.8 \times 10^{23} \qquad (12\text{-}14)$$

This is an astonishingly large number! We had suspected all along, to be sure, that Avogadro's number must be very great, but this almost unimaginably large value is quite unexpected. We

---

† Divide equation 12-5 through by $V$. Then, since $N/V = n_0$ and $\frac{1}{2}(mv^2)_{av}$ is constant for constant temperature, $P$ is directly proportion to $n_0$.

shall see in succeeding chapters that other methods, more recent than Perrin's work, give very precise values of this universal constant. But, in addition to giving the first reliable figure for $N_0$, Perrin's method is of interest because it is based upon a phenomenon that gives convincing evidence of the existence of molecular motions and closely simulates a direct observation of the actual molecules.

Once Avogadro's number is known, the calculation of molecular (and atomic) masses is simple arithmetic. Since, for instance, 32 grams of $O_2$ contains Avogadro's number of molecules, *one* $O_2$ molecule, according to equation 12-14, has a mass of $4.8 \times 10^{-23}$ gram.

Avogadro's number, combined with the observed deviations of real gases from the ideal-gas law, determines the size of the molecules. The very good agreement between the ideal-gas law and the behavior of actual gases, as observed in the laboratory, indicates that these gases at normal pressures and temperatures do indeed act as though there were no intermolecular forces and that molecules have no volume. At sufficiently low temperatures and high pressures, however, all real gases liquefy, and very strong intermolecular forces then come into play. Between these two extremes one would expect the intermolecular forces and the finite size of the molecules to show some effect. It is found that they do, and the ideal-gas equation must be corrected to take these deviations into account. Such a corrected gas law is van der Waals' equation. It holds well for situations where the deviations from the ideal are small. As the pressure on the gas increases, the molecules are crowded more closely together, and the volume of the molecules themselves, though small, therefore becomes appreciable compared with the volume of the container. If the temperature is low, moreover (though still well above the boiling point), the slower molecules are near each other for a longer time at impact, and the intermolecular forces therefore have a greater opportunity to produce an appreciable effect. For these conditions J. D. van der Waals (1837–1923) found that the equation

$$\left(P + \frac{a}{V^2}\right)(V - b) = nRT \qquad (12\text{-}15)$$

was an accurate description of the experimentally observed behavior of real gases.

This equation says that the effective pressure of a gas is larger than the applied pressure, $P$, of the walls of the container by the amount $a/V^2$, and that the volume occupied by the gas is less than the volume of the container by the amount $b$. The quantities $a$ and $b$ are constants that are characteristic of the particular gas under investigation. Laboratory measurements of several corresponding sets of $P$, $V$, and $T$ will yield the numerical values of $a$ and $b$ for the experimental gas.

The quantity $a/V^2$ accounts for the effect of the intermolecular attractions. If these attractions are appreciable, an applied pressure, $P$, reduces the volume of an actual gas more than the volume of the ideal gas, for not only is the applied pressure *pushing* the molecules closer together, but the intermolecular forces are also *pulling* the molecules closer together; thus the effective pressure is greater than $P$ by $a/V^2$. As high pressure pushes the molecules closer together, the intermolecular forces become greater. As low temperature reduces the speed of the molecules, the strong attractions, during the close approach at impact, have a longer time to act. But, since both high pressure and low temperature result in a decreased $V$, the quantity $a/V^2$ becomes larger. Thus this term accounts for the increased effect of molecular attractions in two ways: both by an increased pressure and by a lowered temperature.

The whole development of the kinetic theory makes clear the idea that the effective volume of a gas is the space available for molecular motion. For an ideal gas this is the total volume of the container since the molecules are considered to be point masses—that is, their volume is zero. But this is not true of actual gases. A molecule must have some, even if a minute, volume; one molecule cannot move into the space occupied by another. The *effective* volume of a gas is therefore somewhat less than the volume ($V$) of the container. This correction appears as the constant $b$, which is a measure of the total volume of the molecules themselves.

At low pressure and high temperatures, as $V$ becomes correspondingly large, the constant $b$

| TABLE 12-2    *Molecular Diameters* | |
| --- | --- |
| GAS | DIAMETER IN METERS |
| $H_2$ | $2.76 \times 10^{-10}$ |
| $O_2$ | $2.93 \times 10^{-10}$ |
| He | $2.66 \times 10^{-10}$ |
| $H_2O$ | $2.89 \times 10^{-10}$ |
| Hg | $2.38 \times 10^{-10}$ |

we already know the number of molecules in one mole of gas, it is simple arithmetic to calculate the volume and therefore the diameter of one molecule. Some representative diameters of molecules, determined from van der Waals' constant *b* and Avogadro's number, are given in Table 12-2. Two aspects of these values are of interest. First, the minute size of the molecules explains the remarkable success of the second simplifying assumption for the calculation of the pressure of an ideal gas. To be sure, the molecules of a gas at normal pressure and temperature have an average separation of only about $3 \times 10^{-9}$ meter. But this is still ten times as great as the diameter of the molecules. The second point of interest is that all the different molecules have approximately the *same* diameter; though the diameters vary a little, they are all of the same order of magnitude, $10^{-10}$ meter. But the masses of the molecules listed in Table 12-2 go through a range of a hundred times from $H_2$ to Hg. How could such widely different amounts of matter be contained in approximately equal volumes? Perhaps the picture of an atom as a small uniform sphere, which has been useful in our atomic-molecular theory, is far too simple, and some modification of this picture may be necessary. In later chapters we shall see that this indeed is so.

becomes a negligibly small fraction of $V$ and may be disregarded, and $a/V^2$ also becomes vanishingly small. For these conditions equation 12-15 reduces to the ideal-gas equation. At pressures of from one to two atmospheres, common gases at room temperature (which is far above their boiling points) show inappreciable deviations from the ideal-gas relation. Water vapor, on the other hand, displays marked deviations at 150°C and at pressures not much over atmospheric pressure. Equation 12-15, then, is not a contradiction of the kinetic theory but represents an extension and refinement of the kinetic model of a gas.

The constant *b* is of particular interest for our discussion. It is a measure, as we have seen, of the total volume occupied by the molecules of a mole of gas. Since, from Perrin's work,

## Concepts and Terms

Heat as Mechanical Energy
   change of state
Calculation of Gas Pressure
   root-mean-square speed
   *P-V* product as kinetic energy
   molecular speeds
Absolute Temperature as Molecular Kinetic Energy

Equipartition of Energy
   law of Dulong and Petit
Distribution of Molecular Speeds
Brownian Movements
   determination of Avogadro's number
Deviations from the Ideal-gas Law
   molecular diameters

## Problems

**12-1.** In terms of the kinetic-molecular model of matter discuss: (A) the significance of specific heats and why they are different for different substances; (B) the significance of latent heats. Why "latent," and why should the heat of vaporization be greater than the heat of fusion?

**12-2.** Review the derivation of equation 12-5, and list the various laws of physical science that are either directly or indirectly involved.

**12-3.**

  (A) Show that the kinetic model of a gas is consistent with Boyle's law. (Hint: Consider a cubical volume of edge $L$. If the volume is doubled, $L$ becomes $\sqrt[3]{2}\,L$. This increases the area of a wall and the distances between walls.)

  (B) Show that the model is consistent with the empirical law that, at constant volume, pressure is directly proportional to absolute temperature. (Hint: Remember that doubling the temperature doubles the KE and thus increases the speed by a factor of $\sqrt{2}$.)

**12-4.** Calculate the rms speed of argon at standard temperature and pressure. (Consult Table 12-1, and, remembering Avogadro's law, consult the periodic table for data on relative densities.)
*Ans.* $0.41 \times 10^3$ m/sec

**12-5.** The atmospheric pressure is due almost entirely to nitrogen and oxygen molecules. Approximately 80% of the atmosphere is nitrogen and 20% oxygen. How is the kinetic energy of a sample of air divided between these two gases? Give reasons for your answer.
*Ans.* 0.8 of the total in the nitrogen

**12-6.**
(A) Evaluate the gas constant in joules ($PV =$ energy). Experimentally, 1 mole of any gas at standard conditions fills $2.24 \times 10^4$ cm$^3$. The density of mercury is 13.6 grams/cm$^3$.
(B) Express the gas constant in calories.
*Ans.* (A) 8.31 joules/mole °K
(B) 1.99 cal/mole °K

**12-7.** Using $6.02 \times 10^{23}$ as Avogadro's number, compute Boltzmann's constant.
*Ans.* $k = 1.38 \times 10^{-23}$ joule/molecule °K

**12-8.** Solve equation 12-10 for the rms speed, and show that it is equal to $\sqrt{3RT/M}$ if $M$ is the "kilogram-molecular weight." (That is, for H$_2$, $M = 2 \times 10^{-3}$ kgm/mole. Check the units.) Using the gas law, show that this reduces to equation 12-8.

**12-9.** Using the relation of Prob. 12-8, calculate the rms speed (A) for oxygen at 27°C; (B) for mercury at 127°C (see § 12-3).
*Ans.* (A) $4.84 \times 10^2$ m/sec;
(B) $2.23 \times 10^2$ m/sec

**12-10.** Hydrogen chloride (HCl) and ammonia (NH$_3$) are gases.
(A) Which gas will diffuse through air more rapidly? How many times as rapidly?
(B) A sample of HCl is introduced into one end of a glass tube 1 m long at the same time that a sample of NH$_3$ is introduced into the other end. When the gases meet, they react to form NH$_4$Cl, which produces a white fog. Where will the fog appear?
*Ans.* (A) NH$_3$ diffuses 1.46 times as rapidly as HCl
(B) 40.6 cm from HCl end

**12-11.**
(A) Why does some of an open dish of water evaporate in a short time, but not all of it at once?
(B) The boiling point of alcohol is 78°C, and that of water is 100°C. Why does alcohol spilled on your hand feel cooler than water if both are at room temperature?

**12-12.** The specific heats of six elements of very different atomic weight are given in § 11-1. Calculate the product of specific heat and atomic weight for each of these elements. In view of the large variation of both specific heat and atomic weight, would you call this product a constant? What is the average value of the product? Discuss this result in terms of the kinetic theory of matter.

**12-13.** Do real gases obey the ideal-gas law exactly? Discuss in terms of the kinetic model of a gas. Do the actions of real gases support or refute the kinetic concept of a gas? Discuss.

**12-14.** What were the fundamental assumptions of Perrin's method for the measurement of Avogadro's number? How were these assumptions justified?

# Suggested Readings

1. L. W. Taylor, *Physics the Pioneer Science* (Houghton Mifflin, 1941), pp. 106–109 and 212–215.
2. R. T. Beyer and A. O. Williams, *College Physics* (Prentice-Hall, 1957), Chap. 13.
3. M. Born, *The Restless Universe*, translated by W. M. Deans (Dover Publications, 1951), pp. 1–44. An interesting account of kinetic theory, with marginal "movies." See "To the Reader" opposite the table of contents.
4. L. B. Loeb and A. S. Adams, *The Development of Physical Thought* (Wiley, 1933), pp. 263–294 and 301–306.
5. W. F. Magie, *A Source Book in Physics* (McGraw-Hill, 1935), pp. 178–181 (Dulong and Petit on atomic heat), 247–251 (Bernoulli on kinetic theory), 251–255 (Brown on the Brownian movements), and 255–257 (Joule on the velocity of gaseous molecules).
6. A. Einstein and L. Infeld, *The Evolution of Physics* (Simon and Schuster, 1938). An excellent book written for the layman. Read the preface and pp. 3–67, which trace the growth of the mechanical view through the kinetic theory.

CHAPTER

13

Solutions (I)

IN MOST of our discussion up to this point matter has been considered only in the form of pure substances—elements and compounds. But pure substances are rare; the common form of matter encountered in our environment is the mixture. Of the various types of mixture, the most common, and in many ways the most important, is the special kind of mixture called a *solution*. The reason for this importance is that almost all the transformations of matter, the chemical reactions, take place in solution. All the complex series of biochemical processes that make up the dynamic system called "life" take place in solution; most of the operations of modern manufacturing, from the making of steel to the making of antibiotics, take place in solution; and even such an everyday process as cooking or washing one's face involves solutions. It is apparent, then, that the behavior of matter in solution, whether or not this behavior is understood, determines, to a great extent, our relation to our environment.

These facts are probably more than adequate justification of the study of solutions; but, once again, the primary reason for our consideration of such facts is their relation to theories already advanced in this text and to theories that are still to be developed. The kinetic-molecular theory, which was discussed in the previous chapter, has been extremely effective in interpreting the facts of the behavior of matter in solution; and a detailed consideration of the laws of solution will lead to far-reaching refinements and extensions of the simple mechanical theory of the structure of matter that we have established and accepted and that is the culmination of our study so far.

This chapter will be concerned primarily with presenting the facts and describing the behavior of solutions, with establishing the terminology and conventions that are used in scientific discussion of solutions, and with elucidating the simple laws of solutions. The relation of these laws to the kinetic theory will be pointed out, but the aspects of solutions that lead to new theories will not be considered until the next chapter. Still later chapters will deal with some of the more complex concepts concerning solutions.

## 13-1. *Definitions*

On page 10 a **solution** was defined as a mixture (a form of matter that has a variable composition and can be separated into components by physical means) that is homogeneous by any method of observation. Since then we have developed several new ideas, have refined some old ideas, and have had a good deal of experience in dealing with scientific terms and concepts—all of which we should now apply to expressing a complete and more rigorous statement of this important definition. A completely rigorous definition of the term is: **A solution is a single-phase system consisting of two or more different molecular species that are not readily and spontaneously interconvertible.** This statement is succinct and rigorous, but it needs a good deal of clarification in order to be a complete and useful concept.

The use of the phrase "single-phase system" states the concept of homogeneity explicitly and precisely. A phase has been defined as a part of a system enclosed by a physical boundary—a surface or a discontinuity in properties. In a single-phase system no discontinuity in properties is encountered; the system is therefore homogeneous. The fact that a solution is a sample of matter (or a system) that is made up of several kinds of matter is conveyed in the definition by the statement that solutions consist of two or more different molecular species. The part of the definition that needs the most effort toward clarification is the requirement of non-interconvertibility between the molecular species. To explain this point, we must consider some examples.

Gaseous water exists only as the molecular species $H_2O$. The experimental evidence for this assertion is completely convincing. There is good experimental evidence, on the other hand (it will be considered later in this chapter), that *liquid* water consists, in large part, of aggregates of several molecules—two, three, or even more water molecules held together by rather weak forces (much weaker than ordinary valence bonds). These aggregates of several $H_2O$ molecules can be considered entities and described by the formulas $H_4O_2$, $H_6O_3$, etc. It might seem reasonable to consider pure liquid water a solution of these molecular species in $H_2O$. This interpretation is excluded, however, for these species are readily and spontaneously interconverted. A sample of water, then, is considered a pure substance and *not* a solution even though these aggregated molecular species are known to exist.

The opposite case is illustrated by the two *different substances* oxygen and ozone. Oxygen, of course, has the formula $O_2$, which represents a molecule made up of two oxygen atoms. Ozone, which we can make by passing an electric spark through $O_2$, consists of *three* atoms of oxygen bonded together and has the formula $O_3$. Now it is possible to interconvert these two molecular species, but the process does not take place spontaneously and readily. The two forms of this element are quite stable and can be separated quite easily (the various aggregates of $H_2O$ *cannot* be separated). A system made up of $O_2$ and $O_3$ would properly be considered a gaseous solution of ozone in oxygen.

Another term that will be used frequently in the description of solutions is **component**. Because of the easy and spontaneous interconvertibility mentioned above, a component is not necessarily one of the molecular species *present* in a solution; it is, rather, one of the molecular entities that are needed to make up the solution. Again an example is the best way to describe this subtlety. Carbonic acid was listed in Table 7-8 (§ 7-12) as one of the common acids—or, rather, as the acid corresponding to the common carbonate radical, $CO_3^{-2}$. If one looks closely at the formula of carbonic acid, $H_2CO_3$, one sees that this formula is the sum of the formulas of water and carbon dioxide:

$$H_2CO_3 = H_2O + CO_2 \qquad (13\text{-}1)$$

The relations among these three formulas are much more than a simple coincidence in appearance. Carbonic acid exists, in fact, only in water solution, made by dissolving carbon dioxide in water. Equation 13-1 describes the relations†

---

† These relations are called a **chemical equilibrium.** The concept of equilibrium, an extremely important one, is the essence of many parts of physical science. This concept will be considered in great detail in a

among the three molecular species, *all* of which are present when carbon dioxide is dissolved in water. When the two components, carbon dioxide and water, are mixed, some carbonic acid is immediately formed (which, of course, uses up some of the carbon dioxide and water), and an equilibrium mixture of all three species is present in any solution so made. Such a solution has *only two* components, for only two molecular species were required to make the solution, even though three different molecular species are clearly present in the solution.

Two other terms frequently used in the discussion of solutions are **solvent** and **solute.** The solvent is the component that dissolves the solute, and the solute is the component that is dissolved by the solvent. This terminology is clear enough for liquid solutions made of a liquid component and a solid component; the liquid is the solvent, and the solid is the solute. But, when two liquids are completely miscible (that is, are soluble in each other without limit), it is not at all clear which is the solvent and which the solute. The terms are quite relative, and in such cases this ambiguity is of no importance. In general, in such cases of complete miscibility, the *solvent* is the component present in greater amount, and the *solute* is the component present in lesser amount.

## 13-2. *Classification of Solutions*

Solutions may be classified according to the physical state of the solution and the physical state of the components. All three of the states of matter—gaseous, liquid, and solid—are exemplified by solutions. Most of our interest will be centered on liquid solutions. The detailed study of the other two types is properly a part of advanced courses in physics and chemistry.

GASEOUS STATE. Since all gases are entirely miscible in each other, any mixture of gases is a gaseous solution. All gaseous mixtures are entirely homogeneous (a single phase) by any physically realizable means of observation. Interpretation of the gaseous state according to the kinetic-molecular theory clearly implies discrete molecules and therefore a sub-microscopic discontinuity at the level of molecular size. This, however, cannot be considered *physically observable* heterogeneity.

The requirement of homogeneity (single phase) eliminates the possibility of a liquid or a solid dissolving in a gas to give a gaseous solution. It is true that solids and liquids do evaporate into the air, for example, to give gaseous solutions of these materials. But the first step in this process is the vaporization of the solid or liquid.

The commonest gaseous solution is the air around us. Using the terminology of solvent and solute (which we rarely do in dealing with gaseous solutions), we can consider air a solution of oxygen and water vapor and a few minor components in the solvent nitrogen. The composition of air varies, within fairly narrow limits, mostly in its trace constituents and in its water vapor. Nitrogen makes up about 78 percent of dry air and oxygen about 21 percent. The remaining 1 percent is mostly argon but includes variable amounts of the other inert gases as well as carbon dioxide and hydrogen.

SOLID STATE. The term "solution" is generally applied only to the liquid state. In scientific terminology, however, many solid solutions must be included within the meaning of this term. The common form of solid solution is one solid dissolved in another solid. Such solid solutions of metals are called *alloys*. Examples are the many types of special steels, which are solutions of other metals in iron; brass, which is a solution of zinc in copper; bronze, the alloy of tin and copper; pewter, the alloy of tin and lead; and an extensive array of combinations of components that make special-purpose alloys whose properties meet unique technological needs. Many rocks and minerals are naturally occurring solid solutions of several related solid compounds.

Two other combinations of states give solid

---

later chapter. In this chapter, however, the general idea of equilibrium is used in several instances in the discussion of solutions. An equilibrium is, in general, a situation in which two opposing processes take place at equal rates so that there is no *net* or apparent change. The symbols that imply an equilibrium are the equality sign, as in equation 13-1, and the double arrow, $\rightleftarrows$; in this text the double arrow will generally be used.

solutions. A few gases dissolve in certain solid metals, notably hydrogen in platinum, to give a solid solution of the gas in the metal. Liquid mercury dissolves in certain solid metals to form solid solutions called *amalgams*—for example, zinc amalgam, which is a solid solution of mercury in zinc, and silver amalgam, the solid solution of mercury in silver that is commonly used as dental fillings.

All three types of solid solutions have great technological importance and some theoretical importance to advanced parts of physical science. In the rest of this course, however, we shall be concerned not at all with solid solutions and very little with gaseous solutions; our primary interest will be with the much more extensive and interesting problem of liquid solutions.

LIQUID STATE. All three possible combinations of the states of matter give rise to liquid solutions: gas in liquid, liquid in liquid, and solid in liquid. We have already considered a gas dissolved in a liquid, carbon dioxide in water, which is, in essence, ordinary carbonated water. Solutions of liquids in liquids, such as oil in gasoline or alcohol in water, are also common in our ordinary experience. Solutions of solids in liquids are much commoner. Such solids as salt and sugar, dissolved in water, form liquid solutions that are as common in our environment as sea water or the morning cup of coffee. These liquid solutions will be the major concern of this chapter, and those in which the solute is a solid will receive the major attention.

## 13-3. Concentration

In any precise, quantitative discussion of a solution, it immediately becomes necessary to state the relative amounts of the various components of the solution. A statement of these relative amounts is a statement of the **concentration** of the solution. In this chapter we have already used one common expression for concentration. The composition of air was expressed as 78 percent nitrogen and 21 percent oxygen. This is one of several useful ways of expressing the concentration of oxygen in this solution (or

of any solute in a solution). The statement of the percentage of the constituents is a precise and unambiguous statement of concentration and contrasts strongly to the usual way of expressing concentrations in non-technical language. The description "strong" or "powerful" is a part of our ordinary vocabulary and suffers both from ambiguity of the term and from quantitative indefiniteness. Yet this *is* an expression of concentration. In scientific usage the terms "concentrated" and "highly concentrated" are used in contrast to "dilute" to convey an intentionally indefinite statement of relative concentrations of solutions. But it is clearly necessary, in any quantitative discussion of solutions, to introduce precise and definite terms and methods of stating concentrations.

Any statement that includes relative amounts of any two of the three factors—solute, solvent, and solution—is a quantitative expression of concentration. Many different expressions for concentration have been introduced into science, and any student who continues the study of science will encounter them and will be expected to be familiar with their meanings. Any system of describing concentration can be applied to any solution; and, since the statement of concentration in terms of one expression conveys the necessary information on the relative amounts of solute and solvent, it is possible to calculate the concentration in terms of any other expression of concentration.

The amount of any substance can be expressed in mass or in volume; there are various units of mass and of volume; and the amount of solute, the amount of solvent, and the amount of solution can be expressed in any of these units. The permutations and combinations available for expressing concentrations are, then, numerous—as becomes distressingly apparent to students of classical introductory science courses.

For this text we shall reduce the number of different expressions of concentration to the minimum necessary for presenting the ideas. Of the almost limitless number of expressions of concentration that have been used for special purposes in science, only four will be used in this course. Three of these are new terms and represent new ideas that must be learned.

## 13-4. *Percentage Concentration*

The first of these is *percentage* concentration. We have already used this expression of concentration in describing a gaseous solution, air, but it is not used extensively in scientific work and will be rarely used in this course. The term hardly needs explanation, for it is common in our non-scientific vocabulary. *Percent* means "parts per hundred parts" and, when used to describe concentrations, expresses the number of grams of solute per hundred grams of *solution*. In somes cases, when concentrations of gaseous or liquid solutes are expressed, the term *volume percent* is used, which, obviously, means "parts per hundred parts *by volume*." For example, a solution made by mixing 10 grams of alcohol in 90 grams of water has a concentration of 10 percent alcohol. A 10 percent *by volume* solution of alcohol in water is somewhat different in concentration; it is made by diluting 10 cm³ of alcohol with water to make 100 cm³ of solution.

A commoner way of expressing concentrations is by the mass of solute in a given mass of solvent, usually 100 or 1,000 grams. The solubility curves in Figure 13-1, for example, are expressed in grams of solute per 1,000 grams of water (the solvent in this case).

## 13-5. *Molar Concentration*

For most purposes it is much more useful to express concentrations in the number of *moles* rather than the number of grams of solute. Two common expressions of concentration, *molar* and *molal,* use this method. The more frequently used and the more generally useful is **molar,** which is a statement of the number of **moles of solute per liter** (1,000 cm³) **of solution.** A one molar (1 M) solution is made by dissolving 1 mole of the solute in enough solvent to make 1 liter of solution. Obviously a greater or lesser amount of the solution could be made by using greater or smaller numbers of moles of solute and diluting to a proportionately greater or lesser volume. Similarly, a solution of greater or lesser

concentration could be prepared (depending on the limits of solubility; see § 13-10) by using a greater or lesser number of moles of solute in the same volume of solution. A one molar solution of alcohol in water, for example, would be made by dissolving 46 grams (1 mole) of alcohol in enough water to make just 1,000 cm³ of solution. If 10 liters of such a solution is needed, obviously 10 moles, or 460 grams, would be dissolved in water to make 10 liters of solution. Or, if only a small quantity were needed, 4.6 grams would be dissolved to make 100 cm³ of solution, or 2.3 grams to make 50 cm³ of solution. To make a solution having a concentration of 3 moles per liter (a 3 M solution) of alcohol in water, it would be necessary to dissolve $3 \times$ 46 grams or 138 grams of alcohol in enough water to make 1 liter of solution, or 13.8 grams to make 100 cm³ of solution. A 0.1 M solution would be made by diluting 4.6 grams of alcohol to 1 liter with water. For substances other than alcohol the corresponding molecular weight or multiple or fraction would be used. A 1 M solution of HCl would take 36.5 grams per liter; of NaCl, 58.5 grams; of NaOH, 40 grams; etc.

The usefulness of this expression of concentration lies in the fact that the amount of the solute is determined in *moles* per unit volume of solution. Thus a given volume of any solution having a certain molar concentration contains the same number of moles as the same volume of any other solution of that molar concentration. Since the relative quantities of reacting substances are determined, not directly in grams, but in moles, chemically equivalent quantities of solutions are most easily determined if the concentrations are expressed in the molar system. For example, the reaction of sulfuric acid with sodium hydroxide to produce sodium sulfate and water goes according to the equation

$$H_2SO_4 + 2NaOH \longrightarrow Na_2SO_4 + 2H_2O$$

One would probably bring about this reaction by mixing solutions of the two reactants. The equation states that 1 mole of sulfuric acid will react quantitatively with 2 moles of sodium hydroxide. It would require a bit of calculation to determine what quantity of solutions to mix if the concentrations were expressed in percentage or in grams of solute. If the solutions have the same *molar* concentration, it is immediately apparent that just twice the volume of the NaOH solution is needed to react with a given volume of the $H_2SO_4$ solution. Two liters of 1 M NaOH would just react with 1 liter of 1 M $H_2SO_4$; 20 cm³ of 10 M NaOH would react with 10 cm³ of 10 M $H_2SO_4$; and 100 cm³ of 6 M NaOH would react with 100 cm³ of 3 M $H_2SO_4$.

## 13-6. *Molal Concentration*

In certain other situations it is more convenient to know the concentration of a solution as the number of moles of solute in a given number of moles of solvent rather than a given volume of solution. This type of concentration expression is useful when we are dealing with properties that depend on this relation between the number of particles of solute and the number of particles of solvent. Such properties are called **colligative properties** and are considered in detail in the next chapter. In general, if one is interested in interactions between solute and solvent, this method of expressing concentrations will be used, for the magnitudes of such interactions are determined by the relative numbers of particles of solute and solvent.

There are two methods of stating concentrations in such a way that the relative numbers of particles of the components of the solution are emphasized. The first of these is the use of the expression **molal,** which states the number of **moles of solute dissolved in 1,000 grams of solvent.** A 5 molal solution of alcohol in water is made by dissolving 5 moles ($5 \times 46 = 236$ grams) of alcohol in 1,000 grams of water; a 0.3 molal solution of sugar in water is made by dissolving 0.3 mole of sugar in 1,000 grams of water or 0.03 mole in 100 grams of water. The molecular weight of sugar is 342; it therefore requires $0.3 \times 342 = 102.6$ grams of sugar in 1,000 grams of water, or one-tenth of this, 10.26 grams in 100 grams of water, to make a 0.3 molal solution. It is apparent that, if the mass of the solvent remains fixed, the number of solvent molecules remains fixed; thus a comparison of solutions whose concentrations are expressed as

molal concentrations is a comparison of the number of molecules of solute in a fixed number of molecules of solvent.

## 13-7. *Mole Fraction*

The last expression for concentration that we must consider is *mole fraction.* This also expresses concentration in such a way that relative numbers of particles (molecules) are emphasized. This expression differs from molality in that mole fractions express the number of moles of both the solute and the solvent in the term for concentration. **The mole fraction of a component of a solution, symbolized by X, is the ratio of the number of moles of that component to the total number of moles of all components.** The simplest cases are the two-component solutions we have been describing up to this point. A solution might be made by mixing 1 mole of alcohol (46 grams) and 1 mole of water (18 grams). The mole fraction of each component would then be 0.5. The total number of moles present is 2; there is 1 mole of alcohol, and the ratio of 1 to 2 is 0.5. The solutions described in illustration of molality can also be described in mole-fraction concentrations. The solution of alcohol in water was made by dissolving 5 moles of alcohol in 1,000 grams of water. Since the molecular weight of water is 18, there are $1,000/18 = 55.5$ moles of water in 1,000 grams of water. This solution is therefore made by mixing 5 moles of alcohol and 55.5 moles of water. The total number of moles is, then, $5 + 55.5 = 60.5$, and the mole fraction of alcohol in this solution is $5/60.5 = 0.083$. Similarly, the mole fraction of water in this same solution is $55.5/60.5 = 0.917$. The mole fraction of sugar in the 0.3 molal solution is determined by the ratio of the moles of sugar to the total number of moles, which is $0.3 + 55.5 = 55.8$. $X_{sugar} = n_{sugar}/n_{total} = 0.3/55.8 = 0.054$.

Concentrations expressed in mole fractions are particularly useful when the distinction between solute and solvent is not emphasized and there are more than two components in the solution. The general method of calculating mole fractions is indicated by equations 13-2. An equation of the same form applies to each component.

$$X_1 = \frac{n_1}{n_1 + n_2 + n_3 + \cdots},$$

$$X_2 = \frac{n_2}{n_1 + n_2 + n_3 + \cdots}, \quad \text{etc.}$$

(13-2)

In these equations $X_1$ is the mole fraction of component 1, $X_2$ is the mole fraction of component 2, $n_1$ is the number of moles of component 1, $n_2$ is the number of moles of component 2, etc.

A three-component solution could be made by mixing, for example, 100 grams each of sugar, water, and alcohol. The first step in calculating the mole fraction of each component is to calculate the number of moles in the 100 grams of each. The molecular weights are 342, 18, and 46 respectively. The number of moles in 100 grams are, then: moles of sugar = 100/346 = 0.29; moles of water = 100/18 = 5.55; moles of alcohol = 100/46 = 2.18. The total number of moles is, then, 0.29 + 5.55 + 2.18 = 8.02. The mole fraction of each component is then calculated: $X_s = 0.29/8.02 = 0.036$; $X_w = 5.55/8.02 = 0.692$; $X_a = 2.18/8.02 = 0.272$. The sum of the mole fractions of all the components of any solution must, of course, add up to unity:

mole fraction of sugar    = 0.036
mole fraction of water    = 0.692
mole fraction of alcohol = 0.272

total = 1.000

## 13-8. Interconversion of Concentration Units

An important point about expressions of concentration is that a concentration expressed in one system can be converted to any other system by simple calculation. Any statement of the concentration of a solution is the statement of an empirical fact. It does not change that fact to state the concentration in different units of quantity of the components, just as it does not change the empirical fact of the length of a table to describe that length in meters rather than feet. The conversion among the units of concentration that express the relative amounts of the components in terms of mass (grams or moles) is practically self-evident. Such conversions were made in the illustrative examples above. If the amounts of any of the components are expressed in volumes, as in molarity, it is necessary to change this volume to an equivalent mass in order to convert the concentration to one in which the amounts are expressed in units of mass. It is therefore necessary to know the density of the solution or of the component whose relative amount was expressed in volume units. If, for example, we wish to find the mole fraction of sodium chloride in a 2 molar solution of sodium chloride in water (such a solution has a density of 1.2 grams/cm$^3$), we must express the quantity of water in moles. In order to do this, we must first calculate the *mass* of the water that dissolves the 2 moles of NaCl. From the density of the solution we can calculate the mass of the solution that contains just 2 moles of NaCl, and by difference we can calculate the mass of the water. One liter (1,000 cm$^3$) of solution contains 2 moles. The mass of this volume of solution is 1,000 cm$^3 \times$ 1.2 grams/cm$^3$ = 1,200 grams. The mass of NaCl in this amount of solution is calculated from the molecular weight of NaCl, which is 58.5. Two moles of NaCl has a mass of 2 × 58.5 = 117 grams. The 1,200 grams of solution therefore contains 117 grams of solute, the remainder being water. The mass of the water in this solution is therefore 1,200 − 117 = 1,083 grams. The molecular weight of water is 18; the number of moles of water in this mass of water is therefore $n_w$ = 1,083/18 = 60.2, and the total number of moles is $n_w + n_{NaCl}$ = 60.2 + 2 = 62.2. The mole fraction of NaCl is 2/62.2 = 0.032, and the mole fraction of water is 60.2/62.2 = 0.968.

## 13-9. Saturated Solutions

In our discussion of concentration expressions we tacitly assumed that any solvent could dissolve any amount of any solute. We referred to solutions that contained small amounts of solute and to others that contained large amounts of solute and did not raise the question whether or not it is possible to dissolve so much solute in the specified quantity of solvent, whether such high concentrations are possible. Among the examples considered were several in which alcohol was dissolved in water. These two components are completely miscible in each other; that is, there is no limit on the amount of one that can be dissolved in a given amount of the other. It is therefore possible to prepare solutions made up of these two components in which the concentration has any value desired. But this situation is rather exceptional. There is usually a distinct limit on the solubility. If the concentration of such a solute is continuously increased (by introducing more and more of the solute into a fixed quantity of the solvent), a point is finally reached where the added solute does not dissolve. The solvent is then **saturated** with solute, and the solution is said to be a **saturated solution.**

The concentration of a saturated solution of any pair of components (solvent and solute) is a characteristic property of the pair. We shall see in the next section that this concentration varies with temperature; it is therefore necessary to state the temperature of the saturated solution in order to use this property without ambiguity. The equilibrium in a saturated solution is not static. The solute has not ceased to go into solution; rather, the rate at which the solute comes out of solution has finally reached the point where it just equals the rate at which the solute goes into solution. This is a good example of equilibrium—two equal opposing effects canceling each other out to give an appearance of no change at all.

## 13-10. Solubility

The concentration of solute in a saturated solution is the **solubility** of that solute in the particular solvent under the particular conditions. The terms "solubility" and "saturated solution" have no meaning with respect to solutions of components that are completely miscible. There is no such thing as a saturated solution of alcohol in water for there is no limit to their solubility in each other. Usually, however, the solubility of a solute is limited. Some compounds are highly soluble in water, and others are virtually insoluble. Silver nitrate has a solubility of 2,134 grams per liter in water at 18°C; this means that the concentration of silver nitrate in a saturated solution of this substance in water is 2,134 grams per liter. The molecular weight of silver nitrate is 170; the molar concentration of this solution is therefore $2{,}134/170 = 12.6$ M. Silver chloride, on the other hand, is quite insoluble in water. The concentration of its saturated solution, and therefore its solubility, is $1.5 \times 10^{-3}$ gram per liter $= 1 \times 10^{-5}$ M. Silver sulfate is said to be only moderately soluble in water because the concentration of its saturated solution is 8 grams per liter. Its molecular weight is 312; its solubility can therefore be expressed as $8/312 = 0.026$ M.

The statement that silver chloride is quite insoluble in water is, obviously, not literally true. The solubility is extremely slight and for most purposes is insignificant, but it is not zero. Actually there is no such thing as absolute insolubility. In some precise analytical work the solubility of glass in water cannot be ignored even though for most purposes it is completely insignificant.

The solubility of a particular solute is not a constant property. There is extreme variation in the solubility of any solute in different types of solvent, and there is also considerable variation in the solubility of a given solute in a given solvent with changes in the conditions of the system. It is necessary, therefore, to examine in detail the quantitative effects of these various influences on solubility.

## 13-11. Polar and Non-polar Solvents and Solutes

The widest variation of solubility is observed when we compare a given solute with various solvents or various solutes with a given solvent. Water is the commonest and most widely used solvent. Many substances are extremely soluble in water, and vast numbers of substances are at least moderately soluble. The three solutes considered in the previous section illustrate the widely varying solubility of salts in water. But there is also a quite different class of substances that must be considered insoluble or only sparingly soluble in water. This class consists of the substances called **non-polar.**† The reason for their insolubility, as we shall see, is quite different from the reason for the insolubility of salts such as silver chloride. The non-polar substances are generally **organic** (compounds of carbon) and are usually more soluble in organic solvents than in water. One such organic, non-polar solvent is gasoline. Water and most of the substances that are soluble in water are very slightly soluble, if at all, in gasoline. On the other hand, gasoline is a good solvent for many things, such as grease, fats, oils (non-polar substances in general), that are quite insoluble in water.

From these rather unorganized comments a pattern is beginning to emerge. Substances appear to be classifiable on the basis of their tendency to dissolve in two opposite types of solvent. On the one hand are the water-type solvents and the substances that are soluble in water or other polar solvents, and on the other hand are the oil-type solvents and the substances that are soluble in non-polar solvents. This division into two types of solvents and solutes is expressed by the hackneyed old aphorism "Oil and water don't mix." It is true that oil and water are not soluble in each other, and it is also true that they are representative of two large classes of substances.

The tendency of polar solvents to dissolve polar solutes, and vice versa, illustrates a generalization that describes solubility tendencies qualitatively. This generalization is: "Solvents tend to dissolve chemically similar substances." Another example of the similarity in chemical structure of substances that are soluble in each other is seen in the structural resemblance of both sugar and alcohol to water. Both of these substances are highly soluble in water and much less so in organic solvents even though they are organic substances themselves. The reason for this is that the chemical nature of sugar and

alcohol is largely determined by the presence of hydroxyl groups (–OH) in the molecules. Water has the structure H–OH; alcohol has the structure $C_2H_5$–OH; and sugar, a much larger molecule, has 8 OH groups in its structure: $C_{12}H_{14}O_3$–(OH)$_8$. This similarity accounts for the high solubility of these substances in water.

## 13-12. *Solute-solvent Interaction*

Another factor that is dependent on the relation between solute and solvent will strongly influence solubility: the possibility of chemical reaction between the two. We have considered one example of this phenomenon in the dissolving of carbon dioxide in water. Most gases—hydrogen, helium, nitrogen, oxygen, carbon monoxide—have very limited solubility in water. Carbon dioxide is between 100 and 1,000 times as soluble as these gases. This difference is not explained by the difference in chemical structure. The explanation is that the carbon dioxide reacts with water according to the equilibrium of equation 13-1. A complete explanation of this situation must await a more thorough study of the principle of equilibrium, but it can be touched on at this point. Equation 13-1, if written in the opposite direction (note that it is still the *same* equation since the forward and reverse reactions are both going on at the same time; see § 13-2)—

$$CO_2 + H_2O \rightleftarrows H_2CO_3$$

—indicates the process of $CO_2$ dissolving in water as the forward reaction. It is reasonable that the system is able to "tolerate" more $CO_2$ than other gases because some of the $CO_2$ is effectively removed from the system by conversion to a different molecular species, $H_2CO_3$ in this case. Similar situations obtain with the gases ammonia and nitrogen dioxide. Large amounts of ammonia dissolve in water because this gas reacts with water to form ammonium hydroxide according to the equilibrium equation

$$NH_3 + H_2O \rightleftarrows NH_4OH \tag{13-3}$$

Similarly, nitrogen dioxide, $NO_2$, is extremely soluble in water because it reacts with water to form nitric and nitrous acids.

---

† The meaning of the term "non-polar" and its antonym, "polar," must await the development of the ideas of electricity for full explanation. The polar or non-polar character of a substance is a reflection of its sub-microscopic structure and determines to a large degree its physical and chemical properties, including solubility.

## 13-13. Solvation

This explanation of high solubility on the basis of clear-cut chemical reaction between solute and solvent applies to several solute-solvent pairs, but another situation, much commoner, is less clear-cut. We have referred to the tendency for water molecules to associate with each other in aggregates. This type of association of molecules of liquids is also found in other substances though never to as great an extent as in water. Association into loosely bound aggregates also takes place frequently between different substances. When one of the substances is a solvent, the process is called **solvation;** when the solvent is water, the process is called **hydration.** The solvation of a solute is the association of a solute particle with one or more solvent molecules in loose aggregates similar to those described earlier for water. These aggregates are held together by forces that are much weaker than ordinary valence bonds, and it is usually not possible to determine exactly how many molecules of solvent are associated with each solute particle. This process of solvation is a powerful solubilizing influence. Solute-solvent combinations that tend toward a high degree of solvation are those that give high solubility. The solvent may be said to form a sort of protective buffer round each solute particle; this buffer prevents association or aids the dissociation of the individual solute particles from the undissolved phase. The evidence for the existence of the solvation aggregates in solution depends on rather involved and subtle physical-chemical experiments, but the fact that many salts crystallize from water solution in association with one or more molecules of **water of hydration** shows that the aggregates do exist. Such salts are called **hydrates** and are invariably quite soluble in water. If the crystalline hydrate is stable, it is possible to state how many molecules of water are associated with each solute particle, and this information is indicated in the formulas for the hydrates. One such hydrate is copper sulfate, which crystallizes with five molecules of water of hydration. Its formula is $CuSO_4 \cdot 5H_2O$. Solvation occurs with other solvents but most commonly with water.

## 13-14. Partition of Solute Between Two Solvents

Our generality concerning two classes of solutes (and of solvents) is not absolute. Many substances are soluble in both types of solvents. An interesting question about such solutes concerns their tendency to go from one solvent to another when there is competition between two solvents. Iodine, for example, is moderately soluble in water, the archetype of the polar solvents; it is about 250 times as soluble in chloroform ($CHCl_3$), which is a typical oily, or non-polar, solvent. Water and chloroform are insoluble in each other. The question is now posed: "What is the distribution of $I_2$ between $H_2O$ and $CHCl_3$ when the two solvents are placed in competition for the solute?" We can answer this question experimentally by shaking pure chloroform with a solution of iodine in water until solubility equilibrium is established. It is observed that the iodine distributes itself between the two solvents in proportion to its solubility in them. This experimental generalization, which holds for all combinations of solute and two immiscible solvents, is called the **law of partition** and can be expressed by the equation

$$\frac{c_1}{c_2} = \frac{s_1}{s_2} \tag{13-4}$$

In this equation the subscripts 1 and 2 refer to the two solvents; the $c$'s refer to *concentrations* of the solute in the two solvents, and the $s$'s refer to the *solubilities*. We stated that the solubility of iodine in chloroform is 250 times its solubility in water. The ratio of $s_{CHCl_3}$ to $s_{H_2O}$ is therefore 250, and the ratio of the concentration of iodine in the chloroform to its concentration in the water must also be 250. A saturated solution of iodine in water contains about 1 gram of iodine in 1,000 grams of water. If this much iodine-in-water solution is shaken with 1,000 grams of chloroform, the distribution of iodine between the two solvents is determined by the ratio of concentrations, and most of the iodine passes from the water to the chloroform. Thus all but 1/250 of the 1 gram of iodine is removed from the water solution. A second extraction of the water solution with 1,000 grams of chloroform would again remove 249/250 of the iodine from the water, leaving only $(1/250)(1/250) = 1/62,500$ of the original gram of iodine, or 1.6 $\times 10^{-5}$ gram. In actual practice the same result could be achieved much more economically by using a smaller quantity of chloroform in several extractions. For example, five extractions with 25 grams of chloroform would reduce the concentration of iodine in the water to about $1 \times 10^{-5}$ gram per 1,000 grams of water.

This process of **extraction,** which makes use of the law of partition, is extremely useful in the isolation and purification of industrially useful chemicals. Many interesting drugs are isolated from plant tissues by use of this technique on an industrial scale. The production of a number of hormones, such as cortisone, from animal products that were only waste a few years ago depends on extraction; the isolation and purification of most of the antibiotics use the same technique; and in preparative chemistry the application of the principle of distribution of a solute between two solvents is a common and useful method of purification.

## 13-15. Temperature-solubility Relations

Of the various physical conditions of a system, only temperature has a generally significant effect on solubility. The solubility of gases is affected by pressure also (see § 13-18), but the effects of pressure on the solubility of liquids and solids is inconsequential to our discussion of solutions. Temperature changes, however, have quite sizable effects on the solubility of most solutes, regardless of their physical state. A simple statement of the relation of temperature to solubility is that the solubility of most solids and liquids increases with rising temperature while the solubility of most gases decreases. The simplest way to describe the variation of solubility with temperature is by means of graphs. Such graphs are called **solubility curves;** some examples are shown in Figure 13-1.

Before we discuss the individual curves of Figure 13-1, we must explain how such sets of

data are obtained. Each point on these curves represents the concentration of the saturated solution at the corresponding temperature. The experimental problem, then, is to establish equilibrium between the solute phase (a solid in all the cases shown in Fig. 13-1) and the saturated solution of the solute in water. We do this by adding the solute to a sample of the solvent (water in this case), which is maintained at a particular temperature in a carefully controlled thermostat, until no more solute dissolves. When saturation is ensured (by proper agitation, using a finely divided solute, and waiting a long enough time), we analyze a sample of the solution to determine the mass of solvent and the mass of solute in the sample. We could do this for the solutes of Figure 13-1 by weighing the sample of solution, then evaporating all the solvent, and weighing the residue, which is pure solute. The mass of the solvent would then be determined by difference. An analysis of this sort would be carried out at intervals of a few degrees over the range from 0° to 100° for each of the solutes indicated in the figure. The unit of concentration used in Figure 13-1, mass of solute per 1,000 grams of solvent, is the conventional unit for such comparisons of solubilities.

The first type of information obtainable from this figure is a general estimate of the tendency toward solubility of each of the solutes. Ammonium nitrate, potassium iodide, and silver nitrate are extremely soluble. This fact is apparent from the position of the curves for these salts near the top of the graph. One thousand grams of water is capable of dissolving about 1,200 grams of one of these salts even at 0°C. Potassium perchlorate, on the other hand, is soluble in water, at room temperature and below, only to the extent of a few grams per 1,000 grams.† These curves show, then, the wide range

---

† Substances having solubilities of this magnitude are classed as "moderately soluble," not "slightly soluble" or "insoluble," even though they are clearly *much* less soluble than the most soluble substances in this group. An insoluble substance or one of extremely low solubility, such as silver chloride, could not be represented at all on this graph because its solubility at all temperatures would appear to be zero. All of the substances shown in the figure would be classed as moderately or highly soluble in water.

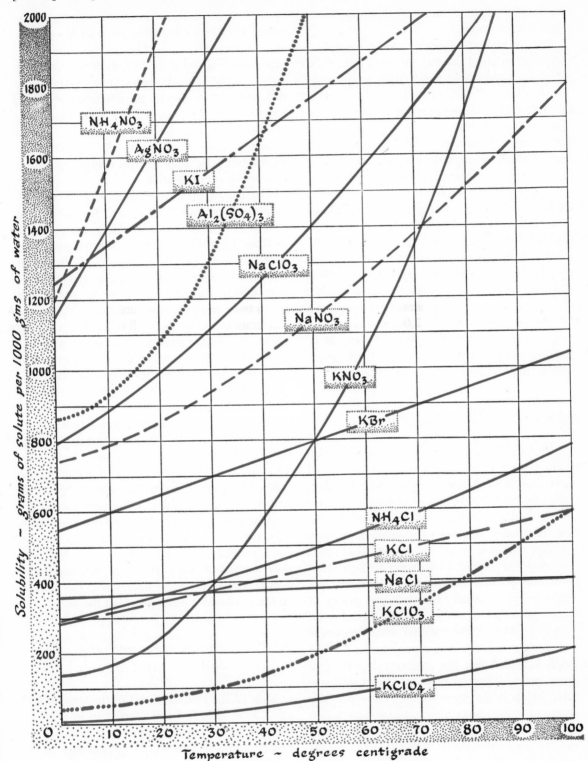

FIGURE **13-1** *Solubility curves.*

of **solubility** of these rather similar salts in the same solvent, water.

A more interesting aspect of these graphs is the presentation of the way in which the solubility of each substance varies with temperature. The fact that *all* the curves rise in going from lower to higher temperatures bears out the generalization that most solids increase in solubility with rising temperature. The *slope* of these curves, which indicates the extent of the increase in solubility for a given increase in temperature, varies widely from one solute to another. Sodium chloride, for example, shows a very slight change in solubility over the entire range of temperatures in the graph: at 0°, 355 grams will dissolve in 1,000 grams of water, and this increases only to 390 grams at 100°, an increase of only about 10 percent. The solubility of potassium nitrate, on the other hand, increases twenty times (2,000 percent) in the same temperature range: it is 130 grams per 1,000 grams of water at 0° and increases to 2,000 grams per 1,000 grams with a temperature rise to about 85°.

## 13-16. Crystallization

Solubility curves are used in an important method for the separation and purification of substances. This method is called **crystallization.** To understand the process of crystallization, we must consider what happens if a saturated solution is cooled. Consider a solution of ammonium chloride that is saturated at 80°. The graph of Figure 13-1 shows that the concentration of such a solution is 660 grams per 1,000 grams of water. One hundred grams of water, saturated at 80°, therefore contains 66 grams of $NH_4Cl$. Now consider what happens if this sample of solution is cooled to 10°C. The graph indicates that the solubility is only 340 grams per 1,000 grams of water at this temperature, which is the same as 34 grams per 100 grams of water. Since this is the concentration of the saturated solution at this lower temperature, we know that the 100 grams of water cannot hold in solution more than 34 grams. Obviously, then, the excess above this amount (32 grams), which was in solution at 80°, must

come out of solution during the cooling. The solute is said to **crystallize** out, and the process is called crystallization. The method is useful for separation and purification only if the solubility curves of the two substances to be separated are different, and the greater the difference, the more effective is the method. If one chooses the proper solvent (guided by solubility curves), it is almost always possible to obtain a sufficient difference in solubility to separate the components of a mixture by crystallization.

The use of the method can be illustrated by another hypothetical situation, for which we choose widely differing solubility curves, such as those for sodium chloride and potassium nitrate. Imagine an equal mixture of these two salts from which it is desired to obtain some pure $KNO_3$. First we saturate some water with the mixture at high temperature. At 75°, for example, all of the $KNO_3$ (1,500 grams) in a sample of the mixture having a mass of 3,000 grams dissolves in 1,000 grams of water, but only about 380 grams out of the 1,500 grams of NaCl dissolves. We then remove the solution from the undissolved NaCl (which is now nearly pure) and cool it to cause crystallization. The solubility of the $KNO_3$ is sharply decreased while the solubility of the NaCl is hardly affected. At 0° only 130 grams of $KNO_3$ remains in solution; the other 1,370 grams crystallizes out. Of the original 380 grams of NaCl, 355 grams remains in solution at 0°, and only 25 grams crystallizes out with the $KNO_3$. One repetition of this process gives virtually pure $KNO_3$, contaminated with only a trace of NaCl. It is true that some loss occurs, but this can be tolerated if the desired end is to obtain a pure sample of the salt.

## 13-17. Temperature and the Solubility of Gases

Most of the characteristics of the solubility of gases have already been referred to in previous sections of this chapter. The two that will be discussed in this section, the dependence of the solubility of gases on temperature and on pressure, are also a familiar part of everyday experience. Ordinary tap water is saturated with air.

| | SOLUBILITY | |
|---|---|---|
| GAS | (GRAMS/1,000 GRAMS) | TEMP. |
| Oxygen | $4.3 \times 10^{-2}$ | 20° |
| | $7.9 \times 10^{-3}$ | 90° |
| Hydrogen | $1.95 \times 10^{-3}$ | 0° |
| | $1.5 \times 10^{-3}$ | 25° |
| Carbon monoxide | $4.4 \times 10^{-2}$ | 0° |
| | $1.8 \times 10^{-2}$ | 50° |
| Carbon dioxide | 3.35 | 0° |
| | 1.45 | 20° |
| | 0.6 | 60° |

TABLE **13-1** *Solubilities of Gases in Water*

We have all observed that, if a glass of very cold water is allowed to warm up to room temperature, a mass of tiny bubbles collects on the surface of the glass. These bubbles are air that has come out of solution because the solubility of the gases that make up air (primarily oxygen and nitrogen) *decreases* as the temperature rises. This behavior is the opposite of that of most liquid and solid solutes but is typical of most gases. Solubility curves such as those of Figure 13-1 are not available for gases, but the tendency to lower solubility at higher temperature is indicated by the data of Table 13-1, which includes the solubilities at different temperatures of several common gases.

## 13-18. Pressure and the Solubility of Gases (Henry's Law)

The effect of changing pressure on the solubility of gases in water is also a part of ordinary non-scientific experience. Carbonated drinks, such as beer and soda, are essentially solutions of carbon dioxide in water, which are maintained in sealed containers at pressures somewhat higher than atmospheric pressure. The opening of the container decreases the pressure on the solution to atmospheric pressure, and it is a common observation that, when this is done, gas is released from the solution. The solubility of the gas (carbon dioxide) in the solvent (water) must, then, be less at the lower pressure. This

behavior is typical of gases. A qualitative statement of the variation of solubility of gases with changing pressure is that the solubility decreases with decreasing pressure and increases with increasing pressure. A quantitative statement of the same empirical fact is contained in **Henry's law,** which states: "The concentration of a gas in solution is proportional to the partial pressure of the gas that is in equilibrium with the solution." This information is conveyed most succinctly by the equation

$$p = kc \qquad (13\text{-}5)$$

in which $p$ is the partial pressure of the gas in the gaseous phase, $k$ is a proportionality constant (characteristic of each gas), and $c$ is the concentration of the gas in the solution phase that is in equilibrium with the gaseous phase.

The most useful form of this equation is a proportion that relates two sets of conditions:

$$\frac{p_1}{p_2} = \frac{c_1}{c_2} \qquad (13\text{-}6)$$

As an example of a calculation based on this form of Henry's law, suppose that we wish to determine, from the data of Table 13-1 and the composition of air, the amount of oxygen dissolved in water that is in equilibrium with air at 1 atmosphere pressure. Table 13-1 states that the concentration of $O_2$ in $H_2O$ that is in equilibrium with pure $O_2$ at 1 atmosphere pressure and 20° is $4.3 \times 10^{-2}$ gram/1,000 grams of water. We can let these numbers be $p_1$ and $c_1$ and determine $c_2$ by letting $p_2$ be the partial pressure of $O_2$ in air. Air contains 21 percent $O_2$; the partial pressure of $O_2$ in this gas mixture at 1 atmosphere total pressure is therefore 21 percent of an atmosphere. Thus $p_2$ in our substitution in equation 13-6 is $0.21 \, p_1$. Making these substitutions, we get

$$\frac{p_1}{0.21 p_1} = \frac{4.3 \times 10^{-2} \text{ gram/1,000 grams}}{c_2}$$

and then, solving for $c_2$, we get

$$c_2 = 0.21 \times 4.3 \times 10^{-2} \text{ gram/1,000 grams}$$
$$= 9.0 \times 10^{-3} \text{ gram } O_2/1,000 \text{ grams } H_2O$$

the concentration of oxygen in water that is saturated with air at 1 atmosphere pressure and at 20°C.

## 13-19. Heat of Solution

When a solute is dissolved, an exchange of heat is usually observed. When sulfuric acid is poured into water, the solution becomes hotter, the amount of heat "liberated" being proportional to the amount of sulfuric acid added. It is possible to make the water boil simply by adding acid to it. The heat effect in this case is extremely large, but in most cases there is some such heat exchange. The exchange may be the liberation of heat, as with sulfuric acid, or it may be the absorption of heat, in which case the solution cools as the solute dissolves. In a few cases no detectable heat exchange takes place. The heat exchange that accompanies the dissolving of a solute is called the **heat of solution** and is expressed quantitatively in calories per mole of solute; the direction of the exchange is indicated by the sign of the $\Delta H$ of solution. The $\Delta H$ of solution of sulfuric acid, for example, is $-18,000$ cal/mole. The minus sign indicates that the change in heat content of the system is negative; that is, heat is given off when sulfuric acid dissolves.

The heat of solution of most solid substances in liquids is positive; that is, heat is absorbed and the solution cools during the process of dissolving. Conversely, heat is given off during crystallization, and the solution becomes warmer as the solid precipitates. On the other hand, when most gases dissolve in water, there is a liberation of heat; the heat of solution is negative, and the solution warms up as the gas dissolves. There are many exceptions to these generalizations, particularly when there is strong interaction between the solute and the solvent. The kinetic theory's explanation of these empirical facts is one of the most interesting applications of that theory to the subject of solutions and will be considered in a subsequent section.

## 13-20. Rate of Solution

A number of factors influence the speed with which solutes are dissolved by solvents—that is, the time necessary for all of a sample of solute to be dissolved or for equilibrium to be reached in the case of saturated solutions. Most of the empirical generalizations are well known from ordinary experience. A spoonful of sugar will dissolve in hot coffee much more quickly than in iced coffee, and stirring speeds the process in both cases. A spoonful of sugar will dissolve more quickly than a cube of sugar; and, if the sugar is finely ground, it will dissolve even more quickly. Here are three factors that increase the speed of solution: higher temperature, agitation, and finer particles of the solute. All of these factors may affect all solutes, and all can be interpreted neatly on the basis of kinetic theory.

## 13-21. Kinetic Theory's Interpretation of the Behavior of Solutions

The rather long parade of descriptive and factual information that has made up the preceding part of this chapter does not contribute much to the development of the science of matter if we just let these facts stand for themselves and do not try to integrate them. But the integration of just these facts is one of the most effective accomplishments of the kinetic-molecular theory that was outlined in Chapter 12. Not all of the facts mentioned in this chapter can be included in a kinetic explanation, but most of them can be, and a general picture of solutions based on the kinetic-molecular theory is a necessary supplement to theories that will be invoked later to explain those other facts of the behavior of solutions.

The process of dissolving a solid solute in a liquid solvent can be viewed as a close analogy to the process of fusion (melting) of the solid. The solute particles become distributed among the solvent particles in the closely packed but randomly organized structure of the liquid. The solute particles are surrounded by solvent molecules and are prevented from coalescing to reform solid clusters by the interference of this atmosphere of solvent molecules. Solvation, in which solvent molecules are specifically combined (though loosely) with solute particles, is particularly effective in preventing the recombination of the solute. Thus the tendency of solvation to increase solubility is explained.

The dissolving of a solid requires the pulling away of the solute particles from the solid phase against the cohesive forces of the solid. Since this energy must come from the thermal energy of motion of the solvent particles, most solids have a positive $\Delta H$ of solution (that is, heat is absorbed and the solvent cools during the process of dissolving). The cohesive forces that must be overcome in dissolving are the same as those that are disrupted by melting. Thus the heat effect just described should be the same as the heat of fusion of the solid. In *many* cases this equivalence of the heat of solution and the heat of fusion is experimentally observed. If there are other processes, such as chemical reaction, between the solute and the solvent, or if there is extensive solvation, no such equivalence is observed, for the heat of solution then includes the heat effects of these other processes as well as the energy of disrupting the cohesive forces of the solid-phase solute. In part, at least, solids become more soluble with rising temperature because the increase of thermal energy supplies the heat of solution that is needed to bring the solute into the liquid phase. A complete and rigorous analysis of this point requires the use of the principle of equilibrium, which will not be considered until a later chapter.

In a similar way the dissolving of a gas in a liquid can be compared to the condensation of the gas. The experimentally observed negative heats of solution and the decrease of solubility with rising temperature can be related to this analogy just as the opposite relations for solids were related to the analogy of melting.

The rate at which a solute dissolves is determined by the ease with which particles of the solute can escape from the surface of the solid into the liquid phase. Obviously, the greater the solid surface that is exposed to the solvent, the greater the rate of this escape. A finely divided solute has much greater surface area, and will therefore dissolve more quickly, than the same solute in coarse particles. The effect of agitation is to distribute the dissolved solute continuously throughout the bulk of the solution. If the bit of solvent immediately in contact with the solute became saturated, it would prevent the further dissolving of the solid. Diffusion would in time spread the solute throughout the solution, but stirring aids the process. The effect of a rise in temperature is to increase the thermal energy of the solute particles (and also of the solvent, of course). As the average energy of the particles increases, more of the solid-phase particles have sufficient energy to break away from the cohesive forces that have held the solid phase together. Thus more particles escape into the liquid phase in a given time, which is one way of saying that the rate of solution is higher.

This brief discussion of some of the properties of solutions in terms of the kinetic-molecular theory serves mainly to illustrate the way in which this new organizing concept is used. The theory is a mechanical one and in some ways represents the peak of subtlety and refinement of the purely mechanical view of physical phenomena. It should be realized that the kinetic-molecular theory is still a very active and effective part of theoretical physical science. It is susceptible of much more complete and sophisticated treatment in relation to solution behavior and to many other areas of science, particularly in the mathematical form that is encountered in more advanced science courses. But the purely mechanical view of the structure of matter that is implicit in this theory is insufficient to deal with the facts of science. The next chapter, a continuation of the discussion of solutions, introduces the experimental reasons for modifying this mechanical theory of the structure of matter.

## Concepts and Terms

Solution
Solute
Solvent
Component
Classification of Solutions
  gaseous
  liquid
  solid
Alloy
Concentration
  molar
  molal
  mole fraction

Saturated Solution
Solubility
Polar and Non-polar
Solvation
  hydration
  water of hydration
Distribution
  law of partition
Solubility Curves
Crystallization
Solubilities of Gases

## Problems

**13-1.** Define in your own words the following terms with respect to solutions: solute, solvent, concentration, homogeneous, component, mole fraction, molar, molal, solubility, solvation, solution.

**13-2.** What volume of a 0.12 molar solution of sodium hydroxide would contain 0.5 mole of NaOH?

*Ans.* 4.16 liters

**13-3.** How many grams of NaCl must be dissolved in 200 cm$^3$ of water to make a 1 molar solution? *Ans.* 11.7 grams

**13-4.** What would be the mole fraction of alcohol ($C_2H_5OH$) and of water in a solution made by dissolving 46 grams of alcohol in enough water to make 100 grams of solution?

*Ans.* $H_2O$, 0.75; $C_2H_5OH$, 0.25

**13-5.** What would be the molal concentration of alcohol in the solution of Prob. 13-4?

**13-6.** Describe how you could make a solution having the following composition: mole fraction of benzene ($C_6H_6$), 0.10; mole fraction of carbon tetrachloride ($CCl_4$), 0.85; mole fraction of bromine ($Br_2$), 0.05.

**13-7.** Calculate the *molal* concentration of a 10% solution of each of the following solutes in water:

  (A) NaCl
  (B) Sugar ($C_{12}H_{22}O_{11}$)
  (C) Glycerine ($C_3H_8O_3$)
  (D) $CaCl_2$
  (E) $H_2SO_4$
  (F) $Na_2CO_3$
  (G) HCl
  (H) Methanol ($CH_4O$)
  (I) A protein having a molecular weight of 60,000

**13-8.** Calculate the mole fraction of the solute in each of the solutions of Prob. 13-7.

**13-9.** Making use of Fig. 13-1, determine the solubility of each of the salts included in that figure at 20°C.

*Ans.* $NaNO_3$, 850 grams/1,000 grams of water

**13-10.** Suppose that you have a mixture made up of about equal amounts of crude sodium chloride and crude sodium nitrate. Making use of the information in Fig. 13-1, devise a method for separating this mixture into pure samples of NaCl and $NaNO_3$.

**13-11.** Could you use the same technique to separate ammonium chloride ($NH_4Cl$) and potassium chloride? Could you use the technique to separate ammonium nitrate ($NH_4NO_3$) and ammonium chloride? Explain your answers.

**13-12.** The measurement of the solubility of an organic solid in an organic liquid (both are non-polar, and there is little solvation effect) is frequently difficult to distinguish from the measurement of the melting point of the mixture. Discuss this statement with respect to the kinetic-molecular theory of solution behavior.

**13-13.** Discuss the relation between heats of solution and heats of fusion and vaporization.

**13-14.** Describe a method, using extraction and crystallization, of separating the components of a solid mixture of equal amounts of iodine, potassium iodide, and potassium chloride. The two salts, KI and KCl, are not soluble in non-polar solvents. Describe how you would prepare a pure sample of each of the three solids from this mixture.

## Suggested Readings

1. F. T. Bonner and Melba Phillips, *Principles of Physical Science* (Addison-Wesley, 1957), Chap. 21.

2. L. Pauling, *College Chemistry,* second edition (W. H. Freeman, 1955), first half of Chap. 18.

3. H. H. Sisler, C. A. VanderWerf, and A. W. Davidson, *College Chemistry—A Systematic Approach* (Macmillan, 1953), first half of Chap. 13.

4. W. F. Ehret, *Smith's Introductory College Chemistry* (Appleton-Century-Crofts, 1950), first half of Chap. 12.

IN CHAPTER 13 some properties of solutions were considered, and most of them were interpreted according to the kinetic-molecular theory. Most of them were distinctive for each particular combination of solute and solvent. It was observed, for example, that, although the solubility of most solids increases as the temperature rises, the *amount* by which it changes for a given change in temperature is unique for each solute. It was also observed that heats of solution vary in an unpredictable way for each combination of solute and solvent. In contrast to this capricious variation from one solute to another is a group of properties that show a steady and predictable dependence *only* on the number of particles of solute in a given amount of solution. These properties are called **colligative properties,** and in all cases the magnitude of the effect is strictly dependent on the relative numbers of solute and solvent particles.

## 14-1. The Four Colligative Properties

The four colligative properties of solutions are (1) **the lowering of the vapor pressure;** (2) **the elevation of the boiling point;** (3) **the lowering of the freezing point;** (4) the development of an **osmotic pressure.** The first two of these are probably entirely new concepts to a student of elementary science, but the last two are a part of general experience. It is well known that we may melt ice on slippery streets by putting salt on it. The ice melts, even though the temperature of the system remains well below the freezing point of water, because the freezing point of the solution of salt in water that results from adding salt to the system is below the temperature of the environment. The process of osmosis is one of the commonest demonstrations of school science courses. The demonstration usually employs a tube containing a sugar solution separated from water by a membrane. It is observed that the water rises in the tube. If this demonstration has not been seen, at least the rise of sap in plants has been inferred from the oozing of sap from a wound in a plant. In this natural situation the solution is the plant

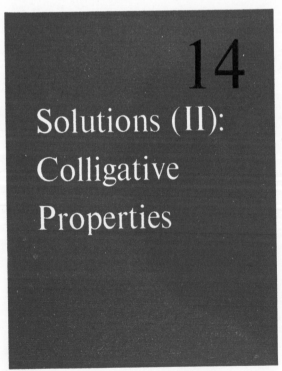

CHAPTER

14

Solutions (II):
Colligative
Properties

sap and the membrane is the living plant tissue. The phenomenon of osmosis was first investigated, in fact, by botanists.

These empirical facts are of interest in themselves, but the purpose of introducing them in a discussion of the science of matter is to advance the theoretical interpretation of the structure of matter. A study of these properties—and, in particular, a careful investigation of an anomaly in our explanation of them—will lead to a tremendous step forward from the simple mechanical view of matter that is implicit in the atomic and molecular theories.

The four colligative properties will be considered in turn with respect to the kinetic-molecular theory. The empirical facts will be stated, and then they will be interpreted. The four properties are closely related, and the interpretations will therefore be related. The most fundamental of the four effects of solutes on solutions is the depression of vapor pressure. The other three can be derived from this one, which will therefore be considered first even though it is the most complex. But before it is possible to consider the lowering of vapor pressure by the presence of a solute, it is necessary to consider in detail the vapor pressure of a pure substance; in particular we must consider the kinetic explanation of the phenomenon.

## 14-2. Vapor Pressure

If an open dish of water is left at room temperature in a free atmosphere, it will, after a time, have entirely evaporated. A more volatile liquid, such as ether, will evaporate much more quickly under the same circumstances. The kinetic interpretation of this phenomenon is that some of the liquid molecules approach the surface of the liquid with sufficient kinetic energy to escape the cohesive forces of attraction and pass into the atmosphere as gas molecules (molecules that are so far apart from other molecules that the forces of attraction are negligible). The same process of evaporation takes place from the surface of solid substances. The evaporation of moth crystals and that of Dry Ice (solid carbon dioxide) are common, well-

known examples of the evaporation of solids. The disappearance of such substances under these conditions is, then, the process of evaporation into a free, unenclosed atmosphere. A question is now posed: "What happens if a solid or a liquid is placed in a *closed* system from which the vaporized molecules are not allowed to escape?" We can establish such a situation by placing a bell jar over a sample of the solid or liquid substance. Figure 14-1 shows what happens. (It must be understood that the spheres representing the molecules of the substance are *vastly* magnified and are extremely simplified representations of actual molecules, and that the separation of the molecules in the vapor phase would be many times greater compared with the size of the molecules.)

## 14-3. Evaporation into a Closed Space

In diagram "a" of Figure 14-1 the solid or liquid substance is represented by a group of closely packed molecules enclosed in a bell jar. It occupies only a small fraction of the space of the container, the rest of the space being a vacuum. But this situation would last only a short time. Diagram "b" represents some of the molecules escaping from the surface of the solid or liquid substance and beginning to fill the space. The individuals escaping are those that combine the circumstances of position at the surface, sufficient kinetic energy to escape, and the direction of their motion toward the free space. In this situation, where there is no appreciable number of vaporized molecules, the direction of movement is entirely away from the solid or liquid phase, toward vaporization. In diagram "c" the space is almost entirely "filled" with vaporized molecules, and now there is considerable tendency for some of the molecules to condense. The ones that condense are, naturally, those that combine the circumstances of low enough kinetic energy and approach to the surface in the right direction. Diagram "d" represents the final situation, in which the rate of escape is just equal to the rate of condensation. This is a dynamic state in which both vaporiza-

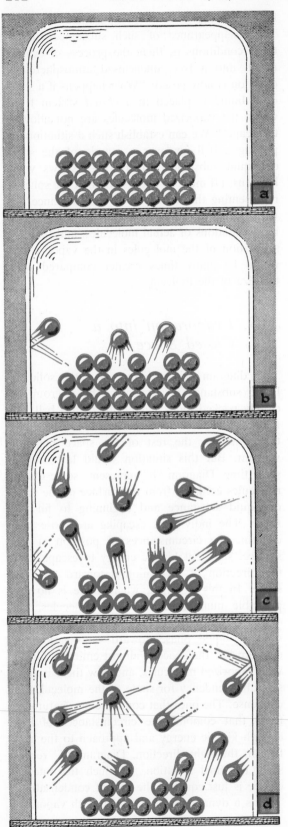

tion and condensation are going on at the same time; because the rates are the same, there is *no net change* in the amount of substance in either phase. This situation is defined as the state of *equilibrium* between the solid or liquid phase and the gas phase.

## 14-4. Vapor-liquid Equilibrium

In this state of equilibrium there is a definite amount of gas in a fixed space (volume); the gas therefore exerts a definite pressure. This pressure, exerted by a vapor that is in equilibrium with a condensed phase of the same substance, is called the **vapor pressure** of the substance. At a given temperature the vapor pressure of a substance is a fixed, characteristic quantity. But it is clear, from consideration of the kinetic theory, that the vapor pressure must vary with temperature. As the temperature is raised, the average kinetic energy of the molecules of the condensed substance is increased, and therefore a greater fraction of the molecules will have sufficient kinetic energy to escape the cohesive forces and vaporize. At the same time fewer of the molecules in the gas phase will have sufficiently low kinetic energy to be "captured" by the condensed phase when they approach the surface. The process of boiling is simply the special situation that obtains when the vapor pressure is equal to the atmospheric pressure. At this temperature the kinetic energy of the condensed-phase molecules is so high that bubbles of gas begin to form in the body of the liquid and *all* of the condensed phase volatilizes.

All condensed substances exhibit a vapor pressure. But the vapor pressure of metals, glass, and extremely non-volatile liquids is immeasurably small. There is very little tendency for substances such as steel or glass to disappear by evaporation at normal temperatures. For the

FIGURE **14-1** *Vapor pressure: diagram of evaporation into an enclosed space. As the condensed phase evaporates* (a–c), *the proportion of molecules in the gaseous phase increases until equilibrium is reached* (d), *in which exchange of molecules between the gaseous phase and the condensed phase continues at equal rates.*

purposes of this discussion we shall be mainly concerned with substances that have easily measurable vapor pressures at normally realizable temperatures.

## 14-5. *Vapor-pressure Curves*

Figure 14-2, with its **vapor-pressure curves** for several liquids, shows the variation of vapor pressure with temperature. Liquids whose vapor pressures near room temperature are much greater than that of water are generally considered to be *volatile*.

A complication arises when we draw the vapor-pressure curves for solids. The vapor pressure of a solid, like that of a liquid, increases as the temperature rises. But at some temperature the solid will melt. This is the temperature at which the kinetic energy becomes so great that thermal agitation overcomes the lattice forces that hold the molecules in the orderly array of the crystalline state. Below this temperature the *solid* is in equilibrium with the vapor, and above this temperature the *liquid* is in equilibrium with the vapor. At the melting point, where there is a transition from solid to liquid, the two condensed phases are in equilibrium with each other. They must therefore *both* be in equilibrium with the vapor phase at this

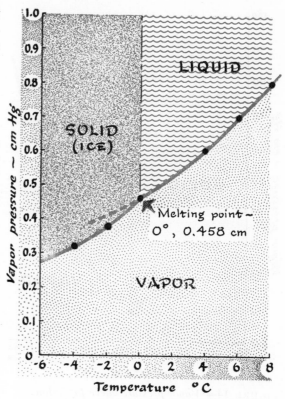

FIGURE **14-3** *Vapor-pressure curve for water near its melting point. The broken line, a continuation of the vapor-liquid curve, represents cooling of the liquid below its freezing point.*

temperature. Figure 14-3 shows the vapor-pressure curve for water in the neighborhood of the melting point, 0°C. The pressure ordinate is greatly expanded on this graph compared with the curve for water in Figure 14-2. This curve shows the increase of the vapor pressure of ice as the temperature rises, up to 0°. At this point there is a discontinuity in the curve because here *both* liquid and solid water are in equilibrium with the water vapor. The vapor pressure at this point is 0.458 cm of Hg. Thus the vapor pressures of the solid and the liquid are the same at the melting point. Above this temperature the curve is simply the vapor-pressure curve for liquid water, as in Figure 14-2. Figure 14-4 is a similar curve for iodine. Below 114° (the melting point of iodine) the curve represents the vapor pressure of solid iodine, and above this point it represents the vapor pressure of liquid iodine. In both cases this is the pressure of the

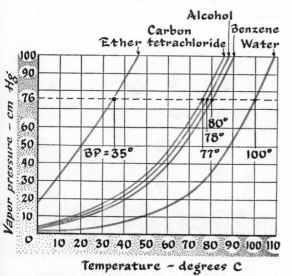

FIGURE **14-2** *Vapor-pressure curves.*

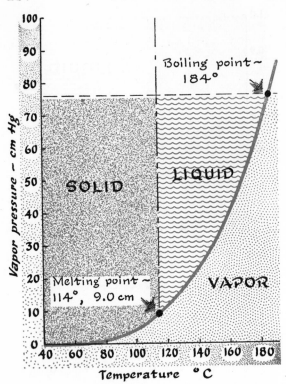

FIGURE **14-4** *Vapor-pressure curve for iodine.*

molecules in the solution; out of each ten molecules, 2 are solute and 8 are solvent). The effect of the solute molecules is to "dilute" the solvent molecules; that is, some of the positions at the surface, which are favorable to escape into the gas phase, are occupied by solute molecules to the exclusion of solvent molecules. This would, of course, decrease the escaping tendency. But, while the tendency to vaporize is thus lowered by the presence of the solute molecules, the tendency to condense (that is, for molecules of the gas phase to strike the surface of the liquid and to be "captured" by the condensed phase) is just as great as it is for the pure solvent, as indicated in Figure 14-1d. This tendency to condense depends on the number of particles present in the gas phase and on their kinetic energy, neither of which is affected directly by the presence of solute particles. The effect of the solute molecules is, then, to shift the equilibrium toward condensation, the result being that *fewer* molecules are in the gas phase in a given volume. At the same temperature these fewer molecules exert less pressure than the larger number in equilibrium with the pure solvent. The effect of the solute is, then, to *lower* the vapor pressure below that of the pure solvent. This interpretation is borne out by experimental observation: the vapor pressure of all solutions of non-volatile solutes is lower than the vapor pressure of the pure solvent at the same temperature.

gaseous substance that is in equilibrium with the condensed phase at the particular temperature. At the melting point the vapor pressures of both the solid and the liquid are the same, 9.0 cm of Hg. Similar vapor-pressure curves describe the variation of vapor pressure with temperature for all condensed substances that have measurable vapor pressures.

## 14-6. Depression of the Vapor Pressure

Let us now consider, by the use of diagrams similar to those of Figure 14-1, the effect of a non-volatile solute on the vapor pressure of a volatile solvent. Figure 14-5 represents such a situation. The solute molecules, which have no tendency to escape to the gas phase because they are non-volatile, are depicted by black spheres. The mole fraction of the solute is represented as 0.2 and that of the solvent as 0.8 (there are four times as many solvent molecules as solute

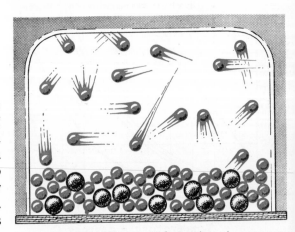

FIGURE **14-5** *Diagram of depression of vapor pressure by a dissolved solute.*

## 14-7. Raoult's Law

From Figure 14-5 we can also decide *how much* the vapor pressure is lowered for a given concentration of solute. If we consider a large enough surface (and the surface of any real sample of liquid would, of course, cover the area occupied by *huge* numbers of molecules), the fraction of the total area occupied by the non-volatile solute molecules would be just the mole fraction of the solute. The area occupied by the solvent molecules that are capable of vaporizing would be $X_{solvent}$ times the total area. In the pure solvent, however, the *total* area is occupied by solvent molecules. It is therefore reasonable to expect that the vapor pressure of the solution would be equal to the mole fraction of the solvent, $X_{solvent}$, times the vapor pressure of the pure solvent at the same temperature—that is, that

$$p = Xp_0 \qquad (14-1)$$

if $p$ is the vapor pressure of the solvent in the solution, $p_0$ is the vapor pressure of the pure solvent, and $X$ is the mole fraction of the *solvent* in the solution. Equation 14-1 expresses the empirically observed relation between the vapor pressure of a solution and that of the pure solvent. It describes the degree to which the presence of a solute lowers the vapor pressure of the solvent. This relation was first observed in 1887 by a French chemist, F. M. Raoult, and is known as **Raoult's law.**

Equation 14-1 describes the change in the vapor pressure of the solution described in the first paragraph of this section, in which the mole fraction of the solute is 0.2 and that of the solvent is 0.8. This equation holds at any temperature and therefore describes the vapor pressure of the solvent in the solution, $p$, in terms of the vapor pressure of the pure solvent, $p_0$, at any temperature. The vapor pressure varies with the temperature, as we observed in the previous section of this chapter. The $p_0$ value could be obtained from tables of such data for pure substances or from a curve of vapor pressure such as those of Figure 14-2. The vapor pressure of the solution could then be calculated

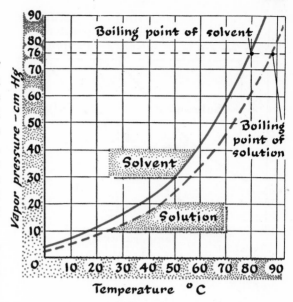

FIGURE **14-6** *Vapor-pressure curves for a solution and the corresponding solvent.*

for any temperature by the use of equation 14-1. It would also be possible to construct a vapor-pressure curve for the solution. The height of such a curve would obviously be less than that of the curve for the pure solvent because the presence of the solute lowers the vapor pressure at all temperatures. The amount by which the curve for the solution is below the curve for the solvent is shown by the relation expressed in equation 14-1. The solution curve will have an ordinate that is the mole fraction of the solvent, $X_{solvent}$, times the ordinate of the pure-solvent curve at each temperature. A curve of this type for a 0.2-mole-fraction solution of a non-volatile solute such as naphthalene in the solvent benzene is compared with the curve for the pure solvent in Figure 14-6. The lower curve is always just 80 percent as high as the pure-solvent curve.

## 14-8. Elevation of the Boiling Point

The second of the colligative properties of solutions—properties whose magnitude depends not on the specific solute but only on the *number of particles* of solute—is the elevation of the boiling point of a solution above the boiling

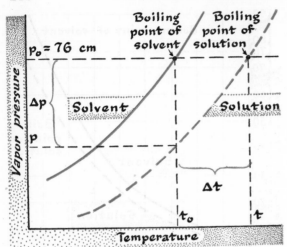

FIGURE **14-7** *Boiling-point elevation by a dissolved solute.*

point of the pure solvent. This is a statement of empirical observations, but it is possible to develop a reasonable explanation on the basis of the kinetic-molecular theory. The explanation is similar to the explanation of the depression of vapor pressure. If we examine the two curves of Figure 14-6 and somewhat magnify the area near the boiling point, as in Figure 14-7, the explanation of a rise of the boiling point due to the presence of a solute becomes almost self-evident. The presence of the solute displaces the whole curve downward so that at $t_0$ (the boiling point of the pure solvent), which is the temperature at which the vapor pressure becomes equal to atmospheric pressure, the vapor pressure is lowered by the amount $\Delta p = p_0 - p$. If we wish the vapor pressure to equal the atmospheric pressure (at which point the solution will boil), we must raise the temperature by $\Delta t$ in order to extrapolate the vapor pressure of the solution along the lower curve until it intersects the horizontal line representing atmospheric pressure (76 cm).

The kinetic interpretation of this situation would follow very closely that of the lowering of vapor pressure. The primary effect of the solute molecules is to lower the vapor pressure of the solvent by lowering the tendency of the solvent molecules to escape from the solution (as described in the previous section). It is therefore necessary to increase the escaping

tendency of the condensed-phase molecules to offset this effect of the solute. We can accomplish this by increasing the thermal agitation of the condensed-phase molecules to the point where more of them—enough to offset the interfering effect of the solute molecules—have sufficient kinetic energy to escape.

It is possible, by fairly advanced mathematical methods, to relate the elevation of the boiling point to the depression of the vapor pressure. This is done by considering Figure 14-7 and relating $\Delta p$ to $\Delta t$. The relation between solute concentration and boiling-point elevation is established empirically, however, and the equation that is normally used is simply a statement of this experimentally determined relation. This empirical equation, which will be used in this text, has the form

$$\Delta t_B = k_B c \qquad (14\text{-}2)$$

in which $\Delta t_B$ is the amount by which the boiling point is elevated (that is, is $t - t_0$, the boiling point of the solution minus the boiling point of the pure solvent), $k_B$ is the molal-boiling-point-elevation constant for the particular solvent, and $c$ is the *molal* concentration of the solute in the solution (moles of solute per 1,000 grams of solvent). The form of this equation does not emphasize the kinetic explanation of boiling-point rise due to the presence of the solute, but it is the most convenient form for experimental use. We can evaluate the molal-boiling-point-elevation constant, $k_B$, by using a solute whose molecular weight is known (see the next section). Then, once we know this constant for the particular solvent, we can use the measurement of boiling-point rise and equation 14-2 to determine the molecular weight of unknown substances. In practice the elevation of the boiling point is not used much for the purpose of determining molecular weights, for it is usually much simpler and more precise to use the depression of the freezing point. The rationale and explanation of the method, which is, in principle, the same for both boiling-point rise and freezing-point lowering, will be taken up in the next section. Table 14-1 lists the molal-boiling-point-elevation constants for several common solvents. It should be noted that the

TABLE **14-1** *Molal-boiling-point-elevation Constants*

| SOLVENT | $k_B$ DEGREES/MOLE |
|---|---|
| Water | 0.52 |
| Alcohol | 1.19 |
| Ether | 2.11 |
| Benzene | 2.65 |
| Chloroform | 3.86 |
| Carbon tetrachloride | 4.85 |

constant for water is much lower than most of the others.

## 14-9. Depression of the Freezing Point

It is common knowledge that the freezing point of a solution is lower than that of the pure solvent. We have already mentioned the use of salt to lower the freezing point of ice (and thereby to cause its melting) on slippery streets. Another common cold-weather experience is the use of anti-freeze to prevent the freezing of the cooling water of automobile radiators. A solute such as alcohol or ethylene glycol is added to the radiator water, and the freezing point is thereby lowered 20° or more. This phenomenon, which is well known to contemporary non-scientists, has been known to scientists for many years and has been the subject of investigation for almost a century. In 1883 Raoult first stated the quantitative law that relates the concentration of the solute to the extent of the lowering of the freezing point. Raoult observed that, for any given solvent, the freezing point is lowered by a fixed amount for each *mole* of *any* solute dissolved in a given amount of the solvent. This generalization can also be stated as follows: **The freezing-point depression for a given solvent is proportional to the molal concentration of the solute.** The same law in the form of an equation is

$$\Delta t_F = k_F c \qquad (14\text{-}3)$$

in which $\Delta t_F$ is the number of degrees by which

the freezing point is depressed (that is, is $t_0 - t$, the freezing point of the pure solvent minus that of the solution), $k_F$ is the molal-freezing-point-depression constant for the given solvent, and $c$ is the *molal* concentration of the solute in the solution (moles of solute per 1,000 grams of solvent).

Equation 14-3 is a useful empirical statement of the relation between freezing-point depression and concentration, but it does not point up the kinetic theory of the phenomenon. The kinetic explanation is best approached in a manner similar to that used for the boiling-point rise. Consider Figure 14-8, which is a magnified picture of vapor-pressure curves of the type shown in Figure 14-6. The upper curve shows the vapor pressure of the pure solvent as it varies with temperature. At the freezing point of the solvent, $t_0$, the vapor is in equilibrium with *both* solid and liquid phases of the solvent, which are also in equilibrium with each other. At the freezing point there is a discontinuity in the vapor-pressure curve; below this temperature the vapor is in equilibrium only with the solid phase of the solvent. The lower curve of Figure 14-8, the vapor-pressure curve for the solution, is displaced below the curve for the pure solvent by an amount determined by equation 14-1.

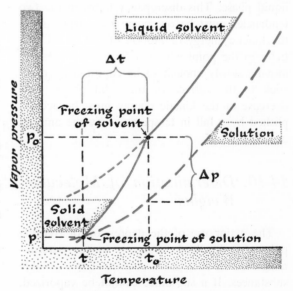

FIGURE **14-8** *Freezing-point depression by a dissolved solute.*

This curve continues to decline with falling temperature, always remaining below the curve for the solvent, and reaches $t_0$, the temperature at which the pure solvent would condense to the solid state, below the upper curve by an amount indicated by $\Delta p$. But the solvent *cannot* condense to the solid state (freeze) from the solution at this temperature, for the vapor pressure of the solid-state solvent at this temperature is $p_0$, which is greater than the vapor pressure of the solution by $\Delta p$. It is therefore necessary to continue the lower curve (by cooling the solution further) down to $t$, which is $\Delta t°$ lower than $t_0$, at which temperature the vapor pressure of the solid-state solvent is equal to the vapor pressure of the solution. Again it is possible to relate $\Delta t$ and $\Delta p$ by the mathematical methods of thermodynamics, but for the purposes of this course the empirical equation (14-3) is sufficient.

The kinetic picture of this situation views the solute particles as interfering by their presence with the tendency of the solvent molecules to condense on the surface of the solid phase. The effect is a dilution of the particles of the solvent. Since the frozen solvent (solid phase) is pure solvent, there is no such dilution in the solid and therefore no interference with the tendency of the particles to escape from the solid to the liquid phase. This discrepancy between the two tendencies must be overcome by a decrease in the kinetic energy of motion of the liquid particles to the point where sufficient numbers are moving slowly enough to be captured by or to stick to the surface of the solid phase. This decrease of the kinetic energy must be accomplished by a fall in temperature by the amount $\Delta t$.

## 14-10. Determination of Molecular Weights

The major use of the depression of freezing points by dissolved solutes is in the determination of the molecular weights of non-volatile substances. If a substance cannot be vaporized, its molecular weight cannot be determined by measurements of its vapor density. (See Chap.

10 and Appendix II.) Like equation 14-2 and the boiling-point elevation, equation 14-3 and the freezing-point depression can be used to determine the molecular weight of an unknown substance once the constant, $k_F$, is known. We can determine the $k_F$ for any solvent by measuring the freezing-point depression caused by a known molal concentration of a solute whose molecular weight is known from gas-density measurements. We can then use this value for $k_F$ in equation 14-3 to determine the molecular weight of solutes that cannot be vaporized at ordinary temperatures or would decompose rather than vaporize when heated.

### EXAMPLE 1

The freezing point of pure benzene is 5.60°C. A solution of 2 grams of naphthalene ($C_{10}H_8$) in 10 grams of benzene ($C_6H_6$) freezes at −2.35°C. Calculate the $k_F$ for benzene.

First calculate the molal concentration of the solution: The molecular weight of naphthalene is 128 (from the formula); 2 grams is therefore $2/128 = 0.0156$ mole. This is dissolved in 10 grams of solvent; the concentration is therefore determined by the proportion $\dfrac{0.0156 \text{ mole}}{10 \text{ grams}} = \dfrac{c \text{ moles}}{1{,}000 \text{ grams}}$:

$c = 1.56$ moles/1,000 grams $= 1.56$ molal

Next calculate the extent of the freezing-point depression:

$\Delta t_F = 5.60° - (-2.35°) = 7.95°$

Finally, substitute these values in equation 14-3, and solve for $k_F$:

$$k_F = \frac{\Delta t_F}{c} = \frac{7.95°}{1.56 \text{ moles}} = 5.10°/\text{mole}$$

### EXAMPLE 2

A solution of 1.7 grams of hexachloroethane in 8 grams of benzene has a freezing point of +1.05°C. Calculate the molecular weight of hexachloroethane.

First calculate the concentration in grams of solute per 1,000 grams of solvent:

$$\frac{1.7 \text{ grams}}{8 \text{ grams}} = \frac{c}{1{,}000 \text{ grams}}$$

$$c = \frac{1.7 \times 1{,}000}{8} = 212 \text{ grams}/1{,}000 \text{ grams}$$

Next calculate the concentration of this solution in *moles* per 1,000 grams of solvent by using equation 14-3 and the data given above:

$$\Delta t_F = 5.60° - 1.05° = 4.55°$$

$$\Delta t_F = k_F c$$

$$c = \Delta t_F / k_F = \frac{4.55°}{5.10°/\text{mole}} = 0.894 \text{ mole}$$

Finally, equate the two expressions for the same concentration, the one expression in *grams* per 1,000 grams of solvent and the other in *moles* per 1,000 grams of solvent:

$$c = 0.894 \text{ mole}/1,000 \text{ grams}$$
$$= 212 \text{ grams}/1,000 \text{ grams}$$

0.894 mole = 212 grams

1 mole = 212/0.894 = 237 grams

The molecular weight is therefore 237.

TABLE **14-2**  *Molal-freezing-point-depression Constants*

| SOLVENT | $k_F$ DEGREES/MOLE |
|---|---|
| Water | 1.86 |
| Chloroform | 4.67 |
| Benzene | 5.10 |
| Naphthalene | 7.0 |
| Phenol | 7.3 |
| Camphor | 40.0 |

Table 14-2 lists $k_F$ values for several common solvents. Again the constant for water is a good deal lower than the others. The remarkably high value for camphor, plus the fact that many organic chemicals are soluble in camphor, makes this substance one of the most useful solvents for determination of the molecular weights of new synthetic compounds.

## 14-11. *Osmotic Pressure*

The process of osmosis, which is the movement of liquids under the influence of osmotic pressure, is illustrated by Figure 14-9. A solution is separated from a sample of the pure solvent by a **semi-permeable membrane,** which allows the solvent molecules to pass through but prevents the passage of solute particles. The level of liquid in the tube rises because some of the solvent passes through the membrane into the solution. The direction of movement of the solvent, as grossly observed, is always toward the more concentrated solution. That solution, which is inside the tube, becomes more and more dilute as more solvent enters, and the process continues until the hydrostatic pressure of the column of solution in the tube (see § 9-2) becomes high enough to prevent the inflow of the solvent. The pressure that is just sufficient to stop the entry of solvent by osmosis is called the **osmotic pressure** of the solution. A rigorous

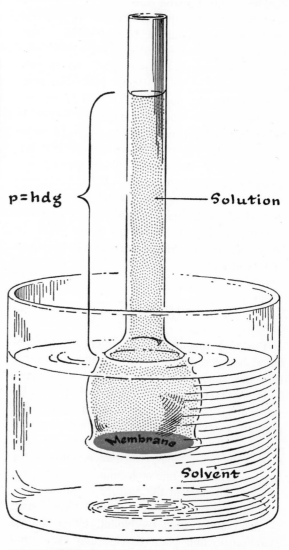

FIGURE **14-9** *Osmosis; measurement of osmotic pressure.*

definition of osmotic pressure is: **The pressure that must be exerted on a solution to prevent the passage into it of the solvent when the solution and the solvent are separated by a semi-permeable membrane is called the osmotic pressure of the solution.**

The first recorded experiments on osmosis were those of J. A. Nollet. In 1748 he reported that an animal's urinary bladder, if filled with alcohol and placed in a container of water, became swollen with water that passed through the tissue membrane. The alcohol inside became diluted with water, which could pass into the bladder, and, because the alcohol could not move out through the membrane, the pressure inside increased until the bladder finally burst. From the time of this first observation the phenomenon of osmosis has interested physiologists, chemists, and physicists. Many biological processes involve the passage of materials through membranes, and the maintenance of tissues in living functional condition depends very much on the maintenance of a proper osmotic environment. One of the most striking natural exhibitions of osmosis (coupled with several other effects of membranes) is the forcing of liquid through the root hairs of plants with sufficient pressure to drive it to the top of the plant. In some cases this pressure is measured in hundreds of feet of water.

## 14-12. Van't Hoff's Law

The first quantitative statement of the relation between osmotic pressure and concentration was made by a Dutch physical chemist, J. H. van't Hoff, in 1886. Van't Hoff also developed a theoretical interpretation of osmotic pressure (and other properties of solutions) in terms of the kinetic-molecular theory. He also coined the term *semi-permeable membrane* for barriers that allow one molecular species to pass through but prevent the passage of others. The first such membranes were natural tissues such as the bladder used by Nollet. Other animal membranes, thin plant tissues, and even such bulky tissues as a whole carrot will function as semi-permeable membranes in osmosis. Most of

these, however, are not perfect in their exclusion of solute particles—they are "leaky" membranes. For this reason most careful experimental work on osmosis is now done with synthetic membranes. A very common and useful semi-permeable membrane is cellophane, and very thin sheets of certain other plastics can be used. The most useful and most nearly perfect semi-permeable "membrane" is formed by precipitation of an insoluble copper salt, copper ferrocyanide, in the pores of unglazed porcelain cups.

Van't Hoff's contribution was to synthesize the experimental work of many investigators into a comprehensive statement. He did this primarily by seeking in osmosis and other properties of solutions an analogy between the molecules of dissolved solutes and the freely moving molecules of gases. His comprehensive description of osmotic pressure is remarkably similar to the general gas equation that describes the pressure of confined gases. It had been discovered that the osmotic pressure, $\pi$, varies directly with the concentration of dissolved solute if the temperature remains constant. Van't Hoff expressed the concentration in moles per liter of solution (*molar* concentration) and, to describe the variation of $\pi$ with concentration, wrote the equation

$$\pi = \frac{n}{V} \times \text{constant}$$

in which $n/V$ is the molar concentration. If this equation is multiplied through by $V$, it becomes strikingly similar to Boyle's law:

$$\pi V = n \times \text{constant} \tag{14-4}$$

It had also been shown that the osmotic pressure of a solution of fixed concentration varies directly as the absolute temperature:

$$\pi = T \times \text{constant} \tag{14-5}$$

If these two equations are combined into one that states the variation of osmotic pressure with both temperature and concentration, equation 14-6 results:

$$\pi V = nKT \tag{14-6}$$

The similarity of this equation to the universal gas equation is obvious. But what is much more

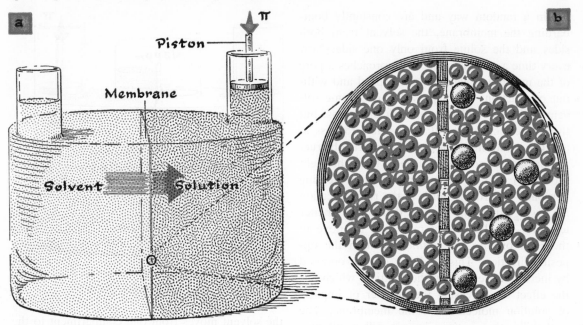

FIGURE **14-10.** *Diagram* (a) *of osmosis and osmotic pressure and* (b) *of the molecules in the vicinity of the membrane.*

remarkable is that, when the constant of equation 14-6 is evaluated, it turns out to have the *same value* as the gas constant, *R*! This quantity can then be substituted in equation 14-6 to give

$$\pi V = nRT \qquad (14\text{-}7)$$

which is entirely analogous to the gas equation, even to the value and units of *R*.†

## 14-13. Kinetic Interpretation of Osmotic Pressure

We can interpret osmotic pressure kinetically by considering, with the benefit of van't Hoff's analogy of solute particles to gas molecules, an experiment for the measurement of osmotic pressure. Such an experiment is diagramed in Figure 14-10a. The solvent, the solution, and the membrane are placed in a container that is fitted with a piston so that an opposing pressure

may be applied against the tendency of the solvent to cross the membrane into the solution. This opposing pressure, $\pi$, which just balances the tendency and prevents any movement of solvent, is the osmotic pressure. If we now consider, on the molecular scale, the motion of the molecules in the vicinity of the membrane (Fig. 14-10b), it becomes apparent why the solvent tends to cross the membrane into the solution. By definition the membrane does not allow the solute particles to pass through. This may be viewed in a somewhat oversimplified way as the action of a simple sieve: the solute particles are prevented from passing simply because they are too big to get through the pores of the membrane.† The diagram indicates this difference by representing the solute particles as black spheres that are too large to pass through the pores of the membrane and the solvent molecules as colored spheres that are small enough to pass through freely. Both types of molecules are mov-

---

† If *R* is used in the units of $\dfrac{cm^4}{mole\ degree}$, the concentration, $n/V$, must be in moles per $cm^3$. Or, if the concentration is expressed in moles per liter, *R* must be in appropriate units, and its value is then $R = 6.23 \dfrac{liter\ cm}{mole\ degree}$.

† The sieve-like character, which prevents the passage of solute particles simply because of their size, is only one of many causes that contribute to the semipermeability of membranes. The properties of membranes are only partly understood, but it is known that many factors are involved in this one.

ing in a random way and are constantly bombarding the membrane, the solvent from both sides and the solute from only one side. Now every time a moving molecule approaches a pore of the membrane with sufficient speed and without obstruction, it will pass through. Some solvent molecules will pass in *both* directions, but the solute molecules will not be able to pass at all. The solute molecules will, however, obstruct the passage of solvent molecules from the right (solution) side of the membrane by preventing approach toward the pores in the right direction for passage through. There is therefore a greater tendency for the solvent molecules to move to the right or *into the solution* than in the opposite direction. This tendency can be opposed by increased pressure on the solution, which has the effect of increasing the number of impacts of solution molecules on the membrane. The probability that a given impact will result in a successful passage through remains less for the molecules on the solution side than for those on the solvent side. The rate of successful impacts has been increased by increasing the total number of impacts. It is possible to derive van't Hoff's equation (14-7) for osmotic pressure by applying a mathematical treatment to this situation.

## 14-14. Relation of Osmotic Pressure to Depression of Vapor Pressure

It is also possible to derive equation 14-7 by relating the osmotic pressure to the difference in vapor pressure between the solution and the pure solvent. This is done by considering a device similar to that of Figure 14-10, in which the solvent and the solution are allowed to be in equilibrium with the vapor of the solvent. This experimental situation is diagramed in Figure 14-11, in which a small chamber of vapor is in contact with both the solvent and the solution. If the solvent and the solution are put into the two compartments and no external pressure is applied to the solution, the solvent vaporizes into the small chamber and then condenses into the solution, the result being that

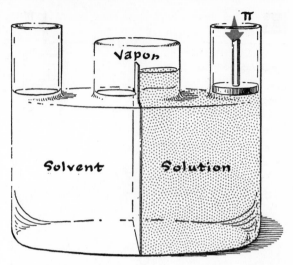

FIGURE **14-11** *Diagrammatic comparison of osmotic pressure and vapor pressure.*

the solvent moves from one compartment to the other just as if the two were separated by a semi-permeable membrane rather than by the communicating chamber. This happens because the vapor pressure of the solvent is greater than that of the solution. The gaseous solvent in the communicating chamber must be at $p_0$, the vapor pressure of the pure solvent. But, since the vapor pressure of the solution is *lower* than $p_0$ by $\Delta p$, the gaseous solvent condenses into the solution. This condensation can be prevented by any influence that increases the vapor pressure of the solution. We can do this by increasing the external pressure, $\pi$, on the solution. If we calculate the external pressure that will increase the vapor pressure of the solution by $\Delta p$ (so that it becomes equal to the vapor pressure of the pure solvent), it turns out to be exactly the osmotic pressure of the solution. If this pressure, $\pi$, is expressed mathematically, equation 14-7 results.

Measurements of osmotic pressure can be used to determine molecular weights, just as measurements of gas density, freezing-point depression, or boiling-point elevation are used. The method has had particular usefulness in determining the molecular weights of very large molecules, such as proteins and some other naturally occurring substances. All proteins have molecular weights that are enormous compared with those of the ordinary compounds we have mentioned in this text. A protein molecule with a molecular weight of 50,000 is considered small; some proteins have molecular weights as high as several million. With such great molecular weights it is impossible to dissolve enough to get accurately measurable freezing-point effects. Osmotic pressure, even though difficult to measure, is therefore preferred for determining the molecular weights of such large molecules.

## 14-15. Ideal and Non-ideal Solutions

In all of the previous discussion of the colligative properties of solutions an assumption has been made but has not yet been stated. The relations between the magnitude of the colligative properties and the concentration of the solute are rigorously true only if the solution is *quite dilute*. Raoult's law of vapor pressure, the freezing-point and boiling-point equations, and van't Hoff's osmotic-pressure equation describe actual solutions only if the concentration of the solute is no greater than about 0.01 molar. Above this concentration the laws are approximately true and can be used for approximate calculations. These deviations from "ideal" behavior are quite analogous to the deviations from ideality of actual gases at low temperature and high pressure. In general, the deviations of solutions from ideality are greater than those of gases and are less easily corrected by modification of the equations. But the reason for the deviations is the same. The postulates of the theory include the assumption of no interaction between solute particles. At high concentrations this assumption is not even approximately true; deviations from theory must therefore be expected.

## 14-16. Anomalous Colligative Properties

But there is another class of deviations from the colligative properties predicted by the theory advanced in this chapter. These deviations are much more pronounced than those due to non-ideality of the solutions and are much more interesting from the theoretical point of view. They are interesting because they are totally unexpected and cannot *possibly* be explained by the atomic and molecular theories we have developed up to this point.

It was known in the 1880's, at the time when the explanations of colligative properties were being developed, that a large class of compounds simply had to be excluded from the explanation or else the currently accepted theories of the structure of matter had to be modified. The problem was that solutions of a large number of substances showed anomalously high colligative properties. A 1 molal solution of alcohol in water freezes at about $-1.86°$, as expected; but a 1 molal solution of sodium chloride freezes at about $-3.6°$. The effect of sodium chloride on the freezing point is nearly *twice* as great as expected. These two substances are examples of two large classes of compounds, of which one class (the alcohol type) shows normal colligative properties in solution and the other class (the salt type) shows colligative properties that are higher than normal by factors of 2, 3, or, in some cases, 4. The first class of compounds, whose solutions have normal colligative properties, includes sugar, glycerine, naphthalene—all non-polar substances, organic compounds in general. The other class includes most salts, acids, and bases—polar, inorganic substances in general.

An adequate explanation of this anomalous behavior was advanced in the late nineteenth century in the form of the **ionic theory of dissociation.** This theory, which will be considered in great detail in Part Two of this text, was conceived because of a remarkable parallelism between two sets of facts concerning solutions. The anomalous colligative properties are one of these sets of facts; the other set has to do with the conduction of electricity by some solutions. It was first observed in 1771 by Henry Cavendish that a solution of salt in water will conduct an electric current. This phenomenon was investigated through most of the nineteenth century by Michael Faraday and others. It was not until 1887 that the parallel between conductivity in water solution and anomalously high colligative properties was emphasized by Svante Arrhenius, a Swedish physical chemist.

The remarkable fact is that the solutes that show anomalously high freezing-point depression in water solution also form conducting solutions in water. Pure water will not conduct electricity; solutions of alcohol or sugar in water also do not conduct it; but a solution of salt in water, or a water solution of an acid or a base —any solution that shows abnormally high colligative properties—is an excellent electrical conductor.

A serious problem is posed by the fact of anomalous colligative properties. An excellent theoretical explanation of normal colligative properties on the basis of the kinetic-molecular theory was advanced. But it fails entirely to account for the many solutes that show abnormally high colligative properties. Science faces another choice in this situation. The theory must be rejected, leaving *all* the colligative properties (plus many other aspects of the structure of matter) with no rational explanation, or the theory must be radically modified. The explanation was based on the *number of particles* of solute, and in the preceding discussion this number of particles was, by implication, equated with the number of molecules of the solute. If the theory has any meaning or value in the interpretation of physical phenomena—in short, if the theory is to be retained—we must postulate that the compounds having abnormally high colligative properties dissociate into anomalously large numbers of *particles* in solution—each molecule giving rise to two, three, or four particles. And, because of the perfect parallel between electrical conductivity and high colligative properties, we must further postulate that these sub-molecular particles that exist in solution have *electrical* properties. The structure of matter must therefore be more complicated than the "billiard ball" model of molecules that we have postulated in our simple mechanical view of the atomic and kinetic-molecular theories. Matter must have a sub-molecular structure, and this structure must be, in part, electrical in nature. Part Two of this text will take up the idea of electricity, its nature, source, and properties, and will consider the structure of matter in terms of electricity.

## Concepts and Terms

Vapor Pressure
   vapor-pressure curves
   depression of vapor pressure
   Raoult's law
Elevation of Boiling Point
Depression of Freezing Point

Determination of Molecular Weights
Osmotic Pressure
   van't Hoff's law
Kinetic Interpretations
Ideal and Non-ideal Solutions
Anomalous Colligative Properties

## Problems

**14-1.** Define the term "colligative properties of solutions"; list these properties, and explain how each is measured.

**14-2.** Define vapor pressure, and give in your own words the kinetic explanation of vaporization and of the variation of vapor pressure with temperature.

**14-3.** Making use of Fig. 14-2, state the vapor pressure of each of the five substances at 45°C.
   *Ans.* benzene, 23 cm Hg

**14-4.** Explain the discontinuities in Figs. 14-3 and 14-4. Explain why the freezing point of water is a good standard reference point for defining a temperature scale (see § 9-11). Could the melting point of iodine be used in this way as a reference point of temperature?

**14-5.** The vapor pressure of a solution can be calculated by use of the equation $\Delta p = X_{solute} p_0$, in which $\Delta p$ is the lowering of the vapor pressure caused by the solute ($\Delta p = p_0 - p$) in a two-component solution. Starting with Raoult's law, show that this equation is true. (Hint: In a two-component solution the sum of the mole fractions of the solute and the solvent is 1; that is, $X_{solute} + X_{solvent} = 1$.)

**14-6.** Construct curves similar to those of Fig. 14-6 for a 0.4-mole-fraction solution of ethylene glycol in water. Use the vapor-pressure curve for pure water from Fig. 14-2.

**14-7.** From your curve of Prob. 14-6 read the vapor pressure of the solution at 100°C. Also read the boiling point at atmospheric pressure (that is, read the temperature at which the vapor pressure reaches 76 cm).

**14-8.** Calculate the freezing points of solutions C, H, and I in Prob. 13-7.

**14-9.** Calculate the osmotic pressure of the solutions of Prob. 14-8. Why is measurement of osmotic pressure preferred to measurement of freezing-point depression for the determination of the molecular weights of proteins?

**14-10.** Describe the deviations of actual solutions from ideal-solution behavior. Discuss the assumptions, in the kinetic explanation of solution behavior, that are associated with these deviations.

**14-11.** A solution of 2.0 grams of an unknown substance in 50 grams of camphor has a melting point of 167°. The melting point of pure camphor is 175°C. Calculate the molecular weight of this substance.

*Ans.* 200

**14-12.** If the freezing point of a water solution is −4.65°C, what is its boiling point?

*Ans.* 101.3°C

**14-13.** A compound contains 24.25% C, 4.05% H, and 71.70% Cl. A solution made by dissolving 1.2 grams of this compound in 15 grams of benzene has a freezing point of +5.6°C.
(A) Calculate the empirical formula of the compound.
(B) Calculate the molecular weight of the compound.
(C) What is the true formula?

*Ans.* (C) $C_2H_4Cl_2$

**14-14.** A 5% solution of ethylene glycol in water has a density of 0.92. The formula of ethylene glycol is $C_2H_6O_2$.
(A) Calculate the molal concentration of ethylene glycol in this solution.
(B) Calculate the molar concentration of ethylene glycol.
(C) Calculate the mole fraction of each component.
(D) Calculate the freezing point of this solution.
(E) Calculate the osmotic pressure of this solution at 22°C.
(F) The vapor pressure of pure water at 22°C is 2.0 cm. Calculate the vapor pressure of this solution at 22°C.

# Suggested Readings

1. H. M. Leicester and H. S. Klickstein, *A Source Book in Chemistry* (McGraw-Hill, 1952). Biographical sketches and brief histories of the contributions of Raoult (pp. 471–475) and van't Hoff (pp. 445 and 453–458).
2. L. Pauling, *College Chemistry*, second edition (W. H. Freeman, 1955), second half of Chap. 18.
3. H. H. Sisler, C. A. VanderWerf, and A. W. Davidson, *College Chemistry—A Systematic Approach* (Macmillan, 1953), second half of Chap. 13.
4. W. F. Ehret, *Smith's Introductory College Chemistry* (Appleton-Century-Crofts, 1950), second half of Chap. 12.
5. D. C. Gregg, *Principles of Chemistry* (Allyn and Bacon, 1958), Chap. 15.

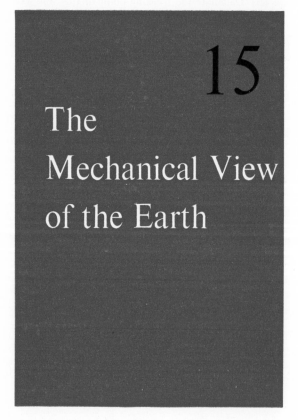

CHAPTER

15

The
Mechanical View
of the Earth

THE CENTRAL purpose of this text is to present the scientific view of the structure of matter and to instill into young students an understanding of the great intellectual and cultural structure called Science. Our development up to this point has established several great physical principles and has presented a unifying conceptual scheme of much of the structure and behavior of our natural environment. But this development has been concerned largely with abstractions—motions and properties of remote planets and stars, the structure of sub-microscopic atoms and molecules, the behavior of invisible gases, and the nature of imponderable quantities such as energy, force, and momentum. There has been a concomitant neglect of the tangible, everyday, near-at-hand parts of our environment. This method, the use of information not for its descriptive value but as a basis for concepts and theories, was established in the preface to this book. It will now be profitable, however, to return to the mundane environment in order to consider some of the ways in which man has used the great physical principles to understand, to describe, and sometimes to control his physical surroundings.

Such an approach might be called applied science and would include subject matter from several of the branches that are commonly included in physical science. Some of these branches are geology, astronomy, meteorology, applied (or industrial) chemistry, mineralogy, metallurgy, and engineering. Obviously, only very fragmentary parts of selected branches of applied science can be included in this discussion. The point of this chapter is to exemplify the scientific use of established principles that we have already used in the development of our science of matter.

## 15-1. Structure of the Earth

An obvious way to begin an application of our principles is to describe the earth. It is common knowledge that the earth is a sphere, about 8,000 miles in diameter, possessing a huge but known (though not commonly known) mass. Most people also know that this sphere is composed of a core and several layers, differing in composition and physical properties, and that the whole is surrounded by an atmosphere containing oxygen and nitrogen; that this atmosphere extends some distance (not so well known) upward. It is also common knowledge that the surface of the earth is irregular (but just *how* irregular is it?); that there is constant change in these irregularities; and that the atmosphere constantly suffers spectacular changes— that is, that *weather* happens.

The bare facts of this knowledge of our earth are interesting, often advantageous, and occasionally crucial to our survival. But a much more intriguing question, the answer to which is much more valuable knowledge, is *"How do we know these things?"* The sphere that we call earth has a mass of $6.593 \times 10^{20}$ tons. How do we know this fact—on what balance was the earth weighed? How, even, do we know the earth is a sphere? It is not, in fact, quite spherical; its equatorial diameter is 7,927.0 miles, and its polar diameter is 7,900.4 miles, a difference of 26.6 miles. How are these facts known, and how can such vast distances be measured accurately? The United States Weather Bureau can now predict with a great degree of certainty the location, extent, duration, and intensity of storms (or of "good" weather). Such information is of inestimable value to many activities of our society. But any alert person must prize even more a knowledge of the principles and way of thinking that lead to such valuable information. The broad answer is: The principles established so far in this text, applied by the methods used in this text, provide the answers to these intriguing questions.

## 15-2. Shape, Size, and Mass of the Earth

The ancient notion that the earth is a flat plane was more popular than learned. Certainly the early Greeks knew that the earth is spherical. This knowledge came from the shrewd use of observations that anyone could make. The earth casts a round shadow on the moon in an eclipse; large bodies of water clearly have a curved (and presumably a spherical) surface, as shown by the classical description of a departing ship as "hull down on the horizon." Greek scientists not only knew that the shape of the earth is generally (or nearly) spherical but also established and used methods for measuring its size. One of their methods is essentially the same as that used in the most modern and most precise measurements of this vast geometric object —that is, the measurement of its **curvature.**

Given the problem of measuring an orange, we should most likely try to measure its circumference with a tape measure or its diameter with a caliper, as in Figure 15-1. Either measurement is an explicit determination of size; one can be calculated from the other, and the volume can be calculated from either. But obviously such a direct approach to measurement of the earth is not possible; some indirect approach is necessary—some cosmic caliper or tape measure is needed. This example illustrates a general principle that we invoked again and again in dealing with the problems of physical science. Much of what we should like to know about our physical environment is unavailable to ordinary measurement; to know about these things, we must first make use of nature itself as a measuring device and then reason by indirection and inference to the quantity we want to determine. The use of these indirect methods in our measurement does not mean that there is uncertainty or inaccuracy in the results; indeed, the size of

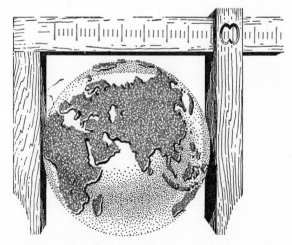

FIGURE **15-1** Cosmic caliper.

the earth and the size of an atom are known at least as certainly and precisely as the size of an orange can be measured. The unique quality of these measurements is that the magnitudes are so profoundly remote from ordinary experience that they can be approached only by indirection.

## 15-3. Measuring the Curvature of the Earth

To return to the orange: another method of determining its size is available; and it is this third method that is used to measure the earth. The method is to measure the curvature of the surface in one local area; then, if it can be assumed that the curvature is constant (that the surface is truly spherical), the circumference and radius of the sphere can be calculated. The problem is diagrammed in Figure 15-2. It is necessary to determine what fraction of the total circumference is represented by a measurable local distance along the arc of the circumference. We

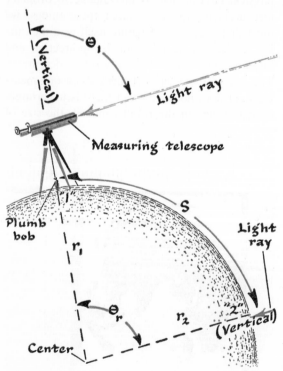

FIGURE 15-2 Determination of the earth's curvature.

accomplish this by measuring, directly or indirectly, the angle $\theta_r$ between the radii, $r_1$ and $r_2$, from the ends of the local arc. Then the distance along the arc, $s$, is the fraction $\theta/360°$ of the circumference. We could apply this technique directly to an orange by simply cutting the orange in half and measuring the angle with a protractor. When we apply the method to the earth, we must use remote astronomical bodies as an observing system, as a "cosmic caliper." From the geometry of Figure 15-2 it is clear that the central radial angle, $\theta_r$, is equal to the angle $\theta_1$ made between $r_1$ and a line parallel to $r_2$. The parallel lines striking the surface of the sphere (the arc in Fig. 15-2) can be rays of light from the sun or, preferably, from a remote star. A modern method of measuring the earth's curvature is to set a telescope at point 1 so that the angle between any celestial object and the vertical (established by a plumb bob) can be measured, to observe a star that is directly overhead at point 2, and at the same instant to observe the angle $\theta_1$ to the same star at point 1.

A classic ancient example of the use of this method was the measurement of the earth by Eratosthenes in the third century before Christ. He used the light from the sun and established point 2 of Figure 15-2 by the fact that just at noon on a particular day of each year the sun shines directly down a deep well in the city of Assuan in upper Egypt. On that particular day, Eratosthenes measured angle $\theta_1$ at point 1, which he chose as Alexandria, 490 miles north of Assuan. There were a number of erroneous assumptions in his method, but fortunately several of his errors compensated each other, and his result was only a few percent higher than the average radius accepted today.

Modern measurements of the curvature of the earth's surface have established with complete certainty that the shape of the earth is indeed generally spherical, and they have established the size of the spheroid with an extremely high degree of precision. These measurements are based on observations of very distant stars rather than the sun, so that the rays of light reaching the earth are much more nearly parallel. They also employ extremely precise angle-measuring devices and compensate for many sources of error that affected the results of ancient measurements. In short, these methods ensure that the conditions assumed in Figure 15-2 are met within extremely close tolerances.

## 15-4. Deviations from Spherical Shape

One interesting result of these measurements was the discovery that the curvature of the earth's surface is less (that is, the surface is more nearly flat) near the poles than near the equator. Another way of stating this fact is that the equatorial diameter is greater than the polar diameter. This difference is shown greatly exaggerated in Figure 15-3. The observations show that a radial angle, $\theta_r$, subtends more surface arc at the poles than the same angle does at the equator. It is necessary, therefore, to presume that the polar radius (and therefore the polar diameter) is smaller than the equatorial. This difference in diameter, just under 27 miles, is a deviation from a perfect sphere of only about 0.3 percent.

We have spoken of the earth's surface as if it were perfectly smooth and quite comparable to similarly shaped objects of our ordinary experience. Yet we are quite aware of the existence of tremendous mountains as irregularities in the surface, and we have just discussed the "flattening" of the polar regions of the earth. It is interesting to compare these irregularities and deviations with the apparently smooth surface and perfect shape of a billiard ball, for example. We have just calculated that the deviation of the earth from a perfect sphere is 0.3 percent in its diameter. This extent of deviation, translated to the size of a billiard ball, which is about 2 inches in diameter, would be 0.3 percent of 2 inches, or about 0.006 inch. It would be a rare billiard ball indeed that would be so nearly perfectly round. The smoothness of the earth's surface is even more remarkable. Mount Everest is the highest known point on the earth and therefore represents the extreme deviation from a smooth surface. Its height above sea level is 29,000 feet, or about 5.1 miles. Compared with the diameter of the earth, this is about $\dfrac{5 \text{ miles}}{8{,}000 \text{ miles}} \times 100 =$

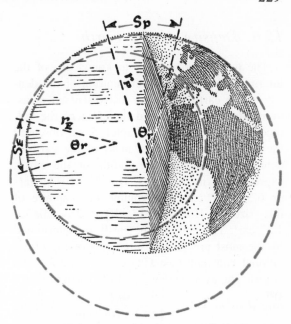

FIGURE **15-3** *Ellipsoidal shape of the earth;* $r_E$ *is the radius of curvature at the equator, and* $r_P$ *is the radius of curvature at the pole.*

0.064 percent. In the billiard ball, this irregularity would amount to 0.064 percent of 2 inches, or just over 0.001 inch. The actual irregularities in the surface of a billiard ball are a good deal greater than this.

## 15-5. Internal Structure of the Earth

The earth is, then, a remarkably smooth spheroid that deviates very slightly from a perfectly spherical shape. Its surface is less interesting in its variation than a billiard ball's. Is its structure no more variant? The surface, obviously, shows a great deal of variation—from mountain to plain, from forest to desert, from land to water, etc.—but we have seen that this variation affects only an extremely minute fraction of the whole depth of the earth. If we delve beneath this fraction of 1 percent of the depth of the earth, do we find more variation? If so, what is the structure? Clearly, such questions as these can be answered only by indirection, just as the outer conformations of the earth must be deduced from indirect observation.

## 15-6. Density of the Earth

The first fact that leads to knowledge of the internal structure is a determination of the density of the earth. We have just discussed measurements of the size (and therefore of the volume) of the earth. In Chapter 5 we observed the method by which the mass of the earth is determined. The average radius of the earth, expressed in metric units, is $6.37 \times 10^6$ meters or $6.37 \times 10^8$ cm. The volume of a sphere of this size is $V = 4\pi(6.37 \times 10^8)^3/3 = 1.083 \times 10^{27}$ cm$^3$. The mass of the earth, as determined by the most precise measurements of the gravitational constant (see Chap. 5), is $5.98 \times 10^{27}$ grams. The average density of the earth is therefore $d = m/V = \dfrac{5.98 \times 10^{27} \text{ grams}}{1.083 \times 10^{27} \text{ cm}^3} = 5.52$ grams/cm$^3$. We must conclude that, if the earth is a homogeneous sphere, this average density must be the actual density of all parts of the sphere, external as well as deep below the surface. But an extensive study of the rocks and minerals near the surface of the earth shows that the earth is not homogeneous. Geological studies and mining operations have supplied us with a voluminous but spotty mass of information about the materials at the surface or within a few thousand feet of the surface of the earth. Careful collation of these extensive data proves that the average density of the substances near the surface of the earth is a good deal less than half of the average density of the earth. In fact, only a very minute fraction of the surface minerals even approaches a density of 5.5 grams/cm$^3$; the average density of the rocks at the surface is 2.7 grams/cm$^3$, and the vast amount of water at the surface has a density of 1.0 gram/cm$^3$. The conclusion is therefore inescapable that the central part of the earth must have a density considerably greater than 5.5 grams/cm$^3$ and much greater than the density of the common substances that make up the surface of the earth.

The materials deep within the earth are, obviously, inaccessible to direct observation. Their nature must therefore be deduced from indirect observations. This study, which falls within a sub-branch of **geology** (study of the earth) called **geophysics,** is one of the most fascinating examples of the ingenuity of scientists in applying the great principles of physical science to the solution of a fantastically complex problem. It has included reasoning by analogy from the composition of meteorites, measurement of the rates and intensities of propagation through the earth of shock waves from earthquakes, detailed study of variations in density, analysis of the rotational inertia of the earth, and many other methods.

## 15-7. Shock Waves and the Earth's Structure

Most of the details of the layered structure of the earth have been deduced from studies of shock waves from earthquakes. Unfortunately, the propagation of waves through solid and liquid media is one theoretical aspect of the great field of physical science that we have not been able to include in this text. But the principles and their use in elucidating the earth's structure can be described very briefly. It is known that waves of this type are reflected from sudden discontinuities in the media. For example, the surface where a material of one density is in contact with a material of a radically different density will reflect shock waves in a manner very similar to the way in which the discontinuity between air and water (the surface of the water) will reflect light waves (see Chap. 25). It is also known that the velocity at which shock waves are propagated through a medium increases as the rigidity of the medium increases, that certain types of these waves will not be propagated at all, though other types will travel very slowly, through a fluid medium. Making use of these and many more subtle generalizations about the behavior of waves, plus the very effective natural sounding device of earthquakes, geophysicists have been able to advance tenable hypotheses, which, though not proven, are consistent with many unrelated observations.

Figure 15-4 shows in a very diagrammatic form these conclusions as to the earth's layered structure and indicates the way in which they were arrived at. Almost every institution of scientific pretensions in the world maintains a seis-

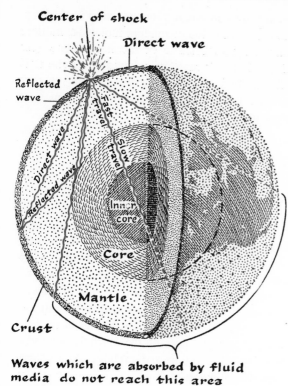

**Center of shock**

**Direct wave**

**Reflected wave**

Fast travel

Slow travel

**Direct wave**

**Reflected wave**

Inner core

**Core**

**Mantle**

**Crust**

**Waves which are absorbed by fluid media do not reach this area**

FIGURE 15-4 *Seismic waves and the layers of the earth.*

mographic sensing station, which consists of automatic recording devices that measure the type, intensity, duration, and exact timing of earth waves. Thus there are records of the waves radiating out in all directions from every earthquake that happens anywhere on the earth. Some of the simplest types of observations are diagramed in Figure 15-4. Sensing stations in the near vicinity of the shock observe direct waves, which are propagated straight through the close surface of the earth. These are timed accurately at several different stations, and their speed of propagation and thereby the distance to the center of the shock are calculated. A little farther away, stations record another series of waves, which, from the time they took in traveling from the center of the quake, must have been reflected off a discontinuity that is fairly near the surface. Much farther away, stations record still other waves that must have been reflected from a much deeper discontinuity. Furthermore, certain areas receive no indication of the type of

wave that will not travel through a liquid medium. The examination of thousands of records of this type has led to the conclusion that two *major* discontinuities in the internal structure of the earth divide the substance into three very broad classifications.

First is the **crust,** which is the very thin layer (tremendously exaggerated in Fig. 15-4) near the surface of the earth. This layer averages about 20 miles thick and ranges from about half to nearly twice this thickness. Subtler studies have also shown that this layer is itself divided into fairly distinct layers of varying density, from the thin veneer of very light sedimentary rock (around 1 mile in average thickness), through a layer of granite, several miles thick, of intermediate density, to a layer of quite dense basalt. Much local variation in these sub-layers is observed; the ocean floors, for example, often do not have the two upper sub-layers at all.

Below the thin crust is a very thick **mantle,** which has a density varying from about 4 near the crust to about 6 near its deep limit. The lower limit of the mantle is about 2,000 miles down, or about halfway to the center of the earth. There are no major discontinuities in the mantle, and the only significant change is a gradation of density, which is deduced from the curved path that shock waves follow through this layer.

At a depth of about 2,000 miles (radial distance from the center about 2,000 miles) there is a very great and sudden discontinuity in the material of the earth. At this point, the outer boundary of the **core,** the density rises abruptly to about 10 grams/cm³. This discontinuity is located by the reflected waves that reach very distant seismic recording stations at a later time than the direct wave. The extent of the core is further established and the fact that it is probably largely liquid is shown by the existence of a "shadow area" in which waves that are not transmitted through a fluid medium are not detected. By careful calculation and a good deal of speculation from these and more complex data of this type, it is possible to deduce the extent and a good deal of the nature of the remotely deep core of the earth. The density of the core material rises continuously from about 10 grams/cm³ at its outer surface to about 12 grams/cm³ at a distance of somewhat less than 1,000 miles from the center. There is some indication that the density again shows a rather sudden discontinuity at this depth and rises considerably higher in the **inner core.** There is also indication that the inner core is solid.

Much of this model of the structure of the earth is quite speculative. It can be said that the model is not in serious disagreement with any considerable number of known facts, and that, though it was deduced largely from seismic records, it is also consistent with much independent observation. For example, calculations of the expected period of the earth's rotation, which depends on the rotational inertia of the earth, which, in turn, depends on the distribution of substances of varying densities about the center of the earth, are in good agreement with the model presented above. Moreover, the gradation of increasing density of the material of the earth as we go from the crust to the center is consistent with the gradation of confining pressures. Obviously, the pressure on the central materials, due to the weight of material in the external layers, becomes stupendous near the center. Such pressures cannot be realized in the laboratory, but extensions of general laws established in the laboratory predict that the atoms will be squeezed together into abnormally close packing and that the substances will therefore become more dense. It is also known that the temperature rises steadily as the depth below the earth's surface increases. It is impossible, of course, to extrapolate from data for the mile or so near the surface through 4,000 miles to the center. But it is possible to make some well-guided guesses as to the temperature within the core of the earth. The temperature of the core is almost certainly less than that of the surface of the sun (6,000°K) and is probably greater than 3,000°K. These extremely high temperatures and the tremendous pressures compensate each other in determining the fluidity (or rigidity) of the various layers of the earth. The facts of propagation of shock waves demand that the crust and mantle be quite rigid solids. At first glance this seems to be an impossibility, for the temperatures deep within the mantle are high enough to melt any ordinary substance at ordinary pressures. But, since the

tremendous confining pressures deep in the mantle prevent the loose, random molecular motions that are characteristic of the liquid state (see Chap. 12), this material behaves as a quite rigid plastic solid. Conversely, the core is at high enough temperatures to ensure a molten state even though the pressures are tremendous.

## 15-8. Surface Conformations of the Earth

The whole question of pressures exerted on each other by the solids of the earth has been studied in great detail in attempts to explain the irregularities of the earth's surface—the existence of mountains and of great depressions in the depths of the ocean. Examination of the surface itself is, of course, a much more satisfactory way of illustrating our principles of physical science, for this part of the earth is accessible to direct observation and even to some experimental manipulation.

Let us next examine the general outward conformation of the earth and seek an explanation of it in terms of the generalities of physical science that we have developed up to this point. We have already seen that the general conformation of the earth is approximately spherical. Why is the earth a sphere? Why not an approximate cube, or a tetrahedron, or an even fancier shape? We know that the major deviation from spherical shape is a flattening at the poles and a bulge at the equator. Isaac Newton predicted the equatorial bulge and the polar flattening. Why had they happened, and why did the originator of systematic mechanics conclude that they must have happened? We are all aware of the local variations in the topography of the earth: the continents and the oceans, mountain peaks, low plains, and ocean deeps. The extreme variation of five miles above sea level at Mount Everest and seven and a half miles below in the Marianas Trench is insignificant compared with the earth's total diameter of 8,000 miles. But to any person who has observed a large mountain, the Himalayas, the Andes, or the Rockies are by no means inconsequential local variations that can properly be ignored. To a scientist, in fact, these magnificently massive piles are a source of wonderment. Why don't they fall down of their own weight? Or at least crush and squeeze the ground rock out from under them? These are real problems and demand, for their explanation, a good deal of fact-finding and some careful application of theories.

## 15-9. *Gravitation Within the Earth*

The two concepts that we shall use to explain the questions posed above are **gravity** and **strength of solids,** both applied to a tremendous system, the material of the earth itself. We examined, in Chapter 5, the theory of universal gravitation; we developed the mathematical statement of this theory, and we applied it to the motions of the planets. We also considered a few examples of the attraction of one small object for another. We must now visualize the whole mass of the earth as exerting gravitational attraction within itself. Clearly, the effect of this force is the basis of the cohesion of the substance of the earth—the explanation of its having *any* shape at all rather than being spread out over the universe or at least over the solar system.

If the material of the earth were fluid, this same force would also explain the spherical shape. Imagine all the particles of the earth in the fluid state—that is, able to move freely with respect to each other. Gravitational attraction would cause all the particles to move toward each other until contact was made. Two particles would join; then, because of the greater mass of the two in combination, they would exert even greater gravitational attraction on neighboring particles (see equation 5-3), which would then approach and join the first pair of particles. This process would continue, all particles taking up a position as close as possible to the center of the aggregate. The geometric figure that meets these requirements is, of course, a sphere. A sample of fluid, if influenced *only* by forces of mutual attraction among its particles, will assume the spherical shape.

In Chapter 1 we defined the fluid state (liquid or gas) as the condition of a substance in which a sample will assume the shape of any container in which it is placed. The question we face now is: What shape will a fluid assume if no container is supplied? We can check our theoretical answer against our own experience by considering a freely falling drop of liquid. The shape it assumes is, of course, a sphere. Thus, *if* the material of the earth were *fluid,* we could explain the spherical shape by simple application of the law of gravitation. But we know, of course, that rocks and earth are solids, not fluids! Or may they not possibly be fluids? The reasoning in this paragraph suggests that perhaps the common-sense notion that rocks are solids should be re-examined. Could it be that, within the fabulously large-scale system we are now considering, rocks might behave somewhat like fluids? The answer is that they do indeed. Under sufficient pressure, rocks will break and flow rather like viscous fluids. To understand this concept, we must first consider the strength of solids, must examine closely and state more precisely the difference between solids and fluids.

## 15-10. *Strength of Materials*

The strength of a material is defined as the pressure (force per unit area; see p. 119) that will cause the material to be permanently deformed. Fluids, obviously, have *zero* strength, for they deform spontaneously without external pressure. The concept of strength, therefore, does not apply to fluids; we could, in fact, revise our definition of a fluid and say that a fluid is a sample of matter in the state in which it has zero strength. A solid, on the other hand, can be distorted by a force applied to it. A steel bar is bent if a force is applied. If the force is below a certain critical value per unit cross-sectional area, the bent bar will spring back when the force is removed. This is *elastic* distortion and is not involved in the concept of strength. We are concerned here with the pressure that is required to bend (or otherwise distort the shape of) the material *permanently;* that is the *bending* strength of the material. We could also measure the *tensile* strength by stretching the bar or the *compressive* (crushing) strength by squeezing it. In the problem at hand, it is primarily the compressive strength that will concern us. **The compressive strength is the pressure required to cause a material to yield continuously by being crushed or by flowing.**

The rocks of the earth, though they have high compressive strengths, can be broken and squeezed by pressure. For example, the compressive strength of granite, one of the commonest rocks of the earth's crust, is about 30,000 pounds per square inch. In our common units of pressure this is 2,000 atmospheres, which is equivalent to a column of mercury 2,000 × 0.76 ≈ 1,500 meters high. The average density of the rocks of the earth's surface is about 2.7. From this fact and equation 9-3 it is possible to calculate the height of rock that a base of granite could support without being crushed. The pressure is directly proportional to the density and the height of the column:

$$P = hdg$$

The same pressure would be exerted by a short column of very dense material and a taller column of less dense material. As we pointed out in § 9-6, the heights of columns of fluid exerting the same pressure are inversely proportional to the densities of the fluids. The height of a column of rock that would exert the pressure we just calculated would be

$$h = 1,500 \ (13.6/2.7) = 1,500 \times 5 = 7,500 \ \text{meters}$$

This calculation indicates that at a depth of 7.5 kilometers, or a little over 4.5 miles, the pressure exceeds the compressive strength of granite. Clearly, if the factors we have considered were the only effective ones, a pile of rock of the size of Mount Everest, which is over 5 miles high, simply could not exist. The base would be crushed out from under it. Other factors do enter; and the main one that saves Mount Everest is the confining pressure exerted on the materials of the base, which increases the compressive strength.

We have clearly established that at depths of several miles the materials of the earth must behave essentially as fluids in the sense that they will flow into the shape of a sphere. In this way the generally spherical shape of the earth is explained. The concept of strength of material will be used again when we face the question of the surface irregularities of the earth. But the next point to be considered should be an explanation of the equatorial bulge in terms of Newtonian mechanics.

## 15-11. Equatorial Bulge

A casual consideration of the diurnal rotation of the earth and of the centrifugal force that is exerted at the surface of a rotating object offers an immediate qualitative explanation of the bulge. An object undergoing uniform circular motion constantly tends to leave the circular path (§ 5-2) and follow a tangential course. An object (or the material of the earth) at the equator thus exerts a force of reaction against the pull of gravity. This force is the *reaction* to the centripetal force, and its magnitude is therefore the same as that of the centripetal force, whose acceleration is given by equation 5-2:

$$a_c = \frac{4\pi^2 r}{T^2}$$

This force is quite small compared with the force of gravity at the equator; objects are in no danger of flying off into space because of it. But it is sufficient to explain the fact that the material of the earth has less weight at the equator than at the poles. If we substitute the values of the radius and the period of rotation into equation 5-2, first for the situation at the poles and then for that at the equator, it becomes apparent that, since the radius from the axis of rotation at the pole is zero, there can be no centripetal acceleration at the poles and no reaction against the force of gravity. The magnitude of the reaction increases steadily in going from either pole to the equator (see Fig. 15-5).

At the equator, $r$ is 4,000 miles, or 6.38× $10^6$ meters, and the period of rotation is 24 hours, or 24 × 3,600 sec. Therefore

$$a_c = \frac{4\pi^2 \times 6.38 \times 10^6}{(8.64 \times 10^4)^2} = 3.38 \times 10^{-2} \ \text{m/sec}^2$$

The measured acceleration of gravity at the equator is equal to the *actual* gravitational acceleration minus the centripetal acceleration. This

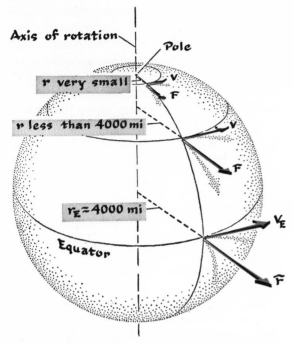

FIGURE **15-5** *Variation of the tangential velocity and centripetal acceleration at the earth's surface with latitude.*

centripetal acceleration is about 0.35 percent of *g*, which is sufficient to account for the observed bulging of the earth. It is also the major factor making the experimentally measured *g* about 0.5 percent less at the equator than at the poles. The other factor is the greater distance (about 13.5 miles) from the center to the surface of the earth at the equator.

## 15-12. *Isostasy*

The explanation of the existence of high mountains and deep ocean depressions is also concerned with the application of the detailed study of gravity and strength of materials to the substance of the earth. It also involves a detailed study of density variation from one area to another. The first step toward the understanding of these extreme surface variations came from the observation that a plumb bob does not always hang exactly vertically. This discrepancy came up in the very precise surveying of India. Apparent errors in the survey were finally traced

to the fact that in the vicinity of the Himalaya Mountains in northern India a plumb bob does not point directly toward the center of the earth but is actually deflected appreciably toward the great mountain mass. In southern India, which is an almost mountainless plain, there was no such effect. When this deviation was observed, it was realized that such an effect should have been expected: the great mass of the mountain range should exert a gravitational attraction on all objects near it, including a plumb bob. The volume and density and thereby the mass of the Himalayas were estimated, and the deviational effect of their gravitational attraction of a plumb bob was calculated. But the interesting result of this calculation was that the correction was *far* too large (Fig. 15-6)! The actual deviation of a plumb bob was only a third of what was expected from the calculated mass of the mountains and their distance from the bob. All the elements of this calculation were known with considerable accuracy except one, the *density* of the materials below the mountain range and below the southern plain. It had been assumed that the subcrustal material was of the same density below the mountains as below the plain—that is, that the mountains were simply a much higher pile

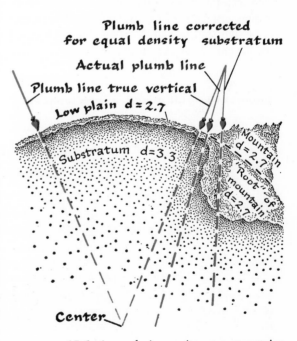

FIGURE **15-6** *Anomaly in gravity near mountains.*

of crustal rock heaped on a common base of the same material below the plain and below the mountains. The English amateur geologist who made these calculations in 1855 (a Reverend Mr. Pratt) was forced by the logic of his calculations to assume that the density of the material below the mountains must be considerably less than that of the material below the low plains. He extended his reasoning beyond this explanation of the double-edged anomaly of the non-vertical plumb bobs and proposed a theory of the "flotation" of mountains.

This theory, which was later called **isostasy,** suggests that mountains (in fact, all surface land features) are blocks of low-density materials "floating" on a substratum of much denser materials. The current concept of isostasy, diagramed in Figure 15-7, is sometimes called the "roots of mountains" theory and is a slight variation on the original theory of Pratt. The best geological evidence has established that the average density of the rock of crustal formations is about 2.7 grams/cm³. The theory suggests that the substratum, of average density 3.3 grams/cm³, acts rather like a fluid (see the discussion of strength in § 15-10) on which the crustal masses float rather as blocks of ice float on water. Each crustal block sinks into the fluid substratum just enough to displace its own weight of the substratum and floats in this position of equilibrium. Thus the height to which a block

rises above the surface is dependent on the total height of the block. Below a high mountain range there is a deep "root" of the less dense crustal rock; below a low plain is a much shallower extension of the less dense rock. The analogy to ice blocks floating in water is applicable to this situation. An iceberg towers above the surface of the water, but only because its "root" extends far below the surface. Conversely, a low, flat ice floe rises hardly at all above the surface of the water because its total thickness, and therefore the amount below the surface of the water, is very slight.

## 15-13. Applications of the Isostasy Theory

It is now apparent how the anomalously small deviation of the plumb bob in northern India came about. The mass of the huge volume of the Himalayas deflected the plumb bob toward itself, but this deflection was only one-third as great as it would have been if the *base* of the mountain had been of density 3.3 grams/cm³. The huge volume of the "root" of these mountains has the lower density of the upper part and therefore less mass and less gravitational attraction for the plumb bob.

The theory of isostasy, as presented here, is clearly an oversimplification. The substratum is not fluid in the sense of having *no* strength; but it does have the property of flowing under the tremendous pressures exerted in these geophysical situations and therefore can be viewed as a fluid in this theory. Also the mountains and other crustal features are not simply blocks that can slide past each other without friction in a vertical direction; they are actually a continuous solid surface covering the earth. But under vast stresses and over vast periods of time, parts of this continuum are capable of vertical movement with respect to each other. This movement makes up the processes of mountain-building, erosional degradation, fault slippage, etc., which take place constantly through geological time.

The concept of isostasy has played a great theoretical role in the study of the features of the earth's surface by serving as an organiza-

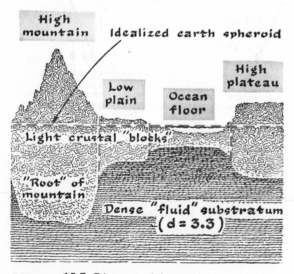

FIGURE **15-7** *Diagram of isostasy.*

tional and integrating basis for vast numbers of observations. It is comparable to several of the theories we have already encountered, such as the kinetic theory and the atomic theory. It is a concept of almost childish simplicity but of stupendous power. It organizes a mass of isolated facts and converts them from trivial single observations into a conceptual whole. And it furnishes a rational basis for extended study and for prediction. In these ways it meets the criteria stated in Chapter 1 for a useful scientific theory.

For a final look at the theory of isostasy we go back to our earlier question: Why do not the Himalayas collapse and ooze out into the Marianas Trench, why can very high mountains and very deep ocean depressions exist? The answer is now obvious. They could not exist if the mountains were simply heaps of rock on a level, continuous substratum or if the deeps were simply holes in this substratum. They do exist because the high mountain block is supported by flotation in the "fluid" substratum and the deeps of the ocean floor are shallow depressions in thin blocks of the same type of rock floating only slightly above the surface of the same substratum.

## 15-14. The Atmosphere

The smoothly spherical object we have been describing, "the earth," is obviously only a part of the world in which we live. Equally important as a part of our environment—and equally interesting as a subject for consideration according to the principles of our sciences—is the *atmosphere*. It says little to describe the atmosphere as a gaseous envelope that surrounds the "solid" earth; much more expressive is the description of Torricelli (§ 9-5) in which he refers to the surface of the earth as the bottom of "a sea of air." This sea of air is a gaseous solution. Since it is a gas, its behavior can be predicted by the general gas laws (Chaps. 9 and 10); since it is a solution, parts of its behavior are predictable by use of the concepts developed in Chapter 13. The constant motion of the atmosphere can be interpreted in terms of the concepts of force and

motion discussed in Chapter 4, and the vast energy exchanges involved in the absorption of the sun's heat and occasionally expended in the magnificent violence of storms illustrate the concepts of energy established in Chapter 11. We are thus amply prepared to deal with the problems of the atmosphere; and, to supply ourselves with a most interesting array of problems whose answers can be instructive and valuable, we need only remember that weather and climate are simply short-range changes and long-range changes in atmospheric conditions.

## 15-15. Physical Description of the Atmosphere

In our experimental study of gases and in the discussion of Chapter 10 it was observed that the quantities that affect the behavior of a gas include its pressure, temperature, amount, volume, and composition (or molecular nature). In Chapter 13 we observed that the factors that influence solubility in gases include the pressure, temperature, and molecular nature of the gases. In Chapter 9 we observed that the pressure of a column of fluid is dependent on the height of the column and the density of the fluid as well as on the acceleration due to gravity, *g*. In view of these considerations, any understanding of the changes and behavior of the atmosphere must be prefaced by a straightforward description of these physical properties of the atmosphere. Then, when we consider the dynamic influences on this physical system in terms of the concepts of mechanics and energetics already referred to, it should be possible to understand and, in some cases, to predict the behavior of the atmosphere—that is, the weather.

In § 13-3 the composition of "dry air" was described as 78 percent nitrogen, 21 percent oxygen, and 1 percent incidental gases including hydrogen, carbon dioxide, and the inert gases. This description of the composition of air is a considerable oversimplification. It does not include, of course, the amount of water vapor in solution; furthermore, it refers to a statistical average of sea-level air. There are sizable non-systematic local variations in the composition of air at the surface of the earth (sea level), and there is an even greater systematic variation with altitude above sea level. There is also a great variation of a very important component, water vapor. The water content of air at sea level averages about 1 percent but varies from very near zero to over 5 percent, depending on a number of factors, such as temperature, availability of water, and ease of evaporation. The systematic variation of composition with increasing altitude consists of a steady decrease in the water content at higher altitudes (primarily because of remoteness from the source of water at the earth's surface), an increase in the amount of nitrogen and other lighter gases, and a concomitant decrease in the amount of oxygen. At an altitude of 60,000 feet the important components of air are, approximately, 80 percent nitrogen, 19 percent oxygen, and less than 0.01 percent water. This tendency of the lighter gases (with the exception of water vapor) to concentrate at higher altitudes is an expected gravitational effect. Gravitational attraction is greater for substances of higher density and produces an effect parallel to the tendency of heavier substances to be concentrated deep within the earth, leaving the less dense rocks at the surface.

## 15-16. Density of Air

It is possible to calculate the densities of the component gases of air and thereby the density of the mixture. From our study of the general gas law, however, it is apparent that the density depends very much on the pressure and temperature of the gases. Any calculation of density must therefore be artificial in the sense that a particular set of conditions must be specified, and it must be realized that the actual conditions of temperature and pressure (and therefore the density of air) will vary through rather wide limits over the surface of the earth. It is, in fact, the variation in these three quantities—temperature, pressure, and density—that gives rise to the motions of the air and therefore to most of our weather phenomena. The general gas equation (§ 10-7) can be modified to include the density of the gas, and in this form the three

variables mentioned above are related. If we solve equation 10-12,

$$PV = \left(\frac{\text{mass}}{\text{mol wt}}\right) RT$$

for the ratio mass/$V$, which is, of course, equal to the density, we have

$$\frac{P}{RT} (\text{mol wt}) = \frac{\text{mass}}{V} = d \qquad (15\text{-}1)$$

Let us select standard conditions of temperature and pressure and substitute these values and the value of the gas constant $R$ into equation 15-1:

$$\frac{76 \text{ cm}}{6.23 \times 10^3 \frac{\text{cm}^4}{\text{mole}^\circ} 273^\circ} (\text{mol wt})$$

$$= d = 4.47 \times 10^{-5} (\text{mol wt}) \text{ gram/cm}^3$$

We can now calculate the densities of the various gases in air at 0°C and one atmosphere pressure. The densities of seven of those gases are presented in Table 15-1. These are, of course, the densities prevailing at sea level during good weather on a cold day. If the temperature rises or the pressure falls, the density will also decrease. A comparison of these densities makes it apparent why there is very little hydrogen or helium near the earth's surface and why these gases are more abundant at great altitudes. It also makes the relative decrease in oxygen at higher altitudes understandable.

The first three gases listed in the table make up the bulk of air and are the ones that effectively determine the density of air under any set of conditions. It is apparent that the density of dry air near sea level (a weighted average of the densities of oxygen and nitrogen) is near 1.3 ×

| TABLE 15-1 | *Gas Densities* |
|---|---|
| GAS | $d$ (GRAMS/CM³) |
| $N_2$ | $1.251 \times 10^{-3}$ |
| $O_2$ | $1.430 \times 10^{-3}$ |
| $H_2O$ | $0.840 \times 10^{-3}$ |
| $CO_2$ | $1.966 \times 10^{-3}$ |
| Ar | $1.783 \times 10^{-3}$ |
| He | $0.179 \times 10^{-3}$ |
| $H_2$ | $0.089 \times 10^{-3}$ |

$10^{-3}$ gram/cm$^3$. It is also apparent that a sizable moisture content will cause the gaseous mixture to have a lower density than normal. Thus three major factors influence the density of air: an increase can result from an increase in pressure, a fall in temperature, or a decrease in water content. These variables are not independent; just as in any sample of gas whose behavior is described by the general gas law, the change in any of the variables will cause related changes in the others.

Listed above, and obviously one of the factors involved in the general gas equation, is the quantity *volume*. A question immediately arises: what volume shall we consider in dealing with the earth's atmosphere? We can hardly refer to the *whole* gaseous envelope of the earth in these considerations; furthermore, what is the outer limit of the atmosphere? And how can we deal with the atmosphere as a confined gas? In most of our dealing with the atmospheric changes exemplified by weather phenomena we can limit the problem by considering *air masses,* which are vast volumes of air (though many orders of magnitude less than the whole atmosphere) that behave, in large part, as isolated samples of gas. This concept of air masses will be considered in detail in a subsequent section. Here we return to the question of the outer limit of the atmosphere. Limits have been set to this dimension of the earth, but any such limit is clearly arbitrary. The outer atmosphere, called the stratosphere, is sometimes defined as extending 30 or 40 miles above the earth's surface. But this only means that the pressure of air is quite low at that height. In Chapter 12 this "thinning" out of the air at great altitudes was discussed in connection with Perrin's determination of Avogadro's number. If we refer to this discussion (pp. 187–189) and Figure 12-6a, this effect becomes understandable. It was pointed out in the discussion that the pressure of the air decreases by half for each 3.5 miles of increase in altitude. At an altitude of 3.5 miles above the earth's surface (sea level) the air pressure would be $\frac{1}{2} \times 76$ cm or 38 cm; at 7 miles it would be $\frac{1}{4} \times 76$ cm; and so on. At 35 miles ($10 \times 3.5$) the pressure would be $(\frac{1}{2})^{10} \times 76$ cm = $(1/1{,}024) \times 76$ cm = 0.074 cm. This is fairly close to a vacuum but is by no means a total absence of gas. It is impossible, in short, to place a precise limit on the earth's atmosphere. Somewhere within 100 miles above sea level the amount of air becomes negligible for most considerations, but there is good evidence that some of the light gases are present beyond this height. It is known, for example, that meteors are observable because these objects enter the earth's atmosphere from outer space and become heated to incandescence by friction in passing through the atmosphere. Most meteors are observed first at altitudes of nearly 100 miles but are occasionally seen at much greater altitudes.

## 15-17. Pressure and Temperature of the Atmosphere

The other two properties of the atmosphere that we shall describe are pressure and temperature. The variation in pressure with altitude was discussed above; but there are also very important local variations at the earth's surface. These are related directly to local fluctuations of the density of the air, and the fluctuations in density are, in turn, dependent on variations in temperature and in water content. Of these two influences the temperature changes are much more striking and violent. The temperature of air near the earth's surface is nearly the same as that of the solid or liquid surface in contact with it. There is, of course, wide variation with season and with latitude. There is also a vertical variation, a fall of about 6°C per kilometer of altitude down to about $-35$°C. Above an altitude of 10 or 12 kilometers (about 8 miles) the temperature remains nearly constant. This over-all temperature equilibrium is maintained by an equality of heat loss and heat gain. The energy from the sun is absorbed, partly by the air but mostly by the ground and water of the surface of the earth. Much of this, after being re-radiated, is partly absorbed by the air and partly lost to outer space. The atmosphere thus acts as a very effective heat insulator, preventing the fluctuations, from extreme heat during the day to abysmal cold at night, that would happen at the surface of a planet without an atmosphere.

## 15-18. Variations in the Properties of Air: Weather

The three factors that largely determine the weather and the climate in a particular locality are (1) the moisture content, (2) the temperature, and (3) the pressure. Short-range changes in these factors, over a period of a few days or weeks, are called **weather,** and the long-range changes, or the average behavior of these variables over periods of years, are called **climate.** If an area always has a very low moisture content in the air and the fluctuations in moisture content are very slight, it is said to have a desert type of climate. If the temperature of another area is always high and the humidity and the rainfall are also high, this area has a typical tropical climate. If the midwestern United States has a few weeks of dry, parching winds, followed by a period of torrential rains, or is visited by a series of tornadoes, these manifestations of variation in temperature, humidity, and pressure are called weather.

The three factors we have listed are completely and inseparably bound up together. Changes in one are caused by changes in the others; when one suffers a change, the others are always correspondingly changed. In describing these changes, however, we shall consider the three in order, outlining how changes are effected and how these changes influence the other variables.

## 15-19. Moisture Content

The moisture content of air and its variations are best understood if we consider the atmosphere a gaseous solution of water in air. If a sample of liquid water (the *ocean,* for example) is in contact with a sample of gas (the atmosphere), a solubility equilibrium will be set up by evaporation of some of the liquid water, which then goes into solution as water vapor in the gaseous phase (see Chap. 13 and §§ 14-2 and 14-3). If the contact is kept long enough, the gaseous phase (air) will become *saturated* with water vapor; that is, the system will reach a true solubility equilibrium. The amount of water that goes into solution is limited by the vapor pressure of the water at the temperature in question. At 0°C, a cold winter day in the temperate zone, the vapor pressure of water is 0.46 cm Hg, which corresponds to a water content of about 0.6 percent; that is, air that is saturated at this temperature has only about 0.6 percent water in it. The vapor pressure of water at 35°C, which would be a fairly warm summer day in the United States, is 4.3 cm Hg, which corresponds to a moisture content in saturated air of about 5.7 percent, or about ten times as much water as in the cold air.

From these facts a large number of generalizations concerning weather can be made. First comes a practical rule on how to design an air-conditioner that will lower the humidity of warm moist air. The air should be cooled, obviously, to a temperature at which the saturated solution can hold only a small percentage of water. (The excess water would condense out, or *precipitate.* See the discussion of saturated solutions in §§ 13-15 and 13-16). After this water-removing step, the air could be warmed to a comfortable temperature, at which it would then be far below saturation in water content.

It is not the total water content of air that determines comfort and thereby the quality of air-conditioning; it is rather the amount by which the water content is below saturation. The major process by which body temperature is maintained is the evaporation of perspiration, which cools; and this process takes place not at all in saturated air, only slowly in air that is very near saturation, and rapidly in air that is far below saturation. For this reason the term **relative humidity** is used. If air is saturated, either very cold air with 0.6 percent moisture or very warm air with 6 percent moisture, it has a relative humidity of 100 percent; if air is dry (has no water content), its relative humidity is 0 percent. The very cold air would have a relative humidity of 50 percent at a water content of 0.3 percent, the very warm air at 3 percent.

This same process—precipitation of water when warm moist air is cooled—happens naturally; it is, indeed, one of the common manifestations of weather. Warm tropical air, saturated with water at high temperatures and therefore with a high moisture content, moves to cooler areas (either upward or northward in the northern hemisphere); as the temperature falls, water vapor condenses. The first manifestation is the formation of clouds, which are accumulations of very fine water droplets (or, in some cases, ice crystals)—so fine that they remain suspended. As more water comes out of solution by further cooling, the droplets grow and are finally so big that they can no longer be suspended; they then fall as rain or snow—that is, as *precipitation*. The tropical rain belts are examples of the constant repetition of this cycle. Surface air in contact with the warm ocean water at the high temperature of the equatorial surface of the earth becomes saturated with water vapor. One of the effects of this increase in water content is a *decrease* in the density. But this lowers the pressure of the air, so that it expands and is forced upward by cooler or less moist air. Then, as the air rises, the temperature falls (this fall is caused both by the lower temperatures at higher altitudes and by the cooling effect of expansion on any gas), and, as the temperature falls, the air can no longer hold all the water in solution. Some of the water must therefore precipitate; vast accumulations of clouds form, and these spill out their water content, maintaining the cycle of evaporation at the surface and precipitation at higher altitudes.

## 15-20. *Heat of Vaporization and Condensation*

One further relation of the moisture content of air has to do with the energy effects of evaporation and condensation—the heat of vaporization (see § 11-1). A large input of heat is needed to evaporate water (540 calories per gram), and this heat must come from the surroundings; the same amount of heat must be given off when water vapor condenses from the air to liquid water, and this heat must be absorbed by the surrounding air. In the absence of sources of or dumping grounds for heat, the processes of evaporation and condensation are therefore self-limiting. In the evaporation part of the cycle, the

sun's radiation and the circulation of the ocean water keep the system operating by supplying heat. But, as air gives up its water content (because of cooling), its temperature must rise because there is no other reservoir to absorb the heat. This effect limits the precipitation process until other factors accommodate the heat gain.

## 15-21. *Radiation and Other Heat Effects*

As we stated above, the major factors raising the temperature of the air are the heat absorbed from the sun and the heat absorbed from the land or sea in contact with the air. Clearly, if the air kept on absorbing the sun's heat without los-

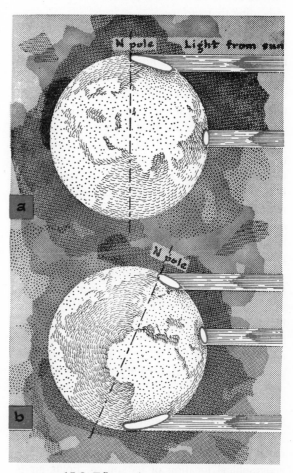

FIGURE **15-8** *Effect of season upon the distribution, and thereby upon the intensity, of the sun's radiation on the earth's surface.*

ing any, its temperature would continue to rise. This absorption of heat must therefore be balanced by loss in the form of radiation back into space. Since the rays from the sun are most effective in heating the air and the surface of the earth if they fall on the earth in a direction perpendicular to the surface, the equatorial regions receive a good deal more heat than the polar regions (Fig. 15-8a). For the same reason the northern hemisphere receives more during its summer, when the tilt of the earth's axis makes the surface more nearly perpendicular to the sun's rays (Fig. 15-8b). At the same time, the southern hemisphere (during its winter) is receiving correspondingly less heat; in the figure we see that a given cross section of solar radiation is spread over a greater area of the surface of the earth and is therefore less effective in heating that surface.

But we know that the temperature fluctuations are always behind the cycle of the tilt of the earth: although the northern hemisphere gets the maximum heat absorption on June 21 and the minimum on December 21, the extremes of temperature come about two months later. This effect is a result of the heat capacity of the earth (§ 11-1). Once heated up during the summer, the earth, including the air, the land, and the water, has a considerable store of heat, which it loses only slowly. Another climatic effect is related to this one. Temperature fluctuations are *much* smaller on seacoasts than in the center of large land masses. The extremes of temperature recorded in New London, Connecticut, are −17°F and 99°F; the extremes recorded in Harding County, South Dakota (at about the same latitude) are −57°F and 114°F. A large body of water adjacent to the land obviously acts as a very effective buffer against temperature changes. Part of this effect is due to the much greater specific heat capacity of water than of soil and rock; the circulation of the sea water also aids by making more water available as source of or dumping ground for heat.

In general, then, the temperature and the moisture content of air are determined by the geographical location of its source. Polar air is cold; it is also dry if its source is a land area and only slightly moist if it originated over a polar

ocean. Air from equatorial regions is hot; it is very moist if the source was over the ocean but may be quite dry if the source was an arid tropical region. These are very loose generalizations, and in the discussion of air masses below it must be remembered that the extent of the polar regions and tropical regions varies with the season. In winter the north polar region extends much farther south than in summer, and the tropical region of the northern hemisphere does not reach as far north.

## 15-22. Circulation of the Air

But it is the movement of air and the encounter of different types of air that really make weather. These movements are caused by differences in pressure. When there is a difference in pressure between two areas, air will move from the area of high pressure to the area of low pressure. If the movement is horizontal (along the surface of the earth), it is called **wind;** if it is vertical (up or down), it is a **current.** We have already explained the reason for the equatorial upward air currents. But, if the air at the surface at the equator moves upward, it cannot leave a vacuum in its place; some other air must move in to occupy this place. And the air to the north and to the south of the equator does this; there is a nearly constant wind toward the equator from higher latitudes in both hemispheres.

The general pattern of the motion of air over the surface of the earth is the quite complex result of a number of factors, which include not only temperature variations, changes in density, and heating effects, which we have already mentioned, but also two others, which we shall now consider. These are, first, the rotation of the earth, with its frictional drag on the atmosphere, and, second, the effect of large land masses on the smooth flow patterns. The best way to attain an understanding of the wind patterns is to set up an idealized model of a smooth sphere that is not rotating and then to introduce successively the complicating factors. In the next sections we shall introduce simplified drawings that show the basic movements but by no means exhaust the scientific analysis of wind patterns.

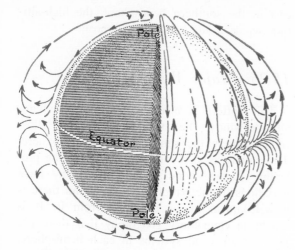

FIGURE **15-9** *Idealized polar-equatorial air circulation.*

## 15-23. *Polar-equatorial Movement*

Figure 15-9 indicates the air movements that would be expected in the simple, idealized situation of a smooth, stationary globe heated by the sun in the way described above. The warm, moist equatorial air would rise vertically. At higher latitudes, where the surface temperatures are lower because less solar energy is absorbed, there would be less rise of air. At the polar regions, which are much colder (and the air drier), the air would fall. Thus there would be higher-pressure regions at the poles and a lower-pressure region at the equator, both at the *surface* of the earth. This would set winds in motion from the poles to the equator at the surface and from the equator to the poles at high altitudes.

The net effect of these movements would be a tremendous heat engine, in which the air mass was expanded by the sun's energy at the equator and compressed by the polar cooling, with circulation between these as diagramed in Figure 15-9. Obviously, if there were a constant input of energy, this circulation would continue to increase in speed (increase in kinetic energy). The limitation on this increase is the frictional dissipation of energy at the surface of the earth and between the two oppositely directed streams of air.

## 15-24. *Effect of the Earth's Rotation*

The next step in considering the over-all pattern of the air movements around the earth is to consider the effect of the earth's rotation on the atmosphere. If there were no north-south movement of the air, the rotation would have *no* effect on the air. The atmosphere is within the earth's gravitational field and would follow the west-to-east motion of the earth's surface in its rotation; the air would be at rest with respect to the surface of the earth; the air at the equator would have the same velocity as the surface of the earth at the equator—that is, about a thousand miles an hour from west to east. Similarly, air exactly at either pole would have zero velocity, and air at intermediate latitudes would have velocities (just as the ground surface at these latitudes do) somewhere between the extremes, depending on the latitude. These velocities would always be in an easterly direction. A sample of air would therefore have a momentum (see § 11-4) that was proportional to its radial distance from the axis of the earth (see Fig. 15-10). This *momentum* would be maximal at

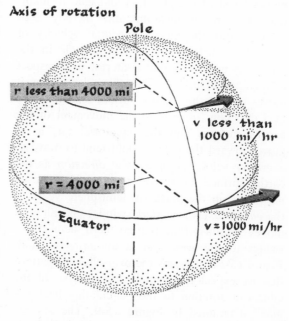

FIGURE **15-10** *Variation of tangential surface velocity with latitude.*

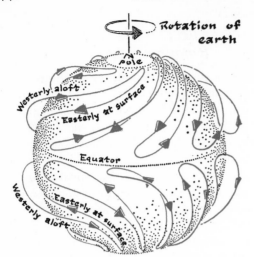

FIGURE **15-11** *Effect of the earth's rotation on the direction of winds.*

the equator and zero at the poles. According to the concept of the conservation of momentum (established in § 11-4), we should expect the equatorial air, as it moves aloft and then toward the poles, to tend to maintain its momentum at the maximal value, corresponding to a velocity of about a thousand miles an hour and a radial distance from the axis of rotation of the earth of 4,000 miles. Similarly, the polar air, as it moves toward the equator, would tend to maintain its zero momentum and thereby zero velocity. But the linear tangential velocity of the earth's surface depends on latitude in the same way as the air that is at rest with respect to the earth's surface. Thus the polar air, as it moves toward the equator, would tend to move in a direction *opposite* to the movement of the earth's surface, and the equatorial air, as it moves toward the poles, would tend to move at a *greater* velocity in the *same direction* as the earth's surface. In general, then, air that moves *northward* in the northern hemisphere veers to the *eastward* (is a *westerly* wind), and air that moves *southward* in the northern hemisphere swings to the *west* and is an *easterly* wind. Figure 15-11 diagrams the over-all wind pattern that we expect if we apply this analysis of the effects of rotation to the "circulating heat engine" diagramed in Figure 15-9. The surface winds would be uniformly from the northeast in the northern hemisphere and from the south-

east in the southern hemisphere; the high-altitude winds would be just the opposite.

## 15-25. *Major Wind Patterns*

This pattern is nearly correct for the high-altitude winds. The so-called **jet streams** follow rather closely the simple pattern set up here. The pattern is also roughly correct for the prevailing surface winds. There are many local variations in the pattern, however, and there is a well-known major deviation from it. It is taught in elementary geography that there are *three* major wind systems in each hemisphere, rather than the single pattern depicted in Figure 15-11, and that there are two transition zones separating the patterns of the two hemispheres. In describing these more complicated patterns, we shall limit ourselves to the northern hemisphere and keep in mind that the southern hemisphere is, in general, symmetrical.

Figure 15-12 diagrams the major wind pattern of the northern hemisphere. The equatorial zone (the geographical location varies somewhat with the season, as mentioned earlier) is the area where the movement of air is generally upward, not horizontal; that is, there is no wind. This area, the separation zone between hemispheres, is called the **doldrums.** From the doldrums (latitude zero) northward to about 30° latitude, the winds are rather constant and

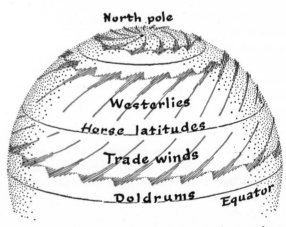

FIGURE **15-12** *Prevailing winds of the northern hemisphere, idealized to exclude the effect of land masses.*

from a northeasterly direction. These are called the **trade winds.** North of the trade winds, in the general vicinity of latitude 30°, is an area of very little wind in which all weather phenomena seem sluggish and without any driving force. This area, known as the "horse latitudes," is a transition between the area of the trades and the area of the **prevailing westerlies.** The area of the westerlies is a belt round the earth, between the approximate latitudes of 30° and 60°, in which the winds blow quite constantly from the southwest. This area resembles the trade-wind area except that the constant winds blow from the opposite direction. North of the westerlies the winds again take a generally southwestward movement (northeast winds). The transition from the westerlies to the northeast winds, sometimes called the **polar front,** is not so well defined as the transition zone at the horse latitudes.

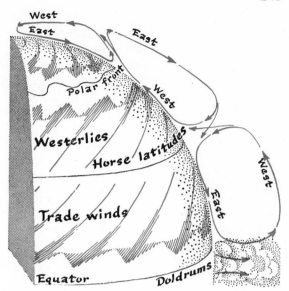

FIGURE **15-13** *Three-cell circulation pattern of winds in the northern hemisphere.*

## 15-26. Three-cell Cycle of Winds

In the polar and equatorial regions the actual pattern parallels fairly closely the general movement outlined in Figure 15-11, but the middle portion, the area of prevailing westerlies, is an inversion of the predicted pattern. This inversion is diagramed in Figure 15-13, in which a cross section of the air movements, both winds and currents, is indicated. The complete sweep of winds from equator to pole at high altitudes and from pole to equator at the surface in one full cycle is broken up into three cells, or subcycles. The polar cell and the equatorial cell operate as predicted in Figure 15-11; but, by a number of very complex causes, including pressure inversions at very high altitudes, the drag of polar air coming down under the air of the middle regions, and eddies in the major cycle of Figure 15-11, the middle, inverted cycle is created. Thus the three cells operate rather like a train of gears, the polar and equatorial cells rotating counter-clockwise (as viewed in cross section from the west) and the middle cell, driven by the other two, rotating clockwise. The horse latitudes are an area of downward moving air, and the polar front is an area where the cold polar air is driving under the warm air

moving northeast in the area of the westerlies. The explanation of the westerly winds at the surface in the middle belt is contained in the discussion of the effect of the earth's rotation in § 15-24. Northward moving air is deflected to the east by the conservation of momentum.

## 15-27. Deviations from the Wind Pattern

Figure 15-13 shows, then, a highly schematic diagram of the major air movements in the atmosphere—winds and currents operating in a three-cell cycle to produce the major belts of steady winds and calm. But this is still a highly idealized view of the actual motions of the air. In the vast ocean area this picture of steady winds blowing in a single direction for weeks on end is not far from the actual situation. But even over the oceans there are periodic major deviations from this pattern, and over the major land areas the pattern is decidedly changed. The primary causes of these deviations are the differences between ground and water in their heating effect on the air above. The continental regions, as pointed out earlier, are much more subject to seasonal temperature variations than the oceanic regions. The amount of energy passed to the air by the land areas therefore fluctuates much more than that passed by the oceanic areas. There is also great local variation in the amount. Some areas of land convey large amounts of energy to the air while others are quite ineffective. The result of all these causes is that the winds over the earth's surface, though in a general and approximate way approaching the pattern of Figure 15-13, are largely influenced by local conditions and vary widely from the pattern with geography and season. Finally, there are short-term local variations that are unexplainable in terms of a global analysis of wind patterns. Such variations are often predicted with much greater accuracy by an observant and experienced amateur than by the weather bureau.

## 15-28. Concept of Air Masses

This tendency for local conditions (on the scale of large continental or oceanic areas) to determine the "quality" of air has given rise to the modern theory of **air masses.** This theory, which is the major basis of long-range weather forecasting, is exceedingly complex in its details and quite beyond the elementary student in much of its application. But, again, like most of the great theories of physical science, the basic concept is quite simple, appearing to be almost trivial. The central idea of air-mass weather analysis is that the major climatic areas of the earth "condition" the air that is in contact with them, and that these masses of conditioned air then move to other areas of the earth and determine the weather in these new areas. The spectacular weather phenomena happen, then, when two different types of air mass encounter each other; the long-range, day-by-day weather is determined by the temperature and moisture of the particular air mass on the particular area. The weather of the United States is largely determined by air masses originating in six geographic areas that surround us, and the type of weather at a particular place and time is determined by the type of air mass that dominates and its reaction in the particular location.

## 15-29. Description of Air Masses

The six types of air mass that affect the United States are (1) polar continental, (2) tropical Atlantic, (3) polar Pacific, (4) polar Atlantic, (5) tropical Pacific, and (6) tropical continental. The first two of these are the most important, in both extent and intensity of their effect; polar Pacific air largely determines the weather of the northwestern United States; polar Atlantic occasionally streams down the eastern seaboard in a northeast storm; tropical Pacific is the major factor in the weather of California; and tropical continental sometimes determines the weather of the southwestern United States. Each of these types of air has a rather definite nature as to moisture content and temperature, determined by the conditions in which it was produced. Polar continental air originates by the pronounced cooling and drying effect of the large, ice-covered continental land mass near the North Pole. The cooling and drying effects decrease from the bottom toward the top of a mass of air. The structure of the air mass is quite stable because the density is greatest at the lowest altitudes. Since the air tends to remain stagnant and in contact with the natural refrigerator of the northern wastes for long times, it becomes quite uniformly cooled and dried. Its motion is generally southerly but is usually deflected to the east. Sometimes waves of polar air flow clear to Texas, Central America, or Florida, and the weather, obviously, becomes unseasonably cold and dry. The usual course of the fronts of polar air is a curving sweep down from the Hudson Bay area, through the northern Middle West, and eastward to the seaboard. Tropical Atlantic air originates in the Gulf of Mexico and the South Atlantic, moves northwestward, then veers eastward, and reaches the midwestern and eastern states as the typical summer southwest wind, which is hot and moisture-laden. Polar Pacific air is cooled and dried over the continent of northern Asia, but the lower layers are warmed considerably and pick up a good deal of moisture as it crosses the ocean to the northern Pacific seaboard of the United States, where it determines the climate.

The climate of southern California is made by the eastward sweep of warm moist tropical Pacific air. Tropical continental air originates in the arid regions of Mexico and the southwestern United States. Its effect on our weather pattern is not great, but on occasion it contributes to a midwestern drought.

## 15-30. *Reactions of Air Masses*

As these air masses move over the land and water, they react to the changing conditions, mostly temperature changes. As the tropical Atlantic air, which is warm and moist, moves northward over cooler parts of the ocean, the air itself is cooled, the solubility of water in the air decreases, and clouds of condensed water form. The same process happens over land during the winter, when the land is colder than the tropical air. As this process continues, the many moisture-laden clouds tend to drop their moisture as rain or snow in a gentle, continuing precipitation. As polar air moves southward over the warmer land or sea, the lower air, on being warmed, acquires an even lower relative humidity and also expands and rises. This causes dry, clear, and cold weather. An interesting sequence of events takes place as the polar Pacific air passes over the mountains of the northwestern United States. The lower layers of this air are relatively warm and moist. As they strike the coastal ranges of mountains, the air is forced upward several thousand feet and thereby undergoes a corresponding decrease of pressure. The first effect is to lower the temperature and thereby to decrease the solubility of the water vapor in the air. The water therefore precipitates in the very heavy rains of the coastal areas of Washington, Oregon, and northern California. When water vapor condenses, the heat of vaporization is made available to heat the air; so, as the air moves on over the mountains and down into the Columbia River basin, it is drier and very much warmer. The air moves on eastward until it is again forced upward, even higher, by the Rocky Mountains at the continental divide. Again the air is cooled, water vapor is precipitated as

rain, and the heat of vaporization reheats the air. The heavy rains of this area—eastern Washington and Oregon, northern Idaho, and western Montana—create its lush evergreen forests and supply the water of the Columbia River drainage area. As the air goes on eastward, it comes down the eastern slopes of the Rockies into Montana, Wyoming, and the Dakotas as a warm, dry, parching wind because it has twice been drained of its moisture and heated in the process. This process has taken place by the natural expansion and compression of passage over the two mountain ranges. The principle is identical to that of an air-conditioning machine, and its theoretical basis lies in the laws of solution behavior and the general gas law.

## 15-31. *Polar Front*

Striking changes in our weather take place when two types of air masses impinge on each other. The two types that are most important in the United States are the polar continental and the tropical Atlantic. The area in which these two come in contact is called the **polar front.** In the winter this area may reach well down into the central United States; in the summer it may be in southern or central Canada. But the polar front is not a line or even a closely limited area; it moves constantly southward and northward in a rhythmic cycle that gives rise to our cyclic weather pattern. The polar air is constantly tending to move to the southeastward while the tropical air is attempting to move to the northeastward. These tendencies, plus the wave pattern mentioned above, make the polar front a rough, broken line extending from the southwest to the northeast and along this line exist cold fronts and warm fronts, depending on which type of air is displacing the opposite type.

## 15-32. *Cold Front*

When a cold front dominates, the cold, dry (and therefore *dense*) air moves as a wedge below the warm air and pushes it up as well as

FIGURE **15-14** *Cold front: cold, dry air moving under warm, moist air.*

back. This effect is diagramed in Figure 15-14, which shows a cold front driving warm, moist air backward and upward. As the warm air is forced upward in this sudden way, big heavy clouds are formed, and, right at the front, a solid bank of black rain clouds is seen. As the cold front moves in from the northwest—and it moves so rapidly that the whole phenomenon may last less than an hour—the torrential rains of a cloudburst come down. Behind the rains come the gusty, violent northwest winds of the summer rain squall. After the squall the weather will be the cool, dry, clear weather, with north-

west winds, that is typical of polar continental air.

## 15-33. Warm Front

A warm front, though made of the same ingredients, is quite different in its behavior. Warm-front weather lasts for days and is much less spectacular. Figure 15-15 diagrams the way in which tropical air dominates polar air. The first difference is that the tropical air moves more slowly than the polar air, and the passage

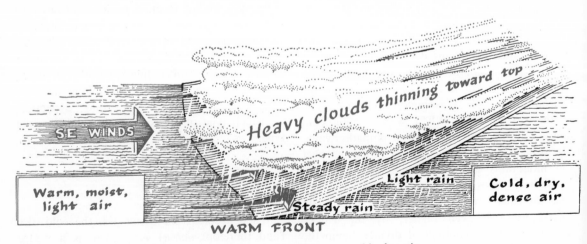

FIGURE **15-15** *Warm front: warm, moist air moving over cold, dry air.*

of a warm front therefore lasts for days. Since the polar air is denser than the warm, moist tropical air, the latter tends to override the polar air, which lies along the ground in a thin wedge. The motion of the tropical air is northeastward, and the warm front therefore moves partially along the line of the cold front as well as over it. As the warm air is pushed upward, it expands and cools in much the same way as the air that is pushed upward by the western mountains. The results are the formation of light, very high clouds at the forward edge of the warm front, and increasing cloudiness at lower and lower levels until, at the foot and some distance in front of the foot, low clouds drop a heavy, steady rain. Behind the front is typical tropical-air weather: warm and humid, with southwest winds. This front extends several hundred miles in each dimension, along the front as well as from the top to the foot, and the whole development takes several days at any particular point. After the tropical air has taken over an area, the weather there is characteristic of that air until another cold front advances into it, bringing its characteristic changes of weather.

Any significant control of or even influence on the vast and powerful effects we call weather is probably beyond the scope of human beings.

It has recently been suggested that atomic explosions have been responsible for abnormal weather patterns. The suggestion is remote from the possibilities. Probably the "abnormal" weather, if not wholly imaginary, is no more than a rather prolonged or extreme fluctuation in the weather pattern. But, whether the abnormalities are real or not, it is hardly possible that they could have been caused by such a puny thing as a nuclear-weapon explosion. Compared with the unbelievably tremendous energies of a hurricane, a tornado, or even a small-scale thunderstorm, these atomic or hydrogen bombs are tiny indeed. The possibility of their sensibly influencing the grand energy exchanges that make our weather is so remote as to be negligible.

Yet, even though we cannot influence the pattern of weather changes, it is of great importance and of social as well as economic value to be able to predict them. The modern science of meteorology, which is simply the application of the laws of physical science to the study of the atmosphere, makes such predictions possible. In spite of popular criticism, the modern weatherman is remarkably accurate and precise in his solution of this tremendously complex problem.

## Concepts and Terms

| | | | |
|---|---|---|---|
| Structure of the Earth | Equatorial Bulge | moisture | Air Masses |
| Methods of Measurement | Isostasy | Weather | Polar Front |
| curvature | The Atmosphere | Climate | Cold Front |
| density | composition | Heat Effects | Warm Front |
| gravity | density | Winds and Air Currents | |
| strength | pressure | three-cell cycle | |
| shock waves | temperature | deviations | |

## Problems

**15-1.** The notion that the earth is a solid sphere is by no means universally accepted even today. Several religious sects have quite different cosmological schemes from that advanced in this chapter and in Chapters 2 and 5. One of these, that the earth is flat and covered by a heavenly dome, was the official view of the government of South Africa in the 1890's. Considerable embarrassment resulted when Captain Joshua Slocum, during his single-handed voyage round the world, called on President Paul Kruger. The fact of Captain Slocum's voyage was rather easily explained as a trip round the *edge* of the world; the embarrassment resulted from his insisting that the voyage was round the *girth* of the world. Discuss, with the use of diagrams, the evidence of the earth's *curvature* as described in § 15-3, and show how this evidence would bear on the flat-earth theory. Consider the case of a sun (or a star) so far away that its rays are parallel at the earth's surface and the case of a sun (or a star) much nearer the earth.

**15-2.** Another view of the structure of the earth, now held by a small group in America, is that, though the earth is indeed spherical, the surface that we know and on which we live is the *inside* surface of the sphere, and the sun and other heavenly objects are near the center of this hollow sphere. Discuss, again with diagrams, the observation of curvature of the surface described in § 15-3, and show how it bears on the hollow-shell theory. Consider the two situations of a very distant sun and a fairly near sun.

**15-3.** In the measurement of the earth's curvature by Eratosthenes, described on page 228, what angle $\theta_1$ should he have observed if his distance along the surface between points 1 and 2 was 490 miles and if the circumference of the earth was 25,000 miles?

*Ans.* 7.05°

**15-4.** If the earth were a completely homogeneous sphere (that is, if the density were constant throughout its structure), would the period of rotation be greater or less than one day? Assume the angular momentum of rotation to be the same in this hypothetical situation as it actually is.

**15-5.** One theory has it that the moon was once a part of the earth. This theory holds that the great basin of the Pacific Ocean was once filled with solid rock; this huge mass of rock broke loose from the earth and flew off into space, where it assumed the spherical shape of the present moon. If this theory is correct, what must the average density of the moon be?

**15-6.** Calculate the pressure at the bottom of the Philippine Deep (6.5 miles or 10.5 kilometers below the surface). Assume for the sea water an average density throughout this depth of 1.2 grams/cm³. Express this pressure in absolute units and in atmospheres, and make an approximate conversion to pounds per square inch.

*Ans.* $1.24 \times 10^8$ newtons/m²; $1.23 \times 10^3$ atmospheres (about 18,000 pounds per square inch)

**15-7.** Describe in your own words the "roots of mountains" theory.

**15-8.** The barometer is the most used weather-predicting instrument. It is often said that the decrease in pressure indicated by a falling barometer causes stormy weather. This is a scientific fallacy. Explain.

**15-9.** Consult the daily weather maps published in the newspaper. Follow these maps and their changes for a week, and analyze the changes in terms of the concepts presented in this chapter.

## Suggested Readings

1. J. Gilluly, A. C. Waters, and A. O. Woodford, *Principles of Geology,* second edition (W. H. Freeman, 1959), Chaps. 10 and 19.
2. U. S. Department of Agriculture Yearbook, *Climate and Man* (1941). Part 4, particularly the section entitled "The Scientific Basis of Modern Meteorology" (pp. 599–655), is a detailed and complete treatment of the science of the atmosphere.
3. H. Shapley, Helen Wright, and S. Rapport, *Readings in Physical Sciences* (Appleton-Century-Crofts, 1948). Part Three includes several sections on various aspects of geology. Those most applicable to this chapter are "Weighing the Earth" (pp. 161–165), "X-Raying the Earth" (pp. 165–172), and "Earthquakes—What Are They?" (pp. 172–176). The last section of Part Three, "What Makes the Weather," is a brief and popularized treatment of air-mass analysis.
4. G. R. Stewart, *Storm* (Random House, 1941). A fictional but informative account of the interaction of air masses along a polar front.
5. L. E. Steiner and J. A. Campbell, *General Chemistry* (Macmillan, 1955). Chap. 6 contains details on the composition of the atmosphere.

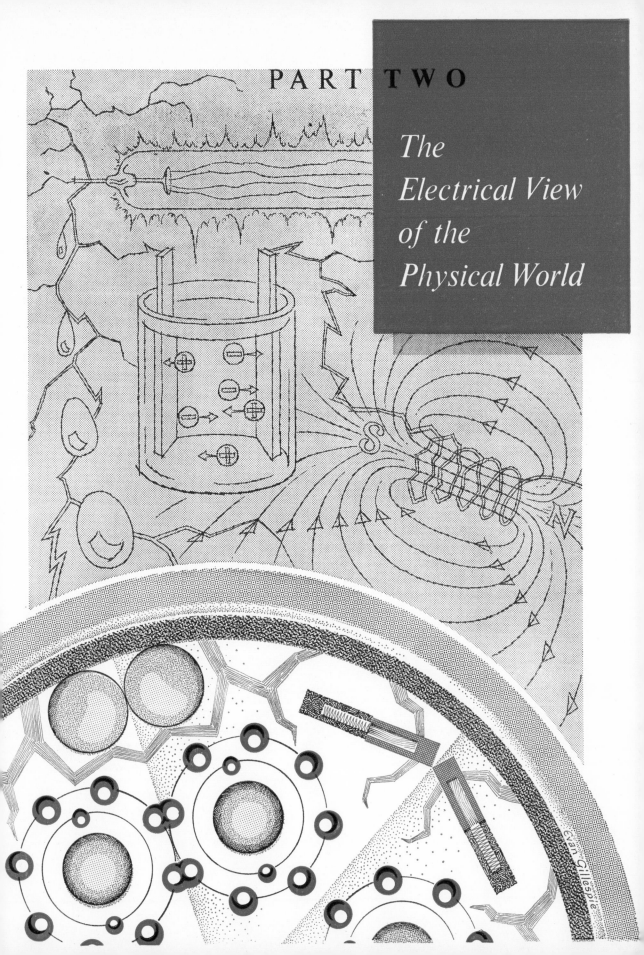

PART TWO

*The Electrical View of the Physical World*

Evan Gillespie

ONE OF the most important scientific achievements of the nineteenth century was the development of the laws of electricity. In line with the currently dominant mechanical view, electrical theory was first developed in terms of an imponderable fluid, which was assumed to be independent of, and apart from, the atoms of matter. In the latter part of the century, however, the facts of electrical conduction through solutions suggested that electricity is intimately associated with the atoms of matter. In the closing years of the century the electron, the minute unit of electricity, was discovered to be an integral part of all atoms. With this discovery the simple "billiard ball" mechanical model of atoms had to be modified to accommodate the electrons. The tendency to interpret all physical phenomena in purely mechanical terms was then forced to give way to interpretations based on electrical as well as mechanical concepts.

THE PHENOMENA of electricity and magnetism present new origins of force that depend upon a fundamental property of matter called *electric charge*. Like the concepts of mass, length, and time, the concept of electric charge is much too fundamental to be defined succinctly in terms of more elementary concepts. In other words, we cannot say what electric charge *is*. We can, however, measure electric charge, develop the fundamental laws that govern its effects, and arrive at an understanding of the concept in terms of the phenomena that it correlates. In this and succeeding chapters we shall consider some of the more important phenomena of electricity and magnetism. In so doing we shall develop a group of concepts and quantitative relations, which, with some necessary definitions, will give us additional and indispensable tools for continuing our study of the nature of the physical world.

## 16-1. Frictional Electricity

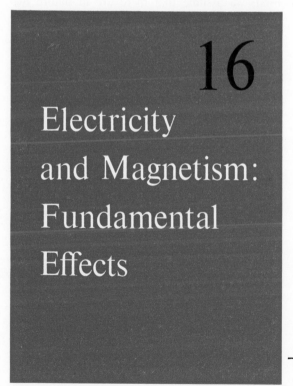

CHAPTER

16

Electricity
and Magnetism:
Fundamental
Effects

If a piece of amber is rubbed with fur, it acquires the property of attracting small light objects. This property was known and recorded by the ancient Greeks as early as 600 B.C. About A.D. 1600 Sir William Gilbert (court physician to Queen Elizabeth I) found that a large number of substances displayed the same property. It was not until the eighteenth century, however, that extensive and systematic studies of the property showed that under proper conditions all substances can be electrified† by friction. We say that such a rubbed substance has acquired an *electric charge,* and we conclude that the observed effect of force is due to this charge. This is a new kind of force. It is clearly not gravitational although it can be shown to act through space without an intervening medium. Gravitational forces between bodies are always present and are always forces of attraction. Electric forces, on the other hand, appear only after a body has been charged (either by friction or by other methods), and *both* attractions and repulsions are observed. And,

† The words *electricity, electrification,* etc. are derived from *elektron,* the Greek word for amber.

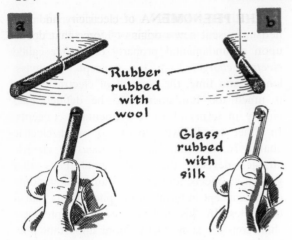

FIGURE **16-1** *Demonstration of* (a) *the repulsion of like charges and* (b) *the attraction of unlike charges.*

finally, the electric forces are much too large to be accounted for by gravitation. Some remarkably simple experiments, which we shall now consider, will lead to some understanding of the nature of these electric forces and of the charges that produce them.

A hard-rubber rod that has been rubbed with wool is suspended by a fine cord so that it is free to rotate in a horizontal plane. If a second rubber rod that has also been rubbed with wool is held near the suspended one, the suspended rod rotates away from the held one; that is, a force of *repulsion* is observed. (See Fig. 16-1a, but ignore the minus and plus signs for the moment.) If now a glass rod that has been rubbed with silk is held near the suspended rod (Fig. 16-1b), a force of *attraction* is observed. The experiment is now repeated with a suspended silk-rubbed glass rod. When another silk-rubbed glass rod is held near the suspended one, a force of repulsion is observed; and, as might be expected, the suspended glass rod is attracted by a wool-rubbed hard-rubber rod. If these experiments are repeated with all the available materials, it is found that the charged materials either repel or attract a wool-rubbed rubber rod. Furthermore, materials that repel the rubber rod also repel each other, and materials that attract the rubber rod also repel each other. Thus all electrified objects are seen to act in the same way as a wool-rubbed piece of hard rubber *or*

as a silk-rubbed piece of glass. And no other effect is ever observed; no material, for instance, ever repels *both* the rubber and the glass.

From these experiments we may draw some conclusions about the nature of electric charge. First, since only two effects are observed, we conclude that there are *two* kinds of electric charge. Quite arbitrarily we call the kind that appears on the wool-rubbed hard rubber a **negative charge** ( − ) and the kind that appears on the silk-rubbed glass a **positive charge** ( + ). (See Fig. 16-1.) The experiments show that positive charge repels positive charge, negative charge repels negative charge, and positive charge attracts negative charge. More succinctly this experimental law states that *like charges repel and unlike charges attract.*

## 16-2. Simple Theory of Electrification

In the light of these experiments it is possible to make some plausible *assumptions* upon which we may build a simple theory of electrification. First, we assume that there are in nature *two different* electric substances, which we arbitrarily name negative electricity and positive electricity. Second, we assume that any electrically neutral (that is, uncharged) body contains *equal* amounts of the two kinds of electricity uniformly distributed throughout the body. Third, we assume that, if during some process a body acquires an *excess* of one kind of electricity, it then acquires the property of electric charge.

The reader will recognize that these assumptions postulate a "fluid" theory of electricity not unlike the caloric theory of heat.† Much of our study will be directed toward determining

---

† We have *postulated* a *two-fluid* theory. In the eighteenth century, however, Benjamin Franklin advocated a *one-fluid* theory, using the plus sign to represent bodies that had more than a "normal" amount of the electric fluid and the minus sign for bodies that had lost some of their normal amount. He had no way of determining experimentally which way the fluid moved, and he assumed that charged bodies that acted the same as silk-rubbed glass had acquired an *excess* of the fluid. We still use Franklin's terminology but shall find that the electricity moves in the opposite direction.

whether electric fluids really exist or whether, as in the case of caloric, the phenomena can be explained in terms of other concepts. In general, both kinds of electricity may move during an electrical process; and we shall see that in gases and liquids both do. Observe, however, that in accordance with our assumptions a body may acquire a certain electric charge either by *adding* some of one kind of electricity or by *losing* some of the other kind. It may be, for instance, that we give a neutral glass rod an excess of positive electricity (and thus charge it positively) by rubbing some positive electricity onto the glass from the silk *or* by rubbing some negative electricity onto the silk from the glass. As yet we have absolutely no criteria for determining which takes place. For reasons that will appear in later chapters, we shall assume that *only negative electricity moves* in solid substances. Let us now consider some further experiments and interpret them in the light of this theory.

## 16-3. *Conductors and Insulators*

We could continue our investigations of electric charge by observing the forces exerted on a suspended charged rod, such as that shown in Figure 16-1. That device, however, is not only awkward but also somewhat insensitive because

of the relatively great inertia of the rod. A much more sensitive instrument is the **electroscope,** illustrated in Figure 16-2a. A vertical, rigid strip of metal is attached to a horizontal metal disc with rounded edges. A very thin, light strip of metal (such as gold foil or aluminum foil), usually called a **leaf,** is suspended from the rigid strip in such a way that it is free to swing away from the strip. If a negative electric charge is brought near the disc (Fig. 16-2c), the leaf is observed to swing out (diverge) by an amount depending on the strength and nearness of the charge. If the charge is removed, the leaf falls back to its original vertical position. The same effect is observed if a positive charge is brought near. Electroscopes can be made extremely sensitive, but even a somewhat crude one is a much more sensitive detector of electric charge than the suspended rod of Figure 16-1.

Now consider the situation shown in Figure 16-3a. A plastic or hard-rubber support, $S$, is placed about one foot from an electroscope, $E$. A negative electric charge, $C$, held in the vicinity of $S$, produces no observable effect on $E$. A glass rod is now supported between $S$ and $E$ (Fig. 16-3b), and again $C$ produces no effect on $E$. If a copper rod is supported between $S$ and $E$ and the charge $C$ is brought near the end on $S$, the leaf of $E$ diverges, indicating the presence of a charge on the end of the rod near $E$ (Fig.

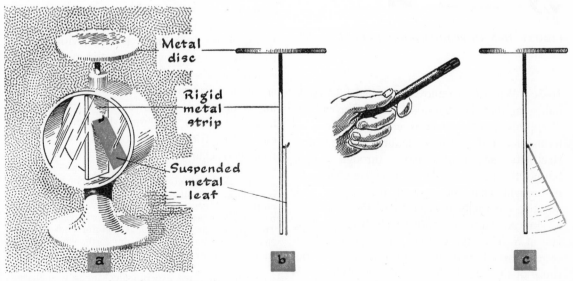

FIGURE **16-2** *A leaf electroscope.*

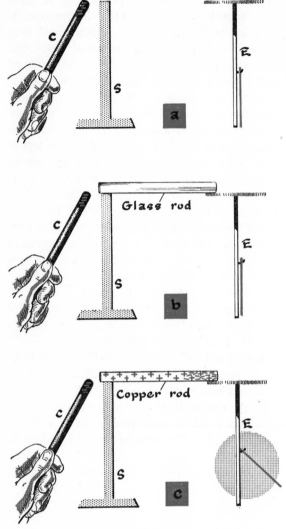

FIGURE **16-3** *Demonstration of electrical conduction.*

16-3c). When C is removed, the leaf falls back, indicating that the charge on the copper rod has disappeared. This effect is easily explained in terms of our theory *if* we assume that negative electricity may readily move through copper but not through glass. As the negative charge, C, is brought near the end of the copper rod, negative electricity is repelled to the end at E, leaving an excess of positive electricity on the end at S. Thus the ends of the copper rod become charged, and the leaf of E diverges because of the negative charge near it. When C is removed, the negative electricity is attracted

toward the positive and flows away from E until there is again a uniform distribution of both positive and negative electricity throughout the copper rod. Thus the copper becomes neutral, and the leaf falls. If the charge C is positive, a similar effect is observed. In the case of the glass rod, however, the electricity must be considered strongly bound (presumably to the molecules) and is not free to move as it is in copper.

Many (in principle, all) substances may be tested in the manner described in the last paragraph. When this is done, it is found that a large group of substances act in the same way as the copper rod; that is, they permit electricity to flow through them. These substances are called **conductors** of electricity. The metallic elements, carbon, the human body, metallic alloys, the ground, and molten salts are conductors. Pure water is not a conductor, but, as we have seen, a water solution of certain solutes is a very good conductor. On the other hand, many substances, such as glass, do not permit the passage of electricity. These are called non-conductors of electricity, or **insulators.** Amber, rubber, sulfur, most plastics, oil, fur, dry wood, textiles, and gases under normal conditions are insulators.

It is now clear why only insulators were used in the experiments on charging by friction. A sufficiently vigorous rubbing of the end of a hard-rubber rod with fur transferred some negative electricity to the rubber rod. Since rubber is a good insulator, the charge remained on the end of the rod long enough for the experiment. If the same experiment is tried with a metal rod, the charges flow through the metal and the experimenter's hand to his body, which serves as an electrical ground,† and no effect of charging is observed. If, however, the metal rod is mounted in an insulating handle, it can be charged by friction just as the rubber and glass rods were charged.

---

† An electrical ground is a conducting body that is so large (and therefore contains so much of both positive and negative electricity) that electricity may be added to it without producing an appreciable excess. The symbol for the ground is therefore not shown as charged. The best ground is the earth, which contains enormous amounts of electricity. For the small amounts of electricity involved in charging an electroscope, however, the experimenter's body is sufficiently large to serve as a ground.

## 16-4. Charging by Induction

Convincing evidence of the correctness of the explanations presented in the preceding section is obtained from the following experiment: In the situation shown in Figure 16-3c, we cut the copper rod in two at the middle while the charge, *C*, is in the position shown. Then, when *C* is removed, the negative electricity cannot flow back to neutralize the positive electricity, and the two halves of the rod should be charged with opposite kinds. To perform this experiment, we need an instrument that would not only detect the presence of a charge but also indicate the *kind* of charge. Such an instrument is a *charged* electroscope.

Consider the sequence of events shown in Figure 16-4. The disc of an electroscope is connected to an electrical ground by a conductor. (This could be a metal wire connected to the earth, or the experimenter could touch the disc with his finger.) As a negative charge is brought near the disc, some negative electricity is repelled along the conductor to the ground. This leaves the disc with an excess of positive electricity—that is, charged positively (a). The conductor to the ground is removed, and a positive charge is trapped on the disc (b). When the negative charge is removed, some negative electricity is attracted to the disc from the leaf and the rigid strip, and equilibrium is quickly established. Since the leaf and the strip are now both positive, the force of repulsion between these charges pushes the leaf away (c). The electroscope is now charged positively. If a positive charge is now brought near the disc, more negative electricity is attracted to the disc, and the leaf, being left more positive, diverges still more. On the other hand, if a negative charge is brought near the disc, some negative electricity is repelled down to the leaf. This neutralizes the leaf, which therefore falls toward the vertical position. If, on the other hand, we begin the experiment by bringing a positive charge near, the electroscope will be charged negatively. In this case a negative charge brought near the electroscope will cause the leaf to diverge farther, and a positive charge will cause the leaf to fall.

An attentive reader will have noticed that in this argument we have *used* the effect that we set out to prove. Nevertheless, whether the explanation is correct or not, a charged electroscope is observed *to act in the way described,* and it thereby furnishes an empirical and definitive method for the identification of electric charge. To summarize: the leaf of a charged electroscope will diverge if a charge of the same kind is brought near it and will fall if an unlike charge is brought near it.

Performing the experiment outlined in the first paragraph of this section (cutting the copper rod in two) would be very awkward. The same result may be obtained more simply in the following manner. Two metallic spheres, *A* and *B*, are mounted on insulating rods and placed in contact with each other. In this position the two spheres form a single conducting body. A negative charge, *C*, is brought near *A*, and ac-

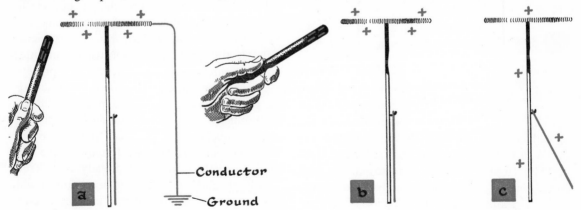

+ + +
+ +

+ + +
+ +

+ + +

+

—Conductor

+

+

a

—Ground

b

c

FIGURE **16-4** *Method of charging an electroscope.*

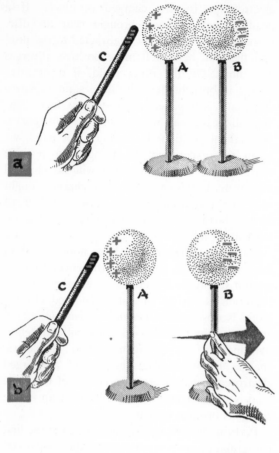

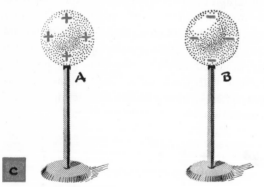

FIGURE **16-5** *Charging two insulated spherical conductors by induction.*

*positively* charged electroscope, the leaf diverges; when *B* is brought near it, the leaf falls; this shows that *A* and *B* are, in fact, charged as shown. When the experiment is repeated with a positive charge on *C*, *A* is observed to have acquired a negative charge and *B* a positive charge. These results are in complete agreement with our theory and strengthen our confidence in the assumptions on which the theory is based.

We have in these experiments an example of a *second* method of producing electric charge. Neither of the spheres was rubbed with some other substance; but, by the repulsion or attraction of a near-by charge, some negative electricity was made to move. This left one part of the conducting medium with an excess of positive electricity and another part with an excess of negative electricity; that is, positive and negative charges were produced. Charges produced in this manner are called **induced charges,** and the method is called *charging by induction.* Clearly, the electroscope in Figure 16-4 was charged by induction.

## 16-5. Conservation of Electric Charge

In all of the discussion so far there has been the idea that, when electric charges are produced, two different electric fluids, which are normally contained in equal amounts in all substances, are partially separated as the result of some process. This expresses the principle of the *conservation* of electric charge, one of the fundamental postulates of electric theory and one that is amply verified by all experience with electric phenomena. Electricity, in other words, is *not created* during a charging process; it is merely separated. If so, then in any charging process *both* positive and negative charges are produced, and the *amounts* of the positive and negative charges produced must be *equal.* These conclusions may be tested for the two charging methods we have already considered.

A hard-rubber rod that has been rubbed with a piece of wool is tested with a charged electroscope and is found to have a negative charge.

cording to the arguments outlined above we should have the situation shown in Figure 16-5a. With *C* still in position, *B* is separated from *A* (Fig. 16-5b). When *C* is removed, the captured charges distribute themselves uniformly, and we should have the situation shown in Figure 16-5c. When *A* is now brought near a

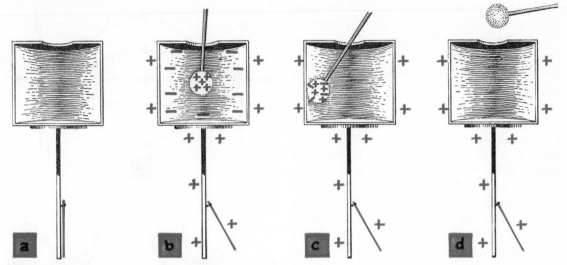

FIGURE **16-6** *The "ice pail" experiment.*

The wool is tested and is found to have a positive charge. When the wool is now wrapped round the end of the rubbed rod, the combination produces *no effect* on the electroscope; that is, the combination displays the property of electrical neutrality. When, however, *without further rubbing,* the wool is now unwrapped from the rod, the electroscope shows that the rod still has its negative charge and the wool its positive charge. Similar results are found when charges are produced by friction between any two substances. Thus we find that charging by friction always produces opposite charges and that the *amounts* of the two charges are equal.

Charging by induction may also be shown to produce equal and opposite charges by the experiment diagramed in Figure 16-6. A metal can† is placed on the disc of an electroscope and thus becomes, electrically, a part of the electroscope system. The system is grounded temporarily and therefore is neutral, and the leaf hangs vertically (a). A positively charged metal sphere on an insulating support is lowered into the can without touching it. The leaf is observed to diverge. This is due to the fact that the positive sphere induces a negative charge

on the inside of the can, which leaves the outside of the can and the electroscope with a positive charge (b). When the sphere is now brought into contact with the inside of the can, *no change* in the divergence of the leaf is observed (c). The sphere is now removed (d) and *by test* is found to be uncharged; and *by test* the electroscope is found to have a positive charge. The induced negative charge and the positive charge on the sphere must have been exactly equal, for they neutralized each other and left the sphere uncharged. Furthermore, the induced positive charge was exactly equal to the induced negative charge since no change in the divergence of the leaf was observed in situations "b" and "c." If the experiment is repeated with a negative charge on the sphere initially, the results are the same except that the electroscope is found to have acquired a negative charge. Hence, in charging by induction, equal charges of opposite sign are produced.

## 16-6. *Field Concept*

The fundamental phenomenon of electric charge is the force of interaction between charges. For these forces to act, however, the charged bodies do not need to be in contact; like the gravitational force, the electric forces act through space without any material con-

---

† This experiment was first performed by Michael Faraday (1791–1867). Instead of a metal can he used an ice pail that happened to be in the laboratory, and the experiment is therefore called the "ice-pail experiment."

nection between the charges. Even if the space is highly evacuated, the forces are still observed. No one knows *why* this happens. It is an experimental fact that charged objects exert on each other forces that do not appear if the objects are uncharged.

It is useful to think of an electric charge as altering the space around it in such a way that forces are exerted on other charges in this space. Such a region of altered space is called an **electric field.** When a charge is placed at any point in an electric field, one considers that a force is exerted on the charge *by the field*. In Figure 16-1b, for instance, the positive charge produces, or sets up, an electric field in the region surrounding it. When the negative charge is placed as shown, the field exerts a force on it, and the rod is observed to move. On the other hand, one could equally well consider the negative charge as setting up a field that exerts a force on the positive charge.

One may think at first that we gain little by introducing the concept of a field. In the experiments we have considered so far, the charges setting up the fields are known. Such charges, however, are not always known. Any electric field, to be sure, is due to a charge or distribution of charges, but we do not need to know this distribution in order to detect and investigate the field. To determine whether or not an electric field exists at any point, one simply places a small charged body, which is called a **test charge,** at the point and observes whether or not an electrical force is exerted on it. By repeating this experiment at various points, we may explore and specify the field without specific knowledge of the charges setting up the field. There are many situations where this has distinct advantages.

The field concept is very general and is applicable to other than electrical phenomena, such as gravitational fields and magnetic fields. An aid in visualizing any field is the concept of a **line of force.** *A line of force is an imaginary line drawn in such a way that at any point the direction of the line* (that is, the direction of the tangent) *points in the direction of the force exerted by the field at that point.* For a gravitational field only one direction is possible since

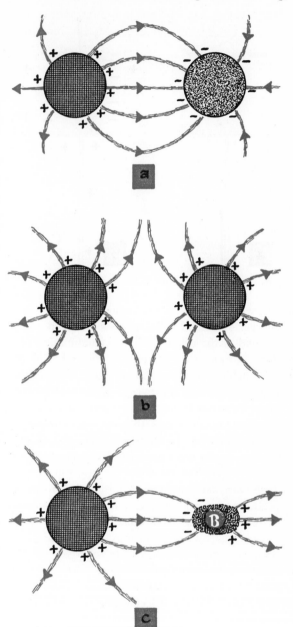

FIGURE **16-7** *Electric lines of force near* (a) *two equally and oppositely charged spheres,* (b) *two equally and positively charged spheres, and* (c) *a positively charged sphere and an initially uncharged conductor.*

gravitational forces are always forces of attraction toward the mass setting up the field. For electric fields, however, there are two possibilities, depending on whether the test charge is positive or negative. The *direction* of an electric field is defined as the direction of the *force on a positive test charge.* By observing the forces on a positive test charge, then, we may map the lines of force in an electric field.

Figure 16-7a shows some lines of force associated with two equally but oppositely charged conducting spheres. If the spheres are both charged positively, the map of the field is like Figure 16-7b. From an isolated positively charged sphere the lines would diverge radially. (See Fig. 17-2.) If, however, an initially uncharged conductor, *B*, is placed near the charged sphere, charges are induced on it, and the field becomes as shown in Figure 16-7c.

In mapping fields we may draw as many lines of force as we wish. To be complete, in fact, a map should have an infinite number of lines since the field exerts a force on a test charge at every point. It is impractical, of course, to fill the entire surface of the diagram with lines, for then no line would be distinguishable. A moderate number of lines is sufficient to indicate the direction of the field at all points.

The lines of force specify the direction of the force on a test charge but do not specify the magnitude of the force. A qualitative estimate of the magnitude of the force is indicated by the spacing, or "density," of the lines. The force on a certain positive test charge is greater in the space between the oppositely charged spheres of Figure 16-7a than in the space between the two similarly charged spheres of 16-7b, and in the former diagram the lines are more closely spaced than in the latter.

Electric lines of force originate on positive charges and terminate on negative charges. In Figure 16-7 the unterminated lines continue to negative charges induced on the walls of the laboratory or on adjacent objects. And, finally, lines of force never intersect. This would mean two different forces exerted by the field on the test charge at the point of intersection. In exploring electric fields, however, we observe only one force acting on the test charge at any point.

It should be emphasized that *line of force* is a purely imaginary concept. Lines of force are of great use in the representation and analysis of electric and magnetic fields, but they have no physical reality.

## 16-7. Field Inside a Charged Conductor

In the diagrams of Figure 16-7 the plus and minus signs are placed on the surface of the conductors, and no lines of force are shown inside the conductors. This implies that the charge of a charged conductor resides on the surface and that there is no electric field *inside* a charged conductor. These two statements, which can be

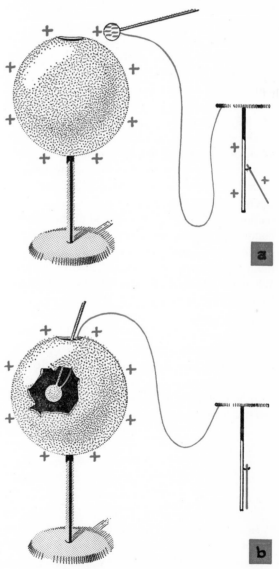

FIGURE **16-8** *Demonstration that there is no electric field inside a charged conductor.*

deduced theoretically, may be verified by two simple experiments.

A hollow conductor such as the "ice pail" of Figure 16-6 is mounted on an insulated stand and given a charge. A **test plane** is prepared by attaching a small metal disc to the end of an insulating rod. The test plane, originally neutral, is placed in contact with the outside surface of the conductor and then placed in contact with the disc of an electroscope. The leaf of the electroscope is observed to diverge, showing that it has acquired a charge, and by test the charge is found to be of the same sign as that on the conductor. In other words, the test plane transferred some charge from the *outside* surface of the conductor to the electroscope. If now the neutral test plane is inserted into the conductor and brought in contact with the *inside* surface, the electroscope does not respond when touched by the test plane.

The second experiment is illustrated in Figure 16-8. An insulated hollow conductor is given a charge. The test plane is connected to the disc of an electroscope by a long thin wire. The electroscope is placed far enough away to be inappreciably affected by the field of the charged conductor. As the test plane is carried near the conductor and thus enters the field, charges are induced, and the electroscope leaf diverges (a). When the plane is inserted into the conductor, however, the leaf falls (b). There is, we conclude, *no field inside* the charged conductor. This fact makes it possible to shield sensitive electrical devices (such as electroscopes and certain parts of radio circuits) from the effects of neighboring charges by merely surrounding them with a hollow conductor. This absence of an electric field inside a conductor is also very useful in the design of particle accelerators and other apparatus of atomic research.

## 16-8. Electric Current

In all the phenomena we have considered so far in this chapter, the observed effects of force have been between stationary charges. These effects and others, along with their quantitative developments, comprise the subject of electro-

statics. Another set of effects is exhibited, however, whenever electricity is moving. Moving charges suggest the idea of an electric current, similar to a current of water through a pipe or along a stream. Momentary currents exist, of course, during the charging or discharging processes we have considered. But these are temporary, erratic, and not easily controlled and therefore do not lend themselves readily to an investigation of the properties of moving electricity. What is needed is some method of producing charges that will supply them just as rapidly as they move away along a conducting path and will thus maintain a *steady* current. Such a method was discovered by Alessandro Volta in 1800. He found that, if a strip of zinc and a strip of copper were placed in a cup of brine, the zinc acquired a negative charge and the copper a positive charge. Experiments since that time have shown a similar result from any two metals placed in any of a wide variety of solutions. In this case the energy required to separate the charges is supplied by a chemical reaction between the substances in the cup. A study of these reactions is very informative and will be considered in some detail in a later chapter. We are interested now in Volta's device (called a voltaic cell) because it is a third and very convenient way of producing electric charge. Several voltaic cells connected together (in order to enhance the effect) comprise an electric battery, such as those used in flashlights, portable radios, automobiles, etc.

If one terminal of a battery is connected momentarily to the disc of an uncharged electroscope, the leaf diverges and remains so, showing that charge has flowed onto the electroscope. The electroscope is tested with a charged rod and is found to have a positive charge. The electroscope is discharged and then connected momentarily with the other terminal of the battery. The leaf again diverges, but this time the electroscope is found to have acquired a negative charge. The leaf diverges, moreover, by the same amount in both instances, showing that the two terminals of the battery are charged equally. Two metal wires from the two terminals of the battery are now connected with an electric lamp. These connections furnish a conducting path be-

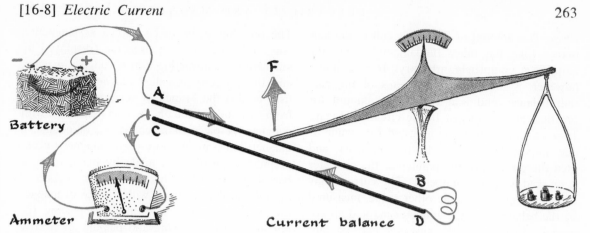

FIGURE **16-9** *Demonstration of the current balance and calibration of an ammeter.*

tween the terminals of the battery. The negative charge flows from the negative terminal through the lamp to the positive terminal, and the lamp glows. The uniform and steady intensity with which it glows indicates a constant and uniform flow of electricity through it. What is happening, obviously, is that, just as rapidly as negative charge flows, *outside* the battery, from the negative to the positive terminal, the chemical reaction goes forward and supplies the energy to transfer negative charge from the positive to the negative terminal *inside* the battery and thus maintains a continuous flow of electricity. In effect, the energy released by the chemical reaction is transferred by the moving charge to the lamp, where it appears as heat and light.

Soon after this source of steady current became available, the properties of moving electricity were discovered and subjected to quantitative investigation. One of these discoveries is represented schematically in Figure 16-9. A stiff wire, *AB*, is mounted on the end of the beam of an equal-arm balance, and the system is brought into equilibrium by adding known weights to the pan. A second stiff wire, *CD*, is mounted rigidly below and parallel to *AB*. A battery, an ammeter, and the two stiff wires are connected by conducting wires as shown. When this conducting path is completed, negative charge flows round the circuit as indicated by the arrows. Two things are observed to happen. First, the pointer on the ammeter moves to a certain position. (The details of the ammeter mechanism need not concern us now. It is sufficient to know that its

deflection is directly related to the amount of current passing through it.) Second, and more important, the wire *AB* is moved upward by a force of repulsion between *AB* and *CD*.† We can measure this force directly by observing how much the weight on the pan must be reduced to restore the equilibrium of the balance. If more cells are added to the battery, the current increases, and so does the force. The force also increases if *AB* and *CD* are made longer, but it decreases if the distance between the wires is increased. The results of such quantitative observations are summarized by the empirical relation

$$F = K \frac{I^2 L}{s} \tag{16-1}$$

in which *I* is the amount of current, *L* is the length of *AB*, *s* is the distance between the wires, and *K* is a proportionality constant. This relation is used to define a unit of current. Units for *F*, *s*, and *L* have already been defined; that leaves either *K* or *I* to be assigned an arbitrary value. Both for historical reasons and for convenience the constant *K* is arbitrarily assigned the numerical value $2 \times 10^{-7}$. Thus we get the definition that *one unit of electric current is the constant current that, as it flows through two parallel wires one meter long and one meter apart, gives rise to a force of $2 \times 10^{-7}$ newton between the*

† If the circuit is connected from *B* to *C* and from *D* to the ammeter, so that the current in *AB* and that in *CD* are in the same direction, the force is one of attraction. Balance is restored by adding weights to the pan.

*wires.* This amount of current is called one **ampere.**† Like the other fundamental units, the ampere is completely arbitrary. It is definite, however, is measurable by means of the current balance, and is a convenient amount for practical measurements. In the circuit of Figure 16-9 the current may be adjusted to a value of one ampere (determined by the balance), and then the position of the pointer of the ammeter is marked with the number 1. The current may then be changed to some other value, measured by the balance, and the ammeter marked appropriately. In this way the ammeter may be calibrated to indicate the number of amperes passing through it. Such a calibrated ammeter is a much more convenient instrument than the current balance and is the one generally used in laboratory investigations of currents.

From the ampere we derive a unit for the measurement of the *quantity* of electric charge. Just as a constant stream of water will carry a definite amount of water past any point in the stream every second, so will a current of one ampere transport a definite amount of electric charge every second. This amount of electric charge is called one **coulomb.**‡ The coulomb is a derived unit in terms of amperes and seconds. If $Q$ represents the quantity of electricity carried past any point in the circuit by a current of $I$ amperes in $t$ seconds, then, by definition,

$$Q = It$$
$$\text{coulombs} = \text{amperes} \times \text{seconds} \qquad (16\text{-}2)$$

Amperes, clearly, may be expressed as coulombs per second.

## 16-9. Magnetism

A certain iron ore ($Fe_3O_4$) has been known since ancient times to have the property of attracting small pieces of iron. This ore, which was well known to the ancient Greeks, was plentiful in the district of Magnesia near the Aegean coast.

The ore thus came to be known as magnetite. Any body that has the property (displayed by magnetite) of attracting iron is called a *magnet,* and the property is called *magnetism.* Magnetism is also the branch of science that evolved from the study of the phenomena associated with magnets. A piece of magnetite is, of course, a magnet, but a much more useful magnet for experimental purposes is made by magnetizing a bar of iron or steel. This may be done by stroking the bar several times with a piece of magnetite or, much more efficiently, by placing the bar inside a coil of wire and passing an electric current through the wire.

One of the first facts to be noticed in experimenting with a bar magnet is that the property of attracting iron is not uniformly distributed along the bar. The attracting force appears to be greatest at two regions, usually situated near the ends of the bar. If the magnet is dipped into a pile of iron filings, for instance, the filings cluster around the ends of the bar, and very few, if any, adhere to the center. These regions of maximum attraction are called *magnetic poles.* Every magnet has at least two (and most magnets have only two) poles. The line joining the two poles is called the *magnetic axis* of the magnet.

If a bar magnet whose magnetic axis coincides with its geometrical axis is suspended or pivoted at its mid-point so as to be free to rotate in a horizontal plane, it will rotate into such a position that its axis points approximately north and south. If disturbed from this position, it will swing back and come to rest with the same pole always pointing north.† This pole is called the north-seeking pole or, more briefly, the N pole, and the other is called the south-seeking, or S, pole. Once the magnet comes to rest, there is no tendency for it to move along the north-south line in either direction. This indicates that the forces on the two poles are equal and opposite and thus that the poles are of equal strength.

A simple experiment, very similar to the one illustrated in Figure 16-1, will yield the qualita-

---

† The unit of current is named in honor of A. M. Ampère (1775–1836), who made important contributions to the formulation of the laws of interactions between electric currents.

‡ Named in honor of C. A. de Coulomb, who, late in the eighteenth century, formulated the quantitative law for forces between static point charges.

---

† This, of course, is the principle of the magnetic compass. It seems to have been known to the Chinese as early as 100 B.C., and among Europeans it was in common use as an aid to navigation as early as the twelfth century. Magnetic compasses are still widely used to determine directions both on land and at sea.

tive law for forces between magnetic poles. Instead of charged rods, bar magnets are used. A bar magnet is suspended from its mid-point and allowed to come to rest with its axis in a north-south direction, and the N and S poles are marked. The procedure is repeated for a second bar magnet. When the N pole of one magnet is held near the N pole of a suspended magnet, the latter is observed to rotate away from the former. A similar force of repulsion is observed between the two S poles. An N pole and an S pole, however, are always observed to attract each other. Thus we discover that *like poles repel and unlike poles attract*. And, like electrostatic forces, magnetic forces become greater as the poles approach each other.

Not all substances can be magnetized. In fact, only three elementary substances (iron, cobalt, and nickel)† and a few alloys display the property of magnetism. This is very different from electrostatic properties, for, as we have seen, *all* substances can be charged. Another difference is observed when an attempt is made to isolate one kind of magnetic pole. This is illustrated in Figure 16-10. A bar magnet (a) is broken at its mid-point. Instead of getting an N pole only on one piece and an S pole on the other, we get *two new* poles at the broken faces (b); that is, two complete magnets are produced. If each piece is broken, new poles again appear, and we have four complete magnets (c). The poles of each new magnet, furthermore, are again observed to be of equal strength. This process may be repeated to microscopic subdivision, and always a magnetic dipole is produced. This result,

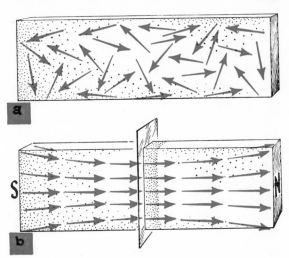

FIGURE **16-11** *Arrangement of elementary dipoles in* (a) *an unmagnetized bar and* (b) *a magnetized bar.*

along with some others,‡ suggests a model upon which to base a simple theory of magnetization.

We *assume* that any sensible sample of magnetic material consists of a very large number of small, elementary magnetic dipoles. If the sample is unmagnetized, the elementary magnets lie with their axes in all directions in a random distribution. This is represented in Figure 16-11a, where a small arrow represents the elementary dipole, the head of the arrow being the N pole. In such a random arrangement the effect of any one dipole is always counterbalanced by the effect of some oppositely oriented one, and the bar as a whole shows no magnetization. Under the action of a magnetic field,§ the elementary

† Note that these are three successive elements in the periodic table.

‡ For instance, a bar of iron shows slight changes in length and volume upon being magnetized, but no change in mass.

§ The reader may inquire about the source of such a magnetizing field. The earth is one source. The action of a compass needle shows that the earth has magnetic poles near the geographic poles, with (by definition) an S magnetic pole in the north. It must *not* be assumed, however, that the earth contains a huge bar magnet. The source of the earth's magnetic field is not yet completely understood. The earth's magnetic field accounts for the magnetization of the naturally occurring magnetite, which may be used to magnetize pieces of iron. In the next section we shall see that the magnetic effect of electric current gives rise to a much more powerful and convenient magnetizing field.

FIGURE **16-10** *Demonstration that a magnetic pole cannot be isolated. Whenever a magnet is broken, two new poles appear.*

magnets are forced to wheel round and align themselves in the direction of the field, somewhat as shown in Figure 16-11b. In this situation equal numbers of N and S poles lie close together throughout most of the bar and therefore produce no net effect. At one end of the bar, however, an "excess" of N poles appears, and their cumulative effect produces the observed macroscopic N pole of the magnet. The other end similarly becomes an S pole. By their mutual repulsion the elementary poles turn somewhat toward the sides of the bar so that the macroscopic poles do not appear only at the end surfaces but are distributed over regions near the ends. This is in agreement with observation (see p. 264). If the magnetized bar is broken (as along the plane drawn in Fig. 16-11b), new regions of excess elementary poles are exposed, and the two pieces become complete magnets, each with an N and an S pole, the effect illustrated in Figure 16-10.†

Because the process of magnetizing a piece of iron appears very similar to the process of charging by induction, it is called *magnetic induction;* but careful consideration of the two inductions reveals important differences. First, in the electrostatic case the induced charges always disappear when the inducing field is removed; in magnetic induction this is only partially so. If pure "soft" iron is used, the induced magnetism also disappears quickly after removal of the magnetizing field; but, if the iron (or, better, steel) is very hard, the induced magnetism remains for a long time, and we have a permanent magnet. Once the elementary magnets are aligned, some combination of internal forces presumably hold them in position even though the action of the magnet's poles tends to destroy the alignment. Second, during electric induction electricity flows and charges are separated, as we can show by separating the conductor while it is under induction and thus capturing the induced charges (Fig. 16-5); as we have seen, this never happens with a magnetized rod, but dipoles are always produced if the rod is separated. Finally, *all* conductors can be charged by induction, but only iron, cobalt, and nickel can be magnetized.

A magnet may be demagnetized by destroying the alignment of the elementary dipoles. Repeated, random jarring will knock the dipoles out of alignment and destroy the magnetism of a magnet. Thermal agitation also will dealign the dipoles. The thermal agitation of ordinary temperatures is sufficient to destroy the magnetization of soft iron almost immediately after the magnetizing field is removed. A hard steel magnet at ordinary temperatures will show very little loss of magnetization even after several years, although in time it too will become demagnetized; but, if it is heated to a high temperature, it quickly loses its magnetization as a result of the increased kinetic energy of the thermal agitations.

All the effects we have been discussing are completely consistent with our *postulation* of elementary permanent dipoles. Such consistency gives confidence in the usefulness and validity of the model. Yet none of these effects reveals the *nature* of the elementary dipoles or tells us why they exist at all. Before we can answer questions of this kind, we must acquire a deeper understanding of the nature of magnetism and of the structure of matter.

## 16-10. *Field Round a Bar Magnet*

A magnetic field may be mapped in a manner very similar to that used in mapping electric fields. The field is considered to exert a force on a small test magnetic pole, and the direction of that force at any point specifies the direction of the magnetic field. Two possibilities exist, depending on the kind of test pole used. By definition *the direction of a magnetic field at any point is the direction of the force on a small N pole.* As we have seen, it is not possible to obtain a single N pole; but, if a small magnetic compass is placed at any point in the field, the needle will come to rest with its magnetic axis along a line of force and with its N pole pointing in the direction of the field.

If the test compass is placed near the N pole

---

† Fig. 16-11 is very schematic and shows the elementary dipoles as much too long. The dipoles must be considered exceedingly small, and any sample of magnetic material contains an exceedingly large number of them. The process of dividing a magnet into smaller ones can therefore be repeated many times.

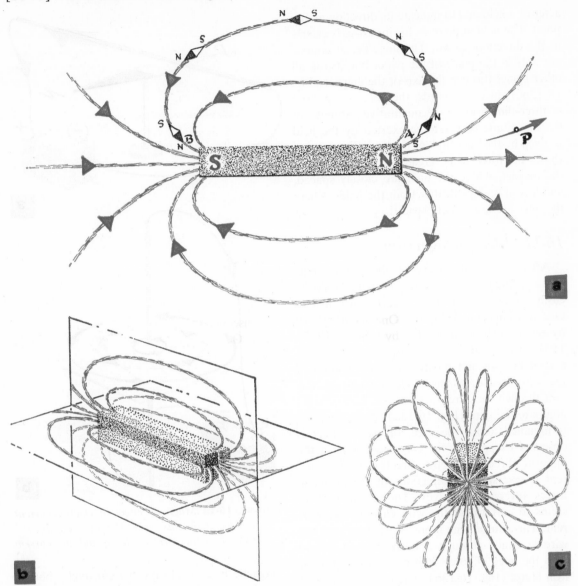

FIGURE **16-12** *Magnetic lines of force round a bar magnet. The lines lie in all planes through the axis of the magnet.*

of a bar magnet, it comes to rest with its N pole pointing away from the magnet as shown in Figure 16-12a. After the direction of the axis of the compass is marked, the compass is moved slightly farther away, and the axis direction is marked again. In this manner a line such as *A–B* may be traced (several typical alignments of the compass are shown). Clearly, such a line lies, at all points along its length, in the direction of the magnetic field indicated by the alignment of the compass needle. Starting from a different point,

other lines of force are traced, and the pattern of Figure 16-12a is obtained.†

As in the case of electric fields, a moderate number of lines suffice to map the general char-

---

† This pattern may be obtained more quickly and (with some care) just as accurately by the use of iron filings. If the filings are scattered on a horizontal plane on which the magnet is resting, each bit of iron, magnetized by induction, swings round and points along a line of force. Thus the iron filings align themselves along the lines of force and a pattern like that of the figure is obtained.

acter of a field and to indicate its direction at any point. The field at point *P*, for instance, is clearly in the direction shown. The lines lie, of course, not only in the plane of the paper but also in all other planes through the axis of the magnet (Fig. 16-12bc); in other words, the complete pattern is three-dimensional. A qualitative estimate of the magnitude of the force exerted by the field is given by the "density" of the lines. Experiment shows the force to be greater near the poles of the magnet, where the lines are closely spaced, and less in regions farther from the poles, where the lines are less closely spaced.

## 16-11. Electromagnetism

After Volta's discovery of the electric battery (p. 262), steady electric currents could be easily produced and their effects investigated. One very important effect was discovered in 1819 by the Danish scientist H. C. Oersted (1777–1851). He found that a compass mounted under a straight wire and pointing in the direction of the wire, would, when an electric current was sent through the wire, turn and set itself at right angles to the wire (Fig. 16-13a). If the compass is mounted above the wire, the same effect is observed except that the compass points in the opposite direction. If the direction of the current is reversed, the directions of the magnetic forces reverse themselves. The magnetic field seems to curl round the wire carrying the current. This can be seen more easily if we pass the wire vertically through a horizontal plane and map the lines of force with a small compass or iron filings (Fig. 16-13b). The magnetic lines of force are found to be concentric circles about the current, with their planes at right angles to the direction of the current.† If the current is reversed, the direction of the lines reverses itself. If the current is stopped, the magnetic field disappears. Here is a new and fundamental property of electricity. Whenever electricity *moves*, there appears, in addition to electrostatic attractions and repulsions, an associated magnetic field. Furthermore, while the electrostatic forces are always along the line joining the charges, the

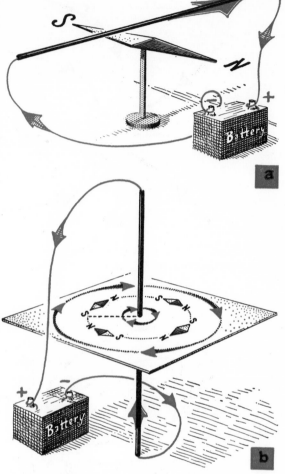

FIGURE **16-13** *Magnetic effect of electric current: (a) Oersted's discovery; (b) magnetic lines of force as concentric circles round the current.*

magnetic force is always *at right angles* both to the direction of the current and to the line from the current to the test compass (broken line in Fig. 16-13b). This magnetic effect of a current is too fundamental in nature to be explained in terms of simpler concepts, but it has many useful applications and sheds new light on the nature of magnetism. (A very simple rule will help you to remember the observed direction of the magnetic field. Grasp the wire in the *left hand* in such a way that the thumb points in the direction of the current. Then the fingers will curl round the current in the direction of the magnetic lines of force.)

Consider a wire bent in the form of a circular

---

† To be consistent with the assumption on p. 255, we shall always define the direction of electric current as the direction of flow of negative electricity.

loop, as shown in Figure 16-14a. When a current flows through the loop, magnetic lines of force appear as shown. Here the current is shown flowing up the nearer part of the loop and down the farther part. The lines of force pass through the loop, emerge from the right side, bend round outside the loop, and enter from the left side. (If the current is reversed, the lines of force reverse their directions.) But this is precisely the pattern that would be set up by a very short and wide dipole with its N pole just at the right of the loop and its S pole at the left (or vice versa with the currents reversed). In other words, a current-carrying circular loop is a magnetic dipole with its axis perpendicular to the plane of the loop.

These magnetic effects of electric currents indicate that magnetism, far from being a unique property, is an aspect of electricity—specifically, a property of *moving* electricity. But the theory of magnetization we developed earlier needs to be altered in only one respect. The postulated elementary dipoles, which were considered microscopic permanent magnets, must now be thought of as due to minute circular loops of current similar to that in Figure 16-14a. With this modification, models such as that of Figure 16-11 would otherwise be unchanged. Shortly after Oersted's discovery, this view was incorporated into magnetic theory by Ampère, and the minute currents became known as amperian currents. This development was an advance in that it included magnetism in the expanding science of electricity and removed the necessity of postulating a separate magnetic substance, but it brought up new questions—about the nature and source of the amperian currents. Answers to these questions, as we shall see later in this book, were not found until well into the twentieth century.

## 16-12. *Rowland Experiment*

We have considered an electric current as a stream of moving electric charges but have en-

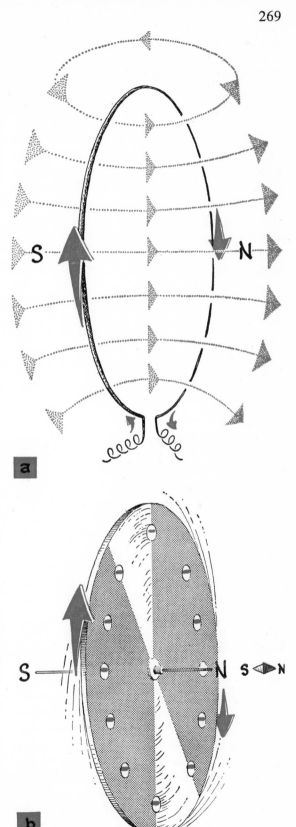

FIGURE **16-14** *Magnetic effect of electric current:* (a) *magnetic field of a circular loop of current;* (b) *Rowland's experiment.*

countered little evidence to support this view. In 1878 H. A. Rowland (1848–1901) performed the following experiment. He mounted a solid wheel of insulating material so that it could be rotated rapidly about an axis through its center (Fig. 16-14b). A series of small metal discs were fixed along a circle near the outer edge of the wheel. These discs were then negatively charged. When the wheel was rapidly rotated in the direction shown by the arrows, a near-by compass needle was observed to align itself along the axis of rotation in the direction illustrated. When the direction of rotation was reversed, the compass alignment was reversed. Great care was taken to shield the compass from electrostatic effects of the charges and from air currents set up by the rotating wheel. Thus a line of charges rotated mechanically round a circle produced a magnetic dipole. This is precisely the effect observed when an electric current moves round a circular loop (Fig. 16-14a). Rowland concluded that an electric current does in fact consist of a stream of moving charges.

## 16-13. Electromagnets

If a conducting wire is bent into a spiral coil and a current is sent through it, a magnetic field, as might be expected, appears near the coil. If the lines of force are mapped with a small compass (or iron filings), a pattern such as that of Figure 16-15 is obtained. Here the lines continue through the coil, emerge from one end, curve round the coil, and enter the other end. The situation diagramed shows the current going into the plane of the paper at the top of each loop and coming out of it at the bottom of each loop. In this case the lines are observed to come out of the right end of the coil and to enter the left end. If the current is reversed, the pattern remains the same, but the lines reverse direction. Such a current-carrying coil has all the magnetic properties of a bar magnet (compare Fig. 16-12a) and is called an electromagnet. The end from which the lines emerge is the N pole, and the other end is the S pole. If such a coil is suspended so that it may rotate in a horizontal plane, it will swing round when the current flows and take up a north-south direction, exactly as

a bar magnet does. If the current is reversed, the coil reverses its alignment, thereby indicating a reversal of the poles. And, finally, if the current is stopped, the magnetic field disappears.

Electromagnets are very convenient devices for the production of magnetic fields, for the fields may be turned on or off and their magnitude changed. Experiments show that the magnitude of the magnetic field is directly proportional to the current and to the number of turns of wire in the coil. If a bar of iron is placed inside the coil, the magnetic field becomes many times greater than with the coil alone. This effect is due to induced magnetism in the iron. Under the action of the magnetic field produced by the current, the elementary dipoles of the iron swing into alignment (see Fig. 16-11b) and produce poles that add themselves to the poles of the coil. If the iron is very hard, it retains its magnetization after the current is turned off and becomes a permanent bar magnet; if it is very soft, it quickly loses its magnetization after the current is stopped.

If the iron core of an electromagnet is bent round so that the two poles face each other (Fig. 16-16), we have a type of electromagnet that is widely used in experiments on atomic structure. Throughout most of the region between the poles there is a strong *uniform* magnetic field, as indicated by the parallel lines of force. We shall see

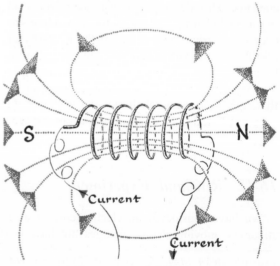

FIGURE **16-15** *Magnetic field of a current-carrying coil.*

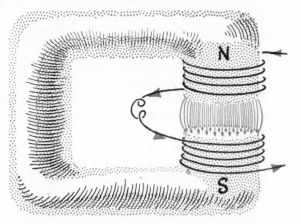

FIGURE **16-16** *Diagram of an electromagnet. A uniform magnetic field is produced when the current flows.*

that such uniform and controllable magnetic fields are very useful in many atomic investigations.

## 16-14. *Electromagnetic Induction*

After Oersted's discovery of the magnetic effect of an electric current, it was natural to speculate on the possibility of the reverse effect. That is, could electric currents be produced by magnets? Faraday soon became interested in this problem and as early as 1822 wrote in his notebook: "convert magnetism into electricity." He needed another decade, however, to discover the central clue and to show that the phenomenon existed. Here again the central clue was *change*. *While* a magnetic field is *changing*, an electric field appears in its vicinity, and electric currents flow in circuits that contain no other source of electrical energy. This inducing of an electric field is called **electromagnetic induction.** Like the magnetic effect of moving charges, this electric effect of a changing magnetic field is fundamental in nature and cannot be explained in terms of simpler concepts.

Electromagnetic induction may be achieved in many ways, and a description of some of them will help us to understand the phenomenon. In Figure 16-17 a loop of wire† is connected to a sensitive ammeter. Since the ammeter has its

† A flat coil of *N* loops increases the effect *N* times, but for clarity only one loop is shown.

zero position in the center of the scale and may deflect in either direction, it indicates not only the flow of current but also the *direction* of flow. A bar magnet whose axis is perpendicular to the plane of the loop is held with the N pole pointing at the loop. If now the magnet is moved toward the loop at speed *v*, current is observed to flow through the loop in the direction shown by the arrow (a) *as long as the magnet is moving.* When the motion stops, the current stops. If the

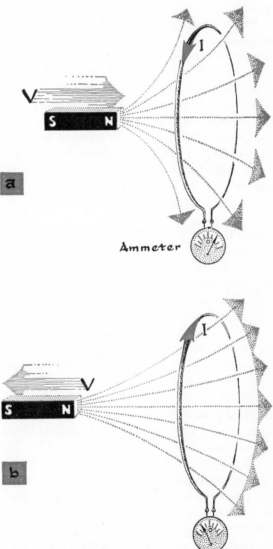

FIGURE **16-17** *Current induced in a conducting loop by a moving magnet. In both cases the magnetic field of the induced current opposes the motion of the magnet.*

magnet is now moved away from the loop, current again flows during the motion, but in the *opposite direction* (b). If, instead of moving the magnet, we move the loop toward the magnet (a) and away from the magnet (b), identical results are observed: it is the *relative motion* that is effective. If the experiment is repeated with the S pole toward the loop, similar effects are observed except that the induced currents are reversed in each instance. And, finally, if the relative speed $v$ is greater, the induced currents are greater.

In each situation the magnetic field in the neighborhood of the loop was changing; *during the change* an electric field was induced, and this caused the current to flow in the loop. Furthermore, the magnitude of the induced electric field was seen to be proportional to the *rate* at which the magnetic field was changed. These generalizations may be visualized in terms of magnetic lines of force. Figure 16-17 shows an arbitrarily small number of lines. Five lines are shown passing through the loop in part "a," but, as the magnet and the loop approach each other, the number through the loop increases to seven, as shown in part "b." The lines may be thought of as cutting across the wire and into the loop during the relative motion. When the magnet and the loop withdraw from each other, the lines again cut across the wire while moving out of the loop. Thus the magnitude of the induced electric field depends upon, and is proportional to, the rate at which magnetic lines cut into or out of the loop of wire. If we let $\phi$ represent the total number of lines threading through the loop at any instant, the magnitude of the induced electric field is proportional to $\Delta\phi/\Delta t$. It was in this form that Faraday generalized the results of his experiments.

The direction of the induced currents yields further understanding of the phenomenon. While the current is flowing, the loop becomes a magnetic dipole (p. 269). In Figure 16-17, while the N pole is approaching the loop, the induced current makes the left side of the loop a magnetic N pole, which repels the approaching N pole of the magnet. That is, it *opposes* the motion. When the magnet and the loop are separated, the induced current is reversed and makes

the left side of the loop an S pole, which, by its attraction, again opposes the motion of the receding N pole of the magnet. This characteristic of induced currents is always observed in electromagnetic induction and was first stated as a law by H. F. E. Lenz (1804–1865): *An induced current is always in such a direction as to oppose the inducing action.*

Lenz stated his law in 1834, before the principle of the conservation of energy had been established (about 1850), but we now understand the law as a statement of a particular case of that conservation. The flow of electricity will, according to the circuit, light lamps, run electric motors, etc., and will always generate heat in the conducting path. Thus electric current indicates the appearance of energy, which, according to the conservation principle, must come from some other part of the system. In the situations of Figure 16-17 the energy is derived from the mechanical work that is required to move the magnet against the opposing magnetic field of the induced current. Here, then, is another method of generating electrical energy: a *direct* transformation of mechanical into electrical energy.

An electromagnet may be used to induce electric currents in a coil. A coil, $A$ (Fig. 16-18), is connected to a battery; when the switch is closed, current, $I$, will flow as shown. Some of the magnetic lines due to $I$ will thread through coil $D$; but, as long as $I$ is steady, no current is observed in $D$. Of course, $A$ or $D$, or both, if moved, will produce induced currents as shown in Figure 16-17, since the current-carrying coil, $A$, has a magnetic field similar to that of a bar magnet. But, even though neither coil is moved, if $I$ is increased, current is induced in $D$ in the direction shown *as long as* I *is changing.* When $I$ becomes steady, the current in $D$ stops. If $I$ is now *decreased,* current is again induced in $D$ during the change, but in the *opposite* direction. If $I$ is changed more rapidly (for instance, by closing and then opening the switch), the induced currents in $D$ are larger. And, finally, if $A$ and $D$ are filled with iron, similar results are observed, but the induced currents are very much larger. A careful analysis of these situations will show that the observed effects are consistent with Faraday's rule for electromagnetic induction and

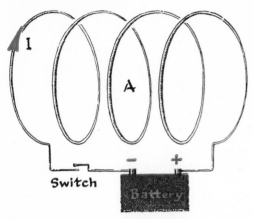 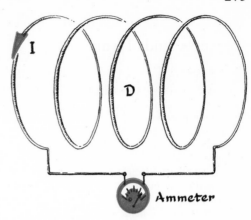

FIGURE **16-18** *Current is induced in coil* D *while the current in coil* A *is changing.*

with Lenz's law for the direction of induced currents.

One more method of electromagnetic induction should be mentioned. While maintaining a steady current in *A*, we may rotate *D* about a vertical axis and thus produce a change in the number of lines through *D*, by virtue of the changing direction of the coil.† Thus continuous rotation of *D* will continuously produce induced currents in it, which may be passed through other electrical devices than an ammeter. When so arranged and used, *D* is called a dynamo and is the usual source of electrical energy for commercial purposes. Dynamos may be made very large and may be rotated by powerful heat- or water-driven engines. Thus large amounts of mechanical energy are converted into electrical energy.

## 16-15. Summary

In this chapter we have considered some fundamental effects in nature, effects we have ascribed to the properties of a universal substance called electricity. We have *assumed* two kinds of electricity, which we *arbitrarily* named positive and negative.‡

The observed effects are force effects, which we ascribe to the action of fields. The forces between static charges, like the gravitational force between masses, act along the line joining the charges; and, as we shall see in the next chapter, they also vary inversely as the square of the distance between the charges. But the electrodynamic effects present forces that are not only new in origin but also new in character. The magnetic field set up by a moving charge is neither in the direction of motion nor in the direction of the line joining the charge to the point of observation, but acts along a line *at right angles* to both of these directions. Furthermore, this mutual perpendicularity exists between an electric field and the changing magnetic field that induces it. And, finally, the magnitudes of the effects also depend upon the velocity of the moving charge and the rate of change of the magnetic field. These inextricably related phenomena are not easily described, as purely mechanical effects were, in terms of simple forces acting at a distance. Thus there began in the last half of the nineteenth century an elaboration of the field concept that related the electrodynamic phenomena. A complete quantitative formulation of the field concept is a topic for advanced courses in physical science. Certain quantitative formulations for some simple fields, however, are necessary for our further study of matter and will be considered in the next chapter.

---

† When *D* is in the position shown in Fig. 16-18, a maximum number of lines will thread through it. When it is in a position with its axis perpendicular to the paper, very few (ideally no) lines will thread through it.

‡ It should be emphasized that none of the topics discussed in this chapter *proves* the existence of *two* electric "fluids." It is possible to follow Franklin's suggestion and relate the phenomena by means of a *one*-fluid theory; and at this stage of our development there are no criteria for choice between the two points of view. To establish the view that we have chosen to use in this chapter, two kinds of electricity would have to be isolated and identified. In later chapters we shall see that this has been accomplished.

## Concepts and Terms

Electric Charge
  positive and negative charge
  forces between charges
Two-fluid Theory
Conductors and Insulators
  electroscope
Induced Charges
Conservation of Electric Charge
  ice-pail experiment
Field Concept
  direction of the field
  electric lines of force
  field inside a conductor
Electric Current
  ampere
  coulomb
Magnetism
  magnetic poles
  forces between poles
  magnetic and non-magnetic substances
  inability to isolate poles

Theory of Magnetism
  induced magnetism
Magnetic Field of a Bar Magnet
  direction of the field
  magnetic lines of force
Electromagnetism
  magnetic effect of electric current
  mutual perpendicularity of force, current, and
    distance
  magnetic field about a current—the left-hand
    rule
  magnetic field about a circular loop of current—
    implication for magnetic theory
  magnetic effect of moving electric charge
Electromagnets
  magnetic field about a current-carrying coil
  effect of an iron core in the coil
Electromagnetic Induction
  induced currents
  directions of induced currents
  Lenz's law—conservation of energy

## Problems

**16-1.** Discuss the process illustrated in Fig. 16-3 if $C$ is a positive charge.

**16-2.** In reference to Fig. 16-4a the statement is made in the text that *some* negative electricity is repelled to the ground, implying that not *all* of it is repelled off the disc. Explain why this is so. (Hint: Consider the negative electricity that is repelled to ground as going in successive small amounts.)

**16-3.** A single metallic sphere is mounted on an insulating stand. Describe (with diagrams) how it can be given a positive charge.

**16-4.** An electroscope is charged by induction with a glass rod that has been rubbed with silk. Is the electroscope charged positively or negatively? Explain with the aid of diagrams. How will this electroscope respond to a positive charge brought near it? to a negative charge? Explain in detail.

**16-5.** Imagine the spheres of Fig. 16-7 mounted on insulating rods on a laboratory table. Complete the lines of force shown.

**16-6.** What would be the force on a test charge placed midway between the spheres of Fig. 16-7b?

**16-7.** Show lines of force for the situations illustrated in Fig. 16-6bc.

**16-8.** During a thunderstorm clouds acquire large electric charges, which induce charges upon the ground and upon objects on the ground under the cloud. Make approximate sketches of the electric field under a positively charged cloud that is (A) over a flat meadow, (B) over a wet tree, (C) over a steel structure such as an office building. (D) Where would it be safest for a person to be? (If the charge is great enough, the field becomes strong enough to break down the insulating properties of the air, and lightning strikes.)

**16-9.** Two parallel wires, each 1.5 meters long, are 50 cm apart. When they are connected and a current is sent through them, there is a force between them of $24 \times 10^{-7}$ newton. What is the current?

*Ans.* 2 amperes

**16-10.** How much charge does the current of the previous problem carry through the wires in 5 minutes?

*Ans.* 600 coulombs

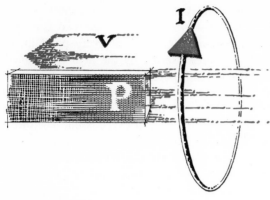

FIGURE **P16-16**

**16-11.** In a certain electrolysis experiment it is required to pass 9,650 coulombs through the apparatus. If a steady current of 5.0 amperes is sent through, how long must the current be on?

*Ans.* 32 min 10 sec

**16-12.** Suppose that one of the magnets of Fig. 16-10b is cut in half *lengthwise*. How are the poles of the new magnets arranged? Are they as strong as the original poles?

**16-13.** If an unmagnetized bar of steel is held in a north-south direction and struck several sharp blows with a hammer, it will develop magnetic poles. Explain this effect. Which end of the bar becomes the N pole? (Steel ships become magnetized by the repeated pounding of the riveting hammers during construction. The field must be neutralized in the neighborhood of the ship's compass.)

**16-14.** Sketch the magnetic field about two magnets, each 9 cm long, whose axes lie on the same straight line with the N pole of one magnet 3 cm from the S pole of the other magnet.

**16-15.** Develop a left-hand rule for determining *directly* the polarity of a current-carrying coil.

**16-16.** In Fig. P16-16 current is induced in a coil in the direction shown when a bar magnet moves as shown. Is *p* an N or an S pole? Give reasons for your answer.

*Ans.* N pole

**16-17.** In Fig. P16-17 current is *increasing* in the direction shown. (A) In which direction will the induced current flow in the other coil? (B) In which direction if the current in the first coil is *decreasing?* Give reasons for your answers.

*Ans.* (B) In the same direction as the inducing current

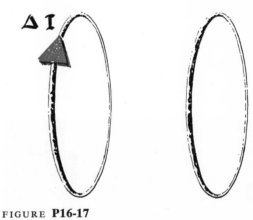

FIGURE **P16-17**

## Suggested Readings

1. L. W. Taylor, *Physics the Pioneer Science* (Houghton Mifflin, 1941), pp. 576–626, 630–643, and 683–689. Interesting reading including much historical background.
2. L. Hogben, *Science for the Citizen* (Knopf, 1938), pp. 617–647.
3. A. Einstein and L. Infeld, *The Evolution of Physics* (Simon and Schuster, 1938), pp. 71–94 and 129–148. An excellent book written for the layman.
4. J. B. Conant, *On Understanding Science* (Yale University Press, 1947), pp. 65–73 (on Volta's discovery of the electric battery).
5. D. Roller and D. H. D. Roller, *The Development of the Concept of Electric Charge* (Harvard University Press, 1954). A Harvard case history. Traces the development of electricity to the end of the eighteenth century.
6. W. F. Magie, *A Source Book in Physics* (McGraw-Hill, 1935), pp. 387–393 (Gilbert on magnetism and electricity), 394–398 (Gray on conductors and non-conductors), 398–403 (Du Fay and Franklin on two- and one-fluid theories), 427–431 (Volta), 436–441 (Oersted on the magnetic effect of current), 446–456 (Ampère on the force between currents), 472–485 (Faraday on induced currents), 489–492 (the ice-pail experiment), 538–541 (Rowland on the magnetic effect of moving charges).

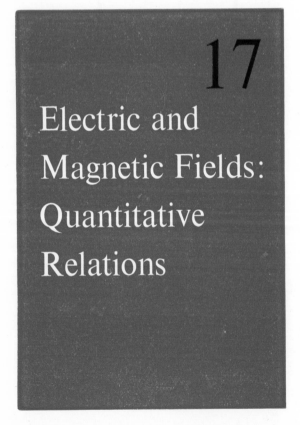

CHAPTER

17

Electric and
Magnetic Fields:
Quantitative
Relations

IN FORMULATING the quantitative relations that describe fields, we use two concepts. One of these is force. If, at every point in the field, the force exerted by the field is specified, that property of the field is completely described. Since forces are vectors, such a description requires a statement of both the direction and the magnitude of the field at every point. The direction is most conveniently represented by lines of force. The magnitude can be determined by an experiment that records at various points the force exerted by the field on a test charge. This can be accomplished, in principle, for any field, whether or not the distribution of the entities creating the field is known. If the distribution of these entities is known, as well as an appropriate law of force, the field may be computed instead of experimentally determined.

The second concept used in describing fields is energy. For instance, to move an electric charge from one point to another in an electric field requires an exchange of energy. If the charge is moved *against* the force exerted by the field, work is done on the charge by the moving agency; if the charge is allowed to move *in the direction* of the field, work is done on the charge by the field. It is clear that these energy changes are changes in the *potential energy* of the moving charge, such changes being due to the charge's changing position in the electric field. If, either by experiment or by computation, these changes in the potential energy of a test charge between all points in the field are determined, a complete description of the field in terms of energy is obtained.

These two ways of describing fields are not independent of each other but are related by the fact that the energy changes represent the work done by or against the forces of the field. In general, therefore, if one description is determined, the other may be derived from it. (This often requires a mathematics that is too advanced for this book. We shall, however, consider one simple example of this general principle.) Hence, in describing a field, we shall have to compute both potential energy changes and forces for different points in the field. We must, therefore, before formulating these relations, discuss the experimental law of force between point charges.

## 17-1. Coulomb's Law

To conduct a quantitative investigation of the forces between static charges, we must measure the distance between the charges, the relative amounts of the charges, and the force of interaction between the charges. If the experimental charges are placed on *small,* insulated conducting spheres, the distance between the charges is the distance between the centers of these spheres; that is, the charges may be considered as *point* charges. The relative amounts of charge may be measured by means of a calibrated electroscope. Consider the arrangement shown in Figure 16-6b. When a small charged sphere is lowered into the can, the leaf diverges as shown. The amount of charge on the sphere is arbitrarily defined as one unit. The position of the leaf, observed on an appropriate scale, is marked with the figure 1. The charge is removed *without touching the can,* and the leaf falls. A second sphere is charged so that it produces the same deflection when lowered into the can. The second charge also is, then, one unit. When both spheres (that is, two units of charge) are lowered into the can, the leaf diverges more widely; its position against the scale is marked 2. Continuing in this manner, we may calibrate the whole scale. The electroscope will then indicate the relative amounts of charge on various spheres that are lowered into the can.

To measure the force between the charges, we use a torsion balance, shown schematically in Figure 17-1. A thin insulating rod, which carries small conducting spheres at its ends, is suspended by a fine wire from a knob that may be rotated along a scale. If a force is applied to one sphere along the line *s*, the rod will tend to rotate in the direction shown by the lower arrow (1). This tendency to rotate can be counterbalanced by a torsion in the wire, produced by turning the knob in the direction shown by the upper arrow (2). By successively applying several known forces to the sphere, we may calibrate the scale so that it will indicate the magnitude of an applied force. Such a torsion balance, if its wire is very fine, is quite sensitive.

A known amount of charge, $q$ (measured by the electroscope), is placed on a sphere of the torsion balance. Another measured charge, $Q$, is placed on a small insulated sphere and situated at distance $s$ from $q$. We measure the interacting force between the two charges by adjusting the knob so as to hold $q$ at its original position. Now, if $Q$ and $s$ are kept constant and $q$ is made successively larger, the measured force is found to be directly proportional to $q$. Similarly, if $q$ and $s$ are held constant and $Q$ is increased, the force is observed to be directly proportional to $Q$. The force between the charges is therefore proportional to the product $Qq$ if the distance $s$ is constant. If both $Q$ and $q$ are kept unchanged and $s$ is increased, the force is found to be *inversely* proportional to $s^2$. The results of all these experiments may be summarized by the equation

$$F = C \frac{Qq}{s^2} \tag{17-1}$$

in which $C$ is a proportionality constant. This experimental law was first published by Coulomb in 1785 and is called **Coulomb's law.**†

---

† Note the similarity between Coulomb's law and Newton's law of gravitational force between point masses (§ 5-3). Both are "inverse square" laws, and both are concerned with fundamental properties of matter—mass and electric charge. Although this similarity is undoubtedly more than sheer coincidence, its full significance is not yet thoroughly understood.

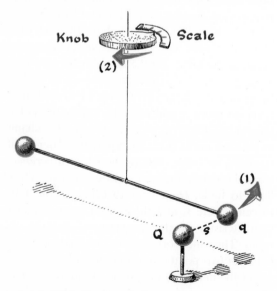

FIGURE **17-1** *Torsion balance for measuring the force between electric charges.*

The value of the proportionality constant in Coulomb's law depends upon the choice of units for the other factors involved, and several combinations are possible. In this book we have already defined units for force, quantity of charge, and distance. In these units, if the charges are *in a vacuum,* the constant has the value†

$$C = 9 \times 10^9 \frac{\text{newton meter}^2}{\text{coulomb}^2} \qquad (17\text{-}2)$$

If the experiment of Figure 17-1 is performed in air instead of in a vacuum, the forces are slightly less (approximately 0.06%), and C is accordingly less. If the space between the charges is filled with insulating materials other than gases, the forces (and thus C) are considerably reduced. For petroleum oil, for instance, the forces are 1/2.2 times the forces between the same charges in a vacuum; for pure water the factor is 1/81. Such an insulating material is called a *dielectric,* and the amount of its characteristic diminution of the electric force between charges is called its *dielectric constant.* The dielectric constant of petroleum oil, for instance, is 2.2, and that of water is 81. A dielectric constant is a pure number, for it gives the ratio of the electric force between charges in a vacuum to the force between the same charges immersed in the dielectric material. We shall assume, unless we specify otherwise, that charges are in a vacuum (or air) and shall use the value of C given by equation 17-2.

Coulomb's law gives the magnitude of the force between two point charges and also indicates the direction of the force. As we have seen, like charges repel. Clearly, if both Q and q are either positive or negative, equation 17-1 yields a positive value for F, which is interpreted as a force of repulsion. If one of the charges is positive and the other is negative, the algebra of equation 17-1 yields a negative value for F, which is interpreted as a force of attraction.

## 17-2. Intensity of an Electric Field

The **intensity,** or *strength,* of an electric field at any point is *defined* as the *ratio of the force* on a small test charge to the magnitude of this charge. If we let E represent the strength of the field, then, by definition,

$$E = \frac{F}{q} \qquad (17\text{-}3)$$

The field intensity E is a vector along the line of action of F if q is positive. In other words, it is the force per unit positive charge. No particular name is given to E, but it is expressed in newtons/coulomb, as required by equation 17-3. Obviously, if E is known (either from computation or from experiments), equation 17-3 permits the calculation of the force on charges in the field. If q is positive, the force has a positive value, which indicates that the force is in the direction of E. If q is negative, F is negative, which indicates that the force is in a direction opposite to the field.

## 17-3. Potential Difference

As pointed out in the introduction to this chapter, fields of force may be characterized by changes in potential energy between points in the field. We have already encountered this idea in our study of the potential energy of a mass in the gravitational field of the earth (§ 11-6). To lift a mass from the floor to a table, for instance, requires an amount of work equal to $mg(\Delta h)$ if $\Delta h$ is the height of the table above the floor. This work measures the *potential-energy difference* between the table and the floor for the particular mass moved. This difference would, of course, be greater if a larger mass were lifted; but, if we agree to move a unit mass (1 kgm), the potential-energy difference depends only on the change in position in the field. Such potential-energy differences, or, more briefly, *potential differences,* could be determined for various changes (from floor to table, from floor to ceiling, from table to ceiling, etc.), and these differences would be characteristic of the gravitational field in the room. Then the work required to carry any mass between two points would be given by the product of the mass and the potential difference. Fur-

---

† More precisely, $C = 8.98776 \times 10^9$, which differs from equation 17-2 by about 0.1%.

thermore, as we have seen, the path along which the mass is lifted (straight up, along an inclined plane, etc.) has no effect upon the work required. Only the starting and ending points of the path determine the work done.

There is an almost exactly analogous situation in an electric field. A test charge at any point in an electric field experiences a force, and to move it to some other point therefore requires the expenditure of energy. But there is one difference from the gravitational field. In the gravitational field the force at any point is always in a certain direction. At any point in an electric field, however, the force is reversed if the test charge is replaced by one of the opposite sign. During any motion of the test charge, therefore, work may be done *on* the field or *by* the field, according as $q$ is positive or negative. Either kind of charge may be used for defining potential differences, and we arbitrarily specify that the test charge be positive. Then, *by definition,* the **potential difference** between any two points in an electric field *is the work done in moving a small positive test charge from one point to the other, divided by the value of the charge.* If we represent the potential difference by $V$, this definition is expressed by the equation

$$V = \frac{W}{q} \qquad (17\text{-}4)$$

The unit of $V$ is clearly joules/coulomb. This unit is called a *volt* in honor of Alessandro Volta (§ 16-8).

Potential difference is a scalar quantity and, in any fixed field, depends only on the positions of the two points in the field. Consider any two points, $A$ and $B$, and assume for the time being that in moving a positive charge from $B$ to $A$ along a certain path *less* work is done than along some other path from $B$ to $A$. The following would then be possible: A positive charge is moved from $B$ to $A$ along the *first* path, and energy is *given to* the system (field and charge). The charge is then allowed to return to $B$ along the *second* path, and the system *delivers more energy* than it had received. We could readily construct a device that would, by repetition of this process, continuously extract energy from the field. But, since the field is stationary, there

are no sources for this energy, and such a situation would violate the principle of the conservation of energy. Hence the work needed to carry a charge along either path must be the same and, by similar argument, must be equal to the work needed to carry the charge from $B$ to $A$ along *any* path. The potential difference between any two points therefore depends *only* on the position of the points in the field; and, in applying equation 17-4, we need not consider the path along which the test charge is moved.

As indicated in the last paragraph, energy may be either *given to* or *extracted from* the system (charge and field) during the motion of a charge in the field. We specify the direction of the exchange by arbitrarily assigning the algebraic plus or minus sign according to the following convention: if the moving charge *gains potential energy,* the work is positive; if it *loses potential energy,* the work is negative.

This convention for the algebraic sign of the work done in moving charges leads to a definition of "higher" and "lower" potential. Suppose that, when a positive test charge is moved from some point, $B$, to another point, $A$, in the field, work is supplied by the moving agency (so that the charge gains potential energy). Then the work is positive and, by equation 17-4, so is $V$. In this case we say that $A$ is at a "higher potential" than $B$. This is analogous to lifting masses to higher elevations in the earth's gravitational field. It follows that a potential difference is considered positive if the motion is from lower to higher potential, negative if the motion is from higher to lower potential. If, for instance, a positive charge, $q$, is allowed to move from $A$ to $B$, then $V$ (in equation 17-4) is a minus number and $W$ is negative, showing that the charge *lost* potential energy. If, on the other hand, a negative $q$ is moved from $A$ to $B$, then $W$ is positive, showing that the negative charge *gained* potential energy. These algebraic results are clearly consistent with the physical facts of the situations. If the definitions and conventions are kept in mind, equation 17-4 will always yield a unique and unambiguous result. Yet, since plus and minus signs are easily "lost," any result should also be interpreted in terms of the "physical sense" of the particular situation.

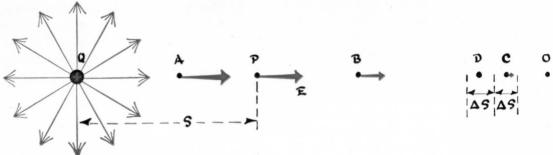

FIGURE **17-2** *Electric field of an isolated point charge.*

## 17-4. *Potential at a Point*

The discussion in the last paragraph implies the concept of *potential at a point* in the field. This concept is easily clarified if some reference point may be assigned the value of *zero* potential. Then *the potential* at any point in the field would be the *potential difference* between that point and the reference point of zero potential. In the earth's gravitational field, sea level may be assigned zero potential and other potentials referred to it. In an electric field no such convenient reference exists. It is always possible, however, to find some point sufficiently removed from the charges setting up the field so that a test charge at that point would experience a negligible force. Such a point, which is effectively outside the field, is said to be "infinitely" distant or to be at infinity.† The **potential** at any point in an electric field is, then, *by definition, the potential difference between the point and infinity.* According to the character of the field, a positive test charge moving in from infinity may experience a force of either repulsion or attraction and thus may either gain or lose potential energy. Hence the potential at a point in the field may be either positive or negative. If we know the potentials at any two points in a field, we may find the potential difference between the points by subtracting the smaller (lower) potential from the larger (higher) potential.

The defining equations, 17-3 and 17-4, along with the conventions for the algebraic signs, are

quite general and are applicable to any electric field. Depending on the distribution of the charges setting up the field, however, the mathematics required for such applications may be simple or somewhat complex. The fields that we shall need to consider arise, fortunately, from simple charge distributions and may be described by elementary algebra.

## 17-5. *Field of a Point Charge*

The simplest electric field is that due to a single, isolated point charge. The field in this important case is easily *computed* with the aid of Coulomb's law. Suppose that the field is due to a point charge of $+Q$ coulombs, as shown in Figure 17-2. To compute the field at some point, $P$, imagine a test charge of $+q$ coulombs placed at $P$. Then $q$, according to equation 17-1, would experience a force $F = +CQq/s^2$. The plus sign shows that the force is one of repulsion and therefore is directed away from $Q$. Then, by equation 17-3,

$$E = \frac{F}{q} = \frac{CQq/s^2}{q}$$

or

$$E = \frac{CQ}{s^2} \qquad (17\text{-}5)$$

This is represented in Figure 17-2 by the vector, $E$, drawn from $P$. Similarly, a larger vector from $A$ and a smaller one from $B$ represent the field at those points. A line from $Q$ through $A$, $P$, and $B$ would always be in the direction of the field at any point and is therefore a line of force. In like manner other lines of force are straight

---

† This is not necessarily a great distance. It might be several meters, or it might be a small fraction of a centimeter, depending on the magnitude of the charges setting up the field.

lines radiating away from $Q$. The field intensity at any point along a line of force is given by equation 17-5 when the appropriate value of $s$ is substituted.

Suppose that point $O$ is sufficiently far from $Q$ so that the field at $O$ is negligible; that is, $O$ is at infinity. Then, to find the potential at any point, such as $P$, we have to calculate the work needed to carry a positive test charge from $O$ to $P$. This is not a simple force-times-distance computation, for the force continuously increases as the charge moves toward $P$ (Coulomb's law); but the work may be computed for successive small steps, the sum of which will be the total work. Suppose that $C$ is the first point at which the field is appreciable and that $\Delta s$ is a small displacement through $C$. If $\Delta s$ is small enough, the force on the positive test charge $q$ will not change as it moves through $\Delta s$.† Then the force at $C$ (from equation 17-1) times $\Delta s$ gives the work needed to move the test charge through this first small step. Similarly, the force at $D$ (a bit larger than at $C$) times $\Delta s$ will give the work for the next small step. This process is repeated until point $P$ is reached. The sum of all these small amounts of work is clearly the work needed to carry $+q$ from $O$ to $P$. We cannot perform this summation (which involves calculus), but we shall write out the result: $W = CQq/s$. The potential difference from $P$ to $O$ is given by equation 17-4 as

$$V_P = \frac{W}{q} = \frac{CQq/s}{q}$$

or

$$V_P = \frac{CQ}{s} \tag{17-6}$$

The subscript $P$ indicates that this is the potential difference from $P$ to infinity—that is, by definition, *the potential at* $P$. Clearly, the potential at $A$ is higher than that at $P$, $V_P$ is higher than $V_B$, etc. Although we calculated $V_P$ by bringing the test charge in along the line $OP$, we must remember that the *same* result is obtained no matter what path the charge is carried along. Equation 17-6 gives the potential at *any* point that is at a distance $s$ from $Q$.

† Remember that $\Delta s$ may be made small enough so that the force through $\Delta s$ is the instantaneous force at $C$.

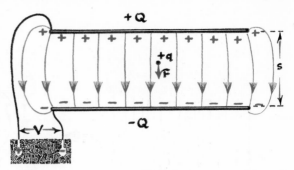

FIGURE **17-3** *Electric field between equally and oppositely charged parallel plates.*

If the point charge setting up the field is $-Q$, equations 17-5 and 17-6 give the numerical value of $E$ and $V_P$. The minus sign of $E$ means that the force is one of attraction; so the lines of force are still radial but pointing *in* toward $Q$. The minus sign for $V_P$ means that the positive test charge *lost* potential energy as it moved in from $O$; that is, $+q$ was *attracted* in to $P$, and energy was extracted from the field. In this case the potential at $A$ is *lower* than at $P$,† $V_P$ is *lower* than $V_B$, etc.; the point of *maximum* potential is at $O$—that is, at infinity. This is the situation for an electron in the nuclear field of an atom (§ 28-1).

If an electric field is due to more than one point charge, the charges being arranged in some fixed distribution, the field intensity may still be calculated with the aid of equation 17-5. At any point the field due to each point charge alone is calculated, and the sum of these is the intensity of the field at that point due to all the charges. This is a vector sum since $E$ is a vector quantity. Similarly, the potential at any point in the field is the sum of the potentials at that point due to each charge in the distribution, as calculated by equation 17-6. But here the sum is algebraic since potential is a scalar quantity.

## 17-6. *Field Between Parallel Plates*

A very useful electric field appears in the space between two *parallel* metallic plates that are equally and oppositely charged. Figure 17-3 is

† Remember that $-13$ is *smaller* than $-7$.

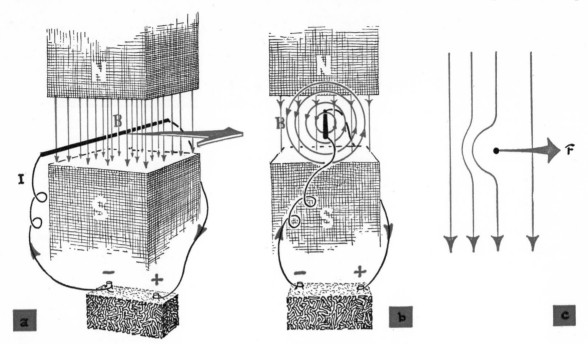

FIGURE **17-4** *A current in a magnetic field experiences a force that is perpendicular to both the current and the field.*

an edgewise view of the situation. Here $+Q$ and $-Q$ are not point charges but are distributed uniformly on the surfaces of their respective plates. The force on a test charge at *any* point between the plates (if not too near the edges) is found to be always of the same magnitude and always along a line perpendicular to the plates. Thus the lines of force are parallel and uniformly spaced, as shown. Such an electric field has two advantages. First, it provides a sizable region throughout which the intensity of the electric field is constant—that is, a uniform electric field.† Second, there is a simple relation between the field intensity, $E$, and the potential difference, $V$, between the plates. The work needed to carry a test charge, $+q$, from the bottom plate to the top plate along a line parallel to the field can be found by a simple force-times-distance calculation since the force, $F$, is the *same* at all points: the work is $W = Fs$ if $s$ is the perpendicular distance between the plates. The work is positive since $+q$ is gaining potential energy. But, in *any* electric field, $W = Vq$ in accordance with equa-

tion 17-4. These two expressions for the work are therefore equal, and we have $Fs = Vq$. Then $Fs/q = V$; but by equation 17-3 $F/q = E$, and therefore $Es = V$. A more useful form of this equation is†

$$E = V/s \qquad (17\text{-}7)$$

We can easily change the potential difference, $V$, by changing the battery producing it, and we can easily measure it with a voltmeter. And $s$ is obtained by direct measurement. Thus a uniform, controllable, and easily measured electric field is produced.

## 17-7. Magnetic Induction

We could formulate the quantitative relations of magnetic fields by starting with an experimental law of force between magnetic poles in a

---

† This is analogous to the uniform magnetic field between the parallel faces of the poles of a large electromagnet (§ 16-13).

† This is a simple example of deriving the force description of a field from the known potential-energy description. In general, for any field, $E = -\Delta V/\Delta s$ if $\Delta V$ is the change in potential along a small displacement, $\Delta s$, parallel to the field. The minus sign describes the fact that, for $\Delta V$ to be positive, $\Delta s$ must be in the *opposite* direction to $E$.

manner very similar to that used for electric fields.† But the process is complicated by two facts. First, as we have seen, magnetic poles cannot be isolated but always appear in N-S pairs. Second, the location of a pole in a magnet is not a definite point but is a region where the lines of force are densest. We shall use another fundamental effect to develop a quantitative statement for the strength of a magnetic field. That effect is the interaction of a magnetic field and an electric current, shown diagrammatically in Figure 17-4a. The N and S poles of an electromagnet produce a uniform magnetic field, $B$. A stiff wire placed at right angles to the field is connected to a battery. When current, $I$, flows as shown, the wire moves out of the magnetic field—the movement indicating that a force, $F$, is acting on the wire in the direction shown. When the wire gets out of the field, the force disappears; if the current stops, the force disappears. Here again is the mutual perpendicularity characteristic of all electrodynamic forces (§ 16-15). The field, the current, and the force are mutually perpendicular. When the current flows, it sets up a magnetic field, and the effect may be considered as the interaction of this field with that of the electromagnet. Figure 17-4b shows an end view of the wire, looking in the direction in which the current, $I$, is flowing. The magnetic lines of force due to the current are shown by circles (§ 16-11) and are seen to be *in the direction* of $B$ on the left side of the wire and *opposite* to $B$ on the right side. Thus the two magnetic fields add on the left side and subtract on the right side of the wire. This is shown in Figure 17-4c, where the lines of the resultant field are "denser" on the left. The wire moves *away from the stronger* and *toward the weaker* portions of the resultant field. If either $B$ or $I$ is reversed, the force reverses its direction.

Instead of permitting the wire to move, we could attach it to a mechanical balance that would indicate the force needed to hold it in position and could thus measure $F$. Experiments of this kind show that, if $I$ is held constant, $F$ is di-

rectly proportional to the length of wire, $L$, that is in the field. (The wire can be placed, for instance, across one corner of the pole piece so that only half as much of it is in the field as before; the force is then observed to be half as great.) If $L$ is held constant, $F$ is observed to be directly proportional to $I$. And, finally, if both $L$ and $I$ are held constant and $B$ is increased (by increasing the current in the coils of the electromagnet), $F$ is observed to increase. Whether this is a direct proportion is indeterminable since we have no unit for the measurement of $B$. We may, however, *define* the strength of the magnetic field so that it is directly proportional to $F$ (with $I$ and $L$ constant). All these results may be summarized by the equation

$$F = BIL \qquad (17\text{-}8)$$

in which $B$ is a measure of the strength of the magnetic field. $B$ is called the **magnetic induction** of the field. Equation 17-8 is the defining equation for magnetic induction. A field has 1 unit of magnetic induction if a current of 1 ampere flowing in a wire 1 meter long at right angles to the field experiences a force of 1 newton. Clearly, the units of $B$ are $\dfrac{\text{newton}}{\text{ampere meter}}$. If $B$ is known from other measurements, we may use equation 17-8 to calculate the forces on currents flowing in the field. We shall see that this equation expresses a very useful relation.

## 17-8. *Motion of Charged Particles in Electric and Magnetic Fields*

Consider the circuit shown schematically in Figure 17-5. $A$ and $C$ are metallic terminals, called **electrodes,** which are connected to the poles of a battery or some other source of electric potential difference. $A$, which is connected to the positive terminal, is called the **anode,** and $C$, connected to the negative terminal, is called the **cathode.** Thus $A$ is at a higher potential than $C$, and the potential difference between $A$ and $C$ may be measured by a voltmeter, $V$. A small particle carrying a charge, $+q$, near $A$ will

---

† By using long, thin magnets so that he could approximately work with isolated poles, Coulomb discovered that the law of force between magnetic poles is also inverse-square. The statement of the law has the same form as equation 17-1.

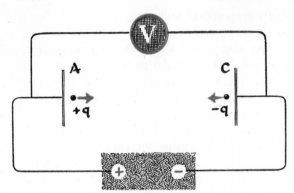

FIGURE **17-5** *Motion of a charged particle in an electric field.*

be moved by the electric field to $C$, while a small particle with charge $-q$ near $C$ will be moved to $A$. (These particles might be charged atoms or molecules or some other, perhaps smaller, charged particles.) In each case, since the work done in moving the charge is negative, energy is being extracted from the field, and the amount of this energy is $Vq$. If the space between $A$ and $C$ is filled with some substance, each charged particle, if it can move at all, will, by repeated impacts, deliver the energy $Vq$ to the molecules of the substance. This energy may take the form of heat (increased motion of the molecules) or light (if the substance is a gas) or may take other forms.

On the other hand, if the space between $A$ and $C$ is highly evacuated, each particle will be continuously accelerated by the field and will arrive at the opposite electrode with some speed, $v$. If the particle started from rest and has a mass $m$, it will have gained kinetic energy equal to $\frac{1}{2}mv^2$. By the conservation of energy this *gain* in kinetic energy must be equal to the *loss* of potential energy of the particle; therefore

$$Vq = \tfrac{1}{2}mv^2 \qquad (17\text{-}9)$$

Since it is possible to generate potential differences of several million volts, small charged particles can be accelerated to very high speeds. Notice that for any particle with constant $q$ and $m$ the speed depends only on the potential difference, $V$. The particle may travel along any path, and the field accelerating it may be nonuniform. Only the potential difference between the starting and ending points of the flight will

determine the speed of arrival. (Compare § 11-8.)

Rowland's experiment (§ 16-12) showed that a stream of moving charges has the same magnetic properties as an electric current. Such a stream moving through a magnetic field would experience a force, and with the aid of equation 17-8 we can calculate the force on *one* of the charges.

Consider a stream of particles, each carrying the same charge, $q$, and all moving with the same constant speed, $v$, as shown in Figure 17-6. Such a stream would constitute a steady current. At some instant a certain particle (the black one) will be at point 1, and $t$ seconds later it will be passing point 2. But during this time *all* the particles initially between those points will have passed point 2, and an equal number will have passed point 1 to take their place. If we let this number be $n$, the total charge passing either point in $t$ seconds is $nq$, and by definition the current is $I = nq/t$. The length of the current between the points is $L = vt$; and, if there is a magnetic field perpendicular to the direction of flow, the force on this section of the stream is, by equation 17-8,

$$F = BIL = B\,\frac{nq}{t}\,vt = Bnqv$$

But this force is distributed over all $n$ of the charged particles; hence the force on one particle is

$$\frac{F}{n} = \frac{Bnqv}{n}$$

or

$$F_q = Bqv \qquad (17\text{-}10)$$

the subscript $q$ indicating that the force is that

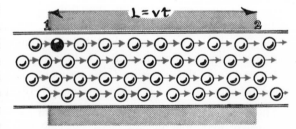

FIGURE **17-6** *A stream of charged particles constitutes an electric current.*

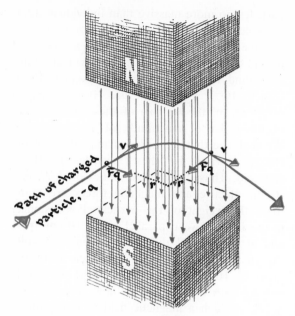

FIGURE **17-7** *A charged particle moving at right angles to a magnetic field is deflected along a circular path.*

on a single moving charge $q$. $F_q$ is perpendicular to both $B$ and $v$ (§ 17-7).

Suppose a charged particle that has been accelerated to speed $v$ enters a uniform magnetic field at right angles to the field. If the particle has charge $-q$, the force $F_q$ is at right angles to both the velocity and the magnetic field, as shown in Figure 17-7. But a force at right angles to the instantaneous velocity is a centripetal force and causes the particle to move along the path of a circle (§ 5-2). The charged particle will therefore move along a circle of radius $r$ with a constant speed since at every point $F_q$ is perpendicular to $v$. The centripetal acceleration is $v^2/r$, and therefore, by Newton's second law and equation 17-10,

$$F_q = Bqv = \frac{mv^2}{r}$$

or

$$mv = Bqr \qquad (17\text{-}11)$$

in which equation $m$ is the mass of the charged particle and $B$ is the magnetic induction of the field.

## 17-9. Velocity Selector

If the moving charged particle is an atom or a molecule or some other sub-microscopic particle, a direct observation of the velocity, $v$, is impossible. We can determine $v$, however, by the use of a velocity selector, which is an arrangement of an electric field and a magnetic field at right angles to each other. Two charged parallel plates (§ 17-6) are placed at opposite sides of the magnetic field between the poles of an electromagnet (Fig. 17-8). Consider a particle carrying charge $-q$ and moving with velocity $v$ in the direction shown. The electric field will exert force $F$ on the particle, and the magnetic field will exert the opposite force, $F_q$. If the fields are adjusted to make these forces equal in magnitude, the net force on the particle is zero, and it travels straight through the space between the plates without deviation. $F_q$ is given by equation 17-10 and $F$ by 17-3; hence

$$Bqv = Eq$$

or

$$v = \frac{E}{B}$$

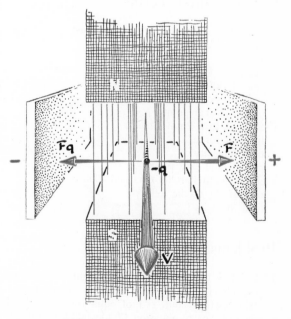

FIGURE **17-8** *Velocity selector.*

Replacing $E$ with the aid of equation 17-7, we get

$$v = \frac{V}{sB} \qquad (17\text{-}12)$$

Since all quantities on the right of this equation are easily measured, the velocity of an undeviated particle passing through the crossed fields is determined.

If particles traveling with different velocities enter the device, only those with a velocity given by equation 17-12 will get through; the others will be deflected out of the path of flight. Thus the device *selects* as well as measures velocity.

## 17-10. *Weight of Charged Particles*

In all of our discussions of the motion of charged particles, the *weight* of the particles has been neglected. If the particle is a sensible piece of matter (even if quite small, such as a tiny drop of liquid), its weight must be taken into account as one of the forces acting on it. However, as we shall see, the relations developed in this chapter will usually be applied to charged particles no more massive than individual atoms or molecules. From the known atomic weights and the approximate value of Avogadro's number (§ 12-5), the masses of individual atoms are found to range from approximately $10^{-27}$ kgm to $10^{-25}$ kgm. If we use $10^{-26}$ kgm as a rough mean, the weights of these particles are of the order of magnitude of $10^{-25}$ newton. We shall see that the order of magnitude of the charges carried by these particles is $10^{-19}$ coulomb. Thus, for modest values of $v$, $E$, and $B$, the electric and magnetic forces are many times the weight of the particle. For instance, in the field between parallel plates 10 cm apart and at a potential difference of only 15 volts the electric force on such a particle is of the order of $10^{-17}$ newton. And, if the particle is moving with the (relatively) low speed of 300 m/sec through a magnetic field of induction of $0.5 \frac{\text{newton}}{\text{amp m}}$, the magnetic force is also of the order of $10^{-17}$ newton. These forces are one hundred million times as large as the weight of the particle. The weight is therefore completely negligible and need not be considered in such applications.

## Concepts and Terms

Law of Force Between Point Charges
  dielectric constant
Electric-field Intensity
  vector aspect
Potential Difference
  scalar aspect
  potential at a point
Field Due to a Point Charge
  lines of force
  field intensity
  potential at any point
Field Between Parallel Charged Plates
  uniformity of the field
  field intensity

Force on a Current in a Magnetic Field
  mutual perpendicularity of force, field, and current
  magnetic induction
Energy Exchange of Moving Charge in Electric Field
  gain of KE for motion through vacuum
Force on Charge Moving in a Magnetic Field
  direction of force
  circular path of moving charge
Velocity Selector

## Problems

**17-1.** Show that the units of the right side (A) of equation 17-6 yield volts; (B) of equation 17-7 yield newtons/coul; (C) of equation 17-10 yield newtons; (D) of equation 17-11 yield kgm m/sec; (E) of equation 17-12 yield m/sec.

**17-2.** Two small spheres charged with $7 \times 10^{-7}$ coul and $3 \times 10^{-7}$ coul respectively are 0.3 m apart. What force do the charges exert on each other?

*Ans.* 0.021 newton repulsion

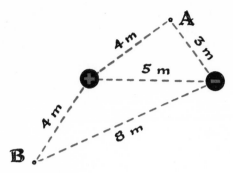

FIGURE **P17-10**

**17-3.** Two charges of $5\times10^{-8}$ coul and $-3\times10^{-7}$ coul are 10 cm apart. What is the force between the charges?

Ans. 0.0135 newton attraction

**17-4.** What would be the forces in Prob. 17-2 and 17-3 if the charges were immersed in petroleum oil?

**17-5.** Calculate the electric field at a point 0.3 m from a small sphere charged with $4\times10^{-7}$ coul.
Ans. $4\times10^4$ newtons/coul radially out from the charge

**17-6.** By experiment the force on a test charge of $2\times10^{-9}$ coul was found to be $3\times10^{-4}$ newton toward the west.
(A) What is the field at the point of the test charge?
(B) If the charge, $Q$, setting up the field is 2 m west of the test charge, what is $Q$?
Ans. (A) $1.5\times10^5$ newtons/coul west
(B) $-6.67\times10^{-5}$ coul

**17-7.**
(A) What is the potential at a point 2 m from a small sphere charged with $8\times10^{-6}$ coul?
(B) How much work would be required to place a test charge of $3\times10^{-8}$ coul at the point?
Ans. (A) $3.6\times10^4$ volts
(B) $1.08\times10^{-3}$ joule

**17-8.** A test charge of $-2\times10^{-8}$ coul absorbs $5\times10^{-4}$ joule of energy while moving from point $A$ to point $B$. Which point is at the higher potential, and what is the potential difference?
Ans. $B$ is $2.5\times10^4$ volts above $A$.

**17-9.** A potential difference of 120 volts between the terminals of an electric heater maintains a current of 8 amperes through the heater. At what rate is heat generated?

Ans. 229 cal/sec

**17-10.** A positive and a negative charge, each of $1.6\times10^{-6}$ coul, are situated as shown in Fig. P17-10.
(A) What is the electric field midway between the two charges?
(B) What is the electric field at point $A$?
(C) Compare these answers with Fig. 16-7a.
Ans. (A) $4.62\times10^3$ newtons/coul toward the negative charge
(B) $1.83\times10^3$ newtons/coul $29°$ above the 3 m line

**17-11.** In the situation of Fig. P17-10 calculate the potential (A) midway between the two charges, (B) at point $A$, (C) at point $B$. (D) How much work is involved in transporting $2\times10^{-7}$ coul from $A$ to $B$? Is this work supplied by the field or by an external source?
Ans. (A) zero; (B) $-1.2\times10^3$ volts; (C) $1.8\times10^3$ volts; (D) $6\times10^{-4}$ joule, external

**17-12.** Calculate the electric field between two parallel horizontal plates 10 cm apart if they are charged to a potential difference of $3\times10^3$ volts and the top plate is positive.
Ans. $3\times10^4$ newtons/coul down

**17-13.** A small drop of oil, whose mass is $1.5\times10^{-8}$ kgm, when placed between the plates of Prob. 17-12, is found to be in equilibrium, neither rising nor falling. What is the charge on the drop?

Ans. $-4.9\times10^{-12}$ coul

**17-14.** By experiment a force of 0.45 newton is found to act on a long wire carrying 5 amp at right angles to a uniform magnetic field. If 30 cm of the wire lies in the field, what is the magnetic induction?

Ans. 0.3 newton/amp m

**17-15.** When current is passed through the wire shown in Fig. P17-15, the wire moves toward the onlooker. Which way is the current flowing?
Ans. to the right

FIGURE **P17-15**

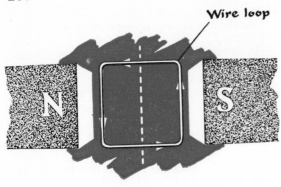

**Wire loop**

FIGURE **P17-16**

**17-16.** A rectangular loop of wire is free to rotate about a vertical axis as shown in Fig. P17-16. When current flows throught the loop as shown, which way will the coil rotate? Will it rotate continuously or come to rest in some other position? Give detailed explanations of your answers.

**17-17.** A helium atom carrying a charge of $3.2 \times 10^{-19}$ coul moves through an evacuated space between electrodes that are at a potential difference of $3 \times 10^6$ volts.
(A) What is the gain in kinetic energy of the charged atom?
(B) If the mass of the atom is $6.68 \times 10^{-27}$ kgm, what speed does it attain?

Ans. (A) $9.6 \times 10^{-13}$ joule
(B) $1.7 \times 10^7$ m/sec

**17-18.**
(A) If the charged atom of Prob. 17-17 enters, at right angles, a magnetic field with induction of 1.5 newtons/amp m, how much force does the field exert on it?
(B) What is the radius of the circle along which it moves?

Ans. (A) $8.16 \times 10^{-12}$ newton
(B) 23.6 cm

**17-19.**
(A) Consider the plates of a velocity selector to be horizontal and the top plate negative (Fig. P17-19). What must be the direction of the magnetic field in order that a small positive charge may travel between the plates from left to right without deviation?
(B) If the plates are 5 cm apart and at a potential difference of 360 volts, what is the velocity of the charge if $B = 0.6$ newton/amp m?

(C) If the charge moves less rapidly, which way will it deflect? Which way if it moves more rapidly?

Ans. (A) at right angles to the velocity and toward the observer
(B) $1.2 \times 10^4$ m/sec

**17-20.** Explain the action of the current balance (§ 16-8) in terms of the force on a current in a magnetic field.

**17-21.** Consider Fig. 17-4.
(A) Show that the work required to carry the test charge $+q$ from the bottom plate to the top plate along a vertical path is $Eqs$.
(B) Show that the work required to carry the charge along any inclined path within the uniform field is also $Eqs$. (Compare Fig. 11-3.)

**17-22.**
(A) No work is required to carry a test charge at constant speed round a circular path centered on a fixed point charge, $Q$. Explain why this statement is true.
(B) Considering the statement of A, explain why the potential at a point due to charge $Q$ (§ 17-5) is independent of the path along which the test charge is carried in from infinity. (Hint: Consider a sequence of concentric circles about $Q$, with radii increasing by $\Delta s$. Any displacement along the path between two of these circles may be resolved into rectangular components along a radius and along an arc of a circle.)

**17-23.** One may explore a gravitational field by observing the force on a *test mass* in the field.
(A) Define the intensity of a gravitational field.
(B) Show that for the gravitational field of the earth the intensity is $g$ newtons/kgm.
(C) Show that the intensity of the earth's gravitational field for any point outside the earth is $Gm_E/s^2$ if $s$ is the distance from the center of the earth and $m_E$ is the mass of the earth. Show that the units are newtons/kgm.

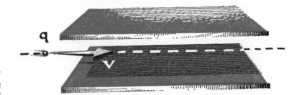

$q$

$V$

FIGURE **P17-19**

# Suggested Readings

1. L. W. Taylor, *Physics the Pioneer Science* (Houghton Mifflin, 1941), pp. 644–661.
2. H. E. White, *Modern College Physics*, third edition (Van Nostrand, 1956), pp. 475–490, 500–505, 511–539, and 543–547. An excellent presentation of the fundamentals of electricity and magnetism. The author anticipates the discovery, which we discuss in the next chapter, that negative electricity consists of discrete, minute charges called electrons. (Also note that the units employed are consistent with those of our text.)
3. R. F. Humphreys and R. Beringer, *First Principles of Atomic Physics* (Harper, 1950), pp. 129–146 and 160–185. The authors use electrostatic units (esu), which are related to those used in our text, at various places in this reference.
4. W. F. Magie, *A Source Book in Physics* (McGraw-Hill, 1935), pp. 408–420 (on Coulomb's laws of force between electric charges and between magnetic poles).

IN OUR discussion of electrification in Chapter 16 we arbitrarily assumed that only negative electricity was transferred during a charging process, and in our discussion of electric currents in metallic conductors we assumed that only negative electricity flowed through the conducting wires. In this chapter, as we take up the experimental evidence concerning this point, we shall discover, not only that our assumptions were justified, but also that negative electricity is particulate in nature, that the particles have the universal property of inertia, and that these particles must be integral parts of all atoms. The idea of the particulate nature of electricity (that is, the "atomicity" of electric charge) was first suggested by the results of experiments on the conduction of electricity through solutions that display anomalously high colligative properties (§ 14-16). The results of such experiments were first summarized by Michael Faraday in 1833 in his laws of electrolysis. These laws will be discussed and interpreted in detail in succeeding chapters. Now, however, we need to anticipate this discussion somewhat and to indicate certain conclusions that are pertinent to the materials of this chapter.

## 18-1. The Charge on Ions

The facts of electrolysis show that, when certain solutes are dissolved, the molecules dissociate into components each of which is charged electrically. Silver nitrate, for instance, dissociates into a positively charged silver atom and a negatively charged nitrate group. We symbolize this by writing $Ag^+$ and $(NO_3)^-$, the sign indicating the kind of charge carried by the particle. These charged particles are called **ions.** Presumably some negative electricity has been transferred from the silver atom to the nitrate radical, and, in the process of dissolving, these two ions are separated and set free to move about in the liquid. The charges on the two ions are the same in amount, but the number of coulombs on either is unknown. This picture is consistent with the ideas of electrification developed in Chapter 16 and represents an extension of the electrical properties of matter to

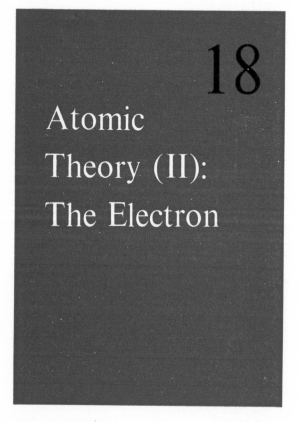

**CHAPTER**

18

Atomic
Theory (II):
The Electron

the sub-microscopic world of molecules and atoms. If any sensible sample of silver nitrate is dissolved, the solution contains a very large number of these ions. Imagine such a solution to fill the space between the electrodes of Figure 17-5. Since the ions are free to move about in the liquid, the electric field will cause the silver ions to migrate to the cathode and the nitrate ions to migrate to the anode. On arrival at the cathode the silver ions will acquire some negative electricity, become neutral silver atoms, and come out of solution as elementary silver. At the anode the nitrate ions cause the release of some negative electricity, which is carried round the circuit to the cathode by the action of the battery. This flow of electricity may be measured by an ammeter in the circuit. Though the situation within the solution is different from that in the connecting wires, since both positive and negative charges move in the solution, the process, in effect, transfers negative electricity through the solution from the cathode to the anode, and thus a steady current round the circuit is maintained.

Clearly, the mass of silver that comes out of solution during any given time may be determined by weighing; and the number of coulombs delivered by the cathode in accomplishing this is, of course, the product of the time and the current. Such measurements yield a completely unexpected result. To bring 1 gram atomic weight of silver out of solution requires $9.65 \times 10^4$ coulombs, and *exactly the same number of coulombs* will release at the cathode 1 gram atomic weight of hydrogen from a solution containing hydrogen ions. But, by Avogadro's law, 1 gram of hydrogen and 108 grams of silver contain exactly the same number of atoms. The two ions in solution ($H^+$ and $Ag^+$) must therefore carry the same amount of charge. If the solution contains copper ions, $19.30 \times 10^4$ coulombs is required to release one gram atomic weight of copper at the cathode. But this is *exactly twice* $9.65 \times 10^4$ coulombs. Hence we symbolize the copper ion as $Cu^{+2}$ (that is, $Cu^{++}$). Here the superscript indicates not only the kind of charge carried by the ion but also the *amount* of charge *compared* with the amount carried by the hydrogen ion. Similarly, the

aluminum ion is found to be $Al^{+3}$, the sodium ion is $Na^+$ (that is, $Na^{+1}$), the barium ion is $Ba^{+2}$, and so on. *Always* the charge on any ion is found to be some *small whole number* times the charge on a hydrogen ion. This relation between the quantities of electric charge on ions suggests that electricity exists as discrete charges, just as the integral ratios of combining masses suggested the atomic nature of matter. The existence of such discrete charges was first suggested in 1874 by C. J. Stoney, who gave the name **electron** to this fundamental piece of electricity. According to this view, the formation of the ions of electrolysis consists in the transfer of one or more electrons but *never* of a fractional part of this elementary unit of charge.

## 18-2. q/m *for Ions*

Electrolysis experiments yield the empirical law that the mass of substance released from solution is directly proportional to the quantity of electricity passed through the apparatus. It is found, for instance, that $9.65 \times 10^4$ coulombs is required to release 108 grams of silver, $9.65 \times 10^2$ coulombs to release 1.08 grams, 9.65 coulombs to release 0.0108 gram, and so on. Always a smaller mass requires a proportionally smaller number of coulombs. This process could, in principle, be continued for smaller and smaller samples until the mass of one single ion was observed. In all cases $q$ is directly proportional to $m$ and $q/m$ equals a constant that is characteristic of the particular ion under observation. Notice that this tells us nothing about the amount of charge carried by the ion or the mass of the ion;† but it does give the *ratio* of these two quantities. The values of $q/m$ for some ions are given in Table 18-1. These experimentally determined values are consistent with our picture of ions in solution. If, for instance, both $H^+$ and $Ag^+$ carry the same charge, $q/m$ for $Ag^+$ should be 108 times as small as $q/m$ for $H^+$ since the Ag atom is 108 times as massive as

---

† Clearly, both the charge and the mass of one ion can be calculated if the value of Avogadro's number is known. But even an approximate value for $N_0$ was not determined until early in the twentieth century (§ 12-5).

| TABLE 18-1 | *Ratio of Charge to Mass of Ions* |
|---|---|

| ION | $q/m$ (COUL/KGM) |
|---|---|
| $H^+$ | $9.58 \times 10^7$ |
| $Al^{+3}$ | $1.07 \times 10^7$ |
| $Cu^{+2}$ | $0.304 \times 10^7$ |
| $Ag^+$ | $0.0895 \times 10^7$ |
| $Ba^{+2}$ | $0.140 \times 10^7$ |

the H atom; and, if $Cu^{+2}$ carries *twice* the charge of $H^+$, $q/m$ for $Cu^{+2}$ should be $63.54/2 = 31.8$ times as small as $q/m$ for $H^+$. These ratios, and similarly predicted ones for the other ions, may be easily verified from the data of Table 18-1. Another aspect of these data, which, as we shall see, is very significant, is that the *largest* value of $q/m$ is the one for $H^+$. This is generally so. Extensive experiments show that $q/m$ for no other ion has a value as large as that for the hydrogen ion.

This view of electricity as a substance composed of tiny pieces, or "atoms," satisfying though it may be for the explanation of the facts of electrolysis, raises many questions. Can the "atoms" of electricity be isolated and their properties determined by experiment? If so, do they display the universal property of inertia, and what is the charge of each? Without such information the status of the electric "fluid" might be no different from that of the caloric "fluid," and the concept, like the earlier one, might in time be replaced by other concepts. (We have, however, encountered one difference: the conservation of electric charge; see §16-5.) The answers to such questions were not forthcoming till more than twenty years after Stoney's suggestion; and with them came a general acceptance of the electron theory.

## 18-3. Cathode Rays

The next clue to the existence of electrons came out of a study of the conduction of electricity through gases. Ordinarily, gases are rather good insulators. But any insulator will conduct electricity if a sufficiently large potential difference is applied. In this situation we can pic-

ture the flow of electricity as the migration of ions through the gas in a manner very similar to the passage of electricity through an electrolytic solution. But for such a picture we need some ions, and gas molecules are electrically neutral. If sufficient energy in the proper form is available, however, some electricity is separated, and positive and negative gaseous ions are produced. This energy is supplied by the natural radioactive and cosmic rays that are always present. (These rays will be studied later.) The ions, of course, attract each other and, because of their great mobility in the gaseous state, move together, recombine, and revert to neutral molecules. Ions are constantly being formed, however, and thus an equilibrium state is reached such that, at any instant, a few ions are present in any sample of gas.

Suppose now that a sample of gas is between the electrodes of a circuit such as that of Figure 17-5. A greatly magnified and somewhat schematic representation of the situation is shown in Figure 18-1. Consider two of the primary ions at the instant the potential difference is applied. Because of the electric field each ion experiences a force ($F = Eq$) and is accelerated in the direction of the force. The neutral molecules are, of course, in random thermal motion but, on an average, are a certain distance apart. As the accelerated ions move through this distance, they gain kinetic energy. If this energy is sufficiently large when they collide with neutral molecules, some electricity is separated, and two more pairs of ions are produced. Thus from the original two come six. Each of these six, accelerated by the field, produces two more, and so on. Thus, very quickly, this cumulative ionization produces

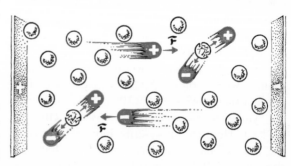

FIGURE 18-1 *Schematic representation of the conduction of electricity through a gas.*

large numbers of ions, which, streaming across the space toward the appropriate electrode, constitute electric currents. As the positive and negative ions stream past each other, some will recombine and give up their ionization energy. This energy takes the form of radiated light,[†] and the path of the ions is made visible by these luminous molecules. At ordinary pressures the path of the discharge follows an erratic zigzag course, which is continuous as long as the electrodes are kept at a constant potential difference by the battery. If, on the other hand, the electrodes are statically charged conductors, the arrival of the ions neutralizes the charge, and the accelerating field disappears. Such a momentary discharge constitutes the familiar spark that jumps between two oppositely charged bodies or, on a grander scale, the bolt of lightning between a highly charged cloud and the earth.

At ordinary pressures the average distance between molecules is extremely small. Hence the force $F$ (and thus $E$), acting through this small distance, must be very large in order to give the ions sufficient energy to maintain the necessary cumulative ionization of the gas. Conduction through only 1 cm of atmospheric air between charged spheres requires a potential difference of about $3 \times 10^4$ volts.[‡] If the pressure is reduced, however, the molecules, as we know, are farther apart, and an ion therefore has a longer flight between impacts, and a less intense electric field will supply the ionizing energy. In the second half of the nineteenth century techniques for obtaining a good vacuum were developed, and the conduction of electricity through gases at reduced pressure began to be investigated. The details of the phenomena are complex and are still a subject for research. Certain aspects are significant for our study of the nature of electricity.

In Figure 18-2 a long glass tube with electrodes sealed into the ends is connected to a

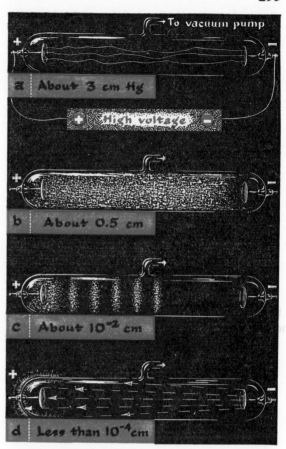

FIGURE **18-2** *Conduction of electricity through a gas at various pressures.*

pumping system. The electrodes are connected to a source of potential difference of several thousand volts. With the gas at atmospheric pressure no conduction is observed; but, as the vacuum pump continues to reduce the pressure, a series of phenomena is observed. At a pressure of about 3 cm of Hg (a) thin, erratic streamer-like discharges appear. At this pressure the distance traveled by the molecules between impacts is large enough for the primary ions to absorb sufficient energy from the field to start the cumulative ionization described above. As the pressure is reduced, more streamers appear until the whole tube is filled with light (b).[†] At still lower pressures (c) a dark space appears near the cathode. With decreasing pressure this

---

† The color of the light is characteristic of the particular gas—pink for nitrogen, bright red for neon, bluish white for mercury vapor, and so on. The nature of this radiation will be considered in later chapters.

‡ This fact makes a bolt of lightning somewhat awesome: it is a discharge across a potential difference of a billion volts or more.

---

† At about this pressure the conductivity of the gas is greatest, and one or two thousand volts will maintain the discharge through a tube several meters long. This is the familiar neon sign.

dark space extends toward the anode and at very low pressures completely fills the tube. The molecules are now so widely separated that an ion might easily travel the full length of the tube without undergoing a collision; the chance of recombination becomes negligible, and the glow disappears. But, by this same argument, the cumulative ionization would disappear, and we should expect the current in the circuit to cease. But *electricity continues to flow in the circuit*. What, then, are the nature and the origin of the ions that carry electric charge across this almost empty space between the electrodes?

When the dark space fills the tube, a new effect appears. The glass walls of the tube glow with a greenish light that is more intense at the anode end. If the polarity of the tube is reversed, the effect reverses itself. Thus invisible "rays" seem to be streaming across the tube and, upon striking the walls, to cause the glass to fluoresce. Because the rays seem to be streaming from the cathode (broken lines in Fig. 18-2d), they were named **cathode rays.** Materials other than glass (for example, zinc sulfide) fluoresce brilliantly when placed in the space between the electrodes; a screen coated with zinc sulfide and placed in the tube glows brightly, and, if some solid object is placed between the cathode and the screen, a sharply defined shadow is formed on the screen. If the object is placed between the anode and the screen, no shadow is formed. The rays, it is clear, move away from the cathode, and the character of the shadow indicates that they move along straight lines.

The cathode rays display the property of inertia. This was first demonstrated by the use of the specially designed and highly evacuated discharge tube shown schematically in Figure

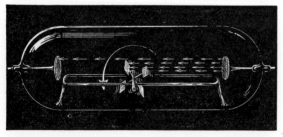

FIGURE **18-3** *Demonstration of the inertia of cathode rays.*

18-3. A paddle wheel, free to roll along a horizontal double glass track, is arranged so that the top paddle is directly between the cathode and the anode. When voltage is applied to the tube, the wheel rolls away from the cathode and toward the anode. If the polarity of the electrodes is reversed, the wheel reverses its direction. The cathode rays, in streaming across the tube, strike the paddles and impart momentum to them, and the wheel rotates. It follows, from the conservation of momentum, that the cathode rays must have momentum and therefore also the other mechanical properties of matter: mass, velocity, and kinetic energy. Thus the picture emerges of a stream of small particles flying away from the cathode through the evacuated space with (probably) high velocity. Since these highly evacuated tubes conduct electricity, the particles must be ions; and, since the ions move away from the cathode, they must be negative ions.

## 18-4. e/m *for Cathode Rays*

The next question that arose was: Are all the negative ions of the cathode rays alike? We have already seen that, for the ions of electrolysis, a characteristic quantity is the ratio of the charge to the mass of an ion. A similar ratio for cathode rays may be determined, but the experimental procedure is completely different from electrolysis. The apparatus, enclosed in a highly evacuated glass tube, is sketched in Figure 18-4a and diagramed in 18-4b. The cathode and anode are connected to a potential difference of several thousand volts. The anode has a small hole in it and the space to its right is shielded (§ 16-7) from the large field of the high voltage by a grounded metal shield (not shown). Thus a narrow beam of cathode rays will go through the hole in the anode, emerge into a field-free space, and, by Newton's first law of motion, continue between the parallel plates in a straight line with constant speed until it strikes the fluorescent screen at $O$, where a fluorescing spot appears. However, if a small potential difference (50–100 volts) is applied to the plates, the upper being positive, the beam is deflected upward by the electric field, $E$, between

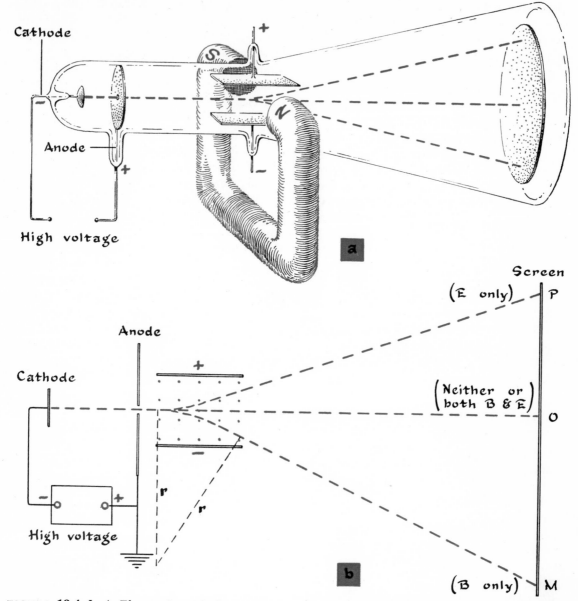

**Cathode**

**Anode**

**High voltage**

a

**Screen**

(E only) P

(Neither or)
both B & E) O

(B only) M

**Anode**

**Cathode**

**High voltage**

r

r

b

FIGURE **18-4** *J. A. Thomson's method of measuring the ratio of charge to mass of cathode rays.*

the plates, and the spot moves to *P*. When this potential difference is removed, the spot returns to *O*. If the poles of a magnet are arranged so that a uniform magnetic field (induction *B* and into the plane of the paper) fills the space between the plates, the beam is deflected downward, and the spot moves to *M*.† The po-

tential difference between the plates is again connected; as its value is increased, the spot moves up until at a particular value of *V* the spot is again at the undeviated position *O*. But this is precisely the situation described by Figure 17-8, and equation 17-12 yields the velocity of the cathode particle. The velocity comes out to be very large (millions of meters per second) and, as might be expected, increases with higher voltage between cathode and anode.

† The electric and magnetic forces causing these deflections are convincing evidence that the cathode particles are negatively charged.

The potential difference between the plates is now removed, and the particles, while in the magnetic field, move along a circular path of radius $r$ and then continue in a straight line to $M$. The distance $OM$ is easily measured, and that, combined with the geometry of the tube, gives the value of the radius $r$. This situation is precisely that described by Figure 17-7, and equation 17-11 applies. By convention the letter $e$ is always used to represent the charge on a cathode particle. Using this, we solve equation 17-11 for the ratio of the charge to the mass of the cathode particle, substitute for $v$ from equation 17-12, and obtain

$$\frac{e}{m} = \frac{V}{sB^2r} \tag{18-1}$$

Every factor of the right side of this equation is directly measurable in the experiment, and thus $e/m$ is determined. The surprising result is that the value of $e/m$ is always the same. The residual gas in the tube may be of any kind, and the metal of the electrodes may be any one of a wide variety, and always the value comes out to be

$$\frac{e}{m} = 1.76 \times 10^{11} \frac{\text{coul}}{\text{kgm}} \dagger \tag{18-2}$$

Clearly, the cathode particles are not charged atoms, for $e/m$ would then vary with the varying atomic masses, just as the ions of electrolysis do (Table 18-1). Furthermore, the value of equation 18-2 is almost 2,000 times (more precisely, 1,836) as *large* as the *largest* value for any charged atom in electrolysis—namely, $q/m$ for $H^+$. This very large value may be due to either a large value of the charge, $e$, or a very small value of the mass, $m$. However, as we have seen, the charged atoms in electrolysis always carry the same fundamental electric charge or *small* multiples of it, never many times the charge on a hydrogen ion. It is reasonable to infer that the cathode particles also carry a small charge and presumably just the elementary amount of Stoney's electron. If so, the very large value of $e/m$ must be attributed to an extremely small mass of the cathode particle, a mass *only*

*1/1,836 of the mass of a hydrogen atom.* Such were the conclusions arrived at by J. J. Thomson, who in 1897 was the first to measure $e/m$. He concluded that the cathode particles are fundamentally different from the atoms of the periodic table, that the cathode rays consist of free electricity and give evidence of being *free electrons.* He also concluded "that *atoms are not indivisible,* for negatively electrified particles can be torn from them by the action of electrical forces."

This view, that negative electricity can be freed from the atoms of all matter, is strengthened by two other phenomena. The first was discovered by Thomas A. Edison in 1883 during the development of the electric light. In Figure 18-5, $F$ is a conducting filament that we may heat to incandescence by passing a current through it (circuit not shown). $A$ is a metal plate, and both $A$ and $F$ are sealed into a highly evacuated tube and connected to a battery as shown. When $F$ is cold, no current flows in the circuit; when $F$ is heated, current flows and is indicated by the ammeter. If the polarity of the battery is reversed, the current stops. Thus negative charges are freed from the glowing filament and allowed to move across the evacuated space in the tube when $A$ is the anode. The value of $e/m$ for these charges may be measured if we replace the cathode in Figure 18-4 with a glowing filament. When this is done, $e/m$ is found to be exactly the same as for cathode rays. The material of the filament has no effect on the measured value; always the value of equation 18-2 is obtained.

The second phenomenon is the release of elec-

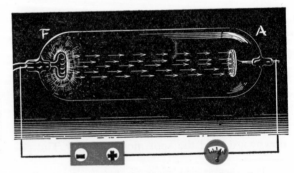

FIGURE **18-5** *Apparatus to demonstrate the production of thermal electrons.*

---

† As a result of many very precise determinations this quantity is now known to six significant figures: $1.75888 \times 10^{11}$ coul/kgm.

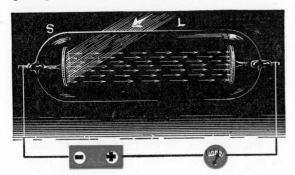

FIGURE **18-6** *Apparatus to demonstrate the production of photoelectrons.*

tricity from substances by the action of a beam
of light. This **photoelectric effect** is illustrated
in Figure 18-6. When a beam of light, *L*, falls
on the surface of *S*, current is registered by the
meter. If the light is blocked off, the current
stops. The current also stops if the polarity of
the battery is reversed, even though the light
still falls on *S*. Again negative electricity is freed
into the evacuated space in the tube, but this
time by the action of a beam of light. If the
cathode of Figure 18-4 is replaced by such a
surface, the value of *e/m* is found to be the
same as that given by equation 18-2. Many different substances may be used for *S,* but the
result is always the same.†

Thus we see that, if sufficient energy is supplied (by strong electric fields, high temperature, or radiant energy), small negatively
charged particles may be torn from any substance and set free in space. And the particles
are all identical, from any source whatever, as
indicated by the universal constancy of the
measured *e/m*. Greater confidence is now established in Thomson's conclusion that atoms must
have structure, since a fundamental particle may
be extracted from any of them. This revolu-

† In measuring *e/m* for both thermal electrons and
photoelectrons, the voltage used to accelerate the electrons is kept low enough so that no cathode rays will
be emitted. The terms "thermal electrons" and "photoelectrons" do not mean that the electrons are different
from those of the cathode ray; they merely indicate
a different source.
The reader is probably familiar with the technical
importance of thermal electrons as the source of current in radio tubes and similar electronic devices. The
photoelectric effect is the basis of the familiar "electric
eye," whereby many electrical devices may be controlled by a beam of light.

tionary view of Thomson's, as might be expected, was not immediately accepted. The
concept of atoms as indivisible, immutable entities had been so successful throughout the nineteenth century that it had acquired the status
of dogma. This opposition is epitomized by a
quotation from one of Thomson's letters: "At
first there were very few who believed in the
existence of these bodies smaller than atoms. I
was even told by a distinguished physicist who
had been present at my lecture that he thought
I had been pulling their legs."

## 18-5. *Electronic Charge*

The particulate character of electricity would
be verified if other evidence, completely independent of *e/m* measurements, was found to
show that electricity has structure. Such evidence
would consist of direct measurements of electric charges and an inspection of the results for
possible "atomicity." Large charges (like large
samples of matter) appear to be continuous,
and the atom of electricity (if it exists at all) is

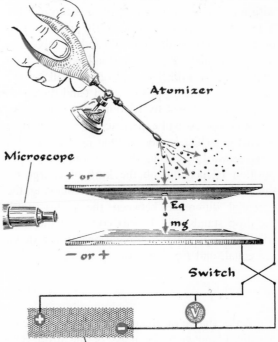

FIGURE **18-7** *Millikan's oil-drop experiment.*

probably very small. A fruitful approach, therefore, would be measurement of the charges carried by extremely small samples of matter. Such measurements (first made by Thomson and subsequently by others) were developed to a high degree of precision by R. A. Millikan, who repeated and extended his measurements for several years from 1906 on.

Millikan's apparatus, quite elaborate in details but very simple in principle, is shown schematically in Figure 18-7. Two parallel and horizontal metallic plates are connected through a reversing switch to a variable source of potential difference. Thus a vertical electric field, directed either up or down as needed, may be established between the plates. The intensity of the field may be changed by variations in the potential difference between the plates. The potential difference is measured by the voltmeter, $V$, and since the distance, $s$, between the plates is fixed, $E$ is known and given by equation 17-7. A small hole (not large enough to distort the field) is drilled through the top plate. A cloud of very fine oil drops is sprayed from an atomizer into the space above the top plate. As these drops, retarded by the friction of the air, fall slowly with a constant speed, one will pass through the hole into the space between the plates. This drop is strongly illuminated and is observed through a microscope as a small point of light against the dark background of the walls of the apparatus. If the drop is charged (and the drops usually are charged by friction in the nozzle of the atomizer), it will experience an electric force when the switch is closed. One may direct this force upward by closing the switch in the proper position (depending on the kind of charge on the drop) and may vary it—by changing the potential difference between the plates—until the drop stands still. In this condition the electric force up and the gravitational force down are equal, and $Eq = mg$, or

$$q = \frac{mgs}{V} \tag{18-3}$$

if $q$ is the charge on the drop (either positive or negative) and $m$ is the mass of the drop. The values of $g$, $s$, and $V$ are directly observable, and $m$ is found by the following method: The switch is opened so that the electric field disappears and the drop falls with a constant speed. This "terminal velocity" is related by a well-known law to the mass of the drop, the density of the oil, and the viscosity of the air. The velocity of fall is observed directly through the microscope, and this, combined with the measured density of the oil and the viscosity of the air, gives the mass of the drop. Thus all factors on the right of equation 18-3 are observable, and the charge on the drop is determined.

Millikan measured the charges on numerous drops and varied the conditions of the experiments in many ways. If, after the charge on a particular drop had been measured, the air in the apparatus was ionized (by X-rays or by radioactive emanations), the drop would accumulate one or more of the ions and acquire a new charge. The difference between this new charge and the original one gave the charges carried by the gaseous ions. Thus not only charges produced by friction but also charges carried by ions were measured. This procedure was repeated many times with a wide variety of gases in the apparatus. Also the substance of the drops was varied widely. Some of the drops were insulators (like oil), some were semi-conductors (like glycerine), and some were good conductors (like mercury). And finally the sizes of the drops and the intensities of the electric fields were varied through a wide range of values. After thousands of such measurements Millikan listed all the values of the charges observed. A few representative values are given in Table 18-2. The charges, both positive and negative, *were always found to be whole-number multiples of a constant minimum charge;* and no charge less than this least common divisor

TABLE **18-2** *Observed Multiples of Unit Charge*

| $q$ (COULOMBS) | MULTIPLES $\times 10^{19}$ |
|---|---|
| $3.20 \times 10^{-19}$ | $2(1.60)$ |
| $11.20 \times 10^{-19}$ | $7(1.60)$ |
| $4.80 \times 10^{-19}$ | $3(1.60)$ |
| $1.60 \times 10^{-19}$ | $1(1.60)$ |
| $8.00 \times 10^{-19}$ | $5(1.60)$ |

was ever found. Millikan concluded that there is a fundamental charge that cannot be subdivided into smaller charges, and that any larger charge consists of an integral number of these fundamental particles of electricity. This elementary charge, this "atom" of electric charge, also represented by the letter $e$, has the value

$$e = 1.60 \times 10^{-19} \text{ coulomb} \dagger \qquad (18\text{-}4)$$

## 18-6. The Electron

The results of $e/m$ measurements, combined with Millikan's measurements of charge, establish the existence of Stoney's electron and specify its properties. Thomson's cathode particle is one elementary unit of electricity (one electron) that has been freed from the atoms of matter. But the cathode particles are *always* negative. Hence the electron is a small *negative* charge of $1.60 \times 10^{-19}$ coulomb. Furthermore, the precise determinations of $e/m$ and $e$ yield the mass of the electron. The value of equation 18-4 divided by the value of equation 18-2 gives for the *mass of the electron*

$$m = 9.1 \times 10^{-31} \text{ kgm} \ddagger \qquad (18\text{-}5)$$

We have already seen, however, that this is 1/1,836 of the mass of the hydrogen atom; therefore $m_H = 1.67 \times 10^{-27}$ kgm. This, combined with the *relative* atomic masses of the periodic table, gives the masses of other atoms. In a later section of this chapter we shall see how the measurement of the ratio of charge to mass for *gaseous* ions leads to the absolute masses of atoms, which masses verify and extend our concept of the relative atomic weights of the periodic table. And in a later chapter we shall see that a knowledge of $e$ leads to a precise value of Avogadro's number, which value agrees with Perrin's, who arrived at his by completely independent measurements (§ 12-5). Consistencies like these (a kind of "double checking") give rise to great confidence in the correctness of the interpretations of Thomson's and Millikan's work. These are but a few of the

---

† The accurate value, as determined by many experiments, is $e = 1.60207 \times 10^{-19}$ coulomb.

‡ More precisely, $m = 9.1085 \times 10^{-31}$ kgm.

many important subsidiary results of the knowledge of the electronic charge.

We now understand why we assumed in Chapter 16 that in the charging process only the negative electricity moves. We consider any atom to contain some positive electricity and some electrons. The positive electricity must be firmly bound in the body of the atom, the electrons less strongly bound and near the periphery of the atom. This picture (suggested by Thomson) is consistent with the facts; atoms are normally neutral, but, when electricity is freed from them, always the negative electrons appear. When frictional charges are produced, electrons leave the glass and go to the silk, leave the wool and go to the hard rubber, and so on. In electrolytic solutions the positive ion is an atom that has *lost* one or several electrons, and the negative ion is an atom (or group of atoms) that has *gained* one or several electrons. Similarly, in gaseous conduction, ions are formed when the molecules lose or gain electrons. But also, in a gas, the electron itself may be a negative ion; and, since it is smaller than the molecules, it moves a greater distance between impacts in an electric field. Thus, in the gaseous discharge, most of the cumulative ionization is due to freely moving electrons. And, finally, conduction through a vacuum is due entirely to a stream of free electrons.

## 18-7. Metallic Conduction

In solid conductors also the current is due to moving electrons. Presumably one electron is *very weakly bound* to an atom of certain substances in the solid state. The structure of these substances, which are good conductors of electricity, may be pictured as consisting of positive ions (the atoms less one electron) held firmly in the crystal lattice and surrounded by a cloud of "free" electrons. The electrons behave like the molecules of a gas and are in temperature equilibrium with the structure of the metal. This picture is shown schematically in Figure 18-8. The particles, of course, are much more numerous and are in constant thermal agitation. The atoms (the large circles with plus signs) vibrate

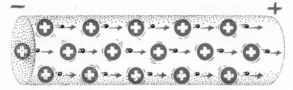

FIGURE **18-8** *Schematic representation of metallic conduction by free electrons.*

about a fixed position while the free electrons (the small dots) move at random. The metal as a whole is electrically neutral since in any volume there are, on the average, equal numbers of positive and negative charges.

If the metal is connected to the poles of a battery, the electrons acquire a velocity in a direction opposite to the electric field, and the electron gas migrates toward the positive pole. Since, for any small volume of the conductor, just as many electrons migrate in as out, the conductor as a whole remains neutral; but the drift of electrons constitutes an electric current.†

As the electrons move through the solid toward the positive pole, they are accelerated by the electric field and acquire additional kinetic energy. This energy, on the average, is lost to the atoms at the next impact, and the process starts again. Thus, as the electrons migrate through the metal, they abstract energy from the electric field and deliver it to the atoms of the metal; that is, heat is generated by the electric current. The rate at which this heat is generated for any given current is a measure of the resistance of the conductor and is clearly directly proportional to the number of impacts per second. If the conductor of Figure 18-8 is made twice as long, there are twice as many impacts per second for the same current (that is, the same rate of flow of electrons), and the conductor displays twice as much resistance. If the length is unchanged but the cross-sectional area of the conductor is doubled, the electrons have to migrate only half as rapidly in order to maintain the same current (that is, to transfer the same amount of charge per second). Between

† To be sure, the electrons are in motion even when the conductor is disconnected from the battery. But, because this motion is random, there is no *net* transfer of charge and hence no current. It is the directional drift superimposed upon the random motion that constitutes the current.

impacts, therefore, the electrons acquire, on an average, only half as much speed and only *one quarter* as much kinetic energy from the field. Hence, although in doubling the area we have doubled the number of impacts, only one-quarter as much energy per impact is delivered, and the *net total* energy delivered is therefore only half as much; that is, the conductor displays only half as much resistance if its cross-sectional area is doubled. All these deductions are in complete agreement with the empirical laws of resistance.

The observed increase in the resistivity of a conductor with rising temperature is also consistent with this view of electronic conduction. As the temperature of the metal in Figure 18-8 rises, the atoms vibrate through a wider amplitude and thus increase the chance of impact with a passing electron. This is somewhat analogous to the situation of a pedestrian standing on a parkway in a stream of traffic. He certainly has a chance of being struck by some car that is headed directly for him; but, if he starts running back and forth across the roadway, his chance of being struck by a car in any one of the lanes of traffic is greatly increased. Hence in any volume of the conductor the chances of electron impact, and thus the resistivity, increase as the temperature rises.

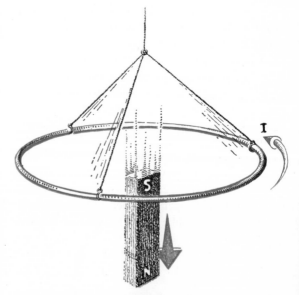

FIGURE **18-9** *Experimental verification of electronic conduction in metals.*

If the temperature is lowered, the conductivity of the substance increases. At a temperature close to absolute zero some metals (although not all) suddenly lose practically all their resistance and exhibit *super-conductivity*. For lead this occurs at about 7°K, for tin at about 4°K. This phenomenon, though not completely understood, permits a striking and informative experi-

ment. Consider a metallic ring suspended so that it is free to rotate and cooled to its super-conducting temperature (Fig. 18-9). A magnet withdrawn from the center of the ring will start a current ($I$) flowing as shown. This current is easily detected by its deflection of a compass needle. As long as the temperature is kept below the critical value for the metal, the current con-

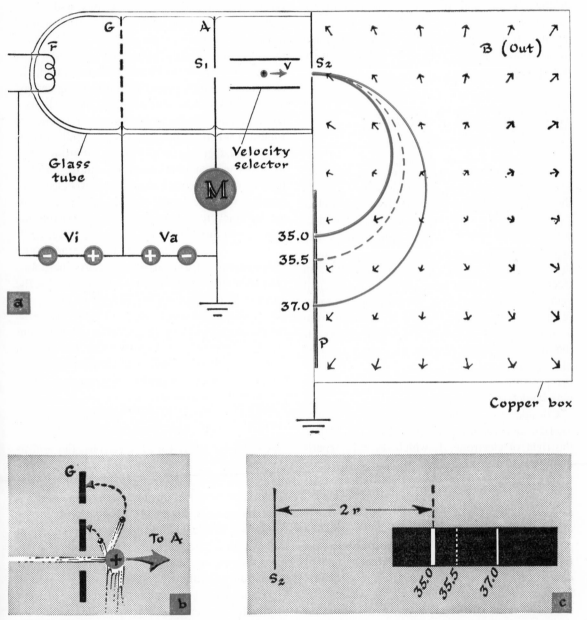

FIGURE **18-10** (a) *Schematic diagram of a mass spectrograph.* (b) *Gaseous ionization by electron impact.* (c) *Mass spectrum of chlorine.*

tinues to flow, diminishing very slowly, and is perceptible several days later. If the temperature is allowed to rise to the critical value, the metal suddenly regains its resistance, and the current stops. If the current is a stream of electrons, however, it has some momentum, due to the finite (if small) electronic mass. Since no external force is applied to the ring when the current stops, the momentum must be conserved in the system, and the ring should rotate in the direction in which the current has been flowing. It is found experimentally that under these conditions the ring does move forward perceptibly!

## 18-8. Ionization Potential; Electron Volt

Electrical conduction in solids, as we have seen, depends upon the "free" electrons. That is, the atoms of good conductors easily lose electrons. In the atoms of insulators, then, the electrons are presumably bound more tightly. But any insulator will conduct electricity if placed in a sufficiently strong electric field; that is, an electron may be freed from any atom if sufficient energy is available. This characteristic amount of energy, required to remove an electron from a neutral atom, is called ionization energy. If the atoms are in the gaseous state, they are free of any intermolecular forces (particularly if the pressure is low), and the ionization energy may be determined electrically.

Consider the apparatus diagramed in Figure 18-10a, and, for the present, neglect the part to the right of electrode $A$, which for this experiment would be solid (that is, there would be no opening at $S_1$). The electrode $G$ is a metallic mesh, and $F$ is a filament that can be heated by an electric current (circuit not shown). $G$ is made positive with respect to $F$ by a variable potential difference, $V_i$, and is also positive with respect to $A$ by a somewhat larger potential difference, $V_a$. As electrons from the heated filament are accelerated to $G$ by $V_i$, some strike the metal wires of the mesh but many shoot on through the holes between the wires. In the space between $G$ and $A$ the field is reversed, and,

since $V_a$ is larger than $V_i$, these electrons are deflected back to $G$. Thus no electrons from $F$ reach $A$, and the meter, $M$, shows no current. The substance to be investigated is introduced into the tube by auxiliary apparatus either directly, if it is a gas, or by vaporization, if it is a liquid or a solid. The pressure is adjusted so that the chance of impact is small until the electrons have traveled from $F$ to $G$. In the neighborhood of $G$, however, electrons with some kinetic energy begin to bombard the neutral atoms of the gas or vapor. If this KE is small, the electrons merely bound off the atom and are attracted back to $G$. As $V_i$ is increased, the electrons strike the atoms with increasing energy, and at a particular value of $V_i$ the meter shows a current. This can be understood by reference to Figure 18-10b, which shows a magnified view of a small region near $G$. The bombarding electron has just enough energy to remove an electron from the neutral atom. The two electrons, moving with negligible speed, are quickly attracted back to $G$, but the positive gaseous ion moves with the field and is accelerated over to $A$. This happens, of course, to many atoms, and thus a stream of ions arrives at $A$. As these ions pick up neutralizing electrons supplied by $V_a$, the meter registers a current. The value of $V_i$, for which the meter first shows current, gives the bombarding electrons the necessary kinetic energy to remove an electron from the neutral atom. This energy, which is the **ionization energy** for the atom, is, according to equation 17-9, given by the expression

$$\tfrac{1}{2}mv^2 = V_i e \qquad (18\text{-}6)$$

Since $e$ is the same for all electrons, the ionization energy is directly proportional to the potential difference $V_i$, which is the particular potential difference through which an electron must move in order to absorb sufficient energy from the electric field to ionize the atom upon impact. This potential difference, which is characteristic of the particular atom, is called its **ionization potential.**

The measured ionization potentials of the first fifty-eight elements of the periodic table are shown graphically in Figure 8-3. Here is one more property displaying the remarkable periodicity that is characteristic of atoms arranged by atomic number. If we start with any Group I element and move across the table, the ionization potential increases to a maximum for the inert gas at the end of the period. Then there is a drastic drop to a low value for the first element of the next period. Certainly the inert gases must be in a very stable situation, at least as far as the energy required for removing electrons is concerned. The Group I elements, at the other extreme, are in an unstable situation since an electron may be removed from them with relative ease. Associated with the change from low to high ionization potential is the change from metallic to non-metallic properties (from the lower left to the upper right of the periodic table). It is not surprising that, as we move from Group I to Group VII, we progress from good conductors to good insulators of electricity. In later chapters we shall find other evidence that is consistent with these relative stabilities of electron structures.

As shown by equation 18-6, the ionization energy was acquired by the motion of one electronic charge moving across a potential difference. This suggests a convenient unit of energy for this and other atomic experiments. The energy absorbed from an electric field by one electronic charge moving across a potential difference of one volt is a definite amount of energy and is called one **electron volt** (abbreviated as ev). This, according to equations 17-4 and 18-4,

would be $1 \frac{\text{joule}}{\text{coul}}$ $1.60 \times 10^{-19}$ coul or

$$ev = 1.60 \times 10^{-19} \text{ joule} \qquad (18\text{-}7)$$

Voltages millions of times as great as this are frequently encountered, and so we speak of millions of electron volts (Mev); and in very high-energy reactions we have billions of electron volts (Bev). Clearly, the electron volt is merely a convenient fraction of a joule and may express any amount of energy, whether it be the kinetic energy of a charged particle or not. Heats of reaction, thermal energies of neutral molecules, and the electrical energy of current-producing cells are examples of energies that may conveniently be expressed in ev for comparison with the energies of sub-atomic particles.

## 18-9. *Isotopes*

In 1815 an English physician, William Prout, impressed by the prevalence of whole numbers among the atomic weights, suggested the fascinating idea that all atoms are built of the same fundamental particle. He proposed the hypothesis that the lightest atom, hydrogen, with atomic weight 1, is the fundamental particle. Then twelve such particles, having coalesced in some manner, would make a carbon atom, sixteen an oxygen atom, and so on. With increasingly precise determinations of atomic weights, however, more and more deviations from this simple whole-number rule were found, and Prout's hypothesis had to be abandoned. An inspection of modern atomic weights will show that, although some are almost exactly whole numbers, many are not, and some (such as that of chlorine) are almost midway between two whole numbers. Nevertheless, almost a hundred years after Prout's suggestion, a discovery led to the revival of his hypothesis and raised new problems. Although this discovery was first made (by Thomson) about neon, we shall discuss it with reference to the more familiar element chlorine.

Refer again to Figure 18-10a, but this time consider the whole apparatus. Two slits, $S_1$ in $A$ and $S_2$ in the side of the copper box, are in a direct line. Chlorine at low pressure is introduced into the apparatus, and $V_i$ is adjusted to the ionization potential for chlorine. As the chlorine ions, $Cl^+$, are accelerated toward $A$, some, moving along the line from $S_1$ to $S_2$, fly straight through the slits and into the copper box. After passing through $S_1$ the ions move with constant speed, since there is no potential difference between $A$ and the box. The speed is determined by the proper adjustment of the velocity selector. When the ions pass through $S_2$, they enter a magnetic field $(B)$ that extends perpendicularly out from the plane of the diagram. (This field is due to a different electromagnet from that of the velocity selector.) Since the copper box shields the ions from any near-by electric field but not from magnetic field $B$, they move through a semicircle and strike a photographic plate, $P$. The energy of the ions reduces the emulsion, and a well-defined line is found on the developed plate (Fig. 18-10c). The relations among the pertinent quantities are given by equation 17-11, which, if solved for the radius of the circular path, yields

$$r = \frac{v}{B}\frac{m}{q} \qquad (18\text{-}8)$$

If we solve for the mass of the ion, we get

$$m = \frac{Brq}{v} \qquad (18\text{-}9)$$

When these experiments were first performed (from 1913 on), all these quantities except $m$ were directly measured. $B$, $r$, and $v$ came from the experimental apparatus, and, since $q$ is the positive charge on the ion due to the removal of one electron, its value, as measured by Millikan, was known (§ 18-5). And the mass of the ion could be computed from the atomic weight and Avogadro's number, both of which were known to good precision.† Thus the *expected* path of a chlorine ion of relative mass 35.5 could be calculated by equation 18-8; it is shown by the dashed semi-circle in Figure 18-10a. A stream of such ions would give rise to a line on the photographic plate (the dotted line of Fig. 18-10c). But, when the experiment is performed, *no such line is observed!* Instead, *two* lines are observed (the solid lines of 18-10c), and they result from paths (the solid semi-circles of 18-10a) of somewhat smaller and larger radii of curvature. These radii, substituted in equation 18-9, yield masses of 35 and 37. There is, it seems, *no chlorine atom of atomic weight 35.5.* There are, however, *two kinds* of chlorine, one of atomic weight 35 and the other of atomic weight 37.‡ In all other properties, however, these two kinds of chlorine are identical and consequently are not distinguishable by other methods of identification. Both therefore appear at the *same position* in the periodic listing of the elements. For this reason they are called **isotopes** of chlorine. (The name derives from two Greek

words meaning "same place.") We now expand our terminology. The position in the periodic table (atomic number) is written as a subscript to the left of the symbol for the element; and the whole-number mass (called the **mass number**) is written as a superscript to the right. Thus the two isotopes of chlorine are $_{17}Cl^{35}$ and $_{17}Cl^{37}$. In general, for any element R we have the symbol $_{Z}R^{A}$, in which $Z$ is the atomic number and $A$ is the mass number. (Note that this terminology still leaves at the right a space for the subscript that we may need in writing chemical formulas.)

Mass-spectrographic analyses of the other elements give similar results again and again. At the present time, approximately 300 stable isotopes of the elements are known.§ Some elements, including Ne (20, 21, 22) and B (10, 11), have, like Cl, only a few isotopes. Other elements, including Ca with six, Ni with five, and Sn with eight, have more. Certain elements, such as F, Na, Al, P, Co, I, and Au, have only one stable isotope each; for these the isotopic mass is the familiar atomic weight of the element. But what are *the* atomic weights of the others?

## 18-10. *Chemical Atomic Weights*

Mass-spectrographic observations give the answer to this question. Refer again to Figure 18-10c. It is *observed* that the line for mass number 35 is approximately three times as dense as the line for 37. There are, accordingly, three

---

† More accurately, this computation gives the mass of an atom, from which the mass of one electron (equation 18-5) must be subtracted. But this small correction may be neglected except in very precise work. For this reason, in the discussion of Table 18-1, we made no distinction between atomic and ionic masses.

‡ The apparatus separates ions of the same mass (and charge) and collects them in sharp lines on a photographic plate. The plate is similar in appearance to the photographs of optical spectra (Chap. 25), and hence the instrument is called a mass spectrograph. Various forms of mass spectrograph have been developed, but they all apply the same principles of electric and magnetic deflection. Such instruments yield very precise measurements. Analysis of the units of equation 18-9 shows that the absolute mass (kgm) of the ion is measured. To this is added the mass of an electron, and this atomic mass times $N_0$ gives the relative atomic "weight" of the periodic table. The two isotopes of chlorine, for instance, have masses 34.9780 and 36.9778. Isotopic masses are always given in this relative scale, and, since they are *always very nearly* whole numbers, they are referred to by the appropriate whole numbers.

§ The much more numerous unstable *radioactive* isotopes will be discussed in a later chapter.

chlorine atoms of mass 35 for every one of mass 37. The mass spectrograph gives the *relative abundance* of the isotopes in any sample of the element. Any naturally occurring sample of chlorine contains 75 percent (75.4%) isotope 35 and 25 percent (24.6%) isotope 37. The two isotopes have identical chemical properties and behave exactly alike in any reaction. Remember, however, that chemical atomic weights are determined from combining weights (§ 7-6) in reactions that involve *large* numbers of atoms, apportioned in accordance with the relative abundance of the isotopes. The chemical atomic weight, therefore, is not a fundamental constant, but is a *statistical average* of the fundamental isotopic masses. The mass of 100 chlorine atoms, for instance, is equal to $75 \times 35$ plus $25 \times 37$ or $2,620 + 925 = 3,545$ units of mass. This, divided by 100, gives 35.45 as the average atomic weight of chlorine; but no atom with this mass exists. Similar calculations give the chemically determined atomic weights of the periodic table.

The discovery of isotopes and the whole-number character of their masses, combined with the measured relative abundance, led to a general law of chemical atomic weights. This law, called the **whole-number rule,** states that any atomic weight that is not a whole number is due to a mixture of isotopes, each of which has a whole-number atomic weight.† On the other hand, the constancy of chemically determined atomic weights indicates that the relative abundance of the isotopes must be very constant in naturally occurring samples of the elements. Repeated mass-spectrographic analyses show that this is so. The reader will remember that, in listing the elements in the order of increasing atomic weight, we were forced to *reverse* the order for three pairs of elements (§ 8-10) in order to place them in a group consistent with all their properties except atomic weight. The isotopic mixtures of these elements explain this arbitrary reversal of order. Argon, for instance, has three stable isotopes with mass numbers and (approximate) percent abundance as follows: 36 (0.3%), 38 (0 1%), and 40 (99.6%). *All* these iso-

topes have the properties of inert gases, but, because of the high abundance of 40, the atomic weight of argon is 39.9. Potassium also has three stable isotopes (all with properties like those of the other alkali metals) as follows: 39 (93.4%), 40 (a trace), and 41 (6.6%). But here, since the *lightest* isotope is the most abundant, the atomic weight is 39.1. The iodine-tellurium case is still more striking. Iodine has only *one* stable isotope, and it has mass number 127. Tellurium has eight stable isotopes ranging from 120 to 130. But the low isotopic masses are in low abundance, whereas 128 and 130 account for 67 percent of the mixture. Hence the atomic weight of tellurium is 127.6. Similarly, cobalt (with one isotope, 59) and nickel (with five, but 68% of 58) are reversed. Thus we see that these reverses are justified by the fundamental property of isotopic masses. In Part Three of this book we shall see that the physical significance of atomic number further verifies the wisdom of neglecting these apparent discrepancies in the increasing order of atomic weight.

## 18-11. *Physical Atomic Weights*

Some elements have very low percentages of all isotopes but one. The isotopes of very low abundance are called *rare isotopes*. Hydrogen is a particularly interesting example. There are two isotopes of hydrogen, $_1H^1$ and $_1H^2$. The precise masses and abundances are 1.00786 (99.98%) and 2.01418 (0.02%). Although the heavy isotope is almost twice as massive, its abundance is so small that it cannot account for the chemical atomic weight (1.0080). Most of the atomic weight of hydrogen is due to the abundant lighter isotope, which makes hydrogen the exception to the whole-number rule mentioned above. The heavy isotope (frequently called deuterium, $_1D^2$) is of great theoretical interest because it is the next simplest atom to hydrogen. Accelerated deuterium ions are very useful "projectiles" in certain atomic researches; and water formed with deuterium ("heavy water," $D_2O$) is useful in atomic-energy developments.

Rare isotopes of other elements were observed, and in 1929 oxygen itself was found to

---

† Hydrogen is the only exception to this rule; but it does have isotopes.

have two rare isotopes. The three isotopes of oxygen are $_8O^{16}$ (99.76%), $_8O^{17}$ (0.04%), and $_8O^{18}$ (0.20%). This fact presents a curious ambiguity in the definition of our standard for atomic weights. For the scale of chemical atomic weights the value 16.00000 is assigned to the *statistical average of all three isotopes*. But this is difficult to interpret for isotopic masses. In mass-spectrographic analysis, 16.00000 is assigned to the isotope of greatest abundance. On this basis then, the relative masses and abundances of the oxygen isotopes give an "atomic weight" for oxygen of 16.00446. Atomic weights based on this value for oxygen constitute the "physicist's scale." Atomic weights on the physical scale are slightly larger than those on the chemical scale. The ratio of physical to chemical scale is easily computed and comes out to be 1.00028. This very small ratio may be neglected in most situations, but the high precision (six or seven significant figures) of mass-spectrographic measurements† requires this distinction if ambiguity in isotopic masses is to be avoided. Hence isotopes are always listed on the physical scale. In Part Three we shall discuss a phenomenon that requires a rigid adherence to one scale.

## 18-12. Atomic Number

Refer once more to Figure 18-10a. Suppose that the accelerating voltage, $V_i$, is made much higher than the ionization potential of the atom under investigation. The energy of the bombarding electrons is now much greater than the ionizing energy of the atom and may well remove more than one electron upon impact. Such doubly or triply ionized atoms are easily detected. Equation 18-8 shows that, if $q$ is $2e$, then $r$ is only half as much; that, if $q$ is $3e$, then $r$ is one-third as much; and so on. Thus the presence of multiple charges on the ions is unambiguously revealed by the position of the line on plate $P$. Such ions have been observed, and many measurements of their charges have been recorded.

---

† Note the precise isotopic masses of chlorine in the second footnote of § 18-9. The masses of the hydrogen isotopes given in this section were reduced to the chemical scale to facilitate comparison with the periodic table.

No amount of mass-spectrographic research, however, has ever revealed a hydrogen ion with more than one electronic charge. We conclude that the hydrogen atom contains only one electron. Similarly, helium has been observed as singly and doubly, but never triply, ionized. The helium atom, therefore, can have only two electrons. Lithium shows a maximum charge of three and carbon of six. As each electron is removed, however, it becomes increasingly difficult to strip another from the atom. Conclusive evidence of this kind for the maximum number of electrons is therefore available for only a few of the lighter elements. For these, however, the number of electrons in the atom is equal to the atomic number; and, since the normal atom is electrically neutral, the number of positive electronic charges in the atom is also equal to the atomic number. This gives us a clue to the significance of the atomic number, which in Part Three we shall see is a general rule throughout the whole periodic table.

## 18-13. Summary

In this chapter we have considered some of the experiments that first required a radical change in our view of the structure of matter. No longer are atoms the ultimate, indivisible particles into which an element can be subdivided. Nor are all the atoms of an element identical (§ 6-5). These results, however, do not vitiate the atomic view of matter but extend and strengthen it. The discovery of isotopes and their very nearly whole-number masses revived interest in the hypothesis that all atoms are built of some fundamental particle. But is the particle hydrogen? Here we run into difficulties. Since, as we have seen, hydrogen has a mass somewhat (almost 1%) larger than 1, four hydrogens add up to 4.03 and not to 4.003, as observed for helium. More serious, perhaps, is the violation of the conservation of charge. Four hydrogens would give helium four electrons, and we have seen that helium contains only two. Thus mass-spectrographic data at once confirm and question Prout's hypothesis. The isotopic masses, furthermore, are not *exactly* whole numbers but deviate (by about 0.1%), as shown by the precise mass-spectrographic measurements.

Thus new knowledge generates new questions. If atoms are built from one or a few fundamental particles, what is their nature? How account for the small but definite deviation of isotopic masses from whole-number values? Can the positive electricity of the atoms be accounted for by some universal and fundamental entity, as the electron accounts for the negative electricity? And, finally, how can the mass of atoms be accounted for, and what is the spatial distribution of the particles within an atom? Much of the rest of this book will be directed toward finding answers to these questions.

## Concepts and Terms

Electrolytic Ions
    integral relation of ionic charge
    ratio of charge to mass
    maximum value of $q/m$ for hydrogen
    Stoney's electron
Conduction Through Gases
    mechanism of discharge—cumulative ionization
    effect of pressure on discharge
Cathode Rays
    fluorescent effects
    source of the rays
    property of inertia
The Electron
    Thomson's method of measuring the ratio of charge to mass for cathode particles
    universality of value of $e/m$
    magnitude of $e/m$; interpretation
    Millikan's measurement of electronic charge
    universality of electronic charge
    mass of electron and of atoms

Electron Theory of Metallic Conduction
Ionization Potentials
    ionization energy
    periodicity of ionization potentials of the elements
The Electron Volt of Energy
Isotopes
    whole-number relative masses
    isotopic nomenclature
Atomic Weights
    relative abundance of isotopes of an element
    chemical atomic weights as statistical averages
    whole-number rule
    rare isotopes
    physical atomic-weight scale
Atomic Number
    total number of electrons in light atoms
    significance of atomic number

## Problems

**18-1.**

(A) In electrolysis sodium forms the ion $Na^+$. What is the value of $q/m$ for this ion? (See Table 18-1 for $H^+$.)

(B) Tin forms the ion $Sn^{+4}$. What is the value of $q/m$ for this ion?

          *Ans.* (A) $4.17 \times 10^6$ coul/kgm
                (B) $3.23 \times 10^6$ coul/kgm

**18-2.** In a certain experiment to determine $e/m$ for cathode rays the deflecting plates were 0.02 m apart and at a potential difference of 800 volts. The electric deflection was neutralized by a magnetic field of $1.5 \times 10^{-3}$ newton/amp m. When the potential difference was removed, the ray moved along a circle of 0.101 m radius. Calculate $e/m$.

**18-3.** In an $e/m$ experiment for cathode rays the deflecting plates were 1 cm apart and at a po-tential difference of 790 volts. The electric de-flection was neutralized by a magnetic field of $3 \times 10^{-3}$ newton/amp m. When the potential difference was removed and the magnetic field reduced to $1.25 \times 10^{-3}$ newton/amp m, the ray was observed to move along a circle of 12 cm radius. Calculate $e/m$.

**18-4.** In a Millikan oil-drop experiment the sepa-ration of the plates was $5 \times 10^{-3}$ m.

(A) With a potential difference of $1.2 \times 10^3$ volts between the plates and the top plate positive, a drop with mass of $1.18 \times 10^{-14}$ kgm was brought into equilibrium. What was the charge on the drop?

(B) The air was ionized, the charge on the drop was changed, and then $9 \times 10^2$ volts, with the top plate negative, was required to bring the drop into equilibrium. What was the new charge on the drop?

(c) Did the drop lose or gain electrons? How many?

> *Ans.* (A) $-4.8 \times 10^{-19}$ coul
> (B) $+6.4 \times 10^{-19}$ coul
> (c) lost 7 electrons

**18-5.**

(A) Calculate the masses of the $Al^{+3}$ and the $Cu^{+2}$ ions. (The data of Table 18-1 are pertinent.)

(B) Calculate the ratio of the mass of the copper ion to the mass of the aluminum ion. Compare with the ratio of their atomic weights.

> *Ans.* (B) 2.34

**18-6.** The current through a 60-watt light bulb is 0.5 amp. How many electrons pass through the lamp per second?

> *Ans.* $3.12 \times 10^{18}$

**18-7.**

(A) Calculate the electric repulsion between two electrons that are $3 \times 10^{-10}$ m apart (this is approximately the diameter of atoms).

(B) Calculate the gravitational attraction (§ 5-3) between the electrons. Use $10^{-30}$ kgm as the electron mass.

(c) How many times larger is the electric force than the gravitational force?

> *Ans.* $F_{elect}/F_{grav} = 3.44 \times 10^{42}$. The gravitational force is indeed negligible!

**18-8.**

(A) The ionization energy for neon is $3.44 \times 10^{-18}$ joule. Convert this to electron volts. Compare the result with the ionization potential for neon, which is 21.5 volts. Discuss.

(B) What kinetic energy in ev would a hydrogen ion, $H^+$, acquire in being accelerated through a potential difference of $10^5$ volts? A deuterium ion, $D^+$? A doubly ionized helium atom, $He^{+2}$?

> *Ans.* (B) $10^5$ ev for $H^+$ and $D^+$;
> $2 \times 10^5$ ev for $He^{+2}$

**18-9.** Calculate the speed acquired by the ions of Prob. 18-8B. The mass of $H^+$ is $1.67 \times 10^{-27}$ kgm. Use 1, 2, and 4 as the atomic weights of H, D, and He. (A little thought will save considerable arithmetic. Be sure the units are consistent.)

> *Ans.* $4.38 \times 10^6$ m/sec for $H^+$; $3.10 \times 10^6$ m/sec for $D^+$ and $He^{+2}$

**18-10.** A particle carrying a charge of $3.2 \times 10^{-19}$ coul moves at right angles to a magnetic field with a speed of $1.96 \times 10^7$ m/sec. The particle is observed to move in a circle of 0.5 m radius.

(A) What is the mass of the particle if the magnetic induction is 0.817 newton/amp m?

(B) The particle is an atomic ion. What is the ion?

(c) How many volts of potential difference were required to give the particle the observed speed? (Hint: Express the kinetic energy in ev.)

> *Ans.* (A) $6.67 \times 10^{-27}$ kgm
> (c) $4 \times 10^6$ volts

**18-11.** The mass numbers and approximate percent abundances of the isotopes of a certain element are 65 (30%) and 63 (70%).

(A) Calculate the atomic weight of the element.

(B) Write the symbols for the two isotopes.

**18-12.** Consider neon as a mixture of $_{10}Ne^{20}$ and $_{10}Ne^{22}$. Calculate the relative abundances of these isotopes.

> *Ans.* 20, 91%; 22, 9%

**18-13.** Write six different formulas for a water molecule.

**18-14.** How many electrons would you expect a chlorine atom to contain? Would this number be the same for both the 35 and the 37 isotope?

**18-15.**

(A) Calculate the values of $q/m$ for the singly ionized $Cl^{35}$ and $Cl^{37}$ isotopes.

(B) Suppose that these ions passed through $S_2$ (Fig. 18-10a) with a speed of $3 \times 10^5$ m/sec. Calculate the separation of the lines on the photographic plate, $P$, if $B$ equals 0.435 newton/amp m.

> *Ans.* (A) $2.74 \times 10^6$ and $2.59 \times 10^6$ coul/kgm
> (B) 5.0 cm

**18-16.**

(A) Consider the segment of conductor shown in Fig. 18-8 to be a copper wire 1 cm long and $10^{-2}$ cm$^2$ in cross section. If each copper atom contributes one free electron as shown, calculate the number, $n$, of free electrons in the segment. The density of copper is 8.89 grams/cm$^3$.

(B) If the current through the segment is 10 amp, calculate the time required for the $n$ electrons to migrate out of the segment, and then calculate the speed of migration. (See § 17-8.)

> *Ans.* (A) $8.42 \times 10^{20}$
> (B) 0.074 cm/sec

# Suggested Readings

1. M. Born, *The Restless Universe,* translated by W. M. Deans (Dover Publications, 1951), pp. 55–69 and 88–95 (on electrons).
2. L. W. Taylor, *Physics the Pioneer Science* (Houghton Mifflin, 1941), pp. 626–629 and 769–788.
3. H. E. White, *Modern College Physics,* third edition (Van Nostrand, 1956), pp. 580–600. Also see p. 798 for a complete list of stable isotopes; the mass numbers in parentheses are those of rare isotopes.
4. R. F. Humphreys and R. Beringer, *First Principles of Atomic Physics* (Harper, 1950), pp. 148–155 and 199–221.
5. R. A. Millikan, *Electrons (+ and −),* revised edition (University of Chicago Press, 1947), pp. 1–89. Readable and authoritative discussion of the electron, with many references to his original work.
6. W. F. Magie, *A Source Book in Physics* (McGraw-Hill, 1935), pp. 563–576 (Crookes on the cathode discharge), 580–583 (Perrin on the negative charge of the cathode rays), and 583–597 (Thomson on the electron).

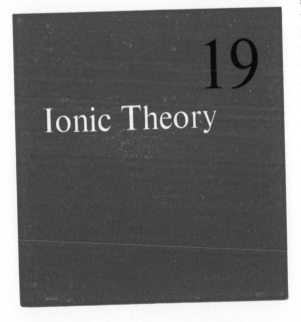

CHAPTER

19

Ionic Theory

THE LAST section of Chapter 14, in considering the anomalous colligative properties of one class of solutes, pointed out that this experimentally observed anomaly threatened the explanation of colligative properties in terms of the kinetic-molecular theory and thereby threatened the whole theory itself. A parallel was drawn between the abnormally high colligative properties of the one class of solutions and the fact of electrical conductance by the same class of solutions. It was further suggested that there is a common explanation of the two observations—conductance and high colligative properties. This explanation was that the molecules of solute dissociate in solution into more than one particle per molecule and that these particles have an electrical quality that allows them to conduct an electric current. This postulate also, by implication, attributed to atoms and molecules an electrical quality that is totally extraneous to the simple mechanical view of the structure of matter on which all of Part One of this text was based. It implied that the atoms are not the simple, structureless, unchanging spheres that were postulated in the first atomic theory of Dalton, and it further suggested that the nature of the chemical bond that holds atoms together in compound substances must be, at least in part, electrical. Consideration of the possibility that some solutes dissociate in solution, which was most tentatively suggested in Chapter 14, has been deferred until this point so that we might first study the phenomenon of electricity; for a knowledge of the nature of electricity and the concepts related to electricity are necessary if we are to pursue successfully the expansion of the suggestion into a coherent theory.

## 19-1. Simple Statement of Ionic Theory

This theory, which is called the **ionic theory,** was first proposed in 1887 by Svante Arrhenius, a Swedish physical chemist who had just completed his work for the Ph.D. degree. Arrhenius considered the two phenomena that we have mentioned, conductance and high colligative properties. He also considered a third phenomenon, which exactly parallels the first two: the rate of chemical reactions in solutions. We shall examine this problem in some detail in a later chapter, but it is possible now to point out the generalization that Arrhenius used. It is observed experimentally that most reactions between salts, acids, or bases in solution take place extremely fast—so fast as to be instantaneous by almost any method of timing. On the other hand, most reactions of compounds such as alcohol, sugar, and glycerine—organic compounds in general— take place slowly. The division into two classes of compounds according to speed of reaction in solution is exactly parallel to the division according to colligative properties and conductance in solution.

Consideration of these three phenomena in the two classes of compounds, as they are summarized in Table 19-1, led Arrhenius to propose the ionic theory. This theory postulates that the substances of Class I dissociate in solution into two or more particles per molecule and that these particles, called **ions,** are electrically charged.

This theory, now completely accepted, has been expanded considerably from the simple statement above. The experimental basis of this acceptance is still, in part, the three phenomena on which it was originally based. These are now readily explained by the kinetic-molecular theory and its extension, the postulates of the ionic theory. But there is also a good deal of independent experimental evidence, some of which will be considered in this and subsequent chapters, that establishes this theory as completely as any scientific theory is ever established.

In this chapter we shall expand the simple statement of the theory, first by considering in detail the relation of the theory to the three phenomena mentioned, and then by considering some of the consequences and extensions of the theory.

## 19-2. *Colligative Properties*

The experimental fact that first led to the consideration of a structure of matter more complex than the simple, indestructible spheres of the original mechanical atomic-molecular theory is the existence of anomalous colligative properties. Certain compounds show, in water solution, colligative properties (changes in vapor pressure, boiling point, freezing point, and osmotic pressure) that differ from the expected "normal" values by factors of 2, 3, or even 4. The "normal" values are those predicted by a theory that assumes that the magnitude of the colligative property depends on the number of solute particles in a given quantity of solvent and that the number of particles is equal to the number of *molecules* of solute. This theory was quite effective in relating this important part of the behavior of substances in solution to the kinetic-molecular theory, which was first postulated for gaseous substances. The theory failed, however, to include large classes of substances (salts, acids, and bases) in the explanation—a failure that threatened the usefulness of the whole kinetic-molecular theory.

This impasse can be avoided, however, if we examine more closely the postulate that the number of *particles* of solute is equal to the number of *molecules*. This postulate is, of course, quite reasonable; indeed, it seems to be an absolute requirement of the theories of the structure of matter that have been the basis of the first part of this text. It is, however, only an *assumption* that molecules remain intact under most circumstances, and it is obviously necessary to assume that they "come apart," or *dissociate,* in chemical reactions. Arrhenius had the boldness to suggest that compounds of one class—Class I of Table 19-1—are always dissociated into submolecular fragments when in solution. This idea was by no means attractive to scientists who had depended on and become attached to the purely

| TABLE **19-1**  *Properties of Solutes* | |
|---|---|
| *Class I* SALTS, ACIDS, BASES | *Class II* ORGANIC COMPOUNDS |
| Conducting solutions | Non-conducting solutions |
| Anomalous colligative properties | Normal colligative properties |
| Instantaneous reactions | Slow reactions |

mechanical theory of the structure of matter. It was necessary, moreover, to advance experimental evidence of such a dissociation of molecules in solution. A good deal of such evidence was available to Arrhenius, and it will be discussed in this and subsequent chapters.

Within Arrhenius' theory of dissociation the multiple values of the colligative properties of Class I substances are no longer anomalous. Sodium chloride, for example, exists in solution, not as the molecule NaCl, but as two separate particles, the Na ion and the Cl ion. A 1 molal solution of NaCl therefore contains *two* moles of particles per 1,000 grams of solvent, 1 mole of Na ions and 1 mole of Cl ions, and the observed freezing point of such a solution, about $-3.6°$, is what would be expected (that is, normal) according to our original interpretation, by which 1 mole of *particles* of solute lowers the freezing point of water about $1.8°$. Similarly, salts such as calcium chloride, $CaCl_2$, and potassium sulfate, $K_2SO_4$, give rise to *three* particles per molecule (one Ca ion and two Cl ions for $CaCl_2$ and two K ions and one $SO_4$ ion for $K_2SO_4$). The experimentally observed freezing-point depression caused by 1 mole of either of these salts in 1,000 grams of water is approximately *three* times the molal-freezing-point-depression constant of $1.8°$ per mole, which is just what would be expected if the postulated dissociation took place. The "anomalously" high colligative properties of the compounds of Class I are perfectly "normal" provided we assume dissociation of the molecules of these substances in solution.

## 19-3. Ionic Charge

In our first encounter with the phenomena associated with electricity in Chapter 16 the concepts of conduction of electricity and separation of charges of opposite sign were established. It was arbitrarily assumed that only the negative charge moves in an ordinary electric circuit, and later, in Chapter 18, the nature of metallic conduction of electric currents was explained, and the basis for the earlier arbitrary assumption was established. A consideration of conduction by solutions raises this question: What is the carrier

of current in solutions? It might seem reasonable to assume again, as in metallic conduction, that freely movable electrons are the carriers. There are two good reasons for avoiding such an assumption. First, we have already postulated freely moving particles, the ions, in such solutions, and it is an unnecessary complication to postulate still another freely moving particle, the electron. It is therefore conservative of assumptions to attribute the carrying of the current to the ions. But the more effective reason for avoiding such an assumption is found in the facts of electrolysis. It is observed experimentally that actual migration of the ions takes place under the influence of the electric field (see Chap. 21). It is therefore necessary to the ionic theory that the current in solution conduction be carried by the ions that arise from the dissociation of the molecules of the solute.

The undissociated form of any substance is electrically neutral. It is therefore obvious that ionic dissociation must give rise to exactly equal numbers of opposite charges among the ions formed. Furthermore, the only reasonable assumption is that all ions of the same element arising from the same compound are similar in charge, both in sign and in magnitude. Thus one type of ion arising from the dissociation of any substance in solution is a negative ion, and the other is a positive ion. The products of dissociation of a molecule of sodium chloride, for example, are an Na ion and a Cl ion, one of which is charged positively and the other negatively. The experimental evidence as to which is positive and which negative will be considered later; at this point it is only necessary to accept the logical requirement that the two types must be charged oppositely and that the total positive charges on the one type must exactly equal the total negative charges on the other type so that the undissociated compound may be electrically neutral. At this stage the decision as to which is positive and which negative is arbitrary; but again, in order to avoid confusion later, we shall make the arbitrary choice in accordance with the actual fact, which will not be proved until later. The sodium ions are charged positively and may be symbolized as $Na^+$; the chloride ions are charged negatively and have the symbol $Cl^-$. In general, the metal ions, such as Cu, K, Mg, Hg, and Ag, have positive charges, the elemental non-metal ions have negative charges, and the negative radicals of Table 7-8, as ions, have negative charges.

## 19-4. *Ionic Conductance*

A physical picture of a solution of sodium chloride in water is indicated in Figure 19-1a. A large number of charged particles (equal numbers of $Na^+$ and $Cl^-$ ions) are freely and randomly dispersed in the water. These particles undergo the constant random thermal motion required by the kinetic theory, and the motions of the oppositely charged particles are entirely independent of each other. The essential difference between this picture and that of a metallic conductor (Fig. 18-8) is that in a solution *both* the positively and the negatively charged particles are free to move but in a metal *only* the negatively charged particles (the electrons) are free.

Figure 19-1b indicates diagrammatically the situation that obtains when a solution becomes a conductor—that is, when a solution becomes one component in an electrical circuit. One metallic plate (the nature of the plate is immaterial except that it be a conductor) is charged positively and the other negatively. This situation is similar to that of Figure 17-5, in which a charged particle is placed between two charged plates. Under these circumstances the particle will suffer a force, the magnitude of which will depend on the magnitude of the charge on the particle and of the electric field between the two conducting plates, and the direction of which will depend on the relative signs of the charges on the particle and on the plates. A positively charged particle will be forced away from the positively charged plate and toward the negatively charged plate, and a negatively charged particle will be forced in the opposite direction. Since the ions (unlike the *atoms* but like the electrons in a metal) are free to move, the effect of the force will be the migration of the ions toward the oppositely charged

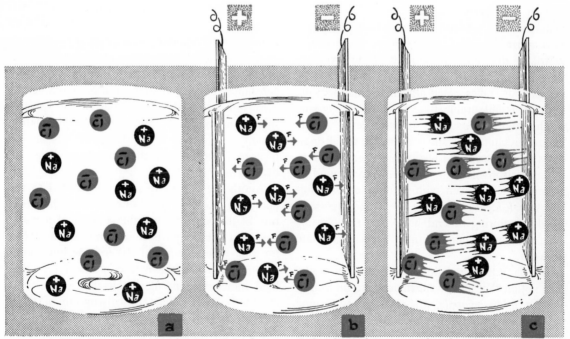

FIGURE **19-1** *Electrolytic conduction:* (a) *the oppositely charged ions are distributed at random;* (b) *the two electrodes, charged by connection to a source of electric current, exert an electrostatic force, F, on each of the charged ions, as in Fig. 17-5;* (c) *each ion, under the influence of the force, moves toward the electrode of opposite charge.*

plates. Both the positive and the negative ions will migrate, and the conduction of the current will be accomplished (Fig. 19-1c) by the motion of charges carried by the ions.

## 19-5. Reaction Rates

A reaction of the type illustrated by sodium bromide and silver nitrate producing sodium nitrate and insoluble silver bromide—

$$NaBr + AgNO_3 \longrightarrow NaNO_3 + \underline{AgBr}$$

—is sometimes called a double decomposition reaction. The substances involved are typical salts, solutions of which have anomalously high colligative properties and are conductors of electric current. A very similar-appearing reaction involves the organic compound ethyl bromide, $C_2H_5Br$:

$$C_2H_5Br + AgOH \longrightarrow C_2H_5OH + \underline{AgBr}$$

But ethyl bromide is quite different in most of its properties from the salts of the first reaction; it is a volatile liquid, very slightly soluble in water, and its solutions are non-conducting and have normal colligative properties. There is also a striking difference in the rates of the two reactions. The first one, which involves only ionic compounds, takes place almost instantaneously, without a measurable time between the mixing of the solutions and the appearance of a pale yellow precipitate of silver bromide, which indicates that the reaction has taken place. The second, which involves the non-ionic compound, is extremely slow; even with heat or other influences to force the reaction, it takes place very slowly, requiring several hours for the appearance of an appreciable quantity of the precipitate of AgBr.

If both of these reactions are viewed under the assumption that all the substances are molecular (that is, *undissociated*), it is necessary to assume that the stages of the reaction must include the disruption of the chemical bonds of the reactants and the formation of the two bonds of the products. Each of these steps requires time, and the rate of the reaction would depend on the amount of time required for the *slowest* step. It is com-

pletely reasonable (and has in recent years been proved) that the slow steps in chemical reactions are the *disruption* of existing chemical bonds. Now the ionic theory of dissociation postulates that ionic compounds (those of Class I in Table 19-1) are already dissociated in solution. There can, therefore, be no delay in disrupting the bonds of the reactants in an ionic reaction. Organic (non-ionic) compounds such as ethyl bromide, however, do not dissociate in solution, and the speed of reactions involving such compounds will therefore be limited by the slow disruption of the chemical bond. The instantaneous reaction of ionic (Class I) compounds serves, then, as a major piece of evidence supporting the ionic theory of dissociation.

## 19-6. Questions Raised by Postulation of the Ionic Theory

Having phrased the ionic theory of dissociation, we must now face some of the questions raised by this theory. The first of these are concerned with the degree of dissociation: Are all ionic substances dissociated entirely in solution, or are they only partially ionized? Is dissociation unique to the dissolved state, or is a solid or liquid substance ionized? If ionization is unique to the dissolved state, what properties of the solvent-solute relation cause ionization? If dissociation is only partial, how is the degree of dissociation measured, and what factors affect the degree of dissociation?

Another group of questions is related to the necessary modification of our views on the structure of molecules: Does the concept of a *molecule* of a compound have any real meaning (a) for ionic compounds and (b) for non-ionic compounds? What is the nature of the forces that hold molecular and non-molecular compounds together? What causes the disruption of these forces? What is the meaning of "valence" in terms of the ionic theory?

Still another group of questions is related to the charges on the ions: What is the sign of the charge on the various ions, and how can it be determined? What is the magnitude of the ionic charge, and how can this be determined? What is the relation of ionic charge to electrons? to valence? to solid-state structure? What is the relation of ions in solution to the gaseous ions?

Many of these questions are interrelated, and the complete answers to some are beyond the scope of this text. But we must consider most of these in order to take advantage of the great step in our understanding of the structure of matter that is offered by the ionic theory.

## 19-7. Degree of Dissociation from Measurements of Colligative Properties

A method of measuring the degrees of dissociation—or of testing whether or not dissociation is complete—is suggested by the experimental facts that first led to the ionic theory. If a compound is not dissociated at all in solution, the amount by which the freezing point is lowered by a given concentration of the compound as a solute can be calculated from the molal concentration and the freezing-point constant, $k_F$. If a compound is *totally* dissociated into ions in solution, the amount by which the freezing point is lowered should be an *exact* multiple of the freezing-point depression calculated from the molal concentration and $k_F$. Any deviation from the exact multiple could then be interpreted as a

deviation from total dissociation. Table 19-2 shows experimental measurements of the freezing points of 0.1 molal solutions of several salts. The last column of this table indicates the ratio of the observed freezing-point depression to the depression that would be expected if there were complete dissociation into the number of ions indicated by the formula of the compound. In all cases the calculated "degree of dissociation" is somewhat less than 100 percent. Such data were originally thought to mean that substances such as these were not totally ionized in solution; it was believed, for example, that 92.7 percent of the KCl in a 0.1 molal solution existed in the ionic form as $K^+$ and $Cl^-$ and the remainder, 7.3 percent, as molecular potassium chloride, KCl. More recent information (some of which will be considered below) indicates, however, that *all* salts and most of the inorganic acids and bases are *totally* ionized. The present interpretation of the data given in the table is that a deviation from complete dissociation is the result of several different types of interaction of the ions with each other and with the solvent (water), so that, in effect, the ions are not able to act entirely independently of each other. One possible contribution to this complex of interactions is the reassociation of some of the oppositely charged ions. But the major factors are probably other than this.

## 19-8. Ions in Molten Salts

The most effective evidence of total ionization of most salts in solution is the fact that these salts are ionized in both the liquid and the solid state. A rather simple demonstration shows the existence of ions in the liquid state of salts. If a simple apparatus for a conductance test, such as that diagramed in Figure 19-2, is set up so that the two electrodes are separated by a solid salt, such as NaCl, no current will flow; the solid salt is an insulator. If the salt is melted, however, the lamp begins to glow and then burns brightly, indicating that the *liquid* salt is now a conductor. This flow of current can only be interpreted as due to ions that are free, in the liquid state, to move under the influence of the potential differ-

| TABLE 19-2 | *Degree of Dissociation from Freezing-Point Depression* | | |
|---|---|---|---|
| COMPOUND | NUMBER OF IONS | FREEZING POINT † | DEGREE OF DISSOCIATION |
| NaCl | 2 | $-0.348°$ | 93.6% |
| KCl | 2 | $-0.345$ | 92.7 |
| HCl | 2 | $-0.356$ | 95.6 |
| $KNO_3$ | 2 | $-0.330$ | 88.8 |
| $MgSO_4$ | 2 | $-0.246$ | 66.2 |
| $Na_2SO_4$ | 3 | $-0.459$ | 80.8 |
| $K_2SO_4$ | 3 | $-0.456$ | 80.4 |
| $BaCl_2$ | 3 | $-0.478$ | 84.4 |
| $K_3Fe(CN)_6$ | 4 | $-0.530$ | 71.5 |

† Freezing point of 0.1 molal solution.

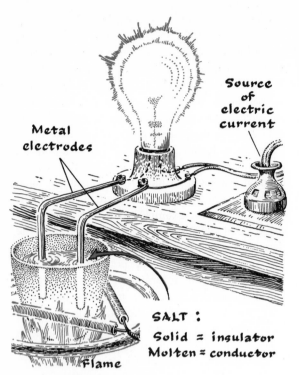

Metal
electrodes

Source
of
electric
current

SALT :

Solid = insulator
Molten = conductor

Flame

FIGURE **19-2** *Demonstration of electrical conduction by a molten salt.*

ence between the two electrodes. The reason why the solid salt does not conduct is not that no ions are present but that the ions, being *fixed* in the solid state, cannot move and therefore cannot carry the electric current. It could be assumed that the heat that melts the salt also causes the formation of ions. This is an unnecessarily complicating assumption, and there is good, even though indirect, evidence that salts are ionized in the solid state.

## 19-9. Ions in Solid Salts

The major evidence that leads us to believe that solid salts are ionized is found in the structure of crystals of salts. It is possible, by a method called *X-ray diffraction,* which will be considered in Part Three, to determine exactly the spacing of the atoms in a crystalline solid. The method is technically difficult, but at this stage it is only the result of the method that interests us. This result is that the spatial arrangement of the atoms in most simple crystals is known with a high

degree of certainty and precision. An example of the crystalline distribution of atoms is indicated in Figure 19-3a. The structure of this crystal (NaCl) is a cube (see § 12-1), and this gross structure is a manifestation of the sub-microscopic arrangement of the Na atoms and Cl atoms in a cubic pattern. It has been proved that this cubic arrangement consists of an alternation of Na and Cl atoms in all three directions, and the spacing of the atoms is *exactly the same* in all of the three mutually perpendicular directions. It is clear that no single Cl atom can be attributed to a single Na atom to make up a molecule of NaCl. Rather, *six* Cl ions are equally associated with each Na ion (Fig. 19-3b), and each of the Cl ions is equally associated with six Na ions (Fig. 19-3c). It is therefore impossible to attribute to NaCl a molecular structure in which an atom of Na is combined with an atom of Cl. The only possible interpretation of such a structure as that of Figure 19-3 is that the atoms are charged and are therefore ions. The ions are held together by coulombic forces, and the structure is disrupted (for example, by melting or dissolving) by the overcoming of these coulombic forces.

Obviously, the fragments indicated in Figure 19-3bc are not electrically neutral. The diagrams simply indicate the immediate environment of a particular Na ion and a particular Cl ion in the crystal. It must be remembered that in any sensible particle of NaCl tremendous numbers of both types of ions are aggregated in this basic cubic pattern. The broken lines in the diagrams indicate lines of coulombic force toward the adjacent, oppositely charged ions, which are left out of the picture to avoid confusion in the drawing. It is apparent that the single charge on an Na ion is "neutralized" by 1/6 of the single charge on each of six Cl ions, and that the charge on each Cl ion is associated with 1/6 of the unit charge on each of six Na ions, to accomplish the necessary electrical neutrality of any gross sample of NaCl.

Another proof of the existence of ions in solid salts is the high melting points of salts. It takes a very high degree of thermal agitation to disrupt the coulombic forces that hold the ions together in patterns like that of Figure 19-3. The melting

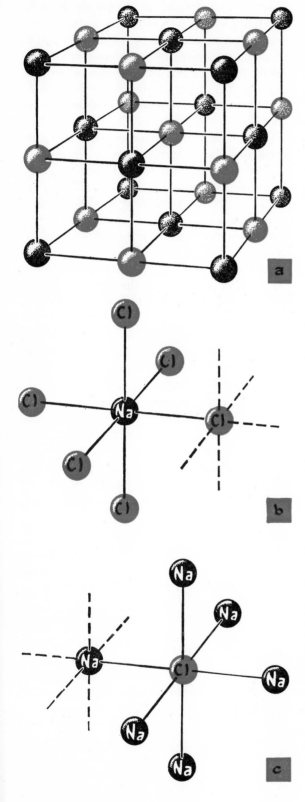

points of most salts are as high as several hundred degrees above zero, whereas most organic compounds, which are molecular in nature and are held together in the crystalline form by forces other than coulombic, have melting points under 200°. Still another fact that supports the postulation of an ionic structure for salts is that salts are generally soluble in strongly polar solvents, such as water, and are insoluble in nonpolar solvents. The role of a polar solvent in dissolving a solute is largely electrical, and such solvents are quite effective in disrupting the forces of electrical attraction that hold ionic lattices together.

This interpretation establishes the concept of salts as totally ionized substances under all circumstances—as solids, as liquids, or in solution. The notion of a *molecule* of a salt such as sodium chloride must be excluded; the concept has no meaning for this class of compounds. But this does not eliminate the notion of molecule entirely; the compounds of Class II of Table 19-1 do exist as molecules. This whole discussion of ionization applies, obviously, only to ionic compounds.

There are compounds, however, that are neither totally ionized nor completely molecular. These compounds are certain acids, bases, and salts that are only partially ionized in solution and are therefore called *weakly ionic* substances. One such weak acid is acetic acid, the sour (acidic) component of vinegar. This compound has the formula $H-C_2H_3O_2$ and ionizes (partially) into hydrogen ions, $H^+$, and acetate ions, $C_2H_3O_2^-$. (The acetate ion is frequently indicated by the symbol $Ac^-$, which is *not* a chemical symbol in the usual sense but is rather an abbreviation for "acetate.") Only about 0.1 percent of the acetic acid in a solution is ionized, the major fraction being present as undissociated molecules of HAc. For such compounds as this the degree of dissociation is a true measure of the degree of ionization. The degree can be determined by measurement of colligative proper-

FIGURE **19-3** *Ionic crystal lattice:* (a) *repeating pattern of oppositely charged ions;* (b) *immediate vicinity of an* $Na^+$ *ion and* (c) *of a* $Cl^-$ *ion in the lattice.*

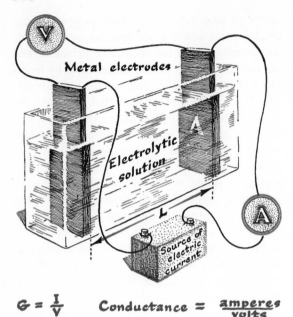

$$G = \frac{I}{V} \qquad Conductance = \frac{amperes}{volts}$$

FIGURE **19-4** *Measurement of electrolytic conductance.*

ties, as in Table 19-2, but more effectively by a study of the conductance of a solution.

## 19-10. Degree of Dissociation from Measurements of Conductance

The second major experimental fact that led to the proposal of the ionic theory of dissociation was that solutions of ionic compounds (Class I in Table 19-1) conduct electric current. For this reason such substances are called **electrolytes,** and the theory of ionization is some-

times called the theory of **electrolytic dissociation.** It is possible, by a quantitative study of the variation of conductance with concentration, to determine the degree of dissociation of an electrolyte. Measurements of conductance, in fact, determine the degree of dissociation much more reliably than measurements of colligative properties.

The variation of conductance with the concentration of an electrolyte can be measured in a cell of the type illustrated in Figure 19-4. The electrolyte solution is put into the cell, and the two inert electrodes are held rigidly so that a constant area is exposed to the solution. A current is then passed through the solution, and the voltage, $V$, and the current, $I$, are measured on the two meters. The **conductance** of the electrolyte solution is defined as the ratio of the current to the voltage; $G = I/V$. Conductance is, then, a quantitative statement of the ease with which electric current can flow through the conductor—in this case a solution of a particular concentration of a particular electrolyte having a certain length and cross-sectional area.

In studies of electrolytic dissociation, the conductance of an electrolyte is measured as its concentration is varied. It is observed for all electrolytes that the conductance increases as the concentration increases. This qualitative generalization is, of course, exactly what would be expected. As the concentration of the electrolyte increases, more ions are present in the space between the electrodes and are available to carry the current. The relation is not, however, a simple one; in general, the conductance does not increase as rapidly as the concentration.

| TABLE **19-3** *Degree of Dissociation, $\alpha$, from Conductance Measurements* | | | | |
|---|---|---|---|---|
| ELECTROLYTE | $5 \times 10^{-4}$ M | $10^{-3}$ M | $10^{-2}$ M | $10^{-1}$ M |
| HCl | 0.994 | 0.990 | 0.967 | 0.919 |
| NaOH | 0.990 | 0.988 | 0.961 | 0.891 |
| NaCl | 0.985 | 0.979 | 0.938 | 0.844 |
| NaAc | 0.980 | 0.973 | 0.921 | 0.801 |
| $Na_2SO_4$ | 0.968 | 0.957 | 0.866 | 0.693 |
| $CuSO_4$ | 0.910 | 0.864 | 0.622 | 0.379 |
| HAc | 0.173 | 0.126 | 0.042 | 0.013 |

We interpret this fact by assuming that at higher concentrations the ions begin to interfere with each other and that, if dissociation were complete, conductance and concentration would exactly parallel each other. By a rather involved mathematical analysis of conductance measurements, deviations from parallel increases in conductance and concentration are expressed as quantitative statements of degree of dissociation, $\alpha$. Table 19-3 lists degrees of dissociation from conductance measurements at several concentrations for a few representative electrolytes.

Modern physical-chemical theory regards conductance as a more significant indicator of degree of dissociation than colligative properties (§19-7). The numbers listed in Table 19-3 are taken as reliable indications of the extent of the dissociation of these electrolytes into independent ions in solution. It should first be noted that the degree of dissociation of all the electrolytes in this list increases as the concentration decreases from $10^{-1}$ M to $5 \times 10^{-4}$ M. But more important is the evidence that such measurements separate electrolytes into two classes: those such as HCl, NaOH, and NaCl, which are almost totally dissociated in moderately dilute solutions, are called **strong electrolytes;** those such as HAc, which are only slightly dissociated, are called **weak electrolytes.** The $\alpha$ values for HAc show that this typical weak electrolyte varies widely in the extent to which it is dissociated. In the ordinary range of concentrations only a very small percentage is dissociated, and it is only at extreme dilution that the major fraction dissociates. This fact is generally interpreted as meaning that weak electrolytes are only partially ionized and that the degree of dissociation is actually a measure of the extent of ionization. The values obtained in this way are very useful in determining equilibrium constants and in the general study of equilibrium. These uses will be discussed in Chapter 23.

## 19-11. *Ionic Charge*

We have assumed that the products of dissociation, the ions, carry an electric charge. We have even assumed, arbitrarily, that metal ions and hydrogen ions have positive charges, nonmetal ions and negative radicals negative charges, though no experimental evidence has been quoted. We shall now be concerned with two questions: How are ionic charges determined? What are the magnitude and sign of the charge on the various ions? The basic experimental information that answers these questions comes from the quantitative study of the process known as **electrolysis.**

The process of conduction by solutions of electrolytes has been explained as the migration of charged particles of the electrolyte, the ions, under the influence of the electric charge on the two conducting plates, or electrodes, in a conductance cell (see Fig. 19-4). Our explanation of the process required that the positive ions migrate toward the negative electrode and the negative ions toward the positive electrode. If it were possible to detect the arrival of particular ions at the two electrodes, it would be possible to decide which charge an ion carries by the sign of the charge on the electrode toward which it migrated. Experiments on electrolysis, described in detail in Chapter 21, supply this information. It is observed in such experiments that metals, such as silver and copper, and hydrogen all migrate toward the negative electrodes; the ions of these elements must therefore have positive charges; for, according to the laws of electrostatic attraction, a particle that moves toward a charged electrode must have the opposite charge. By exactly similar experiments it would be possible to examine the ions of *all* elements and radicals and determine the sign of the charge on each. It would not be necessary, however, to examine all possible ions. From the information already quoted and the formulas of compounds it is possible to state the sign of the charge on many negative ions as well as that of the silver, copper, and hydrogen ions. Nitrate and sulfate, for example, *must* be negative, for electrically neutral compounds are formed by the combination of these with positively charged silver and copper ions. From direct experimental measurement and from the reasoning from such measurements it is possible to make the generalization that the charge of the ions of various elements and radicals has the same sign as the arbitrarily established sign of the *valence* as indicated in Tables 7-7 and 7-8 and in Chapter 7 in general. This experimentally established sign of the charges on the ions gives a logical reason for the arbitrary choice of valence sign that was made in § 7-11. It is now obvious that that choice, even though no justification was given for it at that time, was made in the proper direction so that valence and ionic charge should correspond in sign.

This correspondence in the *signs* of the valence and the ionic charge raises the question whether the correspondence may be complete—that is, whether there may be a relation between the *magnitude* of the valence, as established in Chapter 7, and the magnitude of the ionic charge. The simplest way to answer this question is to assume that the ionic charge and the valence *are* the same in both sign and magnitude and then to see whether the results of the electrolysis experiment verify the assumption. The valence of silver is $+1$, and the valence of copper is $+2$; the transformation of the atoms to charged ions would require two units of charge for each copper atom and one unit of charge for each silver atom. Without considering at this time the *absolute* magnitude of these charges in coulombs, we are able to deduce that a given quantity of electric charge (a given number of coulombs) should convert *twice* as many silver ions to silver atoms (or atoms to ions) as copper atoms to copper ions. We obviously cannot count directly the number of atoms of each element, but we can measure the number of moles of each element that undergo the transformation between atom and ion for a given quantity of electricity. Such observations, made in electrolysis experiments, were cited in § 18-1. The number of moles of silver transformed per coulomb was just twice the number of moles of copper. The experimental observations are, then, exactly what we should expect if the magnitude of the ionic charge were the same as the magnitude of the valence. This experiment and many similar experiments have established that the valence of ions is the same in magnitude and sign as the charge on the ions. The valence discussed in Chapter 7 is therefore called the **ionic valence** or the **electrovalence.**

## 19-12. *Stability of Ions*

We have still not established the absolute magnitude of the unit of ionic charge even though the obvious presumption is that this unit is probably the same as the electronic charge— that a unit of ionic charge is the same as the charge of one electron. In order to establish this fact, however, we must consider the ions of solution in relation to the gaseous ions considered in Chapter 18. There is one obvious difference between the two types. It takes considerable energy to form most gaseous ions, such as those of helium or neon; for these ions are unstable and have a very strong tendency to lose their charge and revert to the atomic state. In contrast, the ions present in electrolytes are extremely stable, exist under all types of circumstances, and require energy to be converted to the atomic state. This generalization is not absolute, however; some electrolytic ions are much less stable than others, and it is possible to *obtain* energy from the reversion of some ions to atoms (see Chap. 21). But, certainly, the mere existence of ions in salts indicates a high degree of stability.

In Chapter 18 it was established that the smallest unit of electrical charge ever carried by a gaseous ion must be equated with the charge of one electron. This fact can be carried over to ions of electrolytes. Some gaseous ions are the same entity as some electrolyte ions, and their identity can be proved, including the unit of ionic charge. In all electrolysis experiments, moreover, the lowest ratio of coulombs to moles is the ratio found for silver; many substances show *multiples* of this value, but none ever shows a *fraction*. The only possible assumption is, therefore, that the charge on an ion arises from the deficiency or excess of *one* electron per atom for each unit of ionic charge. A silver ion, $Ag^+$, is an atom of silver that lacks one electron; a copper ion, $Cu^{+2}$, is an atom of copper that lacks *two* of its usual complement of electrons; and a chloride ion, $Cl^-$, is an atom of chlorine that has one electron in excess of its usual number in the atomic state.

A question now arises: Why is this deviation

from neutrality, this excess or deficiency of electrons (which is characteristic of the quite stable ionic state of many elements) possible, and how does it come about? The complete answer to this question is probably not known to scientists. Much of what is known about the explanation will be considered in Part Three. At this stage we can only emphasize that this distribution of electrons in configurations other than those characteristic of the neutral, uncombined atoms *is* a stable situation; indeed, such distributions constitute the chemical bond. Without these redistributions of atomic electrons, compound matter would not exist; the only form of matter would be monatomic molecules of elemental substances. This whole question of the electronic nature of the chemical bond will be taken up in the next chapter.

## 19-13. Ionic vs. Molecular Compounds

In this chapter we have been emphasizing the ionic nature of one class of compounds. It would be easy for the student to get the impression that *all* compounds are ionic or at least that compounds that are not ionic (those that are molecular) are of little importance. This impression should certainly be avoided. It is true that ionic compounds make up a large and important class of substances, but they are by no means the only type of matter, nor is this class the most important. There is, moreover, no clear and absolute distinction between the two types of compounds. Acetic acid, for example, exists largely as a molecular compound, but we have seen that in solution a small amount of it (the amount varying with concentration) dissociates into ions according to the equation

$$HAc \longrightarrow H^+ + Ac^-$$

In one sense the degree of dissociation of acetic acid, $\alpha$, could be looked upon as a measure of the ionic character of the compound; that is, in a 0.1 molar solution acetic acid is 98.7 percent molecular and 1.3 percent ionic. It is possible to classify many weak electrolytes in a similar way, by the degree of ionic character;

and we observe that there is a complete spectrum of compounds all the way from the totally ionic strong electrolytes to totally molecular, non-polar compounds such as carbon tetrachloride, which has virtually no ionic character.

If we continue this type of examination, we observe that the degree of ionic character often depends, to a considerable extent, on the environment of the compound. Let us consider, as an example, the compound hydrogen chloride. Pure dry hydrogen chloride is a gas; its molecular weight, determined by gas-density measurements (see Chap. 10 and Appendix II), is 36.5; it is moderately soluble in such non-polar solvents as benzene; and such non-polar solutions of it are non-conducting and show normal colligative properties. All of these facts are consistent with the view that hydrogen chloride is a molecular substance having the formula HCl. On the other hand, hydrogen chloride is quite soluble in water; the water solutions are very good conductors of electricity, and their colligative properties indicate that a 1 molal solution gives 2 moles of particles per 1,000 grams of solvent. All these facts indicate that hydrogen chloride is totally ionized in water solution and exists as $H^+$ and $Cl^-$ ions. Thus hydrogen chloride is a typical molecular compound as a gas or in solution in benzene but a typical ionic compound (a strong electrolyte) in water solution. The difference between these two situations can only be attributed to the influence of the solvent, water in this case. Water is the archetypical polar solvent; benzene is a typical non-polar solvent. The presumption is, then, that the difference in the environment in the two cases is due to the different natures of the solvents.

## 19-14. Structure of Water

At this point we shall consider the structure of the water molecule and in particular its polar nature—that is, the meaning of the term "polar," which we have been using for several chapters in referring to water as a solvent. The formula of water has been established as $H_2O$. This combination of three atoms could have several different structures; but, because of the known valences of the two types of atoms, only those in which a central O atom is attached to two H atoms need be considered. This basic arrangement allows at least two possible configurations of the three atoms; they could be arranged in a symmetrical straight line, H—O—H; or they could be arranged in an angular form, H        H,

which has possibilities of asymmetry. Evidence from many different sources has established that the second is the actual structure of the water molecule. The main evidence is the fact that water molecules are electric dipoles; that is, the molecules become oriented in an electric field. This can happen only if there is an asymmetrical distribution of the charge in the molecule. The structure of the water molecule is now known quite precisely to be as indicated in Figure 19-5, which shows the dimensions and angular separation of the two O–H bonds. In this structure there is a concentration of negative charge at the oxygen atom and of positive charge at the two hydrogen atoms. The arrow in part "b" indicates the direction of the electric dipole, which has its negative end at the oxygen atom and points along the bisector of the angle between the two bonds to the hydrogen atoms.

This strongly dipolar, or, more simply, **polar,** structure of the water molecule is the property that has been implied by the reference to water in this and previous chapters as a polar sub-

stance. A perfectly symmetrical molecule such as $CCl_4$ cannot possibly have this asymmetric distribution of charge and therefore cannot be a polar molecule. It is also this polar character that accounts for the extremely high dielectric constant of water, which was referred to in Chapter 17. And it is the high dielectric constant that accounts for the remarkable properties of water as a solvent, both in dissolving ionic substances so vigorously and even in influencing the ionic character of compounds such as hydrogen chloride (discussed above).

## 19-15. Solvent Properties of Water

We can now diagram the way in which the polar structure of the water molecule affects the process of dissolving an ionic compound. Figure 19-6 shows the approach of several molecules of water to the surface of a solid ionic salt (sodium chloride as an example). Electrostatic attraction forces the polar water molecules to approach the surface in such a way that the charged ions of the salt are presented with the oppositely charged ends of the dipoles, the negative ends approaching the $Na^+$ ions and the positive ends approaching the $Cl^-$ ions. Once these associations are formed between the ions and the water molecules, the "hydrated" ions are repelled by the surrounding ions of the salt and move away from the surface of the solid— that is, go into solution. This effect is exactly

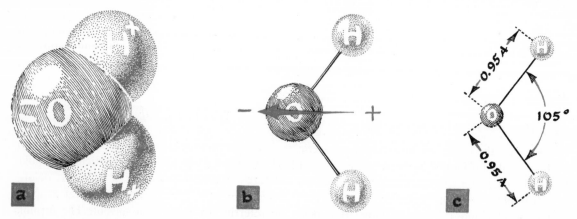

FIGURE **19-5** *Structure of the water molecule:* (a) *approximate physical shape;* (b) *electric dipole;* (c) *bond angle and bond lengths.*

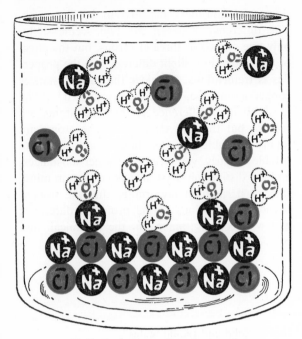

FIGURE **19-6** *Hydration of an ionic solute.*

similar to the effect of any substance of high dielectric constant in reducing the force effects between any two charges when the dielectric fills the space between the two charges as described in Chapter 17. And this neutralization of the forces of attraction between the $Na^+$ ions and the $Cl^-$ ions continues in solution and prevents the reassociation of the ions—a process that would be the first step in coming out of solution.

## 19-16.  Hydrates

Almost all positively charged ions form quite definite hydrates in water solution with four, six, or (some of the large ions) even nine molecules of water to each ion. These complexes, or **hydrates,** are often so stable that they remain in association even when the salt crystallizes, and the solid then contains the corresponding number of molecules of **water of crystallization.** The common forms of some solid salts, for example, are $CaCl_2 \cdot 4H_2O$, $MgCl_2 \cdot 6H_2O$, $AlCl_3 \cdot 6H_2O$, and $CuSO_4 \cdot 5H_2O$. The formulas indicate that four, six, six, and five molecules of water of

hydration remain attached (to the positive ion) in the common crystalline form. The hydrates of the negative ions are not so definite as those of the positive ions and do not remain associated on crystallization, but the association of water molecules with the negative ions contributes to the solubilizing effect of water.

Hydrogen ions also tend strongly to be hydrated in solution. In fact, the probable form of the hydrogen ion in solution is not simply a "naked" $H^+$, but rather the *hydronium* ion, $H_3O^+$, which has the structure indicated. The effect of water as a solvent on hydrogen chloride results, then, from the greater tendency of the hydrogen ion to associate with a molecule of water and form a hydronium ion than for the chloride ion to form a hydrogen chloride molecule. When a hydrogen chloride molecule is approached by a water molecule with the negative (or oxygen end) of the dipole toward the positive hydrogen atom, the compound is, in effect, converted to the ionic form and dissociates a chloride ion, leaving the hydronium ion, $H_3O^+$.

The hydration of ions in solution has a bearing on two topics that were considered earlier in this chapter: the degree of dissociation and the rates of migration of ions during electrical conduction. The dielectric effect is one of the main factors in preventing the interaction of ions; the hydrated ions are electrically "buffered" by the surrounding water molecules, as in Figure 19-6, so that attraction between oppositely charged ions is neutralized. In dilute solutions this neutralization is virtually complete, and dissociation is therefore complete. As for the rate of migration in electrical conduction, one factor is the particle's resistance to movement through the solution, and this would obviously increase with the size of the particle. A small particle would move more rapidly than a larger one, If an ion is hydrated, the moving particle is not simply the ion alone but the aggregate of the ion and the attached molecules of water. The greater the degree of hydration, therefore, the greater the resistance to motion and the slower the ion will be able to move through the solution. The hydronium ion's great mobility in conduction, compared with that of the larger metal ions, is due in large part to its lesser degree of hydration.

## 19-17. Ions and Atoms Compared

A final comment on the nature of ions is necessary to this discussion of the ionic theory. It should certainly be evident by this time, but it often needs emphasis, that an atom and an ion of the same element are *quite different substances*. The two entities have different formulas, but the student frequently ignores the slight difference in the formula—the small plus or minus sign—and considers the two to be the same. The difference between the two seems slight, only one or two or three electrons, but the effect of this apparently slight difference on the properties is tremendous. Consider the two substances copper atoms, Cu, and copper ions, $Cu^{+2}$. The most obvious difference is that the atoms are reddish but the ions deep blue. The atoms are totally insoluble in water, but the ions are quite soluble. Clearly, we have two distinct substances, and the distinction must always be kept in mind. It is of paramount importance that the student be always conscious of the profound difference a few electrons make in the chemical and physical properties of a substance.

## Concepts and Terms

Ionic Dissociation
Ionic Charge
Ionic Conduction
Effect on Colligative Properties
Effect on Reaction Rates
Degree of Dissociation
   from colligative properties
   from conductance

Ions in Solid and Liquid States
Stability of Ions
Ionic vs. Molecular Compounds
Structure of Water
   polar—non-polar
   solvent properties
   hydrates

## Problems

**19-1.** Summarize the various empirical facts that led Arrhenius to postulate the ionic theory of dissociation.

**19-2.** Compare the mechanisms of conduction of an electric current by a solution of an electrolyte with conduction by a metallic conductor.

**19-3.** Phrase succinct answers to all the questions of § 19-6 that you can answer on the basis of your study of this chapter.

**19-4.** The freezing point of a 1 molal solution of alcohol in water is −1.86°C. The freezing point of a 1 molal solution of NaCl is about −3.5°C.
(A) Explain why the freezing points of the two solutions are different.
(B) Explain why the freezing point of the salt solution is not −3.72°.
(C) Calculate from the above data the degree of dissociation of NaCl in a 1 molal solution.

**19-5.** The freezing point of a solution of 2.84 grams of $Na_2SO_4$ in 100 grams of water is −0.87°C. Calculate from these data the degree of dissociation of $Na_2SO_4$.

*Ans.* 78%

**19-6.** Are the degrees of dissociation calculated in Probs. 19-4 and 19-5 true measures of the extent of ionization of the salts in those solutions? Interpret "degree of dissociation" as the term is used in these problems.

**19-7.** Why is molten sodium chloride a better electrical conductor than solid sodium chloride?

**19-8.** Summarize the evidence for the existence of ions in the solid state of salts.

**19-9.** Discuss the meaning of a degree of dissociation derived from conductance measurements, as exemplified by the data of Table 19-3.

**19-10.** Compare gaseous ions, discussed in Chap. 18, with electrolytic ions.

**19-11.** What is the significance of the term "molecule" (A) with respect to ionic compounds and (B) with respect to non-ionic compounds?

**19-12.** Define the term "polar," and describe the difference between polar and non-polar substances.

**19-13.** Describe the action of water as a solvent. Relate such facts as the structure of the water molecule, the dielectric constant of water, the formation of hydrates, and the polarization of solutes such as HCl.

**19-14.** Describe the differences between the two substances in each of the following pairs:

(A) $Na^+$, Na (atom)     (D) $Ag^+$, Ag
(B) $Cl^-$, $Cl_2$ (molecule)     (E) $Cu^{+2}$, Cu
(C) $H^+$, $H_2$

Use information found in this chapter and in previous chapters, particularly Chap. 8.

**19-15.** The law of independence of ions states that the ions of an electrolyte behave independently in solution and that the properties of the electrolyte are the sum of the properties of the individual ions. It is obviously impossible to measure directly the conductivity of a single ionic species. It is possible, however, to use the above law to calculate the conductivities of one electrolyte from the measured conductivities of a complementary group of three other electrolytes. Listed below are the conductivities of 0.1 molar solutions of six electrolytes:

| | | | |
|-----|--------|---------|--------|
| NaCl | 0.0107 | NaOH | 0.0221 |
| KCl | 0.0129 | $NaNO_3$ | 0.0099 |
| HCl | 0.0391 | NaAc | 0.0073 |

The law of independence of ions suggests that the conductivity of NaCl is the sum of the ionic conductivities of $Na^+$ and $Cl^-$, etc. Calculate the conductivities of 0.1 M solutions of (A) KOH, (B) $KNO_3$, (C) KAc, (D) $HNO_3$, (E) HAc.

*Ans.* (A) 0.0243

# Suggested Readings

1. H. M. Leicester and H. S. Klickstein, *A Source Book in Chemistry* (McGraw-Hill, 1952), pp. 483–493 (biographical sketches and short historical treatments of the contributions of Arrhenius and Ostwald).
2. W. F. Ehret, *Smith's Introductory College Chemistry* (Appleton-Century-Crofts, 1950), Chaps. 22, 23, and 24.
3. H. H. Sisler, C. A. VanderWerf, and A. W. Davidson, *College Chemistry—A Systematic Approach* (Macmillan, 1953), Chap. 14.
4. F. T. Bonner and Melba Phillips, *Principles of Physical Science* (Addison-Wesley, 1957), Chap. 21.

IN CHAPTER 19 we raised a number of points concerning the nature of the bonds that hold compounds together, and we associated the bonds with the electrons of the atoms. The time has now come to re-examine the whole concept of the chemical bond and the nature of valence in relation to the atomic theory discussed in Chapter 18. That form of the atomic theory modified our original one by including the fine structure of the atom—a structure that consists of a central body surrounded by electrons. We are not able to say, at this point, how widely the central body and the electrons are separated, but we can say that some electrons must be on the surface of the atom in the sense that they can be more or less easily removed from the fixed central part. We also do not know, at this point, the *number* of such removable electrons or the total number of electrons in any atom. We do know that some electrons—sometimes only one per atom, often more than one—are involved in the valence bonds that link atoms together in compounds. And we already know a good deal about the nature of one type of valence bond, the ionic bond.

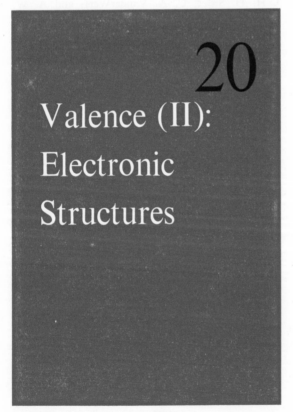

**CHAPTER**

**20**

# Valence (II): Electronic Structures

## 20-1. Periodic Nature of Valence

The point to which a study of the electronic nature of valence should return is the periodic variation of valence. If we re-examine Table 8-3 and the valence chart of Figure 8-1, the striking repetition of valences according to the periodic law and the systematic stepwise change of valence with increasing atomic weight are apparent. We have already associated valence with electronic charge by equating the two for ions of the metals of the first two groups and for the halogens. It is simply an extension of this notion to consider the maximum *positive* valence as equal to the maximum number of electrons that can be *contributed* by an atom to valence bonds and the maximum *negative* valence as equal to the maximum number of electrons that can be *received* by an atom in valence bonds. If we now start at the right-hand side of Table 8-3 and examine the valences of the atoms in the light of this concept, we see that chlorine and fluorine have a maximum of seven electrons to contribute to valence bonds and can *accept* one electron. Oxygen and sulfur can accept two and contribute six; nitrogen and phosphorus can accept three and contribute five; carbon and silicon can accept four and contribute four. The metals are able, apparently, to contribute only three, two, and one, respectively, for the three remaining groups going to the left.

These relations are systematic. In all cases (perhaps excepting the metals of Groups I, II, and III) the arithmetic sum of the extremes of valence, plus and minus, is eight. Within our concept of electrons as the units of valence, this generalization would be: "The sum of the number of electrons that may be accepted and the number that may be contributed in the formation of valence bonds is always *eight*." This emphasis on the number eight may seem reminiscent of Newlands' fascination with the octave relations (see § 8-2). But by this time in our study of science the fact is well established that a simple, systematic, empirical relation usually implies a simple, underlying, conceptual explanation.

## 20-2. Stable Configurations of Valence Electrons

A little thought about this number *eight* in relation to the valences of elements would lead to the postulate that an arrangement of *eight* valence electrons is particularly stable. If, for example, we postulate that a chlorine *atom* has seven valence electrons and that it may reach a stable state *either* by contributing all seven to valence bonds or by accepting one extra in a valence bond, we have a simple conceptual scheme that relates the empirical facts of valence to the electronic concept of valence. In a similar way we could view the sulfur atom as having six valence electrons and being able to reach a stable situation in combination with other atoms either by accepting two more electrons to reach the stable state of eight valence electrons or by contributing all six to reach a stable state of *zero* valence electrons. The carbon atom has four valence electrons in the elemental atomic

state and reaches stable *combined* states either by contributing all four valence electrons to a chemical bond or by acquiring four more to complete an **octet** of electrons. Even the metals can be included in this scheme if we presume that sodium, for example, has a *single* valence electron, reaches stable states in chemical combination by contributing this electron to chemical bonds, but is unable to accommodate the seven that it would have to accept in order to reach the stable state of eight by gaining electrons.

If we turn now from the short (Table 8-3) to the complete periodic table (Table 8-5), which includes the inert gases, we can include these in the scheme we have created here. Since these substances show no tendency to form compounds with other elements, their valence is zero; the configurations of their valence electrons must be remarkably stable. In one sense, they must have *no* valence electrons, for they have no valence; in another sense, they already have the other postulated stable configuration: *eight* valence electrons.

The concept that we are building up in this attempted electronic interpretation of valence is that each element in the periodic table differs from the preceding element by having *one more valence electron*. As each inert gas is reached, a stable configuration of valence electrons is reached, in which there is no tendency for exchange of electrons to form chemical bonds. We can now include the two light gases, hydrogen and helium, in this system. Hydrogen has a common valence of $+1$ and a less common valence of $-1$. We postulate, then, a single valence electron; the atom may lose this electron and reach a stable configuration, or it may gain a single electron and reach another stable configuration. Helium, the next element above hydrogen, has two electrons, and, because helium is chemically inert, with no tendency to form valence bonds, we must assume that the configuration of only two valence electrons is stable for the lightest elements. Element No. 3, lithium, has one more electron than helium, a total of three. But only *one* of these may be a valence electron in the sense of being available for formation of chemical bonds. This electron may be *contributed* to a bond, leaving the lithium with a deficiency of one electron and therefore with a +1 charge and the stable helium configuration of two outer electrons. The next element, beryllium, has a total of four electrons, two of which may participate in valence bonds. In ionic valence these two are lost, leaving the ion again with the stable helium configuration of two outer electrons and a charge of +2. Boron, with one more electron than beryllium, has an atomic configuration made up of the inner, stable, helium pair of electrons and three valence electrons. If these three are lost in the formation of chemical bonds, the stable helium configuration is again reached, but this time with a charge of +3, which again corresponds with the ionic valence. Carbon has a total of six electrons, the two of the first stable state and four valence electrons. Now carbon may contribute all four of these to valence bonds as the smaller atoms do, but there is also the possibility of its *gaining* four valence electrons (which are supplied by some other atom in a chemical combination) to reach the stable state of the next higher inert gas, *neon*. Similarly, nitrogen and oxygen have the original two electrons that form the first stable configuration and therefore are unavailable for chemical combination (are *not* valence electrons), but in addition they have, respectively, five and six that *are* available for the formation of chemical bonds (*are* valence electrons). They reach a stable configuration either by contributing five for nitrogen or six for oxygen to valence bonds or by acquiring three or two other valence electrons to reach the stable configuration corresponding to neon. Fluorine has the two inner electrons, then seven valence electrons, and can most readily reach a stable configuration by acquiring one more electron to reach the neon configuration. In this case the particle has one electron in excess of its atomic quota and therefore has a charge of −1, which is the ionic valence (ionic charge) of the fluoride ion. The next higher element beyond fluorine, neon, is an inert gas and therefore has a stable outer electronic configuration. It has a total of ten electrons, two of which make up the first inner group and the remaining eight the stable octet of electrons.

## 20-3. Electronic Structures

It is possible to go through such a stepwise analysis of the whole periodic table, element by element. Sodium would acquire the neon configuration by losing one electron to form the $Na^+$ ion; magnesium would reach the same stable outer configuration of eight electrons by losing two to become the $Mg^{+2}$ ion; and so on. Chlorine would reach the stable configuration of the next inert gas, argon, by acquiring one more electron to become the $Cl^-$ ion, and sulfur, with one less electron than chlorine, would become the sulfide ion, $S^{-2}$, by accepting two valence electrons—again acquiring the stable valence-electronic configuration of argon. These arrangements of the valence electrons and their possibilities of reaching stable inert-gas configurations are best presented (after the above discussion) by electronic diagrams of the elements. Such diagrams for some of the first elements are shown in Figure 20-1.

One powerful piece of experimental evidence supports this postulate about the numbers of valence electrons in the various atoms. This is the evidence concerning the number of electrons that may be removed in the production of gaseous ions by bombardment. It was stated in § 18-12 that *only one* electron may be removed from the hydrogen atom, and this fairly easily. It is very difficult (high ionization potential) to disrupt the atom of helium, but two, and *only* two, electrons may be removed from it. Lithium loses one electron easily and then two more with great difficulty for a total of three; two can be knocked out of beryllium easily and two more with difficulty for a total of four; boron has five and carbon a total of six electrons. These experiments are entirely consistent, even in the detail of relative ease of loss of the electrons, with the postulate of the preceding section when it is applied to the first six atoms. It is a reasonable presumption that the same pattern applies to the remaining elements of the periodic table.

These postulates of the electronic theory of valence may be summarized as follows: Each atom has associated with it, as part of its structure, the number of electrons indicated by the

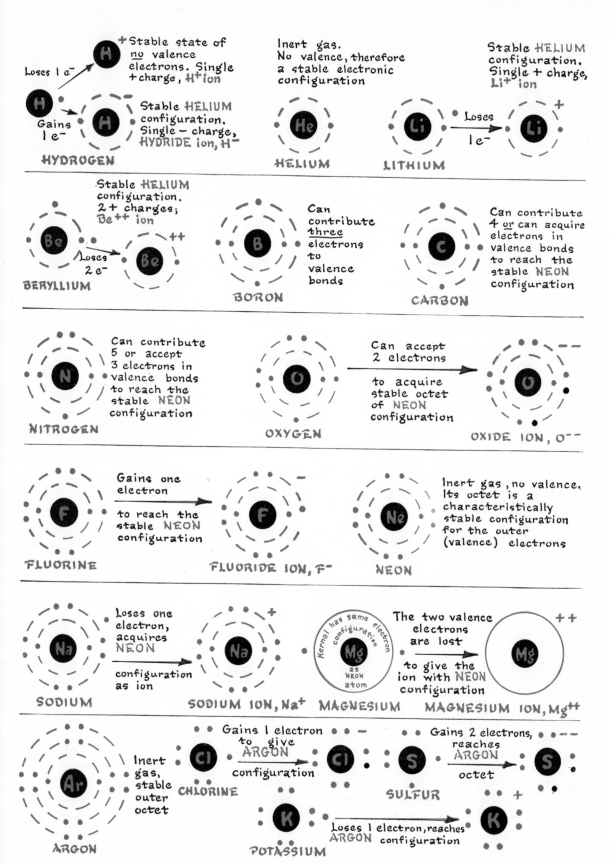

FIGURE **20-1** *Representative electronic structures and transitions of atoms and ions.*

atomic number of the element. Only a few "outer" electrons, which are easier to remove than the "inner" ones, are involved in valence bonds, and they are therefore called valence electrons. The inert-gas configuration of valence electrons, two for helium and eight for the other inert gases, is a particularly stable state. The element next higher in atomic number than each inert gas has one valence electron; the next still higher has two, etc., up to the halogens, which are the elements next before the inert gas of the next period. The halogens have seven valence electrons. Elements other than the inert gases enter into chemical combination by gaining or contributing electrons so as to reach the nearest inert-gas configuration of valence electrons.

## 20-4. Ionic Valence

We can now use this electronic theory of valence in interpreting the facts of ionic valence that have already been established. We have accepted the notion that chemical bonds—or valences—are formed when the atoms involved contribute or accept electrons. It is possible to conceive of at least two ways in which the contribution or acceptance of electrons in valence bonds could be accomplished. At least two atoms are always involved in the formation of a molecule, one contributing and the other accepting electrons. This exchange could be accomplished either by the outright transfer of one or more electrons from one atom to the other or by some sort of sharing of valence electrons between the two atoms. The first of these possible mechanisms would result, obviously, in the formation of ionic valences, and we shall examine this mechanism first.

The idea that a positive ion results from the loss of electrons and a negative ion from the gain of electrons has been well established. The next logical step is the conclusion that a reaction between two elemental substances that produce an ionic compound proceeds by the total transfer of one or more valence electrons from one atom to the other. For example, the reaction of sodium

with chlorine to produce sodium chloride would be visualized as

$$\text{Na} \cdot + \cdot \overset{\times\times}{\underset{\times\times}{\text{Cl}}} \colon \longrightarrow \text{Na}^+ \colon \overset{\times\times}{\underset{\times\times}{\text{Cl}}} \colon ^-$$

in which the single valence electron of sodium is transferred to the chlorine atom, the result being an Na$^+$ ion having the stable neon configuration of outer electrons and a Cl$^-$ ion having an outer group of eight electrons corresponding to the stable configuration of argon. Another example would be the reaction of magnesium with fluorine to form magnesium fluoride by the transfer of the two valence electrons of magnesium to *two* fluorine atoms:

$$\cdot \text{Mg} \cdot + \cdot \overset{\times\times}{\underset{\times\times}{\text{F}}} \colon + \cdot \overset{\times\times}{\underset{\times\times}{\text{F}}} \colon \longrightarrow \text{Mg}^{+2} \colon \overset{\times\times}{\underset{\times\times}{\text{F}}} \colon ^- \colon \overset{\times\times}{\underset{\times\times}{\text{F}}} \colon ^-$$

In this case the magnesium atom has reached the stable neon configuration of Mg$^{+2}$ by the loss of both valence electrons, and each of the fluorine atoms has acquired one electron to complete the outer octet that characterizes the stable electron configuration of neon. Finally, in the formation of calcium sulfide from the elements,

$$\cdot \text{Ca} \cdot + \overset{\times\times}{\underset{\times\times}{\text{S}}} \colon \longrightarrow \text{Ca}^{+2} \colon \overset{\times\times}{\underset{\times\times}{\text{S}}} \colon ^{-2}$$

the calcium atom reaches the stable argon configuration of the ion, Ca$^{+2}$, by the loss of both its valence electrons, and the sulfur atom reaches the stable argon electronic configuration in the S$^{-2}$ ion by the gain of the two electrons, which join the original six to make an octet.

## 20-5. Energy of Ionic Valence

This explanation of the formation of an ionic bond is clear enough and certainly quite logical except that there must be some explanation of the atoms' spontaneous departure from electrical neutrality. In our study of electrostatics it was established that the separation of charges requires work; the spontaneous event is the *attraction* of opposite charges: if charges are left to themselves, they tend to approach and neutralize each other. In our explanation of the formation of ionic valence bonds, however, just the opposite of this spontaneous event takes place. Obviously, the work needed to separate the electron from the positively charged central part of the atom must be supplied from some other source. At this stage we cannot explain this phenomenon. We can only point out that the natural tendency to electrical neutrality is here opposed by another, conflicting natural tendency—the tendency toward the stable configuration of eight (or two) external valence electrons. In the metals and halogens the tendency toward an inert-gas configuration of valence electrons is greater than the opposing tendency toward electrical neutrality of the individual atoms. The work needed to separate the charges is supplied by the spontaneous tendency toward the octet of valence electrons.

It is an experimentally observed fact that the metals of Groups I and II and the non-metals of Group VII, the halogens, have a very strong tendency to form ions. For these elements the difficulty of removing or adding electrons and thereby destroying the electrical neutrality of the atoms is much more than compensated by the tendency to reach a stable configuration of the valence electrons (an inert-gas configuration). It is also experimentally observed that the elements of Group VI have a lesser, but considerable, tendency to form ions having two negative charges, and that the elements of Group III have some tendency to form ions having three positive charges. For these elements the loss of three electrons or the gain of two, with the accompanying change from electrical neutrality of the atom, is just slightly overcompensated by the tendency toward the stable octet. The other possible changes that might result in ions—the loss of more than three electrons or the gain of more than two—do *not* take place; these deviations from electrical neutrality require more work than can be supplied by the tendency toward the stable octet of valence electrons. There is considerable variation within the groups of the periodic table in the ease with which the ions may be formed. Fluorine, for example, tends much more strongly toward the ionic state than chlorine, which is more stable as the ion than bromine or iodine. Similarly, cesium gives

up an electron more easily than the elements above it in Group I of the periodic table. Another example of this difference is in Group III. Aluminum forms the tervalent ion $Al^{+3}$, but boron does not form the corresponding $B^{+3}$.

These tendencies to form ions correspond exactly to the degree of metallic (or non-metallic) character, which was discussed in our first encounter with valence and the periodic table in § 8-13. The metals form positive ions easily; the strong non-metals form negative ions easily; the metalloids are intermediate and have no strong tendency to form elemental ions of either charge. In the next chapter we shall observe a method of measuring quantitatively this tendency to form ions. At this point of the discussion it is only necessary to accept the notion that the formation of ions results when the natural tendency of the atoms to remain electrically neutral is overpowered by the opposing tendency to form octets in the valence-electron shell.

In a qualitative sense it is apparent that it would require much more energy to remove three or four electrons from an atom than to remove one, and that it would be extremely difficult to introduce three or four electrons to a neutral atom. From Coulomb's law it is apparent that such changes in electrical neutrality are quite improbable and would require extremely large amounts of energy. In this sense our interpretation of these facts of electrovalence (or ionic valence) is quite consistent with our general knowledge of electrical phenomena.

## 20-6. *Covalence*

The tendency of the elements near the two extremes of the periodic table—the metals and the non-metals—to form ionic valences is understandable, we have seen, as the result of a competition between two opposing tendencies—toward the stable octet of valence electrons and toward electrical neutrality. For ionic valences the tendency toward the stable octet is more powerful. A question now arises: What form of chemical combination is available to elements near the middle of the periodic table, where the tendency toward the stable octet of valence electrons is not sufficient to overcome the tendency toward electrical neutrality? The answer to this question is found in the other possible method of "contributing" or "accepting" an electron in a valence bond, a method referred to in § 20-4. This second method is some sort of sharing of electrons between two atoms in such a way that the electron is not actually transferred from one to the other; rather, each atom maintains at least a partial interest in all of its own valence electrons. If we look at an example, we shall see how an atom can fill its octet of valence electrons and at the same time maintain its electrical neutrality.

We know experimentally that pure, dry hydrogen chloride is not an ionic compound; it has a clearly established molecular structure, HCl, in which the two atoms are bonded directly to each other. We also know that the neutral hydrogen atom has *one* valence electron and can reach a stable combined state by acquiring one more electron, in which case it has the stable configuration of the inert gas helium. Chlorine atoms have seven valence electrons and can reach the stable combined state in which they have the configuration of valence electrons corresponding to the inert gas argon by acquiring one more electron. Clearly, *both* types of atoms cannot reach these stable states by the outright transfer of electrons between the two. But they *can* complete their groups of valence electrons (to two for hydrogen and eight for chlorine) if the atoms are able to *share* two electrons. If the hydrogen atom contributes its sole electron and the chlorine atom contributes one of its seven electrons to a *shared pair* of electrons,

$$\text{H}\cdot\ +\ \cdot\overset{\times\times}{\underset{\times\times}{\text{Cl}}}\colon\ \longrightarrow\ \text{H}\colon\overset{\times\times}{\underset{\times\times}{\text{Cl}}}\colon\dagger$$

———

† In this and other diagrams of electronic configurations in this chapter different symbols indicate that the electrons were originally contributed to the valence bond by different atoms. It must be remembered, however, that all electrons are identical, and the difference in symbol must not be interpreted as implying any difference in the electrons. In the diagram above the dot means the electron that originally belonged to the hydrogen atom, and the x's mean the seven valence electrons of chlorine. The shared pair is made of one of each. But *all eight* electrons in the diagram are indistinguishable.

then *both* atoms have completed a stable group of valence electrons and have done so without affecting their electrical neutrality. Each of the two atoms, hydrogen and chlorine, still maintains a half interest in the shared pair. The hydrogen atom is surrounded by a completed group of two electrons, but it has only a half interest in this pair from the electrical point of view and thus, in effect, has one unit of electronic charge round the central part of the atom, which carries a single unit of positive charge. Thus the atom as a whole is electrically neutral. The chlorine atom has a central positive charge of +7 (the central part of the atom—that is, all except the valence electrons—being conveniently referred to as the **kernel** of the atom) because there are seven valence electrons, each with a unit negative charge. In the compound hydrogen chloride the chlorine atom has six electrons that it "owns" outright, no other atom sharing any part of them; in addition to these six it also has a half interest in the pair of electrons that makes up the bond between the atoms. One of these was contributed to the bond by the chlorine atom, but the other was contributed by the hydrogen atom. The half interest in the pair is electrically equivalent to a single unit of negative charge; thus the chlorine atom has $6 + 1$ (the 1 being $\frac{1}{2} \times 2$) units of negative charge, which just balances the 7 units of positive charge on the atomic kernel.

Such a shared pair of electrons is called a **covalence** and is, by all odds, the most important force that holds compound substances together. The ionic bond, discussed in previous sections of this chapter, is limited to the salts and some acids and bases. The covalent bond, on the other hand, is a part of the molecular architecture of every compound substance except the few binary salts that are exclusively ionic. The importance of this electronic configuration in the building of molecules is demonstrated by the fact that G. N. Lewis, who discovered the nature of covalence, referred to this as *the chemical bond*.

The spatial distribution of the electrons of a shared pair (a covalent chemical bond) cannot be specified at this point. Neither can we state clearly the nature of the bonding force of a covalent bond. In Part Three we shall be able to consider the most modern views on these problems and to place the physical fact of the sharing of an electron pair by two atomic kernels on a rational basis. But we shall see that an explicit and precise localization of these electrons is impossible—is, in fact, excluded by experimental, theoretical, and even philosophical considerations. Clearly, some motion of the electrons in the neighborhood of the kernels of the two atoms is necessary if the same pair of electrons is to be a part of the electronic environment of both. Even so, we shall continue to use a pair of dots between the symbols of two atoms to represent a shared pair of electrons, and this symbol will imply both the sharing in a covalent bond and the motion that enables the electrons to contribute to the valence-electron configurations of *both* atoms. For brevity in the drawing of covalent structures the shared pair of electrons is often symbolized by a line connecting the two atoms. The structure of hydrogen chloride may be symbolized by any one of the following:

$$\overset{\cdot\cdot}{\underset{\cdot\cdot}{H:Cl:}} \quad H:\overset{\cdot\cdot}{\underset{\cdot\cdot}{Cl}} \quad \overset{\cdot\cdot}{\underset{\cdot\cdot}{H-Cl:}} \quad H-Cl$$

All of these symbolize exactly the same thing. The first shows *all* of the valence electrons; the second shows only those of the covalent bond; and the third and fourth symbolize the covalent bond by a line.

## 20-7. Elemental Covalent Bonds

The simplest and purest covalent bonds are those that hold the two atoms together in the molecules of diatomic gases, and the simplest of such molecules is that of hydrogen. The covalent structure and electronic configuration of this molecule are represented by H:H or H–H, in which both hydrogen atoms have acquired the electronic configuration of helium by allowing the other atom a half interest in its single valence electron. The electronic structures of the diatomic molecules of the halogens are

$$\overset{\cdot\cdot}{\underset{\cdot\cdot}{:F}}\overset{\cdot\cdot}{\underset{\cdot\cdot}{F:}} \quad \overset{\cdot\cdot}{\underset{\cdot\cdot}{:Cl}}\overset{\cdot\cdot}{\underset{\cdot\cdot}{Cl:}} \quad \overset{\cdot\cdot}{\underset{\cdot\cdot}{:Br}}\overset{\cdot\cdot}{\underset{\cdot\cdot}{Br:}} \quad \overset{\cdot\cdot}{\underset{\cdot\cdot}{:I}}\overset{\cdot\cdot}{\underset{\cdot\cdot}{I:}}$$

Several facts of covalence are brought out by consideration of the covalent structures of these gas molecules and of those of hydrogen and hydrogen chloride.

The first is that covalence, unlike ionic valence, does not have a positive and negative character. Ionic compounds are formed *only* between ions having opposite charges. But we have already seen that the hydrogen atom, which normally forms positive ions, can form a covalence either with another hydrogen atom or with a chlorine atom, which forms only negative ions. We can ascribe a *magnitude* (see below) to the covalence of an atom, but we cannot ascribe a sign to it.

The second fact of covalence is that covalences may be formed between two (or more) atoms of the same element. This behavior offers a self-evident explanation of the diatomic nature of the common gases, which was difficult for Dalton to accept in his first postulation of the atomic theory and was important in the first extensions of the theory by Avogadro. It is also apparent why the inert gases are exceptions to this tendency for the elemental gases to exist as diatomic molecules. The inert gases have stable configurations of valence electrons as uncombined atoms. The other elements must reach some stable arrangement of their valence electrons even in the uncombined state; they do this by sharing electrons among several atoms of the same element to form covalent bonds, and this sharing allows the formation of stable octets (a pair in the unique case of hydrogen) of valence electrons.

Another important fact of covalence becomes apparent when we consider the possible electronic configurations of the other elemental gases. From its position in the periodic table it is apparent that the oxygen atom must have only six valence electrons. If two oxygen atoms share a pair of electrons—

$$\overset{\cdot\cdot}{\underset{\cdot}{:O}}\overset{\cdot}{\underset{\cdot\cdot}{:O:}} \quad \text{or} \quad \overset{\cdot\cdot}{\underset{\cdot}{:O}}\overset{\cdot}{\underset{\cdot\cdot}{-O:}}$$

—the structure still does not have a stable octet of valence electrons for either atom. We can imagine two possible electronic structures of the oxygen molecule: a second pair of valence electrons may be shared by the two atoms, as indicated here,

$$\overset{..}{O}::\overset{..}{O}\overset{.}{.} \quad \text{or} \quad \overset{..}{O}=O\overset{..}{.}$$

in which case the stable octet configuration *is* accomplished for both atoms; or the first of the two structures diagramed exists as a stable molecule in which there are two unpaired, or *odd,* electrons. We can distinguish experimentally between the two possible forms: unpaired odd electrons, as in the first diagram, and multiple covalent bonds, as in the second diagram. The multiple-bond configuration, as in the double-bonded oxygen atoms, is by far the commoner of the two possibilities. *Very* few compounds show the unpaired-electron configuration, but double bonds between atoms, and even triple covalent bonds, are extremely common. Unfortunately for the present discussion, oxygen is the notable exception to this generalization. Oxygen possesses an extremely rare property for a gas, that of being highly magnetic. This property is associated with odd electrons in the molecular structure; we must therefore presume that the structure of oxygen is the one that includes odd electrons.

The next elemental gas, nitrogen, illustrates the general existence of multiple covalent bonds. The nitrogen molecule has the electronic structure

$$:N:::N: \quad \text{or} \quad :N\equiv N:$$

in which three pairs of valence electrons are shared between the two atoms. Both atoms have the requisite eight valence electrons and are able to maintain electrical neutrality. Of the original five electrons round the kernel of each atom, three are contributed by each to the formation of covalent bonds between them; the remaining two are an unshared pair in the valence octet of each, which is made up of the six shared and the two unshared. Electrical neutrality is maintained by the half interest of each atom in the six shared electrons for three units of negative charge plus the two electrons owned outright. These five negative charges just balance the five positive charges on the kernel. The nature of molecular nitrogen is consistent with this triple covalent bond. The bond is somewhat shorter

than an ordinary single covalent bond involving the nitrogen atom and is also very difficult to break. Nitrogen is an extremely stable substance and enters into reactions (which would necessarily break the bond between the nitrogen atoms) only under the most violent conditions.

The triple bond also occurs in the structure of gaseous phosphorus at high temperature $(:P:::P:)$ and in many compound substances. The double covalent bond is even commoner in compound substances and in many complex ions (radicals).

## 20-8. *Structure of Elemental Carbon*

If we examine the molecular structure of some other non-metallic elements, we shall notice another important property of covalent bonds. First let us consider the structure of elemental carbon. Pure elemental carbon exists in two quite different forms, graphite and diamond, which have extremely different properties. The form known as **graphite** is a soft, opaque, black substance with dull metallic luster, showing a gross structure consisting of flat layers, or plates, with hexagonal symmetry. The layers are loosely bound together; in fact, they slip over each other so easily that graphite is often used as a lubricant between sliding surfaces. The gross structure of graphite is represented somewhat diagrammatically in Figure 20-2. The crystals of graphite are very easily broken between the plates and much less easily in directions parallel to the plane of the plates. The nature of diamond is, of course, quite different. Diamond is a highly refractive, brilliantly lustrous, colorless, crystal-

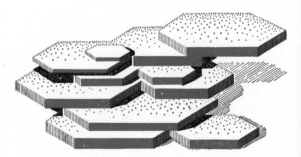

FIGURE **20-2** *Crystalline structure of graphite.*

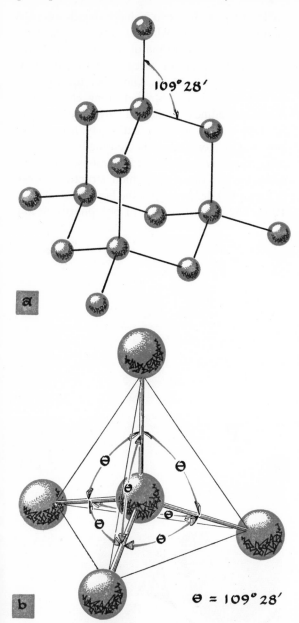

109° 28′

a

b

Θ ≈ 109° 28′

FIGURE **20-3** *Crystal lattice of diamond:* (a) *repeating pattern of tetrahedrally oriented carbon atoms;* (b) *tetrahedral arrangement of four atoms round one central atom.*

line substance, the hardest known material. Its density is half again as great as that of graphite, and the crystals have a high degree of symmetry in all three directions.

These extreme differences in properties between two forms of the same element can be accounted for only by the structures of the solids.

By X-ray diffraction and other methods it is possible to establish the exact relations of the atoms in both these substances, and, in both, the submicroscopic molecular structure corresponds to the macroscopic gross structure. The atoms of carbon in diamond are arranged in a tetrahedral pattern (Fig. 20-3a) that is the simplest regular solid arrangement. Each atom of carbon is surrounded by four other atoms, and the spacing in all directions is exactly equal, as indicated in Figure 20-3b. The attachment of one atom to another in a diamond crystal is viewed as a regular covalent bond. From the required valence-electron arrangement of four electrons round the kernel, carbon would be expected to have *four* possible covalences, and in all of its covalent compounds the valence of carbon is always four. These facts correspond to the view that the bond joining each carbon atom to its four neighbors in the diamond crystal is an actual covalent bond. Furthermore, the fact that diamond is completely non-conducting (of electricity) indicates that all the valence electrons are firmly bound in covalent bonds. In this view each diamond crystal is actually a huge molecule of carbon containing a tremendous number of atoms held together by covalent bonds.

## 20-9. *Tetrahedral Distribution of Covalent Bonds*

From all this it must be accepted, then, that the four covalent bonds of a carbon atom radiate from the central part of the atom in tetrahedral directions; that is, the four covalences are located at the corners of a regular tetrahedron, the atomic kernel being at the center of the tetrahedron, as in Figure 20-3. It has further been shown that this property is not unique to carbon but is rather the rule for *all* atoms that show covalence. The four pairs of valence electrons in the stable octet are arranged at the corners of a regular tetrahedron. This spatial arrangement is characteristic of all atoms whether the pairs form covalent bonds (are shared) or not. The diamond structure of carbon exemplifies the tetrahedral structure of this atom with a shared pair (a covalent bond) directed toward each of the

angle between the two valence bonds of each sulfur atom is 106°, which is very near the 109° 28' of angular separation of the lines joining the center and corners of a regular tetrahedron, as shown in Figure 20-3b. The other form of elemental sulfur is an extremely long chain molecule, sometimes indicated by the symbol $S_n$, in which $n$ is some extremely large number. In this form also the tetrahedral arrangement of the valence bonds is demonstrated. The molecule has the zigzag chain structure shown in Figure 20-4c, and again the bond angle is near 106°. The elemental form of phosphorus, at low

**a**       $S_8$ molecule

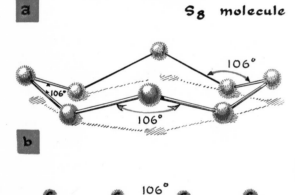

**b**

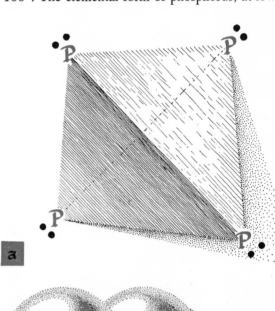

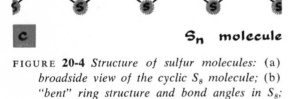

**c**       $S_n$ molecule

FIGURE **20-4** *Structure of sulfur molecules: (a) broadside view of the cyclic $S_8$ molecule; (b) "bent" ring structure and bond angles in $S_8$; (c) "bent" open-chain structure of the $S_n$ molecule.*

corners of a tetrahedron. The molecular structure of elemental sulfur also illustrates this tetrahedral distribution of the pairs of valence electrons. Like carbon, sulfur has two different forms (*allotropes*) of the crystalline solid. One of these has the formula $S_8$ and has been proved to be a ring-shaped molecule that can be diagramed as in Figure 20-4a. The ring is really in a folded form, as shown in Figure 20-4b, in which the

**a**

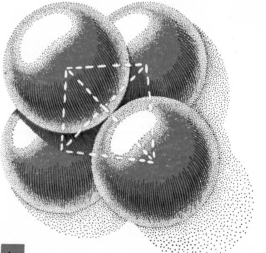

**b**       $P_4$ molecule

FIGURE **20-5** *Tetrahedral structure of the phosphorus molecule, $P_4$.*

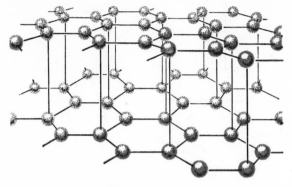

FIGURE **20-6** *Bond structure of graphite.*

temperatures, has the formula $P_4$, and the structure of this molecule also is a regular tetrahedron, as diagramed in Figure 20-5.

## 20-10. *Structure of Graphite*

If we return now to the arrangement of the atoms in the other allotropic form of carbon, graphite, the difference in properties between graphite and diamond can be explained as the result of different types of interatomic bonding. Physical measurements show that the atoms of carbon are arranged in the form of coplanar regular hexagonal rings. Each plane of rings consists of many carbon atoms in a continuous network of covalent bonds; each atom is bonded to *three* other atoms; the angle between the bonds is 120°; and all of the interatomic distances (bond lengths) in the planes are the same. The planes are bonded together by a longer and much less powerful connection. This arrangement is diagramed in Figure 20-6. This structure of graphite explains its properties. The longer bonds between planes of rings mean that the atoms are less closely packed than in diamond, and the substance is therefore less dense than diamond; since such bonds are much less powerful than the other bonds, graphite is easily broken in this direction and the planes are easily displaced with respect to each other. Since not all of the valence electrons are firmly bound up in covalent bonds, graphite is a moderately good electrical conductor. The hexagonal symmetry of graphite crystals is a gross manifestation of the hexagonal arrangement of the atoms in the crystal.

## 20-11. *Diagrams of Tetrahedral Bond Structures*

The structures of multiple covalent bonds can also be diagramed as tetrahedral distributions of the four pairs of valence electrons round the atomic kernel. A double bond would be realized by the attachment of two tetrahedral atoms along one edge of the tetrahedrons, as in Figure 20-7b, and a triple bond by the attachment of the two atoms at *three* corners, which would cause one face of the two tetrahedrons to be coincident, as in Figure 20-7c. These interpretations correspond to the measured angles between the various covalent bonds. In general, the angle between two single bonds is very near the tetrahedral angle of 109° 28′ (Fig. 20-7a); the angle between a double bond and a single bond is near 120°, as required by the geometry of two tetrahedrons attached as in Figure 20-7b; and molecules that include triple bonds are always linear —that is, the angle between a triple bond and a single bond is 180°, as in Figure 20-7c. Finally, in some molecules a single atom may be attached to adjacent atoms by two double bonds (as in carbon dioxide; see below). Such molecules are always linear, as required by the geometry of three tetrahedrons attached at edges (Fig. 20-7d).

It should not be inferred that the actual *shape* of atoms is tetrahedral. They are probably nearly spherical under most conditions. The point of this discussion is that **valence electrons are in pairs at the corners of a tetrahedron** and that **valence bonds are therefore in the direction of lines joining the center and corners of a regular tetrahedron.**

## 20-12. *Covalent-bonded Compounds*

So far we have considered the covalent bond primarily as the attachment of like atoms in elemental substances. But the major importance

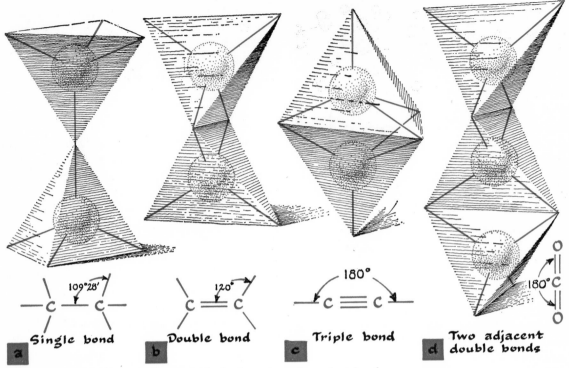

FIGURE 20-7 *Diagram of the tetrahedral orientation of covalent bonds.*

of the bond is in the structure of compound molecules. We have already considered the covalent compound between hydrogen and one of the Group VII elements, chlorine; it will be instructive now to consider in order the hydrides of other non-metals from Groups VI, V, and IV. The next would be the hydride of oxygen, water. Oxygen has six valence electrons and can attain its octet by sharing two pairs; hydrogen reaches the stable configuration of two valence electrons by sharing a single pair. Thus two atoms of hydrogen combine with a single atom of oxygen:

$$\overset{\times\times}{\underset{\times\times}{H:O:H}} \quad \text{or} \quad H-\overset{..}{\underset{..}{O}}-H$$

We know, however, that the four pairs of electrons must be distributed about the oxygen atom in the form of a tetrahedron; the two covalent bonds to the hydrogen atoms must therefore be directed toward two corners of the tetrahedron. For that reason we would not picture the molecule of water as above. (See Fig. 19-5 and the associated discussion of the structure of the water molecule.) In making symbols of substances we

should always be as nearly factual as possible in representation of actual shapes and structures even though the symbols are often very much abbreviated. It is not necessary to draw a three-dimensional picture of water, such as Figure 19-5, each time we want to refer to this substance, but we should keep in mind the fact of tetrahedral distribution of valences and should therefore draw the electronic structure of water as

$$\overset{\times\times}{\underset{..}{H:O:}} \quad \text{or} \quad H-\overset{..}{\underset{}{O}:} \\ \quad\ \ H \qquad\qquad\ \ H$$

rather than as the linear molecule shown above. The two unshared pairs of electrons at the remaining two corners of the tetrahedron (or of the square in the plane projection diagram above) are quite important in explaining the facts of the chemical nature of water. Some of this explanation will be considered in a subsequent section of this chapter.

The hydride of nitrogen, ammonia, which has the formula $NH_3$, has the covalent structure

$$\begin{array}{c} H \\ | \\ :N\!-\!H \\ | \\ H \end{array}$$

in which the three H atoms are bonded to the N atom, again with tetrahedral distribution about the N atom. The fourth corner of the tetrahedron is occupied by an unshared pair of electrons. Carbon, the Group IV element, has innumerable hydrides. The simplest has the name *methane* and the formula $CH_4$. This compound has the covalent structure that would be expected:

$$\begin{array}{ccc} & H & \\ & \cdot\cdot & \\ H\!:\!C\!:\!H & \text{or} & H\!-\!\overset{\displaystyle H}{\underset{\displaystyle H}{C}}\!-\!H \\ & \cdot\cdot & \\ & H & \end{array}$$

All four possible covalences are occupied by H atoms. But carbon has the almost unique characteristic of being able to form virtually limitless numbers of covalent attachments to other carbon atoms as well as to other covalence-forming atoms in its compounds. It also has a strong tendency to form stable multiple bonds, either with other carbon atoms or with "hetero" atoms —that is, with other kinds of atoms (such as oxygen or nitrogen). The covalent structures of a few simple compounds involving carbon atoms

are indicated in Figure 20-8. Most compounds that involve carbon in covalent combination are called **organic compounds.** Thus at last we see the explanation of the use of the two terms "polar" and "organic" as opposite terms.

## 20-13. *Coordinate Covalent Bond*

Before considering the most complex electronic structures, we must consider two more qualities of the shared electrons that make up covalent bonds. The first of these has to do with the exposed unshared pair of valence electrons in such structures as water and ammonia. The nitrogen atom in ammonia has three of its pairs of electrons occupied by covalent bonds to hydrogen atoms, and the combination is a stable, neutral molecule. The pair of electrons not involved in a covalent bond, however, could, under the right circumstances, form a covalent bond with an atom that lacked a pair. Let us consider the likely result of an approach to this molecule by a positively charged hydrogen ion. The $H^+$ ion would be attracted to the two electrons, which represent a concentration of negative charge in the ammonia molecule. The $H^+$ ion is in one stable state, which it has reached by

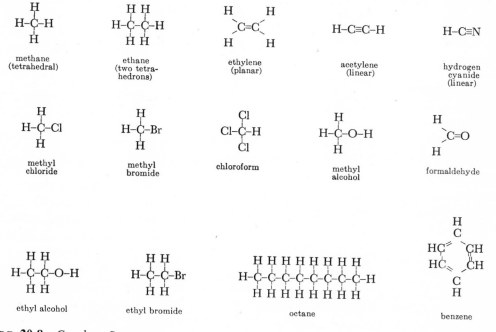

FIGURE **20-8** *Covalent Structures*

losing its only valence electron. But it can also acquire the stable helium configuration of valence electrons if it has *two* electrons in its valence group. It would be reasonable, then, for the $H^+$ ion to attach itself to the ammonia molecule by sharing with the N atom this pair of electrons, which had originally belonged exclusively to the N atom. The resultant complex, $NH_4{}^+$, would still carry the single plus charge that was brought with the $H^+$ ion, but this charge would now be distributed over the *whole* resulting complex, which is called the ammonium ion. Once formed, the covalent bond between the N atom and the new H atom that joined the complex as an $H^+$ ion is identical to the other three; there is no difference whatsoever between the newly formed bond and the others; and the four H atoms have exactly identical characteristics. This bond, formed by the contribution of *both* electrons of a shared pair by one of the two atoms, is called a **coordinate covalence.** It differs from an ordinary covalent bond *only* in the method of formation. There is also, in many cases, an accompanying change in the charge relations of the complex formed, as in the change from the neutral ammonia molecule to the charged ammonium ion. Another simple example of this type is the formation of the hydrated hydrogen ion, or hydronium ion, in water solution (see § 19-16). It is possible for one of the unshared pairs of electrons on the oxygen atom of the water molecule to be shared with an $H^+$ ion to form a coordinate covalence. Once formed, this bond is exactly like the two original H–O bonds of the water molecule. It is possible to prove that, when the hydronium ion dissociates to give a free hydrogen ion, the three hydrogen atoms have exactly the same chance of being dissociated.

## 20-14. Resonance

There are a number of stable compounds that cannot be satisfactorily formulated by a single electronic structure. For example, the ozone molecule, $O_3$ (§ 13-2), cannot be pictured simply by any single covalent arrangement of the three atoms. It is known that the bond lengths between the two end O atoms and the central atom are identical, and any bond structure of the molecule must *show* this identity of the bonds. Neither of the electronic structures shown would be satisfactory. The actual molecule is said to be a *resonance hybrid* of the two forms, and the actual bonds have a character intermediate—a hybrid—between that of single and that of double covalent bonds. We generally indicate this hybrid character by enclosing both (or all possible) forms in brackets or by drawing a double-ended arrow between the various forms. Another example is carbon monoxide, which could be represented, but not entirely satisfactorily, by any of the forms above. The actual molecule must be the resonance hybrid of the three forms indicated.

In some cases the concept of resonance must be invoked even for a compound that can be depicted quite satisfactorily by a single structure. An example of this type is carbon dioxide, which has already been indicated as having the first of the three structures depicted. Physical measurements show, however, that the distances from C to O in $CO_2$ do not correspond perfectly to this structure. The ordinary bond C=O has a length of 1.22 angstroms (1 angstrom, A, $= 10^{-10}$ meter), but the observed distance from C to O in $CO_2$ is only 1.15 A. We can explain this discrepancy by postulating that the actual structure of the $CO_2$ molecule is the resonance hybrid of all three forms depicted. The bond $C-O^-$ has a length of 1.43 A, and the bond $C\equiv O^+$ has a length of 1.10 A. The contribution of all three forms results in the actual measured length of the bond.

This concept of resonance among several possible electronic configurations is extremely important in the modern interpretation of chemical structure. We shall use the concept in this chapter as we consider the structures of more complex compounds, but we shall not be able to explore its vast possibilities in any detail. We must emphasize that the variation in these forms consists *only* in the spatial distribution of the electrons among the atoms that make up the molecule. The spatial relations of the various atoms are fixed, and there is no shifting of the bonds with time. The uncertainty of our specification of interatomic bonds is only a shortcoming of our method of describing the chemical bond.

## 20-15. *Acids and Negative Ions*

The oxygen acids and the negative ions corresponding to these acids, which make up the non-metallic part of many salts, will provide the final examples of the electronic structure of compound substances.

Carbonic acid, $H_2CO_3$:

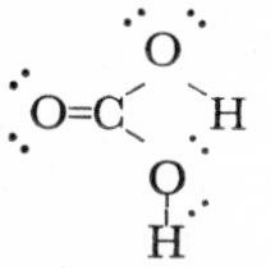

Carbonate ion, $CO_3^{-2}$ (resonance hybrid):

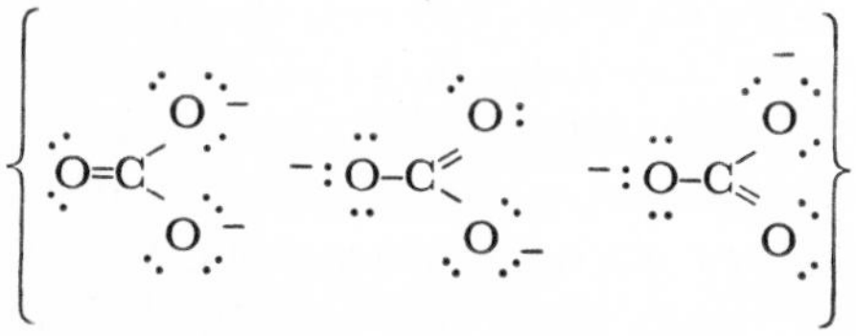

Sulfuric acid, $H_2SO_4$:

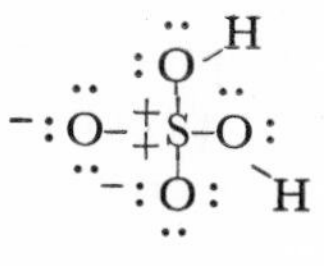

Sulfate ion, $SO_4^{-2}$:

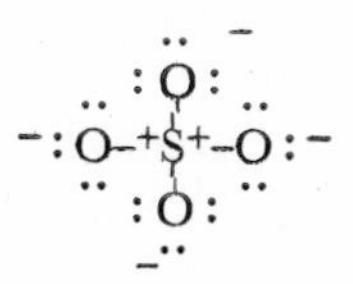

Nitric acid, $HNO_3$:

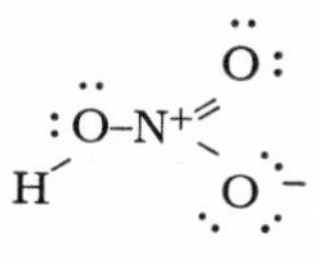

Nitrate ion, $NO_3^-$ (resonance hybrid):

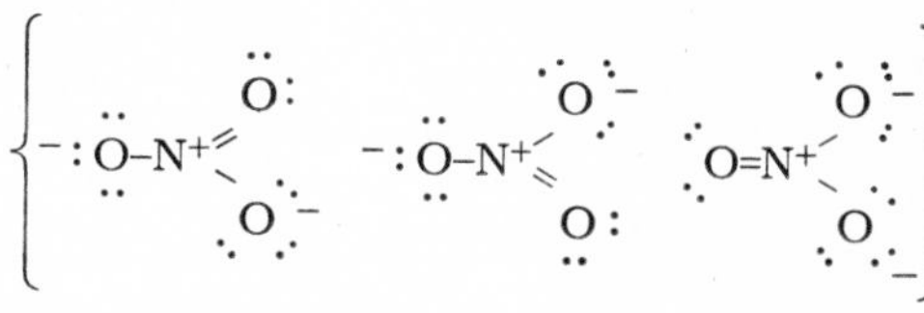

Phosphoric acid, $H_3PO_4$:

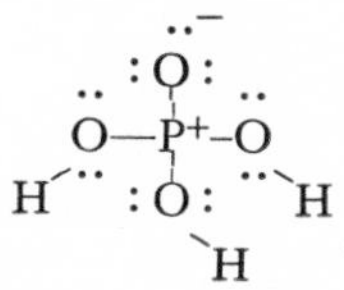

Phosphate ion, $PO_4^{-3}$:

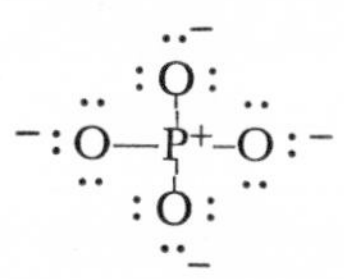

Acetic acid, $C_2H_3O_2H$:

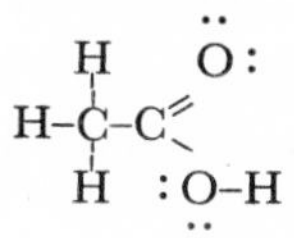

Acetate ion, $C_2H_3O_2^-$ (resonance hybrid):

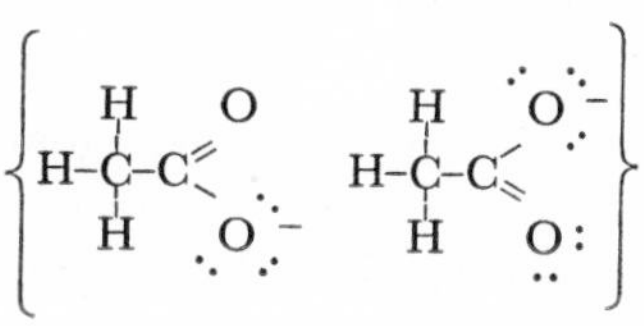

Since most of these acids ionize one or more of the hydrogen atoms as $H^+$ ions quite easily, we must presume that both ionic and covalent bonds are involved in the structures of these substances. Similarly, the salts formed between these negative ions and metals, such as silver nitrate ($AgNO_3$), copper sulfate ($CuSO_4$), and sodium carbonate ($Na_2CO_3$), exhibit both ionic valence and covalence. The structures of the crystals of these substances involve ionic bonds between the positive metal ions and the complex negative ions indicated above. The reason why a salt such as $AgNO_3$ dissociates into only *two* particles is now self-evident. The one ionic bond dissociates in solution, but the four atoms of the nitrate radical are bonded together by covalences that do not dissociate in solution.

## 20-16. Ionic-covalent Character

We have drawn a hard and clear distinction between chemical bonds that are ionic and others that are covalent. But distinctions, scientific and other, are never so perfectly simple in actual situations. The stuff of any chemical bond, ionic, covalent, or intermediate, is two electrons, and the distinction between the two extreme types we have drawn involves only the position of one of those two electrons. As we might expect, a perfectly covalent bond without any ionic character is quite rare. The difference between the two types of bond comes from a difference in the affinity of the two atoms for the electrons of the bond. If the affinity is exactly equal, the electrons are shared, and a covalent bond is the result. If one atom has a much greater affinity for the electrons than the other, it will take over sole possession of both electrons and will thereby acquire a negative charge, leaving the other atom with a positive charge, the result being an ionic bond. In elemental molecules such as $H_2$ and $Cl_2$ the affinity of each atom for the electrons must clearly be the same, and we have here a true covalent bond between the atoms. But, in almost all cases where two different atoms are involved in a bond, one will have a greater affinity for electrons than the other. Let us consider, for example, hydrogen chloride. In different contexts we have referred to this compound's ionic nature and to its covalent nature. As a gas it does exist as a molecule, HCl, but in water solution it is just as certainly ionized and should be written $H^+Cl^-$. Even in the molecular form, HCl has a strong electric dipole, and the electrons must therefore be asymmetrically distributed between the H atom and the Cl atom, as in

$$\left\{ \text{H--}\overset{..}{\underset{..}{\text{Cl}}}: \quad \text{H}^+:\overset{..}{\underset{..}{\text{Cl}}}:^- \right\}$$

the indicated resonance form. This is quite reasonable in view of the known electrical character of the two atoms. Chlorine is a strongly negative element, and hydrogen is at least mildly positive. It would be expected, then, that the Cl atom would have greater affinity for the electrons than the H atom. Hydrogen chloride is a resonance hybrid between the two forms indicated (which differ *only* in the position of the valence electrons). It has been shown that the contribution of the charged form is about 20 percent of the total; the bond is therefore said to be about 20 percent ionic in character. Almost all covalent bonds are thus partially ionic in character. Even in compounds such as methane, $CH_4$, and carbon tetrachloride, $CCl_4$, ionic character makes a small contribution—only a few percent—to the hybrid structure. In general, bonds such as these, and even that of hydrogen chloride, are written as simple covalent bonds—but with the reservation that they are not entirely or perfectly covalent.

The concept of valence is a vast one, almost without limit. Indeed, the whole study of chemistry is a series of variations on the central theme of valence. This chapter has attempted to present some of the basic ideas in a limited form and to move on from the simple statement of the *facts* of combination of atoms to a rational *theory* of combination. This theory, an electronic one, is forced on us and established by our pursuit of the relations between the phenomena of electricity and those of chemical combination. We have been able in this chapter to present a fairly rational statement of the facts of valence in terms of electronic theory, but we have not by any means exhausted the subject. Many aspects have been left in an unresolved state. A few of these are the nature of the forces of a covalent bond, the experimental proof of bond lengths and bond angles, subtler types of valence bonds, and explanations of such crucially important parts of our theory as why *pairs* of electrons and why *octets* are so important. Much of this study is a proper part of much more advanced science courses than this; other parts must be deferred until more background in modern theories and experimental and mathematical methods can be presented.

# Concepts and Terms

Electronic Basis of Valence
Electron Configurations
Stable Configurations
Octet
Kernel
Inert-gas Structures
Ionic Valence
  electron transfer
  stable ions

Covalence
  electron sharing
  tetrahedral distribution
Elemental Molecular Structures
Covalent-bond Structures
Coordinate Covalent Bond
Resonance
Ionic-covalent Character

# Problems

**20-1.** Draw the periodic table through the first three periods (through argon). Under each element indicate the atomic number, the total number of electrons, the number of valence electrons, the ionic valence (for elements that form ions), and the inert gas whose configuration is assumed when the element forms an ion.

**20-2.** Draw electronic configurations for the first twenty elements of the periodic table.

**20-3.** Indicate the ionic valence of the elements in the following compounds by drawing them as dissociated ions:

  (A) NaCl
  (B) LiF
  (C) KI
  (D) $MgCl_2$
  (E) CaS
  (F) $AlCl_3$
  (G) $Na_2O$
  (H) MgO
  (I) $Al_2O_3$
  (J) $K_2S$

      *Ans.* (A) $Na^+$ $Cl^-$
            (D) $Mg^{+2}$ $2Cl^-$

**20-4.** Define (A) electrovalence, (B) ion, (C) covalence, (D) valence electron, (E) octet, (F) shared pair, (G) tetrahedron, (H) coordinate covalence, (I) resonance.

**20-5.** Summarize the evidence in support of the conclusion that the covalent bonds and the unshared pairs of electrons of most elements are directed toward the corners of a regular tetrahedron.

**20-6.** What is the probable shape of a carbon atom? of a graphite crystal? What is the unit shape in the distribution of carbon atoms in a diamond crystal?

**20-7.** What is the electronic structure of the $O_2$ molecule? State the experimental evidence in support of this structure.

**20-8.** Draw covalent-bond structures of the following elemental molecules. Indicate as well as you can the actual spatial distribution of the atoms.

  (A) $F_2$
  (B) $N_2$
  (C) $P_2$
  (D) $P_4$
  (E) $S_8$
  (F) $I_2$

**20-9.** Draw covalent-bond structures for (A) methane, $CH_4$; (B) methyl chloride, $CH_3Cl$; (C) dichloromethane, $CH_2Cl_2$; (D) chloroform, $CHCl_3$; (E) carbon tetrachloride, $CCl_4$.

**20-10.** Draw resonance structures for (A) the ozone molecule, $O_3$; (B) the nitrate ion, $NO_3^-$; (C) the carbon dioxide molecule, $CO_2$; (D) the carbonate ion, $CO_3^{-2}$; (E) the acetate ion, $CH_3-CO_2^-$.

**20-11.** Discuss all of the types of valence bonds found in the compound sodium nitrate, $NaNO_3$.

# Suggested Readings

1. L. Pauling, *College Chemistry,* second edition (W. H. Freeman, 1955), Chap. 10.
2. D. C. Gregg, *Principles of Chemistry* (Allyn and Bacon, 1958), Chap. 11.
3. W. F. Ehret, *Smith's Introductory College Chemistry* (Appleton-Century-Crofts, 1950), Chap. 20.
4. F. T. Bonner and Melba Phillips, *Principles of Physical Science* (Addison-Wesley, 1957), Chap. 20.

IN CHAPTERS 19 and 20 the notion of the electron as the crucial stuff of the chemical bond was well established. The electron is the basic unit of the quantity of electricity, but it is also a fundamental part of the structure of all matter. It is certainly a reasonable expectation, then, that the addition or removal of electrons should profoundly alter the chemical character of any substance. We have already pointed out the great difference between the atomic and ionic forms of the same element: the forms have completely different properties. We have also considered the conduction of electric current by ions in the liquid state (either molten or dissolved electrolytes). We concluded that the conduction must be accomplished by the motion through the liquid of the ions themselves as carriers of charge, but we deferred one very important point: what happens when such an ion reaches an electrode? Since the current flowing through the metallic part of the circuit (Fig. 18-8) can *only* be free electrons, we must presume that there is an exchange of electrons between the charged electrodes of the conduction cell and the ions in the liquid state. In view of the relation of electrons to chemical character, we must expect a chemical reaction to take place at the electrode. Such a reaction does indeed take place, and the process is called **electrolysis.**

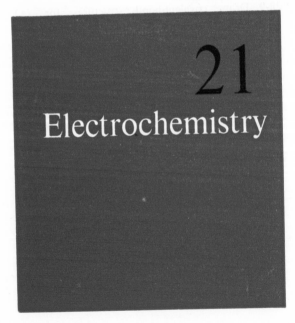

CHAPTER

21

Electrochemistry

## 21-1. *Electrolysis*

The basic experimental facts of electrolysis have been used in previous chapters as necessary parts of the argument that established the ionic theory and the electronic theory of valence. In the present discussion we shall use those theories to rationalize the experimental relations of electrolysis.

The simplest case of electrolysis is the process known as **electroplating.** Two metal plates are put into a solution of a salt of that metal, and a current is passed through the cell. A typical example is the silver–silver-nitrate cell, which is pictured in detail in Figure 21-1 (which is similar to the conductance cell diagramed in Fig. 19-1). The conduction of the current through this cell is by the motion of the two types of ions, $Ag^+$ ions toward the negative electrode and $NO_3^-$ ions toward the positive electrode. (Both electrodes are silver metal.) This motion is due to the electrostatic forces of attraction between opposite charges and of repulsion between similar charges. The new question that electrolysis poses is this: What are the events that take place when an ion arrives at the electrode?

It is simplest to consider first what happens at the negatively charged electrode, the *cathode*. This negative charge is simply a manifestation of the excess of electrons placed on the cathode by an external source of electric current. As a positively charged silver ion, $Ag^+$, approaches the cathode, one of these excess electrons attaches itself to the ion, which is thereby converted to a silver atom. The silver atom, being insoluble, is "plated" out on the surface of the silver electrode and becomes a part of the extension of the atomic lattice of the solid silver metal. Since the single positive charge of the silver ion is neutralized by a single electron, there is an exact 1-to-1 correspondence between the number of electrons entering the electrolysis cell and the number of atoms of silver deposited on the electrode. The gross manifestation of this 1-to-1 relation is that the mass of silver plated out in various situations is always exactly proportional to the amount of electricity passed through the cell.

If we now consider what happens at the positively charged electrode, the *anode*, the first assumption might be that $NO_3$ is released (or that some other change caused by the loss of an electron takes place in the $NO_3^-$ ion) at this electrode. Actually, however, no discharge of the nitrate ion takes place; instead, as the nitrate ions accumulate in the vicinity of the anode, an electronic change involving silver ions and silver atoms takes place. The source of electric power has depleted the anode of electrons, leaving it with a positive charge. This shortage of electrons can be made up if some of the silver atoms of the anode abandon their single valence electron to the circuit and leave the electrode as silver ions, $Ag^+$, which are equivalent to the atoms minus the one valence electron. The silver ions, now soluble, enter the solution, where they are repelled by the anode and attracted to

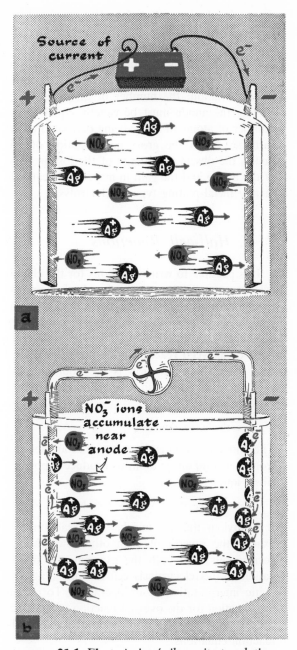

FIGURE **21-1** *Electrolysis of silver nitrate solution.*

the cathode. Thus a steady stream of $Ag^+$ ions moves through the solution from the anode to the cathode as new ones are formed at the anode and others are plated out at the cathode. Again there is an exact 1-to-1 correspondence between the number of atoms changing to ions at the anode and the number of electrons being made available to the circuit through the anode. There must also be an exact 1-to-1 correspondence between the number of electrons leaving the anode and the number arriving at the cathode (driven through by the source of electric power, which acts as a sort of electron pump). Because of this relation, the number of atoms of silver leaving the anode must be exactly equal to the number of atoms of silver being deposited at the cathode. Again the gross manifestation of this fact is the observed equality of the loss in mass of the anode and the gain in mass of the cathode in any metal-plating type of electrolysis.

## 21-2. Half-cell Reactions

It is possible to write equations for the chemical events at the two electrodes. Such electrode equations must necessarily have a quality of incompleteness about them, and the reactions they depict are therefore called either **electrode reactions** or **half-cell reactions.** We have established that the cathode reaction is the addition of a single electron to a positive silver ion to produce a silver atom:

cathode reaction: $Ag^+ + e^- \longrightarrow Ag$

The anode reaction is the removal of an electron from a neutral silver atom to produce a positive silver ion:

anode reaction: $Ag \longrightarrow Ag^+ + e^-$

It is obvious that the two half-cell reactions are exactly the reverse of each other—which fact corresponds with both the experimental observation of this electrolysis cell and the diagrammatic interpretation of its operation. To obtain the equation for the over-all reaction of the electrolysis cell, we need only add the two half-reaction equations:

$Ag^+ + e^- \longrightarrow Ag$ (cathode)
$Ag \longrightarrow Ag^+ + e^-$ (anode)
$Ag^+ + Ag + e^- \longrightarrow Ag + Ag^+ + e^-$ (over-all)

In this particular reaction every quantity that appears among the reactants also appears among the products, and the whole equation cancels out; that is, the over-all reaction in the solution is *no change!* Again, this corresponds exactly to the experimental facts of the operation of this elec-

trolysis cell; changes take place at each electrode (these changes are described by the electrode-reaction equations), but in the solution as a whole the changes are exactly canceled out, and the over-all change is zero. This use of half-cell reactions and their summation to determine the equation for the over-all reaction of the total electrolysis cell appears to be quite pointless in this particular case. In fact, any metal-plating type of cell in which the two electrode reactions are exactly the opposite of each other can be described by an over-all equation that cancels out as this one does. But the general situation is not so simple as this, and half-cell equations will prove to be quite useful in stating an over-all cell reaction.

Electrolysis cells of the metal-plating type are extremely common and important in a variety of industrial applications. The commercial manufacture of silver-plated articles is essentially similar to the process we have just described. The major difference is that the cathode is made of some metal that is not so expensive as silver, the result being that the cheap metal is covered with a thin layer of silver. Many other metals are used in similar cells to produce thin coatings of one metal on another. But an even more important industrial use of the metal-plating type of electrolysis cell is the electrolytic refinement of some metals. Copper is a notable example of substances that are purified in this way. Copper ore generally has a small amount of copper mixed with large quantities of worthless materials. By a combination of several different processes this ore is concentrated from a 1–5 percent concentration of copper to about 95 percent. This impure copper, known as "blister copper," is then cast into large slabs that can serve as anodes in the final electrolytic stage of refinement. Thin plates of pure copper are used as cathodes, and both electrodes are put into electrolytes consisting of soluble copper salts in water solution. As current is passed through the electrolysis cells, extremely pure copper is deposited on the cathode by the plating out of copper ions from the solution. These are replaced by the copper atoms of the anode, which go into solution as ions. The impurities of the blister-copper anode either go into solution and remain there or, if they are

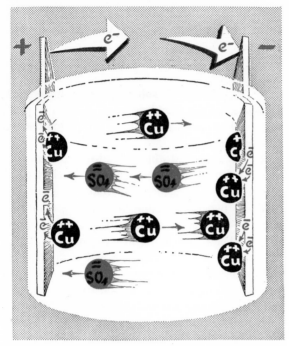

FIGURE **21-2** *Electrolysis of copper sulfate solution.*

insoluble, drop to the bottom of the cell as sludge. The industrial feasibility of this process obviously depends on the availability of cheap electric power. In areas where electricity can be easily generated (by water power, for example) this process and other types of electrolysis cells are of great importance in the industrial production and refinement of many chemicals.

It will be worth while to examine the copper–copper-ion (usually written Cu/Cu$^{+2}$) electrolytic reaction in some detail. Figure 21-2 diagrams the process, which, though similar in principle to the Ag/Ag$^+$ electrolysis shown in Figure 21-1, is different in that each copper ion has *two* positive charges instead of the single positive charge of the silver ion. Again the current is carried by the migration of both types of ions, and again, as in the silver cell, there is no discharge of the negative ion (sulfate in this case) at the anode. The two half-cell reactions are again just the opposite of each other: copper atoms go into solution as ions at the anode by giving up electrons; these electrons are pumped through the external circuit to the cathode, where they change copper ions that are in solution near

the cathode to copper atoms that plate out on the cathode. The two half-cell reactions are

$$\text{cathode reaction: } Cu^{+2} + 2e^- \longrightarrow Cu$$
$$\text{anode reaction: } Cu \longrightarrow Cu^{+2} + 2e^-$$

and the over-all reaction cancels out entirely as before: no net change takes place in the solution as a whole. Sulfate ions accumulate near the anode, but stirring the solution negates even this change, and the electrolyte solution remains totally unchanged by the process of electrolysis. The single difference between the copper cell and the silver cell—but this difference is an extremely important one—is that the copper ion has *two* positive charges and therefore requires *two* electrons in the interconversion of atoms and ions, whereas the silver ion has only one positive charge and requires only one electron for the interconversions.

## 21-3. *Faraday's Laws of Electrolysis*

This ratio of one atom to two electrons at both electrodes in the Cu/Cu$^{+2}$ cell shows that the generalizations made about the Ag/Ag$^+$ cell apply generally to electrolytic reactions: (1) a given quantity of electricity will cause the same amount of substance to participate in the chemical reaction at both electrodes (the gain in mass at the cathode is equal to the loss in mass at the anode); (2) the amount of substance that is chemically altered in an electrode reaction is directly proportional to the quantity of electricity that passes through the cell. Both of these generalizations apply equally to the two electrolysis cells examined. But, if we now compare the two cells, we immediately observe an important difference in the amount of substance entering the electrode reaction for a given quantity of electricity. If one electron passes through an Ag/Ag$^+$ cell, one atom of silver is changed to an ion at the anode, and one ion is changed to an atom at the cathode. But in a copper cell *two* electrons are required to make the change Cu $\rightarrow$ Cu$^{+2}$ or Cu$^{+2}$ $\rightarrow$ Cu. On a gross basis these statements would be that one mole of silver (Avogadro's number of atoms or ions) can be changed from atoms to ions (or vice versa) by Avogadro's number, $N_0$, of electrons, but that, for a change of one mole of copper atoms or ions, twice this number, or $2N_0$ electrons, would be required.

We have long since established the idea that comparison of the amounts of substances is best done by *moles* rather than by grams. We should therefore not expect any simple correspondence between the amount of electricity and the number of *grams* of copper or silver electrolyzed. But we should expect some relation to the number of *moles* of the two substances. It is apparent, however, that the correspondence cannot be direct for the two substances: for a given quantity of electricity, twice as many moles of silver are electrolyzed as of copper. To achieve a direct correspondence, we must include the magnitude of the valence change that takes place in the electrode reaction; and, if we compare the masses of the two substances, not by means of their atomic weights (that is, in moles), but by means of the atomic weights divided by the valence changes, a simple correspondence does result. By considering the quantitative data on *many* electrolysis cells we can make a third generalization about the relation of the amount of electricity to the amount of substance in electrolysis reactions: The amounts of different substances electrolyzed by the same quantity of electricity are proportional to the ratios of the atomic weights (or molecular weights) to the valence changes suffered in the electrolytic reaction. But we have already encountered this ratio of atomic weight to valence (see § 7-6 and Table 7-4); it was, in fact, a necessary step in the establishment of the table of atomic weights of the elements. This quantity is, of course, the *combining weight* of an element.

The generalizations we have been developing in the preceding paragraphs were first established in 1833 by Michael Faraday, an English physical scientist whose whole career exemplifies the unity of the two major branches of science called chemistry and physics. He made many highly important contributions to both sciences as well as many at the border line between the two. His formulation of the laws of electrolysis, which are called **Faraday's laws,** is an excellent example of the complete dependence of each science on the other and illustrates the importance of approach-ing the phenomena of our substantial environment from a point of view that includes both sciences.

The usual statement of Faraday's laws is as follows:

**1. The mass of substance that undergoes change at either electrode in electrolysis is proportional to the quantity of electricity that passes through the cell.**

**2. The masses of different substances that are electrolyzed by the same quantity of electricity are proportional to their combining weights.**

These two laws include the three generalizations we have established in the preceding paragraphs. Their rationality, in view of the particulate nature of both substance and electricity, is self-evident from the discussion of this and the immediately preceding chapters. As was pointed out, the experimental facts summarized by these laws are an essential part of the argument that establishes the particulate nature of electricity and the role of the electron as a part of the structure of atoms.

Several very useful ideas come out of this concept of the process of electrolysis. Implied in both of the laws of electrolysis and in much of our discussion of electrolytic cells is some "given" or "fixed" quantity of electricity. For comparisons of various electrolytic cells, this amount may be any arbitrary quantity; but it would obviously be convenient to relate this arbitrary quantity to some already established quantity involved in electrolysis. The obvious choice among related quantities is the *combining weights,* for these are chemically equivalent for all elements. The standard quantity of electricity for discussion of electrolysis and related topics has been established as **the quantity of electricity that will electrolyze one combining weight of any element.** This quantity is called the **faraday** (abbreviated by the script $\mathcal{F}$ ) of electricity. The combining weight of silver is the same as its atomic weight, 107.88, and the faraday is defined experimentally as the amount of electricity required to deposit 107.88 grams of silver on a cathode in an electrolytic cell. This quantity can be established experimentally with an extremely high degree of precision. The accepted value of this important constant is **$9.650 \times 10^4$ coulombs.**

The determination is so accurate, in fact, that the modern standard of electricity is defined by means of a "silver coulombeter," which is simply an $Ag/Ag^+$ electrolytic cell. The international coulomb is defined as the amount of electricity that will deposit $107.88/9.650 \times 10^4 = 1.118$ milligrams of silver in a silver coulombeter.

## 21-4. Avogadro's Number

A faraday of electricity is enough electrons to change by one unit the valence of one mole of any element (that is, is equivalent to one mole of a univalent element, one-half mole of a bivalent element, etc.). This number of electrons is obviously Avogadro's number, for one mole of any substance contains Avogadro's number of molecules (or atoms if the molecule is monatomic). The value of the faraday in coulombs offers, then, a method of determining Avogadro's number with a high degree of precision. From Millikan's oil-drop experiment we know precisely the charge of a single electron in coulombs (see § 18-5). The accepted value of this constant is $1.602 \times 10^{-19}$ coulomb per electron. From the value of the faraday, which is also known extremely precisely, we can calculate the precise value of Avogadro's number, $N_0$, by dividing the value of $\mathfrak{F} = 9.650 \times 10^4$ coulombs per mole by $1.602 \times 10^{-19}$ coulomb per electron:

$$N_0 = \frac{9.650 \times 10^4 \text{ coulombs/mole}}{1.602 \times 10^{-19} \text{ coulomb/electron}}$$
$$= 6.023 \times 10^{23} \text{ electrons/mole}$$

The units of this number are electrons per mole, which, from our argument above, mean the number of electrons that is chemically equivalent to one mole of a univalent element. Since there are $N_0$ atoms in a mole and an exact 1-to-1 relation between electrons and univalent atoms in electrochemical reactions, this number must be $N_0$. From the results of these two experiments—Millikan's oil-drop experiment and the determination of the faraday—it is thus possible to determine the value of Avogadro's number—that is, to *count* atoms and molecules—with an error of one part in a million.

This concept of a faraday of electricity as equivalent to a "mole" of electrons is extremely useful in electrochemical calculations. Let us consider a calculation involving the use of a silver coulombeter: If a silver electrode in such an electrolytic cell gains 10.79 grams, calculate the number of coulombs that passed through the cell and also the average current if one hour was required for the silver to be deposited. First we shall calculate the number of moles of silver electrolyzed. This is the mass of silver divided by its atomic weight: $10.79/107.9 = 0.10$ mole. We next write the half-cell reaction for the process of deposition:

$$Ag^+ + e^- \longrightarrow Ag$$

The equation shows that a single electron is required for each atom of silver in this reaction; a mole of silver therefore requires a mole of electrons, or 1 faraday of electricity; 0.1 mole requires $0.1 \mathfrak{F}$ or $0.1 \times 9.65 \times 10^4$ coulombs $= 9.65 \times 10^3$ coulombs. We know that a current of 1 ampere is equivalent to 1 coulomb per second. It is therefore necessary to calculate the time of the electrolysis in seconds. One hour is $60 \times 60 = 3,600$ seconds; the average current must therefore have been

$$\frac{9,650 \text{ coulombs}}{3,600 \text{ seconds}} = 2.67 \text{ amperes}$$

## 21-5. Electrolysis of a Molten Salt

What happens at the electrodes in electrolytic reactions other than the simple electroplating of a metal is similar, in principle, to what we have already described. The differences are mainly a matter of detail, but some of the details are of interest in our continuing expansion of the theory of the structure of matter. We shall therefore examine two further instances of electrolysis, in both of which the negative ion not only is involved in the carrying of the current (along with the positive ion) but also is discharged when it reaches the anode. This happens in the electrolysis of molten salts, such as sodium chloride, which is illustrated in Figure 21-3. In this case the electrolyte is the dry salt rather than a solution of the salt in water. Motion of the ions is

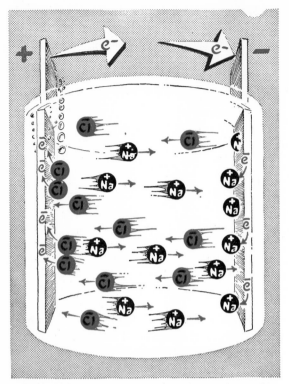

FIGURE **21-3** *Electrolysis of molten sodium chloride.*

rine does not normally exist. If two Cl atoms are produced near each other, they can combine by a covalent bond and form a molecule of $Cl_2$, which escapes as a gas. The equation for this half-cell reaction at the anode is

$$2Cl^- \longrightarrow Cl_2 + 2e^- \text{ (anode reaction)}$$

Just as in the $Ag/Ag^+$ cell described above, these two half-cell reactions describe the chemical events at the two electrodes. There are differences, however, between these equations and those written for the other cell; the anode equation, as written, produces *two* electrons, but the cathode equation consumes only one. But, obviously, the *same* quantity of electricity (and therefore the same number of electrons) passes through both electrodes of the same cell. In order to combine the two half-cell reactions to obtain the equation for the over-all reaction, we must double the cathode reaction so that the same number of electrons will be involved in both halves of the reaction:

$$2Na^+ + 2e^- \longrightarrow 2Na$$

To this equation we then add the anode equation to get the equation for the over-all reaction:

$$2Na^+ + 2Cl^- + 2e^- \longrightarrow 2Na + Cl_2 + 2e^-$$

In this equation the electrons cancel out, as, of course, they must according to the argument above, and the resulting equation describes the over-all reaction. It is apparent that electrolysis of a molten salt, unlike electroplating of metals, causes a change in the electrolyte: the salt, $Na^+Cl^-$, is consumed, and free metallic sodium and chlorine gas are produced. The statement made by the equation corresponds exactly with the experimental facts of the electrolysis of molten sodium chloride.

This particular electrolysis is used for the production of sodium metal and chlorine gas, which are important industrial chemicals. Many other electrolytic decompositions of molten salts have industrial importance, the most notable of which is the Hall process for the production of metallic aluminum. This metal, which is a common item of commerce and even of household hardware, was a chemical rarity only a few decades ago. The widespread use of the metal depended on the development of a feasible and

possible because the salt is kept in the liquid state by being heated above its melting point. The anode, moreover, must be inert—that is, must be incapable of entering the electrode reaction. (Platinum is usually the best inert electrode, but carbon often serves this purpose.) When the electrodes are connected to a source of current, the ions begin to move as expected, the $Na^+$ toward the cathode and the $Cl^-$ toward the anode. The events at the cathode are similar to those in the $Ag/Ag^+$ cell: $Na^+$ ions acquire electrons (one per ion) and are thereby converted to neutral Na atoms, which plate out on the electrode. The half-cell reaction is

$$Na^+ + e^- \longrightarrow Na \text{ (cathode reaction)}$$

At the anode no reaction is possible other than the discharge of the $Cl^-$ ions. Each $Cl^-$ that arrives at the anode gives up an electron (which is driven through the circuit back to the cathode) and is converted to a neutral Cl atom. But we know that the elemental state of chlorine is the diatomic molecule $Cl_2$ and that monatomic chlo-

cheap process for producing it from its naturally occurring salts. The process now used is the electrolysis of a molten aluminum salt that occurs abundantly. The half-cell reaction for the process is

$$Al^{+3} + 3e^- \longrightarrow Al$$

Consideration of this equation in the light of the quantitative relation of coulombs to grams will show why the production of metallic aluminum depends not so much on the availability of salts of aluminum as on the availability of cheap electric power. The equation shows that three faradays of electricity is needed to produce one mole of the metal; that is,

$$\frac{3 \times 9.65 \times 10^4 \text{ coul/mole}}{27 \text{ grams/mole}}$$

is needed to produce each gram. This quantity comes out to be 10,700 coulombs per gram of aluminum (only 893 coulombs is needed to produce a gram of silver in electrolysis).

## 21-6. *Electrolysis of Water*

The final electrolysis that we shall consider is the one we first encountered—the decomposition of water by the electrolysis of dilute aqueous solutions of electrolytes. The gross observation is that the products of the electrolysis of *dilute* solutions of most electrolytes, if inert electrodes are used, are hydrogen and oxygen. These, obviously, are products of the decomposition of water, not of the electrolyte. Again the current is carried by the ions of the electrolyte, and an accumulation of the positive ion near the cathode and the negative ion near the anode (the ions are therefore called **cations** and **anions** respectively) can be proved. But under these circumstances the electrolyte ions are not discharged at the electrodes; the decomposition of water molecules is the more easily accomplished electron transfer and is therefore what happens in most dilute solutions of electrolytes. Figure 21-4 shows diagrammatically what happens to the water molecules at each electrode. At the cathode a water molecule comes in contact with the negatively charged electrode in such a way that the positively charged hydrogen end of the dipole is near-

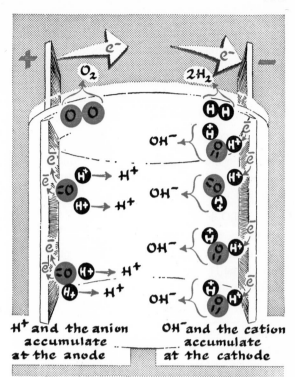

FIGURE **21-4** *Electrolysis of water—a dilute solution of an electrolyte.*

est to the concentration of negative charge (electrons). The hydrogen atom then accepts one electron and releases its largely covalent bond to the oxygen atom, leaving a hydroxide ion, OH⁻, free in solution. Another water molecule suffers the same fate, and the two hydrogen atoms produced (which can exist alone only for an *extremely* brief time) combine by a covalence to form a molecule of hydrogen gas. The half-cell reaction for this process is

$$2H_2O + 2e^- \longrightarrow H_2 + 2OH^- \text{ (cathode reaction)}$$

At the anode a water molecule comes in contact with the electrode, the negative, or oxygen, end of the dipole being attracted by the positively charged electrode. The oxygen then contributes its two extra valence electrons to the anode and thereby becomes a neutral oxygen atom. Another water molecule is similarly decomposed, and the two oxygen atoms combine to form a diatomic molecule of oxygen gas. Each oxygen atom leaves two H⁺ ions free in solution when it gives up its electrons to the anode; these two electrons were each half of the shared pair in the covalence to each of the hydrogen atoms in the water molecule. The electrons are then forced round the external circuit to the cathode as in previous cases of electrolysis. The equation for the production of oxygen gas at the anode is

$$2H_2O \longrightarrow O_2 + 4H^+ + 4e^- \text{ (anode reaction)}$$

We obtain the over-all equation by doubling the cathode reaction (so that the electrons will balance) and adding the two:

$$4H_2O + 2H_2O + 4e^- \longrightarrow$$
$$2H_2 + O_2 + 4H^+ + 4OH^- + 4e^-$$

The electrons cancel, and, if the solution is stirred, the $H^+$ ions and the $OH^-$ ions combine to form water,

$$H^+ + OH^- \longrightarrow H_2O$$

forming $4H_2O$ among the products of the reaction. These four water molecules cancel four of the six $H_2O$ on the left of the equation, and the net over-all reaction is

$$2H_2O \longrightarrow 2H_2 + O_2$$

This is the experimentally observed change that takes place in the electrolysis of dilute aqueous electrolyte solutions: the disappearance of water and the production of the two elemental gases in the volume ratio of two of hydrogen to one of oxygen. If one takes great pains to prevent mixing during the electrolysis, it is possible to show that the cation of the electrolyte and the $OH^-$ ion accumulate at the cathode and that the anion and the $H^+$ ion accumulate at the anode. The electrode reactions account for the appearance of the $H^+$ and $OH^-$ at the respective electrodes, and the conduction of current by migration of ions of the electrolyte accounts for the accumulation of these ions near the electrodes.

## 21-7. Activity Series

Several references have been made in this and the previous chapter to variations among the elements in the ease with which ions are formed or discharged. It was stated that fluorine has a greater tendency to form the fluoride ion, $F^-$, than chlorine has to form the $Cl^-$ ion; that the heavier alkali metals, such as Cs and Rb, have a greater tendency to form the unipositive ion than the lighter alkali metals, such as K and Na. We also encountered, in our consideration of electrolytic cells, a possibility of choice between different ion-electron-atom reactions, such as the choice between the discharge of the $NO^{3-}$ ion and the formation of the $Ag^+$ ion in the silver cell, and the statement was made that there is a greater tendency to form the $Ag^+$ ion than to discharge the $NO_3^-$ ion.

These facts about the ease of forming ions and the difficulty of discharging ions have been organized into a table that compares the tendencies of many elements to form or discharge ions by giving up electrons. This table, called the **activity series,** has considerable usefulness in predicting chemical reactions, including electrolytic reactions. The table is established experimentally by situations in which two elements compete with each other; the successful one is then placed higher in the activity series than the unsuccessful one. If, for example, a piece of metallic zinc is put into a solution of copper sulfate, the zinc goes into solution as $Zn^{+2}$ ions, and the $Cu^{+2}$ ions come out of solution as metallic copper. This situation is clearly one of competition between the tendency of Zn atoms to form $Zn^{+2}$ ions by giving up two electrons and the tendency of $Cu^{+2}$ ions to *remain* ions. It is also obvious that Zn was successful in this competition. We therefore place the zinc half reaction above that of copper in an activity series of the metals. The half-cell reactions for the *formation* of ions in both cases are

$$Zn \longrightarrow Zn^{+2} + 2e^-$$
$$Cu \longrightarrow Cu^{+2} + 2e^-$$

The experiment we have described shows that the tendency of zinc to give up electrons and thereby form an ion is powerful enough to *reverse* the half reaction for copper.

By similar experiments it is possible to place other elements in this series. If metallic zinc is placed in an acid (which contains $H^+$ ions), the zinc is dissolved (as $Zn^{+2}$ ions), and hydrogen gas is liberated; the $H_2/2H^+$ half reaction must therefore be *below* that of zinc in the activity series. Metallic copper will *not* displace hydrogen gas from acid solutions; therefore the $Cu/Cu^{+2}$ half reaction must be below that of hydrogen. Metallic copper will displace silver from solutions of its salts, and for this reason the $Ag/Ag^+$ half reaction is placed below the $Cu/Cu^{+2}$ half reaction. Metallic magnesium will displace metallic zinc from solutions of zinc salts; therefore the $Mg/Mg^{+2}$ half reaction must be *above* the $Zn/Zn^{+2}$ half reaction. By these experiments we have established the short activity series of these metals and hydrogen that is presented in Table 21-1.

| TABLE **21-1** *Activity Series of Metals* |
| :---: |
| $Mg/Mg^{+2}$ |
| $Zn/Zn^{+2}$ |
| $H_2/2H^+$ |
| $Cu/Cu^{+2}$ |
| $Ag/Ag^+$ |

In a similar manner we can establish an activity series of the halogens by opposing two half reactions such as

$$2Cl^- \longrightarrow Cl_2 + 2e^-$$
$$2Br^- \longrightarrow Br_2 + 2e^-$$

If we add $Cl_2$ gas (or chlorine water, which is a solution of $Cl_2$) to a solution of a salt of bromine, which, of course, contains the $Br^-$ ion, the $Cl_2$ is converted to $Cl^-$ ions by accepting electrons, and the $Br^-$ ions are converted to $Br_2$ by giving up electrons. We can demonstrate the fact of this reaction by adding to the solution some carbon tetrachloride, which forms a brilliantly brown solution with elemental bromine, $Br_2$. This information establishes that chlorine has a stronger tendency to form the $Cl^-$ ion than bromine has to form the $Br^-$ ion. If we write the symbols for the half reactions as $Cl_2/2Cl^-$ and $Br_2/2Br^-$, chlorine must be placed above bromine. But to be consistent with the symbolism of the half reactions for the metals, in which we compared the tendency to *give up* electrons, we should always indicate the electrons on the right (as in the half reaction written out above). Then the $2Cl^-/Cl_2$ would

| TABLE **21-2** *Activity Series of Halogens* |
| :---: |
| $2I^-/I_2$ |
| $2Br^-/Br_2$ |
| $2Cl^-/Cl_2$ |
| $2F^-/F_2$ |

be *below* $2Br^-/Br_2$. If similar comparisons are made of the other halogens, fluorine comes out below chlorine (fluorine is able to displace the $Cl^-$ ion from its salts by forcing the ion to give up its electron), and iodine comes out above bromine (iodine is displaced by all the other halogens), as indicated in the activity series of the halogens presented in Table 21-2.

It is now possible to incorporate both of these sets of data into a single table of decreasing tendencies to *give up electrons* in ion-atom reactions. If metallic silver is placed in a solution of bromine, the silver will be converted to the $Ag^+$ ion and the bromine to the $Br^-$ ion; iodine will not accomplish this transformation on silver, but it will on copper. Copper must therefore be above iodine and silver between iodine and bromine in a complete table. The combined activity series that includes these few metals, hydrogen, and the halogens is shown in Table 21-3. This table could be extended by similar experiments to include most of the elements of the periodic table.

Table 21-3 is a list of elements in the order of decreasing metallic character. The very strong metals are at the top, and metallic character decreases as we go down the table. The very strong non-metals are at the bottom, and non-

| TABLE **21-3** *Activity Series* |
| :---: |
| $Mg/Mg^{+2}$ |
| $Zn/Zn^{+2}$ |
| $H_2/2H^+$ |
| $Cu/Cu^{+2}$ |
| $2I^-/I_2$ |
| $Ag/Ag^+$ |
| $2Br^-/Br_2$ |
| $2Cl^-/Cl_2$ |
| $2F^-/F_2$ |

metallic character decreases as we go up the table. This table furnishes qualitative answers to two questions: Which elements tend more strongly toward the formation of ions, and which ions are therefore more likely to be discharged in an electrode reaction in electrolysis? The next step in our development is an effort to make *quantitative* predictions of these tendencies.

## 21-8. *Current-producing Cells*

The activity series of the elements, presented in an abbreviated form in Table 21-3, is a list of chemical changes in the order of decreasing tendency to happen spontaneously. Each chemical change listed in this table has a greater tendency to happen—has a greater spontaneity—than any listed below it. But we have now set ourselves the task of establishing this degree of spontaneity on a quantitative basis. The first difficulty is to establish the concept of relative spontaneity on a basis that is amenable to quantitative treatment. In order to do this, we must carefully examine just what we mean by "relative spontaneity" in the comparison of these half reactions. If two half reactions are to be combined in a whole reaction (for example, the $Zn/Zn^{+2}$ half reaction with the $Cu/Cu^{+2}$ half reaction, as in the preceding section), it is necessary that one of them be able to do the *work* of reversing the other. In the zinc-copper example the transformation of zinc metal to zinc ions liberates enough energy to force copper ions out of solution as metallic copper. The crux of the quantitative problem in the comparison of these half reactions is, then, a measurement of the work done (or the energy liberated) by the reactions.

But how can *chemical* energy, or the work of a chemical reaction, be measured? We have methods of measuring several forms of energy or work, including electrical, mechanical, and heat energy, and we have observed that these can be related to each other. A convenient way to measure electrical work, for example, is by the heat effect of the current passing through a resistor; and mechanical work can be measured

by the heating caused by friction. It would be logical, then, to look for some way to measure the work produced by a chemical reaction in terms of one of the other forms of energy. The clue to the sort of measurement that would be of use is found in the facts of electrolysis. The passage of an electric current through an electrolyte (and the utilization of electrical work in the process) causes a valence change in some of the elements of the electrolyte. Would it not be reasonable to expect that the reverse might also happen? If a chemical reaction in which elements change valence is carried out under the proper circumstances, should not this process (the reverse of electrolysis) produce an electric current and be capable of doing electrical work? The answer to this rhetorical question is that such transformations of chemical energy into electrical energy do indeed take place. The "batteries" with which we are all familiar are chemical reactions set up in such a way that we can obtain electrical energy from their "spontaneity." Furthermore, a careful measurement of the electrical work produced by such reactions offers us a method of measuring the chemical energy liberated in the reactions and thereby a method of assigning quantitative values to the activity series.

Many chemical reactions proceed quite readily (are spontaneous) and are capable of delivering considerable energy. But, unless the physical set-up of the reaction is properly arranged, this energy is wasted as heat. All such reactions, in principle, can be carried out in such a way that the energy liberated can be harnessed and measured as electrical work; and most can be so carried out in practice. Two requirements must be met if the useful work of the system is to be made available as electrical energy: (1) The two half cells must be physically separated from each other; the two electrolytes must be prevented from mixing, and the electrodes (usually the atomic form of the metal or an inert electrode for non-metals) must not be in contact. (2) There must be electrical contact between the two electrolytes; electrons must be able to pass freely from one half cell to the other. We shall discover the reasons for these requirements and the experimental methods of meeting them by examining one such current-producing cell in detail.

## 21-9. *Zinc-copper Cell*

We can demonstrate the measurement of heat liberated in a chemical reaction by adding some metallic zinc to a solution of copper sulfate. The observable facts of this demonstration are that the zinc dissolves, the copper ion (blue in solution) comes out of solution as metallic copper (the solution turns colorless), and some heat is evolved (the temperature of the solution rises). The equation for this reaction is

$$Zn + Cu^{+2} \longrightarrow Zn^{+2} + Cu$$

(The $SO_4^{-2}$ does not enter into the reaction; indeed, the results are the same whatever salt of copper is used as long as it is soluble and gives $Cu^{+2}$ ions in solution.) The amount of heat given off is observed to be $5.1 \times 10^4$ calories per mole. The same reaction is commonly carried out in such a way that the energy of the reaction appears not as heat but as electrical energy. The zinc-copper current-producing cell is known as a **Daniell cell** and is usually set up in one of the forms shown in Figure 21-5. In one of these, known as a **gravity cell** (Fig. 21-5a), the denser copper sulfate (and the copper electrode) are placed in the bottom of the container, and then zinc sulfate solution is carefully poured in on top of the copper sulfate solution. The zinc electrode is suspended near the top of the container in the zinc sulfate solution. If the cell is not jarred or shaken, there will be very little mixing of the two electrolyte solutions. The physical separation of the two electrolytes is thus accomplished by gravity. Another, more convenient way of accomplishing this separation (Fig. 21-5b) is to pour one electrolyte solution into a porous cup and then to place the cup in a beaker of the other electrolyte solution. The proper metal electrode to make up the half cell is then dipped into each electrolyte solution. The third common way of setting up this cell (and all three methods are generally applicable to other current-producing cells) is to place the two electrolytes in separate beakers (Fig. 21-5c)

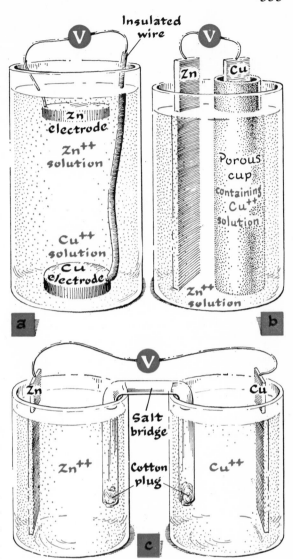

FIGURE **21-5** *Various arrangements of the Daniell cell: (a) gravity cell, in which the two electrolytes are in contact but mixing is prevented by gravity; (b) a porous cup and (c) a salt bridge provide electrical contact and prevent mixing.*

and connect the two by a **salt bridge,** which is a tube of a strong electrolyte solution (the nature of the ionic solute is immaterial) that allows free movement of ions but does not allow a solution to pass from one beaker to the other, the ends of the salt bridge being plugged with cotton or the whole salt bridge being made of a gel such as agar or gelatine. In all three cases there is free electrical contact between the two half cells *without* mixing of the two electrolyte solutions.

This discussion of the physical set-up of a current-producing cell makes the source of the term "half cell" apparent. The zinc–zinc-ion half cell consists of the zinc metal electrode and the solution of zinc sulfate (which anion is unimportant; $Zn(NO_3)_2$ would do as well; it is the $Zn^{+2}$ ion that is a component of the half cell). The equation for this half reaction is

$$Zn \longrightarrow Zn^{+2} + 2e^-$$

The other half cell consists of the copper metal electrode and the solution of copper sulfate (or other soluble copper salt), and the equation is

$$Cu^{+2} + 2e^- \longrightarrow Cu$$

All current-producing cells are set up in a similar way: two half cells are combined to make a single whole cell. The term "battery" comes from the fact that, in actual use, several such cells are combined in a single piece of apparatus (a "battery" of cells). The battery of an automobile has either three or, in recently built automobiles, six cells.

## 21-10. Cell-potential Difference

The voltage developed by a Daniell cell varies slightly with the relative concentrations of the copper and zinc ions in the electrolyte solutions, but for 1 molar solutions the potential difference is 1.10 volts, the zinc electrode being negative. This voltage is a direct measurement of the energy produced by the cell. One volt is equivalent to one joule of work for each coulomb of electricity transferred from the zinc electrode (cathode) to the copper electrode (see § 17-3). It is possible to calculate from this information the energy delivered by the cell per mole of reacting zinc. From the half-cell reaction, $Zn \rightarrow Zn^{+2} + 2e^-$, we see that each atom of zinc gives up two electrons, or each mole of zinc gives up two faradays. Thus a mole of zinc reacting in a Daniell cell would cause $2 \times 9.65 \times 10^4$ coulombs to flow through some external circuit, and each coulomb would do 1.10 joules of work. The work done by the electricity generated by

the reaction of a mole of zinc would, then, be $2 \times 9.65 \times 10^4 \times 1.10$ joules, and we can express this amount of energy in calories by dividing by the conversion factor, 4.18 joules per calorie. The energy per mole from the Daniell cell is, then,

$$\mathcal{E} = \frac{2 \times 9.65 \times 10^4 \times 1.10}{4.18} = 5.07 \times 10^4 \text{ cal}$$

This value is, of course, very close to that of the energy released as heat by this reaction, as measured in a calorimeter, when the two solutions are mixed. The crucial difference is that this energy is available for useful work in the one case but in the other case is wasted as heat and accomplishes no useful purpose. There is actually a slight difference between the maximum useful energy that can be obtained from this reaction and the amount of heat generated. It is never possible to realize *all* the energy of a system as useful work—a fact that is related to the impossibility of removing all friction from any mechanical machine. This subtle difference is of great importance in a branch of physical science called thermodynamics but is too abstract and involved to pursue further in an introductory course.

By this detailed examination of the operation of a Daniell cell we have discovered that the $Zn/Zn^{+2}$ half cell can produce enough work to reverse the $Cu/Cu^{+2}$ half cell and 50,700 cal/mole (or 1.10 volts) *in excess*. Here, then, is a quantitative statement of how much greater the tendency of zinc metal to form $Zn^{+2}$ ions is than the tendency of copper metal to form $Cu^{+2}$ ions. And we have outlined a valid method of comparing any pair of half-cell reactions. As when we established the activity series, the method is to set one half reaction in competition with another; the difference is that the half reactions are set up as current-producing cells, such as the Daniell cell. The voltage is a quantitative measure of the excess in energy of one half reaction over the other.

It is necessary, of course, to establish which of the half cells is the more energetic, not just how much they differ. This information also is supplied by the voltage measurements in the following way: It was stated above that the zinc

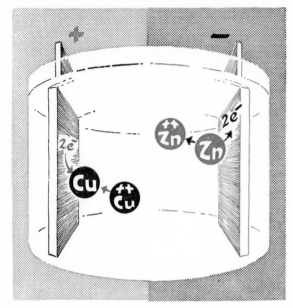

FIGURE **21-6** *Diagram of the operation of a Daniell cell.*

electrode in a Daniell cell is negative; that is, its potential is *lower* by 1.10 volts than that of the copper electrode. We know from the activity series that the $Zn/Zn^{+2}$ half cell is more energetic than the $Cu/Cu^{+2}$ half cell. It is reasonable, then, to generalize and say that the negative electrode in any cell whose voltage is being measured is that of the more energetic of the two half cells. This generalization is consistent with the electronic interpretation of the operation of the Daniell cell, diagramed in Figure 21-6. The half reactions tell us that at the zinc electrode Zn atoms are leaving the metal plate as $Zn^{+2}$ ions. To do so, they must each leave two electrons behind, causing an accumulation of electrons, or a negative charge, on this electrode. At the copper electrode copper ions, $Cu^{+2}$, are going from the solution to the metal plate as metallic copper atoms. This change can be accomplished only by their acquiring from the electrode the two electrons they need to become atoms, leaving the electrode with a deficiency of electrons, or a positive charge. Thus, in general, the negative electrode in a current-producing cell is the one at which electrons are *given up* in the electrode reaction. And, since we have chosen to write the half reactions for the activity series with the electrons on the right

(among the *products*), the greater tendency for the reaction to go must be associated with the *negative* electrode.

## 21-11. *Electrode-potential Series*

The possibility of combining different pairs of half reactions to make current-producing cells is almost without limit. We can use any reaction in which two elements change valence in opposite directions if the reaction can be carried out within the required physical set-up described in § 21-8. Furthermore, the potential differences of the cells can be measured, and with such measurements we can set up a table of quantitative statements of the tendencies of reactions to take place. The table set up in this way is very similar to the activity series of Table 21-3 except that it gives the **half-cell potential,** or **electrode potential,** for each half reaction. In a manner quite similar to that described for the Daniell cell, the $Zn/Zn^{+2}$ half cell can be set

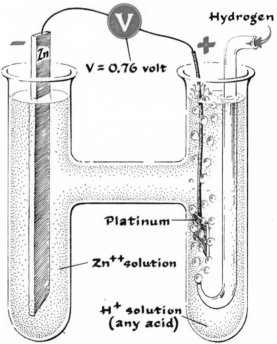

FIGURE **21-7** *Hydrogen electrode coupled with a $Zn/Zn^{+2}$ electrode.*

**TABLE 21-4** *Electrode-potential Series*

| REDUCING AGENT | OXIDIZING AGENT | VOLTS |
|---|---|---|
| Cs | $Cs^+$ | +3.02 |
| Li | $Li^+$ | +3.02 |
| Rb | $Rb^+$ | +2.99 |
| K | $K^+$ | +2.92 |
| Ba | $Ba^{+2}$ | +2.90 |
| Sr | $Sr^{+2}$ | +2.89 |
| Ca | $Ca^{+2}$ | +2.87 |
| Na | $Na^+$ | +2.71 |
| Mg | $Mg^{+2}$ | +2.34 |
| Be | $Be^{+2}$ | +1.70 |
| Al | $Al^{+3}$ | +1.67 |
| Mn | $Mn^{+2}$ | +1.05 |
| Zn | $Zn^{+2}$ | +0.76 |
| Cr | $Cr^{+2}$ | +0.71 |
| $S^{-2}$ | S | +0.51 |
| Fe | $Fe^{+2}$ | +0.44 |
| Cd | $Cd^{+2}$ | +0.40 |
| Ni | $Ni^{+2}$ | +0.25 |
| Sn | $Sn^{+2}$ | +0.14 |
| Pb | $Pb^{+2}$ | +0.13 |
| $H_2$ | $H^+$ | 0.00 |
| $Sn^{+2}$ | $Sn^{+4}$ | −0.15 |
| As | $As^{+3}$ | −0.30 |
| Cu | $Cu^{+2}$ | −0.34 |
| As | $As^{+5}$ | −0.50 |
| $I^-$ | $I_2$ | −0.53 |
| $Fe^{+2}$ | $Fe^{+3}$ | −0.75 |
| Ag | $Ag^+$ | −0.80 |
| $Br^-$ | $Br_2$ | −1.06 |
| $Cl^-$ | $Cl_2$ | −1.36 |
| Au | $Au^+$ | −1.68 |
| $F^-$ | $F_2$ | −2.85 |

*Increasing strength as reducing agent* (left vertical axis)

*Increasing strength as oxidizing agent* (right vertical axis)

up with an $Ag/Ag^+$ half cell. The potential difference of this cell is 1.56 volts, with the zinc electrode negative. The copper-silver cell has a potential difference of 0.46 volt, with the copper electrode negative.

It is also possible to use a hydrogen electrode in current-producing cells and for measurements of differences in cell potential. The $H_2/H^+$ half cell consists of an inert electrode, such as platinum, immersed in a solution that contains $H^+$ ions (any acid) and through which $H_2$ gas bubbles (Fig. 21-7). A cell made up of such a hydrogen electrode and a $Zn/Zn^{+2}$ electrode has a potential difference of 0.76 volt, with the zinc electrode negative. A copper-hydrogen cell has a voltage of 0.34 and a silver-hydrogen cell a voltage of 0.80, both with the hydrogen electrode negative.

All of these voltages are potential *differences,* and in all cases we are *comparing* reaction tendencies. Like previous comparisons such as atomic weights and valences (Chap. 7), this one is most useful if we select some value as an arbitrary standard against which other values can be measured. Cell-potential differences have been placed on such a basis by defining the electrode potential of the hydrogen half cell as zero and by adopting an arbitrary sign convention. The agreement is that all half reactions *above* hydrogen in the activity series (Table 21-3)— that is, those that tend more strongly to *give up* electrons—shall have a *plus* sign; those with a lesser tendency to give up electrons (or a stronger tendency to accept electrons) shall have a *minus* sign. By applying these conventions and comparing each half-cell reaction with the hydrogen electrode, we can assign a quantitative value and the conventional sign to the electrode potential of any half-cell reaction. Thus the $Zn/Zn^{+2}$ half cell is assigned a value of $+0.76$ volt from the voltage measurement shown in Figure 21-7; $Cu/Cu^{+2}$ has a half-cell potential of $-0.34$ volt; and $Ag/Ag^+$ has $-0.80$ volt. Table 21-4 gives the electrode-potential series established in this way for many of the common elements.

## 21-12. *Examples of Use of Electrode-potential Series*

The usefulness of the electrode-potential series can best be demonstrated by examples of problems.

### EXAMPLE 1

Calculate the potential difference developed in a cell made up of a $Pb/Pb^{+2}$ electrode and a $2Cl^-/Cl_2$ electrode. Write the half-reaction equations and the over-all equation.

The half-cell equations and the electrode potentials are obtained from Table 21-4:

$$Pb \longrightarrow Pb^{+2} + 2e^- \qquad +0.13 \text{ volt}$$
$$2Cl^- \longrightarrow Cl_2 + 2e^- \qquad -1.36 \text{ volts}$$

But both of these equations are written in such a way that electrons are *given off* at the electrodes;

one or the other must be reversed. From the direction of the long arrow in Table 21-4 we can judge that the half reaction for chlorine probably goes in the other direction; when the potentials are combined, we can be sure of the reverse direction of this half reaction:

$$2e^- + Cl_2 \longrightarrow 2Cl^- \qquad +1.36 \text{ volts}$$

Now, if we add these two half reactions and the potentials of the individual half cells—

$$Pb + Cl_2 \longrightarrow Pb^{+2} + 2Cl^- \qquad +1.49 \text{ volts}$$

—we obtain an over-all reaction for the cell as a whole, and the potential difference of the cell is 1.49 volts. From the half-cell reactions it is apparent that the lead electrode is negative.

The fact that the cell-potential difference came out positive establishes the fact that the reaction will go as written. In general, **if the cell-potential difference is positive** (as calculated from electrode potentials from Table 21-4), **the reaction will go in the direction written; if the potential difference is negative, the reverse reaction will happen; and, if the potential difference is zero, the reaction will go in neither direction.**

This calculation also illustrates another generalization about the use of Table 21-4. All of the half reactions are written in the direction of giving up electrons. In any total reaction, obviously, the electrons given up by one half reaction (or at one electrode) must be balanced by the electrons accepted by the other half reaction (either from the electrode or directly from the first half reaction). For this reason one of the two half reactions written in Table 21-4 must always be reversed when we write the equation for the whole reaction. It also may be necessary to multiply one half-reaction equation by some factor so that the *number* of electrons given up by one half cell will just balance those accepted by the other.

### EXAMPLE 2

Calculate the voltage developed by a cell with $Cd/Cd^{+2}$ and $Al/Al^{+3}$ electrodes, and write the over-all equation.

The half-cell equations and potentials are

$$Cd \longrightarrow Cd^{+2} + 2e^- \qquad +0.40 \text{ volt}$$
$$Al \longrightarrow Al^{+3} + 3e^- \qquad +1.67 \text{ volts}$$

Both these half cells have positive potentials;

since the aluminum electrode has the greater potential, it will be the negative electrode, and the equation for the cadmium electrode must be reversed:

$$2e^- + Cd^{+2} \longrightarrow Cd \qquad -0.40 \text{ volt}$$

But now we observe that the aluminum half cell delivers three electrons and the cadmium half cell accepts only two. If they are to be coupled in a whole cell, the number of electrons produced in the one must be accepted by the other; it is therefore necessary to multiply each electrode reaction by the appropriate factor to arrive at this balance of electrons. This is done in the same way as in the balancing of chemical equations: the one must be multiplied by the factor 2 and the other by 3 so that the electrons in each amount to six:

| | |
|---|---|
| $2Al \longrightarrow 2Al^{+3} + 6e^-$ | $+1.67$ volts |
| $6e^- + 3Cd^{+2} \longrightarrow 3Cd$ | $-0.40$ volt |
| $2Al + 3Cd^{+2} \longrightarrow 2Al^{+3} + 3Cd$ | $+1.27$ volts |

Note that the voltages of the half cells are *not* multiplied by the factors that balance the electrons. The electrode potentials are a statement of the energy liberated *per coulomb* by any amount of the substance suffering the electrode reaction; doubling or tripling the equation doubles or triples the *amount* of substance and thereby the number of coulombs of electricity, but it does not affect the amount of work produced per coulomb, which is the half-cell voltage.

The final point of interest about the electrode-potential series is that here, for the first time, is a method of predicting the course of chemical reactions. In our first discussion of chemical equations, in Chapter 8, we stated that knowledge of whether or not a reaction will actually happen "can come only from experience and from certain more complex ideas, some of which will be considered later in this book." The concept and use of electrode potentials in predicting

the direction of reactions are those "more complex ideas." One can propose a reaction by writing an equation; then, if the reaction can be separated into half-cell reactions that are found in Table 21-4, one can decide whether or not it will happen.

### EXAMPLE 3

The balanced equation for the dissolving of antimony in an acid ($H_2SO_4$, for example) is

$$2Sb + 3H_2SO_4 \longrightarrow 2Sb^{+3} + 3SO_4^{-2} + 3H_2$$

Does this reaction actually happen?

The two half reactions are

| | |
|---|---|
| $2Sb \longrightarrow 2Sb^{+3} + 6e^-$ | $-0.10$ volt |
| $6e^- + 6H^+ \longrightarrow 3H_2$ | $0.00$ volts |

(Note that the $SO_4^{-2}$ ions do not actually enter this reaction and are really immaterial in this calculation.) The antimony half reaction has a potential of $-0.10$ volt, and the hydrogen half reaction has a potential of $0.00$; the voltage of the whole reaction (if operated as a cell) is $-0.10$ volt. The fact that this potential difference is negative proves that the reaction would *not* proceed as written.

This last example emphasizes the point that the cell potential can be calculated and is of real value *whether or not* the reaction is carried out in such a way that the energy of reaction can be harnessed as electrical work. The calculations are valid and extremely useful in predicting reactions even if the reaction is carried out by a simple mixing of the ingredients. This fact was established by the copper-zinc reaction of § 21-10, in which it was shown that the heat of the reaction could be calculated from electrode potentials just as well as from calorimetric measurements on a reaction initiated by a mixing of solutions.

## Concepts and Terms

Electrolysis
Electrode
  anode
  cathode
Half-cell Reaction
  electrode reaction
Faraday's Laws of Electrolysis

Determination of Avogadro's Number
Faraday of Electricity
Electroplating Reactions
  silver coulombeter
Electrolysis of Molten Salts
Electrolysis of Water
Activity Series

Current-producing Cells
  Daniell cell
  cell-potential difference
  energy of reaction

Hydrogen Electrode
Electrode Potentials
  electrode-potential series

# Problems

**21-1.** Describe in your own words and by the use of diagrams and equations the events taking place in a silver-plating electrolytic cell. Consider the changes at each electrode and in the solution and the movement of charge within the solution and through the external circuit.

**21-2.** In what ways does the $Ag/Ag^+$ electrolysis reaction differ from the $Cu/Cu^{+2}$ electrolysis reaction? In what ways does it differ from the electrolysis of molten sodium chloride?

**21-3.** State in your own words Faraday's laws of electrolysis. Summarize the evidence in support of each of these laws.

**21-4.** Define the faraday of electricity. How is it measured?

**21-5.** Define Avogadro's number. Describe two methods for the determination of $N_0$. Which is more precise?

**21-6.** Describe, with diagrams and equations, the electrolytic decomposition of water.

**21-7.** Describe in your own words the basis and meaning of the activity series of the elements, including the conventions about the direction of the half-cell reactions, and tell which tendency is placed at the top of the series. Describe how you would decide where to place the $Zn/Zn^{+2}$, $Ag/Ag^+$, and $H_2/H^+$ half cells with respect to each other.

**21-8.** Describe all the physical requirements for making a current-producing cell. Illustrate these requirements by constructing a cell that has a potential difference of 1.56 volts. Refer to Table 21-4.

**21-9.** Calculate the energy of reaction, in calories per mole of $H_2$ produced, for the reaction

$$Zn + 2H^+ \longrightarrow H_2 + Zn^{+2}$$

*Ans.* $3.51 \times 10^4$ cal/mole

**21-10.** Calculate the cell-potential difference for each of the following reactions:

(A) $Zn + Cu^{+2} \longrightarrow Zn^{+2} + Cu$
(B) $Zn + 2Ag^+ \longrightarrow Zn^{+2} + 2Ag$
(C) $2Al + 3Zn^{+2} \longrightarrow 2Al^{+3} + 3Zn$

**21-11.** Calculate the energy of reaction, in calories per mole of zinc, for each of the reactions of Prob. 21-10.

**21-12.** Calculate the number of coulombs needed to produce 50 grams of each of the following metals in the electrolysis of a solution of a salt of the metal: (A) Ag, (B) Zn, (C) Al, (D) Cu, (E) Pb.

*Ans.* (B) $1.48 \times 10^5$ coulombs

**21-13.** How long would it take to produce the 50 grams of each of the metals in Prob. 21-12 if the current through the cell were 3.0 amp?

*Ans.* (B) $4.94 \times 10^4$ sec $= 13.7$ hours

**21-14.** In an electrolysis of fused KCl, the current was passed through the cell long enough to produce 200 cm³ of $Cl_2$ gas measured at 76 cm pressure and 27°C.
(A) Calculate the mass of potassium metal produced in this experiment.
(B) Calculate the number of coulombs of electricity used in this experiment.
(C) If the experiment took 2 hours, what was the current used?

*Ans.* (B) $1.57 \times 10^3$ coulombs

**21-15.** Calculate the potential difference of each of the following cells. State which electrode is negative and which positive in each case: (A) $Cl^-/Cl_2$–$Sn^{+2}/Sn^{+4}$, (B) $Cr/Cr^{+2}$–$Br^-/Br_2$, (C) $Sn/Sn^{+2}$–$Pb/Pb^{+2}$, (D) $Cd/Cd^{+2}$–$H_2/H^+$.

**21-16.** Write balanced equations for the half reactions and for the over-all reactions of the cells of Prob. 21-15. Be certain that the equations are written in the direction in which the reactions actually take place.

## Suggested Readings

1. W. F. Magie, *A Source Book in Physics* (McGraw-Hill, 1935). Pages 472–511 contain a biographical sketch of Faraday and a statement of his most important work; his laws of electrolysis are described on pp. 492–498. Alternative discussions of electrochemistry are contained in the following references.

2. F. T. Bonner and Melba Phillips, *Principles of Physical Science* (Addison-Wesley, 1957), Chap. 18.

3. L. Pauling, *College Chemistry,* 2nd edition (W. H. Freeman, 1955), Chap. 12.

4. D. C. Gregg, *Principles of Chemistry* (Allyn & Bacon, 1958), Chap. 13.

5. M. J. Sienko and R. A. Plane, *Chemistry* (McGraw-Hill, 1957), Chap. 14.

IN THE discussion of electrochemistry in Chapter 21 a large number of reactions were considered. All these reactions had one event in common: a change in valence. The general term for such reactions is **oxidation-reduction reaction.** The term "oxidation" originally had only the meaning implied by the word itself, the combination of some element with oxygen to form an oxide. Hydrogen is oxidized in the reaction

$$2H_2 + O_2 \longrightarrow 2H_2O$$

Magnesium is oxidized in the reaction

$$2Mg + O_2 \longrightarrow 2MgO$$

Carbon is oxidized in the reaction

$$C + O_2 \longrightarrow CO_2$$

All these reactions are oxidations in the restricted sense: they are combinations with oxygen to form oxides. But these reactions also have another characteristic in common: the element other than oxygen *increases* its valence. Many other reactions also have this characteristic. Any of the elements named above will react in a similar manner with chlorine,

$$H_2 + Cl_2 \longrightarrow 2HCl$$
$$Mg + Cl_2 \longrightarrow MgCl_2$$

with sulfur,

$$C + 2S \longrightarrow CS_2$$
$$Mg + S \longrightarrow MgS$$

or with any of many other non-metallic elements. In each case the one element increases its valence. The term oxidation has been given a general meaning that includes all of these similar reactions.

## 22-1. General Sense of Term "Oxidation"

An **oxidation** is therefore any reaction in which an element increases its valence. This general definition obviously includes reactions in which oxygen is the oxidizing agent as well as those in which some other element or compound causes the increase in valence. In the examples considered, sulfur and chlorine, as well as oxygen, acted as oxidizing agents.

CHAPTER

22

Oxidation-
Reduction

If the oxidizing agents of such reactions are considered, another characteristic becomes apparent—one that the cell reactions of Chapter 21 might have led us to anticipate. In each of the oxidations we have considered, the oxidizing agent *decreases* its valence from zero to −1 or to −2. If we examine the number of units by which the valence changed, we observe that in each case the total increase in valence is exactly equal to the decrease in the valence of the oxidizing agent. The accepted term for a reaction in which the valence of an element decreases is **reduction.** The two processes always go on together; it is impossible to have a reduction without having some other substance undergo exactly the same amount of oxidation. The whole reactions are therefore called, as we have seen, oxidation-reduction reactions.

If we consider the electrons, we see that oxidation is the *removal* of electrons from the substance oxidized and reduction is the *addition* of electrons to the substance reduced. It then becomes apparent that each of the reactions cited above can be separated into two half-cell reactions, of which one donates electrons and the other absorbs electrons. It is also apparent that all the reactions of Chapter 21, including the reactions of both electrolytic and current-producing cells, are, in fact, oxidation-reduction reactions. This chapter is, then, a continuation of the discussion of the ideas of Chapter 21, with emphasis on the chemical reaction rather than on the electrical events.

## 22-2. Definitions

An **oxidation-reduction reaction** is a reaction in which one element increases its valence (loss of electrons) and another element decreases its valence (gain of electrons).

**Oxidation** is the half reaction in which electrons are *donated,* the valence of the element donating electrons being *increased.*

**Reduction** is the half reaction in which electrons are *accepted,* the valence of the element accepting electrons being *decreased.*

The **oxidizing agent** is the reagent that *accepts* electrons from the other half reaction and thereby causes the increase in valence of some other element.

The **reducing agent** is the reagent that donates electrons to the other half reaction and thereby causes the decrease in valence of some other element.

The **unit of oxidation-reduction** is the *electron.* A unit of oxidation is the loss of one electron; a unit of reduction is the gain of one electron.

## 22-3. Types of Half Reactions

From these definitions it is apparent that oxidation-reduction is a *single,* concerted reaction; neither process ever takes place without an exactly equal amount of the other. It is convenient, in discussion and in the analysis of the over-all process, to separate the two *half reactions.* But in total reactions—which actually happen—each half of the process must be accompanied by the opposite half.

The simplest types of oxidation or reduction half reactions are those we have already considered: transformations between atoms and simple ions of elements. These are clearly included in the definitions above. But many more complex transformations must also be included. The next simplest type is the conversion of a multivalent simple ion from one valence to another. Iron, for example, can have either a +2 or a +3 valence, and it forms ions with each of these. The *ferrous* ion is $Fe^{+2}$, and the *ferric* ion is $Fe^{+3}$. It is therefore possible for the ferric ion to act as an oxidizing agent in the half reaction

$$e^- + Fe^{+3} \longrightarrow Fe^{+2}$$

and for ferrous ion to act as a reducing agent:

$$Fe^{+2} \longrightarrow Fe^{+3} + e^-$$

In both of these half reactions the transformation is between two different ionic states and does not include the atomic, or *zero*-valence, state. Such transformations are commoner than the simpler atomic transformations. Even more common are transformations between two valence states of the central atom in complex ions or in covalent molecules. An example of such a transformation is the oxidation of sulfurous acid to sulfuric acid by oxygen. Sulfur has a valence of $+4$ in sulfurous acid, $H_2SO_3$, and a valence of $+6$ in $H_2SO_4$. It therefore requires two units of oxidation (the acceptance of two electrons) to transform $H_2SO_3$ to $H_2SO_4$. These electrons are accepted by oxygen atoms in the transformation from the zero valence of elemental gaseous oxygen to the $-2$ valence of oxygen in combination. Clearly, an atom of oxygen is also required to balance the substance of this reaction. The balanced equation for the reaction is

$$2H_2SO_3 + O_2 \longrightarrow 2H_2SO_4$$

This reaction can be balanced quite easily by inspection of the formulas, and it is possible to decide which is the oxidizing agent and which the reducing agent from the preceding discussion of the valences of oxygen and sulfur. In most cases, however, the balancing of oxidation-reduction equations is much more complicated, and success can come only from using a system. The system to be proposed is entirely logical and uses ideas that have already been established in this and a few preceding chapters. It places the whole question of oxidation-reduction reactions and the balancing of the equations on a logical, rational, and theoretically sound basis. Many oxidation-reduction equations can be balanced by trial and error, and for this reason students frequently attempt to avoid the use of the rational system. There are two good reasons for abandoning the trial-and-error method and accepting, learning, and using the rational, systematic method. The first is that the systematic method makes use of the central concepts and ideas of the structure of matter, the development of which is the major purpose of our dealing with these reactions in the first place. The second is that the systematic method, if used properly, is *always* successful, whereas the trial-and-error method, in many cases, cannot possibly be successful.

## 22-4. Oxidation Number

We have already encountered several different forms of valence and have used several different concepts of valence. A slight variation on the ideas of valence already used, which is called the **oxidation number,** is particularly convenient for dealing with equations of oxidation-reduction reactions. The oxidation number is a form of valence and, like the other forms of valence we have encountered, is closely associated with the outside group of electrons of the atom. The electron is the unit of oxidation-reduction; it is also the unit of electrovalence and of covalence; and it is the unit of oxidation number. The oxidation number is used because, for many complex ions and covalent molecules, it is difficult to decide, on purely logical grounds, which atom gives up or gains electrons in oxidation-reduction reactions. It is an *arbitrary* method of assigning the gain and loss of electrons within the molecule or complex ion. The following definitions and rules will make the concept understandable.

1. **The charge on the ion is the oxidation number for monatomic ions.** The oxidation number is $+1$ for $Na^+$, $H^+$, $K^+$, $Li^+$, $Ag^+$, etc; it is $+2$ for $Mg^{+2}$, $Ca^{+2}$, $Cu^{+2}$, $Fe^{+2}$, $Mn^{+2}$, $Pb^{+2}$, $Sn^{+2}$, etc; it is $+3$ for $Al^{+3}$, $Fe^{+3}$, etc; it is $+4$ for $Sn^{+4}$, etc. The negative ions have minus oxidation numbers: $-1$ for $Cl^-$, $Br^-$, $I^-$, etc; $-2$ for $O^{-2}$, $S^{-2}$, etc.

2. **The oxidation number of all elemental substances is zero.**

3. **The sum of the oxidation numbers of the atoms in a compound is zero.**

4. **The sum of the oxidation numbers of a complex ion is the charge on the ion.**

5. **In covalent compounds and complex ions the shared pairs of electrons are assigned to the more negative of the two bonded atoms, and the charge remaining on all of the atoms is then the oxidation number of the atoms.**

6. **In an oxidation-reduction reaction the increase in the oxidation number of one atom is exactly balanced by the decrease in the oxidation number of some other atom or atoms.**

## 22-5. Examples of Assignment of Oxidation Numbers

A careful consideration of these rules will show that the oxidation number defined by them is very similar to the valence used in Chapter 7. The difference is that the concept has been refined to include covalent bonds. The significance and usefulness of this concept and the use of the rules that define it are best established by consideration of several examples.

## EXAMPLE 1: Binary Ionic Compounds

Rule 1 makes the assignment of oxidation numbers self-evident—they are simply the ionic charges.

In $Na^+Cl^-$ the oxidation number of $Na^+$ is obviously $+1$ and that of $Cl^-$ is $-1$. In $AlCl_3$, the oxidation number of the aluminum ion is $+3$ and that of each chloride ion is $-1$; the *three* chloride ions represent a *total* oxidation number of $-3$, which balances the $+3$ of $Al^{+3}$ so that the *compound* has a net oxidation number of zero (rule 3).

## EXAMPLE 2: Covalent Compounds

Rule 5 assigns oxidation numbers to all the atoms of such compounds; it is necessary, however, either to write out the electronic structure of the compound or to make a mental assignment of the shared pairs to the negative atoms and thereby to arrive at the charges on the atoms.

In methane, $CH_4$, we know that the H is more positive and the C more negative; all the valence electrons are therefore assigned to the C atom, giving it 8 negative charges against the charge of $+4$ on the kernel. (This fact comes from the position of carbon in Group IV of the periodic table.) The net charge (assigned *arbitrarily*) is therefore $-4$, and the oxidation number of carbon in this compound is $-4$. The H atoms have each lost (by *arbitrary* assignment) their only electron and therefore have an oxidation number of $+1$. In carbon tetrachloride, $CCl_4$, the Cl atoms are more negative than the C atom; the electrons are therefore assigned to the Cl, leaving the C atom with an oxidation number of $+4$ and the four Cl atoms with oxidation numbers of $-1$. These facts are apparent from the electronic structures of the compounds:

$$
\begin{array}{cc}
\text{H} & \text{H}^{+1} \\
\cdots & \cdots \\
\text{H:C:H} = \text{H}^{+1}\text{:C:}^{-4}\text{H}^{+1} \\
\cdots & \cdots \\
\text{H} & \text{H}^{+1}
\end{array}
$$

$$
\begin{array}{cc}
:\text{Cl}: & :\text{Cl}:^{-1} \\
:\text{Cl:C:Cl}: = :\text{Cl}:^{-1}\text{C}^{+4}:\text{Cl}:^{-1} \\
:\text{Cl}: & :\text{Cl}:^{-1}
\end{array}
$$

In these simple examples it is obviously not necessary to draw the electronic structures in order to assign the oxidation numbers; they can be determined by simple consideration of the formula, the relative negativities, and the kernel charges. These two structures do emphasize a point that should be remembered: the *arbitrary* character of oxidation number. The covalent bonds in methane and carbon tetrachloride are essentially similar, and the covalence of carbon is the same in both compounds. But the oxidation number, as determined by the rules for its use, is quite different in the two compounds.

## EXAMPLE 3: Complex Compounds

In $H_2SO_4$ sulfur has an oxidation number of $+6$. The two H atoms (which are easily ionized in solution) are stripped of their electrons and thus given an oxidation number of $+1$; the four O atoms are each awarded a complete octet for oxidation numbers of $-2$; this leaves the S atom stripped of all valence electrons and therefore with an arbitrary charge of $+6$:

$$
\begin{array}{cc}
:\text{O}: & :\text{O}:^{-2} \\
\text{H:O:S:O:} = \text{H}^{+1}\text{:O:}^{-2}\text{ S}^{+6}\text{:O:}^{-2} \\
:\text{O}: & :\text{O}:^{-2} \\
\text{H} & \text{H}^{+1}
\end{array}
$$

In sulfurous acid, $H_2SO_3$, the sulfur atom has an oxidation number of $+4$. Again the two H atoms are given oxidation numbers of $+1$; each of the three O atoms is awarded the pair of electrons that it shares with the S atom; the sulfur is then left with only two of its valence electrons, which cancel 2 of the $+6$ kernel charge for an oxidation number of $+4$:

$$
\begin{array}{cc}
\text{H:O:S:O:} = \text{H}^{+1}\text{:O:}^{-2}\text{ S}^{+4}\text{:O:}^{-2} \\
:\text{O}: & :\text{O}:^{-2} \\
\text{H} & \text{H}^{+1}
\end{array}
$$

Note that in each compound the sum of the oxidation numbers is zero. In sulfuric acid the H atoms contribute $2 \times +1$ and the S atom contributes $+6$ for a total of $+8$; the four O atoms each have a $-2$ for a total of $-8$. In sulfurous acid the sum is $H (2 \times +1) + S (+4) + O (3 \times -2) = 0$.

In phosphorus trichloride, $PCl_3$, the Cl is the more negative. The shared pairs are therefore assigned to Cl, giving each Cl a complete octet for a charge of $-1$ and therefore an oxidation number of $-1$. The P atom has only two electrons left and therefore a charge of $+3$ (the kernel charge of $+5$

minus the two negative charges of the two electrons):

In phosphoric acid, $H_3PO_4$, the phosphorus has an oxidation number of $+5$. The shared electrons are all assigned to the O atoms, leaving the P atom with no electrons and a charge equal to the kernel charge, which is $+5$:

EXAMPLE 4: Complex Ions

The assignment of oxidation numbers is essentially the same for complex ions (which are held together by covalent bonds) as for covalent complex compounds. The difference is that these oxidation numbers add up to the charge on the ion.

The carbonate ion, $CO_3^{-2}$, has the structure shown below:

The oxidation number of carbon in this ion is $+4$ because the assignment of all the valence electrons to the more negative oxygen leaves the C with the bare kernel, which has a charge of $+4$. The sum of the oxidation numbers [$C = +4$, $3O = 3(-2) = -6$] is then $+4 + (-6) = -2$, which is the same as the charge on the ion.

The nitrogen atom in the nitrate ion, $NO_3^-$, has an oxidation number of $+5$ when we assign all the valence electrons to the O atoms:

The N atom ends up with no valence electrons and therefore has the kernel charge of $+5$. The sum of $+5$ and $3(-2)$ is $-1$, the charge on the ion, as required by rule 4.

One useful generalization will simplify the calculation of oxidation numbers. This is that, in almost all compounds and complex ions, oxygen has an oxidation number of $-2$ and hydrogen has an oxidation number of $+1$. Frequently the oxidation number can be calculated directly from these facts and from the rule that the sum of oxidation numbers in a compound is zero.

## 22-6. *Balancing Oxidation-Reduction Equations*

The rational system of balancing oxidation-reduction reactions is divided into several steps. First we express the simple fact of reaction by an "unbalanced equation." Then, after deciding which is the oxidizing agent and which the reducing agent, we write the two half reactions (unbalanced). Next we consider the two half reactions separately, balancing each first in **oxidation number** by adding electrons to the appropriate side, then in **electric charge** by adding water and its products of ionization, $H^+$ ions and $OH^-$ ions, to the appropriate side, and finally for **substance.** We now multiply the two balanced half reactions by the factors that will allow the electrons (units of oxidation-reduction) to cancel out, and we add the two half reactions (or multiples) to get the over-all reaction. We used exactly this procedure in writing over-all reactions for the current-producing cells in Chapter 21. The only difference is that those reactions were quite simple and some of the steps in the process were therefore not necessary.

The first step of this procedure, the writing of the unbalanced equation, is exactly the same as the first step in balancing the equation for any reaction. This usually consists simply of translating a verbal statement into chemical symbols.

To select the oxidizing and reducing agents, we determine which elements suffer changes in oxidation number by examining the formulas of the substances and calculating or assigning the oxidation numbers. The element that changes in a positive direction (goes to a higher positive number or a lower negative number) is the one that is oxidized, and the element that changes in a negative direction is the one that is reduced.

The compounds specified in the unbalanced over-all equation must be included both in the half-reaction equations and in the balanced over-all equation; but attention is focused on the element that suffers the change in oxidation number.

Since the unit of oxidation-reduction is the electron, the first step in balancing the half reactions is to include the proper number of electrons on the proper side of the equation. A decrease in oxidation number obviously requires the addition of electrons to the element being reduced; the electrons are therefore introduced on the left side of the equation, among the reactants. Oxidation is the giving up of electrons, which would therefore appear on the right of the half reaction for the substance being oxidized. In current-producing cells and in electrolysis these electrons pass from the reducing agent to the oxidizing agent through the external circuit and thereby give a physical demonstration of their involvement in the reaction. In the more general case of oxidation-reduction reactions in which the two half reactions are *not* physically separated, the electrons are still passed from the reducing agent to the oxidizing agent, even though there is no physical evidence of the passage. This direct participation of electrons in the reaction and the role of electrons as units of oxidation-reduction make it apparent that the primary operation in balancing these equations must be the balancing of the electrons between the two half reactions; the electrons accepted by the one half reaction must be exactly equal to the electrons given up by the other.

The electron, however, is not only the unit of oxidation-reduction but also the unit of electrical charge. When electrons are added to one side of an equation for a half reaction, the electrical charge is frequently thrown into imbalance. Before being added together the two half reactions must be brought to electrical balance; that is, the same number of electrical charges, including those of ions and of electrons, must appear on each side of the equation. If the charges are not balanced, we can balance them only by adding some entity that is present in the reaction mixture and that appears as a charged particle (an ion) on one side of the

equation and as a neutral molecule on the other. The substance that meets these requirements is water. Almost all of the oxidation-reduction reactions that we deal with take place in water solution, and those that do not will *never* need this balancing of charges. We can therefore consider water as a possible reactant or product in these reactions. Furthermore, water dissociates into ions (to a very slight extent; see Chap. 23) according to the equation

$$H_2O \longrightarrow H^+ + OH^-$$

All three of these entities, $H_2O$, $H^+$, and $OH^-$, are therefore available in any water solution and can be used as participants in reactions. We balance a half reaction electrically, then, by adding enough hydrogen ions, $H^+$, to the side that has the greater negative charge (or lesser positive charge) and the appropriate number of neutral water molecules to the opposite side of the equation. Note that the hydrogen and the oxygen, both in water and as $H^+$ and $OH^-$ ions, have their usual oxidation numbers of $+1$ and $-2$ and so are *not* directly involved in the oxidation-reduction.

The final balance of the half reactions is the balance with respect to substance—the requirement that the same number of atoms of each element appear on each side of the equation. For this balance the ionic state of the atoms is immaterial. Differences between different ionic states are, in fact, differences in numbers of electrons, and these have been balanced separately. A noteworthy fact about these reactions is that the three quantities that are balanced, oxidation number, charge, and substance, *are not independent* of each other. When two of them are in balance, the third always follows. It is necessary, however, to check this fact by counting the various atoms on both sides of the half-reaction equations.

We have already shown that the units of oxidation must exactly balance the units of reduction; the number of electrons accepted by one half reaction must be the same as the number given up by the other. It may be necessary, therefore, to multiply one or both of the half-reaction equations by a factor such that, when the two equations are added, the electrons will cancel.

The final step in writing complete oxidation-reduction reactions is to add the two half reactions just as we added the oxidation-reduction reactions of electrolytic or current-producing cells in the previous chapter. In the over-all equation the electrons do not appear, for they are neither reactants nor products. They function as mediators of the reaction but are neither consumed nor set free in the process.

## 22-7. Examples

If the student re-examines, from the point of view elaborated in this chapter, the reactions that were balanced in Chapter 21, he will see that they were balanced according to the principles outlined above, even though not all details of the method were needed in all cases. We can now best develop the systematic method of balancing oxidation-reduction reactions by considering two further examples.

### EXAMPLE 1

Copper metal can be dissolved in nitric acid. The copper goes into solution as the cupric ion, $Cu^{+2}$; the other product of the reaction is nitric oxide, NO, which escapes as a gas. We are to write a balanced equation for this reaction.

The statement of the reaction in symbols (an unbalanced equation) is

$$Cu + HNO_3 \longrightarrow Cu^{+2} + NO$$

This is clearly an oxidation-reduction reaction, for there is a change in the oxidation number of copper from 0 to +2. We know that there must also be a corresponding decrease in the oxidation number of some atom in the oxidizing agent; this is probably the N atom. The half reaction of oxidation is

$$Cu \longrightarrow Cu^{+2} + 2e^-$$

The two electrons are put on the right of this equation to balance the oxidation number. (The Cu atom is zero, and the $Cu^{+2}$ ion is +2, leaving a net of +2 on the right; this must be balanced by the two electrons, each of which is a −1 unit of oxidation number.) The addition of the two electrons on the right also balances the charge. And the equation is also obviously in balance with respect to substance.

The reduction half reaction must involve the conversion of nitric acid to nitric oxide:

$$HNO_3 \longrightarrow NO$$

In order to balance this half reaction, we must first assign oxidation numbers. The N in $HNO_3$ must have an oxidation number of +5 so that the total for the compound is zero. (Oxygen has −2; the three O atoms then represent a total of −6; hydrogen is +1. These add up to −5 and can be balanced only if the N is +5. The same result comes from calculating oxidation numbers by arbitrarily assigning the covalent electrons to the O atoms, as in § 22-5.) From similar considerations, the N atom in NO has an oxidation number of +2. These numbers are written below the atoms in the unbalanced half-reaction equation:

$$HNO_3 \longrightarrow NO$$
$$(+5) \qquad (+2)$$

The first step in balancing this equation is the balancing of the oxidation number, which is unbalanced by three units. We balance by adding electrons to one or the other side—since the left side is three units more positive, by adding three electrons to the left side:

$$3e^- + HNO_3 \longrightarrow NO$$
$$(-3) \quad (+5) \qquad (+2)$$

This is necessary, of course, if the half reaction is to be a *reduction*, as it must be to be coupled with the oxidation of copper.

The equation is now unbalanced in electric charge. We balance the charges on the two sides by adding $H^+$ ions to the more negative side and water molecules (neutral) to the less negative side. The left side of the equation is three units more negative in charge; we therefore add three $H^+$ ions to this side. These and the hydrogen ion arising from the $HNO_3$ would give rise to two water molecules:

$$3H^+ + 3e^- + HNO_3 \longrightarrow NO + 2H_2O$$

The equation is now in balance with respect to oxidation number and charge. We must finally see if the substance (the number of the various atoms) is in balance. Simple counting of each type of atom on the two sides shows that this is true, and the equation is therefore completely balanced.

The next step is to combine the two half-reaction equations in such a way that the units of reduction (electrons) supplied by the one half reaction just balance the electrons used in the other. The $Cu/Cu^{+2}$ half reaction produces *two* electrons, and the $HNO_3/NO$ half reaction consumes *three*. It is therefore necessary to multiply the first equation by 3 and the second by 2 so that *six* electrons are involved in each half reaction:

$$3Cu \longrightarrow 3Cu^{+2} + 6e^-$$
$$6H^+ + 6e^- + 2HNO_3 \longrightarrow 2NO + 4H_2O$$
$$\overline{6H^+ + 2HNO_3 + 3Cu \longrightarrow 2NO + 3Cu^{+2} + 4H_2O}$$

When we check this over-all equation for balance of substance and electrical charge by counting up each type of atom on each side and by counting the ionic charges, it meets this final test of balance and is therefore an acceptable answer to the question asked in this example. It should be noted that the six $H^+$ ions on the left would be added as nitric acid and that the six $NO_3^-$ ions thereby added would appear on the right of the equation, balancing the three $Cu^{+2}$ ions. These $NO_3^-$ ions are not a necessary part of the equation, for they do not enter into the oxidation-reduction reaction.

## EXAMPLE 2

The deep purple of a solution of potassium permanganate, $KMnO_4$, can be bleached by the addition of a solution of sodium sulfite, $Na_2SO_3$. The products of this reaction are $Mn^{+2}$ ion (*manganous* ion) and sulfate ion, $SO_4^{-2}$. We are to write a balanced equation for this oxidation-reduction reaction.

Since the potassium and sodium ions do not enter into this reaction, we focus attention on the entities that *are* involved, the permanganate ion, $MnO_4^-$, and the sulfite ion, $SO_3^{-2}$, and write the statement of the reaction (an unbalanced "equation") in terms of these ions:

$$MnO_4^- + SO_3^{-2} \longrightarrow Mn^{+2} + SO_4^{-2}$$

Clearly, one half reaction involves $SO_3^{-2} \longrightarrow SO_4^{-2}$ and the other involves $MnO_4^- \longrightarrow Mn^{+2}$, but we must determine the changes in oxidation number before we can state which is the oxidation and which the reduction. The oxidation number of S in $SO_3^{-2}$ is $+4$ and in $SO_4^{-2}$ is $+6$; this must therefore be the oxidation half reaction, and, clearly, two electrons are needed to accomplish this change in oxidation number:

$$SO_3^{-2} \longrightarrow SO_4^{-2} + 2e^-$$
$$(+4) \qquad (+6) \quad (-2)$$

The oxidation numbers are now balanced, but we must add two $H^+$ ions on the right in order to balance the charge and must add one $H_2O$ molecule on the left. This water molecule also provides the O atom that is needed to balance the substance of the reaction:

$$H_2O + SO_3^{-2} \longrightarrow SO_4^{-2} + 2H^+ + 2e^-$$

We now check this equation to make sure of complete balance in oxidation number, charge, and substance. It meets these tests and is therefore the balanced equation of the reduction half reaction.

The oxidation number of Mn in $MnO_4^-$ is $+7$.

(The four O atoms represent $-8$, of which 1 must be the charge on the ion; the remainder must be the oxidation number of Mn.) The oxidation number of $Mn^{+2}$ is, of course, $+2$. The change in oxidation number is therefore $-5$, which is accomplished by the acceptance of five electrons. The half reaction is therefore written as

$$5e^- + MnO_4^- \longrightarrow Mn^{+2}$$
$$(-5) \quad (+7) \qquad (+2)$$

This half reaction must now be balanced in charge and in substance. There is a total of six negative charges on the left and two positive charges on the right; the *difference* is *eight* units of charge, with the left side more negative. We can balance the charges by adding eight $H^+$ ions to the left side of the equation and four $H_2O$ molecules to the right to accommodate these. Since the four water molecules *also* accommodate the four O atoms from the $MnO_4^-$, the equation is completely balanced:

$$5e^- + 8H^+ + MnO_4^- \longrightarrow Mn^{+2} + 4H_2O$$

The first half reaction must be multiplied by 5 and the second by 2 so that the number of electrons is 10 in each half reaction. The two are then added; the electrons cancel out (and also some of the $H_2O$ molecules and $H^+$ ions); and the over-all equation is obtained:

$$5H_2O + 5SO_3^{-2} \longrightarrow 5SO_4^{-2} + 10H^+ + 10e^-$$
$$\underline{10e^- + 16H^+ + 2MnO_4^- \longrightarrow 2Mn^{+2} + 8H_2O}$$
$$6H^+ + 2MnO_4^- + 5SO_3^{-2} \longrightarrow 2Mn^{+2} + 5SO_4^{-2} + 3H_2O$$

Again we check the final equation for balance in substance and in charge.

This discussion of oxidation-reduction reactions has been concerned primarily with the systematic method of balancing the equations. The process of balancing is important in itself because most chemical reactions involve valence changes and therefore fall within the classification set up in the definition of oxidation-reduction reactions. Even the simple elemental reactions considered in Chapter 6, where the quantitative relations in chemical reactions were first established, are oxidation-reduction reactions. The formation of copper sulfide and the decomposition of mercuric oxide are reactions in which the valences of two elements change in opposite directions and must therefore be classed as oxidation-reduction reactions. In these simple cases it was not necessary to go through the detailed method outlined in this chapter in order to establish balanced equations for the reactions. The equations could be written quite readily by trial and error and checked by inspection. Even in these simple cases, however, the over-all re-action is the coupling of two half reactions—one of oxidation and one of reduction.

The real value of this consideration of oxida-tion-reduction reactions lies not in the facility it gives us in writing balanced equations for complex reactions but in the practice it gives us in the use of the concepts that relate valence, electrons, and chemical reactions. In order to understand oxidation-reduction reactions and to use successfully the method of balancing them that has been developed in this chapter, we must understand the electronic theory of valence. And one of the best ways to acquire understanding of valence is practice in dealing with oxidation-reduction reactions.

## Concepts and Terms

Oxidation
  oxidizing agent
Reduction
  reducing agent

Oxidation-reduction
  balancing equations
Oxidation Number
  relation to valence
  electronic interpretation

## Problems

**22-1.** Define the following terms: (A) oxidation, (B) reduction, (C) oxidizing agent, (D) reducing agent, (E) oxidation number.

**22-2.** Describe the electronic interpretation of oxidation-reduction.

**22-3.** State all the assumptions and arbitrary con-ventions used in assigning oxidation numbers.

**22-4.** State the oxidation number of the chlorine atom in each of the following compounds: $KClO_4$, $KClO_3$, $KClO_2$, $KClO$, $KCl$.

**22-5.** Name each of the compounds in Prob. 22-4.

**22-6.** Assign an oxidation number to the nitrogen atom in each of the following: $NO$, $N_2O_5$, $NH_3$, $N_2$, $N_2O$, $N_2O_3$, $NO_2$.

**22-7.** Balance the following oxidation-reduction reactions:

(A) $Cr_2O_7^{-2} + SO_3^{-2} \longrightarrow Cr^{+2} + SO_4^{-2}$
(B) $Cl^- + MnO_4^- \longrightarrow Cl_2 + Mn^{+2}$
(C) $MnO_4^- + Sn^{+2} \longrightarrow Mn^{+2} + Sn^{+4}$
(D) $ClO_3^- + HNO_2 \longrightarrow Cl^- + NO_3^-$
(E) $MnO_2 + HCl \longrightarrow MnCl_2 + Cl_2$
(F) $S_2O_3^{-2} + I_2 \longrightarrow S_4O_6^{-2} + I^-$

## Suggested Readings

1. D. C. Gregg, *Principles of Chemistry* (Allyn & Bacon, 1958), Chap. 12.
2. W. F. Ehret, *Smith's Introductory College Chemistry* (Appleton-Century-Crofts, 1950), Chap. 26.

Most of the readings suggested in Chap. 21 also discuss oxidation-reduction and the methods of balancing equations for such reactions.

A NUMBER of general concepts recur throughout all parts of physical science. One of these, we have seen, is the concept of conservation: there are, we know, specific laws of the conservation of mass, the conservation of energy, the conservation of charge, etc.; the concept impinges on all the experimental information, is involved in all the theories, and is even deeply involved in the philosophical interpretations, of all the parts of the science of our physical environment; it is, indeed, so general that it encompasses many fields of knowledge other than science. Another of these very general concepts—one that is used in the interpretation of many areas of experimental information and is a part of many of the grand theories of science—is the notion of **equilibrium.**

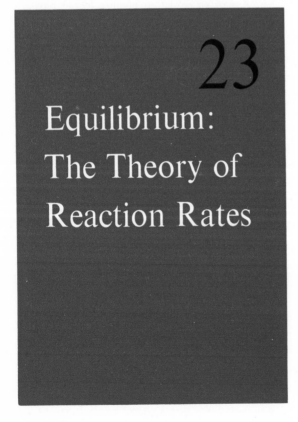

CHAPTER

23

Equilibrium:
The Theory of
Reaction Rates

### 23-1. *Concept of Equilibrium*

The basic concept of equilibrium is an extremely simple one and is illustrated in many physical situations: a state of balance between two opposing influences, which, because they cancel each other out, produce no net change in the system. This is the concept in its simplest and barest form. The word "equilibrium" means literally *equal balance,* and the general use of the word implies just this literal meaning.

We have already encountered the concept in many situations in earlier sections of this text. Two examples of mechanical equilibrium, in which the opposing influences are *forces,* are shown in Figures 9-1 and 9-2. The force exerted on the piston is opposed by the pressure of the confined gas on the opposite side of the piston; the weight on the spring is opposed by the reaction of the spring upward; and in each case the opposing forces just balance each other so that no motion results. Many examples of mechanical equilibrium were encountered in the study of electrostatics, where an electrical force was opposed by an equal and opposite force. One example is the Millikan oil-drop experiment (§ 18-5), in which the electrical force, $Eq$, is just balanced by the weight, $mg$, of the droplet —a balance, an equilibrium, that maintains the droplet's suspension in the field. Another example is the velocity selector (§ 17-9), in which the magnetic force and the electrostatic force on a moving charge just balance each other, the result being that the moving particle (if its velocity is right) does not deviate but moves as if neither of the forces were acting. A final example of this type of equilibrium is the current balance, which relates the electrical force between moving currents (and thereby the magnitude of the unit of current) to mechanical forces; the electrical force was just balanced (§ 16-8) by the gravitational force on the weights at the other end of the balance.

We have mentioned other, more subtle cases of equilibrium. We included the exchange of heat between a body and its surroundings in this concept by describing the situation of constant temperature—the temperature being the same as that of the surroundings—as a "thermal equilibrium" in which the gain of heat and the loss of heat are the same. The whole kinetic theory (Chap. 12) was concerned with equilibrium in several applications, the most interesting being the sub-microscopic consideration of the processes of vaporization (vapor pressure) and dissolving (saturated solutions). In both cases equilibrium (which is the state that defines the vapor pressure of a liquid and the solubility of a solute) was established when the rate of escape of particles from the condensed phase became just equal to the rate of return of particles from the dispersed phase to the condensed phase.

## 23-2. *Chemical Equilibrium*

Another field in which the concept of equilibrium has proved to be a useful tool is the study of chemical reactions. We have already considered many reactions that are, in fact, equilibrium reactions, but we have not yet emphasized that fact. It is necessary to emphasize it at this point if we are to understand the process of chemical reaction. Of more general interest, however, is the fact that the concepts and techniques established in the study of chemical equilibrium are of major interest and are frequently applicable to other parts of science and to problem-solving situations in general.

Most chemical reactions do not go to completion; that is, a reaction, which proceeds by the consumption of the reactants and the production of the products, appears to stop before all of the reactants are converted into products. It is frequently possible, furthermore, to *start* with the products of a particular reaction and, by mixing these products, to bring about—at least to some extent—the *reverse* reaction. In both cases an *equilibrium* is reached in which, it is postulated, the forward and reverse reactions are both going on at the same rate so that there is no net change in the amount of any of the components of the reaction. This interpretation of equilibrium in chemical reactions emphasizes the dynamic situation of two opposing influences operating constantly and at equal rates. Some of the reactants are being converted to the products, and the products are being converted back to the reactants at an equal rate. One such chemical equilibrium is the dissociation of hydrogen iodide into its elemental constituents, hydrogen and iodine, in the gaseous reaction

$$2HI \longrightarrow H_2 + I_2$$

which takes place at elevated temperatures. If a sample of hydrogen iodide is enclosed in a sealed tube and heated to a certain temperature, it will dissociate according to the reaction of the above equation, but will *not* completely dissociate. The tube will contain all three entities involved in the reaction, HI (the reactant in the equation as written) and $H_2$ and $I_2$ (the products of the reaction). The relative amounts of the three components vary with changing temperature but are quite constant at any particular temperature. At room temperature this dissociation is extremely small; at 1,000°C it is 29.0 percent.

It is also possible to reach exactly the same equilibrium by starting with a mixture of pure hydrogen and iodine gases. If these two gases are mixed in a sealed tube and the tube heated to the same temperature as was the tube of HI, the two gases will combine to produce HI according to the equation

$$H_2 + I_2 \longrightarrow 2HI$$

This equation is, of course, the reverse of the equation for the dissociation reaction above. It is observed that the relative amounts of the three gases arising from this combination of the elements to produce HI are exactly the same as those arising from the dissociation of HI at the same temperature. At 1,000°, for example, 71.0 percent of the substance is in the associated form, as HI, and 29.0 percent is dissociated as $H_2$ and $I_2$.

The most logical interpretation of these observations is that the two reactions are in equilibrium: in either case, dissociation or combination, the forward reaction proceeds until the concentration of the products becomes high enough so that the reverse reaction begins to take place; the rates then change until the forward reaction slows down and the reverse reaction speeds up enough so that they become equal; both then continue at this rate with no net change in the relative amounts of the three components of the reaction. If this interpretation is accepted, the equation should show that both reactions are going on. It does by the use of a double arrow for an equilibrium (or reversible) reaction:

$$2HI \rightleftarrows H_2 + I_2$$

Such equations are usually written with the dissociation in the forward direction, as above. The double arrow indicates that the reaction is reversible, that both the forward and the reverse reaction are going on at all times, and that the same equilibrium can be reached from either direction.

## 23-3. Proof of Dynamic Nature of Chemical Equilibrium

This interpretation of the dissociation of hydrogen iodide and similar reactions as equilibria, in which *apparent* total inactivity masks the underlying dynamic state of constantly opposing reaction, is reasonable and makes good sense in terms of the kinetic theory. It is necessary, however, to establish direct experimental proof of such an important concept. Proof of the dynamic nature of equilibrium reactions has become possible in fairly recent years through methods of "tagging" particular atoms. By "tagging" an atom we mean establishing some way

in which a particular atom (in practice this means *large numbers* of atoms) can be distinguished from other atoms of the same element even though the atoms are involved in chemical reactions. With the intense interest in nuclear energy that accompanied World War II, there became available, as by-products of the development of atomic energy, a large group of **radioactive isotopes** of almost all the elements (see Chap. 18 and Part Three). We have already seen that the different isotopes of an element have identical chemical properties; radioactive isotopes differ by having different mass numbers but also by having the easily recognized property of emitting energetic rays. The iodine isotope having a mass number of 131 behaves chemically exactly like the naturally occurring iodine, which has an atomic weight (mass number) of 126.9, but is easily identifiable by its spontaneous emission of detectable energy. This isotope of iodine is, then, a "tagged" atom of iodine in the sense that it can be identified under any circumstances of combination—as the free element or in any compound.

The experiment that proves the dynamic nature of the equilibrium of the dissociation of hydrogen iodide is carried out as follows: The equilibrium mixture of the three gases at a given temperature is known. Such a mixture is created by the mixing of *radioactive* iodine gas with $H_2$ and with HI gas that contains only *normal* iodine. If the equilibrium is perfectly static and the forward and reverse reactions do not go on, the radioactivity should remain *only* in the form in which it was added to the mixture—that is, as $I_2$. If the two reactions do go on, as postulated in the concept of a *dynamic* equilibrium, the radioactive iodine would be distributed in *both* substances, HI and $I_2$. If we use the symbol I* to indicate a radioactive iodine atom, this exchange of the radioactivity between the $I_2$ and the HI can be shown by the equations for the forward and reverse reactions:

$$2HI \longrightarrow H_2 + I_2$$
$$H_2 + I_2^* \longrightarrow 2HI^*$$

Analyses of the equilibrium mixtures of tagged $I_2$ and normal HI show that the radioactive iodine is very rapidly distributed between the $I_2$

and the HI even though the amounts of both substances in the equilibrium mixture remain unchanged. This could happen only if the two opposing reactions take place at rapid and equal rates.

## 23-4. Principle of Le Châtelier

An extremely important qualitative generalization concerning equilibria was made by a French chemist, H. L. Le Châtelier, in 1888. This principle, which was formulated by a chemist to describe chemical systems, has proved to be one of the most useful and generally applicable concepts of physical science. It has been extended to include many types of physical, biological, and even economic and sociological equilibria. Any system that is in a *dynamic* state of balance (that is, a true equilibrium) will respond to stress in a predictable way. The principle of Le Châtelier offers a means of predicting qualitatively what that response to stress will be. The statement of this important principle is: **If a system at equilibrium is subjected to a stress, the equilibrium will shift in such a way as to tend to nullify or minimize the stress and to restore the original conditions.**

## 23-5. Le Châtelier's Principle and Physical Equilibria

The application of this rule to the simplest physical equilibria is so obvious as to be almost trivial but should serve to establish the meaning of the concept. Consider the equilibrium of a weight attached to a spring. In Figure 23-1a the equilibrium is undisturbed; the force of the weight downward is just balanced by the equal force of the distended spring upward. If the system is now subjected to the stress of having an extra weight placed on the spring, as in 23-1b, it is no longer in balance (is *not* in equilibrium) and must respond to the stress by shifting. The principle of Le Châtelier offers a means of predicting the response of the system to this stress. In this trivial case the response is perfectly obvious: the spring will stretch further, as in 23-1c. But Le Châtelier's rule does predict this response. The added force downward of the extra weight must be compensated for by an *equal* increase in the upward force supplied by the spring to restore the equilibrium. This can only be accomplished by an increase in the distortion of the spring (the force of reaction of the spring in-

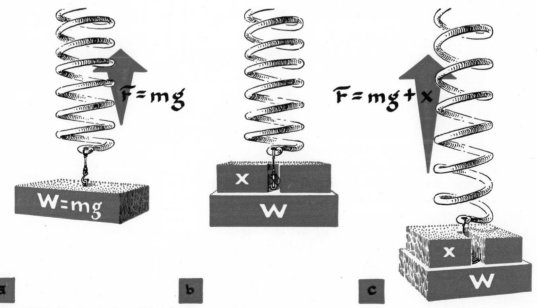

FIGURE **23-1** *Mechanical equilibrium illustrated by a loaded spring.*

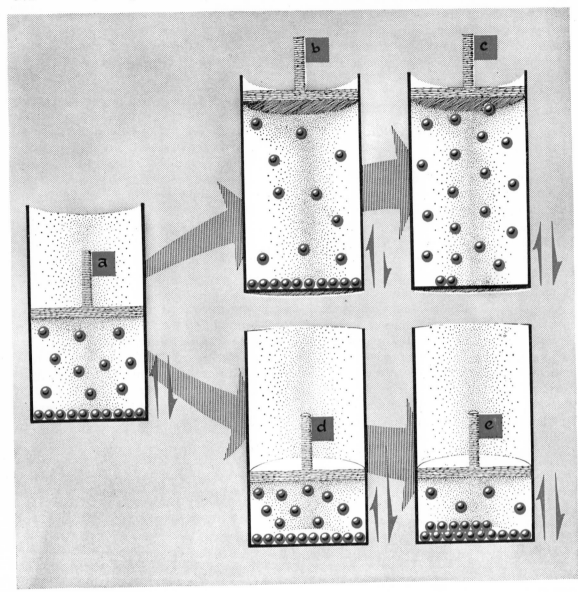

FIGURE **23-2** *Vapor-pressure equilibrium.*

creases with an increase in the distortion or stretching from its original shape).

A somewhat subtler case of equilibrium and its response to stress is the equilibrium between a liquid and its vapor in a closed container (see Fig. 14-1). A condition of equilibrium will obtain when the rate of escape of molecules from the liquid phase just equals the rate of condensation of the gas-phase molecules back into the liquid. The pressure exerted by the gas phase of the substance is defined as the vapor pressure.

Le Châtelier's rule states that, if the system is subjected to the stress of a change in pressure, the equilibrium must shift in such a way as to tend to nullify the effect of this change in pressure. Figure 23-2 shows the effects of both an increase and a decrease in the pressure on this system. Figure 23-2a shows the system at equilibrium before the stress is applied. If we decrease the pressure, as in 23-2b, by increasing the gas volume (sliding the piston up), the rate of impact of the gas-phase molecules with the surface of the liquid (and all other surfaces of the container) is decreased. This lowers the rate of condensation of the gas-phase molecules and leaves the rate of evaporation of the liquid-phase molecules the same as before. The result is that *more* molecules evaporate (Fig. 23-2c) until the two rates are again equal. The rates will be equal only when the pressure in the greater volume has reached the vapor pressure of the substance. Thus the change in pressure has been completely nullified by the evaporation of more of the liquid. Note that, if all the liquid evaporates, the system is no longer an equilibrium, and Le Châtelier's principle no longer applies.

Figure 23-2de shows the effect of compressing the gas phase. The rate of impact of the gas molecules with the surface of the liquid is increased and the rate of condensation correspondingly increased over the rate of evaporation. The effect is a condensation of gas molecules into the liquid phase until the rates are equal. This will again happen when the pressure of the gas in the vapor phase has reached the original pressure of Fig. 23-2a, which is the vapor pressure.

## 23-6. *Le Châtelier's Principle and Chemical Equilibria*

The principle was first expounded in terms of chemical equilibria and was used to predict responses in chemical systems. We should therefore consider some examples of chemical equilibrium. The dissociation of hydrogen iodide, mentioned earlier, can serve as an example. The definition of equilibrium in chemical reactions is made in terms of the relative concentrations of the entities involved. In the dissociation of HI—

$$\text{heat} + 2HI \rightleftharpoons H_2 + I_2$$

—the equilibrium is defined by a statement of the relative concentrations of HI, $H_2$, and $I_2$. One of the most obvious stresses that could be applied to this system would be a change in the concentration of one of the components. Consider, for example, the effect of increasing the concentration of HI. If this is done, it is observed that some of the added HI dissociates to form $I_2$ and $H_2$; that is, the system shifts in such

a way as to decrease the concentration of HI and increase the concentration of $H_2$ and $I_2$— which is just the shift that tends to nullify the effect of the stress. Similarly, the addition of one of the products (either $H_2$ or $I_2$) causes the reverse reaction to proceed so that some of the added $H_2$ or $I_2$ combines with the other product of the forward reaction to form some HI. Again this shift is the one that tends to nullify the effect of the stress—just what the rule of Le Châtelier predicts.

The equation for the dissociation includes the heat that is involved in this reaction. It indicates the experimentally observed fact that the dissociation of HI takes place with the *absorption* of heat; the heat of reaction ($\Delta H$ of reaction) is positive. This fact, plus Le Châtelier's rule, enables us to predict the effect of a rise in temperature on this equilibrium. The stress in this case is the addition of heat to the system. Le Châtelier's rule states that the equilibrium will respond in such a way as to minimize the effect of this added heat—that is, to *absorb* heat. The experimental fact is that, as the temperature rises, the equilibrium shifts to the right—that is, toward increased dissociation into $H_2$ and $I_2$.

An industrially important use of Le Châtelier's principle is found in the reaction of hydrogen and nitrogen gases to produce ammonia gas:

$$N_2 + 3H_2 \rightleftharpoons 2NH_3 \qquad (\Delta H \text{ is negative})†$$

This reaction, which is the basis of the Haber process for the synthesis of ammonia, is still of great industrial importance but was of paramount strategic importance in World War I because ammonia is a crucial intermediate in the manufacture of many explosives. Since this synthesis, developed in 1913, uses only hydrogen, which is commonly available industrially, and atmospheric nitrogen, it made German explosives production independent of imported nitrates and thus able to continue despite the British blockade.

---

† This reaction could, of course, have been written in the opposite direction, $2NH_3 \rightleftharpoons N_2 + 3H_2$, which is the conventional way to write dissociation reactions. In this case, however, we are particularly interested in the *synthesis* of ammonia. Note that, if the reaction is reversed, $\Delta H$ is positive; that is, heat is *absorbed* in the dissociation reaction.

The equation above shows that heat is evolved in the forward (synthesis) reaction; the effect of a higher temperature would therefore be to shift the equilibrium toward dissociation (in the reverse direction) and thus to prevent the synthesis of ammonia. There is another stress, however, that shifts the equilibrium in the desired direction of synthesis. Le Châtelier's principle was actually used to predict a way to make this process industrially feasible by the manipulation of this other stress. The equation shows that the volume of the gaseous mixture decreases as the reaction proceeds in the forward direction. There are four gaseous molecules on the left (one $N_2$ and three $H_2$) and only two gaseous molecules (both $NH_3$) on the right. From Avogadro's hypothesis we know that the total volume of a gaseous mixture is determined by the total number of molecules; the products of this gaseous reaction must occupy less volume than the reactants. The effect of an increase in the pressure on the system is therefore to shift the equilibrium in the direction that produces the least number of molecules and therefore the least volume. An increase in pressure therefore shifts the equilibrium toward the synthesis of ammonia. A decrease in pressure would, of course, have the opposite effect, causing the equilibrium to shift toward the dissociation of ammonia into nitrogen and hydrogen.

This reaction is immeasurably slow at ordinary temperatures. If the temperature is raised to several hundred degrees, the reaction takes place in a reasonable time (§ 12-4). At such temperatures, however, the equilibrium is shifted so far to the left (toward dissociation) that no useful synthesis takes place. But now, if the pressure is increased to several hundred atmospheres, the equilibrium is shifted back toward synthesis sufficiently to make the use of the reaction industrially practical. It was also found that the addition of certain *catalysts* raised the rate of reaction enough so that still lower temperatures could be used (see the discussion of reaction rates in § 23-8). The Haber process is a classical example of the use of Le Châtelier's principle in predicting and manipulating reaction conditions so as to favor a desired chemical process.

## 23-7. *Reaction Rates*

Equilibrium in chemical reactions is defined as the state in which the rate of the forward reaction is just equal to the rate of the reverse reaction. It is therefore incumbent on any study of equilibrium to investigate the rate of chemical reactions. We have already considered reaction rates very briefly on several different occasions in earlier parts of this text. In Chapter 19, in the discussion of the ionic theory, we referred to the difference in rate between purely ionic reactions and reactions involving covalent bonds; and in this chapter we have examined briefly the influence of several factors on reaction rates.

The extreme variation in rate of reaction, from "instantaneous" to immeasurably slow, was pointed out in Chapter 19. Ionic reactions, in which the reactants are already dissociated, take place *extremely* rapidly. In contrast, most reactions involving covalent bonds, in which existing bonds must be broken and new bonds formed, take place slowly. Many oxidation-reduction reactions, in which at least the valence electrons must be rearranged and frequently, in complex ions or molecules, covalent bonds must be broken and re-formed, take place very slowly.

The study of reaction rates is called *chemical kinetics*. This branch of physical science is concerned with the measurement of rates of reaction and with the formulation and use of theories of reaction rates. The foundation of kinetics is the definition of the rate of a chemical reaction, equation 23-1. The rate is equal to the ratio of a change in concentration of one of the participants (decrease in concentration of a reactant or increase in concentration of a product) to the time necessary for that change:

$$\text{rate} = \Delta c / t \qquad (23\text{-}1)$$

The experimental problem of measuring reaction rates is, then, the problem of measuring concentration at various times. These continuous or repeated instantaneous measurements of concentration often require very complicated and elegant apparatus. Such measurements can be based on any easily observable property of one of the participants in the reaction. If one of the reactants is colored, we can measure the rate of the reaction by observing the rate at which the color disappears. If a product is colored, the increase in intensity of the color is an index of the reaction rate. All kinetic studies depend on measuring the rate of change of a concentration and the influence of various factors on this rate.

The view of the mechanism of chemical reactions that we have been building up is essentially a kinetic one, and we shall explain the effects of various influences on reaction rates in terms of the kinetic-molecular theory (Chap. 12). We have considered above the variation of reaction rates with the nature of the reactants. In § 12-4 we discussed the influence of temperature on reaction rates. That discussion should be carefully studied again at this point. Many other factors can influence reaction rates, but this chapter will be limited to only three: catalysis, pressure, and concentration.

## 23-8. *Catalysis*

In the discussion of the Haber process for the synthesis of ammonia we mentioned the use of catalysts in accelerating this reaction to the point where it became industrially usable. Many hundreds of chemical reactions, of paramount importance in the economy of our modern technological society, depend on the use of catalysts. Much industrial developmental research consists of a search for new and more effective catalysts. In general this search is purely empirical, for there is no general theoretical explanation of the mechanism of catalysts and therefore no way of predicting the nature of possible catalysts for a particular reaction.

The first general study of **catalysts** was made in 1835 by J. J. Berzelius, a Swedish chemist, who also invented the term **"catalyst."** He summarized a considerable body of isolated and frequently conflicting facts concerning substances that have the property of strongly influencing the rates of chemical reactions without apparently being changed themselves. Berzelius called this process **catalysis** (Greek, to loosen) because he thought that the catalyst contributed some "force" that weakened the chemical bonds of the reactants. The mechanism of action is not generally understood even now, but several types of catalytic action are being successfully investigated by modern research methods.

Three criteria must be met if a substance is to be classed as a catalyst and if its effect on a reaction is to be classed as catalysis.

1. *The catalyst must be quantitatively recovered in unchanged chemical form at the end of the reaction.* This requirement was originally interpreted as excluding the possibility of the catalyst's actually being involved directly in the reaction. It is now known that in many cases (probably in all cases) the catalyst *is* a direct participant in the reaction; but *all* of the catalyst must be regenerated by the reaction in the same form as at the beginning. Many ionic substances, such as heavy metal ions (including $Cu^{+2}$, $Fe^{+3}$, and $Mn^{+2}$), function as catalysts and probably enter the reaction to the extent of suffering valence changes. But these are always regenerated in the original valence states as products of the reaction and therefore meet this first requirement of true catalysts. Similarly, hydrogen ions, $H^+$, function as catalysts in a great many reactions, in many of which they do enter the reaction, but they are invariably regenerated in amounts exactly equal to the amounts that entered the reactions.

Catalysis often takes place at the surface of insoluble substances such as metals, including platinum, iron, and nickel, and a number of metal oxides such as $MnO_2$. The decomposition of hydrogen peroxide, $H_2O_2$, into water and oxygen is a reaction catalyzed by $MnO_2$. The role of these substances in catalysis is not well understood except that the *surface* of the insoluble catalyst is its crucial characteristic. Often physical changes take place in the surface, such as the pitting of a smooth metal surface or the disintegration of large particles into powders. But these changes always leave the catalyst in the same chemical condition in which it started, and in the same amount.

2. *Small amounts of the catalyst are effective in influencing the reaction of extremely large amounts of the reactants.* Some of the metals and metal ions are effective at tremendously low concentrations. For example, 1 part of platinum in

a colloidal suspension in $10^7$ parts of hydrogen peroxide solution produces a measurable increase in the rate of its decomposition. In many industrial operations a single charge of catalyst operates for years in accelerating a reaction in which the reacting materials are continuously passed over the surface of the catalyst in a reaction chamber.

3. *The catalyst has exactly the same effect on the rates of both the forward and the reverse direction of an equilibrium reaction.* This requirement is frequently stated as an exclusion of any effect of the catalyst on the position of the equilibrium; the exclusion is, of course, a necessary consequence of the equal effect on both rates. In our discussion of equilibrium it has been established that the rates of the forward and reverse reactions must be equal in an equilibrium. If the catalyst changes both rates to the same extent, clearly the position of the equilibrium will be unaffected. From these considerations it is clear that the only effect a catalyst can have on an equilibrium reaction is to speed the attainment of the equilibrium. The position of the equilibrium—that is, the relative concentrations of the reactants and the products—is determined by other factors, such as the temperature or the pressure of the system.

The chemical reactions that take place in living tissues are also influenced by catalysts. The catalysts of these biochemical reactions are called **enzymes.** They meet the three requirements of catalysts in general but usually have a fourth characteristic that is not found in the catalysts of non-living systems. This characteristic is specificity. Nearly all enzymes each catalyze one single reaction of specific reactants and have no effect on very similar reactions or compounds. The enzymes and the biochemical reactions they catalyze are of particular importance in the study of catalysis. Their high degree of specificity offers many advantages in the effort to unravel the complex mechanism of catalytic action. Furthermore, these complex biological catalysts combine some of the surface effects of the catalytic metals and metal oxides with the effects of soluble substances that enter into the reaction. The mechanism of the catalytic process in several enzyme reactions is completely established.

## 23-9. Heterogeneous Reactions

In the previous section the action of some catalysts was attributed to reaction at the *surface* of the catalyst particles. This is an example of a *heterogeneous reaction*—one in which the reactants are in two or more phases. Since the site of reaction can only be at the interface between the phases, the rates of heterogeneous reactions are strongly affected by factors that determine the amount of surface presented by one of the reactants. The two most obvious factors are the physical form of the reactants and the degree of mixing. If a solid is very finely divided, it clearly has more surface than if it is present as one lump or as coarse particles. We can greatly raise the rate of any heterogeneous reaction by making the subdivisions of both reactants as small as possible and thereby increasing the surface. An example of this is the burning of coal. A large lump of coal is not easily ignited and burns only slowly. Coal dust, when mixed with air, is as inflammable as gasoline; such mixtures are explosive and can be detonated by a tiny spark. Another example of the spectacular effect on reaction rate of finely divided solid condition is the extreme inflammability of suspensions of flour in air. It would be rather difficult to burn a large bulk of flour or a pile of wheat. If this same material is ground to the fine particulate condition of flour and then scattered in air, the mixture becomes extremely inflammable. The reaction between the flour and oxygen is so fast as to be almost instantaneous—which is one way of describing an explosion.

These two examples illustrate the accelerating effect on reaction rates in heterogeneous systems of mixing the two phases. If the increased area of the small particles is to be effective in reaction, the phases must be mixed. The particles are effective only if they are well dispersed in the gaseous or liquid phase of the system.

## 23-10. Theory of Rate of Homogeneous Reactions

An account of the effects of catalysts on reaction rates and of rates of heterogeneous reactions is largely a collection of empirical generalizations without any generally adequate theoretical explanation. The commonest reaction situation, however, is a single-phase (homogeneous) system in which either substances in solution in the liquid state or gaseous mixtures react. For this situation there is a well-established and conceptually sound theoretical interpretation of the variation of the rate of reaction with concentration. This theory, like most theories, is idealized in the sense that the assumptions on which it is based are only approximately approached in most actual situations. Even so the theory has been most useful in establishing the mechanisms of many reactions and is an excellent approach to the mathematical description of equilibrium in reversible chemical reactions.

The simplest possible type of chemical reaction is the decomposition of a single substance into some products:

$$A \longrightarrow B + C$$

One such reaction, called a **first-order** or **unimolecular** reaction, is the decomposition of dinitrogen tetroxide into nitrogen dioxide:

$$N_2O_4 \longrightarrow 2NO_2$$

This reaction, which happens in the gaseous state at slightly elevated temperatures, can be easily followed because the product, $NO_2$, is a deep-red gas. We have defined the rate of reaction as the ratio of the change in concentration of a reactant (or a product) to the time in which that change takes place. Another way of saying this is to define the rate as the number of moles reacting per unit time (one second). The chemical interpretation of this reaction is that a single chemical bond in the $N_2O_4$ molecule breaks. This bond breaks in a particular molecule when the energy of vibration in that molecule becomes great enough to overcome the bonding forces. The energies of the molecules in any sample of the substance vary, according to a distribution curve of the type shown in Figure 12-4, from a few with very low energies to a few with energies high enough to break the chemical bond. The curve shows the *proportion* of molecules having the various energies; in any sample the *number* of molecules having sufficient energy to react will therefore be proportional to the total

number of molecules in the sample, or to the *concentration* of the reacting substance—$N_2O_4$ in this case. The rate of a first-order reaction can therefore be expressed by the following equation:

$$\text{rate} = k(c_A) \tag{23-2}$$

In the decomposition of $N_2O_4$, the rate is expressed as

$$\text{rate} = k(c_{N_2O_4})$$

In both of these equations $k$ is a constant of proportionality and is called the **rate constant** for the reaction.

It is characteristic of first-order reactions that the rate goes down steadily with time because the concentration of the reacting substance decreases as the substance is consumed in the reaction. A second characteristic is that the time necessary for some certain *fraction* of the reacting substance to disappear is a constant for a constant set of conditions and is independent of the amount of the substance present at the start of the reaction. For this reason the rate of a first-order reaction is usually stated as a **half-life**—that is, the time it takes for *half* of any sample to be consumed. The rate of decomposition of many unstable substances is often specified by a statement that the half-life is so many seconds. The most notable use of this term is for the rates at which radioactive isotopes decompose (see Chap. 27). Many of these isotopes have half-lives of only a few seconds or minutes, but others have half lives of thousands of years.

The next more complex type of reaction is the **second-order,** or **bimolecular,** reaction. The general equation is of this type:

$$A + B \longrightarrow \text{products}$$

One such reaction is that of hydrogen and iodine gases to produce hydrogen iodide, which was used as an example earlier in this chapter:

$$H_2 + I_2 \longrightarrow 2HI$$

In this reaction a molecule of $H_2$ must collide with a molecule of $I_2$, and the impact must have enough energy to disrupt the valence bonds holding the two atoms of each together in the molecular structure. The energy of the impact is a function of temperature, and the probability of an impact involving so much energy is governed by the relations shown in the energy-distribution curves of Figure 12-4. But, whatever this probability, the *number* of such impacts, or the actual *frequency* of successful impacts, will be proportional to the concentrations of the reacting particles, the $H_2$ and $I_2$ molecules. Consider a single $H_2$ molecule. Its likelihood of reacting with an $I_2$ molecule depends on the probability of collision with an $I_2$ molecule. If no $I_2$ molecules are present, there is no possibility of reaction; if only a few $I_2$ molecules are present (that is, if the concentration of $I_2$ molecules is very low), the likelihood of impact and therefore of reaction between the $H_2$ and an $I_2$ molecule is slight; if many $I_2$ molecules are in the reaction mixture, the likelihood of impact and reaction between the $H_2$ and an $I_2$ molecule is great. Clearly, then, the probability of a reaction between the single $H_2$ molecule and an $I_2$ molecule to produce HI is proportional to the concentration of $I_2$ in the mixture.

Now if, instead of a single molecule, we consider *two* $H_2$ molecules, the probability of a collision and reaction between any $H_2$ and any $I_2$ molecules will be doubled. In general, then, the probability of the reaction $H_2 + I_2 \longrightarrow 2HI$ is proportional to the product of the concentrations of $H_2$ and $I_2$:

$$\text{rate} = k(c_{H_2})(c_{I_2})$$

This argument, which we have advanced for the reaction of hydrogen and iodine gases, is applicable to *any* second-order homogeneous reaction, gaseous or liquid. We can therefore write a general second-order rate equation:

$$\text{rate} = k(c_A)(c_B) \qquad (23\text{-}3)$$

The special bimolecular reaction in which $A$ and $B$ are the same substance—that is, a reaction in which two individuals of the same molecular species collide—is still of the second order, and the equation above describes the rate, the concentration of the reacting species being squared:

$$\text{rate} = k(c_A)(c_A) = k(c_A)^2 \qquad (23\text{-}4)$$

An example of this type of second-order reaction is the association of nitrogen dioxide to form dinitrogen tetroxide:

$$2NO_2 \longrightarrow N_2O_4$$

$$\text{rate} = k(c_{NO_2})^2$$

This argument could be continued to higher and higher orders of reaction, in which three or four or more molecules must collide simultaneously in order to react. The general chemical equation for such reactions is

$$aA + bB + \cdots \longrightarrow \text{products}$$

and the general rate equation is

$$\text{rate} = k(c_A)^a(c_B)^b \cdots \qquad (23\text{-}5)$$

In practice, however, there is an inescapable limit to this analysis. Even the most casual consideration of probabilities must exclude any reaction that depends on an event so unlikely as, for example, the simultaneous collision of five molecules with enough energy of impact to cause reaction. Even third-order reactions are improbable, and it is quite safe to exclude completely any mechanism of reaction that would require more than three molecules to collide simultaneously. Reactions whose equations appear to require the simultaneous collision of several molecules almost certainly proceed by a series of simpler reactions that are much more probable.

As we stated at the outset, this theory of reaction rates in homogeneous systems is somewhat idealized. In practice most reactions proceed in sequences of several steps and with considerable complication from side reactions and competing reactions. The study of chemical kinetics has a long way to go before the actual mechanisms of all reactions are established. Most of the difficulty in these studies comes from trying to sort out the rate-determining processes from these confusing and interfering reactions. When this can be done, the rate theory discussed here can usually be applied with considerable success to the theoretical analysis of the reaction.

## 23-11. Equilibrium Constant

We have defined the general state of equilibrium as the condition of a system in which two opposing influences are operating but produce no net effect because they cancel each other out. This general definition includes reversible chemical reactions that do not go to completion. In this particular subdivision of the general topic of equilibrium, the two equal and opposite tendencies that are going on continuously, maintaining the dynamic quality of equilibrium, are the forward and reverse reactions. It is therefore possible to describe equilibrium in chemical reactions by a mathematical equation that states this quality of the two opposing effects:

$$\text{rate}_{\text{forward}} = \text{rate}_{\text{reverse}} \qquad (23\text{-}6)$$

This equation is the fundamental description of the state of equilibrium in chemical reactions. But we can manipulate it to obtain a relation that is much more useful in the quantitative description of equilibrium.

We manipulate equation 23-6 by substituting in it the expression for the two rates of equation 23-5 or one of the simpler rate equations that apply to particular reactions. In the dissociation of hydrogen iodide, for example, which we considered earlier ($2HI \rightleftarrows H_2 + I_2$), the rate of the forward reaction is specified by equation 23-4 in the form

$$\text{rate}_f = k_f(c_{HI})^2$$

and the rate of the reverse reaction by equation 23-3 in the form

$$\text{rate}_r = k_r(c_{H_2})(c_{I_2})$$

If these two expressions are substituted into equation 23-6, an equation involving the two rate constants and the equilibrium concentrations of the three reacting entities is obtained:

$$k_f(c_{HI})^2 = k_r(c_{H_2})(c_{I_2})$$

The most useful form of this equation is that in which all the concentrations are on one side and the two constants are on the other side:

$$\frac{(c_{H_2})(c_{I_2})}{(c_{HI})^2} = \frac{k_f}{k_r}$$

The quantity on the right of this equation, the ratio of the two rate constants, is itself a constant. This ratio is called the *equilibrium constant* of the reaction:

$$\frac{k_f}{k_r} = K_{equ} \qquad (23\text{-}7)$$

This equation is completely general; it describes

all chemical equilibrium reactions. We have already observed that both the rate of chemical reaction and the position of equilibrium vary as the temperature of the system varies. It is therefore to be expected that the quantities in equation 23-7 change with changing temperature. These "constants" are constant only as long as the temperature remains the same. If the effect on the two rate constants is the same (if both the forward and the reverse reaction are influenced in the same direction and to the same extent), the position of the equilibrium (the value of $K_{equ}$) is not affected by changes in the temperature of the system.

When equation 23-7 is applied to the dissociation of HI, the equilibrium expression becomes

$$\frac{(c_{H_2})(c_{I_2})}{(c_{HI})^2} = K_{equ}$$

which specifies the relative concentrations of the three participants in the reaction when the system is in equilibrium. This relation among the three concentrations, here stated *quantitatively,* was qualitatively predicted by the principle of Le Châtelier.

We can put this equilibrium expression into words as follows: "The ratio of the product of the concentrations of the products of an equilibrium reaction to the product of the concentrations of the reactants is a constant at constant temperature." If the concentration of one of the products—$H_2$, let us say—is raised, there *must* therefore be a corresponding *fall* in the concentration of $I_2$ or *rise* in the concentration of HI, or both, in order to keep the ratio of the concentrations (the expression on the left of the equation) constant. This is, of course, the very response to a change in the concentration of a product of the reaction that is predicted by the rule of Le Châtelier. Similarly, if the HI concentration is raised, the $I_2$ and $H_2$ concentrations must be correspondingly raised to maintain a constant concentration product.

If $K_{equ}$ is large, the dissociation of HI is great (nearly complete); if $K_{equ}$ is small, the dissociation is slight. In the discussion of this reaction earlier in this chapter we pointed out that the reaction is very slow and the dissociation slight at low temperatures. At high temperatures the reaction is fast and the dissociation great. These effects can be interpreted as follows: At low temperatures the equilibrium constant must be very small. Consideration of equation 23-7 shows that the rate constant of the reverse reaction, even though very small itself, must be much larger than that of the forward reaction in order for $K_{equ}$ to be very small. The effect of a rise in temperature is to raise *both* rates, but the rate of the forward reaction must rise more rapidly in order that $K_{equ}$ may increase.

## 23-12. General Equilibrium Expression

This particular equilibrium expression, derived above from the reaction-rate equations for the dissociation of hydrogen iodide, can be generalized and applied to all homogeneous reversible chemical reactions. The general equilibrium expression also can be derived from the rate expressions of the general equation for reversible chemical reactions:

$$aA + bB + \cdots \rightleftarrows dD + eE + \cdots \qquad (23\text{-}8)$$

The two rate equations would have the form of equation 23-5, applied to the reaction above in the forward and reverse directions:

$$\text{rate}_f = k_f(c_A)^a(c_B)^b \cdots$$
$$\text{rate}_r = k_r(c_D)^d(c_E)^e \cdots$$

These two expressions are then combined as in equation 23-6, are rearranged to give the ratio of the concentrations on one side and the ratio of the rate constants on the other, and are then set equal to the equilibrium constant:

$$\frac{(c_D)^d(c_E)^e \cdots}{(c_A)^a(c_B)^b \cdots} = \frac{k_f}{k_r} = K_{equ} \qquad (23\text{-}9)$$

Equation 23-9 is the completely general equilibrium expression and is applicable to *any* chemical equilibrium reaction. In many cases the equation will be somewhat less complex than the complete expression of equation 23-9.

When applying this general expression to particular reactions, one must follow certain rules and conventions, all of which have been stated earlier, either explicitly or implicitly, in the deri-

vation of the rate and equilibrium expressions. These conventions are:

1. The concentrations of the components on the *right* of the reaction equation (23-8), which are the *products* of the reaction, appear in the *numerator* of the equilibrium expression (equation 23-9); the components on the left (the *reactants*) appear in the *denominator*.

2. The coefficients (lower-case letters) in the chemical equation (23-8) appear as *exponents* in the equilibrium expression (23-9).

3. A reversible chemical equation (23-8) is usually written so that the *dissociation* reaction goes from left to right. (Note that, if the equation is written in the opposite direction, the equilibrium constant and the equilibrium expression will be the reciprocal of equation 23-9).

## 23-13. Evaluation of Equilibrium Constants

The general equilibrium expression has been derived from the rates of the forward and reverse reactions. This derivation, starting from the fundamental definition of equilibrium in equation 23-6, is logically consistent and has value in that it relates the expression to this definition. If this derivation is examined rigorously, however, as in more advanced courses in physical science, the logic is seen to be not perfect, particularly when the rate equations are of a high order (implying simultaneous impact of several molecules in the reaction mechanism). It is possible, however, to derive exactly the same equilibrium expression (23-9) from considerations that are completely independent of the reaction rate. This is done in the sub-science called *thermodynamics,* which is a consideration of energy relations—applied, in this case, to chemical systems. *The equilibrium expression is, then, perfectly rigorous and is still generally applicable because it does not depend on the rate theory.*

It is possible, in many cases, to evaluate the equilibrium constant of a reaction by measuring the two rate constants and calculating $K_{equ}$ from equation 23-7. This method, obviously, is applicable only to rates that are neither too high nor too low to be measured with some degree of accuracy. It is also a requirement of this method that the observed rates of the reactions be of the same order as the chemical equations written for the forward and reverse reactions, and that the two reactions be uncomplicated by competing or side reactions. The fact that this requirement is not often met is the major flaw in the application of rate theory to equilibrium.

An example of the use of this method for the evaluation of the equilibrium constant can be found in the reaction that we have used as an example in most of this chapter, the dissociation of hydrogen iodide. Kinetic studies have shown that the rate constant for the combination of $H_2$ and $I_2$ to form HI is 800 times as great as that for the dissociation of HI at room temperature. That is, in the reversible reaction written with the dissociation as the *forward* reaction (2HI $\rightleftarrows H_2 + I_2$) $k_r = 800k_f$. We can now calculate the equilibrium constant for this reaction by substituting this value for $k_r$ in equation 23-7:

$$\frac{k_f}{800k_f} = K_{equ} = \frac{1}{800} = 1.25 \times 10^{-3}$$

The $k_f$, top and bottom, cancel out, and the $K_{equ}$ can be calculated as (in this case) a pure number with no dimensions.

Another way of evaluating the equilibrium constant for a particular reaction is to determine the concentrations of the participants when the system is at equilibrium. That is, we can evaluate $K_{equ}$ by measuring all of the concentrations that appear on the left side of equation 23-9. This determination is effective in all cases to which the equilibrium concept applies and does not have the limitations of the evaluation based on rate constants. The method can be illustrated by calculations based on the concentrations in the equilibrium mixture that arises from the dissociation of dinitrogen tetroxide (cited earlier in this chapter). In an experiment carried out slightly above room temperature, a particular equilibrium mixture consisted of 0.05 molar $NO_2$ and 0.025 molar $N_2O_4$. The reversible equation for this dissociation and the equilibrium expression are

$$N_2O_4 \rightleftarrows 2NO_2$$

$$\frac{(c_{NO_2})^2}{c_{N_2O_4}} = K_{equ}$$

The equilibrium concentrations of the two gases are substituted in the $K_{equ}$ expression and the value thereby determined:

$$\frac{(5 \times 10^{-2})^2}{2.5 \times 10^{-2}} = \frac{25 \times 10^{-4}}{2.5 \times 10^{-2}} = 1 \times 10^{-1} = K_{equ}$$

A third method of determining equilibrium constants for particular reactions is to determine the degree of dissociation, $\alpha$, of the substance at dissociation equilibrium. This important application of the concepts developed in this chapter to ionic equilibria will be considered in detail later in the chapter, in a section that deals with the ionization equilibrium of weak electrolytes in water solution.

Many other methods of evaluating equilibrium constants for particular reactions are available, but most of them involve the subtleties of thermodynamics, which are beyond the scope of this introductory course. One such method exploits the relation between the cell-potential difference and the equilibrium constant in oxidation-reduction equilibrium reactions. It is possible to derive a rather simple mathematical relation between these two important quantities, both of which indicate the tendency of a reaction to proceed.

We have here stated that some oxidation-reduction reactions are reversible. But in the discussion of current-producing cells in Chapter 21 we left the impression that these reactions go one way or the other (the direction being determined by the sign of the cell-potential difference) with no hint that they might go in either direction, as required for reversible reactions. This was an example of pedagogical oversimplification. In fact, the reactions discussed are at least theoretically reversible; but most of them go so nearly to completion in the direction written that the extent to which they are incomplete is not detectable. We stated, for example, that zinc metal will displace copper ions from solution and that copper metal will *not* displace zinc ions. If this is an equilibrium reaction, and in the strictest sense it is, the statement cannot be rigorously true. Zinc metal does not displace *all* the copper ions from solution, and copper metal does not *totally* fail to displace zinc ions. Calculation of the equilibrium constant for the reaction

$$Zn + Cu^{+2} \rightleftarrows Zn^{+2} + Cu$$

from the measured potential difference of 1.10 volts (using the thermodynamic relation referred to above) shows that the equilibrium constant for this reaction is of the order of $10^{20}$. The ratio of $Zn^{+2}$ ions to $Cu^{+2}$ ions at equilibrium is therefore about $10^{20}$. Obviously, this reaction goes to "completion" in any practical sense. The magnitude of $K_{equ}$ depends on the magnitude of the cell-potential difference; and, in general, reactions that have potential differences of more than a few tenths of a volt are, for all practical considerations, irreversible.

## 23-14. Types of Chemical Equilibria

We have developed the concept of equilibrium in chemical reactions by considering gaseous reactions. A number of such reactions have been used as examples, and many details of equilibrium that are unique to gaseous reactions have already been discussed. But most of the details and the whole general concept of equilibrium in reactions are applicable to *all* types of reversible chemical reactions and are not limited to those that take place in the gaseous phase. We have referred very briefly to equilibrium in oxidation-reduction reactions in solution, and we shall make no further study of this type of equilibrium in this text. Two major types of equilibria remain to be considered in this chapter: (1) reactions involving reversible ionic dissociation; (2) solubility equilibria. Before going on to these we must consider a few more details of gaseous reactions.

## 23-15. Gaseous Equilibria

In all the gaseous reactions considered previously in this chapter, the rates and equilibrium expressions have been put in terms of *concentrations* of the gases. We emphasized concentration as the method of stating relative amounts of reacting substances because the relations so obtained are generally applicable to *all* types of equilibria. But the usual method of expressing relative amounts of gases in mixtures is not by

the concentrations but by the partial pressures (§ 10-9) of the gases. It is therefore common practice to put gaseous equilibrium expressions in terms of such partial pressures, in which case the constant is symbolized as $K_p$. The form of the equilibrium expression is the same in terms of either pressures or concentrations, and the magnitude of the constant in terms of either can be readily calculated from the other by the relation between the pressure and the concentration of a gas, as stated in the general gas equation (10-10):

$$pV = nRT$$

If this equation is solved for $p$ and the symbol $c$ is substituted for the ratio $n/V$, which is an expression of concentration (moles per unit volume)—

$$p = \frac{n}{V} RT = cRT$$

—it becomes apparent that the pressure and the concentration of a gas in a mixture at a particular temperature are directly proportional and are related by the factor $RT$.

The dissociation of hydrogen iodide can be used to illustrate this comparison of $K_p$ and the $K_{equ}$ based on concentrations. The equilibrium expression for this reaction is

$$\frac{(c_{H_2})(c_{I_2})}{(c_{HI})^2} = K_{equ}$$

Each of the concentrations in this equation is now replaced by its equality in partial pressures ($c = p/RT$):

$$\frac{\left(\frac{p_{H_2}}{RT}\right)\left(\frac{p_{I_2}}{RT}\right)}{\left(\frac{p_{HI}}{RT}\right)^2} = K_{equ} = \frac{(p_{H_2})(p_{I_2})}{(p_{HI})^2} = K_p$$

In this expression $(RT)^2$ appears in both the top and the bottom of the fraction and cancels out, leaving the equilibrium expression in terms of pressures. Thus, for this reaction, $K_{equ}$ and $K_p$ are equal. This equality of the two expressions for the equilibrium is true for any gas reaction in which there is no volume change— that is, one in which the same number of moles of gas appears among the products as among the reactants.

The dissociation of dinitrogen tetroxide is an example of reactions in which there is a change in volume and in which $K_{equ}$ and $K_p$ are not equal. The two expressions are

$$\frac{(c_{NO_2})^2}{c_{N_2O_4}} = K_{equ}$$

$$\frac{(p_{NO_2})^2}{p_{N_2O_4}} = K_p$$

If $p/RT$ is substituted for $c$ in the $K_{equ}$ expression, it becomes apparent that $K_p = RTK_{equ}$. In general, the relation between the two constants involves the factor $RT$, raised to a power equal to the difference between the numbers of moles of gas on the two sides of the equilibrium equation.

The rates of gaseous reactions can also be expressed in partial pressures, and the equilibrium constant, $K_p$, can be derived from these equations. The observation of pressure changes is often used as a method of measuring reaction rates and evaluating equilibrium constants in gaseous reactions.

As an example based on a gaseous equilibrium, let us calculate the partial pressures of the three components of the equilibrium mixture resulting from the dissociation of pure HI at room temperature and one atmosphere total pressure. The equilibrium constant for this reaction has been calculated to be $1.25 \times 10^{-3}$; that is,

$$\frac{(p_{H_2})(p_{I_2})}{(p_{HI})^2} = 1.25 \times 10^{-3}$$

From the equation for the dissociation—

$$2HI \rightleftharpoons H_2 + I_2$$

—it is apparent that, for each mole of $H_2$ formed, one mole of $I_2$ is also formed. The partial pressures of these two gases in the mixture must therefore be equal: $p_{H_2} = p_{I_2}$. When this equality is substituted, the equilibrium expression becomes

$$\frac{(p_{H_2})^2}{(p_{HI})^2} = 1.25 \times 10^{-3} \quad \text{or} \quad (p_{H_2})^2 = 12.5 \times 10^{-4}(p_{HI})^2$$

We can now obtain the partial pressure of $H_2$ in terms of $p_{HI}$ by taking the square root of both sides of this equation:

$$p_{H_2} = \sqrt{12.5 \times 10^{-2}}p_{HI} = 3.53 \times 10^{-2}p_{HI}$$

This is also, of course, the partial pressure of $I_2$:

$$p_{H_2} = p_{I_2} = 0.0353p_{HI}$$

Since the total pressure of the gas mixture is 1 atmosphere, the sum of the partial pressures of the three components of the mixture must be 1 atmosphere:

$p_{H_2} + p_{I_2} + p_{HI} = 1$ atmosphere

$0.0353p_{HI} + 0.0353p_{HI} + p_{HI} = 1$ atmosphere

$1.0706p_{HI} = 1$ atmosphere

$p_{HI} = 1/1.0706$ atmosphere $= 0.934$ atmosphere

$0.934 \times 76$ cm $= 71$ cm

The partial pressures of iodine and hydrogen are now obtained by the previously established relation $(p_{H_2} = p_{I_2} = 0.0353p_{HI})$:

$$p_{H_2} = p_{I_2} = 0.0353 \times 71 \text{ cm} = 2.50 \text{ cm}$$

Thus the partial pressures of the three gases are HI $= 71$ cm, $H_2 = 2.50$ cm, and $I_2 = 2.50$ cm.

## 23-16. *Ionic Equilibria*

The commonest and certainly the most important type of chemical equilibrium that can be treated in terms of the concepts outlined in this chapter is the equilibrium of the dissociation of weak electrolytes in water solution. As we saw in Chapter 19, strong electrolytes such as NaCl and $HNO_3$ (most salts, strong acids and bases) are considered to be totally ionized under all circumstances, including water solutions, but weak electrolytes are only partially ionized in water solution. The reversible dissociation of weak electrolytes, partially described in Chapter 19, is an equilibrium reaction and is therefore best and most completely described in terms of the equilibrium concept and the equilibrium expression (equation 23-9).

One such weak electrolyte is acetic acid, $H-C_2H_3O_2$, which we have chosen to symbolize as HAc. The dissociation takes place according to the equation

$$HAc \rightleftharpoons H^+ + Ac^-$$

and the equilibrium expression is

$$\frac{(c_{H^+})(c_{Ac^-})}{c_{HAc}} = K_{equ}$$

We already know something about this reaction: we know that the ratio of the product of the concentrations of the $H^+$ ion and the $Ac^-$ ion to the concentration of the un-ionized HAc is very low, or that the degree of dissociation of HAc is small. In other words, the equilibrium constant for the reaction is a small number. This qualitative statement provides only a limited description of the reaction. The value of the equilibrium expression is that it describes reversible reactions *quantitatively* and can be used to calculate the exact nature of equilibrium systems—in this case solutions of acetic acid.

Obviously, if we are to consider this equilibrium reaction quantitatively, we must first evaluate $K_{equ}$. But how? Since the reaction is ionic and therefore takes place exceedingly rapidly, the use of rate measurements is out of the question. Since the reaction is not an oxidation-reduction, the equilibrium constant cannot be calculated from measurement of the potential difference. The concentrations of the three components, from which it would be possible to evaluate $K_{equ}$, are not easy to measure. The best method of evaluating $K_{equ}$ for acetic acid, and also for most weak acids and bases, is to calculate it from the degree of dissociation, as measured by conductance.

It is possible to express the equilibrium constant in terms of the degree of dissociation, $\alpha$, and the *total* concentration of acetic acid, $C$. This concentration is the amount of acetic acid added to water to make up the solution and includes what dissociates as well as what remains undissociated. Consideration of the equilibrium reaction

$$HAc \rightleftharpoons H^+ + Ac^-$$

shows the relation of the concentration of each of the reacting entities to $\alpha$ and $C$. Each molecule of HAc that dissociates gives rise to one $H^+$ ion and one $Ac^-$ ion; thus the concentrations of these are equal in a solution of HAc in which there is no other source of $Ac^-$ or $H^+$ ions. The amount of each of these is equal to the amount of dissociated HAc, and their concentration is $\alpha$ times the original concentration of HAc:

$$c_{H^+} = c_{Ac^-} = \alpha C$$

Furthermore, the concentration of undissociated HAc is equal to the total concentration *minus* the concentration that is dissociated:

$$c_{HAc} = C - \alpha C = (1 - \alpha)C$$

These quantities are now substituted in the equilibrium expression:

$$K_{equ} = \frac{(\alpha C)(\alpha C)}{(1 - \alpha)C} = \frac{\alpha^2 C^2}{(1 - \alpha)C}$$
$$= \frac{\alpha^2 C}{1 - \alpha}$$

Experimentally determined values of $\alpha$ and the corresponding values of $C$, the total HAc concentration, are now substituted in this equation to determine the value of $K_{equ}$ at the various concentrations. Table 19-3 shows that the degree of dissociation at $10^{-3}$ M concentration is 0.126. When these values are substituted in the equation above, we can complete the calculation:

$$K_{equ} = \frac{(0.126)^2 \times 10^{-3}}{1 - 0.126} = \frac{1.59 \times 10^{-2} \times 10^{-3}}{0.874}$$
$$= 1.82 \times 10^{-5}$$

Obviously, from the argument on which the equilibrium concept is based, $K$ should be the same for all concentrations. This is not exactly true, but the variation over a rather wide range of concentrations of HAc remains nearly within the limits of experimental error. The same calculation, using the data for other concentrations (Table 19-3), gives values of $K$ for acetic acid varying from $1.71 \times 10^{-5}$ to $1.85 \times 10^{-5}$. The accepted value for this constant is $1.8 \times 10^{-5}$.

Ammonium hydroxide is a weak base (a weak electrolyte that gives rise to a hydroxide ion on ionization) that dissociates according to the equilibrium reaction

$$NH_4OH \rightleftharpoons NH_4^+ + OH^-$$

The equilibrium constant for this reaction is $1.75 \times 10^{-5}$, and the equilibrium expression has the form

$$\frac{(c_{NH_4^+})(c_{OH^-})}{c_{NH_4OH}} = K_{equ} = 1.75 \times 10^{-5}$$

This constant has been evaluated by methods very similar to those used for the evaluation of the constant for the dissociation of acetic acid. That method is generally applicable to any weakly ionic compound.

The use of equilibrium constants and the equilibrium expression in quantitative description of the behavior of equilibrium systems can best be shown by calculations based on these expressions.

## EXAMPLE 1

Calculate the concentration of H+ ion present in a 2.0 molar solution of HAc.

From the equation for the dissociation it is apparent that one Ac− ion is produced for each H+ ion produced. If no other source of either Ac− ions or H+ ions is present, the concentrations of these two ions must be equal. It is also apparent from the magnitude of the dissociation constant that the fraction of HAc that ionizes will be small. Because of these two facts it is possible first to equate $c_{Ac-}$ and $c_{H+}$ and then to regard $c_{HAc}$ as equal to the total concentration of HAc—that is, as 2.0 molar. (The second of these decisions amounts to making the justified assumption that the fraction of HAc that dissociates is negligibly small.) When these equalities are substituted into the equilibrium expression, it becomes

$$\frac{(c_{H+})^2}{2.0} = 1.8 \times 10^{-5}$$

which then reduces to

$$(c_{H+})^2 = 3.6 \times 10^{-5} = 36 \times 10^{-6}$$

Note that we made the last change in the equation in order to make the exponent an even number so that we can take the square root of both sides of the equation and still get a whole-number exponent:

$$\sqrt{(c_{H+})^2} = \sqrt{36 \times 10^{-6}}$$
$$c_{H+} = 6 \times 10^{-3} \text{ molar}$$

## EXAMPLE 2

Calculate the concentration of OH− ion in a 0.1 molar solution of ammonium hydroxide to which enough ammonium chloride has been added to make the solution 0.5 molar in ammonium chloride.

Ammonium chloride is a strong electrolyte and is totally ionized in solution. The concentration of ammonium ion that arises from this salt in the solution is therefore 0.5 molar. (The Cl− concentration has the same value, but this fact has no bearing on the dissociation of NH₄OH and can be ignored in this problem.) It also can be assumed that the dissociation of NH₄OH gives rise to a negligible concentration of NH₄+, compared with that from the NH₄Cl, and that the amount of dissociation is also negligible when we state the concentration of undissociated NH₄OH. The equilibrium equation therefore becomes

$$\frac{(c_{OH-}) \times 0.5}{0.1} = 1.75 \times 10^{-5}$$
$$c_{OH-} = \frac{0.1}{0.5} \times 1.75 \times 10^{-5} = \frac{1.75}{5} \times 10^{-5}$$
$$= 0.35 \times 10^{-5} = 3.5 \times 10^{-6} \text{ molar}$$

## 23-17. *Ionization of Water*

Water itself dissociates into ions. The degree of dissociation is extremely small, and water must therefore be classed as a very weak electrolyte. This dissociation, which was referred to briefly in Chapter 22 and several times earlier, gives rise to H+ ions and OH− ions according to the equilibrium reaction

$$H_2O \rightleftarrows H^+ + OH^- \tag{23-10}$$

The production of H+ ions and OH− ions by this reaction, which is taking place in *all* water solutions, obviously has a very special significance in relation to the acid-base equilibria exemplified by the dissociation of acetic acid and of ammonium hydroxide. Water can be considered a weak acid because it produces H+ ions. It can also be considered a weak base because it produces OH− ions. Because the degree of dissociation is exceedingly slight, water is extremely weak both as an acid and as a base, and the number of ions produced can often be ignored, particularly when we are dealing with strong acids and bases. There are several situations, however, in which this dissociation is of great importance; and a rigorous treatment of any equilibrium that involves H+ or OH− ions and that takes place in a water solution must take account of the dissociation equilibrium of water.

The conventional equilibrium expression for the dissociation of water would be

$$\frac{(c_{H+})(c_{OH-})}{c_{H_2O}} = K_{equ}$$

In a water solution, however, the concentration of water, $c_{H_2O}$, is constant. A liter of water has a mass of 1,000 grams, which is 1,000/18 =

55.5 moles. The constant concentration of water in pure water (or in a dilute water solution) is therefore 55.5 molar. Since $c_{H_2O}$ is constant, it can be incorporated into the equilibrium constant to give another constant:

$$(c_{H^+})(c_{OH^-}) = (c_{H_2O})K_{equ} = K_w$$

Because of this special relation of the dissociation of water to all acid-base equilibrium reactions, this expression and the constant are given special emphasis and a unique name. The constant, $K_w$, which has been evaluated by methods similar in principle to those described in § 23-13, is called the *ion-product constant* for water, and the whole expression is called the ion-product expression for water:

$$(c_{H^+})(c_{OH^-}) = K_w = 1.0 \times 10^{-14} \qquad (23\text{-}11)$$

From the equilibrium equation (23-10) it is apparent that in a pure sample of water the $H^+$ ion concentration must be exactly equal to the $OH^-$ ion concentration. One each of both kinds of ion arises from the dissociation of a molecule of water; the concentrations of the two must therefore be equal. By using the ion-product expression we can calculate the concentration of these two ions in the special case of pure water that has no other source of either ion:

$$(c_{H^+})(c_{OH^-}) = 1.0 \times 10^{-14} = (c_{H^+})^2 = (c_{OH^-})^2$$

Or, if we take the square root:

$$c_{H^+} = c_{OH^-} = \sqrt{1.0 \times 10^{-14}} = 1.0 \times 10^{-7} \text{ molar}$$

This statement tells us that pure water has $H^+$ ion concentration of $10^{-7}$ molar and an equal $OH^-$ ion concentration. This equilibrium mixture, then, represents the point of neutrality on an acid-base ($H^+ = OH^-$) concentration scale.

The ion-product expression also shows that in any water solution there are always *some* $H^+$ ions and some $OH^-$ ions—even in a solution of a strong acid or a strong base. For a solution that is 10 molar in $H^+$ ion from a strong acid, the $OH^-$ ion concentration can be calculated as follows:

$$c_{OH^-} \times 10 = 1 \times 10^{-14}$$

$$c_{OH^-} = 1 \times 10^{-15} \text{ molar}$$

This, obviously, is an exceedingly small concentration of $OH^-$ ions, but it is greater than zero. Similarly, the $H^+$ ion concentration in a 1 molar base is $10^{-14}$; in a 0.1 molar base it is $10^{-13}$, and so forth. This reciprocal relation between the $H^+$ and $OH^-$ concentrations, plus the fact that the concentrations of these ions in many systems are extremely important, has led to a method of expressing the $H^+$ ion concentrations in terms of an exponential unit called pH. The pH is defined as the negative exponent to the base 10 of the $H^+$ ion concentration. Thus a solution that has a $10^{-1}$ molar concentration of $H^+$ ion is said to have a pH of 1.0; a solution that is $10^{-4}$ molar in $H^+$ ion has a pH of 4.0; and pure water has a pH of 7.0. The same system can be used to describe basic solutions because of the reciprocal relation between $H^+$ ion and $OH^-$ ion concentrations. Thus a solution that has a $10^{-1}$ molar concentration of $OH^-$ must have a $10^{-13}$ molar concentration of $H^+$ ion and therefore a pH of 13; a $10^{-5}$ molar basic solution has an $H^+$ ion concentration of $10^{-9}$ and therefore a pH of 9. This system of expressing the acidity or basicity of a solution has the obvious advantage of simplicity and is therefore much used in industrial and research operations. Because biological materials are extremely sensitive to changes in acidity, the pH system is also in common use in medical research and practice and in biochemical research. The pH of animal tissues is about 7.4, and a deviation of more than a few hundredths of a pH unit will cause the death of the tissue. Most plant tissues are somewhat more acid, having a pH of about 6.5, which is just on the acid side of the neutral point on the acid-base scale.

## 23-18. Hydrolysis

The dissociation of water by the equilibrium reaction of equation 23-10 is, as we pointed out, one of the conditions of any water solution. $H^+$ and $OH^-$ ions are available in these solutions from this dissociation and in many cases must be considered with respect to other ionic equilibria involving $H^+$ and $OH^-$ ions. This relation is illustrated by the experimental fact that solutions of many salts are *not* neutral. It is well known, for example, that a solution of washing soda is basic. The basic quality is due, of course, to an excess of $OH^-$ ions in the solution, and it is the basic quality that makes this compound useful as a washing agent. Washing soda is sodium carbonate, $Na_2CO_3$, which is the salt of a weak acid (carbonic acid, $H_2CO_3$) and a strong base (sodium hydroxide, NaOH). Such salts generally form basic solutions in water. Salts of strong acids and weak bases (for example, ammonium chloride, $NH_4Cl$, which is the salt of HCl and $NH_4OH$) generally form *acidic* water solutions. This phenomenon and the mechanism by which the excess of $H^+$ or $OH^-$ ions is produced are called **hydrolysis.** The explanation of the mechanism and the quantitative description of the process require the application of *two* equilibrium expressions, one for the dissociation of water and the other for the dissociation of the weak electrolyte (acid or base) corresponding to one of the ions of the salt.

One such hydrolytic reaction is that of sodium acetate, the salt of the strong base NaOH and the weak acid HAc, which forms a basic solution in water. Our analysis of the reaction must explain the formation of an excess of $OH^-$ ions in solution in water. The salt itself is, of course, a strong electrolyte and is completely dissociated into $Na^+$ ions and $Ac^-$ ions. The dissociation of water produces some $H^+$ ions (and $OH^-$ ions as well), and the $H^+$ ions are capable of combining (or associating) with the $Ac^-$ ions to form undissociated HAc according to the equilibrium equation for this reaction shown on page 387.† There is, then, a competition for the $H^+$ ions between $OH^-$ ions to form water molecules and $Ac^-$ ions to form HAc molecules. Both are partially successful in this competition, and both of the undissociated species will therefore be present. The net result of these reactions is the accumulation of free $OH^-$ ions by the removal of $H^+$ ions from water molecules. We can show the relation between the two equilibrium reactions and this competition by writing the equations of the two equilibria (as well as the total

---

† There is, of course, no corresponding tendency for $Na^+$ ions and $OH^-$ ions to associate because sodium hydroxide is a strong electrolyte (totally dissociated into ions).

dissociation of NaAc) together to point up the three reactions involved:

$$NaAc \longrightarrow Na^+ + Ac^-$$

These three equations, written in this way, make it apparent that for each $H^+$ ion that enters the association reaction with $Ac^-$ ions, a free $OH^-$ ion is left. The solution therefore accumulates $OH^-$ ions and becomes basic; and the degree to which this association takes place determines how *many* such free $OH^-$ ions accumulate in the solution and thereby how basic it becomes. The extent of this association to form HAc is determined by *both* the $K_{equ}$ for this reaction and the ion-product constant for water, $K_w$. We can describe the relation between them mathematically by combining the two equations describing the two equilibria that determine the conditions of the whole system.

The concentration of $H^+$ can be expressed in terms of the $OH^-$ concentration and $K_w$:

$$c_{H^+} = \frac{K_w}{c_{OH^-}}$$

This value is then substituted in the equilibrium expression that describes the HAc equilibrium:

$$\frac{(c_{H^+})(c_{Ac^-})}{c_{HAc}} = K_{equ} = \frac{\frac{K_w}{(c_{OH^-})}(c_{Ac^-})}{c_{HAc}} = \frac{K_w(c_{Ac^-})}{(c_{OH^-})(c_{HAc})}$$

$$(c_{OH^-})K_{equ} = \frac{K_w(c_{Ac^-})}{c_{HAc}}$$

$$c_{OH^-} = \frac{K_w}{K_{equ}}\frac{c_{Ac^-}}{c_{HAc}}$$

If there is no other source of HAc than the association reaction (that is, if the solution contains only sodium acetate), the concentration of $OH^-$ ions and the concentration of undissociated HAc are equal. This is apparent from the reactions indicated above, in which each $H^+$ ion that associates with an $Ac^-$ ion to form a molecule of HAc leaves one free $OH^-$ ion in solution. In this special situation it is therefore possible to simplify the equation above by substituting the equality $c_{HAc} = c_{OH^-}$:

$$c_{OH^-} = \frac{c_{Ac^-}}{c_{OH^-}} \frac{K_w}{K_{equ}}$$

$$(c_{OH^-})^2 = (c_{Ac^-}) \frac{K_w}{K_{equ}}$$

We could use this equation to calculate, for example, the concentration of hydroxide ion in a $10^{-1}$ molar solution of sodium acetate:

$$(c_{OH^-})^2 = (10^{-1}) \frac{1.0 \times 10^{-14}}{1.8 \times 10^{-5}} = \frac{1}{1.8} \times 10^{-10}$$

$$c_{OH^-} = \frac{1}{\sqrt{1.8}} \times 10^{-5} = \frac{1}{1.35} \times 10^{-5}$$

$$= 0.74 \times 10^{-5} = 7.4 \times 10^{-6} \text{ molar}$$

## 23-19. Solubility Equilibria

The final type of chemical equilibrium that we shall consider is that between sparingly soluble ionic compounds and their saturated solutions. The terms "soluble," "insoluble," and "sparingly soluble" are relative and describe qualitatively equilibria that can be described completely and quantitatively only by the equilibrium expression. For very soluble substances, the most satisfactory way to state solubility is the way we have done it up to now—by specifying a certain mass of solute per unit amount of solvent or solution. But many ionic substances are only slightly soluble, and for them the commonest and most complete way to state solubility is to apply the equilibrium expression to the special case of solubility equilibria. The special form that the expression takes for this type of equilibrium is called the **solubility-product expression,** and the equilibrium constant is called the **solubility-product constant,** $K_{sp}$, or simply the solubility constant.

Silver acetate, a sparingly soluble salt, will illustrate solubility equilibria. Silver acetate dissolves by dissociation according to the equation

$$AgAc \rightleftarrows Ag^+ + Ac^-$$

and is present in solution as the dissociated ions. Instead of writing the general equilibrium expression (equation 23-9) for this equilibrium, we shall put the expression into a simpler form that is similar to the ion-product equation for water. The effective concentration of the undis-

sociated (and undissolved) AgAc is constant† and can be incorporated into the $K_{equ}$, as we did with the constant for the dissociation of water, to form a new constant, $K_{sp}$. The equilibrium equation then becomes

$$(c_{Ag^+})(c_{Ac^-}) = K_{sp} = 3.6 \times 10^{-3}$$

As we stated above, this expression is called the solubility-product expression for silver acetate. The general form of the solubility-product expression is implied by this special case: the product of the concentrations of the ions formed when the substance dissociates in solution, set equal to the solubility constant. The general equation for a salt $A_aB_b$ is

$$(c_A)^a(c_B)^b = K_{sp} \qquad (23\text{-}12)$$

We can evaluate the solubility constant most simply by measuring the concentrations of the ions present in a saturated solution. For example, the concentration of $Ag^+$ ion in a saturated solution of AgAc at room temperature is $6.05 \times 10^{-2}$ molar. Obviously, the concentration of $Ac^-$ ion must be the same in this solution, for each silver ion that dissolves is accompanied by one acetate ion. These concentrations can be substituted in the solubility-product expression:

$$(c_{Ag^+})(c_{Ac^-}) = K_{sp} = (6.05 \times 10^{-2})(6.05 \times 10^{-2})$$

$$= 36.5 \times 10^{-4} = 3.65 \times 10^{-3}$$

The response of a solubility-equilibrium sys-

---

† In all analyses of equilibria in solution, the concentration of any solid substance is considered to be constant in the equilibrium expression. This is frequently rationalized in elementary textbooks in one of two ways.

(1) The density of a solid is constant; therefore the mass per volume is constant, whether expressed as grams/cm³ or as moles/liter. Thus the *concentration* of a solid substance is constant.

(2) The concentration that enters the equilibrium expression is not that of the *solid* phase itself but that of dissolved but *undissociated* substance, which is in equilibrium with the solid phase as well as with the dissociated substance in solution. Thus *two* equilibria are involved, illustrated in the case of silver acetate by the expression

AgAc (solid) $\rightleftarrows$ AgAc (dissolved but undissociated) $\rightleftarrows$ Ag$^+$ + Ac$^-$

It is then further explained that the concentration of dissolved but undissociated substance is constant, regardless of how much solid phase is present.

Both explanations lead to the same $K_{sp}$ expression.

tem to the stress of an added concentration of one of the ions of the salt illustrates a qualitative generalization that is quite useful in dealing with solutions of sparingly soluble substances. A general statement of this qualitative rule, called the **common-ion effect,** is: "In the presence of an excess of either of the ions of a sparingly soluble salt, the solubility of the salt will be less than in pure water." This is really a special application of Le Châtelier's rule to this kind of equilibrium. The common-ion effect can be illustrated by an example: The solubility-product constant for silver chloride is $1.2 \times 10^{-10}$; the concentration of $Ag^+$ ion in a saturated solution of AgCl is therefore

$$c_{Ag^+} = \sqrt{1.2 \times 10^{-10}} = 1.1 \times 10^{-5}$$

But, if excess $Cl^-$ ion is added to this solution, some AgCl will precipitate (fall out of solution), leaving a *lower* concentration of $Ag^+$ ion in solution. If $10^{-1}$ molar HCl, for example, is added, the concentration of $Ag^+$ (and therefore the solubility of AgCl in this solution) is

$$c_{Ag^+} = \frac{1.2 \times 10^{-10}}{10^{-1}} = 1.2 \times 10^{-9} \text{ molar}$$

The discussion of equilibrium in this chapter, lengthy as it is, constitutes only the barest and simplest introduction to a few aspects of the subject. Each of these few special topics within the general concept of equilibrium has been considered only in part. In more advanced courses the discussion of each is expanded tremendously in detail and complexity. This chapter has been primarily concerned with chemical equilibrium; but even in this limited area only a very few of the many possible applications of the concept to chemical systems have been mentioned.

The main purpose of this chapter has been to demonstrate a mathematical, analytical method of almost unlimited applicability. This method starts from an extremely simple concept —the dynamic opposition of two competing influences. By a straightforward application of this concept to many different systems, making use of the theories and facts that have been developed in the first two parts of this text, we have been able to analyze, quantitatively and in great detail, the behavior of those systems. The method has extreme precision and tremendous power in solving chemical problems. The fundamental concept is applicable, furthermore, to a vast number of situations in science and to many problems in other fields of human study.

## Concepts and Terms

Equilibrium
  physical
  chemical
  gaseous
  ionic
  solubility
Dynamic Equilibrium
Le Châtelier's Principle
Catalysis
  catalyst
Heterogeneous Reactions

Reaction-rate Theory
  first order (unimolecular)
  second order (bimolecular)
  higher orders
Equilibrium Constant
  ion-product constant
  solubility-product constant
Ionization of Water
  ion-product constant for water ($K_w$)
  hydrolysis

## Problems

**23-1.** Define in your own words the concept of equilibrium (A) in general, (B) in terms of forward and reverse rates, (C) in chemical reactions, (D) in terms of the equilibrium expression.

**23-2.** Give your own definitions of the following terms: reaction rate, second-order reaction, catalyst, equilibrium constant, unimolecular reaction, common-ion effect.

**23-3.** State the criteria for true catalysis.

**23-4.** List and explain the conventions used in writing equilibrium expressions for dissociation reactions.

**23-5.** Describe an experiment and list the equipment needed to demonstrate the dynamic nature of the equilibrium between nitrogen dioxide and dinitrogen tetroxide:

$$2NO_2 \rightleftharpoons N_2O_4$$

**23-6.** Powdered coal is sometimes used as a fuel in industrial heating plants and power-generating stations. It has the obvious advantage of ease of handling because it can be pumped through pipes. What other advantage over lump coal as a fuel does powdered coal have?

**23-7.** A piece of coal in the shape of a cube and 10 cm (about 4 inches) on an edge has a surface area of 600 cm$^2$ (six sides, each 10 cm square) and a volume of 1,000 cm$^3$.
(A) Calculate the surface area this same amount of coal will have if it is broken into cubes 1 mm on an edge.
(B) What would be the total surface if the particles were 1 micron ($10^{-3}$ mm) on an edge (a fine powder)?
    *Ans.* (B) $6 \times 10^7$ cm$^2$ = about 1.5 acres

**23-8.** The rates of most biochemical reactions follow the generalizations outlined in this chapter for ordinary chemical reactions. If a certain food is known to spoil in one day if left at a temperature of 30°C, how long is it safe to store it in a refrigerator at about 0°C? How long in a deep-freeze at −30°C?
    *Ans.* About 1 week; about 2 months

**23-9.** The gaseous reaction of the oxidation of sulfur dioxide,

$$2SO_2 + O_2 \rightleftharpoons 2SO_3$$

is an important step in the industrial synthesis of sulfuric acid. The reaction liberates considerable heat ($\Delta H$ is negative) and proceeds very slowly at room temperature. Finely divided platinum is added to the gas mixture in the industrial use of the reaction.
(A) State the effect of a rise in temperature on (1) the rate of the forward reaction; (2) the rate of the reverse reaction; (3) the position of the equilibrium.
(B) State the effect of an increase in the total pressure on the two rates and on the position of the equilibrium.

(C) State the effect of the added platinum on the two rates and on the position of the equilibrium.
(D) State the effect of an increase in the concentration of $O_2$ on the two rates and on the position of the equilibrium.
(E) Predict what temperature, pressure, and concentration of $O_2$ would probably be used in the industrial operation of this reaction.

**23-10.** The equilibrium constant for the reaction of Prob. 23-9 at 300°C is $8 \times 10^3$; at 500° it is 30; and at 1,000° it is 0.3. Calculate the ratio of the concentration of $SO_3$ to the concentration of $SO_2$ in the equilibrium mixture at each of the three temperatures if the concentration of $O_2$ is kept at $10^{-1}$ mole per liter in each situation.
    *Ans.* At 300°: 28.3

**23-11.** Calculate the H$^+$ ion concentration in $10^{-1}$ molar solutions of the following weak acids:

(A) HAc $\rightleftharpoons$ H$^+$ + Ac$^-$    $K_{equ} = 1.8 \times 10^{-5}$
(B) HCN $\rightleftharpoons$ H$^+$ + CN$^-$        $4.0 \times 10^{-10}$
(C) HF $\rightleftharpoons$ H$^+$ + F$^-$          $6.7 \times 10^{-7}$
(D) HN$_3$ $\rightleftharpoons$ H$^+$ + N$_3^-$      $1.0 \times 10^{-4}$
(E) HNO$_2$ $\rightleftharpoons$ H$^+$ + NO$_2^-$    $4.5 \times 10^{-4}$

    *Ans.* (B) $6.3 \times 10^{-6}$ M

**23-12.** Calculate the Ag$^+$ concentration in a saturated solution of each of the following silver salts:

(A) AgBr    $K_{sp} = 3.3 \times 10^{-13}$
(B) AgCl            $1.7 \times 10^{-10}$
(C) AgI              $8.5 \times 10^{-17}$
(D) Ag$_2$S          $1.0 \times 10^{-51}$
(E) Ag$_2$SO$_4$     $1.2 \times 10^{-5}$

    *Ans.* (D) $1.26 \times 10^{-17}$ M

**23-13.** Calculate the concentration of the negative ion of each of the salts of Prob. 23-12 in a solution containing $10^{-1}$ mole per liter of Ag$^+$ ion and saturated with the salt.
    *Ans.* (E) $c_{SO_4^{-2}} = 1.2 \times 10^{-3}$

**23-14.** A hypothetical weak acid is found to be 0.1% dissociated in a $10^{-3}$ molar solution. Symbolize the acid as *HA* and its dissociation as

$$HA \rightleftharpoons H^+ + A^-$$

Calculate the degree of dissociation (degree of ionization) of this acid in a $10^{-2}$ molar solution and in a $10^{-4}$ M solution. (Hint: First calculate the dissociation constant from the data given; then use this constant for calculating the degree of dissociation.)

**23-15.** Calculate the equilibrium constant at each of the four concentrations for acetic acid from the data given in Table 19-3.

*Ans.* At $10^{-2}$ M $1.84 \times 10^{-5}$

**23-16.** A hypothetical gaseous reaction is symbolized by the equilibrium equation

$$2A + B \rightleftharpoons C$$

(A) What effect would doubling the concentration of $A$ have on the rate of the forward reaction?

(B) What effect would doubling the concentration of $B$ have on the rate of the forward reaction?

(C) What effect would doubling the concentrations of both $A$ and $B$ have on the rate of the forward reaction?

(D) What effect would doubling the concentrations of both $A$ and $B$ have on the rate of the reverse reaction?

Give logical reasons for your answer in each case.

**23-17.** Assume that you have methods of analysis for the concentrations of $A$, $B$, and $C$ in the reaction of Prob. 23-16. Describe a practical experiment for proving that the system is at equilibrium.

# Suggested Readings

1. H. M. Leicester and H. S. Klickstein, *A Source Book in Chemistry* (McGraw-Hill, 1952). A biographical sketch of Le Châtelier and his own statement of the principle that bears his name appear on pp. 480–483.

The next three references contain detailed and quite rigorous treatments of rate theory and equilibrium.

2. J. H. Hildebrand and R. E. Powell, *Principles of Chemistry*, 6th edition (Macmillan, 1952), Chaps. 11 (rates of chemical reactions), 12 (chemical equilibrium), 13 (types of equilibrium).

3. L. Pauling, *College Chemistry*, 2nd edition (W. H. Freeman, 1955), Chaps. 19, 20, and 21.

4. M. J. Sienko and R. A. Plane, *Chemistry* (McGraw-Hill, 1957), Chaps. 12 (rates) and 13 (equilibrium).

The three following references, less detailed and less complete, are probably easier for beginning students of physical science.

5. W. F. Ehret, *Smith's Introductory College Chemistry* (Appleton-Century-Crofts, 1950), Chaps. 21 and 24.

6. D. C. Gregg, *Principles of Chemistry* (Allyn & Bacon, 1958), Chaps. 14 and 18.

7. F. T. Bonner and Melba Phillips, *Principles of Physical Science* (Addison-Wesley, 1957), Chap. 22.

THE CULTURAL ages of Man have been named after the materials of his chief implements: the Stone Age, the Bronze Age, the Iron Age, and the variously named present age. Our current culture has been called the Atomic Age, but a better name, arising from a longer perspective, would probably be the Age of Energy. All the implements alluded to are of mineral origin. A sharp piece of flint, a bronze sword, a steel cannon, a supply of petroleum, the uranium from which to make an atom bomb—all are obtained from the earth's crust. In each age the dominant influence in culture and power has been associated with a combination of two things: an abundant supply of these materials and the ability to use them. The paramount social issues of our time are associated with the control of the mining and refining of petroleum and the mining and application of uranium. The international struggle over these resources is the cause of great tensions—both the tension that creates new civilizations and the tension that frightens individuals and nations into self-destruction through witless acts and refusals to act. No doubt prehistory was dominated, with wonderful and awful results, by similar tensions over the control of the mining and fabrication of sharp flints. It will be worth while to consider briefly the scientific background of the problems associated with these culturally dominating tensions, to raise—and possibly to answer—such questions as: Where do mineral deposits occur? What conditions cause the formation of minerals? How are they found? And how mined, extracted, and used? These and many related questions are primarily problems of applied chemistry. And while we are considering these "geochemical" problems, it will be worth while also to discuss a few related examples of applied chemistry.

## 24-1. Chemical Composition of the Earth

In Chapter 15 we considered the over-all physical characteristics of the earth, its distribution of densities, its layered structure. We also considered in some detail the chemical compo-

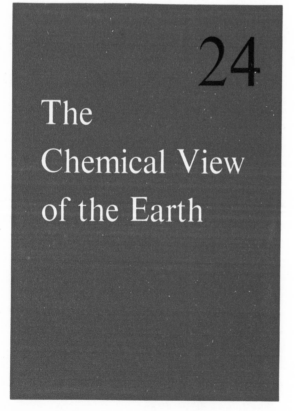

CHAPTER

24

The
Chemical View
of the Earth

sition of the atmosphere. We shall now consider the distribution of the few compounds that make up most of the substance of the earth. Though our direct knowledge of the composition of the earth is limited to extremely superficial parts of the outer crustal layer, it is possible to extend our knowledge well beyond the area of direct observation by reasoned arguments from indirect, presumptive information and by established generalizations about the parts we know directly.

Of the 102 elements listed in the periodic table, eighty-eight have been shown to occur naturally; that is, the part of the earth of which we have direct knowledge—the crust, the oceans, and the atmosphere—is made up entirely of these eighty-eight elements. There are, however, great variations in relative abundance. As indicated by Table 24-1, two elements, oxygen and silicon, make up by far the largest part of the surface material of the earth; and the ten elements listed account for all except traces.

Some of these elements, to a limited extent, occur free in nature. Elemental oxygen is, of course, a major component of air, as is nitrogen, but the total amount of substance represented by the atmosphere is such a small fraction of the earth's crustal mass that it has only a minute effect on the over-all percentages. Nitrogen does not even make up 0.5 percent of the total, and most of the oxygen is present in the crust in

chemical combination, as are almost all of the other elements. A few, including silver, copper, gold, sulfur, and traces of others, do occur as free elements. Most of the metals occur as *oxides* and *silicates,* and most of the silicon and oxygen are present in these compounds, such as the oxides of iron, hematite ($Fe_2O_3$) and magnetite ($Fe_3O_4$), which are the principal ores of iron, quartz ($SiO_2$), and the complex silicates of iron, aluminum, magnesium, sodium, and potassium. These silicates have very complex formulas in which several metal ions are combined with the quadrivalent silicate ion, $SiO_4^{-4}$. In addition to these minerals, which make up the bulk of the earth's crust, there are economically valuable deposits of metal carbonates and sulfides, including the major minerals of zinc (sphalerite, $ZnS$), lead (galena, $PbS$), and copper (chalcopyrite, $CuFeS_2$) as well as marble and limestone ($CaCO_3$).

These minerals and the elemental composition indicated in Table 24-1 are found in the directly observable surface. All evidence as to the composition of the inner parts of the earth must come from indirect observations and deductions (see Chap. 15). Variations in density and the analogy of meteorites indicate that the composition of the inner layers (Fig. 15-4) is probably as follows: The dense basaltic layers ($d = 3.5$–$4.0$) of the lower crust are underlain by even denser rocks, in which compounds of the heavy metals, particularly iron compounds, are more abundant; the percentage of iron and nickel in these rocks increases with depth through the mantle. The core is probably composed almost entirely of elemental iron and nickel.

| ELEMENT | ABUNDANCE IN CRUST, SEA, AND AIR | ABUNDANCE IN CRUST |
|---|---|---|
| Oxygen | 49.5% | 46.4% |
| Silicon | 25.8 | 27.8 |
| Aluminum | 7.5 | 8.1 |
| Iron | 4.7 | 5.1 |
| Calcium | 3.4 | 3.6 |
| Sodium | 2.6 | 2.6 |
| Potassium | 2.4 | 2.5 |
| Magnesium | 1.9 | 2.1 |
| Hydrogen | 0.9 | 0.2 |
| Titanium | 0.6 | 0.6 |
| All others | 0.7 | 1.0 |

TABLE **24-1** *Elemental Composition of the Earth*

## 24-2. *Distribution of Crustal Substances*

The elements that make up the earth were formed, in the proportions that now exist, at the formation of the earth† (see Chap. 31). Since then these elements have been constantly com-

† One obvious minor exception to this statement is the radioactive transmutation of elements discussed in Chap. 30. This process, except for a short time right after the formation of the earth, cannot have been of great quantitative importance.

bining and recombining in the formation of compounds. Here we can be concerned only with the processes that take place in the earth's crust, in the seas, and in the air—in the part of the earth that is open to direct chemical observation. If all the substance of the earth's crust were uniformly distributed, there would be no such thing as mineral deposits. All the elements except oxygen and silicon would be economically unobtainable rarities. But there is, of course, no such equal distribution. Great beds of iron ore, containing 70 percent iron, occur in Minnesota; western Pennsylvania is underlain by vast coal fields that are 90 percent carbon; tremendous concentrations of petroleum occur in Texas and in the Middle East; and within a fairly small area of South Africa occur large deposits of gold and diamond ore. In one, elemental gold is disseminated in very small particles; in the other, vertical "pipes" of earthy blue rock contain the rarer but more valuable crystals of pure carbon (diamonds). Both gold and carbon are trace elements of the crustal material; gold makes up less than $5 \times 10^{-7}$ percent and carbon less than 0.07 percent. Obviously, selective processes of distribution have been in operation; and, equally obviously, our culture, which is dependent on the use of such substances, owes its existence to those processes.

The study of the formation and selective distribution of minerals is called **mineralogy.** We shall consider here, very briefly, a few of the mineralogical processes.

Most of the crustal rocks and minerals began as **igneous rocks**—that is, as molten mixtures beneath the present surface of the earth. The formation of igneous rocks can be observed now in volcanic activity. In the fluid condition, at extremely high temperatures and pressures, the elements listed in Table 24-1 would form a number of compounds, including quartz and the oxides, sulfides, and silicates of several metals. These substances flow as fluids, come into contact with other types of rock, intrude into crevices, are sorted gravitationally, and undergo other processes that tend to separate them. When these igneous rocks reach the surface (by volcanic activity, upheaval, or erosion of overlying material), they are there exposed (over geologic

ages) to the process of **weathering.** Weathering reduces massive rock to smaller fragments, transports material from one place to another, and even chemically transforms a compound by introducing oxygen, carbon dioxide, or water into, or eliminating part of, the original molecule. One of the major processes is transportation by run-off water, which also sorts the particles and ends with their redeposition as **sedimentary rocks.** Much of the outer crust consists of igneous rocks covered by sedimentary rocks. Where intrusive contacts of these two have brought about changes, a third type of rock is formed. This is called **metamorphic rock.**

A special kind of sedimentary deposition is the deposition of vast accumulations of the remains of living organisms, either from the sea or from the surface of the land. Much of the vast amount of limestone and marble (calcium carbonate) arose by the piling up of the skeletons of marine organisms, which were subsequently compacted by the pressure of more layers of sediment and in some cases were changed by the heat of igneous intrusions. Coal and petroleum deposits arose from similar accumulations of plant and animal remains, compacted and protected from weather by subsequent deposits of sedimentary material. Another cause of the selective distribution of minerals is the solvent action of surface and sub-surface water. In some cases a valuable **ore body** (an economically usable accumulation of minerals) has been formed when the ground water dissolved out useless materials from a large area of rock and left the useful part behind. In other cases the useful mineral has been leached out of a tremendously large area by ground water and then deposited by precipitation from solution in a smaller area, which then became the ore body.

## 24-3. Winning of Minerals

Many valuable substances exist in nature in the form in which they are economically useful. In these cases the only problems are to find a deposit of the mineral and to devise a way to obtain it from the earth—that is, to mine it. Gold, diamonds, sulfur, and coal are minerals of this type. Gold occurs almost entirely as "native" —that is, *elemental*—gold, and all commercial production is from such sources. Gold, as its position in the electrode-potential series of Table 21-4 indicates, is a very unreactive element. It has extremely little tendency to form metallic ions and even less to form complex ions; its stable state is therefore the uncombined element. It is formed in igneous rocks of high quartz or silicate content and in ore bodies is almost universally associated with quartz, in which it is present as an "impurity" consisting of threads, flakes, or small chunks of the pure metal. From these primary igneous sources the gold is frequently moved by weathering and sedimentation into deposits of sand and gravel along stream beds. In all gold-producing areas gold is first discovered in these *placer* deposits and is first mined by methods that are some variation on the technique of "panning." This consists of shaking a mass of gravel with water to allow a settling out of the denser parts of the gravel and the washing away of the lighter parts. Since gold has a density of 19.3 grams/cm³ and quartz only 2.6, separation by this method is quite easy. The gold rush in 1849 in California was started by discoveries of placer deposits in the streams of the Central Valley, just west of the Sierra Nevada mountains. These easily worked stream-bed deposits soon gave out, and the substantial gold-mining industry then depended on the location of the "mother lode," where the primary deposits of gold-bearing quartz had been laid down by igneous activity. In the mother lode —the area of the high Sierras east of the Central Valley—great veins and dikes of gold-bearing quartz were discovered and were mined very intensively until quite recently.

Diamonds also occur most commonly in deposits of gravel or clay and are associated with quartz. Their primary formation took place in eruptive masses of igneous rock, where extremely high temperature and pressure allowed pure carbon to crystallize from solution (in molten rock) slowly enough to form fairly large crystals. The mining process is simply some way of sorting the few small crystals of great value from immense amounts of worthless "ground" rock.

Sulfur is formed in several different ways and in some places is associated with volcanic activity. Deposits of sulfur collect in isolated pockets. Sulfur can be formed by the partial oxidation of metallic sulfides or hydrogen sulfide:

$$2H_2S + O_2 \longrightarrow 2H_2O + 2S$$
$$2CuS + O_2 \longrightarrow 2CuO + 2S$$

Elemental sulfur may also be formed by the reduction of metallic sulfates, which is frequently accomplished by living micro-organisms. The major deposits of sulfur are located in the Louisiana-Texas coastal region, where massive layers of nearly pure sulfur, a hundred feet thick, occur at depths of a few hundred feet. The most effective way of mining this sulfur is to drill two wells through the overlying rock, melt the sulfur by piping high-pressure steam down one well, and force the mixture of molten sulfur (melting point about 120°C) and water up the other well.

## 24-4. *Coal*

Coal is quite different from the minerals already mentioned. It is a primary sedimentary rock of living origin. Vast layers of plant material are laid down, and new layers are constantly piled on top of them. The new layers protect the lower layers from oxidation and begin the process of compaction by pressure. Ordinary sedimentary rocks pile on top of this organic deposit and continue the compression over many geologic ages. The original organic material is made up primarily of compounds of carbon and hydrogen, which contain some oxygen, smaller amounts of nitrogen, and traces of sulfur. The several types of coal represent stages in this gradual process of formation. **Peat,** which is not included among the coals because it is hardly compacted at all, can be seen in the process of formation at the present time in bogs in dense woodlands. Peat has a good deal of inorganic soil in it and contains well-recognized, unaltered plant remains. It has little value as fuel but is so used in many areas. The next stage in the process is **lignite,** or brown coal, which is only slightly compacted and changed from the original organic material. If the water it contains —as much as 35 percent—is removed by drying, the dry lignite contains 20–35 percent oxygen and 5–7 percent hydrogen in chemical combination with the residual carbon. **Bituminous coal,** the next stage, is harder than lignite, is more compacted, and contains less oxygen (about 10 percent) and hydrogen (about 5 percent) and no water. The hardest coal, the ultimate stage in the progress of dead plant material toward pure carbon, is called **anthracite.** Hard and lustrous, it contains 85–95 percent carbon, very little volatile hydrocarbon, and virtually no oxygen.

Coal occurs in layered beds varying in thickness from a few inches (not economical to mine) to more than a hundred feet. These beds are often of tremendous lateral extent and occur in many parts of the earth's surface. The shallower beds, within a few hundred feet of the surface, are now mined by stripping off the surface soil and rock and scooping out the coal. Coal is most frequently used as a fuel, as a source of the energy required by our energy-oriented industrial culture, but in recent years it has also been used as an intermediate in the production, by chemical manipulation, of more efficient and more easily transported fuels. Coal has also become increasingly important as a source of material for the synthesis of an almost unlimited number of chemical substances. The starting materials—volatile mixtures of compounds of carbon, hydrogen, oxygen, and nitrogen—are obtained by distillation of the softer coals. Another major use of coal is in the production of coke, which is the residue left after most of the volatile material is driven from certain types of soft coal. Coke is the major component other than iron ore in the making of steel (see § 24-7).

## 24-5. Ore Deposits

Most of the minerals of the earth occur as chemical compounds rather than as free elements—for example, the iron oxides from which pure iron (steel) is obtained, copper sulfides, carbonates, and oxides, and aluminum hydroxide (bauxite). The problem of winning the useful substance, the metal in each case mentioned, is twofold: first the location and mining of the compound ore and then the refining of the ore, by which process the free elemental metal is obtained.

The value of bodies of ore of this type is an economic question rather than a geologic question. If located near steel mills and coal mines, iron-mineral deposits containing less than 50 percent iron are good ore, but deposits containing 60 or 70 percent iron are not usable if the cost of mining or transporting them to steel mills is too great. At Bingham, Utah, where a whole mountain has been cut almost level for the sake of ore that contained less than 1 percent copper, an enormous body of ore and the means of obtaining the copper from the ore were near each other. In northern Michigan, however, huge blocks of pure copper were worthless because they were so difficult to remove from the earth. Bauxite is a worthless rock unless it is associated with a huge source of very cheap electric power.

In a large region near Lake Superior lie some of the greatest deposits of iron ore in the world. The mineral in the most profitable deposits is hematite, $Fe_2O_3$, and it occurs almost pure, in huge ore bodies, in northeastern Minnesota and adjacent areas of Michigan and southern Canada. These bodies of ore probably arose by the leaching of iron oxide out of the general rock over a tremendous area and the subsequent deposition of the almost pure compound in geological troughs of impervious rock. This ore often occurs in a soft, easily crushed form that can be mined by power shovels; transportation by ship to the steel foundries of Ohio and Pennsylvania is readily available, and those foundries are located in excellent coal-producing areas; and, finally, carbonates, the third element in the production of steel, are also available. These factors make the Great Lakes region an ideal steel-producing combination.

## 24-6. Metallurgy

The processes by which metals are produced from their ores date from the beginning of history. Until the nineteenth century and the beginning of rational chemistry these processes were purely arts; little was known of them except that they worked. The ancient art of metallurgy was one of the major sources of the practical lore that made possible the theoretical organization of chemistry as a science: it accumulated the mass of unrelated empirical facts that is a necessary part of the foundation of any science. Modern metallurgy is one of the industrially most important parts of applied chemistry. In this chapter we shall briefly consider three metallurgical processes. Each involves the use of oxidation-reduction reactions to produce the free metal; the metal is reduced from the positive valence that it has in the compound of the ore to the zero valence of the free elemental state.

## 24-7. Steel Production

The iron ore of the Lake Superior region is mixed with coke obtained from the Pennsylvania and Ohio coal fields and with limestone ($CaCO_3$) or iron carbonate. The mixture is loaded into a blast furnace, which is a tall cylinder (up to 150 feet tall) built so that preheated air can be forced in at the bottom and up through the mineral charge. As the air, heated to about 1,500°C, enters the bottom, some of the coke burns to carbon dioxide and carbon monoxide. The carbon dioxide is then reduced by the coke to carbon monoxide:

$$2C + O_2 \longrightarrow 2CO$$
$$C + O_2 \longrightarrow CO_2$$
$$CO_2 + C \longrightarrow 2CO$$

The hot carbon monoxide then reduces the iron oxide ($Fe_2O_3$) to elemental iron:

$$Fe_2O_3 + 3CO \longrightarrow 2Fe + 3CO_2$$

An excess of carbon monoxide is needed to drive this reaction to completion, and a good deal of hot carbon monoxide therefore escapes from the top of the blast furnace. This is used as a fuel to preheat the air that enters the bottom. It is possible to operate the furnace continuously by this use of the excess carbon monoxide and by continuous additions of iron ore and coke at the top. The function of the carbonate is to neutral-ize any silicates that are present in the ore. Since the silicates are acidic and the carbonates basic, the two react to form a neutral slag of waste products. The temperature of the furnace is high enough to keep the iron molten; the metal, because of its high density, settles to the bottom of the furnace and can be tapped off. The molten slag, after the iron has been removed, can also be tapped off.

The product of a blast furnace, called pig iron, still contains considerable impurities of carbon, silicon, sulfur, phosphorus, and a few other metals. It can be cast, but it is rather brittle and is of little use as such. To make steel, one must reduce the impurities by any of several methods, including the open-hearth, Bessemer, and crucible processes, all of which reoxidize the impurities by atmospheric oxygen while the pig iron is molten. Various types of steel are produced when the impurities are reduced to various low levels, and various alloys are produced when definite amounts of various other elements are introduced. The basis of all types of steel is very nearly pure iron; the minor constituents are controlled to give particular properties.

## 24-8. Copper Production

The production of copper metal from its ores varies greatly with the type of ore. Low-grade ores, such as those of Bingham, Utah, require a preliminary concentration. The rock is crushed, and the fragments are sorted by "flotation," the ore-bearing fragments being saved and the worthless rock discarded. The concentrate is then used as the charge in the **smelting** process. The compounds are usually copper sulfides, which are reduced by roasting in air and by a treatment similar to the Bessemer process of steel production. The sulfur of the copper sulfide is oxidized to sulfur dioxide, and the free elemental copper is left:

$$Cu_2S + O_2 \longrightarrow 2Cu + SO_2$$

If the ore is a mixed sulfide of copper and iron, the iron (which is waste in copper refining) is converted to iron silicate by the silica present in the waste rock. The iron and other silicates are discarded as slag. The sulfur dioxide escapes as a gas and is usually caught and converted to sulfuric acid by further oxidation to sulfur trioxide, $SO_3$, and reaction with water. The copper from this process, about 99 percent pure, is called blister copper because of the bubbly form given it by the escaping gas. It is cast into slabs, which are used as the anodes in the electrolytic refining process described in § 21-2. In this process the copper atoms go into solution at the anode—

$$Cu \longrightarrow Cu^{+2} + 2e^-$$

—and are deposited on the cathode by the reverse half-cell reaction. The copper so deposited, called *electrolytic copper,* has less than 0.01 percent impurities. This high purity is ensured by maintaining the cell potential at such a point that copper is the *only* metal plated. Elements of higher electrode potential, such as iron, remain in solution; those of lower potential, such as silver, gold, and platinum, never go into solution and fall to the bottom of the anode part of the cell as sludge. This anode sludge, of great value because of its precious metals, contributes greatly to the economical operation of copper refineries.

## 24-9. Aluminum Production

Aluminum is the most abundant metal in the earth's crust; yet, until the end of the nineteenth century, metallic aluminum was a chemical curiosity of great price and rarity. Its position in the activity series (Table 21-4) shows that reduction of the ion to the free element is extremely difficult, and all attempts at chemical reduction on a commercial basis have failed. The successful process, mentioned on page 350, is an electrolytic reduction according to the half-cell reaction

$$Al^{+3} + 3e^- \longrightarrow Al$$

From this equation it is apparent that it requires three faradays of electricity to reduce one mole of aluminum, or 10,700 coulombs per gram. Cheap electric power is therefore the first requisite for the successful economic operation of the process. The second is an adequate solvent for aluminum ores in the electrolytic cell. Water

would not do, obviously, since the electrode potential for the reduction of aluminum is well above that for the decomposition of water; the only result of an attempt to electrolyze a water solution of an aluminum compound would be the decomposition of water.

This problem was solved in the 1890's by an American chemist, Charles Hall. His process depends on the use of another salt of aluminum as a solvent for the principal ore, which is bauxite, aluminum hydroxide contaminated with iron oxide. Originally molten cryolite, a mixed fluoride of aluminum and sodium ($Na_3AlF_6$), was used as the solvent; modern operation replaces cryolite, which is not widely available, with a mixture of aluminum fluoride, $AlF_3$, and sodium fluoride, $NaF$. The mixed fluorides are placed in a carbon-lined iron box, which acts as the cathode; an electric arc between this cathode and the carbon anode melts the fluorides. The bauxite ore, which has been purified by removal of iron compounds and dehydrated to the oxide—

$$2Al(OH)_3 + heat \longrightarrow Al_2O_3 + 3H_2O$$

—is then added to the molten fluorides and immediately dissolves. Under the influence of the cell potential (maintained at about five volts) the $Al^{+3}$ ions migrate to the cathode, which makes up the bottom of the cell, and are there reduced. Oxygen gas is liberated at the anode as the other decomposition product of the aluminum oxide. The electrolyte is maintained in the molten state (about $1,000°C$) by the electrical heating of the cell, which has a fairly high resistance. This process, in an age when electrical power is a major commodity, has, in a few decades, converted aluminum metal from a rarity into a commonplace.

## 24-10. Petroleum

Coal provided the basic energy of the Industrial Revolution, and in the middle of the twentieth century it still supplies well over half of the energy used throughout the world. But through the last half century its importance as a fuel has decreased steadily, its place being taken largely by petroleum and partly by natural gas. The probability is that petroleum and natural gas will dominate as the major energy sources of our industrial system for many decades to come. Furthermore, the use of these two mineral resources, like that of coal, as sources of materials other than fuels, is constantly increasing.

**Petroleum** (rock oil) and natural gas are always found together and are always found in sedimentary rocks. The origin of oil and gas is, ultimately, the decomposition of ancient living matter. There is still argument among geologists and chemists as to whether it is formed from plant or animal remains. In either case, the source is most likely micro-organisms whose remains have accumulated in the marine ooze at the bottom of ancient seas. The organic matter is there incorporated into the general sediment, and the whole is compacted by the pressures of layer upon layer of accumulating sediment. These layers protect the organic matter from oxidation by the air and contribute to the changing of the substances from highly oxygenated living matter to the **hydrocarbons** (compounds of hydrogen and carbon only) that make up petroleum and natural gas. It is quite probable that bacteria contribute to this deoxidation of the organic matter in the ooze.

The process of compaction continues until the ooze is transformed into the rock called *oil-bearing shale*. Except in a few regions, including wide areas of the western United States, oil-bearing shales are of no economic value as sources of petroleum. Other geologic processes must bring about the conditions that give rise to usable oil "pools." **Oil pools** are not actually caverns filled with oil but are porous rock formations in which oil can accumulate and through which oil can flow. There must also be an impervious cap rock above the porous pool rock to prevent the oil and the gas from escaping. In general, then, the formation of an oil deposit requires a large area of source rock in which the organic matter was originally deposited, above this a porous pool rock into which the oil can rise or be forced by ground water (petroleum has a density of from 0.6 to 0.85 grams/cm³ and is therefore forced upward by ground water, which has a density of 1.0), and above the pool an impermeable cap rock. Since these conditions

are well known, it is possible to predict with some accuracy which areas are likely to contain petroleum and which certainly do not. The major oil-producing areas of the world are the Persian Gulf area, the southwestern United States, Venezuela, and the Caucasus region of the Soviet Union. These areas account for most of the current production and for 45, 30, 10, and 10 percent, respectively, of the known reserves.

The removal of the oil from the earth, once a deposit is located, requires drilling through the cap rock a series of holes (wells) through which the oil may be forced by the pressure of the fluid in the pool. Sooner or later, however, the pressure becomes insufficient, and the oil must be pumped out. The oil removed from the well is usually a dark, viscous, foul-smelling liquid, which contains hundreds of different compounds. To be useful in our industrial system, this mixture must be separated, not into individual compounds, but into mixtures of more limited composition having usable properties. This process of making petroleum usable takes place in the oil refineries, to which crude petroleum may be shipped from halfway round the world.

## 24-11. *Refining of Petroleum*

Petroleum, we have seen, is a mixture of a large number of hydrocarbon compounds. One class of hydrocarbons have the general formula $C_nH_{2n+2}$. The simplest of these is methane, $CH_4$; the next is ethane, $C_2H_6$; then come propane, $C_3H_8$, and butane, $C_4H_{10}$, and so on up to molecules having more than fifty carbon atoms and correspondingly large numbers of hydrogen atoms (102 for the $C_{50}$ compound). This group of compounds have the generic name **paraffins.** Another class of hydrocarbons, called **olefins,** contain smaller percentages of hydrogen and have the general formula $C_nH_{2n}$. Other classes have even smaller percentages of hydrogen, and still others have such complexities as ring systems, complex branching, and other variations. The major constituents of petroleum are paraffins and, to a lesser extent, olefins. The chemical properties of these compounds vary only minutely, and the physical properties, such as viscosity, boiling point (or volatility), and physical state (solid, liquid, or gas) vary systematically with the molecular weight. The lower members of each series, up to about four carbon atoms, are gases; these compounds make up natural gas, are dissolved in petroleum to a sizable extent, and are produced in great quantities in the process of refining oil. The next higher members, from about $C_5$ to $C_9$, are volatile liquids and make up the currently most valuable part of petroleum, gasoline. Above these, up to about $C_{18}$, are the constituents of fuel oil and Diesel oil; around $C_{20}$ are lubricating oils of various viscosities; and above these are the compounds that make up such materials as heavy greases, petroleum jelly (Vaseline), paraffin wax, tar, and asphalt.

The refining of petroleum consists, then, of separating these compounds into the useful fractions, for the most part by the process of **fractional distillation,** in which the crude petroleum is heated until the volatile materials are vaporized through a tall heated tower. The most volatile substances (of low molecular weight) rise through the tower, whose temperature is lowest at the top and highest at the bottom, and are piped off from the top. The next higher-boiling fraction (of higher molecular weight) is condensed and piped off some distance below the top, where the temperature of the column is higher. Taps are made at various levels, depending on the fraction wanted, until at the bottom the least volatile material, the asphalt or tar, is removed as a non-volatile residue. The most valuable fraction, and the one most used in our economy, is gasoline, which makes up only one quarter or less of the whole petroleum mixture. It is possible, by recently developed methods, to convert almost all of this mixture to the most desirable substances, those of intermediate molecular weight. By the first of these two new methods, called **cracking,** the substances of high molecular weight are broken down into smaller molecules by passing over catalysts at very high temperatures and pressures. By the second method, called **alkylation,** molecules of low molecular weight combine to form compounds having molecular weights in the gasoline range. This also is a catalytic process, carried out at high temperature and starting either with natural gas, the most volatile fraction of petroleum, or with the products of the cracking process that have very low molecular weights.

An interesting reversal in the production of motor fuels has taken place over the last several decades. When petroleum was first used to a large extent, in the early part of this century, the most valuable components were kerosene (about $C_{10}$–$C_{15}$) and fuel oil. With the development of the gasoline engine and the tremendous expansion of its use in automobiles and airplanes, the whole petroleum industry concentrated on the production of the most and best gasoline. Kerosene became an almost worthless by-product. This development reached its peak in World War II. Immediately afterward, in the late 1940's, the jet engine began to dominate in military aircraft, and it is now taking over all aircraft. It turns out that the best fuel for a jet engine is kerosene. It has also developed that some rocket fuels are based on kerosene. So now the petroleum industry is reversing itself to increase the production of kerosene and is even exploring ways in which the $C_5$–$C_{10}$ compounds of gasoline can be converted to the $C_{10}$–$C_{15}$ compounds of kerosene.

## 24-12. Petrochemicals

Although the primary usefulness of the organic mineral deposits, coal, petroleum, and natural gas, has been from the beginning, and still is, as fuels, as the supply of energy that keeps our industrial system in operation, a by-product of the refining of these minerals has steadily been growing in importance. As we said above, in connection with the use of coke in steel manufacture, much of the carbonaceous material of coal consists of hydrocarbons that are removed by distillation in the production of coke. Part of this material comes off as volatile liquids and another part as a viscous black substance called **coal tar.** For over a century these fractions of coal have been investigated by chemists. The volatile liquids have long been used as solvents, as liquid fuels, and for other economically low-grade purposes. The coal tar has become more and more valuable as a source of many different chemicals that are used as starting materials in the synthesis of organic substances. The range of these synthetic substances is extremely broad, from aspirin to plastics, from nylon to artificial rubber, from vitamins to TNT, from weed-killers and insecticides to household cleansers. Each of these materials is an *organic* compound—that is, a compound of carbon and hydrogen with small amounts of oxygen, nitrogen, or other elements. Their synthesis generally starts with molecules made up of half a dozen or so carbon atoms and ten or fifteen hydrogen atoms and very rarely an oxygen atom or a nitrogen atom. These rather simple molecules are modified by controlled reactions that generally increase the size as well as the complexity of the molecule by the introduction of new atoms and the rearrangement of the old atoms. The branch of applied chemistry that is concerned with the winning of the starting materials for these syntheses from coal and petroleum is called **petrochemistry,** and the substances obtained from the organic minerals and delivered to the synthetic chemical industry are called **petrochemicals.**†

Originally coal tar was the major source, indeed the only source, of industrially significant amounts of the simple organic compounds used in synthesis, and the organic compounds first synthesized from these materials were dyes. The older lore of synthetic chemistry is therefore associated with the "coal-tar dyes." In fact, however, no pigment of any value is isolated directly from coal tar; the relation between coal tar and the magnificent colors that are now a commonplace of the textile industry is no more than the relation between a cheap, simple, crude starting material and the complex, highly valued, *synthetic* final product. Bituminous coal is still the major source of one type of organic starting material, but there is no logical distinction among coal, oil, and natural gas as sources of the raw material of the tremendous modern chemical industry.

The use made of a particular sample of or-

---

† This term, which is now part of technical terminology, is perhaps unfortunate. From its etymology it should mean "rock chemicals" rather than "petroleum chemicals."

ganic mineral is determined by economic factors. If the demand is greatest for heating fuels, then natural gas, the volatile by-products of petroleum cracking and distillation, and the volatile by-product of coke manufacture will be used as fuels. If the demand is greatest for liquid motor fuels, a large part of these substances will be converted to gasoline. If the demand is greatest for synthetics, the substances will be used as sources of starting materials. Obviously, there is never a complete concentration of these substances in any one of the possible uses. But the demands and the consequent values in one use may greatly influence prices and availability in the others.

## 24-13. *Synthetic Chemistry*

The petrochemical industry depends chiefly on the synthetic chemical industry as a market for its products. And the synthetic chemical industry was started, and the demand for petrochemicals was thereby created, a little more than a century ago. The whole thing began when, in 1856, William Henry Perkin made the first synthetic dye. At that time most of the systematizing concepts of chemistry that we have been studying had not yet been developed, and the great complexities of organic chemistry resulting from the structural relations among the many atoms of the typical organic compound were hardly realized. Intense experimentation revealed many facts and relations, but the concepts that would organize these facts into a science were still lacking. Organic chemistry did not become an organized science for two more decades.

One of the major chemical interests during the second quarter of the nineteenth century was the analysis and attempts at synthesis of naturally occurring organic compounds. Compounds were isolated from a host of sources: plant pigments, poisons, medicinals, foods, and many others. First the empirical formulas were determined and then the molecular weights and thereby the true formulas. Because the structural complexities were not realized, the attempts to synthesize these complex molecules were often naive. Most such attempts were never formally reported, in fact, because nothing came of them. But a few attempts achieved spectacular—though unexpected—results. One of these was the dye *mauveine.*

In 1853, at the age of fifteen, W. H. Perkin entered the newly founded Royal College of Chemistry in London. The director of this institution, which was the major force in the training of chemists in Britain, was a German chemist, A. W. von Hofmann, who had been interested for some time in a nitrogen-containing compound obtained from coal tar and named *aniline* ($C_6H_8N$). Hofmann had suggested that it might be possible, and certainly would be of value, to synthesize the anti-malarial drug quinine ($C_{20}H_{24}N_2O_2$) from aniline or a compound ($C_{10}H_{13}N$) related to aniline and also obtainable from coal tar. Perkin had proved to be a very apt student; by the age of seventeen he had become the assistant to the great Hofmann and seemed well on the way to a spectacular career of pure research in organic chemistry. During the Easter vacation of 1856 he attempted the synthesis of quinine. He reasoned that the oxidation of two molecules of the $C_{10}$ compound might cause them to combine and produce quinine by the elimination of a molecule of water:

$$2C_{10}H_{13}N + 3O \longrightarrow C_{20}H_{24}N_2O_2 + H_2O$$

It is not at all surprising that this synthesis failed; the basic rationale of the experiment was fantastic in the light of modern knowledge of the extremely complicated structure of the quinine molecule. But what did come of these efforts was a small amount (about 5 percent yield) of a purple dye, which Perkin first called aniline purple and later called mauve or **mauveine.**

Much against the protests of his teacher, Hofmann, young Perkin, at the age of eighteen, decided to abandon his scientific career and formed the first company for the manufacture of synthetic dyes. The coal and coke industries were persuaded to increase the output of aniline and other petrochemicals, and in this way both the petrochemical industry and industrial synthesis arose from the discovery of mauveine. Perkin's venture into industry was spectacularly successful; although at first the new dye cost a little more than platinum (about $500 per pound), it

was accepted immediately and used in great quantity—so great, in fact, that the period became known as the "mauve decade." The price fell steadily with greater efficiency in production and in ten years was less than fifty cents per pound. After making a fortune by this venture, Perkin retired, at the age of thirty-six, and continued his career in research. His success stimulated others to produce more and better dyes and to synthesize other interesting and valuable chemicals on an industrial basis.

The early development of the synthetic chemical industry took a rather peculiar turn, which has had powerful sociological, economic, and political implications right up to the present time. Germany, for some time, had been the center of learning and training in pure chemistry, and she had a beginning chemical industry. As industrial synthesis, which had started with dyes, proceeded immediately to synthetic perfumes, drugs, explosives, and other substances, the German government did everything possible to encourage expansion of chemical industry and research. Hofmann was enticed back to Germany in 1864 with the offer of two very attractive professorships. Chemical research was subsidized, favorable economic and trade policies were adopted, and new industries were encouraged. Of the thirteen major chemical-manufacturing companies in Germany in 1914, the ten largest had been started as dye manufacturers between 1862 and 1880. At the same time, the policies of the British, French, and American governments were just the opposite. All financial policies were designed to aid the textile industries and the production of dyes from natural sources. The result of this policy was that by 1900 more than 95 percent of the world's dye market and an even greater percentage of the market for other synthetic organic chemicals, which naturally developed as outgrowths of the synthesis of dyes, were controlled by German industry. When World War I started, Germany was more than self-sufficient in the production of dyes and—what was even more important—in the production of munitions and other synthetics. During that war, however, the American and British chemical industries were greatly developed and encouraged, and in large part the German monopoly was broken. Then, in the years between the two great wars, German industry made a powerful effort to regain its dominance by the formation of a huge cartel of chemical industries with wide international involvement. This cartel is called the *Interessen-Gemeinschaft für Farbenindustrie,* which means partnership of dye-industry interests, and is popularly known as I. G. Farben. The effort was partially successful but was countered by the formation of an opposing British cartel called Imperial Chemical Industries and in the United States by an extremely robust free enterprise in the chemical industry.

In the latter part of the nineteenth century many thousands of new compounds were synthesized in efforts to make new dyes. Most of these compounds were useless as dyes, but several hundred were extremely successful. Most of the naturally occurring dyes were synthesized, and during the twentieth century dyes from natural sources (plant and animal tissues mostly) have been entirely supplanted by synthetics. But of much greater significance than even the huge dye industry has been the expansion of the techniques and theoretical knowledge of organic chemistry in all other fields. In the decades immediately following Perkin's discovery the rational, theoretical basis of organic chemistry was laid, a development that was greatly advanced by the information gained by the frankly profit-motivated search for new synthetic compounds.

## 24-14. *Nitrogen Cycle*

Compounds of nitrogen play a leading role in several aspects of our chemical culture. The very important class of foods called *proteins,* which are the basic substance of all living things, contain nitrogen as well as carbon, hydrogen, and oxygen. As we pointed out in the previous section, many interesting and valuable compounds are made from petrochemicals by the introduction of nitrogen atoms into the molecule. Almost all the conventional explosives, including trinitrotoluene, nitroglycerine (the active component of dynamite), and nitrocellulose (the active component of guncotton), are compounds of nitrogen. The fact that many nitrogen-containing compounds are so unstable, or so "energetic," as to be explosive is related to the fact that molecular nitrogen, $N_2$, is a very *stable* compound, and related to both of these facts is the great difficulty of obtaining nitrogen in a usable form even though unlimited quantities of $N_2$ are available in high concentration (about 80 percent) in the atmosphere.

There are sizable quantities of nitrogen circulating throughout our chemical system. All living organisms contain a significant percentage of nitrogen—about 10 percent of the dry weight of animal tissues and a slightly lesser percentage of the dry weight of plant tissues. The nitrogen in these living tissues remains in a more or less closed cycle. Plant tissues are eaten by animals; part of the nitrogen of the plant is incorporated into the animal tissue; part is excreted and thereby fertilizes the soil; ultimately, when the animals die, the whole substance of their bodies returns to the soil, and the nitrogen becomes available for incorporation into new plant tissues. These changes are called the **biological nitrogen cycle.** But nitrogen is lost from this cycle: some of the nitrogen compounds are prevented by artificial means from returning to the soil for re-use; some soil bacteria convert nitrogen compounds, which are usable by plants, to free molecular nitrogen, which escapes into the atmosphere and is not usable; some nitrogen is lost through the synthetic chemical industry. All explosives are made from nitrogen in the "usable" form; when they are consumed, their nitrogen is converted into the unusable form of molecular nitrogen, $N_2$. The same degradation to the lowest energy form is the ultimate fate of the nitrogen in other synthetic compounds.

It is quite apparent from the above discussion that the continued existence of our culture, indeed even the continued existence of life, depends on the introduction into the nitrogen cycle of new **fixed nitrogen** in usable forms to make up for the losses. Two natural sources (minerals) furnish huge amounts of nitrogen to make good this imbalance of accounts. The first of these is the mineral deposits of nitrates, saltpeter ($KNO_3$) and Chile saltpeter ($NaNO_3$), which are mined to the extent of 250,000,000 tons per year. These two compounds are used chiefly as fertilizers (introducing nitrogen into the soil for plants to incorporate into foods) and to make nitric acid, which is then used in the synthetics and explosives industries. The second major mineral source is nitrogen-containing petrochemicals. Both sources arose ultimately from living tissues. The origin of coal and oil, from which petrochemicals are derived, has already been discussed. The deposits of nitrates arose from the weathering of huge deposits of animal excreta, notably guano. Our resources of both of these minerals are, of course, limited, and the conservation of our culture depends upon some system of reversing the losses to the atmosphere— that is, of converting molecular nitrogen, $N_2$, back to the more energetic and therefore usable forms of nitrogen. Such processes are called the **fixation of nitrogen.**

The fundamental problem is the conversion of nitrogen of oxidation number 0 to other valence states. The common oxidation states of nitrogen in its compounds are $+5$ (as in nitric acid, $HNO_3$), $+3$ (as in nitrous acid, $HNO_2$), and $-3$ (as in ammonia, $NH_3$). The $+5$ state of nitric acid and the nitrates (see § 7-12) is used in synthetic chemistry and the manufacture of explosives; it also is the form in which nitrogen occurs in the nitrate deposits. The $-3$ state (ammonia) is the form in which nitrogen is incorporated into living tissues and is that of the nitrogen obtained from petrochemicals. These two valence states are readily interconverted by oxidation-reduction reactions, both chemically on an industrial scale and by living plants and micro-organisms. Thus much of the ammonia obtained from petrochemicals is oxidized to nitric acid for use in synthesis. The nitrates can be used directly as fertilizers because plants are able to absorb them from the soil and reduce them to the $-3$ state for incorporation into protein. The oxidation state is thus changed, probably stepwise, between the positive and negative oxidation states without conversion to the intermediate state of zero valence, which is the most stable state. In this way, either the $+5$ or the $-3$ state is available for easy chemical and biochemical use, and both are therefore called **fixed nitrogen** in distinction from the inert molecular form of atmospheric nitrogen.

## 24-15. Biological Nitrogen Fixation

Many organisms are capable of converting amino nitrogen (valence $-3$) to nitrate or nitrite, some are capable of the reverse conversion, and a few are even capable of converting fixed nitrogen to $N_2$. But only two classes of bacteria can convert $N_2$ to fixed nitrogen. One class includes several types of soil bacteria that live on the remains of dead organisms in the soil and convert atmospheric nitrogen to the $-3$ oxidation state of protein. This nitrogen is then oxidized by other organisms to the $+5$ state of nitrate, which can be absorbed by higher plants growing in the soil.

The second type of nitrogen fixation is quantitatively much more important and biologically more interesting. There is a very widely distributed species of rod-shaped bacteria that live in the soil, enter the roots of plants of the legume family, and there form *nodules*. The nodules are essentially clusters of bacteria intermingled with the plant tissue. In this intimate relation the combination of plant tissue and bacteria is able to absorb atmospheric nitrogen, reduce it to the $-3$ oxidation state, and incorporate it into protein of the bacterial and plant tissue. This close interdependence of two organisms in carrying out a reaction neither can accomplish alone is called *symbiosis;* the process is therefore called **symbiotic nitrogen fixation.** Tremendous quantities of atmospheric nitrogen are fixed in this way and introduced into the biological nitrogen cycle. In addition to the nitrogen of the stem and leaves of the plant, large quantities are left in the soil in the bacteria and in the roots of the plant. Thus a crop of legumes is equivalent to a sizable treatment of fertilizer in enriching the nitrogen content of a soil. It has been estimated that a good crop of alfalfa introduces nearly 500 pounds of fixed nitrogen per acre into a soil by this process of symbiotic nitrogen fixation.

## 24-16. Chemical Nitrogen Fixation

Three other processes are continually replenishing the nitrogen of our chemical and biochemical system. One of these is natural, and the other two are artificial.

When an electric discharge passes through $N_2$ gas, some of the electrons of the very stable valence bond of the $N_2$ molecule are knocked out of the molecule. This is the process of ionization by accelerated electrons (see § 18-8). The ionized $N_2$ molecules are in a much higher energy state and are capable of reaction with many substances toward which they are ordinarily inert. When a bolt of lightning passes through the air, we have an electrical discharge on a grand scale, a stream of accelerated electrons passing through $N_2$ gas. Many $N_2$ molecules are ionized, and these are surrounded by oxygen molecules with which they can react. Thus large amounts of $N_2$ gas are converted to oxides of nitrogen and ultimately to nitrates. The nitrates are dissolved from the air by rain drops and fall to the earth, where they increase the supply of available nitrogen. The amount of nitrogen fixed in this way is not easily estimated but must be extremely large. At one time efforts were made to use this process artificially by passing high-voltage electrical discharges through air, but it has never been economically feasible on a large scale.

A much more successful industrial method of fixing atmospheric nitrogen is based on the **Haber process** (discussed in § 23-6), in which ammonia is synthesized directly from the elements, $N_2$ and $H_2$, by use of high pressures, moderate temperatures, and catalysts. The product of this reaction is ammonia, with an oxidation number for nitrogen of $-3$. The ammonia may be used directly in this form but is more generally oxidized to the $+5$ state corresponding to nitric acid or the nitrate salts.

A second industrial process for the chemical fixation of nitrogen is the **cyanamide process,** in which calcium carbide reacts with nitrogen at high temperature to produce calcium cyanamide. The calcium carbide is made by heating lime (calcium oxide obtained from limestone) and coke in an electric furnace. The equations for this process are:

$$CaO + 3C \longrightarrow CaC_2 + CO$$
$$\text{lime} + \text{coke} \longrightarrow \underset{\text{carbide}}{\text{calcium}} + \underset{\text{monoxide}}{\text{carbon}}$$

The calcium carbide thus formed is heated to about 1,000°C in nitrogen gas obtained by the fractionation of liquid air:

$$CaC_2 + N_2 \longrightarrow CaCN_2 + C$$
$$\underset{\text{cyanamide}}{\text{calcium}}$$

The calcium cyanamide reacts with cold water slowly and with steam very rapidly to form ammonia and calcium carbonate:

$$CaCN_2 + 3H_2O \longrightarrow CaCO_3 + 2NH_3$$

Some of the cyanamide produced by this process is added directly to the soil as a source of ammonia, and a small amount is used directly in synthesis, but most is converted to ammonia for chemical use. The annual production of ammonia in the United States is almost two million tons; about three-quarters of this is produced by the fixation of atmospheric nitrogen in the Haber process, and the remainder is divided about equally between the cyanamide process and petrochemical production. Of the total ammonia production, about three-quarters is used directly as fertilizer, and almost one-quarter is converted to nitric acid; only a few thousand tons are used each year directly in synthesis.

## 24-17. *Chemical Energy*

This chapter opened with a discussion of the implements of mankind. Included among these implements, both in the introduction and throughout the discussion that followed, have been the sources of energy. Energy, indeed, is the paramount implement of any culture since the first cultures were formed on the discovery of the use of fire. We have discussed the mining of the useful metals, precious metals, and gems; we have also considered the creation of new implements in the form of synthetic chemicals. Related to both of these activities are the mining and processing of the mineral fuels—our natural energy resource. The whole driving energy of the industrial activities we have described in this chapter, as of all other industrial activities, comes from the mineral fuels. The energy that heats the blast furnaces in steel production and the roasting furnaces in copper refining, the electrical energy for the electrolysis of blister copper and the electrolytic reduction of aluminum, the whole energy of the synthetic chemical industry, the heat to drive the Haber process and the cyanamide reaction, in which inert nitrogen is raised to a usably high energy level—all come from the burning of coal, gas, and oil.†

A moment's thought about our sources of energy leads us to two startling conclusions. First, our energy resources are limited; second, the origin of these resources is biological. There are prodigious amounts of coal and oil still in the earth, and without doubt they will last a long time even at the tremendous rate at which they are being consumed. But, when the existing supplies *are* consumed, *there is no way of replacing them.* Coal and oil are formed by processes that take geologic ages to complete but are consumed at the breathtaking pace that characterizes the present age. Since there seem to be alternative sources of energy that may substitute for these mineral fuels (see Chap. 30), these comments on the limitation of mineral reserves are especially applicable to the inorganic minerals. Clearly, the cultures of future ages must depend on the law of conservation of mass; they will be forced to re-use metals over and over again because our culture will have consumed all the available deposits of minerals. Such a conservation of substance will depend, in turn, on much greater expenditures of energy.

The biological origin of coal and oil has already been pointed out. And, if we examine the relations discussed, we must conclude that all our common sources of energy, from a gas flame to a candy bar, from an electric light to a stick of dynamite, are traceable directly to biological material. Since this is the ultimate source of energy on the surface of the earth, we must ask: "Where do living organisms obtain this energy?" The answer to this question is: "From the sun's radiation." The obvious next question, then, is: "How does the sun produce the energy?" That question must be deferred until Chapter 31; at

this point only the relation of sunlight to terrestrial energy must be faced.

## 24-18. *Photosynthesis*

Carbon dioxide is a small but very important component of the atmosphere, amounting to about 0.03 percent (§ 15-15). In a way roughly analogous to that of molecular nitrogen, it is an energetically degraded substance; compounds of carbon, such as the hydrocarbons and foodstuffs, as well as elemental carbon itself, can be burned to $CO_2$ with the liberation of sizable quantities of energy ($\Delta H$ of reaction). A natural process carried out by green plants reverses this degradation of carbon compounds. This process, called **photosynthesis,** takes place continuously on an unbelievably huge scale and is the mechanism by which, now and in the past, the energy of the sun has been made available to Man.

Green plants, including the higher plants with which we are familiar, the algae, the seaweed of the oceans, and certain green bacteria, owe their characteristic color to chlorophyll. Chlorophyll, a rather complex organic molecule having the formula $C_{54}H_{71}O_3N_4Mg$, is found in small particles in intimate combination with protein in the leaves of higher plants and the cells of microorganisms. This protein-chlorophyll complex not only imparts their color to these plants but also accounts for the remarkable synthetic activity by which they absorb the energy of visible sunlight (see § 25-4 and Fig. 25-11) and use this energy to convert $CO_2$ and water to sugar, starch, and other organic molecules of high potential chemical energy. The equation for this reaction is:

$$6CO_2 + 6H_2O + \text{light energy} \longrightarrow \underset{\text{sugar}}{C_6H_{12}O_6} + 6O_2$$

The exact reverse of this reaction is the chemical process that supplies the energy of all living functions, the oxidation of sugar to water and carbon dioxide:

$$C_6H_{12}O_6 + 6O_2 \longrightarrow 6CO_2 + 6H_2O + \text{energy}$$

One may also obtain heat by burning sugar in oxygen, and the same equation describes the reaction, with the same liberation of energy, about 680,000 calories per mole. The hydrocar-

---

† Electrical energy from water power is an obvious exception to this generalization. But it is still only about 3 percent of the total energy of our industrial system. Atomic energy is also an exception, but this source (see Chap. 30) is still a totally inconsequential fraction of the whole.

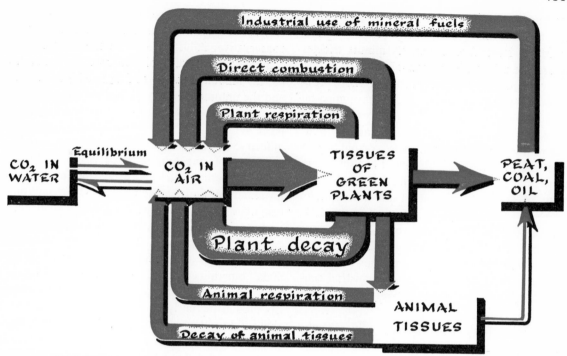

FIGURE **24-1** *Biochemical carbon cycle.*

bons and other organic compounds may also be oxidized in a similar way to produce energy. In each case, burning or **biological oxidation,** we obtain energy by converting the highly organized molecule to $CO_2$; and in each case the potential chemical energy that is made available was introduced into the complex organic structure by the mediation of the chlorophyll of a living plant between the $CO_2$ of the atmosphere and the energy radiated to the earth from the sun.

The magnitude of the photosynthetic conversion of $CO_2$ to the complex organic molecules that make up the substance of plant tissues is almost unbelievably large. It has been calculated that an average acre of land on the earth's surface supports plant growth that converts *two tons* of $CO_2$ per year in this way; this is equivalent to about 500 tons per square kilometer of land surface. And, since there are about $150 \times 10^6$ square kilometers of land surface on the earth, this amounts to a total of *75 billion* tons of substance per year, with the attendant energy, absorbed from the atmosphere by land plants each year. This quantity is stupendous, but it is only a fraction of the total photosynthetic pro-

duction. It is not easy to calculate the average fertility of the surface of the ocean, but it is known to be several times greater than that of the land surface. And there is somewhat more than twice as much ocean surface as land surface on the earth. Thus a careful estimate of the total substance produced by photosynthesis would be several hundred billion tons per year.

But how can this prodigious removal of $CO_2$ from the atmosphere continue year after year through eons of geologic time without totally depleting the atmosphere of $CO_2$? The answer is again, obviously, that a cycle is in operation, that $CO_2$ is returned to the atmosphere as rapidly as it is removed by photosynthesis. This cycle is diagramed in Figure 24-1, the width of the arrows indicating very roughly the magnitude of the various processes. Most of the *fixed carbon dioxide* is returned to the atmosphere directly by decay of plant tissues; sizable amounts of organic substance are consumed by the oxidation that produces the energy for the growth and functioning of living plants and living animals; considerable amounts of $CO_2$ are returned to the atmosphere (and energy is made available) by the direct combustion of plant tissues. It is noteworthy, though, that the greatest single factor in this process is forest fires. Relatively minute trickles of organic substance are converted to coal and oil by the processes discussed earlier. These processes may still be going on, as they have gone on through past geologic ages, but they cannot be a sizable quantitative factor. The use of mineral resources derived from these organic deposits as fuels in industry and general heating, however, is a considerable contribution to the stability of the $CO_2$ content of the atmosphere. There is some evidence, in fact, that the $CO_2$ concentration is raised slightly by the tremendous amount of fuel consumed in highly industrialized and highly populated areas: it is known that the $CO_2$ content of the air near large industrial centers is slightly greater than the average.

The accomplishments and capabilities of the synthetic chemical industry are little short of marvelous. New materials of better quality, greater complexity, and more varied usefulness are constantly being produced by the chemists. Chemists cannot quite make a silk purse out of a sow's ear even though they did, some years ago, accomplish the transformation to a *nylon* purse; it takes a silkworm to make the silk. And this is exactly the point at which synthetic chem-istry suffers by comparison with the syntheses carried out by living tissues. Biosyntheses are conservative; industrial applied chemistry is, by comparison, wasteful of our resources. Plants use the unlimited supply of $CO_2$ and $N_2$ in the air and the unlimited energy of sunlight. Animal tissues use these same sources indirectly to accomplish syntheses. The whole synthetic chemical industry, on the other hand, is based on the consumption of our limited resources of organic minerals, both as fuel and as starting materials. Extremely optimistic chemists view our natural resources as of hardly more than incidental importance. They feel that the synthetic industry can make substitutes for all of our naturally occurring substances, that atomic energy will make our mineral fuels unnecessary. On the other hand, extremely pessimistic conservationists predict the early doom of our industrialized civilization unless we immediately begin to conserve our resources of mineral metals, mineral fuels, natural water supply, forests, etc. Neither extreme view is wholly tenable; but it is certain that only a combination of carefully managed industrial synthesis, reasonable conservation programs, and continued biosynthesis of energy-rich nitrogen and carbon compounds will prevent the substantial and energetic degradation of the earth.

## Concepts and Terms

Composition of the Earth
   crust
   atmosphere
   sea
   distribution
Ores
   coal
   sulfur
   gold
   diamond
   iron
   copper
   aluminum
Metallurgy
   steel
   copper
   aluminum

Petroleum
   hydrocarbons
   refining
   fuels
   petrochemicals
Synthetic Chemistry
Nitrogen Cycle
   fixed nitrogen
   symbiotic nitrogen fixation
   cyanamide process
   Haber process
Photosynthesis
   carbon cycle
Conservation

# Problems

**24-1.** In Table 24-1, whose data are expressed as percentages of total mass, hydrogen is the ninth most abundant element of the crust, sea, and air; if the percentage composition of the earth is expressed in *moles*, hydrogen becomes the third most abundant element. Rearrange the table in the order of decreasing abundance in moles.

**24-2.** Iron pyrite, FeS, is called "fool's gold" because it is often mistaken for gold by amateur prospectors. The mistake is natural because pyrite often occurs in tiny, bright-yellow flecks of a metallic luster in masses of quartz crystals. Knowing prospectors for gold are quite pleased to find such pyrite-bearing quartz in placer deposits; they consider it a favorable clue to the location of real gold. Explain their reasoning.

**24-3.** Explain why gold and silver often occur in the native state. Explain why the most primitive cultures and the earliest civilizations possessed artifacts (implements and ornaments) made of gold, silver, and copper even though these elements are extremely rare as constituents of the earth's crust, and why aluminum, the third most common element, was unknown until the nineteenth century and a rarity until the twentieth century.

**24-4.** Bronze is an alloy of copper and tin, both very minor constituents of the earth's crust. Explain why the production of bronze was the first large-scale metallurgical accomplishment of Man.

**24-5.** Steel and aluminum are the major structural metals of our society; both are characteristic of the highly developed technological culture of the last century. Describe the metallurgy of these materials, and explain why their use came late in history.

**24-6.** Discuss the uses of coal and petroleum.

**24-7.** Define the term *ore*. State what factors other than chemical composition determine whether a particular mineral deposit is an ore or not.

**24-8.** The trace constituents of minerals and the by-products of metallurgical operations are often of great economic importance. The anode sludge of the electrolytic refinement of copper has been mentioned. Small amounts of silver often occur in galena, chalcopyrite, and chalcocite ($Cu_2S$).

Two rather interesting economic phenomena may be explained by these facts. (1) The price of sulfuric acid sometimes determines whether or not lead and copper mines and refineries can operate economically. (2) Western senators argued during and after World War II that government support of the price of silver was a necessary defense measure. Explain these two phenomena.

**24-9.** The reduction of iron ore by coke to elemental iron in the manufacture of steel may be formally summarized by the equation

$$2Fe_2O_3 + 3C \longrightarrow 4Fe + 3CO_2$$

(A) How much coke (assume that coke is pure carbon) would be needed to reduce a 50,000 ton shipload of iron ore (assume that the ore is pure $Fe_2O_3$)?

(B) How many tons of steel (assume that steel is pure Fe) would be produced from this amount of ore?

(C) If the coal from which the coke was made was 70% carbon, how much coal, if there were no loss, would be needed to carry out this process?

*Ans.* (B) 35,000 tons

**24-10.**

(A) How many coulombs are needed to produce one ton of aluminum? (One ton = 2,000 pounds = 907.2 kilograms.)

(B) How many hours would it take to produce this amount of aluminum if the cell operated at 100 amperes?

*Ans.* (B) $2.7 \times 10^4$ hours = 3.1 years

(An aluminum plant, obviously, operates thousands of cells at very high currents.)

**24-11.** Describe the nitrogen cycle, including the processes that deplete the supply of fixed nitrogen and the sources of the nitrogen in usable oxidation states that makes up these losses.

**24-12.** In the reaction of photosynthesis (§ 24-18) the production of $O_2$ is at least equal in importance to the fixation of $CO_2$ in organic compounds. The primary photoreaction of photosynthesis, in fact, is the reduction of water to produce molecular $O_2$. It is known that the maintenance of fish in an aquarium requires that the water be aerated by air pumped through in bubbles. If some green aquatic plants are growing in the aquarium, however, and if the whole aquarium gets adequate light, it is not necessary to aerate the water. Explain this fact.

**24-13.** The operation of a space ship or the colonization of the moon requires that an environment suitable to human occupancy be artificially established. Discuss the problems involved in such a project. Consider both energy and substance, their availability in these situations, and their utilization.

## Suggested Readings

1. J. Gilluly, A. C. Waters, and A. O. Woodford, *Principles of Geology*, 2nd edition (W. H. Freeman, 1959), Chap. 21.
2. H. Shapley, Helen Wright, and S. Rapport, *Readings in the Physical Sciences* (Appleton-Century-Crofts, 1948), pp. 199–209 (formation of mineral deposits).
3. W. H. Perkin, "Origin of the Coal-tar Colour Industry," *Journal of the Chemical Society*, Vol. 69 (1896), pp. 596–637.

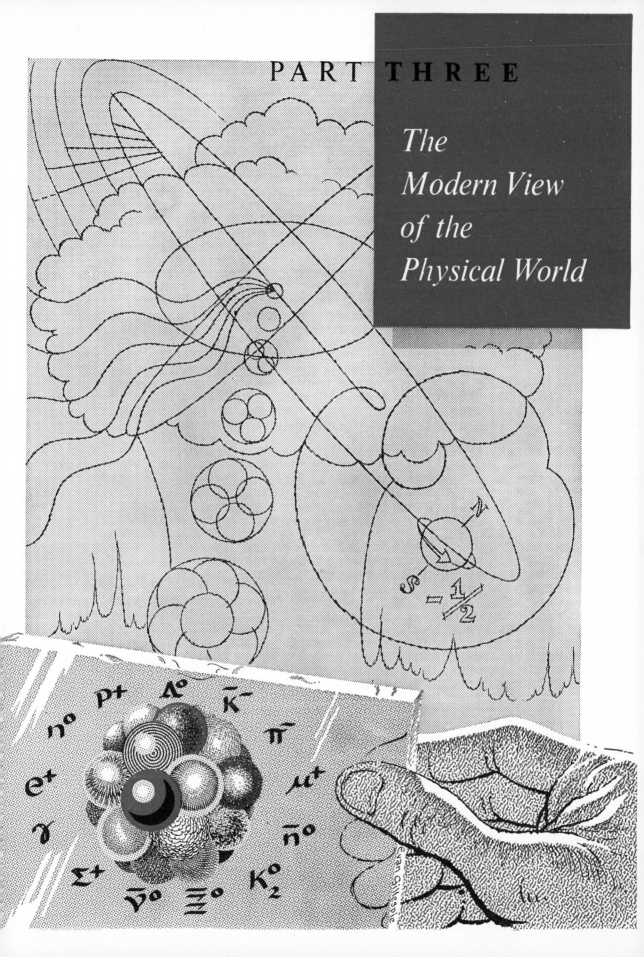

PART THREE

*The
Modern View
of the
Physical World*

THE TERM "modern," applied to science, sometimes means "of the time since Galileo and Newton." More often, however, as in the title of this third part, it means "of the twentieth century." In the decade from 1895 to 1905 the electron, X-rays, and radioactivity were discovered, and the quantum hypothesis and the theory of relativity were formulated. These discoveries and theories and the developments they stimulated have fundamentally transformed physical science. The revolution that took place was not, like that of the seventeenth century, primarily a revolution in method; it was, rather, a revolution in concepts. Fundamental and seemingly self-evident ideas of the physical world were abandoned: mass, length, and time are no longer immutable but change with changing velocity; mass and energy are no longer separate entities but are interconvertible; radiant energy has structure and displays properties formerly attributable only to particles; the atoms, once hard and immutable spheres, are now known to have an extremely complex structure, to be transmutable, and to consist largely of empty space. Disturbing as these concepts may be to our intuition and prejudices, they have been astoundingly successful in explaining the facts of experience and have brought to all of physical science a unity that was not even remotely approached in earlier efforts.

Since many of the new developments arose out of attempts to explain the phenomena of radiant energy, we begin our discussion of the modern view of the physical world by considering light.

THE MOST obvious aspect of light is that it represents the transfer of energy. We sit in the sun and are warmed. The whole earth, similarly, is warmed by the energy of sunlight, without which it would not be a habitable planet. Sunlight supplies the heat of vaporization that forms clouds from the waters of the earth. More subtly, light energy activates the complex reaction of photosynthesis, whereby large amounts of energy are stored in the tissues of growing plants (to be released later through foods and fuels). Also, as we have seen (§ 18-4), light can supply the energy that pulls electrons from the surface of metals. The very process of seeing starts with the stimulation of the nerves of the retina by the energy of the light entering the eye. In all these situations (and many more) energy is emitted by the radiating source, travels through space, and is absorbed by the appropriate receiver. How, then, is this energy transmitted?

## 25-1. Transmission of Energy

There are two ways in which energy may be transmitted through space. One of these we have already considered: Work is done on a material body by the force accelerating it; the body stores up kinetic energy, which it delivers, upon impact, to some distant object. The ionizing energy delivered by a stream of moving electrons is one example. A less important but perhaps more easily visualized example is the following: Suppose we wish to make an object floating in the middle of a pond bob up and down. If we were alongside the object in a boat, we could push it and thus deliver the energy that would start the motion. If no boat were available, we could accomplish the same result by standing on the shore and throwing rocks at the object; and, if our aim and timing were sufficiently accurate, we could maintain the bobbing motion by a series of throws at regular intervals. In situations such as this the energy is transferred by means of the kinetic energy of matter moving across the space between the source and the receiver.

However, as everyone knows, the floating object may be moved by a completely different method. All we need to do is to strike the water

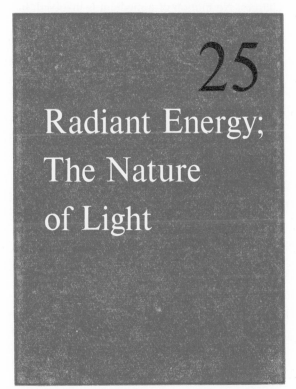

CHAPTER

25

Radiant Energy;
The Nature
of Light

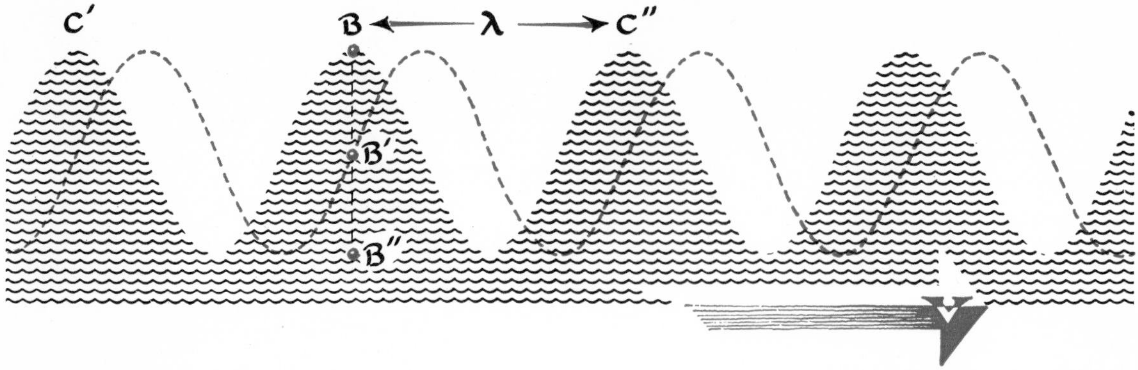

FIGURE **25-1** *Relation between wavelength, frequency, and velocity of propagation of a train of waves.*

at the shore with a paddle. The *waves* thus generated move across the surface of the pond and, on passing the floating object, make it bob up and down. If we strike the water with the paddle at regular intervals, we generate a series of waves, or *train of waves,* which, upon passing the floating object, maintain its bobbing motion. Here, clearly, *energy* is transferred, *but no matter moves from the source to the receiver.* The water moves, to be sure, but *only locally.* The paddle forces some water near the shore to move up and down. This moving water disturbs a neighboring bit, which also begins to move up and down, and this in turn disturbs the next bit, and so on. Thus the energy is passed along from one part of the water to the next as the disturbance moves across the pond. It is the *propagated disturbance* that constitutes the wave and transmits the energy. The water merely serves as a medium for the propagation.

This example makes it clear that periodic motion and wave transmission of energy are intimately related. We considered water waves first because such periodic motion is easily observed. Even if the water were not visible, however, the observed periodic motion of the floating object would be strong evidence of the passing of waves. Waves running along a stretched cord and sound waves passing through an elastic medium are other examples. If one end of a stretched cord is moved up and down, waves are seen to run along the cord and do work on an object at the other end. A vibrating body (such as the vocal cords of a speaker, the sounding board of a musical

instrument) sets up periodic pressure changes in the air around it. Because the air is elastic, these pressure changes are transmitted, and upon arrival at an ear they create periodic stimuli that give rise to the sensation of sound. More subtle is the transmission of electrical energy by radio waves. Here the periodic motion of electrons back and forth along the antenna of the broadcasting station sets up periodic changes in the electric and magnetic fields due to the moving charges. No motion of a medium is involved, but the changing condition of the field is propagated through space, and the wave is detected by the periodic motion of electrons in the antenna of a distant radio. These and other examples of wave motion are fundamentally alike. Some oscillating source sets up a periodic disturbance in its immediate environment. This *disturbance* is propagated from point to point through space and, as it passes an appropriate object, produces oscillations of a material body. Thus *energy* from the source is transmitted through space *without* the actual transfer of material objects.

In the seventeenth century both a particle (corpuscular) theory and a wave theory of the transmission of light energy were proposed. Newton thought of light as a stream of material corpuscles (of unknown character), which, shooting away from the source, carried energy through space. Huygens, Newton's contemporary, thought that light energy was transmitted by waves (also of unknown character). Since both theories adequately explained the optical phenomena known at the time, there were no criteria for choice between them; but Newton's great prestige and the remarkable success of his mechanics led to a general acceptance of the corpuscular theory until the beginning of the nineteenth century. When, at that time, conclusive evidence of the wave nature of light was discovered, the wave theory was revived; and it continued to be developed throughout the nineteenth century. In order to trace this development, we must first discuss some general properties of waves.

## 25-2. *Properties of Waves*

In order to help in visualizing the properties of waves, we shall confine our discussion at first to water waves. It must be remembered, however, that these properties are characteristic of wave propagation in general and therefore of *any* kind of wave. Consider a train of waves moving along the surface of a pond (Fig. 25-1). A floating body, *B*, moves up and down with the water as the waves move past it. A snapshot taken at the instant when *B* is on the crest of a wave shows the situation represented by the rippled lines. A short time later the waves have moved to the right, and a second snapshot shows the waves in the position of the broken line. *B* has now moved down to *B'*. As the waves progress, *B* continues to move down until it is at the bottom of a trough. It then starts to rise and at a certain time is on the crest of the next wave. One cycle has been completed, and the motion just repeats this cycle as succeeding waves move past. While *B* moved down and back up, the crest *C'* moved along to *B*, and the crest originally at *B* moved on to *C''*. Thus, during one complete cycle, the disturbance traveled the distance *BC''*. This distance is called the **wavelength**, $\lambda$ (lambda). The time *B* takes to execute one cycle is called the **period**, *P*, of the wave. Since the wave travels the distance $\lambda$ during *P* seconds, the velocity of propagation, *v*, is $\lambda/P$. The number of cycles per second, called the **frequency**, $\nu$ (nu), of the wave, is clearly $1/P$. The **velocity of propagation** of the wave is, then,

$$v = \lambda\nu \qquad (25\text{-}1)$$

This relation is quite general and applies to any kind of wave.

If the medium transmitting a wave is homogeneous in all directions and is *free of obstacles,* the energy is transmitted along straight lines. This would also be true if the energy were carried by a stream of corpuscles. But, if waves strike an obstacle in which there is a small opening, they display a unique property. The waves bend round the edges of the opening and spread out into the space beyond. A stream of particles, on the other hand, would continue straight on through the opening, just as the electron and ion beams discussed in Chapter 18 do. This characteristic spreading out of a wave as it passes through an opening is called **diffraction** and is displayed by every kind of wave. Sound waves, for instance, when they move through an open door, diffract so that a person in a hall can hear a speaker in the next room even though there is a sound-proof wall between them.

Diffraction is easily observed with water waves. Consider Figure 25-2, in which we are looking down on the surface of water as waves move to the right, from some distant source, toward an obstacle, *S*. The crest of each succeeding wave is represented by a solid line.

Before we go on with our interpretation of the figure, we must say something about the geometrical representation of wave propagation. Everyone knows that water waves from a small source (a "point" source) spread out in concentric circles about the source. If the point source is distant, only a small fraction of the whole circular wave is utilized in any particular observation. As the source becomes more distant, this fraction, becoming smaller and smaller, approaches a straight line. For very distant sources the wave is a straight line. A similar argument applies to the more important cases of energy transmission in three dimensions (sound, radio, and light waves): the waves from a point source are concentric spheres, and at great distances from the source the utilized fraction of the sphere becomes a plane. Hence waves from any distant point source are called **plane waves**.

We also need a way of representing the direction in which energy is transmitted through a medium. As we saw above, water waves from a point source are concentric circles about the source. Energy flows from the source to float-

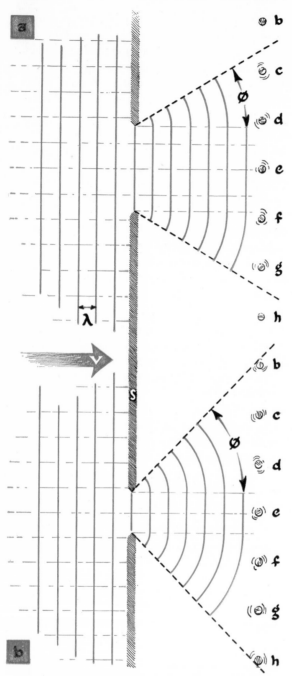

FIGURE **25-2** *Diffraction of plane waves through narrow openings.*

Such a line is called a **ray.** A complete description, of course, would require that the space through which the energy is transmitted be filled with rays; but, as in the case of lines of force (§ 16-6), a few properly chosen rays will represent the situation adequately. The group of rays that represent the flow of energy is called a **beam.** For plane waves the rays are parallel to each other and form a *parallel beam.* For other than plane waves the rays diverge and form a *divergent beam.*

We now return to Figure 25-2a, which diagrammatically represents the *observed* effect. Plane waves strike an obstacle, S, in which there is a small opening. The rays (shown by colored broken lines) are all parallel. Most of each wave is intercepted by S, but a portion of each passes through the opening, and that portion is observed to bend so that the energy spreads out in the region to the right of S. This fanning out (diffraction) of the propagated energy is represented by the divergence of the rays along the edge (black broken line) of the beam. The angle φ is a measure of the *amount* of diffraction of the wave.

Even if the surface of the water were invisible and the waves were therefore not directly observable, the effects of diffraction could be observed. Imagine a row of small corks (b–h) floating on the surface of the water. If there were no diffraction, only d, e, and f would receive energy and move. (This is what would happen if transmission were corpuscular.) But corks c–g are all observed to move; corks c and g, then, must be receiving energy.

If the opening is now made smaller, the angle of diffraction, φ, becomes larger (Fig. 25-2b). This can be observed directly or inferred from the observation that all the corks, b–h, absorb energy and begin to oscillate. As the opening is made still smaller, φ increases; for a very small opening it becomes practically 90°. Thus, as viewed from the right side of S, a very small opening acts like a point source and sends out rays in all directions.

In this discussion of diffraction we have specified that the opening be small. But what is the criterion for smallness? Investigation shows that it is the length of the wave involved. If, for

ing objects along the radii of these circles. Hence the direction in which the energy is transmitted is always at right angles to the wave. A line that is always perpendicular to the waves specifies, then, the *direction of transmission* of the energy.

instance, the impinging waves of Figure 25-2a were longer, the same opening would be *effectively* smaller and $\phi$ would be larger. This is easily demonstrated. The distant source is made to vibrate more slowly (smaller $\nu$). Then, by equation 25-1, $\lambda$ is larger, and the diffracted waves are observed to spread out through a larger angle. This effect is also observed for sound waves. The length in air of the sound wave for middle C on the piano ($\nu = 260/\text{sec}$) is approximately four feet. Since, for this wave, an open door is very small (approximately one wavelength), the sound can be heard 90° away from a direct line through the door. On the other hand, for a sound frequency of 16,000/sec (about the upper limit of audibility) $\lambda$ in air is about ¾ inch. For this wave the open door is very wide (about 65 wavelengths), and in order to hear this sound the listener must stand almost on a direct line through the door to the source. It is this aspect of the effective size of an opening that makes the observation of the diffraction of light difficult. As we shall see, light waves are exceedingly short; for them an apparently narrow opening may be effectively very wide.

Interference is a second unique property of the wave propagation of energy. Consider the situation shown in Figure 25-3. Here only rays are shown (solid lines). Parallel rays (that is, plane waves) from a distant source strike an obstacle in which there are two closely spaced openings, $S_1$ and $S_2$. The openings are so small that the waves diffract through a large angle, and rays are therefore diverging in all directions from both $S_1$ and $S_2$. For the sake of clarity only a few rays are shown in the diagram. The letters $B_1 - B_1'$ mark some of a line of corks floating on the water. If $S_1$ is momentarily closed, waves are observed to diffract out of $S_2$, and all the corks are set into oscillation; this is, of course, a repetition of the situation shown in Figure 25-2b. Similarly, if $S_2$ is closed and $S_1$ is opened, all the corks are observed to oscillate. These two observations show that energy is diffracting out to *all* the corks from *each* opening. If now *both* $S_1$ and $S_2$ remain open, an unexpected result is observed. The cork at $O$ oscillates up and down through a wide amplitude, which shows that it is absorbing a sizable amount of energy. The cork at $I$ oscillates less violently, and the cork at $D_1$ *does not move at all!* Beyond $D_1$ the corks begin to move again: $I_1$ shows a moderate, and $B_1$ a maximum, oscillation. At still greater distances from $O$ the pattern is repeated with a gradual diminution of intensity. An identical pattern is observed on the other side of $O$: corks $I'-B_1'$ show motions identical with those of their counterparts.

Probably the most remarkable aspect of these observations is the lack of motion of $D_1$. From

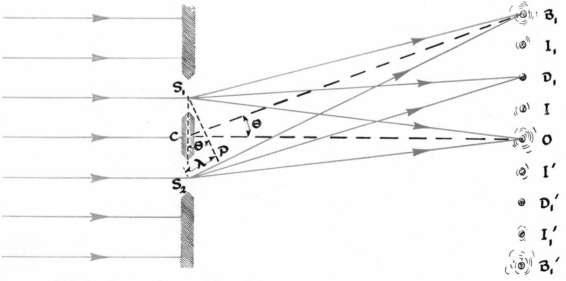

FIGURE **25-3** *Interference of waves diffracted through two openings.*

the first part of the experiment we know that energy is flowing through $D_1$ from *both* $S_1$ and $S_2$. That energy must be flowing in such a way as to produce *no* disturbance at $D_1$. This is impossible if the energy is carried by corpuscles. There is no imaginable way in which *two* streams of particles could arrive at $D_1$ from $S_1$ and $S_2$ and cancel each other's effect. Two trains of waves, however, can do it easily.

Two trains of waves pass the point $D_1$. One train travels along the ray $S_1D_1$ and the other along the ray $S_2D_1$. The two trains must start right "in step"—that is, succeeding crests and troughs leave $S_1$ and $S_2$ simultaneously—because both are diffracted portions of the *same* wave impinging on the left side of the obstacle. But, since the distance $S_2D_1$ is greater than $S_1D_1$, the number of waves that reach from $S_1$ to $D_1$ will not quite reach from $S_2$ to $D_1$. If $D_1$ is situated so that $S_2D_1$ is just one-half wavelength longer than $S_1D_1$, we have the situation shown in Figure 25-4a: when a trough from $S_1$ is at $D_1$, the corresponding trough from $S_2$ has not yet arrived at $D_1$; instead, the preceding crest from $S_2$ is there. Thus the two waves exert equal and *op-*

*posite* forces on $D_1$, and it does not move. Half a period later a crest from $S_1$ arrives, but so does a trough from $S_2$, and the net force on $D_1$ is still zero. Thus the two trains of waves are constantly opposing each other and, as they pass $D_1$, produce no displacement. Either train of waves *alone* would, of course, cause $D_1$ to oscillate. These are the observed effects. This property of waves is called **destructive interference.**

Now consider again the $B_1$ of Figure 25-3. The distance $S_2B_1$ is just one whole wavelength longer than $S_1B_1$. The waves arriving at $B_1$ are therefore "in step," as shown in Figure 25-4b. When a crest from $S_1$ is at $B_1$, the corresponding crest from $S_2$ is still one wavelength away. But the preceding crest is at $B_1$ and reinforces the crest from $S_1$. Thus $B_1$ is acted on with twice the force of either wave alone. One half period later two troughs arrive, then two crests, and so on. Thus the two wave trains continuously reinforce each other, and $B_1$ oscillates through a great amplitude. These again are the observed effects. This property of waves is called **constructive interference.**

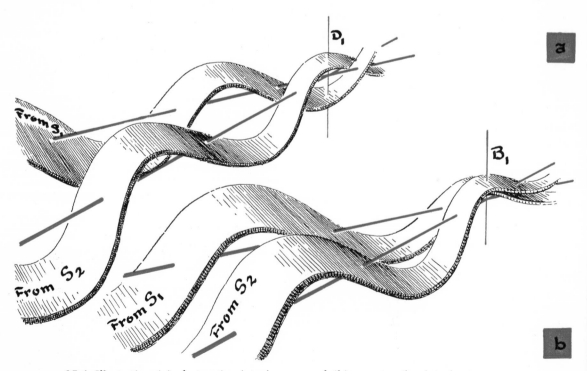

FIGURE **25-4** *Illustrating* (a) *destructive interference and* (b) *constructive interference.*

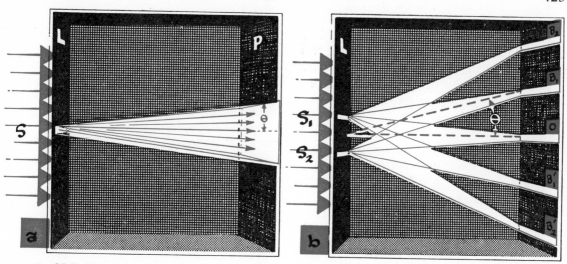

FIGURE **25-5** *Illustrating* (a) *diffraction of light through a single slit and* (b) *interference of light diffracted through two parallel slits.*

In Figure 25-3 the central point $O$ is clearly a region of constructive interference since the distances $S_1O$ and $S_2O$ are exactly equal. The symmetry of the situation indicates that $D_1'$ and $B_1'$ are points of destructive and constructive interference respectively. At intermediate points (such as the $I$'s) the waves are neither completely in nor out of step, and some disturbance is observed. Thus, as the point of observation moves away from $O$, the intensity of oscillation is seen to decrease to zero $(D)$, then increase to a maximum $(B)$, then decrease to zero again, and so on. This pattern of alternate regions of maximum response and zero response is repeated symmetrically on both sides of $O$ as long as the waves from *both* $S_1$ and $S_2$ diffract to the point and produce the appropriate interference.

We have confined our discussion of diffraction and interference to the case of water waves. Such waves are directly observable, and the phenomena of diffraction and interference appear as empirical facts. However, by mathematical reasoning that is too advanced for this book, it can be proved rigorously that these phenomena are fundamental properties of wave motion and thus are general characteristics of any type of wave. It is, then, reasonable to conclude that any transmission of energy that displays these properties must have the character of waves.

Finally, the phenomenon of interference not only establishes the wave nature of the propagated energy but also furnishes a method of measuring the wavelength. Imagine that the surface of the water in Figure 25-3 is not visible but that the motions of the corks are. The observed interference pattern tells us that there is a wave propagation of energy, and the observation of $B_1$ as a point of maximum disturbance tells us that $S_2B_1$ is exactly one wavelength longer than $S_1B_1$. Draw the line $S_1P$ so that $S_1B_1$ equals $PB_1$. Then $S_2P = \lambda$. Let the distance between the openings ($S_1S_2$) be represented by $s$. Then, in the small triangle $S_1PS_2$, we have (see Appendix I)

$$\sin \theta = \frac{\lambda}{s} \qquad (25\text{-}2)$$

From the geometry of the figure we know that angle $B_1CO$ is equal to $\theta$. Thus, from the observed distances $OB_1$ and $CB_1$, $\sin \theta$ is determined; and, since $s$ is directly measurable, equation 25-2 gives the wavelength.

## 25-3. Diffraction and Interference of Light

If light from a narrow and distant source is allowed to pass through a small slit, diffraction is easily observed. In Figure 25-5a the slit, $S$, in an opaque sheet, $L$, is a few tenths of a millimeter wide. In $P$, a receiving screen, which might be the retina of an observer's eye or a photographic plate, either stimulated nerve endings or reduced grains of silver indicate the absorption of energy, just as the floating corks in the discussions of the last section indicated the delivery of energy by the water waves. Parallel rays of light from a distant source falling on $L$ are observed to spread out after passing through $S$. Instead of a sharply defined narrow line of light, a broad band of light is observed on $P$ as shown. If $S$ is replaced by a still narrower slit, the light is observed to diffract through a wider angle—precisely the effect to be expected if light energy is carried by waves (Fig. 25-2). The single slit is now replaced by *two* closely spaced (less than 0.5 millimeter apart) and parallel slits, $S_1$ and $S_2$ (Fig. 25-5b). When either slit alone is open, the screen is continuously illuminated from $B_2$ to $B_2'$; when *both* slits are open, the screen shows a pattern of alternately bright and dark regions. Again this is precisely the result to be expected if the transmission of light energy is by wave propagation (Fig. 25-3). This interference was first observed by Thomas Young about 1800 and was correctly interpreted by him as demonstrating the wave nature of light.

As pointed out in the previous section, interference permits a quantitative determination of the wavelength. Measurements of the situation shown in Figure 25-5b are difficult, however, for two reasons: (1) the angle $\theta$ is very small; (2) since the bright regions are broad and diffuse, the points of maximum intensity are somewhat indefinite.

We overcome the first difficulty by placing the slits closer together. A little consideration of Figure 25-3 will show that, if the distance $S_1S_2$ is made smaller, $B_1$ must be farther away from $O$ in order to fulfill the necessary condition for constructive interference (namely, that $S_2B_1 - S_1B_1 = \lambda$). Thus $\theta$ increases as $s$ decreases; and, if $s$ is sufficiently small, $\theta$ is large enough to be measured easily.

We overcome the second difficulty by using many equally spaced slits instead of only two. Figure 25-6 shows six narrow slits, each sepa-

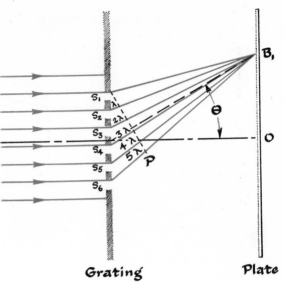

Grating                                Plate

FIGURE 25-6 *Diffraction grating.*

rated from the adjacent one by distance $s$. The distance from any slit to $B_1$ is one wavelength longer than the distance from the slit next above it. Thus all the waves arriving at $B_1$ are in step and by constructive interference produce a bright line on the plate. As in the case of two slits, the line $S_1P$ is drawn so that $S_1B_1 = PB_1$. Then $S_6P = 5\lambda$, and, since $S_1S_6 = 5s$, the sine of $\theta$ is $5\lambda/5s = \lambda/s$. Thus equation 25-2 gives the wavelength for this situation also. With six trains of waves, however, destructive interference occurs at a point much nearer $B_1$ than with only two slits.[†] Thus, as you move away from $B_1$, either toward or away from $O$, the intensity falls quickly to zero, and the bright region becomes more sharply defined. Clearly, the argument will hold for any number of slits. Such an array of many closely spaced slits is called a **diffraction grating.** Gratings used in the student laboratory have approximately 15,000 slits spaced approximately $1.7 \times 10^{-6}$ meter apart. With such a grating $\theta$ is about 20°, and, since

---

[†] This can be proved by methods that are beyond the scope of this book. The effect can be observed, however, if we use first a double slit and then, successively, gratings composed of increasing numbers of identically spaced slits. The distances between the *centers* of the bright regions remain unchanged, but the bright regions become successively narrower. With a very large number of closely spaced slits, the bright regions become so narrow that they appear as sharply defined images of the source.

the bright line at $B_1$ is clearly defined, $\lambda$ may be accurately measured. Gratings with many more slits much more closely spaced, which are used in very precise work, give the wavelengths of light to an extremely high degree of accuracy. (Values reliable to parts per million are not uncommon.)

It has already been mentioned that light waves are exceedingly short. For instance, the characteristic yellow light emitted by glowing sodium vapor, when measured by a diffraction grating, is found to have a wavelength of $5.893 \times 10^{-7}$ meter. A convenient unit for such small lengths is the **angstrom** (abbreviated as A). By definition $A = 10^{-10}$ meter (see Fig. 19-5). For the yellow light of sodium vapor, therefore, $\lambda = 5,893$ A.

## 25-4. *Spectra*

A little consideration of the physical requirements for the production of bright interference lines by a diffraction grating will show that the position of the first bright line, $B_1$ (the "first-order" line), will be farther from $O$ (the "central-order" line) if the wavelength, $\lambda$, is greater. This fact is included in the generalization of equation 25-2 since $\sin \theta$ increases with $\theta$. Hence, if a mixture of different wavelengths passes through a diffraction grating, a bright line will be formed for each, and all will have different positions on the screen. The longer the wavelength the farther from $O$ the line will be formed (that is, the greater $\theta$ will be). Thus a diffraction grating will *disperse* a mixture of wavelengths, form a group of bright lines, and yield data for the measurement of each wavelength present. Such a group of bright lines is called a **line spectrum.** The fact that a certain source emits a characteristic group of wavelengths has great significance.

Line spectra are observed whenever any substance in the gaseous state is excited to luminescence—an event that we can most easily bring about by confining the gas in a tube at low pressure and passing an electric current through it (see Fig. 18-2b). The flame of a Bunsen burner will vaporize and excite some

substances, such as sodium; an electric spark passing between two pieces of the element will do the same for some of the other metals. In all cases, if the source of light is a low-pressure gas, line spectra are observed. The spectrum of a monatomic gas is quite different from that of a polyatomic gas even though the atoms in the molecule are alike. When dispersed by an ordinary grating, the spectrum emitted by a polyatomic gas appears to be a group of bands of light rather than well-defined lines. Each band, however, when produced by an extremely fine grating, is found to consist of many closely spaced lines. The wavelengths of these lines are related in a complicated way. In our discussion, however, we shall be interested primarily in the *atomic spectra* emitted by monatomic gases. Most elements vaporize into monatomic gases. For ele-

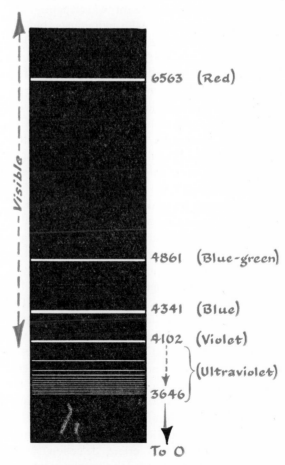

FIGURE **25-7** *Balmer series in the line spectrum of hydrogen.*

ments such as hydrogen the excitation can be made sufficiently energetic to dissociate the molecules, and the atomic spectrum is then emitted. These spectra are characterized by groups of well-defined lines whose wavelengths are simply related.

If the source of light is luminous hydrogen, the lines shown in Figure 25-7 are observed. This represents the neighborhood of $B_1$ on the photographic plate of Figure 25-6. Each line is due to a definite wavelength and its distance from $O$ leads to the numerical value of $\lambda$. The measured $\lambda$'s for some of the lines are given in angstroms. A visual observation of spectra reveals the fact that the sensation of color changes with wavelength. Long wavelengths appear red, and the hue changes through orange, yellow, green, blue, and violet as the wavelength decreases. The human eye is limited in its response to a very narrow range of wavelengths. The range varies somewhat with individuals, but the limits of visibility are approximately 4,000 A (deep violet) and 7,500 A (deep red). Photographic plates (and other devices) respond to other wavelengths also, and thus the range of wavelength "observations" is considerably extended. Wavelengths shorter than about 4,000 A are called **ultraviolet,** and those longer than about 7,500 A are called **infrared.** These arbitrary categories merely indicate, in a general way, the relation of the lines to the visible region.

To return to the hydrogen spectrum shown in Figure 25-7: the lines become closer together as the wavelength decreases, and the group appears to converge toward a definite limit (3,646 A) in the near ultraviolet. Such a related group of lines is called a **spectral series.** Atomic hydrogen has other series than the one shown. The other elements also emit series of wavelengths. The spectra of the heavier elements, however, are very complex, and sorting out their series is a formidable task. Complex as the atomic spectra are, however, it is an astonishing fact that the wavelength series of any element are unique. This fact makes spectra a powerful analytical tool in the laboratories for scientific research, industrial testing, and crime detection. More important, however, are the implications for atomic structure.

The first successful attempt to formulate a relation between the wavelengths of a series was made by J. J. Balmer in 1885. He found that a fairly simple formula would represent all the lines of the hydrogen series shown in Figure 25-7:

$$\frac{1}{\lambda} = \Re_{\mathrm{H}} \left[ \frac{1}{n^2} - \frac{1}{p^2} \right] \qquad (25\text{-}3)$$

Here $n$ and $p$ are integers, and $\Re_{\mathrm{H}}$ is an empirically determined constant whose value is

$$\Re_{\mathrm{H}} = 1.096776 \times 10^7 \text{ meters}^{-1} \qquad (25\text{-}4)$$

This quantity, called the **Rydberg constant,** plays a central role in all spectral-series formulas. The number of significant figures in $\Re_{\mathrm{H}}$ is an indication of the high precision of wavelength measurements.

Balmer found that, if $n = 2$ and $p = 3$, equation 25-3 yields $\lambda = 6,563$ A, which is the first hydrogen line of Figure 25-7. If $n$ is held constant at 2 and $p$ is assigned the values 4, 5, 6, . . . successively, the other lines of the figure are obtained. If $p$ is very large ($p = \infty$), the limit of the series is found to be 3,646 A. In honor of Balmer's contribution, the series of hydrogen lines in Figure 25-7 is called the Balmer series.

In that series $n$ is always equal to 2. It is reasonable that hydrogen should radiate other series in which $n$ has other integral values. A number of such series have been found. Considerable experimental difficulty is encountered in observing the lines since they lie in the far ultraviolet and infrared regions. The series actually observed and named in honor of the discoverers are:

Lyman series (far ultraviolet)
  $n = 1; p = 2, 3, 4, \cdots \infty$
Balmer series (visible)
  $n = 2; p = 3, 4, 5, \cdots \infty$
Paschen series (infrared)
  $n = 3; p = 4, 5, 6, \cdots \infty$
Brackett series (infrared)
  $n = 4; p = 5, 6, 7, \cdots \infty$
Pfund series (far infrared)
  $n = 5; p = 6, 7, 8, \cdots \infty$

We infer that other series exist, but their detection would be extremely difficult. The remarkable simplicity of the Balmer formula, com-

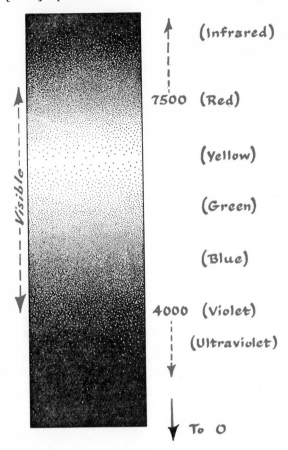

FIGURE **25-8** *Continuous spectrum from an incandescent solid or liquid.*

angstrom, show no break in this **continuous spectrum.** The sources mentioned must emit an infinite number of wavelengths, with values ranging from the ultraviolet into the infrared (Fig. 25-8). In the visible region the familiar rainbow range of colors from violet through red is observed. The ends of the continuous spectrum are not sharply defined but gradually "tail off," indicating an unobservably low intensity rather than an absence of waves. The nature of the spectrum does not depend upon the kind of substance radiating (with minor exceptions due to surface conditions of the radiator) but depends only on its absolute temperature.

An interesting property of continuous spectra is the distribution of the energy among their wavelengths. This property, which, as we shall see, is of great theoretical importance, was investigated during the 1890's by several scientists. The question was: Does a very narrow range of wavelengths in red transmit the same amount of energy as an equal range of wavelengths in blue, and, if not, does the distribution of energy change with the temperature of the radiating source? To answer this question investigators heat the source in a furnace to a known and constant temperature. The radiated light emerges through a small hole in a wall of the furnace and is dispersed into a continuous spectrum. One of the several devices that absorb light energy, convert it into heat, and indicate the amount of energy absorbed per second is mounted be-

pared with the apparent complexity of the series it represents, indicates a correspondingly simple structure in the atoms that account for the radiated spectra. (Notice that here again whole numbers play a central role.) Relations similar to equation 25-3 have been developed for spectral series of atoms other than hydrogen. The Balmer formula is rightly designated as the prototype of all spectral series.

If the radiating source is a hot liquid or a hot solid or even a hot gas under very high pressure, a completely different type of spectrum is produced by the diffraction grating. Instead of a set of discrete lines indicating a finite number of wavelengths, such as those from a luminous gas, a *continuous* band of light, ranging from the ultraviolet to the infrared, is observed. The finest gratings, capable of separating wavelengths that differ by only a small fraction of an

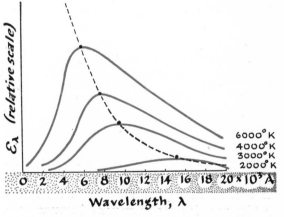

FIGURE **25-9** *Distributions of the energy in the continuous spectra emitted by a hot body at four different temperatures.*

hind a narrow slit at various positions in the spectrum. The position of the slit in the spectrum determines the wavelength carrying the energy absorbed. This energy per unit wavelength ($\varepsilon_\lambda$) is then plotted against the wavelength, $\lambda$, and the curves of Figure 25-9 are obtained. As might be expected, the total energy, $\varepsilon$, transmitted per second by all the waves from one unit area of the radiating source (that is, the area under the curve) increases with rising temperature. A quantitative study of the experimental curves shows that this total energy is directly proportional to the fourth power of the absolute temperature; that is,

$$\varepsilon = aT^4 \qquad (25\text{-}4)$$

if $a = 5.669 \times 10^{-8} \dfrac{\text{joule}}{\text{sec m}^2 \,{}^\circ\text{K}^4}$. In other words, if the temperature of the source is doubled, the radiated energy is sixteen times as large; if the temperature is tripled, the energy is eighty-one times as large; and so on.

All the curves start out with low energy, carried by the short wavelengths; but, as $\lambda$ increases, the energy carried increases up to a maximum value for a definite wavelength ($\lambda_{\text{max}}$) and then decreases (more slowly) with increasing wavelength. Furthermore, the wavelength of maximum energy decreases as the temperature rises. A quantitative study of the graphs shows that this is an inverse proportion (broken curve in Fig. 25-9); that is,

$$\lambda_{\text{max}}T = b \qquad (25\text{-}5)$$

if $b = 2.898 \times 10^7$ A $^\circ$K. Equations 25-4 and 25-5 are the empirically determined laws of temperature radiation. The universal constants $a$ and $b$ are experimentally determined. Once the constants are determined, these relations permit us to measure the temperature of a hot body by analysis of the light it is radiating. This method has many uses in industry, such as the measurement of the temperature of a blast furnace in the manufacture of steel. The surface temperature of stars (including the sun) is measured in a similar way. Of more importance, however, were the attempts to "explain" these curves theoretically, for they led to a radically new concept of the nature of radiant energy (Chap. 26).

## 25-5. Speed of Light

The measurement of the speed with which light energy is propagated through space has interested scientists since the time of Galileo. He attempted this measurement by placing himself and an assistant on opposite sides of a lake at night, each with a covered lantern. Galileo would uncover his lantern and start counting time. When the assistant saw the flash, he would uncover his lantern; when Galileo saw this light, he would stop counting time. Thus it was hoped to measure the time for light to go across the lake and back. The experiment failed, and Galileo concluded that the speed of light must be very great, if not indeed infinite. The experimenter is confronted with the necessity of measuring an exceedingly short time interval if the measured distance of travel is to be of convenient size. Conversely, if the measured time is to be conveniently long, the distance traversed must be enormous.

The second combination was employed in 1675 by the Danish astronomer Olaus Roemer. He observed that the eclipse of the first moon of Jupiter occurred about a thousand seconds later than the predicted time when the earth was at the farthest point from Jupiter but right on schedule when, about six months later, the earth was nearest Jupiter. Roemer assumed (correctly as we now know) that the delay was due to the time required for light to traverse the diameter of the earth's orbit rather than to any irregularity in the orbital motion of Jupiter's moon. Since the diameter of the earth's orbit is about 186,000,000 miles, Roemer concluded that the speed of light must be 186,000 miles per second! This method involves an assumption —which, to be sure, was very plausible. A direct laboratory measurement would have been more convincing. Methods of measuring the extremely short time taken by light in traveling directly measurable distances were developed by A. H. L. Fizeau, J. B. L. Foucault, and others, starting in the middle of the nineteenth century. The methods were refined and improved and in the first quarter of the present century brought to a high degree of precision by A. A. Michelson.

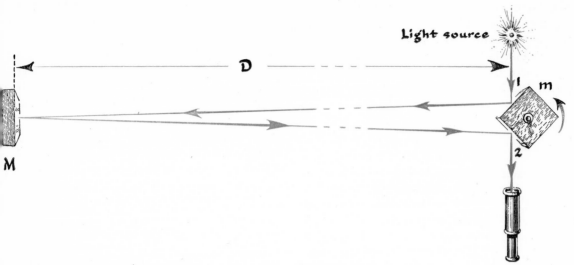

FIGURE **25-10** *Michelson's method of measuring the speed of light.*

Michelson's method is shown in principle (though not in detail) in Figure 25-10. Light from a point source is reflected off one face (1) of a rotatable mirror, $m$, to a distant fixed mirror, $M$. The light is reflected from $M$ to the next face (2) of $m$, from which it is reflected into a reading telescope, $T$, where it forms a sharp image of the source on the cross hairs in the eyepiece. If $m$ is now rotated, face 2 turns through a small angle while the light goes to $M$ and back, and the light, upon reflection from it, misses the telescope, and the image disappears. As the speed of rotation of $m$ is increased, the image reappears in the field of the telescope, and at a particular speed it returns to its original position on the cross hairs. At this critical speed face 1 rotates into the position originally occupied by face 2 during the time the light travels to $M$ and back (a distance of $2D$). From the measured speed of rotation of $m$ the time for one quarter of a revolution is determined. Thus a direct distance-over-time measurement of the speed of light is achieved. Many such determinations of the speed of light (combined with the results of some indirect methods) give the accepted value:

$$c = 2.99793 \times 10^8 \text{ m/sec} \qquad (25\text{-}6)$$

This very important constant of nature is always represented by the letter $c$. The great precision of measurement is indicated by the number of significant figures. Except for the most precise computations, however, the value $c = 3.0 \times 10^8$ m/sec is always used. This value converts to 186,000 miles/sec. This is indeed a great speed! According to the theory of relativity, in fact, this is the maximum possible speed of any object. In order to appreciate the magnitude of the speed of light, consider this hypothetical example. A person standing on the equator and facing east starts a pulse of light, which, for the sake of illustration, we shall assume travels in a circular path round the earth. The person can turn round and face west in about one second. While he does so, the light will have passed him *seven times* going round the earth and will be coming up to meet him on the eighth!

In *free space* all wavelengths of light travel with the speed given by equation 25-6. In air and other gases at normal pressure all wavelengths travel with practically the same speed (there is less than 0.03 percent difference) as in a vacuum. Other media affect the speed more and affect the different wavelengths differently. In glass, for instance, though red light travels as much as 4 percent faster than blue light, the average speed is only about two-thirds as great as in a vacuum. Thus the speed of propagation depends upon the properties of the transmitting medium. The *frequency* of the wave, however, is determined by the radiating source (hydrogen, sodium, etc.) and is an important property of that source. The frequency of light waves is not directly observable; but, after the wavelength is measured by the diffraction grating, the frequency may be computed from the known constant speed by means of equation 25-1.

## 25-6. Electromagnetic Nature of Light

The nature of light waves was first discovered in a completely unexpected manner. The fundamental laws of electricity and magnetism, which were developed during the first half of the nineteenth century, showed that an accelerated charge would cause some distant charge to move —in other words, that electrical energy is radiated by the accelerated charge. Imagine an electron oscillating along a straight wire. This moving charge constitutes an electric current and therefore has a magnetic field associated with it (Oersted's discovery, § 16-11). But the current is continuously changing because the speed of the oscillating electron is continuously changing. The associated magnetic field is therefore also continuously changing. A changing magnetic field induces an electric field and would cause current to flow in a near-by conducting loop (Faraday's discovery of electromagnetic induction, § 16-14). This current would create a magnetic field, which would again induce an electric field in a neighboring loop, and so on. Thus electrical energy would be handed on from loop to loop and transmitted to some distant point. This is not hard to imagine if the loops are present to carry the currents. About 1870 James Clerk Maxwell (who earlier had derived the distribution of molecular speeds) considered this problem and added a very important extension of the ideas. He believed that the induced electric and magnetic fields exist even if the conducting loops are not present. At some point near the oscillating charge, therefore, an electric and a magnetic field, at right angles to each other, would grow to a maximum value and then decrease to zero, would grow to a maximum value in the opposite direction and again decrease to zero; and then the cycle would be repeated at a frequency equal to that of the oscillating charge. These changing fields would induce similar changes at a neighboring point, and so on. This looks very much like a wave, the propagated disturbances being fluctuations in the electric and magnetic fields. When Maxwell formulated these ideas mathematically, the result was indeed a wave equation. The speed of propagation involved electric and magnetic constants that were easily measured in the laboratory. These values, substituted in the equation, gave, for the speed of Maxwell's electromagnetic waves, the value $3 \times 10^8$ m/sec! This, of course, is precisely the speed of light.

It remained to be shown that electromagnetic waves do exist. This was achieved in a series of experiments performed by Heinrich Hertz in 1887 and 1888. He arranged an electric circuit containing two metal rods (each about 12 cm long) in a line, with a short air gap between the ends of the rods. Wires from the rods led to a source of potential difference, which sent periodic pulses of high voltage across the gap. As the electrons surged back and forth across the gap, sparks were observed. An identical pair of rods, included in a similar circuit *but not connected* to a source of potential difference, was placed some distance away. Sparks were observed to jump across this air gap whenever the voltage was applied to the first circuit. Thus electrical energy was transmitted through space. Hertz showed, furthermore, that this electromagnetic radiation has all the properties of light. He diffracted it through single slits and double slits, observed the interference pattern, and measured the wavelength. The wavelength times the known frequency of the oscillator gave the speed of propagation, which was the same as that of light. These waves, still sometimes called Hertzian waves, are the now familiar radio, television, and radar waves and are identical in every way (except visibility) with light waves. Hertzian waves that are somewhat shorter than the deep infrared waves from optical sources have, in fact, been generated.†

---

† An *optical source* is a source, such as a hot solid or liquid or an incandescent gas, that radiates the ultraviolet, visible, and infrared range of wavelengths. We shall also refer to the spectra emitted by optical sources as *optical spectra*. The spectra discussed in § 25-4, for example, are optical spectra.

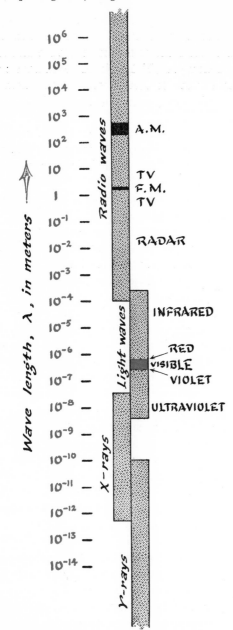

FIGURE **25-11** *Electromagnetic spectrum.*

exception, however, the only difference between the bright green of the mercury spectrum and your favorite radio station is in wavelength. The range of electromagnetic waves is shown in Figure 25-11. The categories are historical and merely indicate the source of the radiation. The various ranges overlap: a deep ultraviolet wave, for instance, might be shorter than a long X-ray.

## 25-7. *Origin of Light Waves*

There is much evidence to indicate that the source of light waves is intimately associated with the atoms of matter. The very high frequency of light waves indicates that the vibrating source must be very small. Any vibrating body is being continuously accelerated, and the acceleration becomes greater as the frequency increases. A material body that experiences the enormous accelerations corresponding to the measured frequencies of light waves must have very little mass; and it is plausible to think of the atoms, or of still smaller masses, as the vibrating source. Another suggestive fact is the unique character of the characteristic spectra: the spectral series emitted by any element are highly stable and characteristic properties of that element.

On the other hand, the electromagnetic nature of light waves requires that the vibrating source be charged electrically. The belief that the source is so charged is supported by the effects of magnetic and electric fields on the spectra of luminous gases. When luminous hydrogen is placed between the poles of a powerful electromagnet, each line of the normal spectrum (Fig. 25-7) splits up into three closely spaced components. When the magnetic induction, *B*, of the field is increased, the space between the components increases; when the field is turned off, the normal spectrum reappears. The effect on the spectra of heavier elements is similar, but the components are often more numerous. This splitting of spectral lines by a magnetic field is called the **Zeeman effect** in honor of Pieter Zeeman, who discovered the phenomenon in 1896. A similar splitting of lines by a strong electric field was

The word "light" now takes on a more general meaning. Light is electromagnetic radiation, and the energy may be carried by any one of a wide range of wavelengths. All the various waves travel through free space with the enormous speed of $3 \times 10^8$ m/sec. A certain small range of wavelengths happen to excite the sensation of vision and are thus "visible light." With this

discovered by Johannes Stark in 1913. An electric charge, whether moving or not, will experience a force in an electric field; and a moving charge will experience a force in a magnetic field (Chap. 17). Thus the nature of the waves and the Stark and Zeeman effects lend strong support to the idea that the source of light waves must be electrical in nature.

If, then, the source is intimately associated with the atoms and is also electrical, it is quite plausible to identify it with the electrons of the atoms. We easily form the qualitative picture of an electron (disturbed from its normal position in an atom by some external agency) executing periodic, accelerated motion under the action of restoring forces within the atom, and thus radiating electromagnetic waves. Our discussion of valence makes it reasonable to assume that the electrons most easily disturbed by external agencies (such as bombardment by free electrons) are the "outer" valence electrons of the atoms. This view is consistent with the fact that the optical spectra of the elements show a periodicity that is just as striking as the periodicity of their other properties. The normal spectra of the un-ionized atoms of Group I all show marked similarities; in particular, the lines are *doublets*. The familiar yellow line of the sodium spectrum, for instance, is found upon careful examination to consist of *two* lines differing in wavelength by six angstroms. Similarly, other lines of sodium and lines of the other Group I elements show this characteristic doubling. Also the arrangements of the series are very similar. For instance, for every series of the sodium spectrum there is a similar series in the potassium spectrum. Although there is no simple relation between the spectra of adjacent elements of the same period (for example, potassium and calcium), there are marked similarities in the spectra of the Group II elements. Here the lines show singlet and triplet structures as well as similarities in the arrangement of series. As we progress across the periodic table, the spectra become more and more complicated, and their analysis into series becomes more and more difficult. However, a vast amount of spectrum analysis amplifies the general rule of marked similarities among the spectra of any one group.

Now refer to Figure 20-1, which shows empirical electronic structures (based on chemical evidence) for some of the atoms. Notice that the Group I elements (H, Li, Na, K) each have *one* valence electron associated with a stable kernel, that the Group II elements shown (Be, Mg) each have *two* valence electrons associated with a stable kernel, and so on for the other groups. If, then, we associate the source of optical spectra with periodic motions of the valence electrons, the similarities discussed in the previous paragraph are to be expected. Furthermore, we should expect the singly charged ion of an element to show a spectrum of the same type as the neutral atom of the preceding element in the periodic table. Suppose, for example, that the exciting agent is sufficiently energetic to remove one electron from an atom of calcium vapor. Then the calcium ions ($Ca^+$) would have only *one* valence electron left, and we should expect them to emit a spectrum of the same type as neutral potassium. By the same argument, we should expect singly ionized aluminum ($Al^+$) to emit a spectrum similar to that of neutral magnesium, and doubly ionized aluminum ($Al^{+2}$) a spectrum similar to that of neutral sodium. These and many similar expectations are completely verified by detailed studies of the spectra of ionized gases.

A non-luminous gas will *absorb* some of the frequencies that it would emit if it were luminous. We have already seen that white light from any white-hot solid, when dispersed by a diffraction grating, gives a continuous spectrum. If a glass tube containing sodium vapor is placed in the path of a beam of white light between the source and the grating, a black line in the yellow portion of the continuous spectrum indicates that a wavelength is missing. The position of this *absorption line* in the spectrum shows which wavelength is missing (equation 25-2), and this is found to be that of the yellow line produced by luminous sodium vapor. Remember that the energy transmitted by the beam of white light is distributed among all possible wavelengths. Presumably part of the energy carried by the sodium yellow wavelength is absorbed by a non-luminous sodium atom. Since the atom quickly re-radiates this energy in *all* directions, only a small fraction of the absorbed energy is re-radiated in the direction of the grating; and, since this process is repeated many times as the beam traverses the sodium vapor, very little, if any, of the energy carried by this wavelength reaches the grating. Hence only a negligible amount of energy from this wavelength remains in the beam of light arriving at the grating, and a black line appears in the otherwise continuous spectrum. Similarly, other characteristic frequencies of the sodium atom are absorbed. Such a group of dark lines is called an **absorption spectrum.** Not all the series that a luminous gas radiates appear in its absorption spectrum. Only the Lyman series, for instance, normally appears as absorption lines for hydrogen. These facts will be seen to be consistent with the theory of radiation discussed in Chapter 28. Absorption spectra are very useful in the identification of gases that are not themselves emitting light. We can, for instance, analyze the atmospheres of planets and stars by studying their absorption spectra.

A phenomenon displayed by any kind of wave, and called the *Doppler effect*, gives further evidence that atoms are the source of light waves. Suppose that a source of waves is approaching the observer with speed $v$. At some instant the source starts a disturbance (say the crest of a wave), which travels away from the source toward the observer with a speed, $S$, that is *characteristic of the transmitting medium.*

That is, once the disturbance is started, it travels with the same speed whether the source is moving or not. Hence, during the time, $P$, that the moving source takes to make one vibration and start the next crest, it gains somewhat on the previous crest. Thus each crest set out in the medium is somewhat nearer the previous one than it would be if the source were stationary. Once started, however, the two crests maintain this nearness since they both travel with the same speed, $S$. The observed wavelength is therefore somewhat shorter than it would be if the source were stationary. Figure 25-12 shows the instantaneous positions of three successive crests at a time four periods (that is, $4P$ sec) after the instant when the source was at $a$. One period after passing $a$, the source is at $b$ and starts another crest, which, at the instant of the diagram, has progressed to $b'$. These, as well as the crest at $c'$, which was started at $c$, proceed to the left with speed $S$. The observed wavelength, $\lambda'$, is the distance between any two successive crests, such as the distance $a'b'$. But $a'b' = aa' - ab' = aa' - (ab + bb')$. Now $aa'$ is the distance traveled by the disturbance during $4P$ seconds, $bb'$ the distance traveled by the disturbance during $3P$ seconds, and $ab$ the distance traveled *by the source* during $P$ seconds. Hence $\lambda' = 4PS - (Pv + 3PS) = PS - Pv$; or $\lambda' = PS(1 - v/S)$. But $PS$ is the distance the disturbance travels during one period and is equal to the observed wavelength, $\lambda$, that would be ob-

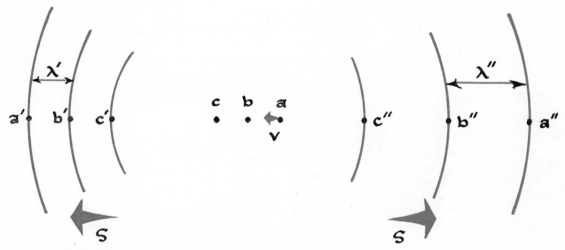

FIGURE **25-12** *Illustrating the Doppler effect.*

served if the source were stationary (§ 25-2). Therefore

$$\lambda' = \lambda \left(1 - \frac{v}{S}\right) \qquad (25\text{-}7)$$

If the source is *receding* from you (if you are on the right in Fig. 25-12) with speed $v$, the observed wavelength, $\lambda''$, is

$$\lambda'' = \lambda \left(1 + \frac{v}{S}\right) \qquad (25\text{-}8)$$

Notice that the change in the observed wavelength depends on the *ratio* of the speed of the source $(v)$ to the speed of propagation $(S)$. Figure 25-12 is drawn to scale for $S = 3v$. For this case the ratio $\lambda''/\lambda' = 2$, which may be verified by measurement. For sound waves in air, $S$ is only about 330 m/sec; the pitch of the bell of an express train $(v \approx 30 \text{ m/sec})$ is therefore noticeably raised (shorter wavelength) as the train approaches and noticeably lowered (longer wavelength) as the train recedes. For light waves, however, $S = c$, which is almost a million times as great as the speed of sound. Even with very precise spectroscopic measurements, therefore, the speed of a source of light waves must be great if a Doppler effect is to be observed.

Such great speeds are attained by gaseous atoms and molecules, as the apparatus shown in Figure 25-13 will demonstrate. Gas at low pressure is enclosed in a glass tube that contains an anode, $A$, and a cathode, $C$, with a hole in the middle. Ions, produced by electron bombardment close to $A$ (electrodes not shown), are accelerated toward $C$ by the electric field and fall through potential difference $V$. Some go through

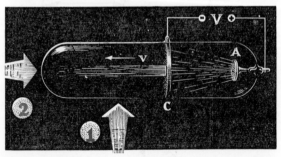

FIGURE **25-13** *Observation of the Doppler effect in the line spectra of moving atoms.*

the hole, coast with speed $v$ into the space to the left of $C$, and, recombining with electrons, emit characteristic spectra. If this stream of luminous atoms is observed through a grating from direction 1, no Doppler effect is to be expected, for $v$ is at right angles to the line of sight, and the atoms are neither approaching nor receding from the observer. If the gas is hydrogen, the spectrum of Figure 25-7 is observed. If, however, the stream is observed head-on, from direction 2, the *same series,* that of Figure 25-7, is observed, but each line is shifted a measurable amount toward the violet end of the spectrum; that is, each line now has a shorter wavelength. This, of course, is the Doppler effect and is to be expected because the waves are emitted from atoms that are approaching the observer. Furthermore, the spectroscopic observations from directions 1 and 2 give $\lambda$ and $\lambda'$ for each line. The known value of $q/m$ for the ions, combined with the observed value of $V$, gives the speed $v$ (equation 17-9). These values for $\lambda$ and $v$, substituted in equation 25-7, give the same value for $\lambda'$ that is observed from direction 2. Thus theory and observation are in complete agreement.

The Doppler effect, in conjunction with kinetic theory, explains the width of spectral lines. The bright orders formed by a grating are "lines" because in all spectroscopic apparatus the source is a narrow slit illuminated with the light being investigated.[†] If the slit were made narrower, we should expect the lines of the spectrum to become narrower; and, up to a point, they do. For a very narrow slit, however, the lines are not correspondingly narrow but have a definite and measurable width. This means that a *small range* of wavelengths is being *observed* but not necessarily that all these wavelengths correspond to characteristic frequencies of the source. If the source is a gaseous atom, it is moving as a result of the temperature of the gas, and the light passing through even the narrowest slit is coming from an enormous number of atoms. In the chapter on kinetic theory we saw that most of the molecules of a gas are moving with speeds close to the rms speed (p. 184). At any instant some would be moving across the line of sight,

---

[†] If the source were an illuminated circular hole, we should have "spectral circles."

and the light from them would show no Doppler displacement. Some would be moving toward and some away from the observer, and the observed wavelengths from these would show a maximum Doppler shift toward shorter and longer wavelengths respectively. Still others, moving at an angle to the line of sight, would have components of speed (less than the rms speed) toward or away from the observer. Thus, if the source is a large number of atoms in *random* motion, each observed line should be a narrow continuous range of wavelengths. This is exactly what is observed. Furthermore, the width of the line, determined from equations 25-7 and 25-8, should be $\lambda'' - \lambda'$ if $v$ is the rms speed for the temperature of the gas and $\lambda$ is the wavelength for the *center* of the line. Careful observations show that this is indeed so. If the gas is cooled, the lines should, and do, become correspondingly narrower. And, finally, the lines of the spectra of two different gases at the *same* temperature should, and do, have different widths, being narrower for the gas of higher atomic weight. The lines from luminous mercury vapor, for instance, are observed to be correspondingly narrower than those from luminous helium at the same temperature.

The discussion so far in this section has been confined to the uniquely characteristic line spectra of the elements. As we have seen, these spectra are obtained only if the element is in the gaseous state. Since atoms in this state are more or less independent of each other's fields of force, the radiated frequencies must be controlled by forces within the atom, which forces might plausibly be different for different atoms. It is observed, however, that, as the pressure of such a gas increases, the lines in the spectrum become broader. (This is independent of the Doppler effect; the temperature of the gas may remain constant as the pressure increases.) At high pressures this "pressure broadening" is considerable, and each "line" spreads out into a range of frequencies. But at high pressures the atoms of a gas are much closer together and collide much more frequently. As the atoms approach each other and collisions become more frequent, therefore, the forces of interaction begin to dominate, and vibrations not uniquely determined by the individual atoms begin to radiate light waves. In the extremely close-packed arrangements of liquids and solids we should expect the characteristic frequencies of the atoms to be completely superseded by a continuous range of frequencies; and we recall that incandescent liquids and solids (and gases under extremely high pressure, such as the core of the sun) give rise to *continuous* spectra, the character of which depends only on the absolute temperature.

## 25-8. *X-rays*

In 1895 W. K. Roentgen reported the discovery of a hitherto unknown type of radiation, which emanated from the region of impact of the cathode rays in a high-voltage discharge tube— either from the fluorescing glass wall of the tube or from the metal of the anode (§18-3). He showed that this emanation was composed, not of cathode rays, but of rays of a different character, which were emitted when the high-speed free electrons struck a material substance. These rays, sometimes called Roentgen rays, are commonly known by the name given them by Roentgen himself—X-rays.

Within a month of Roentgen's announcement, the properties of these rays were being studied all over the world. We omit the details of these investigations and list some of the outstanding properties. (1) X-rays cause a fluorescent screen to glow. (2) X-rays affect a photographic plate the same way as visible light. (3) X-rays ionize a gas through which they travel. (4) X-rays release electrons from metallic surfaces (see the photoelectric effect, § 18-4). (5) X-rays are *not* deflected by electric or magnetic fields. (6) X-rays are very penetrating and pass through many substances with very little decrease in intensity; that is, substances are transparent to these rays. The rays are not completely unabsorbed, however, and the degree of absorption increases with the atomic weight of the absorbing substance. For instance, a sheet of lead 0.2 cm thick will almost completely absorb a certain beam of X-rays (will be opaque), but a sheet of aluminum of equal thickness will absorb only a small fraction of the same beam (will be fairly transparent).

What is the nature of X-rays? This, of course, was immediately a question of central importance. Property 5 ruled out a stream of charged particles. On the other hand, the similarity of properties 1, 2, and 4 to the properties of light waves suggested that X-rays might be electromagnetic waves. Roentgen performed a series of experiments to detect whether X-rays have the properties of light waves, but the results were all negative. This does not mean, however, that X-rays are not waves; perhaps the effects were undetectably small. Recall that, if a wave is to show appreciable diffraction, the aperture through which it passes must be small; and that the criterion for "smallness" is the wavelength (§ 25-2). Thus, if X-rays are very short waves, they may be only slightly diffracted by a slit that is narrow enough to diffract visible light through a wide angle. And this is just what was finally found. In 1909 investigators observed an extremely small effect that *might* be attributed to the diffraction of a beam of X-rays by a very narrow slit. The amount of diffraction indicated that the wavelength was of the order of half an angstrom ($\approx 5\times10^{-11}$ m), or about 1/10,000 of the wavelength of visible light.

The measurement of such a short wavelength raised a serious technical problem. Recall that, to make the angle $\theta$ out to the first bright order sufficiently large for precise measurement, the spacing of the slits ($s$) of the diffraction grating had to be made very small. Specifically, if $\theta$ is to be 30°, we must have $s = 2\lambda$ since sin 30° = 0.5 (Fig. 25-6 and equation 25-2). Thus, if the wavelength is only half an angstrom, $s$ has to be of the order of one angstrom—that is, of the order of $10^{-10}$ m! Technically, this is impossible with even the most delicate ruling machines. But molecules and atoms *are* of this order of magnitude (Table 12-2), and in the closely packed and *orderly* arrangement of the atoms in a crystal we should expect the distances between the centers of the atoms to be only a few angstroms. We might therefore expect the layers of atoms in a crystal to act like a very narrowly spaced grating. As a result of similar reasoning, W. Friedrich, P. Knipping, and M. T. F. von Laue performed the following experiment in 1912. A small beam of X-rays was allowed to pass through a crystal of zinc blende. At some distance behind the crystal was placed a photographic plate. When the plate was developed, a definite and widely spaced diffraction pattern was found. (The pattern was more complicated than that observed through a grating since the atom layers of a crystal are arrayed in three dimensions, not in the two dimensions of a ruled grating.) This important discovery proved the wave nature of X-rays and opened important areas for research. The most important of these areas for a knowledge of the structure of matter is the study of X-ray spectra.

As the electromagnetic waves of a beam of X-rays impinge on the atoms of a crystal, the electrons in these atoms are made to oscillate. The oscillating electrons send out waves. Thus each atom acts as a point source of X-rays, sending out rays in all directions. This process is called *scattering;* that is, the X-rays are scattered by the atoms of the crystal. The waves scattered in certain directions interfere constructively and produce the observed diffraction pattern. In other directions the waves interfere destructively. As a result of the regular arrangement of the atoms in a crystal, it is possible to construct a number of sets of parallel planes through the atoms with each set in a different direction. The planes define possible layers of atoms in the crystal and are called atomic planes. We cannot discuss the involved geometry but will state the result obtained. W. L. Bragg showed that constructive interference is produced only by waves scattered in a direction that makes an angle with an atomic plane equal to the angle made by the incident beam. For this reason the diffracted beam is often considered as being reflected from the atomic plane. The complicated Laue patterns can be interpreted as reflections of the incident beam from the many different sets of atomic planes in the crystal.

A simpler and more easily explained pattern is obtained by an experimental arrangement devised by Bragg. The incident beam is made to fall at an angle on one face of the crystal. The detector, either a photographic plate or an ionization chamber, is placed so that it receives only the beam reflected from the atomic planes that are parallel to the face of the crystal. The con-

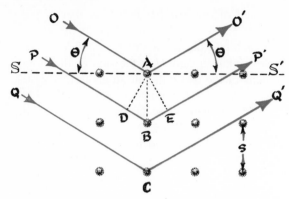

FIGURE **25-14** *Illustrating the derivation of Bragg's equation.*

dition for constructive interference in this beam can be understood with the aid of Figure 25-14, which represents a few of the atoms in a perpendicular section through the face of a cubic crystal. The line *SS'* represents one surface of the crystal, and *s* is the distance between any two adjacent atoms. Imagine a narrow beam of X-rays striking the surface at angle $\theta$. One ray of the beam will hit atom *A* and be scattered. Of the many rays scattered from *A*, one (*AO'*) will make the same angle, $\theta$, with the surface of the crystal as the impinging ray, *OA*. Similarly, *BP'*, parallel to *AO'*, will be one of the rays scattered from atom *B* as a result of the im-

pinging ray *PB*. The lines *AD* and *AE* are constructed with right angles at *D* and *E*. The path *PBP'* is longer than *OAO'* by the distance *DB* + *BE*. Since the atoms in the crystal are uniformly spaced, the path *QCQ'* is also *DB* + *BE* longer than *PBP'*. The diagram is, of course, enormously magnified; any two rays of the reflected beam, such as *AO'* and *BP'*, are, in fact, so close together that they make a single impression on a detector placed in the direction *AO'*. If the waves traveling along these rays are in step, they reinforce each other and produce a measurable intensity at the detector. This condition is met if the distance *DB* + *BE* is equal to one wavelength, for the waves of the incident beam are in step when they enter the crystal. In the two right triangles *ADB* and *AEB* the angles at *A* are each equal to $\theta$, *AB* = *s*, and *DB* = *BE* = *s* sin $\theta$. Hence the condition for constructive interference (*DB* + *BE* = $\lambda$) becomes

$$2s \sin \theta = \lambda \qquad (25\text{-}9)$$

This equation, called Bragg's equation, is fundamental to X-ray spectroscopy.

If the incident beam contains more than one wavelength, angle $\theta$ must be adjusted for each wavelength successively in accordance with equation 25-9. We do this by rotating the crystal about an axis parallel to the reflecting face. The

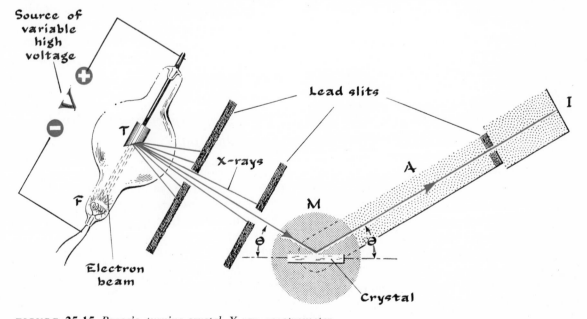

FIGURE **25-15** *Bragg's turning-crystal X-ray spectrometer.*

detector must also be moved, of course, so that it is in a position to receive the reflected beam. This is accomplished with the Bragg turning-crystal spectrometer, shown schematically in Figure 25-15. The X-ray tube consists of a hot filament, $F$ (heating circuit not shown), and a target, $T$, enclosed in a highly evacuated glass tube. Electrons emitted from $F$ are accelerated by the high voltage, $V$, and X-rays are emitted when the electrons strike $T$. Most of the X-rays are absorbed by the lead screens, but a narrow beam passes through the two slits and falls on the crystal at angle $\theta$. The crystal is mounted on a rotatable table, $M$, to which is attached an accurate scale for the measurement of $\theta$. The reflected beam passes through another lead slit into $I$, where it is detected by the ionization it produces in a gas of high atomic weight (such as $Br_2$). $I$ is carried on an arm, $A$, attached in such a way that, when $M$ (and with it the crystal) is rotated, $A$ is rotated twice as much. Thus, when $\theta$ is changed, the incident and reflected beams still make the same angle with the crystal, as required by the Bragg equation. For any given wavelength, an appropriate value of $\theta$ will result in an appreciable ionization in $I$. The amount of ionization, measured by the conductivity of the gas (circuit not shown), gives a measure of the intensity of the ray; and the value of $\theta$ determines the wavelength in accordance with equation 25-9.

For Bragg's equation (and thus his spectrometer) to be useful, the distance, $s$, between adjacent atoms in the crystal must be evaluated. Consider the cubic crystal of NaCl shown in Figure 19-3. The Na and Cl atoms alternate along the edges of repeated cubes. The crystal diagramed has three atoms along each edge, and the total number of atoms in the crystal is $3^3 = 27$ (count them). Considering the enormous value of Avogadro's number, however, this crystal must be imperceptibly small. If we have a crystal 1 cm on edge, the number of atoms along one edge and the number of *spaces between atoms* along the same edge may be considered equal, since the difference is only one out of a very large number. Thus the number of atoms along an edge of a 1 cm cubic crystal is $1/s$, and the total number of atoms in the crystal is $(1/s)^3$.

One-half of this number is the number of *pairs* of different atoms (Na and Cl) in the crystal; and each pair has a mass of $M/N_0$ if $N_0$ is Avogadro's number and $M$ is the sum of the atomic weights of the two different atoms in the crystal. The product of the number of pairs times the mass of one pair gives the total mass of all the atoms in the crystal, which, since the crystal is 1 cm on edge, is equal to the density of the substance. Thus

$$d = \frac{1}{2}\left(\frac{1}{s}\right)^3 \frac{M}{N_0}$$

from which

$$s^3 = \frac{M}{2N_0 d} \qquad (25\text{-}10)$$

The density of rock salt (NaCl) is 2.165 grams/cm$^3$, which leads to $s = 2.814$ angstroms. Similarly, sylvite (KCl), a cubic crystal of density 1.984 grams/cm$^3$, has a value of $s = 3.14$ A. If the same X-ray is measured first with rock salt and then with sylvite on the spectrometer table, we expect $\theta$ to be appropriately smaller for sylvite (since $s$ is larger) in accordance with equation 25-9. Experiment shows this to be so. The complete consistency of such measurements is convincing evidence of the correctness of our picture of the arrangement of the atoms in a cubic crystal. As we pointed out in § 19-9, these measurements of diffraction angles also establish the structure of crystalline salts and thereby furnish convincing evidence that salts are ionized in the crystalline (solid) state as well as in the molten or dissolved state.

## 25-9. X-ray Spectra and Moseley Diagram

The development of the turning-crystal spectrometer opened up the wide and important field of X-ray spectroscopy. Suppose that the target ($T$) of the X-ray tube (Fig. 25-15) is made of silver and that the potential difference ($V$) is held constant at 10,000 volts. Observations of the ionization current at various values of $\theta$ give the relative amounts of energy carried by the different wavelengths in the X-ray beam radiated from the silver target. Under these condi-

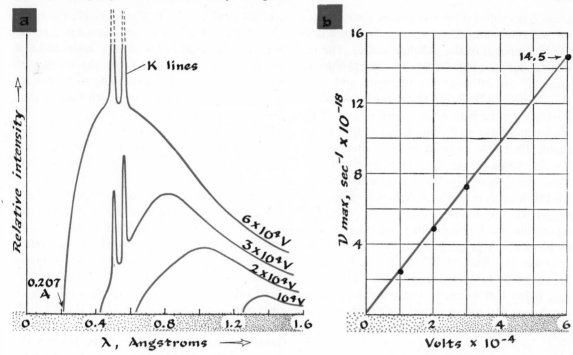

FIGURE **25-16** (a) *Graph of X-ray intensities against wavelengths from a silver target for each of four different potential differences across the tube.* (b) *Direct proportion between maximum frequency and tube potential difference.*

tions it is found that a continuous range of wavelengths from 1.24 angstroms upward is emitted. This distribution is shown by the lowest graph in Figure 25-16a. If $V$ is now increased to $2\times 10^4$ volts, a similar distribution is observed, but the total energy in the beam (the area under the curve) has increased, and the minimum $\lambda$ has decreased to 0.62 A. With $3\times10^4$ volts across the tube, an expanded continuous range of $\lambda$ is again observed, and two intense, sharply defined maxima appear at approximately 0.49 A and 0.56 A. As $V$ is increased still further, the continuous range of $\lambda$ continues to expand toward shorter wavelengths, but the sharp maxima remain at the *same* wavelength. At $6\times10^4$ volts, for instance, the minimum $\lambda$ is 0.207 A, but the sharp maxima (now off scale) are at the same wavelength as before. Thus, at a sufficiently high voltage, the X-ray beam consists of a continuous spectrum with a line spectrum superimposed on it. The lines shown are called the $K$ lines or the $K$ series. No lines of shorter wavelength are observed for a silver target, even at very high voltages. If the curves are extended to the right,

however, another group of lines, called the $L$ series, appears between 3 and 4 angstroms.

If now the silver target is replaced by one of higher atomic number (tungsten, for instance), identical curves are obtained *except* that the $K$ and $L$ series appear at shorter wavelengths. For lower atomic number the $K$ and $L$ lines have longer wavelengths. Thus the continuous X-ray spectrum is independent of the nature of the target and depends only upon the accelerating voltage across the tube—that is, upon the kinetic energy of the bombarding electrons. The line spectrum, however, is a stable property of the particular substance of the target.

These spectra, although similar in many ways to optical spectra, show several striking differences. Optical line spectra are obtained only when the substance is in the gaseous state, but the characteristic X-ray lines of an element are emitted from the solid, the liquid, or the gaseous state. Even chemical combination does not affect the X-ray lines, but the optical spectra of molecules are quite different from those of the constituent atoms (§ 24-4). Another striking difference is exhibited by continuous optical spectra and continuous X-ray spectra, both of which are independent of the radiating source. The radiation curves (Fig. 25-9) for optical spectra "tail off" toward shorter wavelengths and show no well-defined limit, but the X-ray curves (Fig. 25-16a) approach the wavelength axis at sharp angles and have well-defined, accurately measurable limits. A study of these limiting wavelengths yields a surprisingly simple relation. From the data of Fig. 25-16a the graph of Fig. 25-16b is easily constructed. When the frequency ($\nu_{max}$) of the limiting wavelength is plotted against the accelerating voltage, the two are seen to be in direct proportion. At $6\times10^4$ volts, for instance, the limit, 0.207 A, has a frequency ($c/\lambda$) of $14.5\times10^{18}$/sec, and at $3\times10^4$ volts $\nu_{max}$ is just half as much. From the slope of the graph we can easily compute the proportionality constant, and then we have the equation

$$\nu_{max} = \frac{2.42\times10^{14}}{\text{sec volt}} V \qquad (25\text{-}11)$$

We shall refer to this general relation in the next chapter.

Both the X-ray and the optical line spectra are characteristic of the radiating element, but the X-ray spectra are markedly different from the optical in many ways. In Figure 25-17a the X-ray line spectra of a few of the elements are diagramed. The K series for each is shown and also the L and M series that lie in the wavelength range represented. The first thing to be noticed is that the X-ray spectra are much simpler than the optical ones. Each series consists of only a few lines (some cannot be distinguished in the diagram), not of the very numerous lines that appear in optical spectra (Fig. 25-7). Furthermore, the X-ray series of all the elements are very similar, whereas the optical spectra of one group of elements are very different from those of the next group of elements in the periodic table. Perhaps the most remarkable difference, however, is that the X-ray spectra show no trace of the striking periodicity of the optical spectra (and other properties) of the elements. The K lines for potassium, for instance, do not have wavelengths corresponding to those for sodium. With increasing atomic number the X-ray series systematically shift to shorter wavelengths (that is, to higher frequencies). In 1913 H. G.-J. Moseley conducted an extensive study of this systematic shift and discovered simple relations between the frequencies of X-ray lines and atomic numbers. In Figure 25-17b the square root of the frequency for the first line (longest

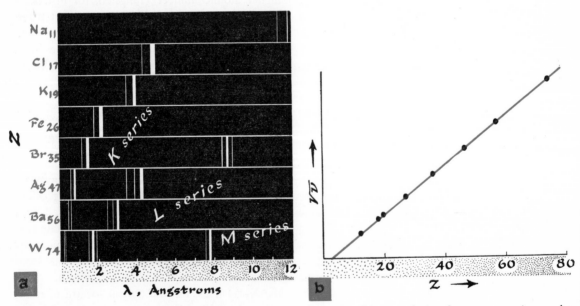

FIGURE 25-17 (a) X-ray line spectra of several elements. (b) Linear relation between atomic number and square root of the frequency of the $K_\alpha$ line.

wavelength) of the $K$ series ($K_\alpha$) is plotted against the atomic number of the element. The result is a direct proportion. This graph, and similar graphs for other lines, rise linearly throughout the whole periodic table, in marked contrast to the periodic repetition for other properties. This result shows that for the $K_\alpha$ line $\nu \propto (Z - 1)^2$. (Note that the graph falls to zero at $Z = 1$.) The proportionality constant determined from the graph leads to the equation

$$\nu = \tfrac{3}{4}c\mathcal{R}(Z - 1)^2 \qquad (25\text{-}12)$$

in which $c$ is the velocity of light and $\mathcal{R}$ is the same empirical constant that appears in the Balmer formula for the hydrogen spectrum.

This remarkably simple but completely general relation must represent some fundamental regularity in the structure of the atoms. Aside from its theoretical interest, it contributes important information about the periodic table. For instance, in order to maintain the linearity of the graphs, Moseley had to list Ar and K, Co and Ni, and Te and I inversely with the atomic weight (§ 8-10). (This was before the meaning of atomic weights as statistical averages of isotopic mixtures was understood; see § 18-10.) Also a kink in the graph at $Z = 43$ led Moseley to predict the existence of Tc, which was discovered years later. (This is Mendeleev's eka-manganese; see § 8-7.) The graphs (similar to Fig. 25-17b) for the various X-ray lines, collectively called the "Moseley diagram," accurately predict the X-ray series for an element of any atomic number. As in the case of Tc, this method predicted the spectra of the few unknown elements in the periodic table and furnished a conclusive test for identifying them when discovered. By the same argument, we now know that in one respect our knowledge of the elements is complete. Elements for all the atomic numbers from 1 through 102 have been identified, and no new element can be fitted between any two of these without disrupting the straight-line graphs of the Moseley diagram. For reasons that we shall discuss in Chapter 30, it appears to be unlikely that elements of atomic number higher than 102 will be found in nature. On the other hand, it appears to be quite likely that such elements of high atomic number will be synthesized.

## 25-10. Applications of X-rays

The useful applications of X-rays are numerous, and only a few can be mentioned here. The penetrating property of X-rays (greater at higher frequencies), and their greater absorption by elements of higher atomic weight, find many uses in medicine. We can, for instance, "see" the bone of a broken arm by placing the arm between an X-ray tube and a fluorescent screen. The X-rays that strike the bone are more strongly absorbed (by the calcium in bone) and thus produce less fluorescence at the screen than those that strike the fleshy tissues, and a well-defined "shadow" of the break is seen on the screen. If we replace the screen by a photographic plate, we obtain a permanent picture that may be studied in detail. Similar X-ray photographs of teeth are of great help to dentists. Similarly, physicians may observe disorders of the alimentary tract by feeding the patient a meal containing substances of high atomic weight (such as barium salts). These are but a few of the many kinds of diagnosis that are possible by the skillful interpretation of X-ray photographs.

Another large area of application is the testing of materials. A steel plate or a casting, for instance, might contain an internal defect, not apparent on the surface, that would seriously weaken its structural strength. Such defects show clearly on an X-ray photograph.

The cells of living tissues are destroyed by the absorption of X-rays. Fortunately, however, diseased tissue, such as a tumor, is destroyed to a greater degree than healthy tissue; and, conversely, the healthy tissue recovers more readily than the diseased. Tumors can therefore be removed by a series of carefully controlled irradiations by X-rays. If the tumor is deep-seated, very penetrating X-rays are used so as to minimize absorption by (and thus destruction of) the skin. For such treatments, some hospitals have X-ray equipment that uses potential differences of more than a million volts.

An extremely important application of X-rays is the determination of the structure of crystals. We have already seen that, if we know the distance between the layers of atoms in a cubic crystal (as determined from the density), X-ray wavelengths may be measured. But the process works the other way also. Suppose that a previously measured wavelength (such as the $K_\alpha$ line of some element) is diffracted from a certain crystal and the angle for constructive interference is measured on the spectrometer. Then the Bragg equation (25-9) yields the distance, $s$, between the atom planes. By repeating this measurement from the various faces of the crystal, we can measure the distances between all sets of planes in the crystal and determine the arrangement of the atoms in the crystal lattice. The geometrical details of the analysis may be complex, but even the most complicated crystal structures are completely specified. And not only crystal structures but also the structures of large organic molecules are revealed by the X-ray diffraction patterns they produce. A quantitative study of these patterns yields the distances between the atoms of these large molecules.

## 25-11. Summary

In this chapter we have considered the more important discoveries and empirical formulations derived from the wide field of spectroscopy.

These results furnish powerful tools for scientific investigations and analyses, and find many applications in medicine and industry, some of which we have mentioned. Light energy is transmitted by waves, which, through the work of Maxwell and Hertz, were found to be periodic variations of electric and magnetic fields. The frequencies of some of the waves (the line spectra) are characteristic properties of the radiating substance; but other frequency distributions (the continuous spectra) are independent of the nature of the radiating substance. And, finally, the source of the waves must be intimately associated with the atoms of the radiating substance.

The electromagnetic theory was so successful in explaining the speed, diffraction, reflection, and other phenomena associated with the *transmission* of light energy, that for a while the nature of light seemed to be completely understood. In the closing years of the nineteenth century and the early years of the twentieth, however, attempts to formulate theoretical explanations (based on Maxwell's electromagnetic theory) of the *emission* and *absorption* of light energy met with catastrophic failure. A radically new concept was required to bring theory and observation into agreement. This concept is the topic of the next chapter.

## Concepts and Terms

Wave Propagation of Energy
   wavelength, frequency, and velocity
   ray and beam
Diffraction
   criterion for smallness of opening
Interference
   destructive and constructive
Diffraction and Interference of Light
   diffraction grating
Spectra
   line spectra
   continuous spectra
Hydrogen Spectrum
   Balmer formula
   hydrogen series
Distribution of Energy in Continuous Spectra
   laws of temperature radiation

Speed of Light
   frequencies of light waves
Electromagnetic Nature of Light Waves
Atoms as Source of Light Waves
   Zeeman effect
   periodicity of optical spectra
   spectra of atomic ions
   absorption spectra
   Doppler effect; shift and broadening of spectral lines
X-rays
   diffraction
   Bragg's equation
   turning-crystal spectrometer
Continuous X-ray Spectra
X-ray Line Spectra
   Moseley diagram
   $K_\alpha$ frequency

# Problems

**25-1.** In wave transmission of energy three quantities—velocity of propagation, wavelength, and frequency—are related as in equation 25-1. The frequency is characteristic of the radiating source, but the other two quantities are characteristic of the transmitting medium. Discuss in detail.

**25-2.** A strip of metal vibrating up and down is so mounted that it strikes the surface of a shallow pan of water at the bottom of each vibration. Ripples are observed to run across the water with a wavelength of 2 cm. If the strip makes 12 vibrations per second, what is the velocity of propagation of the waves?

*Ans.* 24 cm/sec

**25-3.** Waves on the surface of a certain liquid are observed to travel at 80 cm/sec. If the distance between two successive crests is 4 cm, what is the frequency of the source?

*Ans.* 20/sec

**25-4.** Sound waves of various wavelengths travel with the same velocity through air. At normal pressure and 22°C this velocity is 344 m/sec. A typical human ear will respond to wavelengths ranging from 17.2 m to 1.72 cm.
(A) What is the audible frequency range?
(B) Two sounds with a frequency ratio of 2/1 produce the musical internal of an octave. How many octaves are there in the audible range?

*Ans.* (B) approx. 10 octaves

**25-5.** In one series of measurements of the velocity of light, Michelson placed the rotating mirror and the fixed mirror on adjacent mountain tops in California. The distance between the mirrors (about 22 miles) was determined very accurately by the U. S. Coast and Geodetic Survey.
(A) Calculate the speed of light if $D = 3.5 \times 10^4$ m and the mirror (as shown in Fig. 25-10) made $1.07 \times 10^3$ revolutions per second.
(B) Michelson actually used a rotating mirror with more than four sides. What would be the speed of rotation if the mirror had sixteen sides?

*Ans.* (A) $2.996 \times 10^8$ m/sec
(B) 267.5 rev/sec

**25-6.**
(A) How long does it take light to reach us from the sun? (See § 5-5.)

(B) How long does it take light to cross the solar system? (See Table 5-1.)
(C) An astronomical unit of distance is the light-year—the distance light travels in one year. How many miles is this unit?

*Ans.* (A) 8 min 20 sec
(B) approx. 11 hours
(C) $5.9 \times 10^{12}$ miles

**25-7.** A wave from a radar station is reflected from a distant airplane and returns 15 microseconds after emission. How far away is the airplane?

*Ans.* 2,250 m

**25-8.**
(A) Calculate the frequencies of the wavelength ranges shown in Fig. 25-11.
(B) How many "octaves" are in the visible range?

*Ans.* (B) approx. one octave

**25-9.**
(A) Commercial AM radio stations broadcast on frequencies ranging from about 500 to 1,500 kilocycles/sec. What is the wavelength range for these stations?
(B) The center of the FM broadcast band has a wavelength of 3 meters. What is the frequency of this radio wave?

*Ans.* (A) 600–200 m
(B) 100 megacycles/sec

**25-10.**
(A) All light waves travel with the same velocity, $c$, in air. In a certain kind of glass, however, hydrogen red light (see Fig. 25-7) travels with a velocity of 0.610 $c$. What is the wavelength of this light in the glass? (Hint: Consider the statement of Prob. 25-1.)
(B) Hydrogen blue light, in the same glass, has a wavelength of 2,580 A. What is the velocity of this light in the glass?

*Ans.* (A) 4,003 A
(B) 0.595 $c$

(This variation of velocity with frequency in solids and liquids accounts for the dispersion of white light into a continuous spectrum by a glass prism and into a rainbow by drops of water.)

**25-11.** The mercury green line (5,461 A) forms a first-order bright image 30° away from the central order of a diffraction grating. How far apart are the grating slits spaced? (Sine $30° = 0.500$.)

*Ans.* $1.09 \times 10^{-6}$ m

**25-12.** Calculate the shortest wavelength in the hydrogen spectrum.

*Ans.* 912 A

**25-13.** Calculate the wavelength (A) of the first line of the Paschen series, (B) of the third line of the Balmer series.

*Ans.* (A) 18,800 A

**25-14.** The surface temperature of the sun is $6,000°K$. What wavelength carries the maximum energy in sunlight?

*Ans.* 4,830 A

**25-15.** A certain grating has 8,340 slits per centimeter of length.
(A) What is the distance in centimeters from the central bright order to the first bright order for the Balmer series limit if the distance from the center of the grating ($C$) to the first order ($B_1$) is 100 cm? (Hint: See Figs. 25-7 and 25-8 and the definition of $\sin \theta$ in Appendix I.)
(B) What is the length in centimeters of the whole Balmer series? Consider the distance $CB_1$ to be 100 cm in all cases.

*Ans.* (B) 24.3 cm

**25-16.** Analysis of the spectrum of a certain star shows that the wavelength of maximum energy is 483 A.
(A) What is the surface temperature of this star?
(B) Compared with the sun (see Prob. 25-14), how much more energy per square meter does this star radiate each second?
(C) The sun is a yellow-white star. What is the color of the other star?

*Ans.* (B) 10,000 times more

**25-17.** The line spectra of $B^+$ and $B^{+2}$ should be similar to the spectra of what neutral atoms? The spectrum of $Li^{+2}$ should be similar to what?

**25-18.** The speed of sound in air is 344 m/sec, and the wavelength of a certain tone is 78.3 cm.
(A) What would be the wavelength of this tone if it were received from the bell of a train approaching with a speed of 26.8 m/sec?
(B) What would be the wavelength as the train receded?

*Ans.* (A) 72.2 cm
(B) 84.4 cm

**25-19.** Suppose that the apparatus of Fig. 25-13 contains sodium vapor. If the ion stream is observed from direction 1, the short component of the sodium yellow line has a wavelength of 5,890.0 A. If it is viewed from direction 2, the wavelength is 5,884.11 A.
(A) What is the speed of the Na ions?
(B) What is the potential difference, $V$, accelerating the ions? (Hint: Calculate $q/m$ for $Na^+$ from the value for $H^+$ in Table 17-1 and the atomic weights.)

*Ans.* (A) $3 \times 10^5$ m/sec
(B) $1.06 \times 10^4$ volts

**25-20.** At a certain time the spectrum from a particular star on the ecliptic (see § 5-8) shows the wavelength of the hydrogen red line to be the same as determined in the laboratory, 6,563 A. Three months later the wavelength of this line in the star's spectrum is found to be 6,562.35 A. Six months later the line is at 6,563 A again, and nine months later it is at 6,563.65 A. After that the cycle repeats itself at yearly intervals.
(A) How do you interpret these observations? (Hint: For light waves the Doppler effect depends only on the *relative* velocity of source and observer.)
(B) What is the orbital speed of the earth?
(C) What is the mean distance of the earth from the sun?

*Ans.* (B) $2.97 \times 10^4$ m/sec
(C) $1.49 \times 10^{11}$ m

Note: Such observations are further proof of the earth's revolution and furnish a precise method of evaluating the astronomical unit (§ 5-5).

**25-21.** A certain X-ray shows constructive interference in a direction lying 30° ($\sin 30° = 0.5$) from the face of the diffracting crystal. What is the wavelength if the crystal is NaCl?

*Ans.* $\lambda = 2.814$ A

**25-22.**
(A) Why would you expect LiCl to be a cubic crystal? How could you verify that it is?
(B) Calculate the crystal spacing. The density of LiCl is 2.07 grams/cm³.

*Ans.* (B) 2.57 A

**25-23.** The $K_\alpha$ line from silver has a wavelength of 0.56 A.
(A) What would be the sine of the angle for constructive interference with an NaCl crystal on the spectrometer?
(B) Would the angle be smaller or larger with a KCl crystal? (See § 25-8.) What would be the value of $\sin \theta$ with this crystal?

*Ans.* (A) $\sin \theta = 0.0994$ ($\theta = 5°42'$)

**25-24.** With a calcite crystal (one form of $CaCO_3$) on the spectrometer, the $K_\alpha$ line from copper ($\lambda = 1.54$ A) appears at an angle whose sine is 0.254. What is the crystal spacing for calcite?

*Ans.* 3.03 A

**25-25.** Compare X-ray and optical spectra (both line and continuous) as to likenesses and differences.

**25-26.**

(A) What is the highest frequency emitted from an X-ray tube if the potential difference across the tube is $1.5 \times 10^4$ volts and the target is silver? What would be the frequency if the target were tungsten?

(B) What would be the shortest wavelength emitted? Relate your answer to Fig. 25-16.

*Ans.* (B) 0.827 A

**25-27.**

(A) The frequency of the $K_\alpha$ line from sodium is $0.25 \times 10^{18}$/sec. What is the frequency of the $K_\alpha$ line from scandium?

(B) Calculate the wavelength of the $K_\alpha$ line from gold.

(C) Relate your results to Fig. 25-17.

*Ans.* (A) $1.0 \times 10^{18}$/sec

(B) approx. 0.2 A

**25-28. Energy from the Sun.**

(A) The solar constant is $1.36 \times 10^3$ joules/sec $m^2$. By direct measurement it is found that this number of joules falls on one square meter of the earth each second when the earth is at its mean distance from the sun ($1.5 \times 10^{11}$ m). What is the total energy radiated by the sun each second?

(B) The radius of the sun is $6.97 \times 10^8$ m. How many joules per second are radiated per square meter of the surface of the sun?

(C) What is the temperature of the surface of the sun? [Hint: Use equation 25-4. Note: This is the effective temperature, which is the average for all parts of the surface. Spectrum analysis (see Prob. 25-14) shows that the temperature falls from about 6,000°K at the center of the disc to about 5,000°K at the edge. The source of the prodigous outflow of energy from the sun (and other stars) was until recently an unsolved problem of science.]

*Ans.* (A) $3.84 \times 10^{26}$ joules/sec

(B) $6.28 \times 10^7$ joules/sec $m^2$

(C) 5,760°K

Problems 25-29–25-34 will refer to the following data. The *wave numbers* of some of the lines of the hydrogen spectrum are listed in order, starting with the longest wavelength in each series. The wave number of a line is the reciprocal of the wavelength in space—that is, the number of waves per meter.

| LINE | LYMAN | BALMER | PASCHEN |
|---|---|---|---|
| 1 | $82.27 \times 10^5$/m | $15.24 \times 10^5$/m | $5.33 \times 10^5$/m |
| 2 | $97.51 \times 10^5$/m | $20.57 \times 10^5$/m | $7.80 \times 10^5$/m |
| 3 | $102.84 \times 10^5$/m | $23.04 \times 10^5$/m | $9.14 \times 10^5$/m |
| 4 | $105.31 \times 10^5$/m | $24.38 \times 10^5$/m | . |
| 5 | $106.65 \times 10^5$/m | | . |
| . | . | . | . |
| . | . | . | . |
| . | . | . | . |
| ∞ (limit) | $109.70 \times 10^5$/m | $27.43 \times 10^5$/m | $12.19 \times 10^5$/m |

**25-29.**

(A) Verify the wave numbers for the third Balmer line and the Balmer limit.

(B) What is the wavelength of the fourth Lyman line?

*Ans.* (B) 949.6 A

**25-30. Combination Rule.**

(A) Subtract the wave number of the first Lyman line from the wave number of the second Lyman line. Compare the difference with the wave number of the first Balmer line. Now subtract the first Lyman from the third Lyman, and compare with the second Balmer. Continuing this process, show that $L_n - L_1 = B_{n-1}$ if $n = 2, 3, \ldots \infty$ and the letters stand for the appropriate series.

(B) Investigate the Balmer and Paschen series for a similar result.

(C) Investigate the Lyman and Paschen series for a similar result.

**25-31. Limit Relations.**

(A) Subtract the Balmer limit and the Paschen limit from the Lyman limit, and compare the differences with the first two Lyman lines. Also compare the difference between the Balmer and Paschen limits with the first Balmer line.

(B) Divide the Lyman limit by the Balmer limit and by the Paschen limit. Calling the Lyman limit $\mathcal{R}$, express the three limits in terms of $\mathcal{R}$ and integers.

*Ans.* (B) $\mathcal{R}/1^2$; $\mathcal{R}/2^2$; $\mathcal{R}/3^2$

**25-32. Term Diagram.**

Construct a term diagram for hydrogen. Take your clue from the results of the preceding problem. You may find a series of terms, each one a wave number, by successively dividing $\mathcal{R}$ by the squares of increasing whole numbers. The value of the term approaches zero as $n$ becomes very large—that is, as $n \rightarrow \infty$. As found in the preceding problem, the first three terms are the series limits shown in the table. Calculate the next three terms (that is, let $n = 4$, 5, and 6), and round off each to two figures after the decimal point. Now plot these six terms in the following way. Draw two horizontal lines 24 cm apart. In the right-hand margin label the top line $\Re/\infty = 0$ and the bottom line $\Re/1^2 = 109.7 \times 10^5/m$. This effectively plots the first term *down* from the top line on a scale of $\Re = 24$ cm. Plot the second term by a line 6 cm down since $\Re/2^2 = \Re/4$. Plot and label the remaining four terms. These horizontal lines are called *levels*. In the left-hand margin number the levels, starting with the bottom level as No. 1. The resulting diagram will be similar to Fig. 28-3.

### 25-33. Hydrogen Series.

(A) The difference between the terms of any two levels of a term diagram is called a *transition*. Calculate the wave number for the transition from the second to the first level, and compare with the first Lyman line. Represent this transition by a vertical arrow pointed downward between level 2 and level 1. Place this arrow at the left edge of your diagram. Calculate and represent the transitions to the first level from the rest of the levels, including $n = \infty$. (Group the arrows in the left-hand third of your diagram.) Notice that these transitions give rise to the portion of the Lyman series shown in the table.

(B) Repeat part A for transitions terminating on the second level, and compare with the Balmer series.

(C) Repeat part A for transitions terminating on the third level, and compare with the Paschen series.

### 25-34.

(A) Where do the levels from 7 to $\infty$ lie in your diagram?

(B) Notice that in any one series the transitions become progressively *less* different. Relate this to the observed convergence of spectral series.

(C) How would you compute the Brackett series from your diagram?

(D) Relate the Balmer formula to the procedure for calculating spectral series from a term diagram.

Note: Combination rules and term diagrams can be worked out for the spectra of atoms other than hydrogen. Although somewhat more complicated (since the observed spectra are more complicated), these rules and diagrams are similar to those for hydrogen. All observed series converge toward a limit and may be represented by transitions between terms that converge to zero and involve the constant $\Re$. These results, of course, are all empirical but are important for us for two reasons: (1) they enable us to describe an enormous body of spectroscopic observation by rather simple rules; (2) they indicate that a simple and universal structure within the atoms accounts for the emitted spectra.

## Suggested Readings

1. L. W. Taylor, *Physics the Pioneer Science* (Houghton Mifflin, 1941), pp. 394–404, 504–548, 746–749, 761–768, 790–800.
2. H. E. White, *Modern College Physics*, 3rd edition (Van Nostrand, 1956), pp. 386–389, 453–463, 601–611, 624–638.

The interesting topic of color, which we do not discuss, is well presented in the two references above. Chap. 45 of White is a well-illustrated discussion, and Chap. 35 of Taylor is interesting for its historical content.

3. M. Born, *The Restless Universe*, translated by W. M. Deans (Dover Publications, 1951), pp. 106–117. Note the marginal "movie" of electromagnetic waves.

4. A. Einstein and L. Infeld, *The Evolution of Physics* (Simon & Schuster, 1938), pp. 94–126, 148–160.
5. Sir William Bragg, *The Universe of Light* (Macmillan, 1933). An interesting, non-mathematical account based on the popular Christmas lectures given by the author at the Royal Institution of London. See especially Chap. 8, on X-rays.
6. W. F. Magie, *A Source Book in Physics* (McGraw-Hill, 1935), pp. 294–298 (Grimaldi on diffraction), 308–315 (Young on interference), 318–324 (Fresnel on diffraction), 335–344 (Roemer, Bradley, Fizeau, and Foucault on the velocity of light), 360–365 (Balmer on the hydrogen series), 600–610 (Roentgen on X-rays).

THE EMPIRICAL laws of temperature radiation (§ 25-4) were the first laws of radiation to be subjected to theoretical investigation. Attempts were made to derive, from theory, an equation that would fit the energy-distribution curves of the continuous optical spectra (Fig. 25-9). The source of the waves was considered to be the vibrating molecules of the hot radiating object; for, as atoms were known to contain electric charges (Thomson had just discovered the electron), it was thought that vibrating molecules would radiate and absorb electromagnetic waves in much the same way as minute, high-frequency Hertzian oscillators (§ 25-6).

## 26-1. Classical Radiation Theory

A somewhat crude but perhaps helpful analogy is presented in Figure 26-1. A mass is attached to the end of a suspended coil spring, and a thin horizontal cord is attached to the mass. If the mass, originally at $O$, is raised to some point $A$ and released, it will start to oscillate between $A$ and $A'$ with a frequency determined by the mechanical properties of the system. As it oscillates, it will carry the end of the cord up and down, and waves will travel along the cord as shown in part "a." These waves carry energy away from the vibrating system, which energy, by the conservation principle, must come from the energy content of the vibrating mass. Thus the vibrations will gradually die down as represented in part "b," which is a graph of displacements (of the mass) against time. The reverse process works equally well. If waves (from some other source) are traveling to the left in "a," the mass initially at $O$ will *continuously* absorb energy and gradually increase its vibration—that is, trace the graph of "b" from right to left.

In temperature radiation the vibrating molecule plays the role of the mass-spring system, and the waves are periodic changes in the surrounding electric and magnetic fields. Observations show, however, that the radiation contains a wide and continuous range of frequencies: a large number of vibrating electric dipoles of many different frequencies seem to radiate energy to, and absorb energy from, the surrounding

CHAPTER

26

The
Quantum Theory

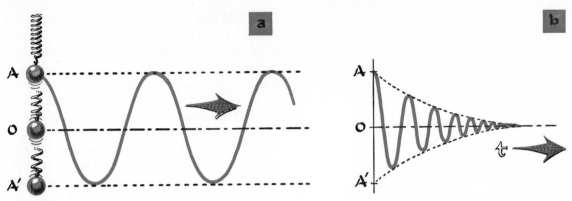

FIGURE **26-1** (a) *Waves along a cord attached to an oscillating mass.* (b) *Graph of displacement against time for the same mass.*

field, the processes reaching equilibrium at a constant temperature. This model is very similar to the kinetic-theory model for temperature equilibrium in a gas; in fact, the statistical methods and fundamental ideas that had been eminently successful in the kinetic theory were confidently applied to this assemblage of electric oscillators in a luminous hot body. In the kinetic theory, the energy is the kinetic energy of the molecules. Since this energy is handed about from molecule to molecule in their frequent impacts, one individual molecule might have, at any instant, *any* amount of kinetic energy from zero on up. In accordance with the principle of equipartition of energy (§ 12-3), however, each molecule, over a period of time, has an *average* kinetic energy of $\frac{3}{2}kT$. Similarly, any one oscillator, during its energy exchanges with the field, was allowed to have, instantaneously, *any* amount of energy from zero on up, and at temperature equilibrium *each* oscillator was assumed to have an average vibrational energy of $\frac{3}{2}kT$. When these ideas were consistently applied, the resulting theoretical distribution of energy among the various frequencies was in drastic disagreement with observation. This disagreement is illustrated in Figure 26-2, where one of the experimental curves of Figure 25-9 is reproduced (solid line). The curve predicted by theory for the same temperature (broken line) is seen to agree well with observation *only* for the longer wavelengths (lower frequencies). For higher frequencies the predicted curve rises too rapidly and approaches indefinitely large inten-

sities. The *observed* intensities, however, reach a definite maximum and then drop off toward zero at still higher frequency (shorter wavelength). Many attempts to make the theory fit the facts met with failure.

## 26-2. Planck's Quantum Hypothesis

In 1900 Max Planck (one of several working on the problem), advancing the hypothesis that the equipartition principle has limitations when applied to vibrating molecules, introduced a bold new assumption that removed all the difficulties. He assumed that the molecules radiate

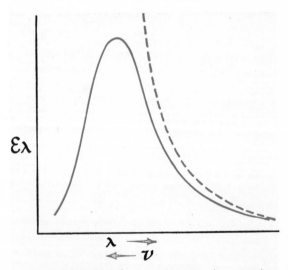

FIGURE **26-2** *Distribution of energy in a continuous spectrum: solid line, experimental; broken line, theoretical, based on classical concepts.*

energy in discrete packets of energy, which he called *quanta,* and that the size of the quantum —that is, the amount of energy in the packet—is directly proportional to the characteristic frequency of the vibrating molecule. This *quantum hypothesis* is expressed algebraically by the equation

$$\epsilon = h\nu \qquad (26\text{-}1)$$

in which $\epsilon$ is the amount of energy in the radiated quantum, $\nu$ is the frequency of the vibrating molecule, and $h$ is a *universal* constant called *Planck's constant.* According to this hypothesis a vibrating molecule must contain its energy in discrete packets; that is, a molecule may have a vibrational energy of 0, of $h\nu$, of $2h\nu$, of $3h\nu$, etc. —always some whole number of quanta, never a fractional amount such as $1.58h\nu$. In other words, Planck assigned structure to the energy content of a molecule.

Strange and (even to Planck) absurd as this assumption may have seemed, it was astoundingly successful in bringing theory into agreement with fact. Without any other assumption that broke with classical † principles, Planck derived an equation that fitted perfectly the energy-distribution curves. The mathematical details are much too complex for an elementary book, but some discussion will help in understanding why the hypothesis was successful. Let us construct a graph (similar to Fig. 26-1b) and for concreteness suppose that the molecule has vibrational energy $2h\nu$ (Fig. 26-3a). On the new theory, no gradual radiation of energy occurs, but at some instant the molecule *suddenly* starts to vibrate with $h\nu$ less energy, and one quantum is radiated; then a second such sudden change radiates the remaining quantum. Thus the molecule seems to "jump" from one energy state to another. This *discontinuous* exchange of energy constitutes the radical departure from classical ideas and is not derivable from any law of the older science.

Now consider a molecule whose characteristic frequency ($\nu'$) is half as large as the one above

---

† Early in the twentieth century, when new discoveries required new concepts that were fundamentally and radically different from established ideas, the body of science formulated at the end of the nineteenth century began to be called "classical science."

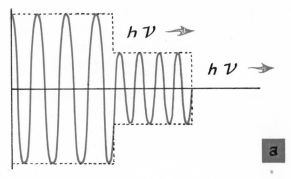

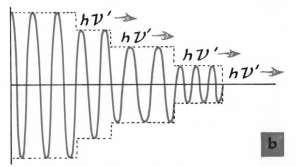

FIGURE **26-3** *Graph of displacement against time of an oscillator according to the quantum hypothesis.*

but whose total energy is initially the same (Fig. 26-3b). Since the quantum is only half as large, the molecule contains $4h\nu'$ in its highest energy state. For this molecule, then, four jumps are possible before all the energy is radiated. Consider now a molecule of very low frequency and (for comparison) with the same initial energy content. For this molecule the highest energy state would contain very many quanta, each one very small, which, when emitted successively, would *appear* to be a continuous emission of energy. A graph (such as Fig. 26-3b) for this molecule would decrease with many small steps and very nearly coincide with the continuously smooth decrease shown in Figure 26-1b.

The energy emitted by vibrating molecules comes from the thermal energy of the hot body. For molecules of low vibrational frequencies the quanta are so small that there is a good chance of receiving at least one quantum during any thermal impact. Such molecules therefore behave approximately as though there were a *continuous* energy exchange and (since this satisfies the statistical requirement for equipartition of energy) have an *average* energy of vibration of $\frac{3}{2}kT$. This, the fundamental assumption of the older theory, explains why prediction was in good agreement with observation for low frequency (Fig. 26-2).

Now consider a molecule of somewhat higher vibrational frequency, such as $v'$ in Figure 26-3. This molecule, to vibrate at all, must be given at least one quantum of energy. Since many thermal impacts do not involve so much energy as this, such molecules, for part of the time, do not vibrate at all. Their *average* energy is therefore somewhat less than $\frac{3}{2}kT$, and the intensity of their radiation is less than that predicted by the classical equipartition theory. At still higher frequencies the quanta are still larger, and the energy required to start the molecules vibrating becomes less likely to be exchanged during thermal impact. Thus, with increasing characteristic frequency, the molecules vibrate for shorter and shorter times, and their average energies become much smaller than $\frac{3}{2}kT$, approaching zero for very high frequency. Hence the intensity of the radiation falls off at high frequencies (short wavelengths). This, of course, is exactly what is observed, as shown by the experimental curves of Figure 25-9.

From his distribution equation Planck derived the radiation laws expressed by equations 25-4 and 25-5. Planck's equations involved the two universal constants $k$ and $h$, and the corresponding experimental laws contained the empirically evaluated constants $a$ and $b$. By equating theory and experiment Planck obtained two equations with only two unknowns and thus was able to compute the numerical values of both $k$ and $h$. The value of Boltzmann's constant, $k$ ($= R/N_0$), divided into the then well-known value of the gas constant, yielded a numerical value for Avogadro's number, $N_0$. Several years later this value was found to be in good agreement with that found by the more direct measurements of Perrin (p. 188). For our present discussion the more interesting result is the value of the new constant, $h$. This† came out to be

$$h = 6.63 \times 10^{-34} \text{ joule sec} \qquad (26\text{-}2)$$

---

† The precise contemporary value is $6.6252 \times 10^{-34}$ joule sec.

(Note that the units are those to be expected from equation 26-1.) This is an astonishingly small number. Even when multiplied by the very high frequencies of light waves ($\approx 10^{15}$/sec), the amount of energy in one quantum is still extremely small. It is not surprising that in our ordinary experience this fine structure of energy is completely unnoticeable. Compared with the energy exchanges in the extremely small regions within a molecule, however, the quantum is of appreciable size, and the discrete structure of energy becomes evident.

Planck's hypothesis was concerned with the energy content of vibrating molecules and not necessarily with the nature of light. Nothing in it implies that light energy, when radiated, maintains a quantum structure. In the first quarter of the twentieth century, however, many discoveries supported the idea that radiated light maintains a quantum aspect. Some of these discoveries will be discussed in the following sections and others in later chapters.

## 26-3. Einstein's Theory of Photoelectric Effect

It is an ironic fact of history that, during the experimental investigations that verified Maxwell's electromagnetic theory of light, Hertz discovered a phenomenon that proved to be incompatible with Maxwell's theory and was destined to play an important role in establishing the quantum nature of light. This was the photoelectric effect (§ 18-4). Qualitatively, the effect is to be expected from the electromagnetic theory. The electric field of the wave, exerting forces on the electrons of the metal, supplies the energy that separates them from the metal and sets them free in the space of the tube. Quantitative studies of the effect, however, presented grave difficulties for the classical electromagnetic theory. What were the results of these studies?

Figure 26-4 shows an experimental set-up for investigating the photoelectric effect. The experimental metal surface, $S$, and a collecting electrode, $C$, are enclosed in a highly evacuated transparent tube. The electrodes are connected through a current meter to a source of potential

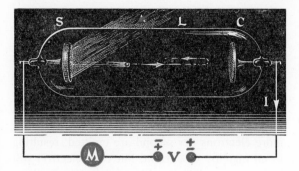

FIGURE **26-4** *Method of measuring the kinetic energy of photoelectrons.*

difference. The voltage, $V$, is variable from zero up and is arranged so that $C$ may be made either positive or negative and $S$ either negative or positive. When monochromatic light (a single frequency) falls on $S$, and $C$ is positive, a steady current, $I$, is indicated by the meter. If $V$ is set to zero, the current continues; and even for small *negative* potential differences (that is, if $C$ is negative) the current still flows in the *same* direction. If this negative potential difference is increased, however, the current finally stops at a sharply defined "stopping potential," $V_s$. These results are easily understood in terms of the electromagnetic theory. Presumably the light wave supplies enough energy to the electrons to free them from the surface of $S$ and start them across the space between the electrodes with a certain kinetic energy. Thus the electrons coast across to $C$ and maintain the current even when $V = 0$. When $C$ is made negative, the electrons move *against* the force of the electric field due to $V$ and thus gain potential energy, which gain must come from their store of KE. If $V$ is not too large, the KE of the electrons still carries them across to $C$. But at a sufficiently large potential difference ($V_s$) the electrons lose all their KE just before reaching $C$, turn round (as in the figure), and fall back on $S$; and the current stops. Since the gain in PE equals the starting KE, we have $V_s e = \frac{1}{2}mv^2$. This is exactly analogous to tossing a ball into the air. We start it up with a certain KE, which all goes into PE at the top of the flight. From the known mass of the ball and the observed height to which it rises, we compute the starting KE.

We now repeat the experiment but with an increased intensity of light. According to the electromagnetic theory, we expect the stronger fields of the more intense waves to eject electrons with greater KE. Such electrons, moving more rapidly, would constitute a larger current than before; and, in fact, the current through the tube is found to increase with the intensity of the light. By the same argument, however, we expect a greater stopping potential to be required for these more energetic electrons. But this is *not* so. No matter how weak or strong the light is made, the same value of $V_s$ is always observed. This has no explanation in the classical theory. From the fact that the current does increase with light intensity, we infer that *more* electrons are released but with the same KE as under the weaker illumination.

Let us now vary the experiment and use light of a higher frequency. $V_s$ is now observed to be greater, although still independent of intensity. As the frequency is raised further, the observed $V_s$ rises linearly. The electrons are released, then, with kinetic energies that are linearly related to the frequency of the impinging light. Since the KE (in electron volts) is equal to $V_s e$, these results are represented by Figure 26-5. If the photoelectric surface ($S$ in Fig. 26-4) is potassium and is illuminated with the hydrogen red line, low-energy ($\approx 0.25$ ev)

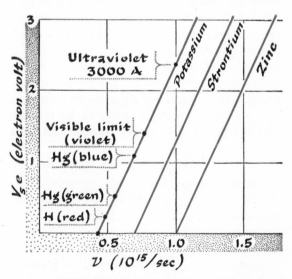

FIGURE **26-5** *Graph of energy of photoelectrons against frequency of light for three different elements.*

electrons are released. With the mercury blue line (higher frequency) the electrons are emitted with about four times as much energy, and with the high-frequency ultraviolet high-energy ($\approx 2.5$ ev) photoelectrons are released. On the other hand, if very deep red or infrared light ($\nu < 0.4 \times 10^{15}$/sec) is used, no photoelectrons are released, *no matter how intense the light.* There is, then, definite minimum frequency (the **threshold frequency**), below which no effect whatever is observed. If now strontium is used for the photoelectric surface, similar results are found *except* that the threshold frequency is higher; as can be seen from the graph, only the blue end of the visible spectrum produces any effect. If the surface is zinc, the threshold is well into the ultraviolet; zinc shows no response at all to visible light.

Fig. 26-5 shows only three out of a large number of experimental graphs for various substances. Each substance shows a sharply defined, characteristic threshold. There is no explanation of such thresholds in classical electromagnetic theory, according to which *any* wave, if sufficiently intense, would exert great enough electric forces on the electrons to free them from the substance, and infrared rays should be as effective as ultraviolet. Also (as noted above), the KE with which the electrons come out of the metal is independent of the intensity of the light but (as shown by Fig. 26-5) is dependent on the frequency of the light and increases in direct proportion with the frequency. These observations are just the reverse of predictions of the older theory. And, finally, the proportionality constant is the same for all substances (that is, is a universal constant), as shown by the fact that the graphs are parallel—that is, all have the same slope.

In 1905, Albert Einstein, a young man of twenty-six, brought theory into agreement with fact by extending the quantum idea and making bold and fundamentally new assumptions about the nature of light. He assumed that light energy is absorbed in concentrated packets, each of an amount $h\nu$. The light quanta are called **photons,** and the two terms are used interchangeably. Einstein further assumed that the energy is so concentrated that a photon, when it enters a sub-

stance, can transfer all its energy to one electron. Einstein then applied these assumptions to the photoelectric effect.

When an electron absorbs a photon, the electron comes out of the surface with a certain KE. If the same light is made more intense, more photons per second strike the surface, but each one still has the same energy as before. Thus more electrons per second are emitted, resulting in an increase of current, but each electron still has the same KE as with the less intense light. If now a light of higher frequency is used, each photon ($h\nu$) contains more energy, and the electrons are ejected with greater KE. All this is in complete agreement with the observations discussed above.

The KE of the electron, however, is less than the energy of the photon because some energy is required to separate the electron from the surface. This amount of energy would, quite reasonably, be different for different substances.† Call this energy $\epsilon_t$. Now for a photon of low frequency, such that $h\nu < \epsilon_t$, no photoelectric emission should take place no matter how intense the illumination. For a particular frequency $\nu_t$ such that $h\nu_t = \epsilon_t$ the electrons should be released but without appreciable kinetic energies. Thus there should be a threshold frequency ($\nu_t$), characteristic of the substance, below which no photoelectric emission of electrons can occur. Again this is in complete agreement with observation.

Following Einstein, we now apply the conservation of energy to these ideas and write

KE of electron = photon − work function

or

$$\tfrac{1}{2}mv^2 = h\nu - \epsilon_t$$

But, as we saw above, the KE is measured by the stopping potential, and, according to theory, $\epsilon_t = h\nu_t$; therefore

$$V_s e = h(\nu - \nu_t) \qquad (26\text{-}3)$$

This equation represents a group of straight-

---

† This energy, called the "work function," is measurable by several methods and is a characteristic property of the substance. It is an interesting correlation that the work function is, in general, smaller for elements toward the top of the electrode-potential series (§ 21-11) and greater for those farther down the series.

line graphs, each starting at some value, $v_t$ (different for each substance), and all rising with the same slope, $h$.† This, of course, is precisely the experimental result shown in Figure 26-5.

Historically, the sequence of events was the reverse of our presentation. In 1905 the data were somewhat qualitative and showed only that Einstein's theory predicted results of the proper order of magnitude. The next year, however, Millikan started his precise determination of the electronic charge, $e$ (§ 18-5), and a decade later completely verified Einstein's equation (26-3) by a series of precise (though technically difficult) experiments. Thus Millikan was able to evaluate $h$ as it appeared in Einstein's equation for the photoelectric effect, and he found it to have the value (equation 26-2) determined by Planck from thermal-radiation data. This constancy of $h$ as determined from widely different phenomena is strong evidence for the universal and fundamental character of this important constant.

## 26-4. *Continuous X-ray Spectrum*

Einstein's quantum theory gave a completely satisfactory explanation of the photoelectric effect by assuming that the energy of a photon was transferred to an electron. The reverse process satisfactorily explains the continuous X-ray spectrum. An electron, accelerated by the large potential difference, $V$, across the X-ray tube (Fig. 25-15), enters the material of the target with high kinetic energy. As it passes through the strong electric field that is due to the positive charges in an atom of the target material, it may be slowed down by the force of attraction and lose some KE. During this encounter, or "impact," the atom is much too massive‡ to be accelerated, but energy is conserved by the emission of a photon equal to the KE lost by the electron. Several such encounters (not necessarily of equal energy loss) will

finally bring the electron to rest. With many electrons in the impinging beam, each radiating quanta as a result of random "impacts," we should expect the emitted photons to have energy less than the KE of the bombarding electrons. Occasionally an electron, stopped by a single encounter, may transfer all its KE to a single photon of maximum energy. We should therefore expect a continuous range of frequencies, with a sharply defined maximum, to be radiated from the target. If the accelerating voltage across the tube is increased, the electrons have greater KE and the largest possible photon therefore has a greater frequency (a shorter wavelength). And, finally, we should expect the maximum of these continuous spectra to be independent of the nature of the target material and to depend only on the voltage across the tube. This is precisely what is observed, as shown in Figure 25-16. (Here we consider only the continuous spectra and defer the discussion of the line spectra to a later chapter.)

In the previous section we equated the KE of the photoelectrons to the energy of the impinging photon. We now reverse this and equate the energy of the photon of maximum frequency to the KE of the impinging electron;† that is, $h\nu_{max} = \frac{1}{2}mv^2$. But, since $\frac{1}{2}mv^2 = Ve$ (in which equation $V$ is the potential difference through which the electrons with charge $e$ are accelerated), $h\nu_{max} = Ve$, or

$$\nu_{max} = \frac{e}{h}V \qquad (26\text{-}4)$$

This relation between $\nu_{max}$ and $V$, since $e/h$ is a constant, represents a straight-line graph through the origin. This is in complete agreement with the observations shown in Figure 25-16b. Furthermore, by equating the slope of equation 26-4 to the empirically determined value (equation 25-11), we determine the value of $h$ as $6.63 \times 10^{-34}$ joule sec. Thus, from a third phenomenon, the emission of X-rays, the quantum constant, $h$, is found to have the numerical value given in equation 26-2. This

---

† Subtracting $\nu_t$ shifts the origin to the right by that amount. We have already encountered this algebraic trick of shifting the origin so that the experimental graph will go through it (§ 10-4).

‡ A silver atom, for instance, is approximately 200,-000 times as massive as an electron.

---

† In this "inverse photoelectric effect" we may neglect the work function of the target material; it is only a few electron volts, and the KE of the electrons is many thousand electron volts.

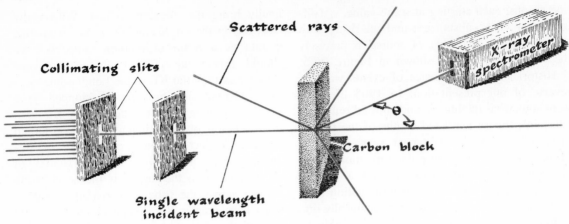

FIGURE **26-6** *Experimental method of studying scattered X-rays.*

method, in fact, is one of the most precise for the measurement of $h$.

## 26-5. Compton Effect

In 1923, A. H. Compton, by his study of scattered X-rays, produced further evidence for the quantum nature of light energy. We have already discussed the scattering of X-rays from the atoms of a crystal and have seen how some of the scattered waves reinforce each other to produce intense beams in certain directions (§ 25-8). It was found that all substances, whether crystalline or not, will scatter a beam of X-rays in all directions—that is, will scatter the rays *diffusely*. According to classical electromagnetic theory, the scattered radiation should include the same wavelengths as the incident X-rays, since the electrons are forced to vibrate with the same frequencies as the incident waves. This assumed, of course, that the electrons were free to follow the varying electric field of the incident waves and were not appreciably constrained by electrical forces in the atoms. This condition should obtain for elements of low atomic number, such as carbon, since the amount of positive electricity in their atoms is small. The results of early investigations of scattered X-rays agreed only moderately well with these expectations. The scattered rays appeared to include some rays of somewhat longer wavelength than the incident rays. When the experi-

ment was tried with short-wavelength (less than one angstrom) incident waves, the discrepancy was marked. The scattered rays were found to include the incident wavelengths in accordance with classical theory; but they also included longer wavelengths that were not in the incident beam. These longer wavelengths cannot be explained by classical theory but can be explained by quantum theory. Compton made a careful study of this effect by a method shown schematically in Figure 26-6. A narrow beam of incident rays included only one wavelength—for example, the $K_\alpha$ line of the target material of the X-ray tube (not shown). By placing an X-ray spectrometer (details not shown here; see Fig. 25-15) in various positions around the carbon block, he could measure the wavelengths in any ray scattered along the direction from the block to the entrance slit of the spectrometer. This direction is specified by the angle, $\theta$, between the directions of the incident and scattered rays.

Compton found that the scattered ray consisted of *two* wavelengths; that is, two lines appeared in the spectrum of the scattered ray, whereas there was only one in the spectrum of the incident ray. One of the lines, the *unmodified line,* always had the same wavelength as the incident ray; the other line, the *modified line,* was of definitely longer wavelength. The increase in wavelength ($\Delta\lambda$) depended on the angle of scattering, $\theta$, being greater for larger $\theta$. Figure 26-7 presents the results for three scattering angles. The intensity of ionization in the spectrometer chamber shows two definite peaks in each case. The shorter-wavelength peak appeared at the wavelength of the incident X-ray; for instance, if the $K_\alpha$ line of silver ($\lambda = 0.56$ A) was used, the shorter-wavelength peak (the unmodified line) appeared at 0.56 A. The longer-wavelength peak appeared at a definitely greater wavelength (not present in the incident beam). The "shift" ($\Delta\lambda$) of this modified line was greater for rays scattered at a greater angle to the incident beam. If another wavelength, such as the $K_\alpha$ line of tungsten ($\lambda = 0.209$ A), was used for the incident beam, the unmodified line appeared at 0.209 A, but the *shifts* (the $\Delta\lambda$'s) of the modified line were the same as before. And, finally, when substances other than carbon were used for the scattering material, the same results were observed. Here again is an effect that is independent of the particular substances involved, that must be related to the scattering process since the shift of the modified line depends only on the angle of scattering.

Compton explained this effect perfectly by boldly applying an extreme quantum picture of radiant energy. He considered the incident X-ray beam to consist of a stream of photons and each photon to be so small (so concentrated in space) that the scattering process may be considered as a single encounter of a photon and an electron. And, finally, he assigned *momentum,* as well as energy, to the photon. He then treated the scattering process as an elastic collision (§ 11-9) between the photon and the electron and applied the laws of conservation of energy and conservation of momentum. With these assumptions, Compton produced a theory that was in complete agreement with the observations.

In order to follow Compton's development, we must discuss his way of describing the mechanical properties of energy and momentum for a photon. The energy, of course, is equal to $h\nu$ in accordance with Einstein's theory of radiant energy. To arrive at an expression for the momentum, we make use of a principle derived by Einstein from his special theory of relativity (also published in 1905). The principle states that there is an equivalence of mass and energy; that is, any mass is intrinsically equivalent to a definite amount of energy, and, conversely, a certain amount of energy represents (is equivalent to) a definite mass; and the "exchange rate" (the proportionality constant) is the square of the velocity of light. In symbols, the principle states that

$$\epsilon = mc^2 \qquad (26\text{-}5)$$

For a photon, however, $\epsilon = h\nu = mc^2$, from which we see that the equivalent mass of the photon is $m = h\nu/c^2$. But the photon is traveling at the velocity of light. Thus we ascribe to the photon a momentum (mass times velocity) of $(h\nu/c^2)c$; that is,

$$\text{momentum of photon} = h\nu/c \qquad (26\text{-}6)$$

(The reader should show that equations 26-5 and 26-6 are consistent in units.)

As a specific example of these relations, consider a photon of the $K_\alpha$ line of silver (p. 439). Here $\lambda = 0.56$ A, and, remembering that $\nu = c/\lambda$, we see that the energy of the photon is

$$\epsilon = \frac{hc}{\lambda} = \frac{6.63 \times 10^{-34} \text{ joule sec} \; 3 \times 10^8 \text{ m/sec}}{0.56 \times 10^{-10} \text{ m}}$$

$$= 3.6 \times 10^{-15} \text{ joule}$$

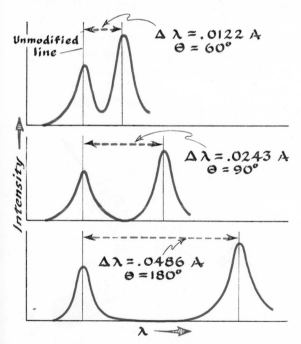

FIGURE 26-7 *Unmodified and modified lines for three angles of scattering.*

Then, applying equation 24-5, we find that the equivalent mass is

$$m = \frac{\epsilon}{c^2} = \frac{3.68 \times 10^{-15} \text{ kgm m}^2/\text{sec}^2}{9 \times 10^{16} \text{ m}^2/\text{sec}^2} = 4.0 \times 10^{-32} \text{ kgm}$$

This is an astonishingly small mass, but it is, compared with the mass of an electron (p. 299), appreciable. The ratio of these masses is $m/m_e$ = 0.044; that is, the equivalent mass of this photon is 4.4 percent of the mass of an electron. According to Compton's theory, if this photon were to collide head on with a "free" electron, we should have the situation shown in Figure 11-6, in which $m_1 = m$, the equivalent mass of the photon; $v_1 = c$, the velocity of light; $m_2 = m_e$, the mass of the electron; and $u_2 = v$, the "recoil" velocity of the electron. Putting these values into equation 11-7 and solving for $v$, we get $v = \dfrac{2m}{m + m_e} c$. If we use the mass of the electron as a unit mass (that is, if $m_e = 1$), we get, for this photon, $v = \dfrac{2(0.044)}{1.044} c = 0.084c$. That is, the electron would recoil with almost one-tenth of the velocity of light. The astonishing fact is that such high-velocity recoil electrons are actually observed and that their measured velocities are equal to those predicted by the theory.

Compton, however, first verified his theory by measuring the wavelengths of the scattered X-rays. He considered the modified line to be due to an elastic collision between the photon and a "free" electron. What is a "free" electron? The electrons, after all, are parts of the atoms of the scattering material. To remove an outer electron from an atom, however, requires only a small amount of energy. For carbon, for instance, this ionization energy is about eleven electron volts. (See § 8-11.) This, of course, must be supplied from the energy of the photon during impact. The energies of X-ray photons are many thousands of electron volts. The photon of the previous paragraph, for instance, has an energy of $(3.6 \times 10^{-15}$ joule$)/(1.6 \times 10^{-19}$ joule/ev$) = 2.3 \times 10^4$ ev—that is, more than 20,000 electron volts. Since the ionization energy is negligibly small, an outer electron may be considered "free." A possible collision is shown

schematically in Figure 26-8. Here a photon, traveling at the velocity of light, approaches, with momentum $h\nu/c$ (equation 26-6) an electron that is at rest (broken circle). After a glancing impact, the photon bounces off, at angle $\theta$ from its original direction, and the electron recoils with velocity $v$. The electron has gained KE, and the photon has lost energy. But, since all photons travel at the constant velocity of light, $c$, and since $h$ is also a universal constant, the only way for the photon to lose energy is to have a lower frequency, $\nu'$—that is, a longer wavelength. This lowered frequency also reduces the momentum of the photon, as required by the conservation of momentum. This photon and others bouncing off at the same angle account for the shift of the modified line toward a longer wavelength. Qualitatively, we can see that photons that strike electrons more nearly head on would give more energy to the recoil electrons and bounce off at greater angles. Thus the modified line would be shifted a greater amount as the angle of scattering increases. This is in complete agreement with the observations (Fig. 26-7).

The quantitative treatment of these collisions would require the use of vectors (see Fig. 11-2). If $\theta = 180°$, however, the collisions are head on, and all the momenta are directed along the same straight line. In Figure 26-9a a photon of energy $h\nu$ is headed directly at a stationary electron of mass $m$. After impact (26-9b) the photon, with reduced energy ($h\nu'$), rebounds in the opposite

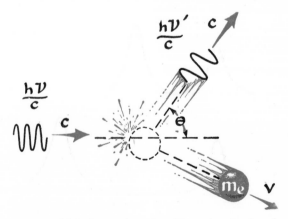

FIGURE **26-8** *Scattering of an X-ray by elastic collision of a photon with an electron.*

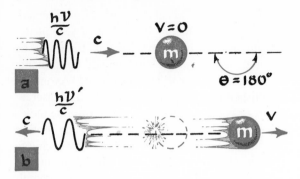

FIGURE **26-9** *Head-on collision of a photon and an electron, with 180° scattering.*

direction ($\theta = 180°$) because its equivalent mass is less than the mass of the electron (§ 11-9); and the electron moves forward with velocity $v$. For this elastic impact we may write

CONSERVATION OF ENERGY:

$$h\nu = h\nu' + \tfrac{1}{2}mv^2 \tag{26-7}$$

CONSERVATION OF MOMENTUM:

$$\frac{h\nu}{c} = mv - \frac{h\nu'}{c} \tag{26-8}$$

These equations involve known constants, the frequencies (and thus the wavelengths) of the incident and scattered photons, and the recoil velocity of the electron. Since we are not interested here in the recoil velocity, we combine equations 26-7 and 26-8 so as to eliminate $v$ and solve for $\nu - \nu'$, the change in frequency due to scattering. From this, since $\nu = c/\lambda$, we get an expression for $\lambda' - \lambda$ (that is, $\Delta\lambda$), $\lambda'$ being the wavelength of the scattered photons of the modified line and $\lambda$ the wavelength of the incident photons. The resulting shift ($\Delta\lambda$) of the modified line for scattering at 180° comes out to be†

$$\Delta\lambda = \frac{2h}{mc} \tag{26-9}$$

Notice that the right side of this equation contains only universal constants. This means that the *shift* of the modified line should be the same for different wavelengths of the incident X-rays and the same for different scattering materials. This prediction is confirmed by observa-

tion. And, finally, by substituting the values of the constants, we can easily compute the amount of shift to be 0.0486 A. This is precisely the observed value, as shown on the bottom graph of Figure 26-7.

The presence of the unmodified line, with the same wavelength as the incident X-rays, is also explained by Compton's theory. Not all of the incident photons will strike "free" outer electrons. Other electrons of the scattering material are so strongly bound to the atoms that the photons have insufficient energy and momentum to knock them free. A photon colliding with one of these electrons is colliding, in effect, with the whole atom, the mass of which is thousands of times greater than that of an electron.† Such photons bounce off the electrons with undiminished energy, just as gas molecules rebound from the wall of a container without losing kinetic energy. They show no shift of wavelength (since $\nu$ is unchanged) and thus account for the unmodified line. This result can also be predicted from equation 26-9: if, for a photon rebounding from a bound electron, the mass of the whole atom (rather than the mass of one electron) is substituted for $m$, $\Delta\lambda$ comes out to be imperceptibly small.

The picture suggested by the Compton effect, then, is of a stream of photons, all of the same energy and momentum, striking the scattering material. Some photons collide with "free" outer electrons, give up some energy to them, and rebound with diminished energy and increased wavelength (the modified line). Other photons of the incident beam, rebounding from the relatively enormous mass of the whole atom, move off with undiminished energy and unchanged wavelength (the unmodified line). The complete and exact agreement between the observations and the predictions of Compton's theory is the most convincing single piece of evidence in support of the reality of photons. This correspondence provides an empirical basis for the quantum of energy comparable to that for the atom and the electron.

---

† The solution for the more general case (Fig. 26-8) comes out to be $\Delta\lambda = h/mc(1 - \cos\theta)$. For $\theta = 180°$ this reduces to equation 26-9.

† Remember that an electron is only about 1/2,000 as massive as a hydrogen atom, and that a carbon atom is therefore almost 24,000 times as massive as an electron.

## 26-6. Summary

In this chapter we have considered one of the radically new concepts that transformed physical science fundamentally during the first decades of the twentieth century.

The quantization of energy was completely new and contradicted all our intuitive ideas concerning energy exchanges. A falling weight apparently changes PE to KE *continuously;* an oscillating pendulum seems to convert its energy to heat continuously and *gradually* to die down. On a subtler level, this same idea of continuous energy exchange underlies the theorem of the equipartition of energy, which is fundamental to much of classical science. But the quantum hypothesis treats this theorem as only an approximation for low frequencies and considers the exchange of energy to take place discontinuously in discrete packages. An oscillator does not give energy continuously as the oscillations die down gradually, but emits energy *only* during very sudden changes in energy content. Between these quantum "jumps" the oscillator emits no radiation and vibrates with constant amplitude. And this, if the oscillator is charged, contradicts classical electromagnetic theory, which requires that an accelerated charge radiate energy at all times. It is not surprising, then, that Planck's quantum hypothesis was received with great misgivings and skepticism. Even Planck himself tried for several years (but with no success) to fit his discovery into the classical theory. But, as we have seen before, when all efforts fail to fit new facts into existing theories, science must adjust the theories, and, if necessary, change fundamental concepts, no matter how deeply ingrained, so as to include the new experience. And we have seen that the quantum hypothesis, proposed by Planck and extended by Einstein in his theory of photons, is extremely successful in relating such widely different phenomena as the energy distribution in continuous spectra, the photoelectric effect, and the production and scattering of X-rays. Still further successes of this new concept will be discussed in later chapters. Thus during the early decades of the twentieth century the quantum aspect of radiant energy became generally accepted.

The quantum theory is the last of several developments that have revealed the structured, or "atomic," nature of the fundamental constituents of the physical world. Dalton and Avogadro established that any mass is composed of discrete atoms or combinations of atoms in discrete molecules. Later heat was identified with the motion of these atoms and molecules. Electric charge (which, along with heat, was treated as an imponderable fluid by the science of the eighteenth century) was seen to have structure with the discovery of the electron. That this particulate nature of the world lay hidden for so long is due to the minute size of the fundamental entities. Even for the very high frequencies of X-rays the photon is an extremely small amount of energy. Any directly observable beam of light is a stream consisting of an enormously large number of photons, just as any sensible piece of matter, however small, represents countless numbers of atoms or molecules. Whenever we consider processes that involve individual entities (such as chemical reactions or the interactions of photons and electrons), the structured nature of these quantities becomes obvious.

The most troublesome of the fundamental entities, conceptually, is the photon. It is tempting to consider a photon a *material* particle carrying energy and thus to revert to the corpuscular theory of light advocated by Newton. But, difficult as it may be, we must regard a photon as a packet of energy that is not attached to any material body. A billiard ball, on impact, may transfer all its KE to another ball, but the original ball is still there—it has only transferred its store of energy. But a photon, during a photoelectric process, transfers its energy to an electron and disappears—it ceases to exist. Another troublesome aspect of a photon is its apparent dual nature. During interactions, as we have seen, the photon displays the properties of a *particle;* but the quantity of energy of the photon ($\epsilon = h\nu$) is determined by the frequency of a *wave*. The difficulty arises primarily from our need to form models and pictures to help in visualizing the concepts. We form these pictures, quite naturally, in terms of our own experience. We observe water waves or waves along a stretched string, determine their properties, and learn how to describe them completely. We observe the patterns of illumination produced by light passing through small openings and find that we can describe them completely by ascribing to light the properties of waves. On the other hand, after observing the motions of billiard balls or other particles during impact, we formulate our observations in terms of the concepts of particle mechanics; and, after observing the results of the interaction of light and matter (as in the Compton effect), we find that we can completely describe these results by ascribing to light the properties of particles.

By now the reader undoubtedly has the uncomfortable feeling of being caught on the horns of a dilemma, which feeling is no different from that felt by the early workers in this field. Does light consist of waves or of particles? The whole classical theory, amply verified by experiment, says waves; the quantum theory, also amply verified by experiment, says particles. Clearly, new developments are required to reconcile these apparently contradictory theories. In the late 1920's, a new, abstract, and highly mathematical theory, called "wave mechanics," began to be developed. The name implies, and in fact the theory effects, a combination of the two opposing views into a unified theory, which is capable

(at least in principle) of solving all problems in the field. At this stage, however, we are not prepared to discuss the ideas underlying this theory. We shall, instead (as did the scientists of the first quarter of this century), hold the two separate views *concurrently*. We shall remember that for transmission phenomena (diffraction, interference, etc.) the wave theory works perfectly, but that for emission and absorption phenomena the photon or "particle" theory is required. Strange and intuitively disturbing as this wave-particle duality may seem, the photon theory is justified by its great power to explain and predict observations and, as we shall see, to stimulate new discoveries.

We have implied that the quantum theory is capable of explaining all the processes of radiation and absorption of light, but we have not discussed the emission and absorption line spectra of the elements. To discuss these uniquely characteristic properties of the atoms, however, we need some picture or model of the structure of atoms. The first clues that led to such a model came from investigations in the field of radioactivity, which also was developing rapidly during the early decades of the twentieth century. These clues and the discoveries to which they led will be the subject of the next chapter.

## Concepts and Terms

Quantum Hypothesis
   quantum energy changes
   temperature radiation
   Planck's constant
Photoelectric Effect
   relation between KE and light frequency
   threshold frequency

Continuous X-ray Spectrum
   inverse photoelectric effect
Compton Effect
   mass and momentum of photon
   photon-electron impact theory
Wave-particle Duality

## Problems

**26-1.** The sodium yellow line has a wavelength of 5,890 A. Calculate the quantum of energy for this light in (A) joules and (B) electron volts.
    *Ans.* (A) $3.39 \times 10^{-19}$ joule; (B) 2.11 ev

**26-2.**
  (A) Determine the value of Planck's constant from the slope of the graphs of Fig. 26-5. What are the units?

(B) Convert the value of Planck's constant (see § 26-2) to (ev) sec. Compare with the result of A.
    *Ans.* (B) $4.14 \times 10^{-15}$ (ev) sec

Note: This value of Planck's constant will be found very useful in many calculations.

**26-3.** Calculate the quantum of energy in ev for each of the first four lines and for the limit of the Balmer series. Use three significant figures. (See Fig. 25-7.)

*Ans.* 1st line, 1.89 ev; limit, 3.40 ev

**26-4.** The ionization energy of hydrogen is 13.6 ev. For what wavelength would this be one quantum of energy? Compare with the limit of the Lyman series. (See Prob. 25-12.)

**26-5.** Compare the change in the work function of the three elements shown in Fig. 26-5 with the change in the electrode potentials of the same elements, as shown in Table 21-4. Is this relation to be expected? Discuss.

**26-6.**
(A) Calculate the work function in ev for strontium. Take appropriate data from Fig. 26-5.
(B) Will the sodium yellow light produce photoelectrons from a strontium surface? (See Prob. 26-1.)
(C) With how much KE (in ev) will photoelectrons leave a strontium surface illuminated with light of 4,000 A wavelength (visible violet limit)? Verify your answer from Fig. 26-5.

*Ans.* (A) 2.8 ev

**26-7.**
(A) The stopping potential is 1.20 volts for photoelectrons ejected from a nickel surface by ultraviolet light of wavelength 2,000 A. What is the work function for nickel?
(B) Place the graph for nickel on Fig. 26-5.

*Ans.* (A) 5.01 ev

**26-8.** An experiment on the photoelectric effect with a cesium surface gave the following data: for yellow light (5,890 A) a stopping potential of 0.21 volt; for ultraviolet light (2,537 A) a stopping potential of 3.00 volts. Evaluate Planck's constant from these data. (Hint: Write Einstein's equation for each set of data. Subtract one of these equations from the other. The result will contain $h$ and observed data.)

**26-9.** The maximum frequency radiated from an X-ray tube was found to be $1.2 \times 10^{19}$/sec. What was the potential difference across the tube? Check your result with Fig. 25-16b.

**26-10.** The $K_\alpha$ line of copper has a wavelength of 1.54 A. What is the least voltage across the tube that will cause this line to be radiated?

*Ans.* $8.07 \times 10^3$ volts

**26-11.** Calculate Planck's constant from equations 25-11 and 26-4.

**26-12.**
(A) The surface temperature of the sun is approximately 6,000°K. Calculate the average kinetic energy per molecule (see § 12-2). Express in ev.
(B) Calculate, in ev, the energy of a photon of light with $\lambda = 5,000$ A. This wavelength is near the peak of the sun's temperature radiation curve. Repeat for $\lambda = 16,500$ A, which is an infrared wavelength in the sun's spectrum.
(C) Would you expect an average molecular impact to cause the radiation of 5,000 A of 16,500 A? Relate your answers to Figs. 25-2 and 12-3.

*Ans.* (A) 0.776 ev
(B) 2.48 ev; 0.752 ev

**26-13.**
(A) What assumptions underlay Compton's theory of the scattering of X-rays?
(B) Why does a photon bouncing off a "free" electron have a longer wavelength?
(C) How do you account for the unmodified line?
(D) In view of the quantitative agreement between the predictions of the theory and the observations (including the speed and directions of the recoil electrons), what would you say about the assumption that photons have momentum, as stated by equation 26-6?

**26-14.**
(A) Calculate the change in wavelength for 180° scattering from a "free" electron. Compare your answer with Fig. 26-7.
(B) Calculate the change in wavelength for 180° scattering from a bound electron in carbon. Could this change be observed?

**26-15.**
(A) The wavelength of the copper $K_\alpha$ line is 1.539 A. What is the wavelength of the modified line scattered at 90°?
(B) What is the wavelength of the modified tungsten $K_\alpha$ line scattered at 60°?

*Ans.* (A) 1.563 A
(B) 0.221 A

**26-16.**
(A) Derive a formula for the speed of recoil of the electron for 180° scattering. (Hint: Express the conservation of momentum, remember that $v = c/\lambda$, and solve for $v$.)
(B) Calculate the recoil speed if the incident wavelength is 1.549 A.

*Ans.* (A) $v = h(\lambda + \lambda')/m\lambda\lambda'$
(B) $v = 0.0311c$

**26-17. Radiation Pressure.** According to the quantum theory, a beam of light consists of a shower of photons. If the light is reflected by a mirror, the photons rebound with undiminished energy and momentum.

A beam of yellow light ($\lambda = 5,900$ A) falls perpendicularly on a mirror of 5 cm² area. The intensity of the beam is such that 0.243 joule falls on the mirror each second. Calculate the force and the pressure exerted on the mirror by the beam of light. (Hint: Calculate the energy of one photon and hence the number of photons striking the mirror per second. The analysis is then the same as in Prob. 11-8.) Compare the pressure with normal atmospheric pressure.

What would be the pressure if the light fell on a surface coated with lampblack?

*Ans.* Pressure on mirror $= 3.24 \times 10^{-6}$ newton/m²

Note: The radiation pressure on delicately suspended mirrors has been measured and found to be in agreement with theory. Radiation pressure undoubtedly plays a large role in the formation of a comet's tail. As a comet, in its very elliptical orbit, swings in close to the sun, it develops a tail. The tail, however, streams out, not behind the comet, but in a direction *away* from the sun. For a sufficiently small dust particle the force due to radiation pressure becomes greater than the gravitational attraction of the sun.

**26-18. Energy-level Diagram.** Consider the term diagram of Prob. 25-33. Each term represents a wave number $(1/\lambda)$ with the unit of 1/meter. Multiplying each term by the constant $(hc)$ would yield a set of discrete energies of different amounts or "levels." As an example, convert to energies the terms for $n = 2$ and $n = 3$. Compare the difference between these energies with a photon of the first Balmer line. (See Prob. 26-3.) In a similar manner the size of the photons of the whole hydrogen spectrum could be obtained by appropriate differences. In Chap. 28 we shall consider the theoretical basis of this fact.

# Suggested Readings

1. R. A. Millikan, *Electrons* (+ *and* −), revised edition (University of Chicago Press, 1947), pp. 232–259. An excellent and readable discussion of the quantum nature of light, including the author's experimental verification of Einstein's photoelectric theory.
2. A. Einstein and L. Infeld, *The Evolution of Physics* (Simon & Schuster, 1938), pp. 263–280. Excellent, non-mathematical discussion of quantum theory.
3. M. Born, *The Restless Universe*, translated by W. M. Deans (Dover Publications, 1951), pp. 117–121, 133–139.
4. R. F. Humphreys and R. Beringer, *First Principles of Atomic Physics* (Harper & Brothers, 1950), pp. 250–259 (quantum theory), 284–288 (Compton effect).
5. H. E. White, *Modern College Physics,* 3rd edition (Van Nostrand, 1956), pp. 652–659 (photoelectric effect), 705–707 (Compton effect).
6. O. Oldenberg, *Introduction to Atomic Physics,* 2nd edition (McGraw-Hill, 1954). An excellent intermediate text. See pp. 75–94 on the quantum of light and pp. 213–217 on the vector treatment of the Compton effect.

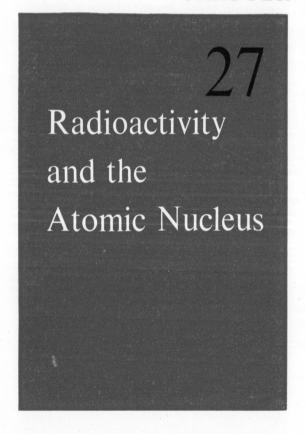

# Radioactivity and the Atomic Nucleus

WITHIN a few months of Roentgen's discovery of X-rays and just a year before Thomson's discovery of free electrons, a new and mysterious type of radiation was discovered. In 1896, A. H. Becquerel was investigating the possibility of a relation between X-rays and visible fluorescence. It was known that the uranium mineral pitchblende would emit X-rays at the anode end of a cathode-ray tube and would fluoresce with visible light when struck by X-rays from some other source. Becquerel's experiment was to find out whether the reverse effect existed —that is, whether the pitchblende would emit X-rays after exposure to visible light. To test this possibility, he wrapped a photographic plate in black paper to protect it from light, placed a piece of pitchblende on the package, and set the combination in strong sunlight for a few days. On developing the plate he found it blackened as if by X-rays. One day, however, when the weather turned cloudy, he set the device in a drawer to await a clear day. The cloudy spell lasted several days, and, not wanting to use an old plate, he developed the one that had been in the drawer. Much to his surprise he found that this plate also was blackened, although the plate and pitchblende had been in darkness. Repeated trials showed that the effect was no accident but that pitchblende (and other uranium minerals) emitted a radiation that was capable, like X-rays, of passing through normally opaque substances. The new rays were found to be very energetic and could, like X-rays, reduce a photographic emulsion or discharge an electroscope by ionizing the surrounding air. But, *unlike* X-rays, they had no apparent source of energy. Although, at the time, neither the nature of X-rays nor the process of their production was understood, the source of their energy could easily be related to the electrical energy supplied to the cathode-ray tube. But the uranium minerals required no treatment, apparently no transfer of energy, to produce the rays. Here, indeed, was a vastly surprising discovery. Apparently these minerals contained an inexhaustible supply of energy, which they continuously and *spontaneously* radiated. Several natural substances and also some man-made ones display this property. They are called **radioactive substances,** and the study of this phenomenon comprises the field of **radioactivity.**

## 27-1. *Radioactive Substances*

The nature of the radioactive emanations immediately became a question of great interest and was investigated by several scientists. Notable among these was a young physicist, Ernest Rutherford, who was working under Thomson at the Cavendish Laboratory in England. Rutherford found that the radioactive emanation contained two components, which he named alpha rays ($\alpha$-rays) and beta rays ($\beta$-rays). Later a third component, called gamma rays ($\gamma$-rays), was discovered. The method of investigation, which is already familiar to us, is shown schematically in Figure 27-1. The radiation is strongly absorbed by lead. Hence, if some radioactive material is placed at the bottom of a long, narrow hole drilled in a lead block, a narrow, well-defined beam of radiation will emerge from the block. This beam is allowed to pass between the poles of an electromagnet and fall on a photographic plate. With no current in the magnet, a well-defined spot (marked gamma ray in the figure) appears on the photographic plate. When the magnetic field is turned on, two other spots, displaced from the original spot, appear. We conclude that the $\alpha$- and $\beta$-rays consist of streams of electrically charged particles, and that the $\gamma$-rays, which are not deflected by the magnetic field, are probably high-frequency electromagnetic waves. The $\alpha$-particles are charged positively, and the $\beta$-particles are charged negatively (verify this from the figure); and the $\beta$-particles are deflected much more than the $\alpha$-particles.

Immediately after Becquerel's discovery, Marie Curie started a systematic search for other radioactive substances. The main component of pitchblende is uranium oxide ($U_2O_8$), and, since pure oxygen does not have any radioactive effect, the activity was ascribed to the uranium. But Mme. Curie found that radiation from *pure* uranium oxide (as measured by the rate of discharge of a charged electroscope) was *less* intense than that from pitchblende; and she rightly concluded that the mineral contained radioactive substances other than uranium. She and her husband, Pierre Curie, then began the chemical analysis of uranium minerals. This was a painstaking and arduous task. Many kinds of chemical separations were applied, and large quantities of minerals had to be handled, for the radioactive elements were found to be present in exceedingly small fractions. The products of the reactions were tested with the electroscope, the inactive parts were discarded, and the active parts were further analyzed. Finally one product, which was mostly bismuth sulfide, proved to be hundreds of times as active as uranium. Since neither bismuth nor sulfur is radioactive, Mme. Curie correctly assumed that the product contained a trace of a new, highly active element that closely resembled bismuth chemically. She named this element polonium ($Z = 84$). Later that same year (1896), the Curies obtained, along with barium chloride, an active product that indicated, since neither barium nor chlorine is active, the presence of a new alkaline-earth metal. This element existed in sufficient quantity, however, so that repeated fractional crystal-

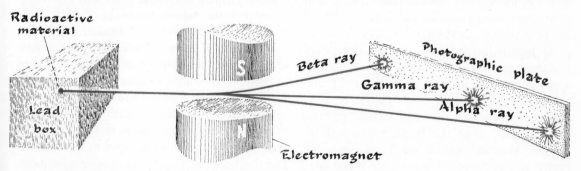

FIGURE **27-1** *Separation of radioactive rays by a magnetic field.*

lizations gradually removed the inactive barium and left the pure chloride of the new element. When, with this, the atomic weight was determined, radium was placed in the periodic table ($Z = 88$). These elements (Po and Ra) were the first to be discovered as a result of their radioactive properties. Soon many other radioactive heavy elements were found. We now know that all atoms from atomic number 84 up are radioactive, many of them being isotopes of the listed elements. These atoms were identified mostly by their radiations but also by such manifestations as the appearance of a hitherto unknown atomic or X-ray spectrum. The atomic number 88 for radium, for instance, was later verified by the position of radium's X-ray spectrum on the Moseley diagram (§ 25-9).

As the radioactive elements, once isolated, supplied much more intense sources of radiation than had been available before, detailed and precise studies of radioactivity became possible. One result was the discovery that a radioactive atom emits either an $\alpha$-particle or a $\beta$-particle, but not both, and that many radioactive elements emit the $\gamma$-ray also. Another result of the early experiments was very puzzling and completely unexpected: a carefully prepared sample of a radioactive substance was observed to change its properties with time, as though its composition were changing! Some substances changed in a few days or even in a few minutes, others more slowly. The astounding fact, of course, was that they changed at all, for, as we have seen, the idea of constant composition is fundamental to our concept of substances. It was found, however, that all radioactive elements are continually creating small amounts of new elements. We shall see, for instance, that uranium (92), as it emits $\alpha$-particles, produces an element with all the properties of thorium (90); this substance emits $\beta$-particles and produces an isotope of protactinium (91). Radium (88) gradually disappears, and the inert gases radon (86) and helium (2) appear.

Here, indeed, is a new and strange process, quite different from the familiar chemical reactions. Mercuric oxide, we know, may be heated and decomposed into mercury and oxygen; and under other conditions oxygen and mercury may be combined to form the oxide. But, although radium continuously decomposes into radon and helium, no one has ever succeeded in combining these two to produce radium. Furthermore, as we have seen (Chap. 23), we can control the rate of chemical reactions by temperature or other factors. But nothing affects the rate of radioactive disintegration. No changes in the applied temperature or pressure, however great, nor even changes in chemical combination, will affect the radiation. The radium in radium chloride, for instance, disintegrates in exactly the same way as the purified metal. But the most astonishing comparison, probably, is between the energies of the reactions. The energy exchanged in chemical reactions is only a few electron volts (§ 21-10); the energy exchanged in radioactive processes, as determined by the observed energy of the rays is several *million* electron volts (Mev).

The facts of radioactivity, which were entirely new and different from any other observations in chemistry and physics, led to the assumption of a hitherto unknown process within atoms. Radioactivity, it seemed, must be a process deep within the atoms, for no external agency affects it. (Chemical reactions, as we have seen, involve the "outer," valence electrons near the surface of atoms.) In 1903, Rutherford and a coworker, Frederick Soddy, proposed the hypothesis that each radioactive atom has an intrinsic tendency to explode. During the explosion an $\alpha$- or a $\beta$-particle is ejected with high energy, which process transforms the atom into an atom of a *different* element. This new atom may itself be radioactive and transform itself into a still different element, which process continues until a stable element is formed. This bold hypothesis postulated the transmutation of elements and disagreed radically with the classical idea of the immutability of atoms (§ 6-5). By an elaborate series of tests Rutherford and Soddy were able to determine which radioactive atoms transformed into which others and the characteristic rate of transformation of each kind of atom. With this information they were able to explain completely the puzzling changes in composition that had been observed in radioactive substances. So convincing were their results that their transformation hypothesis has never been seriously questioned. We cannot discuss their methods, which involved intricate and tedious analyses. At the end of this chapter, however, we shall discuss their radioactive "series" in the light of a new concept of atomic structure proposed by Rutherford in 1911: the nuclear atom.

## 27-2. *Nature of Radioactive Rays*

The determination of the properties of the three types of radiation emitted by radioactive substances constituted much of the research immediately following Becquerel's discovery. Those properties were soon discovered, and in this section we shall discuss some of the results of the research.

γ-RAYS. We have already seen that γ-rays are not deflected by a magnetic field (Fig. 27-1). From this and their ability to penetrate opaque substances we might suspect that the γ-ray consists of high-frequency electromagnetic waves. This was found to be so. The γ-rays from some radioactive substances have wavelengths of about the same magnitude as high-energy X-rays, and these wavelengths can be measured with the Bragg spectrometer (§ 25-8).

The γ-rays from other radioactive substances, however, have wavelengths that are much too short to show measurable diffraction, even with the very fine spacing of a crystal "grating" (Fig. 25-11). These wavelengths are measured indirectly by the energy of the photon ($h\nu$) for the frequencies. Such a photon, for instance, in passing through a thin layer of metal, may produce a photoelectron. By magnetic deflection the speed and thus the KE of this electron can be measured. This measurement then gives the energy of the photon (§ 26-3; here the work function is negligibly small). If the photon experiences a Compton impact and gives only part of its energy to the electron, the theory of the Compton effect will yield its energy (§ 26-5). The experiments are troublesome (since it is not always clear whether the observed electron is a photoelectron or a Compton electron) and involve many ob-

servations and a rather complicated statistical analysis.

These and other methods, however, give consistent results, which show that a γ-ray consists of high-energy photons of a well-defined wavelength, which is characteristic of the particular radioactive substance. Depending on the substance, the energies range from about a half million to several million electron volts (Mev).

β-RAYS. These rays consist of very high-speed electrons. Figure 27-1 shows that they are negatively charged, and by the measurement of their deflections in electric and magnetic fields both the speed and the ratio $e/m$ may be evaluated.† These electrons are ejected with a wide range of velocities, but there is a well-defined maximum velocity for each β-emitting substance. Some of these β-particles have kinetic energies of the order of Mev (Table 27-2) and velocities that approach the velocity of light—a hitherto unheard-of velocity for a material body.

The measurements of $e/m$ for β-particles yielded another surprising result: instead of being constant, as it is for lower-energy electrons, it was found to decrease as the velocity increased. A few representative results are shown in Table 27-1. The measured velocity of the β-particle is

TABLE 27-1 *Ratio of Charge to Mass of High-speed Electrons*

| $v/c$ | $e/m$ ($10^{11}$ coul/kgm) | $\sqrt{1 - v^2/c^2}$ |
|---|---|---|
| 0.100 | 1.75 | 0.995 |
| 0.500 | 1.52 | 0.866 |
| 0.750 | 1.17 | 0.664 |
| 0.998 | 0.0855 | 0.0486 |

given in the first column as a fraction of the velocity of light. Notice that, as the velocity approaches the velocity of light, the value of $e/m$ decreases rapidly: for $v = 0.1c$, $e/m$ is only 0.5 percent less than the standard value ($1.76 \times 10^{11}$ coul/kgm), but for $v = 0.998c$ (almost the ve-

† In Fig. 18-4, for instance, replace the cathode, $C$, with a sample of β-emitting substance, and disconnect the accelerating voltage. The apparatus would then measure the $v$ and $e/m$ of the β-particles.

locity of light), $e/m$ is only about 1/20 of the standard value. This is indeed surprising, for, as we have seen, a great variety of evidence points to the constancy of $e$, the electronic charge. If $e$ is constant, the *mass* of these high-speed electrons must be *increasing with the speed*.

This effect had been predicted by Einstein as a logical consequence of his special theory of relativity (1905). This very general theory of dynamics, derived from observations of phenomena completely different from radioactivity, predicts that the mass of any material body will increase with increasing velocity. The relation between mass and velocity, derivable from the theory, is stated by the equation

$$m = \frac{m_0}{\sqrt{1 - v^2/c^2}} \tag{27-1}$$

in which $v$ is the velocity of the body, $c$ is the velocity of light, and $m_0$ is the "rest mass"—the mass of the body when it is stationary or moving with a velocity that is small compared with the velocity of light ($v/c << 1$). The presence of the velocity of light in the formula explains why this effect is never noticed for bulk matter. If $v/c = 0.1$, for instance, the radical evaluates at 0.995; that is, there is only 0.5 percent increase in mass. Although one-tenth of the velocity of light is small for the motion of $\beta$-particles, for ordinary motions it is enormous (about 19,000 mi/sec; compare with 0.3 mi/sec for a fast jet airplane). Hence the change of mass with velocity is completely unobservable for perceptible bodies, and in Newtonian mechanics the mass of a moving object is therefore considered constant.

If we assume equation 27-1 to be correct, then

$$\frac{e}{m} = \frac{e}{m_0} \sqrt{1 - v^2/c^2}$$

Here $e/m_0$ is the standard value, that of the "slow" electrons in cathode-ray tubes. For "high" velocities the measured value of $e/m$ should be the same fraction of the standard value as the numerical value of the radical. This numerical value is given for the listed velocities in the third column of Table 27-1. When the numbers are multiplied by 1.76, the values of the second column are obtained. This was the first experimen-

tal verification of the several predictions of the relativity theory, and it gave increased confidence in the correctness of the other predictions, such as the mass-energy equivalence that was used effectively by Compton in his theory of X-ray scattering. All the various atomic particles, accelerated to very high velocities in the apparatus of contemporary atomic research, show this increase of mass with velocity. Hence the "relativistic" mass must be used in atomic dynamics. Whenever we speak of *the* mass of a particle, however, we mean its rest mass.†

$\alpha$-RAYS. These rays consist of doubly ionized helium atoms. The deflection of $\alpha$-particles by a magnetic field shows that they are positively charged; and the fact that they are deflected less than $\beta$-rays suggests that they are much more massive than $\beta$-particles (Fig. 27-1). With sufficiently strong electric and magnetic fields, however, the velocity and the ratio of charge to mass of $\alpha$-particles may be determined precisely. The value of $q/m$ for all $\alpha$-particles is found to be $4.83 \times 10^7$ coul/kgm. This is just half as large as the value for hydrogen ions in electrolysis experiments (Table 18-1). As we saw in Chapter 18, the value of $q/m$ for hydrogen is the largest of all atomic ions in electrolysis. Thus the smaller value for the $\alpha$-particles suggested a mass of atomic scale. If the $\alpha$-particle, like the hydrogen ion, was singly charged, its relative mass would be 2, which was at that time an unknown atomic weight. The presence of helium in most radioactive preparations favored the view that $\alpha$-particles might be ionized helium atoms. If so, with an atomic weight of 4, they would have to carry two elementary charges ($+2e$) to give the observed value of $q/m$.

Rutherford identified the $\alpha$-particle as ionized helium in two ways, the first of which can be understood with the aid of Figure 27-2. When an $\alpha$-particle strikes a thin coating of fluorescent

---

† This result furnishes another reason why the photon cannot be considered a *material* particle. Equation 27-1 shows that at the velocity of light ($v = c$) the mass of any material object becomes *infinitely large*. But the photon travels at the velocity of light. Hence its equivalent mass must be all relativistic; that is, it can have no rest mass. This is consistent with the observation that, when the energy of a photon is absorbed (as in the photoelectric effect), the photon disappears.

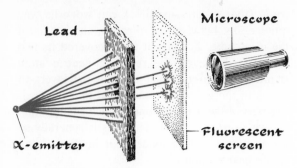

FIGURE **27-2** *Method of counting α-particles.*

material on a glass plate, it causes the material to glow momentarily at the point of impact. By counting these tiny flashes of light (called *scintillations*) one can determine the number of α-particles striking the fluorescent screen.† A lead plate with a hole in it prevents the α-particles from striking the fluorescent screen outside the small area that can be conveniently observed through the microscope. By averaging the counts of many observations, one can determine accurately the number of α-particles per minute. The fluorescent screen is then replaced by a metallic

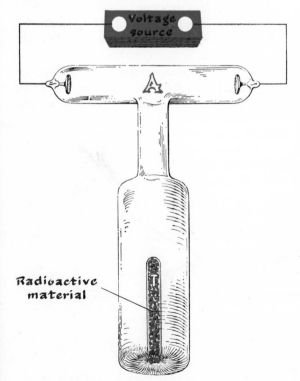

FIGURE **27-3** *Identification of α-particles as helium ions.*

plate connected to a negatively charged and calibrated electroscope. When the α-particles strike the plate, they remove negative charges (equal to their positive charges) and become electrically neutral. From the observed rate of discharge of the electroscope, the total charge per minute carried by the impinging α-particles is determined. This charge, divided by the previously determined number of particles per minute, yields the charge on one α-particle. The value was always found to be $3.2 \times 10^{-19}$ coulomb. This is just twice the electronic charge ($q = 2e$) and, as mentioned above, gives 4 as the "atomic weight" of the α-particle.

The next year (1909) Rutherford produced still more convincing evidence of the identity of α-particles and helium ions. Making use of the ability of α-particles to penetrate thin layers of solid material, he devised the experiment represented by Figure 27-3. A glass tube carried a side arm, $A$, containing sealed-in electrodes, and a thin-walled re-entrant tube, $T$. The apparatus was so highly evacuated that, when the voltage was turned on, no luminous discharge appeared in $A$. Some α-emitting material was then placed in $T$. After several days sufficient gas was found to have accumulated in the apparatus to support a luminous discharge in $A$. When this light was analyzed, it was found to consist of the characteristic line spectrum of neutral helium. Control experiments with helium in $T$ showed that there was no possibility of helium gas leaking into the apparatus. Rutherford concluded that the α-particle was an ionized helium atom, which, while passing through $T$ or by contact with other parts of the apparatus, picked up two electrons and became a neutral helium atom.‡

---

† The fluorescent hands of a watch are coated with a thin film of fluorescent material to which a minute amount of radioactive substance has been added. If the hands of the watch are observed through a magnifying glass in a very dark room, many scintillations —individual atomic explosions!—may be seen. (It is usually necessary first to wait a while in the dark so that the eyes become "dark-adapted."

‡ The results of this experiment, combined with the value of $q/m$, verify an assumption that was made in the method of Fig. 27-2: that *every* α-particle produces a visible scintillation. The reader should develop the logic of this conclusion. The conclusion is important because the counting of α-particles by the scintillation method was one of the most widely used tools of research in the early investigations of radioactivity.

Unlike $\beta$-particles, $\alpha$-particles are ejected with definite velocities that are characteristic of the radiating substances. These velocities are considerably smaller than those of $\beta$-particles, the greatest $\alpha$-particle velocity being only about $0.07c$. An $\alpha$-particle's velocity-induced increase in mass is therefore negligibly small. Yet $\alpha$-particles are so much more massive than $\beta$-particles that their kinetic energies are also of the order of Mev (Table 27-2).

As pointed out in § 27-1, the very high energies of all the radioactive rays indicate that we are dealing with a process very different from ordinary chemical reactions, for this process involves energy exchanges a million times as large. Very small amounts of radioactive substances release sizable amounts of energy. A tube containing a small amount of radium, for instance, is always at a higher temperature than the surroundings. Rutherford and Soddy calculated that the presence of radium as only 1 part in $10^{14}$ would account for the heat lost from the earth by radiation, and they suggested that the heat of the sun may be due to radioactivity. We shall see in a later chapter that we now have a different theory of the heat of the sun, but the heat of the earth is probably due, in part, to radioactive materials.

A rather startling inference must be drawn from the result of the experiment of Figure 27-3. Presumably a helium atom minus its two elec-trons (that is, an $\alpha$-particle) can work its way quite easily between, or *through,* the atoms of the glass tube, $T$. Once it has recovered its two electrons, however, the resulting neutral atom is much too large to get through the layers of atoms in the glass. It seems, then, that the positive part of the helium atom is much smaller than the whole neutral atom. That this is generally so for all atoms will be made clear in some detail in the next section.

## 27-3. Nuclear Atom

In 1911, Rutherford announced a new theory of the structure of atoms—a theory that swept away the last vestige of the classical model of solid spheres. The theory was based on experiments that measured the deflection of $\alpha$-particles by passage through thin metallic foils. Rutherford (who was then professor of physics at the University of Manchester, England) and his collaborators got some completely unexpected results.

The apparatus is quite simple; its essential features are shown in Figure 27-4. A narrow beam of $\alpha$-particles from radium emerges from a small hole in a block of lead. This beam is directed at a thin metal foil (gold in the first experiment), which, before mounting, was tested for air-tightness; there are no holes in it. The

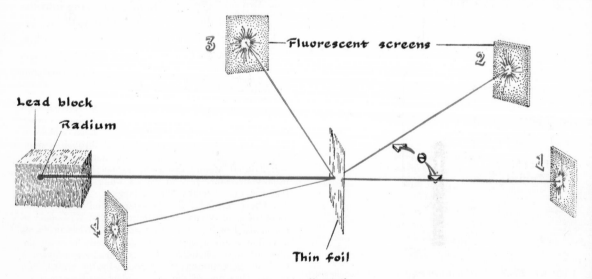

FIGURE **27-4** *Scattering of $\alpha$-particles by a thin metallic foil.*

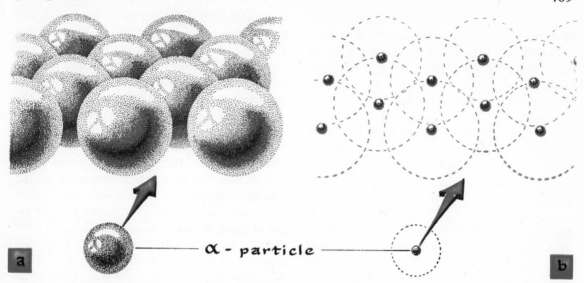

α - particle

FIGURE **27-5** *Diagram of an α-particle approaching thin foil: (a) Thomson's atomic model; (b) Ruther-ford's nuclear model (nucleus greatly magnified).*

α-particles are detected by the scintillations they produce on striking a fluorescent screen. The scintillations are observed through a microscope (not shown) mounted directly behind the screen. The microscope-screen combination is mounted on an arm so that it may be moved round a circle with the foil at the center. Thus α-particles leaving the foil in any direction may be observed, and the scintillations indicate the number moving in each direction. The whole apparatus is enclosed in a vacuum so that any observed deflection will be due to the action of the foil, not to impacts with gaseous atoms.

Let us see if we can predict what will happen. We use the picture of an atom proposed by Thomson after his discovery of electrons. This, you will remember, assumed that the positive charge is distributed uniformly throughout the whole volume of the atom. We have already seen that the atoms of a solid lie very close together, their centers separated by not much more than their diameters—that is, by several angstroms (§ 25-8), which is about the known diameter of atoms (§ 12-5). Hence even a very thin foil ($\approx 10^{-6}$ m) is several thousand atoms thick (remember that 1 A = $10^{-10}$ m). An α-particle approaching such a thin foil is presented with a situation somewhat like that shown in Figure 27-5a except that the thickness must be imag-ined as several thousand atoms instead of the three that are shown. Our first conclusion is that the α-particle (itself a helium atom minus two electrons) would not go through the foil at all. But we have already seen that α-particles do penetrate thin layers of solids (Fig. 27-3). Perhaps the very high kinetic energy of the α-particle enables it to plow right *through* the atoms of the metal. We can picture the result of such a process. If the α-particle should happen to go through the center of a metal atom, it would not be deflected. If it went through the left side of an atom, it would be deflected to the left by the repulsion of that part of the positive charge of the atom which lay to its right. It would then probably go through the right side of the next atom and be deflected to the right. Many such deflections, the amount of each depending on the distance from the center of the atom, would result in a zigzag path through the foil, and the α-particle would emerge from the other side with very little *net* deflection. Applying the laws of probability to this picture, Rutherford and his collaborators found that the net deflection produced by a thin foil should be about one degree. This deduction seemed to be consistent with observation, but the experiment also yielded a completely unexpected result.

Refer again to Figure 27-4. With the screen

in position 1 and the foil removed, the scintillations were observed to occur in a circle, the size of which was determined by the width of the beam. With the foil in place, *most* of the α-particles still struck the screen at 1 but were distributed over a slightly greater area. This was the expectation. But *some* α-particles were observed to be deflected through large angles. At position 2, for instance, with $\theta = 30°$, a definite number of scintillations were observed. The number, to be sure, was only a fraction of 1 percent of the number of α-particles in the beam; but, according to the theory, the chance of observing any at all was completely negligible. Furthermore, a small but varying fraction of the α-particles were found to be deflected through any angle chosen, such as that of position 3 ($\theta$ a little greater than 90°) and that of position 4 ($\theta$ almost 180°). This last was particularly surprising: an α-particle turned back along its path as though it had rebounded from a head-on collision with some massive object. It was impossible to explain these large-angle deflections as multiple deflections by Thomson's type of atoms in the foil.

To account for these observations Rutherford proposed a new atomic model, one that could produce a large α-particle deflection as the result of a *single* encounter. He introduced the hypothesis that the positive charge of an atom (and practically all the mass) is concentrated in an exceedingly small region at the center of the atom, which he called the **nucleus.** Arranged round the nucleus—in such a manner as to account for the known size of the atoms—are sufficient electrons to make the whole atom electrically neutral. An α-particle approaching a thin foil composed of such nuclear atoms would find a situation somewhat like that shown in Figure 27-5b. Here each nucleus is presented as a small globe at the center of a circle (dashed line), which circle represents the sphere that defines the total volume of the atom. It is impossible, unfortunately, to draw this to scale. We shall see presently that, if the nucleus is represented by spots of the size shown, the spheres, on the same scale, should be bigger than a house. We must therefore imagine the diagram as enormously expanded, with relatively vast spaces between

the nuclei. The α-particle, as we have seen, is a helium atom minus two electrons. But a helium atom *has* only two electrons (p. 306). The α-particle is therefore a helium nucleus and, on this hypothesis, is also exceedingly small. With this model, Rutherford worked out, for the deflection of α-particles, a theory that accurately accounted for the observations. We cannot follow the mathematical details, but we shall show, qualitatively, how theory and observation agree.

It is easy to understand why most of the α-particles go through the foil with little deflection. Since, for the minute α-particles of the incident beam, the foil is mostly empty space, most of them pass through it at relatively great distances from the nuclei of the metal atoms. They encounter electrons along the way, to be sure, but their motion is little affected by these collisions between a very large mass and a small one (ratio about 8,000/1)—collisions that are somewhat analogous to a moving automobile's being hit by a golf ball. Many such impacts, however, produce a small deflection of the α-particles, and this accounts for the slight broadening of the direct beam.

Occasionally, however, a few of the many α-particles of the incident beam will pass close to the nucleus of a metal atom. Three such encounters are shown in Figure 27-6. The nucleus, with charge $+Q$, is shown as a black globe. (Again the reader is reminded of the relative distances involved: if the nucleus were as large as

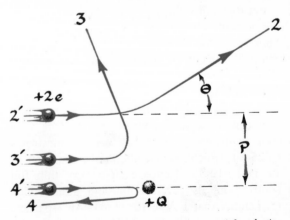

FIGURE **27-6** *Deflection of an α-particle during each of three successively closer approaches to a nucleus.*

its representation in the figure, an adjacent nucleus would be about 400 feet away—that is, in another building of the campus.) Consider an α-particle (a colored globe) approaching from 2′ so that, if undeflected, it will pass the nucleus at some distance, $p$, much smaller than the radius of the whole atom. As it approaches the nucleus, the electrostatic repulsion between $+Q$ and $+2e$ becomes strong enough to affect its motion appreciably. Suppose that this point is just to the right of the position of $+2e$ shown in the figure. The force, which is along the line joining the nucleus and the α-particle and makes an angle with the direction of motion, may be resolved into rectangular components parallel to and perpendicular to the instantaneous direction of the path. The parallel component slows down the α-particle, and the perpendicular component changes the direction of its motion. The detailed mechanical analysis is complicated by the fact that both the magnitude and the direction of the force are continuously changing. At the point of nearest approach to the nucleus, the force on the α-particle is at its maximum and acts at right angles to the path; the direction of motion is changing most rapidly at this point. After this point the parallel component of the force speeds up the α-particle until the force again becomes inappreciable. The α-particle then moves along a straight path toward 2. Detailed calculation shows that the path is a hyperbola and is symmetrical about the point of nearest approach. Thus the α-particle moves off with the same kinetic energy with which it approached the nucleus.† The chance that this α-particle will make another close approach to a nucleus before it emerges from the foil is negligible; it moves along the new direction and produces a scintillation on the fluorescent screen at position 2 (Fig. 27-4). Now consider an α-particle approaching from 3′ so that, if undeflected, it will pass closer to a nucleus than the particle from 2′ (smaller $p$). The repulsive force is now at first more nearly parallel to the line of flight. The particle, during the first part of its encounter, is

† The nucleus is not displaced during the encounter since it is much more massive than the α-particle. Each metallic atom, moreover, is held firmly in the crystal lattice of the metal. In effect, then, the α-particle rebounds off the mass of the whole foil.

therefore slowed down more but deflected less than the one from 2′. Thus it moves nearer to the nucleus before reaching the point of maximum change in direction. The repulsive force at that point is now greater; the particle is deflected through a greater angle and moves off to the screen at position 3. Very infrequently an α-particle, approaching from 4′, moves directly toward a nucleus ($p = 0$). In this case the particle is slowed down until, at a point very near the nucleus, it momentarily comes to rest. It is then repelled along its original path; that is, it is deflected through 180°.

Now even a very narrow beam contains many α-particles and is so wide, compared with atomic dimensions, that it is directed toward a large number of atoms in the foil, the nuclei of which would appear as widely spaced, minute dots. Since the distances between the nuclei are thousands of times as large as the diameters of the nuclei, most of the α-particles in the beam do not pass close enough to any nucleus to suffer more than a negligible deflection. There is a small but definite chance, however, that an α-particle will pass some nucleus at the distance $p$ of Figure 27-6. All such particles will be deflected through angle $\theta$ and will move off to produce a definite number of scintillations on the screen at position 2. Clearly, the chance that an α-particle will approach some nucleus more closely than $p$, as from 3′, is less than its chance to approach at the greater distance, and a smaller number of α-particles should therefore be deflected through the larger angle to the screen at position 3. In other words, the number of α-particles deflected should become smaller as the angle of deflection becomes larger. Rutherford's calculation of the fraction deflected through any angle was found to give the exact number that was observed.

Let us now suppose that the foil is replaced by one twice as thick. As the α-particles go through the foil, they pass twice as many nuclei as before. Clearly, then, the chance for an α-particle to pass a nucleus at a particular distance (such as 2′→2 in Fig. 27-6) is twice as great, and the fraction of the α-particles deflected through a particular angle should therefore be twice as great for this foil. Or, more generally, the number of scintillations observed at a fixed position of the screen (constant $\theta$) should be directly proportional to the thickness of the film. This also is completely verified by experiment. And, finally, if faster $\alpha$-particles are used, the observed deflections should be smaller. Again consider an $\alpha$-particle approaching from 2′ (Fig. 27-6), but with greater speed. As it passes the nucleus, it will experience the same force as the slower particle did. But the force now acts for a shorter time and therefore produces less deflection.† When $\alpha$-particles from different substances, with known speeds, were used, the number of observed scintillations was that predicted by the theory.

In making his calculations, Rutherford assumed (1) that the nuclei are "point" charges and that the force of repulsion between them obeys Coulomb's law (p. 277) even for the extremely small distances involved in large-angle deflections; (2) that the nuclei are so small (and thus so widely spaced) that the observed deflection of an $\alpha$-particle is the result of a single encounter with a nucleus in the foil. The complete agreement between the experimental results and the predictions of theory proved that these two assumptions are indeed correct. The calculation of the path of an $\alpha$-particle becomes, then, a straightforward problem of mechanics. The quantities involved are the mass, speed, and charge of the $\alpha$-particle (all known from other experiments), the angle of deflection (observed), and the charge, $+Q$, on the nucleus of the deflecting atom. Since $Q$ is the only unknown quantity involved, the calculation yields the value of the nuclear charge. The important result is that the positive charge of the nucleus is equal to the atomic number times the electronic charge; in symbols, $Q = +Ze$. Rutherford's collaborators showed this to be a general rule for heavy elements such as gold, copper, silver, and platinum.

We introduced atomic numbers as the ordinal numbers of the elements arranged in order of increasing atomic weight (§ 8-10). But it was necessary to reverse this order for several pairs of elements. Next (§ 18-12) we saw that for the

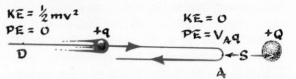

FIGURE 27-7 *Method of measuring the maximum size of the nucleus.*

lighter elements the atomic number is equal to the total number of electrons in the atom and thus (since atoms are electrically neutral) is equal to the number of positive electronic charges in the atom. And now, as a result of the deflection experiments, the atomic number of a heavy element is equal to the positive charge of the nucleus measured in electronic units. By inference this rule is valid for all the elements. We see that the nuclear charge, unlike other properties, shows no periodicity but increases uniformly throughout the whole periodic table. This reminds us of the Moseley diagram for X-ray line spectra (§ 25-9). In our study of the origin of line spectra we shall see that Moseley's law gives further verification of the concept of atomic number as the number of positive electronic charges on the nucleus.

The deflection experiments permit us to measure the size of the nucleus. Consider the 180° deflection shown in Figure 27-7. At some point $D$, "infinitely" far from the metallic atom's nucleus, the approaching $\alpha$-particle has no potential energy. As it approaches the nucleus, the electrostatic force of repulsion increases rapidly (inverse square), and the $\alpha$-particle has to draw on its store of KE to do the work of moving against the electric field of the nucleus. Thus, as it moves in, it loses KE and gains PE. At $A$, the point of nearest approach to the nucleus, the $\alpha$-particle is momentarily at rest, has lost all its KE, and has a maximum PE. This PE is the product of the electric potential at $A$ and the charge on the $\alpha$-particle. But, as we have seen above, the field is a Coulomb-force field due to the point charge of the nucleus. We may therefore use equation 17-6. In this case $Q = Ze$ and $q = 2e$, and we have, according to the conservation of energy,

$$\tfrac{1}{2}mv^2 = \frac{CZe}{s}\,(2e)$$

---

† During a deflection an $\alpha$-particle changes momentum (its direction is changed). We have seen from Newton's second law that $Ft = \Delta M$ (§ 11-4). $F$ is the same for both particles, but $t$ is smaller for the more rapid one, which thus acquires a smaller $\Delta M$.

Solving for *s*, we get

$$s = \frac{2CZe^2}{\frac{1}{2}mv^2} \qquad (27-2)$$

From this we may calculate *s*, for all the quantities on the right are known constants or are independently measurable. For instance, the measured speed of the $\alpha$-particles from one of the isotopes of polonium gives 7.7 Mev as the KE. For these particles deflected back from a gold foil ($Z = 79$) we have

$$s = 2.95 \times 10^{-14} \text{ meter}$$

This, of course, being the distance of nearest approach of the $\alpha$-particle to the gold nucleus, represents the maximum radius of the nucleus; the size of the nucleus is somewhat smaller. Many experiments of this kind, using various bombarding particles and many different elements, consistently give about $10^{-14}$ meter (a little smaller for light elements) as the size of the atomic nucleus. But we have considered evidence (§ 12-5), and there is a variety of other evidence, giving about $10^{-10}$ meter as the size of atoms; that is, the nucleus is *ten thousand times smaller†* than the atom of which it is the major part.

Minute as the nucleus is, it contains practically all the mass of the atom (the electrons account for only about 0.03 percent), and, what is more important, it carries the positive charge of the atom. This nuclear charge is the fundamental factor that controls most of the other atomic properties. When we deal with the kinetic theory of gases, with change of state, with chemical reactions, or (as we shall see in the next chapter) with optical spectra, we deal with phenomena that involve forces among the electrons near the outer reaches of the atoms. But the numbers and motions of these electrons are controlled by the electric field of the nuclear charge. If in some way the number of charges in the nucleus is changed, a different number of electrons, probably in a different distribution, is arranged round this new nucleus, and we have a different element (a different atomic number). On the other hand, there may be nuclei that have

---

† This is the factor that was used earlier in this section for the comparative size of nucleus and atom.

different masses but the same charge. The electronic structures round these nuclei would be the same, and all would be atoms of the same "element" (the same atomic number). Such atoms having identical properties (except mass) would constitute an isotopic mixture (§ 18-9).

## 27-4. *Radioactive Transmutation*

We can now discuss the radioactive process in somewhat more detail. Apparently the nuclei of radioactive atoms are unstable and disintegrate spontaneously and explosively in an uncontrollable way. During the explosions some radioactive nuclei eject helium nuclei ($\alpha$-particles) and others eject high-speed electrons ($\beta$-particles). Since both kinds of particles carry away electric charge, the remaining nuclei have different charges and thus form different atoms. During these violent rearrangements of the nuclear charges, a high-energy photon of electromagnetic radiation (a $\gamma$-ray) is sometimes emitted (mostly in association with $\beta$-emission). The newly formed nucleus, however, may also be unstable; it may emit a particle and become a still different nucleus. Thus a whole *series* of radioactive atoms is formed, each one spontaneously transmuting itself into the next atom of the series, until finally a stable nucleus is formed.

Each daughter atom formed by such a transmutation is related to the parent atom in a definite way that is consistent with the conservation of mass and the conservation of electric charge. For instance, an $\alpha$-particle carries away four atomic mass units and two positive electronic charges. The daughter formed by $\alpha$-emission will therefore have a mass number ($A$) that is four less, and an atomic number ($Z$) that is two less, than those of the parent atom. For instance (Table 27-2), radon ($A = 222$, $Z = 86$) is formed from radium ($A = 226$, $Z = 88$) by $\alpha$-emission. On the other hand, $\beta$-emission results in a daughter atom of unchanged mass number since the electronic mass is only a small fraction of one atomic mass unit. But the $\beta$-particle carries away one *negative* electronic charge and thus leaves the daughter nucleus with one extra *positive* electronic charge. Thus the daugh-

TABLE **27-2** *The Uranium-radium Series*

| NAME | MASS NO. $(A)$ | ATOMIC NO. $(Z)$ | EMISSION | HALF-LIFE | MAX. ENERGY (MEV) |
|---|---|---|---|---|---|
| Uranium I | 238 | 92 | $\alpha$ | $4.6 \times 10^9$ yr | 4.2 |
| Uranium X$_1$ | 234 | 90 | $\beta$ | 24.1 days | 0.2 |
| Uranium X$_2$ | 234 | 91 | $\beta$ | 1.14 min | 2.3 |
| Uranium II | 234 | 92 | $\alpha$ | $2.7 \times 10^5$ yr | 4.76 |
| Ionium | 230 | 90 | $\alpha$ | $8.3 \times 10^4$ yr | 4.68 |
| Radium | 226 | 88 | $\alpha$ | 1,590 yr | 4.78 |
| Radon | 222 | 86 | $\alpha$ | 3.83 days | 5.49 |
| Radium A | 218 | 84 | $\alpha$ | 3.05 min | 6.00 |
| Radium B | 214 | 82 | $\beta$ | 26.8 min | 0.7 |
| Radium C | 214 | 83 | $\beta$ | 19.7 min | 3.17 |
| Radium C' | 214 | 84 | $\alpha$ | $1.50 \times 10^{-4}$ sec | 7.68 |
| Radium D | 210 | 82 | $\beta$ | 22 yr | 0.018 |
| Radium E | 210 | 83 | $\beta$ | 5.0 days | 1.17 |
| Radium F | 210 | 84 | $\alpha$ | 140 days | 5.30 |
| Lead | 206 | 82 | — | Infinite | — |

ter formed by $\beta$-emission will have the same mass number as the parent atom and an atomic number greater by one. The formation of radium C from radium B is an example. If we use the terminology set up in our discussion of isotopes, we may summarize radioactive transmutations in the following way. For $\alpha$-emission:

$$_{Z}R^{A} \longrightarrow {}_{Z-2}R^{A-4} + {}_{2}He^{4} \qquad (27\text{-}3)$$

For $\beta$-emission:

$$_{Z}R^{A} \longrightarrow {}_{Z+1}R^{A} + {}_{-1}e^{0} \qquad (27\text{-}4)$$

Here the electron is assigned a mass number of zero (the nearest integer on the atomic-weight scale) and an "atomic number" of minus one (one negative electronic charge). Note that these reactions balance in mass† and in electric charge.

Starting with the common isotope of uranium, $_{92}U^{238}$, the series of Table 27-2 is formed according to equations 27-3 and 27-4. Each succeeding element is displaced two places down the atomic table or one place up, until the stable isotope of lead, $_{82}Pb^{206}$, is formed. In the light of our knowledge of nuclear charges and the nature of $\alpha$- and $\beta$-particles, this "displacement

† More critically, in mass number. The absolute mass is slightly unbalanced. In a later chapter we shall see that the imbalance is always a very small fraction of one atomic mass unit and is accounted for by Einstein's mass-energy equivalence.

law" now seems obvious. The discovery of the law, however, and the identification of the series, presented a difficult experimental problem. The experiments responsible for the discoveries were largely chemical analyses. Notice that, since the fifteen elements in Table 27-2 have only eight different atomic numbers, seven of the elements must be isotopes of the others. Many, furthermore, are among the actinide transition elements, all of which have similar chemical properties. The tests that established this radioactive series were therefore difficult and elaborate. The results confirmed again the law that the atomic number is equal to the nuclear charge.

The process of transmutation is often called decay. Radium, for instance, decays by $\alpha$-emission into radon. The rate of decay of a radioactive substance is a useful and important concept. Once the radioactive substances had been purified and their atomic weights had been determined, the number of atoms in a pure sample of one of them could be found by appropriate analyses. One thousandth of a mole of radon, for instance, would contain one thousandth of Avogadro's number of atoms. Since these atoms would immediately begin to decay, analysis of the sample at a later time would show fewer radon atoms remaining. Although the techniques were difficult and required the greatest experi-

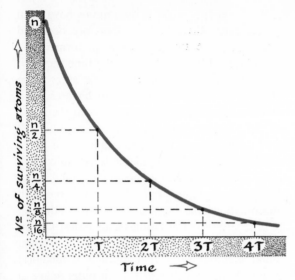

FIGURE **27-8** *Decay curve for radioactive substances.*

mental ingenuity, many experiments of this kind were performed, and they yielded a law that is applicable to any radioactive substance: *The fraction of the number of atoms that will decay per unit time interval is a characteristic constant of the particular substance.* This fraction is called the **decay constant** of the substance. Suppose that the decay constant of one substance is 0.1/sec and that we start with 100 atoms. (Actually, of course, the number in even a minute sample is much greater.) During the first second 10 atoms will decay, and 90 will survive; during the next second only 9 will decay, and 81 will survive; and so on. The number of survivors at any time is shown by the graph of Figure 27-8. The number of surviving atoms decreases rapidly at first, decreases less and less rapidly as time goes on, and approaches zero asymptotically for an indefinitely long time. Hence we cannot specify a finite time at which all the atoms will have decayed. We can, however, specify the time at which any particular fraction of the atoms will have decayed. For convenience the fraction one-half has been chosen. The time, $T$, required for one-half of the atoms to decay is called the **half-life** of the substance. After the interval $T$, half of the original number of atoms have decayed, and half have survived. Since half of these survivors will decay

during the next interval $T$, at time $2T$ one-quarter of the original number will have survived; and so on, as shown in Figure 27-8. Clearly, the half-life and the decay constant are related. Half of the atoms decay in a shorter time for a substance with a large decay constant than for a substance with a small decay constant. The decay curve of Figure 27-8 is valid, however, for all radioactive substances, the only difference being the amount of time represented by $T$. The half-lives of the radioactive substances of the uranium-radium series are given in the fifth column of Table 27-2. Half of a sample of radium E, for instance, would disappear in 5 days, three-quarters in 10 days, seven-eighths in 15 days, and so on. Half of a sample of radium F would take 140 days to decay, three-quarters 280 days, and so on.

Notice the wide range of half-lives in Table 27-2, ranging from a very small fraction of a second (radium C′) to almost five billion years (uranium I). A moderate half-life, such as that of radon, can be measured directly; a long half-life, such as that of radium, would require too long a time for the experiment. Radium, however, since it has a longer half-life, must have a proportionately smaller decay constant, than radon. Radium atoms therefore emit fewer $\alpha$-particles per second than the same number of radon atoms. By comparing the number of $\alpha$-particles emitted per second from equal numbers of radon and radium atoms (say $10^{-3}$ mole of each), we compute the half-life of radium from the measured half-life of radon. Other long half-lives are determined in a similar way. Very short half-lives are derived from an empirical relation between the energy of $\alpha$-particles and the half-life of the emitter. Comparing radon, radium A, and radium F, we see that the energy of the emitted $\alpha$-particles decreases as the half-life increases. The relation is not a simple inverse proportion, but it is definitely determined experimentally. By measuring the kinetic energy of the $\alpha$-particles from radium C′, we can calculate its very short half-life.

We have discussed only the uranium-radium series. Two other series are known to exist in nature. One, called the *actinium series,* starts with the rare uranium isotope $_{92}U^{235}$ ($T \approx 10^{9}$ years) and ends with $_{82}Pb^{207}$. The other, called the *thorium series,* starts with $_{90}Th^{232}$ ($T \approx 10^{10}$ years) and ends with $_{82}Pb^{208}$. A fourth series, not found in nature, which starts with the artificially produced plutonium ($_{94}Pu^{241}$) and ends with a stable isotope of bismuth ($_{83}Bi^{209}$), is called the *neptunium series* because neptunium ($_{93}Np^{237}$) is its longest-lived member ($T = 2.25 \times 10^6$ years).

The fact that the three series found in nature all end with different isotopes of lead (206, 207, 208) places lead in a special situation among the stable elements. We saw in our discussion of isotopic mixtures (p. 305) that the relative abundance of the isotopes is the same for all samples of the substance. This is proved by the very precise and constant atomic weights found by chemical analyses in all circumstances. The atomic weight of chlorine, for instance, always comes out to be 35.457 because *any* sample has the same percentage of 35 and 37. Presumably, at some distant time before the earth solidified, all the various isotopes were thoroughly mixed and have remained in the same proportions. But not so for lead. The atomic weight of lead is found to vary somewhat, depending on the place where it is found. This was a very puzzling fact to chemists before the discovery of radioactive series. Down through the ages these series have been (and still are) producing three different types of lead. Lead found in rocks that also contain radioactive minerals has a different isotopic mixture than lead found elsewhere.

Once the radioactive series had been worked out, it became possible to estimate the "age" of rocks. Suppose that, when a rock was formed, some uranium I was included. Since then the uranium has been decaying and, through the uranium-radium series, has been producing lead 206. The rock is analyzed, and the amounts of lead 206 and uranium are measured. From the known half-lives of the uranium-radium series and the law of radioactive decay (Fig. 27-8) we can calculate the time required to produce the observed amount of lead 206 and leave the observed amount of uranium. If some lead 206 was already present during the formation of the rock, this method, of course, gives too long a time. For each atom of lead *produced,* however, eight $\alpha$-particles have been emitted by the series (Ta-

ble 27-2); that is, eight helium atoms have been formed. Since these helium atoms are occluded in the rock, the amount of helium formed can be determined by analysis and the time required for its formation computed. To be sure, since helium is a gas, some of it might have escaped from the rock, and this method would then give too short a time. Together, the two methods set limits to the correct time and enable us to make reliable estimates. These methods of radioactive dating are powerful tools enabling geologists to trace the geologic history of the earth. From such determinations the "age of the earth" (that is, the time since the formation of the oldest known minerals) is found to be about five billion years. Similar methods show that the age of meteoric material falling on the earth from outer space is about the same as that of the earth.

## 27-5. Summary

In this chapter we have considered the evidence that compelled a radically new view of atomic structure. The complete agreement between observation and Rutherford's predictions led to an immediate acceptance of his nuclear model, even though (as we shall see in the next chapter) it raised serious questions about the stability of atoms. This model immediately suggests an analogy to the solar system. There the very massive sun, attracting the lighter planets by an inverse-square force (Newton's law of gravity), holds them in their orbits. The sun, because of its relatively enormous mass, remains practically stationary at the center of the orbits. Similarly, the (relatively) enormously massive nucleus, attracting the very light electrons by an inverse-square force (Coulomb's law), holds them in orbits round itself. The extremely small size of the nucleus furthers the planetary analogy. In order to make up the comparatively large size of the atom, the electrons (themselves about the same size as nuclei) must revolve round the nucleus at relatively great distances.

This planetary atom implies a separation of atomic study into two almost completely separate parts, a separation that has persisted to the present time. One part is the study of the nucleus, which, minute as it is, clearly must have structure. The heavy radioactive nuclei give evidence of structure by spontaneously ejecting the smaller $\alpha$- and $\beta$-particles. Other nuclei, by inference, have structure but are more stable. In a later chapter we shall return to this question of nuclear structure.

The other part of atomic study is concerned with the arrangment of the planetary electrons. These investigations—the ones most actively pursued during the years immediately following Rutherford's discovery of the nuclear atom—involve primarily only one property of the nucleus, the nuclear charge. In little more than fifteen years of intense activity the electronic structures of the atoms were worked out. With this came an explanation of the periodic system of the elements and an interpretation of their properties, both physical and chemical. We now turn to a study of these developments.

## Concepts and Terms

Radioactivity
  transmutation
  $\alpha$-, $\beta$-, and $\gamma$-rays
  change of mass with velocity
Nuclear Atom
  size of the nucleus
  nuclear charge and atomic number

Radioactive Series
  $\alpha$-emission
  $\beta$-emission
  uranium-radium series
Law of Radioactive Decay
  decay constant
  half-life
  radioactive dating

## Problems

**27-1.** The energy of a $\gamma$-ray photon was found to be 2.0 Mev. What is the wavelength of this ray? Compare with Fig. 25-11. Could this wavelength be measured with the crystal spectrometer?

*Ans.* $6.21 \times 10^{-3}$ A

**27-2.** Verify the data of Table 27-1 for a $\beta$-particle moving with half of the speed of light, on the assumption that Einstein's formula for the increase of mass is correct.

**27-3.** Calculate the kinetic energy in Mev of a $\beta$-particle moving with 0.75 of the speed of light. (The relativistic mass must be used.)

*Ans.* 0.22 Mev

**27-4.** The kinetic energy of an $\alpha$-particle from radium is 4.78 Mev. Calculate the speed of this particle on the assumption that the increase of mass is negligible. Is this a valid assumption? (The mass of a helium atom is $7.35 \times 10^3$ times the mass of an electron.)

*Ans.* $1.51 \times 10^7$ m/sec

**27-5.** Compare the energies involved in the previous problems with the energies of optical and X-ray photons. From what part of an atom would you suspect the radioactive rays to be radiated?

**27-6.** Consider Fig. 27-2. The number of $\alpha$-particles per second passing through the aperture (directly counted), divided by the area of the aperture, gives the number per $cm^2$ arriving at the lead shield. This number times the area of a sphere with radius equal to the distance from the emitter to the shield gives the total number of $\alpha$-particles emitted per second. By such an experiment it is found that 1 microgram ($10^{-6}$ gram) of radium emits $1.48 \times 10^5$ $\alpha$-particles per second. By another experiment it is found that 1 *gram* of radium produces $1.412 \times 10^{-2}$ $cm^3$ of helium (at standard conditions) in 30 days. Determine Avogadro's number from these data. (From the gas accumulation calculate the number of moles, from the counting rate the number of atoms, and then the number of atoms per mole. This is not the most precise method of determining $N_0$, but it is of interest because it involves a direct count of atoms.) The method involves a tacit assumption. What is it? Would the method be valid with similar data for radium F?

*Ans.* $6.06 \times 10^{23}$/mole

**27-7.**

(A) Show that the units of equation 27-2 reduce to $s =$ meter. What unit must be used for the KE?

(B) Verify the value of s for gold stated in the text.

**27-8.** An α-particle from radon (see Table 27-2) is deflected 180° by a thin foil of copper. Calculate the distance of nearest approach to the copper nucleus.

*Ans.* $1.52 \times 10^{-14}$ m

**27-9.** An isotope of actinium with mass number 224 emits α-particles. A rare isotope of potassium with mass number 40 emits β-rays. Write balanced equations for these two transitions.

*Ans.* The products are $_{87}Fr^{220}$ and $_{20}Ca^{40}$.

**27-10.** Write the isotopic symbol alongside the name of each substance in the radioactive series of Table 27-2. (Uranium $X_1$, for instance, is $_{90}Th^{234}$). Verify each by applying equation 27-3 or 27-4 to the successive transitions. How many different elements are in the series? Which elements have the most isotopes in the series?

**27-11.** Graph the uranium-radium series (§ 27-4) in the following manner. Plot mass numbers ($A$) as ordinates along the length of the sheet. Let five small squares equal one unit, and start the scale at $A = 204$. Plot atomic numbers ($Z$) as abscissas, with ten small squares equal to one unit. Start the scale at $Z = 80$. Label each $Z$ with the appropriate chemical symbol. Place a small circle on the graph for each member of the series. Draw an arrow from the circle for uranium I to the circle for uranium $X_1$. Label the arrow "α." Continue, representing each successive transmutation in a similar manner. The resulting graph clearly shows the progression of the series in the periodic table.

**27-12.** The thorium radioactive series starts with the isotope $_{90}Th^{232}$ and ends with the lead isotope $_{82}Pb^{208}$. How many transitions are there in this series, and what are the emissions?

*Ans.* 10 transitions; 6 α's and 4 β's

**27-13.** How long will it take for three-quarters of a sample of radon to disintegrate?

*Ans.* 7.66 days

**27-14.** An automatic counter of α-particles records 1,600 counts per minute from a certain sample of $_{84}Po^{210}$. How many counts will be recorded from this sample 420 days later?

*Ans.* 200 counts/min

**27-15.** In a mixture of radium E and radium F, an atom of which substance has the greater chance of disintegrating in the next second? How many times greater?

*Ans.* radium E, 28 times greater

**27-16.** What percentage of the mass of the sodium atom is due to the electrons? of the uranium 238 atom? ($m_H = 1,836\ m_e$.)

*Ans.* approx. 0.026% and 0.021%

**27-17.** A platinum foil $5.7 \times 10^{-5}$ cm thick was used in an experiment on the scattering of α-particles. The density of platinum is 21.4 grams/cm³.
(A) Calculate the number of atoms in 1 cm² of the foil. (Hint: From the dimensions and density calculate the mass, and then the moles and the number.)
(B) Consider the foil as made up of layers of atoms, each layer one atom thick, the atoms lying side by side. Use $3 \times 10^{-8}$ cm as the diameter of the atom. How many layers thick is the foil? (Hint: The great-circle area of one atom divided into 1 cm² will give the number of atoms per cm² of one layer. This, combined with the result of A, will yield the answer.)
(C) As viewed from an α-particle approaching the foil perpendicularly, what fraction of the area is obstructed by nuclei? Assume that no nucleus lies behind any other one. Use $3 \times 10^{-12}$ cm as the nuclear diameter.
(D) What is the chance that an α-particle will collide head on with a nucleus? What is the chance if the foil is $8.6 \times 10^{-5}$ cm thick?

*Ans.* (A) $3.77 \times 10^{18}$
(B) $2.66 \times 10^3$
(C) $2.66 \times 10^{-5}$

# Suggested Readings

1. H. E. White, *Modern College Physics,* 3rd edition (Van Nostrand, 1956), pp. 612–623 and 691–694.
2. R. F. Humphreys and R. Beringer, *First Principles of Atomic Physics* (Harper & Brothers, 1950), pp. 299–316.
3. M. Born, *The Restless Universe,* translated by W. M. Deans (Dover Publications, 1951), pp. 166–176 (Rutherford's scattering experiment).
4. W. F. Magie, *A Source Book in Physics* (McGraw-Hill, 1935), pp. 610–613 (Becquerel on the discovery of radioactivity) and 613–616 (Pierre and Marie Curie on the discovery of polonium and radium).
5. J. W. Knedler, Jr., *Masterworks of Science* (Doubleday, 1947), pp. 570–595 (excerpts from Marie Curie's book *Radioactivity*).

The following references discuss various aspects of the theory of relativity:

6. A. Einstein and L. Infeld, *The Evolution of Physics* (Simon & Schuster, 1938), pp. 160–260. A non-mathematical discussion written for the layman.

7. M. Born (cited above), pp. 69–88 (increase of mass with velocity and equivalence of mass and energy).

8. Humphreys and Beringer (cited above), pp. 230–246. Includes an algebraic treatment of the special theory of relativity.

WE NOW return to the problem (stated at the end of Chap. 26) of finding an explanation for the characteristic line spectra of the elements. The field of spectroscopy, which had been developing through the latter part of the nineteenth century, had become, by the first decade of the twentieth century, little more than a mass of unexplained experimental results. To be sure, some empirical progress had been made. It had been found, for instance, that the reciprocal wavelengths $(1/\lambda)$ of spectral series could be represented by the differences of empirically determined numbers called "terms." These terms were few compared with the lines in the series. Furthermore, for the hydrogen series, which are the simplest of all atomic spectra, the terms are related by simple whole numbers: any term is $\mathcal{R}/n^2$ if $\mathcal{R}$ is the Rydberg constant and $n$ is an integer. The terms for other elements also involve $\mathcal{R}$ and integers but in a more complicated way. These results not only offered important simplifications of the spectroscopic observations but also suggested that a theoretical explanation of atomic spectra would disclose the nature of atomic structure.

Some efforts to explain line spectra were based on the Thomson atom. This model had the advantage that the electrons in a normal non-radiating atom could be considered at rest. Only after excitation by some external agency would the valence electrons vibrate about their equilibrium positions and, according to the electromagnetic theory, radiate away the excitation energy. But the theoretical frequencies of such an oscillator (somewhat like the overtones produced by a musical instrument) do not converge toward any such limit as is observed in spectral series (Fig. 25-7), and the Thomson atom, therefore, did not lead to an explanation of line spectra. The Thomson atom, moreover, as we saw in the previous chapter, disappeared from the scientific scene with Rutherford's discovery of the nucleus.

The nuclear atom, being mostly empty space, cannot possibly be static. There is no possible way of arranging the negative electrons in a stationary pattern about the positive nucleus. The electrons, by electrostatic attraction, would fall in to the nucleus just as an unsupported ob-

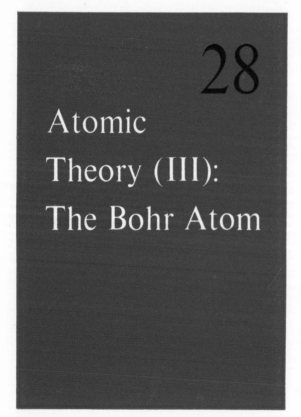

CHAPTER

28

Atomic
Theory (III):
The Bohr Atom

ject falls to the earth. We are therefore forced to accept the planetary atomic model described at the end of the previous chapter. But here new difficulties arise. A planet moving round the sun loses none of its energy. To be sure, it changes some PE to KE, and vice versa, as it speeds up and slows down along its orbit (§ 11-9), but its total energy remains constant, and it therefore moves along a stable orbit. An electron, however, unlike a planet, carries an electric charge, and because of its orbital acceleration it should radiate energy in the form of light. Thus the electron, continuously losing energy, should spiral in toward the nucleus with increasing frequency of revolution (Kepler's third law, § 2-8). Such an atom should, of its own accord, emit a continuous spectrum. This, of course, never happens. The electrons, moreover, would soon spiral into the nucleus, and the atom would collapse. As we know, atoms do not collapse but are very stable structures.

This, then, was the puzzle that faced scientists in 1911 after the discovery of the nuclear atom. How could Rutherford's planetary atom be made stable and be made to account for the observed facts of spectroscopy? The puzzle was soon resolved by Niels Bohr, a brilliant young Dane who had received a scholarship to work with Rutherford. His answer was that the classical electromagnetic theory, clearly, does not work for regions inside the atom, and that in some way the quantum hypothesis must be applied to atomic structure. Bohr's theory (published in 1913) was worked out specifically for the hydrogen atom, but in developing it he used the quantum hypothesis so imaginatively that he opened the way for the solution of the more general problem of the structure of all atoms.

## 28-1. Bohr's Theory of the Hydrogen Atom

Bohr's problem was to adapt the quantum hypothesis† to Rutherford's model of a hydrogen atom and to deduce a formula for the hydrogen spectral series—that is, to obtain the Balmer formula (equation 25-3) from theoretical considerations. Bohr's postulates, implicit in the discussion of the previous section, may be made more explicit by the following three statements:

1. *The electron revolves round the nucleus as a center and moves in accordance with the classical laws of mechanics.* This, of course, accepts the planetary atom as a necessary consequence of Rutherford's experiments.

2. *The electron moves only in certain "allowed" orbits, and while in one of these orbits it does* not *radiate energy.* This is the famous "stationary state" postulate: while moving in one of the allowed orbits, the total energy of the electron remains constant, or "stationary." This postulate is, of course, a flat contradiction of the classical electromagnetic theory. But it is a consistent extension of the quantum hypothesis. In Planck's theory the basic idea of quantum "jumps" implies that the molecule, between jumps, vibrates without radiating energy (see Fig. 26-3). With this postulate Bohr solved the problem of the stability of nuclear atoms by merely stating that the cause of instability does not operate inside atomic structures. An electron can revolve indefinitely in the stationary state of lowest energy‡ without radiation and without spiraling into the nucleus.

3. *An atom emits a photon* (h$\nu$) *when an electron jumps from any stationary state to one of smaller energy.* More succinctly, this postulate states that

$$W_p - W_n = h\nu \qquad (28-1)$$

if $W$ represents the total energy of the electron in an allowed orbit and $n$ and $p$ are integers that give the ordinal number of the orbits in the order of increasing energy. An electron might

---

† At the time Bohr constructed his theory (1913) the quantum hypothesis had been applied to only a small range of problems and had not yet attained the general applicability outlined in Chap. 26. To be sure, Planck had established the usefulness of the quantum concept for calculating the energy content of molecules, and Einstein had developed his theory of the photoelectric effect. But Millikan had not yet performed his precise verification of the photoelectric equation; the Braggs were just developing the X-ray spectrometer (and thus opening the field of X-ray spectroscopy); and Compton's work on the scattering of X-ray photons was still a decade away.

‡ The energy of this lowest state cannot be zero, however, since the first postulate requires the electron to be moving in *some* orbit.

go, for instance, from the fifth orbit ($p = 5$) to the third ($n = 3$) and emit a photon of energy equal to the difference between the energies in the two orbits. This, again, is an extension of the quantum hypothesis, for it specifies quantum (not continuous) changes in the energy content of the atom. The postulate also incorporates Einstein's theory of photons by specifying that the energy is radiated as a photon of light. (Equation 28-1, in fact, came to be known as Einstein's frequency condition.) And, finally, we see that this postulate might be useful in explaining the line spectra of atoms. Each electron jump would result in a definite radiated frequency, and, depending on the arrangement of the allowed orbits, a discrete set of such frequencies would be possible for each kind of atom.

As a fundamental set of postulates, these three statements may seem highly arbitrary—as, indeed, they are. They represent a remarkable combination of principles taken from classical science with principles radically at variance with classical science. The Bohr theory, however, is an excellent example of what frequently happens in the development of scientific theories. In mathematics, for instance, a theory starts from *well-established* postulates and by strictly logical development produces new results that are as valid as the postulates. But in scientific theory the desired result is often known in advance, for it has been given by experiments (for example, the Balmer formula). Hence we reverse the process and *invent* new postulates, often in a "cut-and-try" manner, as starting points for the theory. These postulates often present no apparent revelation of new truth and at times seem contradictory to expectations.† The validity of the postulates is judged by the success of the theory in predicting observed facts and in stimulating further successful developments. From this point of view, Bohr's postulates seem acceptable, for, as we shall see immediately, his theory was astonishingly successful.

We start, as Bohr did, with the simplest situation: a single electron revolving in a circular orbit round a nucleus. This could be a hydrogen

atom, a singly ionized helium atom, a doubly ionized lithium atom, and so on. The first problem is to determine which of the possible circular which the electron may move. The quantum hypothesis does not yield the answer directly since we may have a quantum of energy of any size ($h\nu$) merely by assigning the proper frequency. The clue lay hidden in the quantum hypothesis, however, in the universality of Planck's constant, $h$. As we have seen, the value of $h$ is the same in all circumstances, which fact suggests that in some way this constant may determine the stationary states. An analysis of the units of $h$ makes the suggestion more specific. According to quantum hypothesis, $\epsilon = h\nu$; therefore

$$h = \frac{\epsilon}{\nu} = \text{joules sec} = \text{kgm} \frac{\text{m}^2}{\text{sec}^2} \text{sec} = \text{kgm} \frac{\text{m}}{\text{sec}} \text{m}$$

or

$$h = \text{momentum} \times \text{distance}$$

Apparently this mechanical quantity, the product of momentum and distance, appears in nature in discrete amounts. The fundamental amount is equal to the numerical value of Planck's constant, and no smaller amount can exist. Larger amounts appear as integral multiples of the fundamental unit; that is, there may be amounts equal to $2h$, $3h$, $11h$, etc., but never a fractional multiple such as $4.37h$. At any rate, this seemed to Bohr to be a plausible and fundamental interpretation of the quantum hypothesis, and he used it to specify the "allowed," or stationary, orbits of the electron. According to this scheme, the electron can travel only in orbits for which the momentum times the circumference is equal to some whole number times Planck's constant. With this "quantum condition" for the allowed orbits, the rest is straight going.

Figure 28-1 presents the single-electron atom specified in the previous paragraph. The electron, with mass $m$ and charge $-e$, moves with a constant speed, $v$, along a circle of radius $r$. At the center of the circle is the nucleus, much more massive than $m$ and carrying the nuclear charge $+Ze$. The size of the circle is determined by the quantum condition:

$$mv2\pi r = nh \qquad (28\text{-}2)$$

† This is particularly true of atomic theories because we are prone to judge the plausibility of a process in the light of our daily experience.

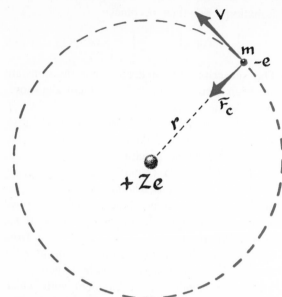

FIGURE **28-1** *Bohr's model of a single-electron atom.*

if $n = 1$, 2, 3, etc. (but not 0). According to the first postulate, the electron moves in accordance with Newtonian mechanics, and we recognize the motion as a centripetal acceleration. The centripetal force, $F_c$, is only the electrostatic attraction between the charges since the gravitational attraction between the masses is completely negligible. We may therefore write (Coulomb's law, § 17-1; Newton's second law, § 5-2)

$$\frac{CZe^2}{r^2} = m\frac{v^2}{r} \qquad (28\text{-}3)$$

From these two equations we may calculate the radius of the orbit by eliminating the unobservable speed, $v$. We square equation 28-2 and solve for $v^2$. We substitute this value for $v^2$ in equation 28-3 and solve for $r$. The result is

$$r = \frac{n^2}{Z}\frac{h^2}{4\pi^2 mCe^2} \qquad (28\text{-}4)$$

Notice that the right side of this equation involves only *known* constants and the integer $n$. Hence the equation defines the set of allowed orbits along any one of which the electron may move. We specify the smallest orbit by letting $n = 1$. The next, for $n = 2$, is four times as large, the next ($n = 3$) nine times as large, etc. Thus

the relative sizes of the allowed orbits, which constitute the possible stationary states, are determined by the value of $n$. The integer $n$ is called the **quantum number** of the stationary state.

The energy of a stationary state is the sum of the kinetic energy and potential energy of the electron. The KE is, of course, $\frac{1}{2}mv^2$. The PE is electrical and is due to the position of the electron's charge in the electric field of the nucleus. From Rutherford's work on $\alpha$-particle scattering we know that this is a coulombic field set up by the point charge of the nucleus. We have studied this type of field and have a formula for the PE at a point (p. 281). As the electron revolves in a circular orbit, it is always at the same distance, $r$, from the nucleus. Its PE, the same at all points in a particular orbit, is equal to

$$V_p q = CZe/r(-e) = -CZe^2/r$$

The minus sign that comes out of the algebra is consistent with the arbitrary definitions used in developing the formulas. Remember that, in fact, we can talk only about changes in PE, and that, when we talk about *the* PE at a point, we are implying that some reference point has been arbitrarily assigned a value of zero. For the electric field this point is taken at "infinity"—that is, a point so far from the charge that the force on a test charge is negligible. For the Bohr orbits this would mean an orbit of infinite radius, and the formula above would yield zero for the PE. But in this case zero is also the *maximum* PE for the electron; for, as the electron moves into orbits of smaller radius, it moves in the direction of the force and loses PE as a stone falling toward the earth does. The *least* PE that the electron can have, then, is in the first ($n = 1$) orbit, with radius $r_1$. Suppose that this comes out to be $-8$ units. If we do work on the electron, we can move it out to the second orbit ($n = 2$). But, as we have seen, $r_2 = 4r_1$, and the PE here would be $-2$ units—an *increase* in PE of 6 units. (Remember that $-2$ is *larger* than $-8$.)

The total energy in any orbit (the $n$th, say) is, then,

$$W_n = \frac{1}{2}mv^2 - \frac{CZe^2}{r}$$

This involves the unobservable quantities $v$ and $r$, but they may be replaced. We solve equation 28-3 for $mv^2$ and substitute this value in the equation above. In the resulting equation we substitute for $r$ the values given by equation 28-4. The result is

$$W_n = -\frac{Z^2}{n^2}\frac{2\pi^2 mC^2 e^4}{h^2} \tag{28-5}$$

Here, again, only known constants and the quantum number $n$ are involved. Hence equation 28-5 specifies the energy for each allowed stationary state. $W_n$ increases (becomes less negative) with increasing $n$ and is a maximum (is equal to zero) for infinite (very large) values of $n$; that is, the electron has a maximum energy with respect to the nucleus when it is at rest *outside* the atom, a minimum energy when it is in the smallest stationary orbit ($n = 1$).

Suppose now that the electron receives sufficient energy to move in one of the higher-energy orbits specified by quantum number $p$. It can spontaneously jump to an orbit of lower energy specified by number $n$. Here $p > n$ ($p = 5$ and $n = 2$ would be one possible combination). According to the third postulate, the energy lost by this jump is radiated as a photon. Then, from the frequency condition (equation 28-1),

$$h\nu = h\frac{c}{\lambda} = W_p - W_n \tag{28-6}$$

Both $W_p$ and $W_n$ are given by equation 28-5 if the appropriate quantum number is inserted. Making this substitution and solving equation 28-6 for $1/\lambda$, we get

$$\frac{1}{\lambda} = Z^2\left(\frac{2\pi^2 mC^2 e^4}{ch^3}\right)\left[\frac{1}{n^2} - \frac{1}{p^2}\right] \tag{28-7}$$

This formula represents a discrete set of wavelengths of which each is determined by a particular pair of integers ($n$ and $p$). The formula becomes simpler when we notice that the parentheses contain only fundamental universal constants and therefore have the same value in all circumstances. We can represent this quantity by a single symbol:

$$\mathscr{R}_{th} = \frac{2\pi^2 mC^2 e^4}{ch^3} \tag{28-8}$$

Equation 28-7 then becomes

$$\frac{1}{\lambda} = Z^2 \mathscr{R}_{th}\left[\frac{1}{n^2} - \frac{1}{p^2}\right] \tag{28-9}$$

The subscript "th" indicates that the constant has been derived from theoretical considerations. We use the same symbol ($\mathscr{R}$) for the *experimentally* determined Rydberg constant because, if we apply the formula to hydrogen ($Z = 1$), equation 28-9 has precisely the *same form* as the Balmer formula (equation 25-3). The only remaining question is whether the $\mathscr{R}_{th}$ of equation 28-8 has the same value as the $\mathscr{R}_H$ derived empirically from the hydrogen spectrum. If so, Bohr accomplished his purpose of deriving from purely theoretical considerations a formula for the observed spectral series of hydrogen.

We can imagine the excitement with which Bohr substituted the values in his formula. The charge and mass of the electron came from Millikan's oil-drop experiments and Thomson's magnetic-deflection experiment, Coulomb's constant from classical experiments in electricity, the velocity of light from Michelson's rotating-mirror experiments, Planck's constant from his theory of temperature radiation and Einstein's theory of the photoelectric effect. Let us set forth these constants determined from widely different fields of investigation:

$$C = 8.98776\times10^9 \ \frac{\text{newton m}^2}{\text{coul}^2} \quad \text{(p. 278)}$$

$$m = 9.1085\times10^{-31} \ \text{kgm} \quad \text{(p. 299)}$$
$$e = 1.60207\times10^{-19} \ \text{coul} \quad \text{(p. 299)}$$
$$c = 2.997929\times10^8 \ \text{meters/sec} \quad \text{(p. 429)}$$
$$h = 6.6252\times10^{-34} \ \text{joule sec} \quad \text{(p. 450)}$$

We now substitute these values in equation 28-8 after rounding off the more precise to five figures in order to be consistent with $m$ and $h$. The result is $\mathscr{R}_{th} = 1.0975\times10^7$ meters$^{-1}$. Compare this with $\mathscr{R}_H = 1.0968\times10^7$ meters$^{-1}$ (p. 426)! When Bohr published his theory, the values of the fundamental constants were not known to the high degree of precision given above, and the values of $\mathscr{R}_{th}$ and $\mathscr{R}_H$ agreed well within the experimental error of measurements.[†] This impressive result represents one of the greatest achievements of detailed numerical agreement

---

[†] We shall return later to the apparent discrepancy (about 0.1%) between the values.

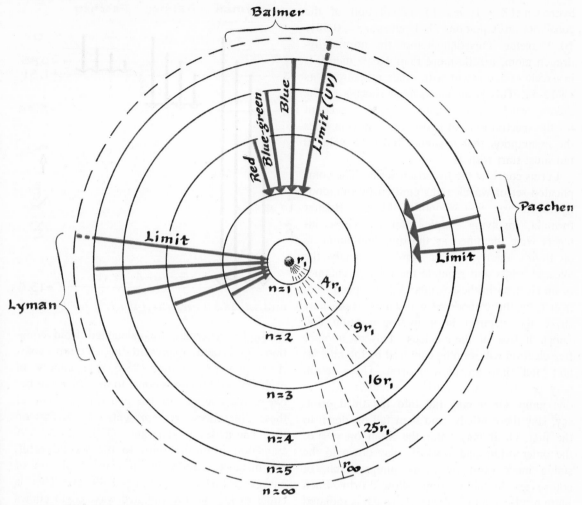

FIGURE **28-2** *Some of the allowed electron orbits for a hydrogen atom.*

between theory and experiment that science has produced. The chance that all the fundamental constants, with their enormous powers of ten, would just happen to combine into the proper number is practically nil. In the light of the success of the theory, the underlying postulates take on greater significance. Since only universal constants derived from a wide variety of experiments are involved, the postulates undoubtedly represent a fundamental process characteristic of other atoms as well as hydrogen.

## 28-2. *Energy-level Diagrams*

Let us now summarize the results of the theory diagrammatically. Figure 28-2 represents

the allowed circular orbits. The nucleus at the center of these circles is, of course, shown much too large (p. 473). The smallest possible orbit ($n = 1$) has radius $r_1$. The other orbits have radii $4r_1$, $9r_1$, etc., as required by equation 28-4. The first three of these are drawn to scale, and the rest are drawn smaller in order to keep the diagram on the page. The broken circle ($n = \infty$) has a radius so large that an electron on it would not be affected by the electric field of the nucleus. An electron would have minimum energy in the smallest orbit. Hence, unless the atom is receiving energy from some external agency, the electron will revolve in the first orbit. The diameter of this orbit, then, should be the size of the atom in its normal state. For hydrogen $(Z = 1, n = 1)$ substitution of the constants in equation 28-4 gives $r_1 = 0.53 \times 10^{-10}$ meter. This diameter of the normal hydrogen atom, a little more than $10^{-10}$ meter, is in excellent agreement with other measurements (§ 12-5). This is an unexpected success of the theory, which was primarily designed to account for the spectral lines of hydrogen. It also justifies the assumption that $n$ cannot have the value 0 but must start with 1.

Let us consider the hydrogen series. The complicated set of wavelengths emitted by luminous hydrogen was first simplified by the Balmer formula, involving simple integers. These integers were identified as the quantum numbers of Bohr's theory, which numbers specify the allowed orbits and regulate the relative energies of an electron in these orbits. A high-speed electron from the cathode of a discharge tube may strike the electron in a hydrogen atom and knock it free of the nucleus. This or another free electron will soon be captured by the nucleus and "fall" into an allowed orbit. The electron may go all the way into the smallest orbit in one jump. Or it may fall into the third orbit, say, stay there briefly, and then fall on down to the first. Or it may enter the atom on one of the outer orbits and work its way down to the stable inner orbit by many jumps, each, of course, terminating on some allowed orbit. Each jump results in a loss of energy, which is radiated as a photon and accounts for a definite line in the spectrum. Some possible jumps are represented by the arrows of Figure 28-2. One group terminates on the innermost orbit. The wavelengths of this group are given by equation 28-9 if $n = 1$ and $p = 2, 3, 4$, etc. This is the Lyman series. Similarly, the jumps terminating on the second orbit $(n = 2)$ give rise to the Balmer series, those terminating on the third orbit to the Paschen series, etc.

Diagrams of the allowed orbits such as Figure 28-2 would, if drawn to scale, extend indefinitely. But the *energies* of the electron in these orbits converge toward the maximum energy of zero for very large $n$. These energies may be plotted along a vertical scale with a horizontal line at the value for each orbit. Such an "energy-level diagram" for hydrogen is shown in Figure

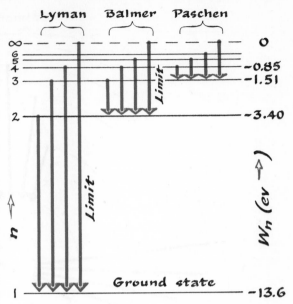

FIGURE **28-3** *Energy-level diagram for hydrogen.*

28-3. The energies are calculated from equation 28-5 and expressed in electron volts. According to equation 28-6, the energy of each emitted photon is equal to the *difference* between the energies of the two orbits. Some of these differences are represented by arrows on the energy-level diagram (Fig. 28-3). A transition from the third to the second orbit, for instance, results in an emitted photon of energy $-1.51 - (-3.40) = 1.89$ ev. This is equal to $h\nu$, and the radiated wavelength comes out as 6,563 A. This is the first Balmer line (red). Similarly, the transition $4 \rightarrow 2$ yields the second Balmer line, which, since $h\nu$ is larger, has a shorter wavelength; $5 \rightarrow 2$ gives the third Balmer line; etc. A large number of excited states† must be imagined for quantum numbers between $n = 5$ and $n = \infty$. Transitions from these states to 2 result in a large number of emitted lines. As $n$ increases toward $\infty$, the energies of the states (proportional to $1/n^2$) increase by successively smaller amounts. Thus the group of lines emitted by transitions terminating on 2 compose a series converging toward

---

† All energy levels greater than the minimum one are called *excited states* since energy from an external agency ("excitation" energy) is required to lift the electron into that level. The minimum energy level, that of the electron in the normal, "unexcited" atom, is called the *ground state*.

a sharply defined short-wavelength limit ($\infty \to 2$; $h\nu = 3.40$ ev). This, of course, is precisely the observation (Fig. 25-7). Similarly, transitions to the ground state give rise to the Lyman series, those to the third state to the Paschen series, etc. Thus an energy-level diagram, with only a few terms, correlates a large amount of spectroscopic observation.

Other simplifications are suggested by the energy-level diagram. For instance, in terms of the energies of the radiated photons, the Lyman limit minus the Balmer limit gives the first Lyman line; the third Lyman minus the first Lyman gives the second Balmer line; the Balmer limit minus the Paschen limit gives the first Balmer line; etc. Such combination principles, for other spectra as well as for that of hydrogen, were known empirically before Bohr's theory and indicate that the theory, designed specifically for hydrogen, contains clues to the solution of the more general problem of atomic spectra.

## 28-3. *Successes of Bohr's Theory*

The first successes of Bohr's theory caused great excitement in 1913 and stimulated many further investigations. The Balmer and Paschen series were known, and Bohr used them in verifying his deductions. The series terminating on the ground state, however, had not been observed. Bohr predicted the series and calculated the wavelengths, and experimentalists began to search for the lines. The wavelengths are very short (about 1,000 A) and are strongly absorbed by air. In 1915, Professor Theodore Lyman, at Harvard University, developed the

vacuum spectrograph. The grating (reflection type), source slit, and photographic plate were all enclosed in an evacuated space. With this Lyman discovered the predicted series, which now bears his name.

When the technique of the vacuum spectrograph became fully developed, the following experiment was possible. Consider the tube shown schematically in Figure 28-4. It contains hydrogen at low pressure. Electrons boiled out of a hot filament, $F$ (heating circuit not shown), are accelerated by the potential difference $V_a$ toward a metallic mesh electrode, $G$. For this experiment the potential difference $V_r$ is set equal to zero so that the metal plate $P$ is at the same potential as $G$. Thus the region between $G$ and $P$ is a field-free space. The source slit of a spectrograph is pointed at this space. (We omit the troublesome technical details of a vacuum spectrograph.) Suppose that the accelerating voltage, $V_a$, is set at 8 volts. Many of the electrons arriving at $G$ with KE = 8 ev will pass through the mesh and coast into the field-free space. Such electrons, when striking the hydrogen atoms, should not be able to dislodge the hydrogen electrons from the ground state, for the energy-level diagram (Fig. 28-3) shows that the first possible excited level ($n = 2$) is 10.2 ev above the ground state. Under these conditions we expect no radiation from the gas, and the spectrograph, in fact, records no lines. With $V_a = 10.2$ volts, however, the bombarding electrons have sufficient energy to raise the hydrogen atoms to the first excited state. After a brief interval these atoms return to the ground state and radiate the energy absorbed from the bombarding electrons as a photon of the first Lyman line. With $V_a = 10.2$ volts the spectrograph records the first Lyman line and *only* that line. As $V_a$ is increased, the first Lyman line continues, at first, to be the only line; then, when the second critical voltage, 12.1 volts, is reached, the bombarding electrons have sufficient energy to raise the atoms to the second excited state ($n = 3$), and three radiated lines are possible: an atom may return directly to the ground state ($3 \to 1$) and radiate the second Lyman line, or it may return in two jumps ($3 \to 2$ and $2 \to 1$) and radiate the first Balmer line and the first

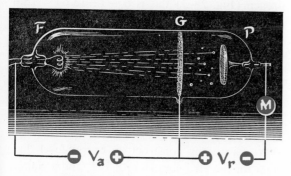

FIGURE **28-4** *Method of measuring energy levels.*

Lyman line. Only these three lines are recorded by the spectrograph when $V_a$ is set at 12.1 volts. As $V_a$ is increased further, more and more of the complete hydrogen spectrum is observed as $V_a$ passes the critical voltages corresponding to the higher energy levels of Figure 28-3.†

Another informative kind of experiment may be performed with the tube of Figure 28-4. The potential difference $V_r$ is held constant at about 0.5 volt. With $V_a$ at 8 volts, the electrons passing through $G$ have sufficient KE to move easily against the retarding potential of 0.5 volt and to travel over to $P$, and a current is registered by the meter, $M$. As $V_a$ is increased, the electrons, having greater KE, move more rapidly to $P$, and a larger current is observed through $M$. This continues until, at a certain critical value of $V_a$, the current *decreases* abruptly. With hydrogen in the tube this critical potential is 10.2 volts, precisely the excitation energy of the first excited state. The interpretation of this result is as follows: At values of $V_a$ less than 10.2 volts (such as the 8 volts above) the bombarding electrons suffer elastic impacts; that is, KE is conserved. The impinging electrons have insufficient energy to raise the atom to the first excited state and hence merely bounce off with undiminished KE. At the critical value of $V_a$ (10.2 volts for hydrogen) the impacts become inelastic. KE is absorbed by the atoms and converted into the energy of the radiated photons. After such impacts the bombarding electrons are left with too small a KE to move against the retarding potential, and the meter therefore shows an abrupt decrease of current. The outstanding result of this kind of experiment is that the *same* critical potentials that were determined by spectroscopic measurements are here determined by purely electrical measurements.

Many experiments of the kinds described in the last two paragraphs were carried out for all elements available as gases or vapors. The excitation energies for a particular element were always found to be the same by both methods. The important result is that the concept of a discrete and characteristic set of energy levels, developed by Bohr for the hydrogen atom, is equally applicable to all atoms. An explanation of these characteristic energy levels would lead to an understanding of atomic structures. We shall return to this question in the next section.

It is clear from the development of Bohr's theory that his equations should be applicable to any single-electron system. Hydrogen is, of course, the only neutral atom containing only one electron. We have already considered direct experimental evidence that for the next lighter elements the *total* number of electrons in the atom is equal to the atomic number (p. 306). Hence singly ionized helium ($He^+$), doubly ionized lithium ($Li^{+2}$), etc. would each be a positively charged nucleus with one remaining electron. How do observation and theory compare for these substances?

The ionization energies give excellent verifications of the theory. We have already discussed an electrical method of measuring these characteristic energies. (See p. 301, and note that the apparatus is the same as that of Fig. 28-4, with the value of $V_r$ set appropriately high.) By this method the ionization energy of hydrogen is shown to be 13.6 ev. According to the Bohr theory, the ionization energy should be the energy required to lift the electron from the ground state with $n = 1$—that is, to lift the electron out to the edge of the nuclear field. For hydrogen (Fig. 28-3) this is $0 - (-13.6) = 13.6$ ev. That is, the ionization energy is the positive energy of the ground state. But this is also the energy of the photon for the shortest wavelength in the spectrum—for hydrogen the limit of the Lyman series. Here again we obtain complete agreement between the electrical and the spectroscopic observations of this characteristic atomic property.

We can easily construct an energy-level diagram for the $He^+$ ion. Here $Z = 2$, and a glance at equation 28-5 tells us that energy levels for

---

† In any experiment we observe the radiation not from only one atom but from a very large number of atoms. If a certain transition is more probable than some other one, a larger number of atoms radiate this photon, and this line appears as more intense in the composite spectrum from all the atoms. In the visible region, for instance, the 3→2 transition of hydrogen has a high probability, which accounts for the reddish hue of luminous hydrogen. One shortcoming of the Bohr theory is that it does not predict these probabilities and the relative intensities of the lines. It gives only the possible transitions.

TABLE **28-1** *Ionization Energies* (ev)
*of Hydrogen-like Ions*

| $Z$ | SUBSTANCE | OBSERVED | THEORETICAL ($Z^2 \times$ H) |
|---|---|---|---|
| 1 | H | 13.6 | 13.6 |
| 2 | $He^+$ | 54.2 | 54.4 |
| 3 | $Li^{+2}$ | 122 | 122 |
| 4 | $Be^{+3}$ | 217 | 218 |
| 5 | $B^{+4}$ | 339 | 340 |

the increasing quantum numbers are just four ($Z^2$) times those for hydrogen. Similarly, the levels of Figure 28-3, multiplied by nine, give the levels for the $Li^{+2}$ ion; multiplied by sixteen, they give the levels for $Be^{+3}$; etc. Hence the ionization energy of hydrogen times the square of the atomic number should give the value for these substances. Table 28-1 gives the results for the first five elements. The experimental values, determined both electrically and spectroscopically, are shown in the third column. Those that differ from the theoretical values, listed in the last column, do so by only a fraction of 1 percent. This variation is well within the experimental precision of the measurements.

The Bohr theory predicts that the ions of the last paragraph will radiate spectral series similar to the hydrogen series but displaced uniformly toward shorter wavelengths. As pointed out above, the energy levels for $He^+$ are just four times those for hydrogen. Thus a particular transition, such as $4 \rightarrow 3$, would give rise to a photon four times as large from $He^+$ as from H; that is, the radiated line would have one-quarter the wavelength of the corresponding hydrogen line. The same result is obtained for all other transitions. This, of course, is just what equation 28-9 tells us. For $He^+$ this equation becomes $1/\lambda = 4\Re[1/n^2 - 1/p^2]$, which, with $n = 1$ and $p = 2, 3, 4$, etc., predicts a series each line of which has just one-quarter the wavelength of the corresponding line of the Lyman series of hydrogen. With $n = 2$ and $p = 3, 4, 5$, etc., a series with lines having one-quarter the wavelengths of the lines of the Balmer series is predicted. Higher series, starting with $n = 3$, $n = 4$, etc., are also predicted. At the time Bohr

published his theory, some of these lines were known but had been incorrectly attributed to hydrogen. Similarly, lithium under high-voltage excitation was found to emit a spectrum described by $1/\lambda = 9\Re[1/n^2 - 1/p^2]$, which is the predicted spectrum of $Li^{+2}$. Corresponding observations for the heavier elements up to oxygen have been obtained. In each case the wavelengths differ from the hydrogen series by the factors 16, 25, 36, etc.—that is, by $Z^2$. Such excellent agreement between fact and theory strengthens our confidence in Bohr's theory. And, since the concept of a nuclear charge of $+Ze$ is fundamental to the theory, these results yield further confirmation of the general law that the atomic number is equal to the number of positive electronic charges on the nucleus.

## 28-4. *Motion of the Nucleus*

The spectroscopic verifications of Bohr's theory outlined in the last paragraph produced an apparent discrepancy—which, however, led to a further success of the theory. The wavelengths from $He^+$ were found to be slightly different from the corresponding wavelengths from hydrogen. The transition $3 \rightarrow 2$ in hydrogen, for instance, gives rise to the intense red line of 6,563 A. The transition $6 \rightarrow 4$ in $He^+$ should radiate the same wavelength according to the simple theory outlined so far.[†] By direct measurement, however, this line is found to have a wavelength of 6,560 A—that is, is about 1 part in 2,000 too small. This variation between the two spectra, though small, could not be attributed to experimental error. Bohr's theory had greatly stimulated spectroscopic investigations, and these had led to more refined and precise techniques for wavelength measurements. It was evident, therefore, that the Rydberg constant must have a slightly smaller value for H than for $He^+$. (We have already encountered this small discrepancy when evaluating $\Re_{th}$ with modern precise values of the constants and comparing the result with an $\Re_H$ evaluated from the Balmer

[†] For $He^+$, $6 \rightarrow 4$ gives $1/\lambda = 4\Re[1/4^2 - 1/6^2] = \Re[2^2/4^2 - 2^2/6^2] = \Re[1/2^2 - 1/3^2]$, which is the hydrogen $3 \rightarrow 2$ transition.

formula.) But, according to the simple theory, $\mathfrak{R}_{th}$ should be the same in all circumstances, for equation 28-8 involves only universal constants. Bohr soon cleared up the difficulty by pointing out that his original theory contained a simplifying assumption.

In presenting Bohr's theory we assumed that the nucleus was *at rest* at the center of the orbits. The mass of the nucleus, then, did not enter into the equations, for, if it was not moving, it contributed no KE to the system. (The nucleus would correspond to an enormously massive sun at the center of a light planet's orbit.) But, as we have seen (§ 5-6), earth and moon revolve about a common center since the moon's mass is an appreciable fraction of the earth's mass. Similarly, the assumption of a stationary nucleus is strictly true only if the mass of the electron is an unobservably small fraction of the nuclear mass. For heavy nuclei this is true, but for lighter nuclei the fraction, although small, is not beyond the precision of spectroscopic measurements. Bohr therefore refined his theory to include the motion of the nucleus. We shall not carry out the complicated calculation. The results are the same except for one simple correction. Wherever the mass, $m$, of the electron appears, it is replaced by the so-called "reduced mass," the fraction $mM/(m + M)$, in which $M$ is the mass of the nucleus. Notice that for heavy nuclei, whose $M$ is much larger than $m$, this reduces simply to $m$, as in the formulas of the simpler theory. For hydrogen, however, $M = 1,836m$, and the reduced mass becomes $1,836m/1,837$, which differs from $m$ by approximately 1 part in 2,000. We put the reduced mass in equation 28-8 and obtain the theoretical value of the Rydberg constant for hydrogen:

$$\mathfrak{R}_H = \frac{1,836}{1,837}\,\mathfrak{R}_{th} = 1.0969 \times 10^7/m$$

The experimental value derived from the Balmer formula is $\mathfrak{R}_H = 1.0968 \times 10^7/m$. These are the same since the variation is only one digit in the fifth figure, the number of figures used for these calculations. A similar calculation gives the value for $\mathfrak{R}_{He}$. When these values are used, the lines predicted for the $He^+$ spectrum are precisely the same as the observed lines—that is, of

slightly shorter wavelength than the corresponding H lines, as pointed out in the last paragraph.

The motion of the nucleus played a central role in the discovery of the rare isotope of hydrogen, $_1H^2$ (§ 18-11). A slight, barely detectable discrepancy was found between the atomic weight of hydrogen ($_1H^1$) determined by the mass spectrograph and that determined by chemical means. This suggested that there might be a heavy isotope of hydrogen. If so, and if its mass was twice that of ordinary hydrogen, a concentration of 1 part in 4,500 would account for the observed discrepancy. But did the isotope exist? The mass spectrograph was not sufficiently sensitive to record such a low concentration. In 1932 H. E. Urey and his associates, G. M. Murphy and F. G. Brickwedde, started a search for this isotope. Their first problem was to prepare a sample of hydrogen that would, if the isotope existed, have a higher concentration of it than natural hydrogen. Relying on the fact, predicted by the kinetic theory, that the heavier hydrogen would evaporate less rapidly than normal hydrogen, they evaporated a large enough quantity of liquid hydrogen so that, if their guess was correct, the residue would contain a detectable concentration of the isotope. This sample was introduced into a discharge tube, and the spectrum was photographed. The normal hydrogen spectrum appeared and in addition, alongside the bright Balmer red line and displaced slightly toward shorter wavelength, a new line. This was exactly what was to be expected if the sample contained a heavy isotope, since the heavier nucleus would not move as much as the lighter nucleus of ordinary hydrogen. The observed wavelength, substituted in Bohr's equation, yielded the value of the reduced mass, from which the nuclear mass of the isotope was found to be 2. Thus this important, though rare, isotope of hydrogen was discovered and identified.

## 28-5. *Extensions of Bohr's Theory*

In the preceding section we have outlined some of the outstanding successes of Bohr's theory for hydrogen-like atoms. The theory was soon found, however, to have a limited validity.

It did not, for instance, accurately predict the spectra of atoms with more than one electron, not even the next simplest one, He (that is, the neutral atom with two electrons, not the ion He$^+$ with only one electron), and the increasingly precise spectroscopic measurements that were stimulated by the theory produced puzzling new observations. For instance, lines that had been considered single (that is, of one wavelength) were found to have *fine structure;* that is, the "line" consisted of several closely spaced lines of slightly different wavelengths. The clue to the analysis of these complex spectra was given, however, by Bohr's theory.

In our discussion of the spectra of hydrogen-like atoms we computed from theory the energy-level diagram and then compared predicted transitions with observed radiations. This process works equally well in reverse. We accept Bohr's fundamental postulate that an emitted photon represents the difference between two discrete energy states of the atom. By measuring the wavelengths in the spectrum, we may determine experimentally the energies of the emitted photons. Then we construct an energy-level diagram so that the application of the equation $h\nu = W_n - W_p$ will give the energies of the observed photons. In this way a characteristic set of levels

is worked out for each element, since, as we have seen (§ 25-4), no two elements emit exactly the same spectrum. The problem, then, was to account for these empirically determined energy levels in terms of possible energy states of the electrons. In a little over a decade from the time Bohr published his theory the problem was worked out. This was a period of intense activity, which exhibited a remarkable interplay of experimental observation and theory, each alternately pointing the way. The final result was a detailed picture of atomic structure that culminated in the interpretation of the periodic table of the elements. We cannot follow the developments in detail, but we shall discuss the important results.

The first extension of the Bohr theory, made in 1916 by the German scientist Arnold Sommerfeld, was to elliptical orbits. Just as the inverse-square force of gravity produces elliptical orbits for the planets, with the sun at a focus, the inverse-square Coulomb's force should produce an elliptical orbit for the electron, with the nucleus at a focus. The quantum condition restricts the electron to certain allowed ellipses, whereas classical mechanics permits ellipses of any size. In applying the quantum condition to circular orbits (equation 28-2), we had to con-

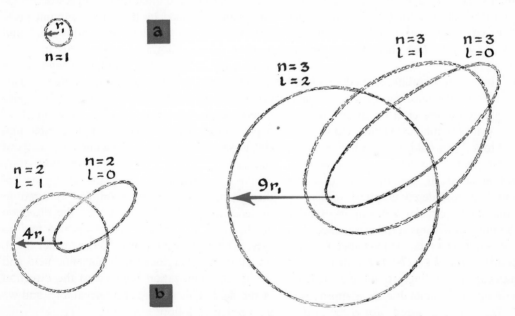

FIGURE **28-5** *Sommerfeld's orbits for the first three principal quantum numbers.*

sider only the rotation of the radius joining the nucleus and the electron since all other factors remained constant. For an elliptical orbit, however, the radius not only rotates but also changes length as the electron swings round the nucleus. Hence there are *two* factors to be quantized. Sommerfeld extended Bohr's quantum condition to these factors, and each one involved an integer times Planck's constant. The results of the complicated mathematics are illustrated in Figure 28-5. The allowed orbits are specified by *two* quantum numbers. One of these is $n$, Bohr's original quantum number, now called the **principal quantum number.** The other is designated by $l$ and determines the eccentricity (the "flatness") of the ellipse. The theory restricts $l$ to integral values starting with 0 and increasing to $(n-1)$. Thus for each principal quantum number there are $n$ allowed orbits. The most elliptical has $l = 0$, and with increasing $l$ the orbits become less elliptical, the final one being a circle for $l = n - 1$. For each $n$, the long diameters of the ellipses and the diameter of the circle are all equal. The nucleus is at the center of the circle and at a focus of the ellipses. The possible orbits for values of $n$ through 3 are shown in Figure 28-5. The size of the orbits increases as $n^2$, just as in the simple Bohr theory. With $n = 4$, for instance, there would be four orbits: a circle and three ellipses for $l = 3, 2, 1, 0$. The radius of the circle and half of the long diameter of each ellipse would equal $16r_1$. And so on for larger values of $n$.

At first the elliptical orbits seemed to represent no advance, for classical mechanics gave the same energy for the electron in any one of the orbits for a particular $n$. Hence a transition from $n = 3$ to $n = 2$ would result in the emission of the same photon no matter which pair of orbits was involved. It was this fact that led Bohr, who had considered elliptical orbits, to use only the simpler circular orbits in his original theory. Sommerfeld, however, investigated the effect of the electron's relativistic change in mass due to its orbital speed (§ 27-2). As the electron in an elliptical orbit swings round the nucleus, it speeds up just as a planet does as it approaches the sun. This varying speed would be somewhat different for the different orbits. A simple

calculation for circular orbits from equations 28-2 and 28-3 shows that the greatest speed is less than 0.01 of the speed of light. This would produce a very small relativistic correction, but the fine structure of spectral lines represents just such small variations. By taking relativity into account, Sommerfeld showed that the energies for the different orbits for each value of $n$ were slightly different. Transitions terminating on $n = 2$, say (such as the Balmer lines), could end up on two slightly different energy levels, one for the circle and one for the ellipse. Thus two very nearly equal but measurably different photons would be radiated. In this way Sommerfeld was able to *predict* the observed elaborate fine structures of the H and He$^+$ spectral lines. The elliptical orbits, then, must represent discrete energy levels of the atoms. The principal quantum number, $n$, determines the size of the orbits, and the quantum number $l$ determines their shapes.

The circular and elliptical orbits discussed so far represent motion only in two dimensions; that is, the orbits are all in the same plane. Sommerfeld next considered the problem of movement in three dimensions, and applied the general quantum condition to each of the three coordinates. As might be expected, the orbits came out to be the circles and ellipses described above and specified by the same quantum numbers, $n$ and $l$. But the plane of an orbit was found to have certain allowable orientations in space; that is, the orbit could be tilted through angles specified by a third quantum number. This orientation of the orbit in space was called **space quantization.** Now we might hold a sheet of paper so that it is inclined at 40° to a table top. But to say that the paper is inclined 40° without stating a fixed reference (such as the table top) would be meaningless. In the mathematical theory the space quantization was referred to the coordinate axes involved. But the direction of the axes is perfectly arbitrary and has no special physical significance. On the other hand, the atom may be placed in a magnetic field and the space quantization referred to the direction of the field. This picture *is* interpretable, and we interpret it as follows.

For the sake of definiteness consider the cir-

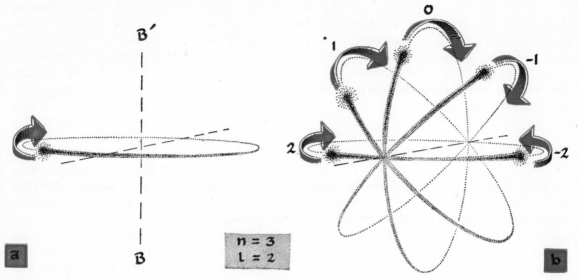

FIGURE **28-6** *Space quantization of an electron orbit.*

cular orbit represented by $n = 3$ and $l = 2$ in Figure 28-5. Suppose that the plane of the orbit is at right angles to some arbitrarily chosen direction, $BB'$, as shown in Figure 28-6a. When this orbit is space-quantized with reference to $BB'$, five orientations are allowed, as shown in Figure 28-6b. (So far we cannot determine experimentally whether or not these predicted orbits exist.) Now consider that the atom is in a uniform magnetic field in the direction $BB'$. The electron, with charge $-e$ and moving with speed $v$ round the orbit, constitutes a current loop, which produces a magnetic dipole along the line $BB'$, with an N pole toward $B'$. This is exactly analogous to a compass lining itself up with the earth's magnetic field. Now to rotate this orbit into position 1 (Fig. 28-6b) would require work in just the same way as to move a compass into a position making an angle with the earth's field would require work. Orbit 1 therefore represents a different energy state from orbit 2. Similarly, the other orbits, round to $-2$, represent different energy states, the differences in energy being supplied by the magnetic field.†

† Orbit $-2$ *looks* the same as orbit 2, but the electron, as viewed along the direction of the field, is going round in *opposite* directions in these two orbits. The radii of 2 and $-2$ are slightly different, moreover, since the force exerted by the magnetic field on the moving electron is away from the nucleus in one case and toward it in the other.

Now a spectral "line" due to some transition from a higher state to these orbits would display just one wavelength when there is *no* magnetic field. *With* the magnetic field, however, the transition would result in a slightly different energy change. Hence, if the atom is in a magnetic field, the line should "split" into several close lines that depend on the particular orbit terminating the "jump." If the magnetic field were made stronger, the differences between the energies of the orbits would be greater, and the line should split into more widely spaced components (that is, the emitted photons would have greater energy differences). This is the Zeeman effect described in § 25-7.

With an enormous amount of spectroscopic analysis of the Zeeman effect, interpreted in terms of space quantization, the allowed orientations of the various orbits were worked out and a general rule evolved. Each space-quantized orbit is specified by a *third* quantum number, $m_l$, which may take on certain integral values determined by the value of $l$. In Figure 28-6 there are five possible values of $m_l$, 2, 1, 0, $-1$, and $-2$. For $l = 1$ (such as $n = 3, l = 1$ and $n = 2, l = 1$ in Fig. 28-5) there are three values of $m_l$, 1, 0, and $-1$. For $l = 0$, $m_l = 0$; that is, there is only one orientation for these orbits. These examples illustrate the general rule: for any given value of $l$ the space quantum numbers are $m_l = l, l - 1$,

. . . 1, 0, −1, . . . −(l − 1), −l; that is, there are 2l + 1 orientations. For higher values of the principal quantum number, n, where l has (n − 1) values, the number of space-quantized states can be quite large. The important result is that here are more actual stationary states for the electrons inside atoms.

## 28-6. Spinning Electron

Precise spectroscopic studies revealed details that could not be accounted for by transitions among the stationary states discussed so far. In particular, certain spectral series displayed a multiplet structure (§ 25-7). These doublets, triplets, etc., were for many years a great puzzle to the spectroscopists. In 1925 two young Dutch physicists resolved the puzzle with their discovery of the spinning electron. They assumed that, as the electron moves along an orbit, it also spins on an axis, very much as the earth rotates on its axis as it moves round the sun. Here, then, was one more motion that would affect the total energy of the electron. The spinning charge of the electron creates a magnetic dipole along the axis of spin. But the orbital motion of the electron creates a magnetic field in the direction of line B in Figure 28-7. How is the axis of spin oriented in space? Space quantization, which here is referred to the direction of the *internal* magnetic field of the orbital motion, gives the simple answer. The electron may align its axis of spin in only *two* directions (Fig. 28-7), each of which is

parallel to the field due to the orbital motion. It may align its magnetic dipole either in the direction of the field (*parallel*) or in a direction opposite to the field (*anti-parallel*). These two possible orientations are specified by a fourth quantum number, $m_s$, which is assigned the values ½ and −½. These two orientations, since it requires work to swing the dipole against the field, represent a small difference of energy, which splits the energy level of the orbit into two slightly different levels. Appropriate transitions between such split levels led to a complete description of the observed multiplet structures of spectral lines.

Having discovered a large number of possible motions for an electron, we have apparently exhausted the possibilities that are consistent with the picture of a planetary atom and with the fundamental quantum hypothesis of discrete stationary states. We have pictured these states as certain allowable orbits for the electrons. These orbits, of course, may not be an accurate description of the electronic motions inside the atoms. But the discrete energies for these orbits, as determined by the four quantum numbers, certainly are the energy states of the atom; for with these states and a few empirical rules for "allowed" transitions (electron "jumps") the spectroscopists were able to account for the vast and complex data of spectroscopy.

The model we have pictured may, in some repects, be disappointing. Some may hope to find an explanation in terms of our more familiar experience, which is the basis of classical science. To us there seems to be no chance of accomplishing this. The basic quantum idea of discrete, discontinuous changes appears to be fundamental to atomic processes. And, as we shall see, the same quantum numbers that completely determine the observed spectral lines also determine the arrangement of electrons about the nucleus. In view of this, the quantum model of atomic structure is fully justified by its enormous success and represents great progress in our understanding of the nature of matter.

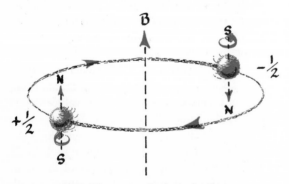

FIGURE **28-7** *Electron-spin quantization.*

## Concepts and Terms

Planetary Atom
Bohr's Postulates
  stationary states
  frequency condition
Bohr's Theory of One-electron Atoms
  quantum condition for stationary states
  orbits
  spectral series
  Rydberg constant
Hydrogen Atom
  electron jumps
Energy-level Diagram
  convergence of energies toward zero
  electron transitions
  critical potentials
  ionization potential

One-electron Ions
Motion of Nucleus
$\mathcal{R}_H$
Extensions of Bohr's Theory
  fine structure of lines
  elliptic orbits
  quantum number $l$
  Zeeman effect
  space quantization
  quantum number $m_l$
  multiplet structure of lines
  spinning electron
  quantum number $m_s$

## Problems

**28-1.** Review the steps in the development of Bohr's theory of the hydrogen atom. Indicate the steps that introduce the postulates of the theory into the development. Also indicate which steps are direct applications of classical science and which are applications of radically new concepts.

**28-2.** Starting with equations 28-2 and 28-3, derive equation 28-7. Include the algebraic steps indicated (but not performed) in the text. Show that equation 28-7 is consistent in units.

**28-3.** Using approximate values (three significant figures) for the fundamental constants, calculate the Rydberg constant.

**28-4.**
  (A) Calculate the diameter of the smallest hydrogen orbit. Compare your answer with the data of Table 12-2. Discuss.
  (B) Calculate the diameter of the third hydrogen orbit.

*Ans.* (A) 1.06 A
  (B) 9.54 A

**28-5.** Calculate the diameters of the first and third orbits of He+. (Hint: How does $r$ vary with $Z$?)

*Ans.* 0.53 A; 4.77 A

**28-6.**
  (A) Derive a formula for the speed of an electron in an allowed orbit in terms of measurable quantities. (If you have done Prob. 28-2, you already have an expression for $mv^2$.)
  (B) Calculate the speed of the first hydrogen orbit, and express it as a fraction of the speed of light. Is the relativistic increase in mass appreciable? (See § 27-2.)
  (C) What is the speed of the electron in the fifth hydrogen orbit? in the "infinite" orbit? Relate these changes in speed to corresponding energy changes.

  *Ans.* (A) $v = 2\pi CZe^2/nh$
    (B) $7.25 \times 10^{-3}\ c$
    (C) $1.45 \times 10^{-3}\ c$; zero

**28-7.** Calculate the energy of the fifth hydrogen orbit. (You have already calculated $\mathcal{R}_{th}$ in Prob. 28-3. Compare equations 28-5 and 28-8, and express $W_n$ in terms of $\mathcal{R}_{th}$. This will save considerable arithmetic.) Enter the answer in the energy-level diagram of Fig. 28-3.

  *Ans.* −0.544 ev

**28-8.** Consider equation 28-5. How do the energies of the orbits vary with the quantum number? Verify your answer numerically by the use of Fig. 28-3.

**28-9.** From the energy-level diagram of Fig. 28-3 calculate the wavelengths of the four visible lines of the hydrogen spectrum and of the limit of this series. (See Fig. 25-7.)

**28-10.** Hydrogen gas is bombarded with electrons that have fallen through a potential difference of 12.8 volts.
(A) How many lines will this gas radiate?
(B) How many will be in the visible range?

*Ans.* (A) six
(B) two

**28-11.** Construct an energy-level diagram for He+ with values for the first six levels. Which transitions among these levels give rise to lines of the hydrogen spectrum? Which hydrogen lines are they? What is the ionization potential of He+ (that is, the *second* ionization potential for helium)?

**28-12.** The sodium yellow line ($\lambda = 5,893$ A) is due to a transition from the first excited state to the ground state. The ionization energy of sodium is 5.12 ev. Calculate the first two energy levels for sodium.

*Ans.* $-5.12$ ev; $-3.01$ ev

**28-13.**
(A) How many different orbits are possible for principal quantum number $n = 2$? How many energy states are possible?
(B) Repeat A for $n = 3$ and for $n = 4$.
(C) Generalize your results for any value of $n$.

*Ans.* (A) 4 orbits, 8 energy states
(C) $n^2$ orbits, $2n^2$ energy states

**28-14.**
(A) White light, after passing through non-luminous sodium vapor, is dispersed into a spectrum. Describe the spectrum. (Consider the information of Prob. 28-12, and see § 25-7.)
(B) If a continuous spectrum of sufficiently wide frequency range is passed through non-luminous hydrogen, what absorption lines would you expect to appear?
(C) In the sun's spectrum the Balmer lines appear as absorption lines. In the laboratory, however, the Balmer absorption lines do not appear after white light is passed through hydrogen gas. How do you account for these facts?

## Suggested Readings

1. S. Hecht, *Explaining the Atom* (Viking Press, 1947), Chaps. 1, 2, and 3. A non-mathematical discussion written for the layman.
2. M. Born, *The Restless Universe,* translated by W. M. Deans (Dover Publications, 1951), pp. 122–133 and 176–185.
3. H. Semat, *Fundamentals of Physics,* 3rd edition (Rinehart, 1957), pp. 774–790.
4. R. D. Rusk, *Introduction to Atomic and Nuclear Physics* (Appleton-Century-Crofts, 1958), pp. 155–185. A more detailed discussion than ours of the Bohr theory and its extensions.

# The Periodic Classification (II): Electronic Configurations of Atoms

IN THE years 1921–1923 Bohr undertook to study the pattern of the periodic table of the elements and to arrive at an atomic model that would satisfactorily explain both the physical and the chemical properties of the atoms. He imagined that one would start with a bare nucleus, add electrons one at a time, and investigate what orbits and energy levels they would enter. At first one might think that, in accordance with the general tendency of physical systems to assume a minimum energy,† the electrons would all crowd into the orbit of the lowest energy. If this were so, however, the list of elements would show none of its striking periodicities. Lithium, with three electrons in such an orbit, would show no similarity to hydrogen, with only one; potassium, with nineteen in one orbit, would be very different from sodium, with only eleven; and so on for other groups.

By correlating the facts of spectroscopy (both optical and X-ray) with the known chemical properties, Bohr assigned the electrons to appropriate orbits that accounted for the known facts, and thus developed a theory of the periodic system. This remarkable achievement of inductive reasoning was one of the most important syntheses in the history of science. It is all the more remarkable when we consider that he worked out his theory without two ideas that we now know are fundamental to such a theory. One of these ideas is that of the electron spin, and the other is the exclusion principle.

## 29-1. Quantum Specification of Electronic Orbits

In the last chapter we saw that the discovery of the electron spin led to a fourth quantum number for determining energy states of an electron in an atom. Let us summarize what these four numbers specify. The principal quantum number, $n = 1, 2, 3, \ldots$, determines the *size* of the orbits, which is larger for higher numbers. For each value of $n$ there are $n$ *shapes* specified by the quantum number $l = 0, 1, \ldots (n - 1)$,

---

† For instance: water runs downhill and reduces its PE; hot bodies radiate heat and cool off; spontaneous chemical reactions give up energy, leaving the products with a smaller total energy; etc.

with the most elliptical shape for $l = 0$ and with ellipticity decreasing to a circle for $l = n - 1$. Each orbit may have $2l + 1$ *orientations* in space, specified by the quantum number $m_l = l$, $l - 1, \ldots 1, 0, -1, \ldots -(l - 1), -l$. In any orbit the axis of *spin* of the electron, either parallel or anti-parallel to the orbital magnetic field, is specified by the quantum number $m_s = +\frac{1}{2}$ or $-\frac{1}{2}$. Any possible combination of these four numbers will determine for an electron a unique motion in which it will have a definite amount of energy different from that of any other combination. In other words, such a set of quantum numbers determines a **stationary state** of the atom. For instance, the numbers $n = 2$, $l = 1$, $m_l = 0$, and $m_s = -\frac{1}{2}$ specify the energy for an electron in the next to the smallest circular orbit, tilted 90°, and with the axis of electron spin anti-parallel to the orbital magnetic field.

## 29-2. *Exclusion Principle*

In the same year that the electron spin was discovered (1925) Wolfgang Pauli proposed a simple and plausible principle that has been found to be of fundamental importance. He stated that within a single atom no two electrons can have exactly the same set of quantum numbers; that is, no two electrons can be in the same stationary state. This is the famous **Pauli exclusion principle.**

We can now build the electronic structures of the atoms with a great deal more ease than did Bohr. We follow his method of adding electrons one by one to a bare nucleus† and are guided by the following two principles: (1) the electrons arrange themselves in accordance with the exclusion principle; (2) the electrons in a neutral unexcited atom fill the lowest available energy levels consistent with the exclusion principle.

## 29-3. *Electronic Configurations*

Hydrogen's one electron is in the only orbit for $n = 1$ and has its spin parallel to the or-

bital magnetic field. Helium's first electron has the same configuration as that of hydrogen; the second, however, can enter the same orbit by aligning its spin anti-parallel to the field. This orbit is now filled. A third electron, to enter this orbit, would have to align its spin parallel to one of the first two. This would give it an identical set of quantum numbers, which is excluded by principle 1. Since, furthermore, this orbit is the only one for $n = 1$, the two electrons of helium completely fill all stationary states for the principal quantum number $n = 1$. The group of all states for a given value of the principal quantum number is called a **shell.** Each shell is labeled by a capital letter, a terminology carried over from the study of X-ray spectra. For $n = 1$ the shell is called the K shell,† for $n = 2$ the L shell, for $n = 3$ the M shell, and so on. In helium the K shell is completely filled. No more electrons can enter it, and the ones that are in it show a great reluctance to leave. This very stable structure is evidenced by the chemical inertness and large ionization potential of helium (Fig. 8-3).

Lithium's first two electrons fill the K shell. The third electron, forced to occupy one of the larger orbits of the L shell ($n = 2$), chooses the lowest energy state, which is the one in the elliptical orbit with $l = 0$ (Fig. 28-5) and spin parallel to the field, $m_s = +\frac{1}{2}$. Beryllium's fourth electron enters this same orbit but has its spin anti-parallel, $m_s = -\frac{1}{2}$. For the next elements the electrons enter the circular orbits for $n = 2$, $l = 1$. There are three of these orbits, oriented according to $m_l = +1$, 0, $-1$, and, since each can accommodate two electrons ($m_s = +\frac{1}{2}$ and $-\frac{1}{2}$), they give six different states. These fill up as we go on from boron until, for neon, the tenth electron completes these orbits. These are all the orbits for $n = 2$, and thus the L shell is filled with a stable structure of eight electrons in addition to the two electrons in the still more stable K shell.

For the next element, sodium, the eleventh electron enters the more elliptical orbit of the M shell ($n = 3$, $l = 0$), which orbit accepts another electron in magnesium. The electrons then begin to fill the more nearly circular ellipse

---

† Remember that, as we go through the periodic table, the positive charge on the nucleus increases by one electronic charge for each succeeding element.

† Not to be confused with the symbol for potassium.

$(n = 3, l = 1)$. For these, as before with $l = 1$, there are three orientations and six states. Filling these carries us to argon with its stable outer group of eight electrons. But the M shell is not complete, for we have not used the five circular orbits for $n = 3$, $l = 2$ (see Fig. 29-1). The nineteenth electron in potassium, however, instead of entering one of these orbits, enters the most elliptical orbit of the N shell $(n = 4, l = 0)$. It does so because this orbit represents a lower energy state than any of the $n = 3$, $l = 2$ orbits. We can understand this in a qualitative way. Although this first orbit of the N shell $(n = 4)$ belongs to a group that are generally larger than the orbits of the L shell $(n = 3)$, it is so elliptical that for part of its path it approaches the nucleus more closely than some of the M orbits do. It is thus more strongly attracted and has a smaller energy, which leads to a smaller average energy for the orbit than might at first be expected. (This is somewhat analogous to the fact that a stone falling toward the earth from a great height has a constantly increasing weight and thus loses more PE per meter of fall the closer it comes to the earth.) The force exerted by the nucleus on an electron in this orbit is further enhanced by the fact that the electron, as it moves round the end of the ellipse nearer the nucleus, is less shielded from the nuclear charge by the other electrons in the atom. There are many such **penetrating orbits**—orbits that penetrate the orbits of lower $n$ value.

The nineteenth electron of potassium, then, enters the penetrating orbit $n = 4$, $l = 0$; the twentieth electron of calcium also enters this orbit but with opposite spin. This orbit is now full. The twenty-first electron of scandium now has both the $n = 4$, $l = 1$ orbits and the $n = 3$, $l = 2$ orbits available. Since the latter have the lower energy states, we begin to fill these and thus complete the M shell. Since $l = 2$, there are five of these orbits ($m_l = +2, +1, 0, -1, -2$), which can accept a total of ten electrons. This carries us through the first group of transition elements to zinc. Here the K, L, and M shells are filled, and there are two electrons filling the $n = 4$, $l = 0$ orbit. Starting with gallium ($Z = 31$), the three $n = 4$, $l = 1$ orbits fill up, and we arrive at krypton ($Z = 36$). Here again, although the N shell is not complete, we have, as in argon, a stable octet in the $l = 0$ and $l = 1$ orbits. Such a stable group within a shell is called **a sub-shell.** Completed sub-shells containing eight electrons—or, more properly, four *pairs* of electrons—characterize the inert gases. In each case the outer, "valence" electrons make up an octet that amounts to a completed sub-shell of four pairs of electrons.[†]

The principles and the pattern for describing the electronic structures of all the atoms of the periodic table have now been established. It is only necessary to mention briefly the way in which these principles operate in "building" the heavier atoms beyond krypton; to show a few specific atoms; and, much more importantly, to relate these electronic structures to the chemical properties of the various elements, to the empirical periodic law, and to the formation of valence bonds in chemical compounds.

The next two elements beyond krypton, the alkali metal rubidium and the alkaline-earth metal strontium, follow exactly the pattern followed in the beginning of the fourth period by potassium and calcium. Rubidium has its thirty-seventh electron alone in the O shell, and strontium has two electrons in this shell. Starting with element 39, yttrium, the energy levels are such that the N shell can expand; such expansion continues through the transition elements to cadmium ($Z = 48$), at which point the N shell is expanded to eighteen electrons and the O shell still has two (valence) electrons. This configuration of eighteen electrons presents another stable situation and therefore another sub-shell of the N shell of electrons, larger than, but otherwise similar to, the stable N sub-shell of eight electrons. Even with the eighteen electrons, however, not all the possible quantum numbers of $n = 4$ are used, and therefore the N electron shell, which corresponds to $n = 4$, is not yet entirely filled. The remainder of this long period is made up by the one-at-a-time expansion of

---

[†] The first inert gas, helium, obviously does not fall within this generalization, for its outermost electron shell is completed with the two electrons, and no possibility of later expansion of the K shell exists. The principle—that a stable configuration of outermost electrons leads to chemical inertness—is the same, however, for helium as for the other inert gases.

the O shell through indium ($Z = 49$), with three electrons, to xenon ($Z = 54$), the next inert gas, which has the stable octet of four pairs of electrons in the O sub-shell to give it the characteristic stable configuration.

The sixth period begins the same as the fourth and fifth periods, the first two electrons starting a new shell (called the P shell) and the first two elements being an alkali metal (one valence electron) and an alkaline-earth metal (two valence electrons). After these first two elements, cesium and barium, we find *three* possibilities for the introduction of more electrons: (1) further addition to the P shell (outermost); (2) expansion of the O shell (next to outside) from its stable sub-shell state of eight electrons; (3) expansion of the N shell from its stable but incomplete configuration of a sub-shell with eighteen electrons. The relative energy levels are such that the third alternative takes place first. Fourteen more electrons are added to the N sub-shell until it is completed with thirty-two electrons. This expansion takes place in elements 57–70, the rare-earth metals, or **lanthanides,** and completes the N shell by utilization of all thirty-two combinations of quantum numbers having $n = 4$. After completion of the N shell at element 70, further addition of electrons takes place by expansion of the O sub-shell (next to outermost) from the stable but incomplete configuration of eight electrons to the next stable sub-shell configuration of eighteen. This expansion corresponds to the ten transition elements of the sixth period, beginning with Lu ($Z = 71$) and ending with Hg ($Z = 80$). As in the two previous periods, the last six elements represent the stepwise addition of single electrons to the outermost shell until the stable octet configuration of the inert gas is reached at radon ($Z = 86$).

The last sixteen elements of the periodic table are the beginning of another long period (seventh period), formed similarly to the sixth period. Two electrons start the formation of a new shell (Q, with $n = 7$) in elements 87 and 88, the alkali metal francium and the alkaline-earth metal radium. The remaining elements begin another series, similar to the lanthanides, in which the electrons enter the second-to-outermost sub-shell, expanding the O sub-shell from

eighteen to thirty-two electrons, the outer shell of electrons remaining constant with two.

## 29-4. *Table of Electronic Configurations*

Figure 29-1 summarizes this brief description of the electronic configurations of the 102 elements. The various orbits allowed by the combination of quantum numbers are indicated by squares, the two oppositely oriented spin quantum numbers ($m_s$) being indicated by the oppositely directed arrows in the squares. The various orbits are very roughly placed vertically to indicate their relative energies. No absolute energy scale is shown, for the energies are not known with certainty in many cases, and the absolute energy varies, moreover, with the nuclear charge, which is, of course, different for each element. The energies of orbits at any position are, in general, greater than those of orbits at a lower position and lower than those of orbits at a higher position. The principal quantum number, $n$, is shown to the left of each shell and each sub-shell, and the broken lines segregate the various sub-shells that correspond to a particular principal quantum number. The quantum numbers for the sub-shells, $l$ and $m_l$, are given above the columns of sub-shells. The placing of the elements follows the rule that each new electron enters the most stable orbit available (the one with the least energy), and we repeat the sequence of the periodic table by starting with the lowest energy, at the bottom (H and He), and going *up* the diagram to the orbits having the next higher energies.[†]

One might use this diagram in describing the complete electronic configuration of an element. We shall use manganese ($Z = 25$) to illustrate

---

[†] The energies of many orbits high in this figure (high values of the atomic number) are so close together that it is uncertain which of the orbits an electron will occupy. In several such cases rigid following of the diagram places the electrons in slightly wrong orbits. For example, while the $n = 3$, $l = 3$ sub-shell is being filled, the $n = 4$, $l = 0$ orbit sometimes contains the two electrons indicated in the diagram but may have only *one* electron for some of the elements. In these cases one electron moves from the outer orbit into the inner sub-shell.

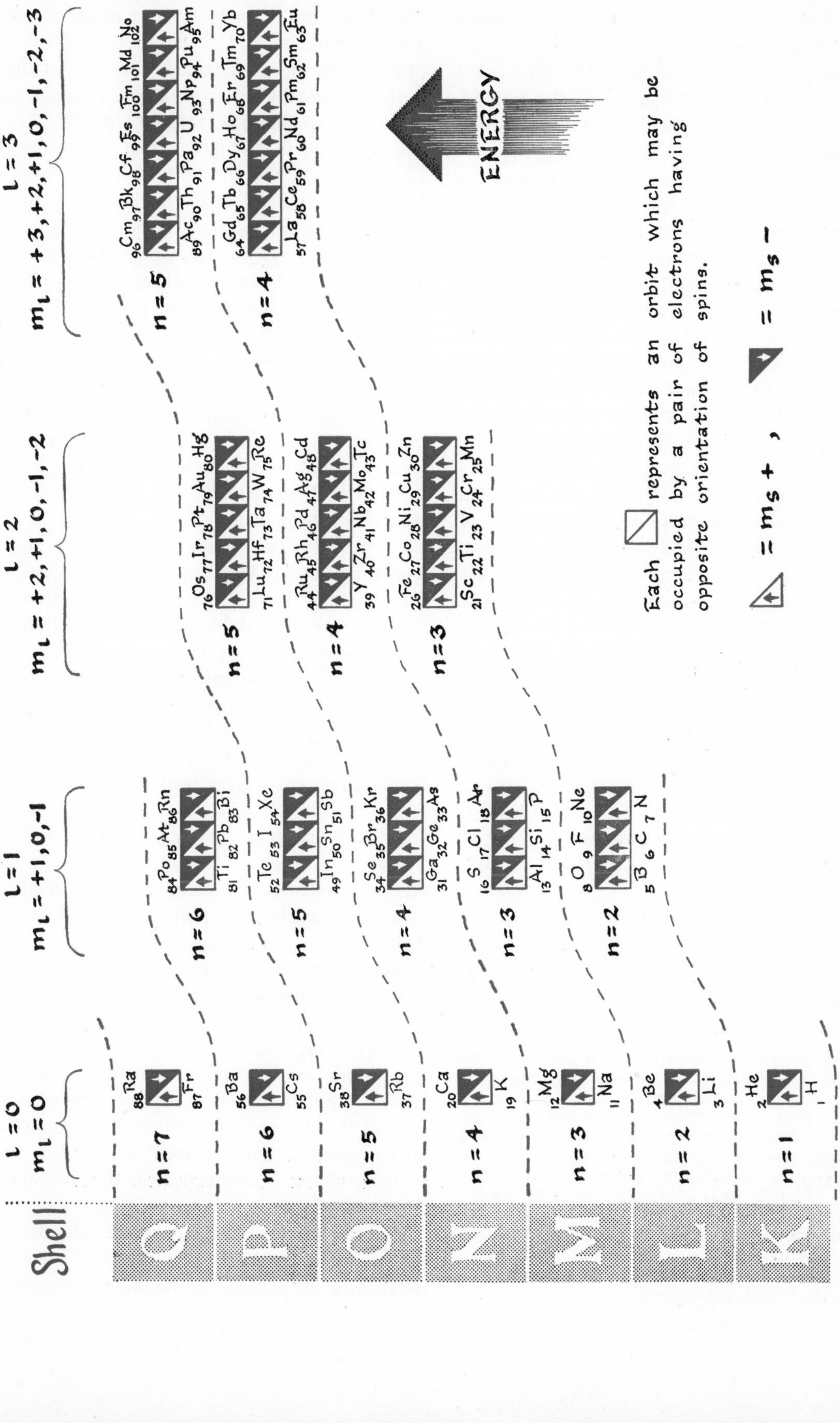

FIGURE 29-1 *Electronic configurations and quantum numbers.*

Each represents an orbit which may be occupied by a pair of electrons having opposite orientation of spins.

= $m_s +$ , = $m_s -$

ENERGY

$l = 0$  $m_l = 0$

$l = 1$  $m_l = +1, 0, -1$

$l = 2$  $m_l = +2, +1, 0, -1, -2$

$l = 3$  $m_l = +3, +2, +1, 0, -1, -2, -3$

Shell

Q  $n=7$  $_{88}Ra$  $_{87}Fr$

$n=6$  $_{84}Po$ $_{85}At$ $_{86}Rn$  $_{81}Tl$ $_{82}Pb$ $_{83}Bi$

$n=5$  $_{96}Cm$ $_{97}Bk$ $_{98}Cf$ $_{99}Es$ $_{100}Fm$ $_{101}Md$ $_{102}No$  $_{89}Ac$ $_{90}Th$ $_{91}Pa$ $_{92}U$ $_{93}Np$ $_{94}Pu$ $_{95}Am$

P  $n=6$  $_{56}Ba$  $_{55}Cs$

$n=5$  $_{52}Te$ $_{53}I$ $_{54}Xe$  $_{49}In$ $_{50}Sn$ $_{51}Sb$

$n=5$  $_{76}Os$ $_{77}Ir$ $_{78}Pt$ $_{79}Au$ $_{80}Hg$  $_{71}Lu$ $_{72}Hf$ $_{73}Ta$ $_{74}W$ $_{75}Re$

$n=4$  $_{57}La$ $_{58}Ce$ $_{59}Pr$ $_{60}Nd$ $_{61}Pm$ $_{62}Sm$ $_{63}Eu$  $_{64}Gd$ $_{65}Tb$ $_{66}Dy$ $_{67}Ho$ $_{68}Er$ $_{69}Tm$ $_{70}Yb$

O  $n=5$  $_{38}Sr$  $_{37}Rb$

$n=4$  $_{34}Se$ $_{35}Br$ $_{36}Kr$  $_{31}Ga$ $_{32}Ge$ $_{33}As$

$n=4$  $_{44}Ru$ $_{45}Rh$ $_{46}Pd$ $_{47}Ag$ $_{48}Cd$  $_{39}Y$ $_{40}Zr$ $_{41}Nb$ $_{42}Mo$ $_{43}Tc$

N  $n=4$  $_{20}Ca$  $_{19}K$

$n=3$  $_{16}S$ $_{17}Cl$ $_{18}Ar$  $_{13}Al$ $_{14}Si$ $_{15}P$

$n=3$  $_{26}Fe$ $_{27}Co$ $_{28}Ni$ $_{29}Cu$ $_{30}Zn$  $_{21}Sc$ $_{22}Ti$ $_{23}V$ $_{24}Cr$ $_{25}Mn$

M  $n=3$  $_{12}Mg$  $_{11}Na$

$n=2$  $_8O$ $_9F$ $_{10}Ne$  $_5B$ $_6C$ $_7N$

L  $n=2$  $_4Be$  $_3Li$

K  $n=1$  $_2He$  $_1H$

most of the subtleties of the diagram. Manganese appears among the transition elements of the third period ($n = 3$, shell M). All orbits below its symbol in the diagram are filled; the K and L shells are completed, the M sub-shell is filled, two electrons are in the lowest energy orbit of the N shell ($n = 4$, $l = 0$, $m_l = 0$), and five electrons have been added to the outer M shell. The quantum numbers for the last five electrons all have $n = 3$, $l = 2$; according to the diagram these electrons differ only in the orientation of their orbits, which, specified by the quantum number $m_l$, is $+2$, $+1$, $0$, $-1$, $-2$ respectively for the five electrons; and all five are indicated as having the same spin orientation; that is, all are unpaired. Actually, it is not known with certainty whether they are all unpaired or not. The energy levels are such that some of these $n = 3$, $l = 2$ electrons might be paired; magnetic data indicate that it is quite probable that some are paired; if so, the $m_l$ and $m_s$ quantum numbers would be different from those indicated. The usual practice in describing electronic configurations of atoms is simply to indicate the *number* of electrons in the sub-shells by a superscript rather than to specify the $m_l$ and $m_s$ quantum numbers for each electron. The $n$ and $l$ quantum numbers are specified for each sub-shell. An example of such a specification of configuration is, for sulfur ($Z = 16$): $(n = 1, l = 0)^2$, $(n = 2, l = 0)^2$, $(n = 2, l = 1)^6$, $(n = 3, l = 0)^2$, $(n = 3, l = 1)^4$. Another example, for copper† ($Z = 29$): $(n = 1, l = 0)^2$, $(n = 2, l = 0)^2$, $(n = 2, l = 1)^6$, $(n = 3, l = 0)^2$, $(n = 3, l = 1)^6$, $(n = 3, l = 2)^9$, $(n = 4, l = 0)^2$.

The relation of the electronic configurations summarized in Figure 29-1 to the periodic law and to chemical properties either is largely self-

---

† The electronic configuration given here is the one indicated by the diagram. It represents one quite probable structure of several that are possible because of the very close energy levels of the $n = 4$, $l = 0$ and $n = 3$, $l = 2$ orbits. The structure usually assigned to the copper atom is very similar to this but differs in having only one electron in the O shell: $(n = 1, l = 0)^2$, $(n = 2, l = 0)^2$, $(n = 2, l = 1)^6$, $(n = 3, l = 0)^2$, $(n = 3, l = 1)^6$, $(n = 3, l = 2)^{10}$, $(n = 4, l = 0)^1$. The experimental evidence, primarily the chemical evidence of a strong tendency for copper to form ions with a valence of $+1$, supports this structure rather than the one obtained from the diagram.

evident or has already been pointed out; but several subtleties and patterns of chemical nature remain to be explained. The first of these is the empirically observed ability of some elements to show multiple valence (see § 8-13). It was observed in Chapter 8 that the transition elements, found in the "b" sub-groups and in Group VIII, show a strong tendency to multiple valence. Iron, for example, commonly has a valence of either $+2$ or $+3$. Up to this point this has been a purely empirical fact with no hint of a theoretical explanation. In Figure 29-1 iron is observed to have six electrons in the partially completed M sub-shell and two electrons in the N shell, all of which are at very near the same energy level. It is therefore quite understandable that the two or three of these that are most loosely bound to the atom could be lost in the formation of an ion and that the difference in the energy (and hence in the stability) of the $Fe^{+2}$ and the $Fe^{+3}$ ions could be very slight. The experimental fact that both of these ions, one of which lost two electrons and the other three, do exist in stable condition can thus be correlated with the electronic configurations. It is also observed, in general, that the other elements of the transition groups, which show multiple valence, have sub-shells that are partially completed and therefore have several loosely bound electrons in very nearly identical energy levels.

In the fourteen lanthanide elements also ($Z = 57$–$70$) a sub-shell is filling up. These elements all have a valence of $+3$ and are almost identical in all of their chemical properties (see § 8-13). This similarity can be explained by the electronic configurations of the elements, through which the N shell expands from the stable sub-shell to a completed shell. The energies of the orbits that are being filled are so very close that the three most loosely bound (valence) electrons can be lost with almost exactly the same ease by each of the elements. The differences among the atoms, moreover, reside deep within them and so have almost no influence on their chemical character.

The last fourteen elements of the periodic table, the actinide series ($Z = 89$–$102$), are all radioactive but chemically resemble the lanthanide series. Again the electronic configurations show that the very close chemical similarity is to be expected because of the very close energy levels of the outermost electrons. The differences among these elements are in the more centrally located electrons rather than in the valence electrons, and hence their chemical nature, which is determined entirely by the most loosely bound electrons, shows remarkably little variation from one element of the series to another. The last ten of these radioactive elements (all beyond uranium, $Z = 92$) have no natural existence; they are man-made. Most of the ten are extremely unstable, and some have been prepared in quantities barely sufficient to prove their existence. It is possible that the list of elements may be extended still further by such synthesis of new elements.

## 29-5. *Quantum View of Valence Bonds*

The quantum theory is essentially a mathematical theory, and its sophisticated use in explaining chemical facts requires an extremely high level of mathematical training. It is possible, however, to continue the rough, non-mathematical, and very qualitative approach that we have used throughout this chapter in approaching several of the unexplained characteristics of valence bonds. It must be understood that this treatment is superficial and in some cases even slightly erroneous because of the necessary oversimplification. These shortcomings are more than compensated for the elementary student, however, by the opportunity he has to get a glimpse of the exciting and profoundly important developments on the frontiers of modern physical science.

In Chapters 7 and 8 the concept of valence was introduced in an extremely rudimentary form and on a purely empirical basis. In Chapter 20 our views of valence were much more highly organized and developed; the electronic foundation of valence was introduced, and the periodicity of the pattern of valence through the periodic table was considered. But the treatment there was largely empirical, was based primarily on the simple assertion of the experimental facts. At this point we must relate these views of valence to our most highly developed picture of the configurations of the electrons of the various atoms —that is, to the quantum theory.

The formation of a chemical bond, ionic or covalent, between two atoms consists of the redistribution of the most loosely bound electrons of each atom into a less energetic and therefore more stable arrangement. This redistribution, as was pointed out in the chapters on valence, can take place by the *loss and gain* or by the *sharing* of valence electrons. We can put this generalization into terms of the quantum view of orbital electrons by saying that the electron orbits of *both* atoms are available to *all* the loosely bound (valence) electrons and that these electrons will distribute themselves about the two atomic nuclei in the configuration of lowest energy. In some cases (formation of ionic bonds) this lowest energy state is reached when an electron abandons its orbit in one neutral atom, leaves the residue of the atom with a positive charge and therefore as a cation, and occupies one of the orbits of the other neutral atom, which thereby acquires a negative charge and becomes an anion. This process can also take place when two or even three valence electrons give doubly or triply charged ions; it can also take place when three or even more atoms give rise to more complicated compounds than the simple prototype, the binary ionic compound sodium chloride. Even with these complications, however, the principle is unmodified: **an ionic bond is formed when one or more loosely bound electrons leave their orbits in one atom and take up orbits in another (or other) atom(s).**

There are limitations on the scope of ionic-bond formation: limitations that were first stated as empirical facts but can now be theoretically explained. Elements never gain more than two electrons and rarely lose more than three in the formation of ionic bonds by this mechanism. This limitation is obviously an electrostatic one; Coulomb's law tells us that the work of removing or adding several electrons to an atom is quite large and becomes greater with each successive electron. The whole driving force toward bond formation is the possibility of reaching lower energy states, and this, clearly, cannot be accomplished by a process that requires the input of energy. Some other process must supply the energy to accomplish this electrostatic work and to lower the energy of the bonded atoms below that of the two separate neutral atoms.

This stabilization that compensates for the work of separating charges to form ions can only come from the more stable configurations—that is, the configurations of lower energy—in the bonded atoms. The most important effect of this type is the completion of shells or sub-shells of electrons to form the characteristic outer electronic shell of the inert gases. It can be proved by mathematical application of the quantum theory, and it is experimentally observed, that either neutral atoms or ions which have acquired a completed octet of electrons are more stable than any alternative structure, in which these sub-shells would be only partially filled. Furthermore, this greater stability of the completed octet is sufficient to compensate for the work of removing or adding a few electrons to neutral atoms against the coulombic forces and still lead to a lower energy in the ionic compound. If the energy of the two unbonded atoms is greater than the energy of the two ions, reaction will take place, and an ionic valence bond will be formed. If the energy difference is very large, the compound will be very stable; if the difference is small, the compound will be unstable. If the energy of the unbonded atoms is lower than that of the bonded compound, reaction will not take place, and no ionic bond will be formed.

## 29-6. Covalent Bonds

An atom such as carbon, which must gain or lose four electrons in order to reach a stable sub-shell, fails to form ionic bonds because the relative energies of the bonded and unbonded conditions are such as to prevent bond formation. But an alternative way of reaching stable electronic configurations is available. This alternative is, of course, the formation of the covalent bond discussed in Chapter 20, where a covalent bond was defined as the attachment of two atoms by the sharing of a *pair* of valence electrons. In the terminology of this chapter a covalent bond is one in which two electrons of opposite spins (an electron pair) occupy orbits round *both* atomic nuclei. As a first example we shall again use the hydrogen molecule. In Figure 29-1 we observe that the hydrogen atom has only one orbit ($n = 1$, $l = 0$), which can accommodate two electrons with oppositely oriented spins ($m_s = \pm\frac{1}{2}$). The neutral atom has only a single electron in this orbit and, as we know, can reach a more stable condition either by losing this one electron to form an $H^+$ ion or by gaining an electron to fill the K shell and form an $H^-$ (hydride) ion. A third alternative is to share its single electron with another neutral hydrogen atom.

It is difficult to visualize two electrons occupying orbits round two different atomic nuclei, and no model or diagram of such an electronic configuration is entirely satisfactory. Yet mathematical calculations, based on extensions of the quantum theory of single unbonded atoms, as presented in this and the preceding chapter, to covalent molecular structures, have established the fact that such spreading of electrons through several orbits does indeed happen, and analysis of *molecular* line spectra has related these mathematical conclusions to experimental observation. Molecular spectra, obviously, are vastly more complicated than the spectra—those of single atoms—that have been discussed in this book; the whole topic, in fact, is well beyond the scope of an introductory text. We mention the subject here only to point out that the quantum theory of the electronic configurations of covalent molecules has the same basis in mathematical analysis of experimentally observed spectra as the atomic structures presented in this chapter.

In spite of the warning against physical models, Figure 29-2 is presented as a reasonably realistic picture of the hydrogen molecule. The two nuclei are a little less than one angstrom apart, and the two electrons move very rapidly (with about 1 percent of the velocity of light) through the region between the nuclei and round each nucleus. Very recent developments of the quantum theory have led scientists to abandon the picture of neat orbits, both in molecules and in the uncombined atoms. The current view is, rather, that the electrons move rapidly round the atomic nuclei through a much less defined area, and that the orbits of the original Bohr theory describe the *most probable* path of the electrons. In movement such as this, the two electrons, each furnished by one of the two hydrogen atoms, can effectively occupy the orbits round *both* nuclei of the hydrogen molecule. The "strength" of this covalent bond thus lies in the work that would raise the electrons from the low-energy level of the shared pair indicated in Figure 29-2 to the higher-energy level of two neutral hydrogen atoms with single unpaired electrons in the K shell.

The carbon atom, which of all atoms, as we pointed out in Chapter 20, has the greatest propensity toward formation of covalent bonds, is clearly a good deal more complicated a problem than the hydrogen atom. In Figure 29-1 we observe that carbon has a completed K shell and four electrons in the L shell. These four electrons are, however, in two different types of orbits. The diagram indicates that two electrons are paired in the $n = 2$, $l = 0$ orbit and that two are unpaired in the $n = 2$, $l = 1$ orbit. This is probably the electronic structure of the neutral carbon atom that is not bonded to other atoms. The implication that the two different types of orbits would give rise to two different types of valence bonds, one corresponding to $l = 0$ and one to $l = 1$, is not borne out by fact. It was pointed out in Chapter 20 that the four covalences of carbon are identical and are directed toward the four corners of a regular tetrahedron.

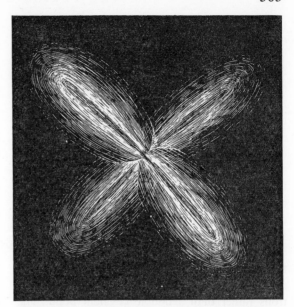

This conclusion is supported by vast amounts of experimental evidence and is contradicted by none. The more advanced quantum theory, which includes the concept of "smearing" out of electrons in **molecular orbitals,**† has established that the four bonds of carbon in covalent compounds such as methane, $CH_4$, are, in fact, resonance hybrids of the $l = 0$ and $l = 1$ orbits of Figure 29-1. This theory describes the **hybridization,** or combining, of the $l = 0$ and $l = 1$ orbits into the four identical and symmetrical **tetrahedral bond orbitals** pictured roughly in Figure 29-3. The methane molecule would be formed by the sharing of a pair of electrons of oppositely oriented spin between the carbon atom and each of four hydrogen atoms. The two electrons of each of the four covalent C–H bonds would occupy the $n = 1$, $l = 0$ orbit of the hydrogen atom and *also* one of the four hybridized $n = 2$ orbits of the carbon atom.

The energy of the covalent bond is due, in

FIGURE **29-2** *Distribution of electrons in the hydrogen molecule.*

---

† In Bohr's original quantum theory the path of an electron was made as simple and as precisely located in space as the orbit of a planet round the sun. In contrast, the modern wave-mechanical view of Schrödinger and Heisenberg (§§ 31-1–31-3) replaces these precise orbits with mathematical expressions of *probabilities* of charge distribution. The term "orbital" refers to the less explicit but more realistic modern view of electron distributions.

part, to the greater stability of the electrons in molecular orbitals, where they are associated with two atomic nuclei instead of one. But it is also, at least in part, due to the greater stability of *paired* electrons. We have seen that the spinning electron is a minute magnetic dipole. We have also seen that the spin axes of a pair of electrons in the same orbit (or orbits) are parallel but must be in opposite directions (exclusion principle: $m_s$ must be different for two electrons in the same orbit). Thus the two electrons, by canceling each other's magnetic fields, produce a situation of lower over-all energy. In some elements and compounds, however, one or more electrons remain unpaired. We encountered in Chapter 20 the example of the oxygen molecule (§ 20-7), which has two unpaired electrons rather than a double covalent bond. The reason cited there for regarding the structure of the oxygen molecule as including unpaired electrons was that the molecule is shown by experimental study of its magnetic properties to be a magnetic dipole. In other elements, particularly among the transition groups, in which unfilled inner shells are being completed, we find *several* unpaired electrons with their spin axes in the same direction. These reinforce each other's magnetic fields and make the atom a strong magnetic dipole. The iron atom, for example, has five such unpaired electrons, which account for the very powerful magnetic property of iron. Here, then, in unpaired electrons, are the "amperian currents" that were fundamental to the nineteenth-century theory of magnetism (§ 16-11).

One final point should be made in the comparison of the ionic and the covalent bond. The fundamental nature of the two is, of course, quite different. The ionic bond is essentially an electrostatic attraction between two oppositely charged particles; the covalent bond is the intermingling or joining of electron orbits of two atoms. Several interesting spatial qualities deduced from these characteristics correspond exactly with the experimental observation of the two types of compounds.

The first is the directional quality of the covalent bond. All the facts of organic chemistry (essentially the study of the covalent bond in carbon compounds) require that covalent molecules have a very definite shape and that each individual atom have a unique position in space with respect to the other atoms of the molecule. The opposite is true of the ionic bond. It is directed equally in all directions, and we find it impossible to specify which atom is bonded to which in an ionic crystal. All semblance of "molecular structure" is lost when an ionic compound is melted.

Another aspect of the spatial qualities of the two types of bonds is the "bond length." The ionic bond, which depends on coulombic forces, tends to be "elastic"; that is, it can be distorted in both direction and length much more than the covalent bond and still remain a chemical bond. If, for example, an ionic bond were stretched to twice its normal length, the force of attraction would fall to one-fourth of the normal (inverse-square law); but, if a covalent bond were stretched beyond the "thickness" of an electronic orbit, one would expect it to break entirely. It can be shown experimentally that covalent bonds will not form unless atoms can approach to within about 0.2 A of the normal covalent bond length, which is about 2 A. A distortion of about 10 percent is therefore sufficient to prevent the formation of a covalent bond or to break an existing one.

Associated with this extremely precise spatial requirement of covalent bonds are the ease and speed of bond formation. It was pointed out in § 23-7 that ionic reactions are extremely rapid, whereas reactions involving the formation of covalent bonds are generally slow. To bring about the formation of an ionic bond, as in the precipitation of an insoluble ionic salt, it is only necessary to have the atoms approach each other closely enough, from any directions, so that the two charged particles come within each other's electrostatic fields. Then coulombic attractions draw the two together. To form a covalent bond, on the other hand, two atoms must approach each other closely enough and from such directions that the directed valence orbitals can overlap. The energy of the impact, moreover, must be great enough for the atoms to approach closely but not so great that they bounce apart (elastic impact, Chap. 12). Similarly, for a reaction involving the rupture of a covalent bond, the spatial conditions must fall within the very close limits described above.

From these theoretical considerations, it is clear, the probability that an impact will result in the formation or rupture of a covalent bond must be quite low. And, according to the kinetic theory of the rates of reaction (Chap. 23), a low probability of successful impact results in a low rate of reaction. Again the gross experimental observations are quite consistent with the extremely refined and sophisticated theoretical picture of orbital electrons in the highest energy levels giving rise to valence bonds by shifting their positions to orbits of lesser energy.

## 29-7. Sizes of Atoms

The atomic model we have built permits an estimate of the sizes of atoms. By "size of an atom" we mean the space within which the electrons travel in their orbits about the nucleus. This is determined by the radius of the largest shell that contains any electrons in the unexcited neutral atom—in much the same way as the radius of the orbit of the planet farthest from the sun determines the size of the solar system. Let us discuss this with reference to a particular atom. Figure 29-4 represents the structure of a ru-

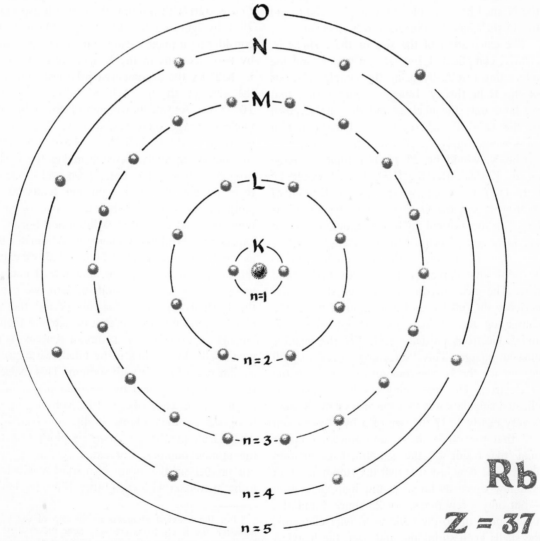

FIGURE **29-4** *Schematic shell model of the rubidium atom.*

bidium atom, which is a representative alkali metal about halfway through the periodic table. The diagram is, of course, highly schematic. The shells, determined by the principal quantum number, $n$, are shown as circles although we know that for $n$ greater than 1 there are ellipses as well as circles. For any shell, however, the average size of the ellipses and the average size of the circles are the same. The K and L shells are drawn approximately to scale, but the sizes of the others are arbitrary in order to keep the diagram on the page. Rubidium, with atomic number 37, has thirty-seven electrons arranged as shown. The K, L, and M shells are filled with two, eight, and eighteen electrons respectively, the N shell has a stable sub-group of eight, and the O shell has the thirty-seventh electron.

The calculation of the size of these shells is, clearly, complicated, but we can understand the interesting results by using the simple relations of the Bohr theory. Imagine, temporarily, that we have only the nucleus and the one electron of the O shell, where $n = 5$. Then equation 28-4 would apply exactly, and the O shell, accordingly, would be 25 $(= n^2)$ times as large as the K shell. But the K shell itself would be only $1/37$ $(= 1/Z)$ as large as the K shell of hydrogen, and the O shell would be $25/37$ as large as the normal hydrogen atom, or about the *same* size. When all the electrons are taken into account, however, the size comes out to be somewhat larger, and we can understand why. The electrons in the M shell do not experience the full force of attraction of the $+37e$ charge on the nucleus, for the intervening K and L electrons partially neutralize the positive nuclear charge. This "screening effect" is still greater for the N electrons and greatest for the O electron. The interesting result of the complicated calculation is that the size of the K shell is very nearly $1/37$ the size of a hydrogen atom and that the other shells are somewhat larger than the result of the simplified calculation above. The conclusion is that the rubidium atom is a few times as large as the hydrogen atom —but only a few times, not 25 times. Similarly, as we move up to the table to heavier elements, the shells keep shrinking, and even the heaviest elements are not much larger than the lightest

ones. The heavy elements contain many more electrons, but the electronic orbits are squeezed in so tightly that they do not extend much farther from the nucleus than in the light elements. Thus the experimental fact that all atoms are of approximately the same size (of the order of $10^{-10}$ m) is consistent with our atomic model. This picture becomes more plausible when we remember that the sizes of nuclei are of the order of $10^{-14}$ m—that is, ten thousand times smaller than the atoms. In other words, there is ample room outside the nucleus for the electronic structures.†

Although the sizes of atoms are approximately the same, they do show an interesting variation. Let us start with lithium. We can still use Figure 29-4 by ignoring the M, N, and O shells and considering a nuclear charge of $+3e$ surrounded by two electrons in the K shell and one in the L shell. By the arguments of the last paragraph the size of the L shell of lithium is about $10^{-10}$ m. As we move across the table, the nuclear charge increases, and we keep adding electrons to the L shell. As we have seen above, the increasing nuclear charge makes the L shell progressively smaller; but, as we add electrons, their mutual electrical repulsion tends to expand the L shell. We thus have two opposing tendencies. At first, for beryllium and boron, we expect the shrinking tendency to dominate; but, as more and more electrons are added, we expect the expanding tendency to dominate. Hence, as we go across the table from lithium, we expect the L shell (and thus for this period the size of the atom) first to decrease in size and then to increase, approaching a maximum at neon. As the next shell (M) begins to be filled, we expect a similar cycle to start with sodium. This expectation is amply verified by the data presented in Figure 29-5. Here the atomic volume, as determined by the volume in the *solid state* of Avogadro's number of atoms, is plotted against the atomic number. For exact agreement with our prediction, the atoms in a solid would have to lie in contact with each other. Since we know,

---

† For the heaviest elements at the top of the table, however, the K electrons are very near the nucleus—a fact that contributes to the instability of these radioactive nuclei.

however, that there is some separation between adjacent atoms in a solid, some discrepancy is to be expected. The sharp maxima of the graph at the inert gases is convincing evidence, nevertheless, of the variation in the size of atoms predicted by our atomic model.

Another correlation is presented by the cycle between potassium and rubidium. Starting with potassium, as the N shell starts to fill, the atomic volume decreases sharply as expected. But from about atomic number 22 to number 30 the curve shows very little change. For these elements (the first transition group) the added electrons are filling up the inner M shell and have little effect on the (for this group) outermost N shell. After the M shell is filled (at zinc), the N shell begins receiving more electrons, and the atomic volume increases rapidly toward a maximum.

A further consistency with theory is furnished by this graph. Notice that with few exceptions the range in volume is about eight times. But, since the radius of a sphere is proportional to the cube root of its volume, the radius of the atoms varies only about two times; that is, the radii of the different atoms are not very different and are all of the same order of magnitude.

This is the conclusion arrived at by calculation of orbital radii.

## 29-8. *Size and Density of Nuclei*

The size of the nucleus, on the other hand, does *not* show a periodic variation. We are familiar, from our discussion of Rutherford's experiments on the scattering of $\alpha$-particles (§ 27-3), with the type of experiment that yields the size of the nucleus. Many experiments of this kind, involving the scattering of other particles as well as $\alpha$-particles, have resulted in the general law that the radius of the nucleus is directly proportional to the cube root of the mass number; that is, $R$ is proportional to $A^{\frac{1}{3}}$. This, of course, means that the size of the nucleus increases steadily as we go up the periodic table and shows no periodicity at all. But again the total range of radius throughout the table is not large. Let us compare the light element sodium ($A = 23$) with the heavy element uranium ($A = 238$). The cube root of 23 is about 2.8, and the cube root of 236 is about 6.2; that is, the uranium nucleus is only a little more than

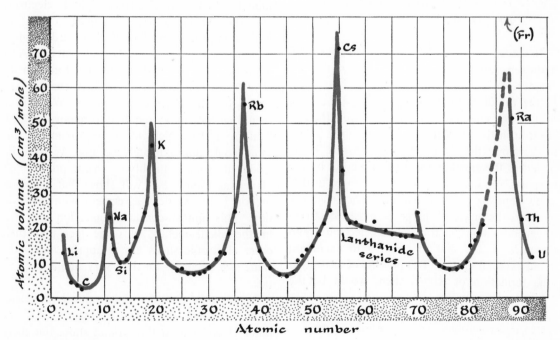

FIGURE **29-5** *Graph of atomic volume against atomic number.*

twice as large as the sodium nucleus, not ten or a hundred times. This is consistent with the "constant" value of $10^{-14}$ m, which we have been using in previous chapters, as the order of magnitude of all nuclei.

A corollary of the law for the radius of the nucleus is that the density of all nuclei, throughout the whole periodic table, is approximately the same. Since the volume of a sphere is proportional to the cube of the radius, the volume of the nucleus is directly proportional to the mass number. The ratio of the mass (as given by the mass number) to the volume of the nucleus is therefore the same for all nuclei.† This surprising result tells us that, when mass units are combined into larger nuclei, the units (whatever their nature) lie closely packed in the nucleus, somewhat like golf balls in a bag. This nuclear density is enormous, for practically all the mass of an atom is in the nucleus, whose volume is only $10^{-12}$ (the cube of $10^{-4}$) times that of the atom. Hence the nuclear density is about $10^{12}$ times as great as the densities of ordinary "solid" matter. A teaspoonful of nuclei would be a formidable mass indeed!‡

## 29-9. Ionization and Spectra of Atoms

In discussing the energy levels and spectra of hydrogen (and hydrogen-like ions) in the last chapter, we had only one electron to consider. In the rubidium atom of Figure 29-4 we have thirty-seven electrons. Clearly, however, the one electron in the O shell is the least tightly bound in the atom; that is, of all the electrons, it experiences the smallest force of attraction by the nucleus. Not only is it, on the average, farther away from the nucleus than any other electron, but also the nuclear charge is most effectively screened for this electron. This O electron would therefore be the first to respond to excitation by an external agency. The process of ionization (the formation of Rb+), then, would be the

removal of this electron from the atom, which process, in our model, would consist of lifting it to a shell of infinite radius with principal quantum number $n = \infty$. The energy for this could be supplied by a bombarding electron or by a sufficiently energetic photon. Let us imagine riding along with this O electron as it moves away and looking back toward the remaining structure. We should see the stable N octet of electrons, in their various rapid motions, forming a kind of cloud of electrons. Somewhat dimly through this cloud we should see the denser cloud of the M shell, and so on. We might not see the nucleus, but we should know that some positive electricity was there, for we could detect the force of attraction on our electron. If we consider these electronic clouds as uniform spherical shells of negative electricity (which, on the average, they approximate), then, as we learned in our study of electricity, each shell would act as though its charge were concentrated at the center. The net attraction on our electron, then, would be that due to just one positive electronic charge: the $+37$ of the nucleus minus 36 for the remaining electrons.

Let us now consider a similar situation for sodium. The reader can easily construct the model with two K electrons, eight L electrons, and one M electron. Here again, during an ionization process, we look back toward a similar structure with a stable octet on the outside. And, as in the case of rubidium, the net force on the electron is that due to one positive charge. And so on for the other alkali metals. We expect, then, that the energy required to remove an electron from these elements is approximately the same (only approximately because we have introduced some simplifying assumptions). A glance at Figure 8-3 will show that this prediction is in excellent agreement with observation. This almost constant ionization potential of the alkali metals, plus the fact that their outer electronic shells are of approximately the same size, accounts for their very similar properties.

Let us now consider some optical properties of these atoms. As shown in Figure 29-4, the outer electron is in the ground state, but there are many unoccupied energy levels in the larger

---

† There is, of course, a *small* difference between the mass and the mass number of a nucleus. This small but important difference will be discussed in the next chapter.

‡ About ten million tons.

shells for $n = 6, 7, 8, \ldots \infty$. Electron transitions between these levels would give rise to many spectral lines, but none of the transitions could be greater than 4.2 electron volts (the ionization potential of rubidium). This, as we have seen, is just the proper range of energies for photons of optical line spectra. Thus we see that this outer valence electron is responsible for the emission of rubidium's characteristic line spectrum. From our previous discussion of the closely similar structures and ionization potentials of all the alkali metals, we expect the line spectra of these elements to be very similar.

Now consider strontium, the next element past rubidium. For this element we revise the structure of Figure 29-4 by adding one positive charge to the nucleus and one more electron to the O shell. We expect that the energy required to remove one of the O electrons will be somewhat greater than for rubidium, since the remaining electron in the large O shell cannot completely shield the added positive charge on the nucleus. And we expect the energy required to remove the second O electron to be about twice that for the first. By experiment the first and second ionization energies for strontium are 5.7 and 11 electron volts respectively, in good agreement with prediction. We also expect the optical line spectrum for strontium to be quite different from that for rubidium, since now there are two electrons available for quantum transitions, and, as a result of their similar structures, we expect the spectra of all the alkaline-earth metals to be similar to strontium. Similarly, as we progress across the periodic table, we expect increasing ionization potentials and increasing complexity of spectra until, after a rare-gas structure, the cycle starts again. These expectations are in complete agreement with the observations discussed in § 25-7. The reader can relate the other observations discussed there with the atomic model we have built; for instance, only lines that terminate on the ground state are expected to appear as absorption lines. The critical-potential experiments (described in detail for hydrogen in § 28-3) are also completely consistent with our atomic model.

In this discussion of spectra we have assumed that there is sufficient space round the atoms for the valence electrons, when excited, to move into the larger unfilled orbits of the higher-quantum-number shells, and that the energy levels of these shells are unaffected by neighboring atoms—that is, that each atom is completely independent of neighboring atoms. This is certainly so in the gaseous state, where the atoms are separated by distances many times as great as their diameters. In the liquid and solid states, however, this is definitely not so. Here the space between atoms is about as big as the unexcited atoms themselves. It is not surprising, then, that the characteristic optical line spectrum of an element appears only when the element is in the gaseous state. Finally, the energy states of the valence electrons are completely different when the atom enters into chemical combination. As we pointed out earlier, the molecular spectra are characteristic of the much more complicated electronic configurations of molecular orbitals. In other words, we do not expect water vapor to produce a spectrum containing the Balmer series; we expect it, rather, to produce a spectrum that is characteristic of the O–H covalent bond.

## 29-10.  *X-ray Spectra*

Let us now relate to our atomic model the properties of X-ray spectra discussed in § 25-9. Because of their very high frequencies, X-ray photons represent large energy changes. A photon of the $K_\alpha$ line from rubidium, for instance, is $1.34 \times 10^4$ ev (compared with only a few ev for optical spectra). This tells us that X-ray photons are emitted by electronic transitions between the inner shells of the atoms, where the attracting force of the nucleus is much larger not only because the electrons are much nearer the nucleus but also because the nucleus is much less screened by intervening shells. In particular, the K series of lines result from transitions to the K shell from the L, M, and N shells; the L series result from transitions to the L shell from the M and N shells; and, for the heaviest elements, the M series from transitions terminating on the M shell. We immediately understand why X-ray spectra are so much simpler than optical spectra. Even for the heaviest elements there are only a few inner shells for electron transitions, whereas the unfilled outer shells offer almost limitless possibilities. Furthermore, the physical state (solid, liquid, or gaseous) and chemical combination involve only the outer shells of electrons. We understand why these factors have no effect upon the emission of X-ray spectra.

As mentioned above, a single line of an optical spectrum may be produced if the atoms are excited by the proper critical energy. It is easy to see why this cannot be done for X-rays. Suppose that we bombard a substance with electrons of just the proper energy to raise a K electron to the L shell (for instance, $1.34 \times 10^4$ ev for rubidium). The K electron cannot absorb this energy and go to the L shell, for this shell is already full and by the exclusion principle cannot accept another electron. What must be done is to bombard the atom with enough energy to knock a K electron all the way out of the atom. Then an L electron can fall into the empty place and emit the $K_\alpha$ line, or (less likely) an M electron can fall into the K shell and emit the $K_\beta$ line. In either case the place that is left may be filled by an electron from a higher shell. In short, the whole line spectrum comes in at once when the atom is supplied with enough energy to ionize the K shell. This, of course, is just what is observed.

We do not expect X-ray line spectra to show the periodicity displayed by optical spectra. As we go up the periodic table, the inner completed shells remain unchanged in structure. The energy differences, however, become greater because of the increased nuclear charge. Thus corresponding transitions give rise to the emission of larger and larger photons. Hence we expect X-ray line spectra to shift uniformly toward shorter wavelengths as we progress to higher atomic numbers (Moseley diagram).

Consider the emission of the $K_\alpha$ line. As the L electron starts in toward the K shell, it finds itself *inside* the L, M, and higher shells. If these shells are uniform shells of negative electricity, they exert no force on the falling L electron (§ 16-7). The remaining K electron, moving close to the nucleus, effectively screens out one unit of the nuclear charge. As the L electron falls, then, it is moving in a field due to $(Z - 1)$ electronic charges. This is a Bohr one-electron system, and we may apply equation 28-9. For the $K_\alpha$ line, then, $1/\lambda = (Z - 1)^2 \Re[1/1^2 - 1/2^2]$. If we multiply through by the velocity of light, the left side becomes the frequency of the $K_\alpha$ line, and we have $\nu = 3c\Re(Z - 1)^2/4$. This is Moseley's law (§ 25-9).

This chapter has presented the most sophisticated view of the extranuclear structure of the atom that a non-mathematical elementary student can possibly grasp. The ideas have been much simplified and do not always represent the last word of the research scientists. But they are not inconsistent with the most modern and highly theoretical views and will, if reasonably well grasped by the student, acquaint him with the quality and flavor of current scientific investigation and thinking.

Much of the gross nature of matter is determined by this extranuclear structure of the atom. All of chemistry and most of classical electricity and magnetism can be explained entirely in terms of this quantum-electronic picture of the extranuclear structure of atoms. Thus we have accomplished a major part of the difficult but rewarding task that we set ourselves in the introduction of this text—the understanding of the structure and transformation of the stuff of our physical environment.

The major question remaining to be answered is that of the structure of the nucleus. The groundwork has been laid for such an answer, and the next chapter will attempt to give it.

# Concepts and Terms

Pauli's Exclusion Principle
Electronic Configurations
   shells
   sub-shells
   penetrating orbits
   energy levels
Valence Bonds
   ionic bonds
   covalent bonds
   molecular orbitals
   hybrid orbitals

Atomic Dimensions
   change of radius of electron shells with atomic
     number
   screening effect
   periodicity of atomic volume
   change of nuclear radius with mass number
Optical Spectra
   valence electrons as source
   periodicities of ionization potential and spectra
   relation to physical state and chemical combi-
     nation
X-ray Spectra
   Moseley's law

# Problems

**29-1.** Contrast the chemical, mechanical, and electronic properties of the ionic and the covalent bond.

**29-2.** Vanadium has two electrons in the N shell. Construct an electronic-shell diagram for this atom.

**29-3.** Write the quantum-number specification of the electronic configuration of the vanadium atom. Refer to Fig. 29-1. What ambiguities are present in this specification? Explain.

**29-4.** Determine the valences of iron and cobalt from Fig. 8-1. Explain these valences by the electronic configurations of the atoms.

**29-5.** Explain the striking similarities in the chemical properties of the elements of the lanthanide series. What could you predict about the chemical properties of the man-made "trans-uranium elements" (elements beyond uranium in the periodic table)?

**29-6.** In § 25-9 certain observed differences between optical line spectra and X-ray line spectra were stated. Relate these differences to the electronic-shell model of atoms.

**29-7.**
(A) The diameter of the K shell for helium is 0.60 A. Assuming the Bohr theory to be approximately correct, calculate the diameter of the K shell for uranium.

(B) If the diameter of the helium nucleus is $10^{-4}$ A, calculate the diameter of the uranium nucleus.

(C) Compare the relative sizes of K shell and nucleus for each atom. (Note that for the heavy element uranium the K shell is still well outside the nucleus although much closer than for helium.)
    *Ans.* (A) $1.3 \times 10^{-2}$ A
       (B) approx. $4 \times 10^{-4}$ A
       (C) He, 6,000/1; U, approx. 30/1

**29-8.** Calculate the wavelengths of the $K_\alpha$ lines for Na, K, Ag, and W. Compare these with Fig. 25-17. (To save time in the computation, first solve the equation for $\lambda$, and combine the constants.)

**29-9.** Rephrase the discussion of resonance of Chap. 20 in terms of the concepts of Chap. 29.

**29-10.** The theory of resonance, as applied to organic chemistry, includes the concept of "resonance energy" of stabilization. This concept can be stated briefly as follows: "If two or more resonance forms are possible for a compound, the compound will be more stable than if only a single form is possible. The greater the number of possible forms and the more closely similar they are, the greater will be the resonance energy of stabilization." Explain this concept in terms of the ideas developed in this chapter.

## Suggested Readings

1. D. C. Gregg, *Principles of Chemistry* (Allyn & Bacon, 1958). Chap. 10 is an alternative elementary treatment of the quantum basis of the periodic table.

2. L. Pauling, *College Chemistry,* 2nd edition (W. H. Freeman, 1955). Chap. 5 includes a description of the periodic table and a theoretical discussion of the electronic configurations of the atoms; Chap. 11 provides a general discussion of covalence, including the quantum basis of covalence.

3. L. Pauling, *The Nature of the Chemical Bond* (Cornell University Press, 1948). This book is a rigorous, mathematical, and detailed discussion of the chemical bond. It is suggested as outside reading, partly to indicate the vastness of the subject of valence and partly as a more detailed treatment of subjects considered in this chapter. Chaps. 1 and 3 are most pertinent and, at least in part, are readable by elementary students.

4. M. Born, *The Restless Universe,* translated by W. M. Deans (Dover Publications, 1951), pp. 210–230 (exclusion principle, periodic table, and magnetism).

5. R. D. Rusk, *Introduction to Atomic and Nuclear Physics* (Appleton-Century-Crofts, 1958), pp. 188–201 (exclusion principle, periodic table, and optical and X-ray spectra).

6. H. Semat, *Fundamentals of Physics,* 3rd edition (Rinehart, 1957), pp. 805–811 (X-ray spectra).

CHAPTER

30

Nuclear
Reactions

THE NUCLEUS, so far, has entered into our discussions in only an elementary way. Except by the very small correction due to the motion of the nuclei of a few light elements, the nuclear mass has not affected the results. The only nuclear property of importance has been the charge of $+Ze$. Yet the nucleus, far from being a simple charged particle, must, as evidence we have already considered shows, be made up of more fundamental particles. The discovery of isotopes and their whole-number masses revived Prout's hypothesis (§ 18-9) that atoms are composed of varying numbers of some fundamental "building block." And these building blocks, it seemed, must be in the nucleus, for the planetary electrons (all of the atom other than the nucleus) are determined, both in number and in arrangement, by the nuclear charge. Further evidence of a nuclear fine structure is offered by the facts of radioactivity: many atoms of large mass number spontaneously eject smaller particles that can come only from the nucleus.

The prevalence of $\alpha$-particles in radioactive emanations suggests that the helium nucleus might be a nuclear building block. If this were the only sub-nuclear particle, nuclear masses would be twice the atomic number and always divisible by four. For many elements this is true; the carbon nucleus, for instance, is equal to three $\alpha$-particles: $_6\text{C}^{12} = 3\,_2\text{He}^4$. Of elements for which this is not true, one might assume, in order to adjust the mass, that hydrogen nuclei also are nuclear building blocks, and, in order to balance the charges, that electrons can be a part of the nucleus. The sodium nucleus, for instance, might be made up as $_{11}\text{Na}^{23} = 5\,_2\text{He}^4 + 3\,_1\text{H}^1 + 2\,_{-1}e^0$. We now know, however, as a result of an enormous number of experiments, that the units of nuclear sub-structure are somewhat different. Yet the fundamental generalization is the same: all atomic nuclei are made up of simple fundamental particles, as Prout had supposed. The nuclear mass, furthermore, is the sum of the masses of the fundamental particles, and the nuclear charge $(+Ze)$ is the sum of their charges.

The experiments that identified the sub-nuclear particles were all based on the same

principle: to decompose the nucleus and examine the products. Particles were knocked out
of the nucleus (we know from the energies of
the radioactive rays that the energy required
for this operation is sizable), and their properties were determined. The methods of observing
these atomic and sub-atomic particles, methods
that effectively extend our observations to *individual* atoms, are so important for an understanding of nuclear structure that some of the
more important techniques will be described.

## 30-1. Methods of Observing Atomic Particles

We have already considered two effects that
are very useful when we wish to observe atomic
particles. The first is the visible fluorescence produced in certain crystals by radiations. In certain
cases this luminescence, when viewed through a
moderately good magnifier, is seen not to be a
continuous glow (as it is for $\beta$- and $\gamma$-rays)
but to consist of sudden sharp flashes of light.
Each of these flashes, or *scintillations,* is produced by the impact of a *single* fast particle, an
$\alpha$-particle or some other high-speed atomic ion.
The visual counting of these scintillations was
one of the most powerful early methods of investigating individual atomic events. Rutherford
made some discoveries of fundamental importance by using this simple but painstaking technique. The method, however, has limitations.
Since the flashes are very faint, there is considerable eye strain involved, and the response of the
eye is so slow that large numbers of slow counts
were required for good statistical averages.

More recent developments permit an electrical
counting of scintillations. Many very elegant
electronic devices, of staggering complexity, have
been developed for counting emitted nuclear
particles and distinguishing the various types.
They are either photo-sensitive devices that
count scintillations or devices that detect the
ionization of a gas by the passage of a particle.
They are capable of very rapid and highly accurate counting but are, in principle, only refinements of the basic method of Rutherford.

Another detection device that depends upon

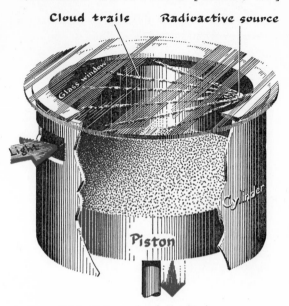

FIGURE **30-1** *Wilson cloud chamber.*

the ionizing property of rays was invented by
C. T. R. Wilson in 1911. This spectacular device, which supplies a great amount of detailed
information, is called the **cloud chamber.** The
vapor-pressure curves for liquids (Fig. 14-2) tell
us that, as the temperature is lowered, the vapor
pressure also is lowered. Hence, if a volume of
gas saturated with the vapor of a liquid is suddenly cooled, the vapor begins to condense to
the liquid phase so as to adjust the vapor pressure to the lower temperature. It is characteristic of this situation that the condensation
will take place only on small foreign particles,
such as dust particles, that are in the gas.

Wilson suspected that, if the gas were free of
dust particles, a gaseous ion would serve equally
well as a center of condensation, and that a
small droplet would appear on each ion. The
apparatus he designed on this assumption is
shown in Figure 30-1. A cylinder, painted black
inside, is closed at the top by a glass plate and
at the bottom by a tightly fitting black piston.
A small amount of liquid (water or alcohol) is
placed on the top of the piston. When the piston
is pushed in, the gas in the chamber is compressed and slightly warmed. A short time is
allowed for temperature equilibrium to be established. The piston is then lowered quickly;
the gas, expanding suddenly, cools, and a cloud

appears. The droplets, illuminated from the side through a window in the cylinder, stand out brilliantly against the black background when viewed through the glass plate. A few cycles remove any dust particles from the gas (they are carried to the walls of the chamber by the droplets), and further cycles produce droplets only on gaseous ions. The droplets, of course, settle slowly to the bottom of the chamber, but immediately after the expansion they definitely locate the ions. A simple mechanism may be arranged to move the piston through repeated cycles and also to trip the shutter of a camera immediately after each expansion. With such a device a large number of photographic records are obtained.

As a charged particle travels through the gas in a cloud chamber, it leaves a train of ionized molecules in its wake. The droplets condensed on these ions form a cloud trail that reveals the path of the particle. Figure 30-2 presents sketches of three typical photographs obtained as α-particles traversed the cloud chamber. Remember that in Rutherford's theory of the nuclear atom, derived from the observed scattering of α-particles by thin metal foils, two kinds of impacts were assumed. The first, and by far the more probable, were impacts with electrons in the atoms, which, on account of the small electronic mass, produced little deflection of the α-particles. The second were infrequent collisions with, or close approaches to, the nucleus, which produced large deflections of the α-particles. These two types of collisions are beautifully

demonstrated by the cloud-chamber photographs. Each minute droplet represents the collision of an α-particle with an electron—in other words, an ionization process. This occurs so frequently that the resulting close spacing of the droplets produces an apparently continuous cloud trail. Almost all the trails are straight lines, as would be expected from electron collisions. These numerous ionizing collisions, however, gradually reduce the KE of an α-particle, which slows down and at the end of the trail picks up two electrons and becomes a neutral helium atom. Hence the length of the trail, or the **range** of the α-particle, gives a measure of the initial KE. Figure 30-2a shows the trails of α-particles from a small amount of a mixture of two different radioactive substances at the bottom of the picture. The velocities characteristic of the two emitting substances are clearly demonstrated by the two well-defined ranges.

Occasionally, toward the end of a trail, a sharp kink is observed, such as that under the arrow in Figure 30-2a, in which the chamber was filled with oxygen. This is produced by a close approach to an oxygen nucleus, which, by its greater mass, strongly deflects the α-particle. Such a deflection is more likely to happen toward the end of a path, where the slowly moving particle would be near the nucleus for a longer time. Rarely—only once in a large number of photographs—a trail is observed to fork. This is the mark of a collision between an α-particle and a nucleus. The nucleus, knocked free of its shells of electrons, moves off with an appreciable

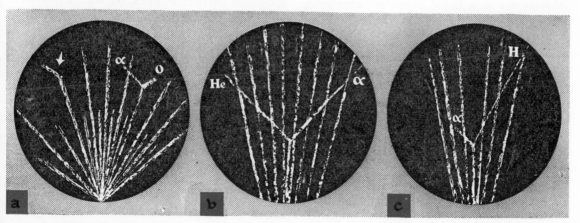

FIGURE **30-2** *Cloud trails produced by α-particles* (a) *in oxygen;* (b) *in helium;* (c) *in hydrogen.*

fraction of the KE of the impinging $\alpha$-particle, and thus both the rebounding $\alpha$-particle and the recoil nucleus leave a trail of droplets. These events obey the laws of mechanics for elastic impacts. In Figure 30-2a the lighter $\alpha$-particle rebounds with greater velocity than the more massive oxygen nucleus. In 30-2b, where the chamber is filled with helium, we have a situation analogous to the impact of two identical billiard balls. In 30-2c, where the chamber contains hydrogen, the lighter hydrogen nucleus recoils with greater velocity than the rebounding $\alpha$-particle. The velocities are easily computed from the known initial velocity of the $\alpha$-particle, the known nuclear masses, and the angles between the velocities after impact, which are measured directly on the photograph. If, as sometimes happens, the collision is head on, all velocities are in the same direction, and calculation is simplified.

By such methods the cloud trails produced by various high-speed nuclei and other particles, such as electrons, could be compared. The range, we have seen, is directly related to the initial energy of the particle. It is also, for particles of equal energy, inversely related to the mass; hydrogen nuclei, for instance, have much greater ranges than oxygen nuclei of the same KE. Another characteristic property is the "density" of the trails—that is, the number of droplets per centimeter. The droplets can be counted on the photograph with the aid of a microscope. The average density of trails in air is $5 \times 10^4$ droplets per centimeter for $\alpha$-particles, only a hundredth as many for $\beta$-particles, about one-quarter as many for hydrogen nuclei, and so on for other particles.† An ionizing particle, then, can be identified and its kinetic energy determined by careful measurements of the range and density of the cloud trail it produces. We can check these conclusions by applying a strong magnetic field at right angles to the direction of the trails. The radius of curvature of the path produced by the magnetic field is directly measured on the

photograph. This, combined with the velocity (derived from the range), leads to the ratio of charge to mass (§ 18-9), which verifies the nature of the particle. And, finally, the observations also give us considerable detailed information about collisions between particles.

The cloud-chamber technique, continually improved and elaborated, has become one of the most powerful tools for the study of atomic phenomena.

## 30-2. The Nucleus Contains Protons

The simplest nucleus is that of ordinary hydrogen. Because, as we shall see presently, this particle is fundamental in nature, it has been given the special name **proton**. The mass of the proton (equal to the mass of $_1\text{H}^1$ minus one electron) is known quite accurately to be 1.007593 units. The charge on the proton is positive and equal to the charge on the electron.

In the last section we mentioned the well-defined and characteristic range of $\alpha$-particles. This range, primarily determined by the KE of the particle, also depends on the pressure of the gas and the kind of gas. If the pressure is reduced, there are fewer ionizations per centimeter, and an $\alpha$-particle travels farther before losing all its KE. At the same pressure, the number of ionizations per centimeter being the same, the loss of KE per centimeter is different for different gases; for, as a result of the different ionization energies of gases, the same number of ionizations requires different amounts of energy. For these reasons the ranges of $\alpha$-particles in various gases were systematically studied.

In 1919 Rutherford, while studying the range of $\alpha$-particles in nitrogen, made a startling discovery. His apparatus was so simple that we need not diagram it. It consisted of a tube closed at one end with a fluorescent screen and containing a rod carrying a small amount of an $\alpha$-emitting substance that could be moved to varying distances from the screen. Nitrogen was introduced into the tube, and scintillations produced on the screen were observed through a low-power microscope. When the radiating

---

† High-energy photons such as $\gamma$-rays produce no trails. They do occasionally eject a photoelectron out of a gas molecule. When this happens, the passage of the photon is detected by the erratic trail of the photoelectron.

source was near the screen, abundant scintillations were observed. As the source was moved gradually farther away, the scintillations continued abundant until, at a distance of 7 cm, the number was drastically reduced. But not all the scintillations disappeared; very rare scintillations continued to be observed for distances as great as 40 cm. Clearly, the range of the α-particles was 7 cm. What, then, were the nature and origin of the long-range particles?

Rutherford soon became convinced that these particles were high-speed hydrogen nuclei (fast protons), and this conclusion,† indicated by their long range, was verified by rough magnetic analysis. At first he suspected that the nitrogen contained a trace of hydrogen as an impurity and that the protons were produced by elastic impacts with the α-particles. This explanation was soon found to be incorrect. A subsidiary experiment with hydrogen only in the tube showed that such recoil protons were indeed produced, but with a maximum range of only 28 cm, even though the same source of α-particles was used. Hence the 40 cm range of protons produced with nitrogen in the tube could not be explained by simple elastic impacts. In a variation of the experiment, the fast protons were observed in directions making various angles with the forward direction of the incident α-particles. Some, observed at angles greater than 90°, had a *backward* component of velocity. This would have been impossible after elastic collision with hydrogen impurities, for after such collisions both particles must have at least a component of forward motion. Such experiments led Rutherford to the conclusion that the fast proton was produced by a disintegration of the nitrogen nucleus under the intense forces of a collision with an α-particle, and that the liberated proton *"formed a constituent part of the nitrogen nucleus."*

This conclusion was amply verified by further studies of the phenomenon with a cloud chamber. These studies, carried out in the next several years after Rutherford's discovery, also revealed the details of the process. P. M. S. Blackett took a large number of photographs of the cloud trails

† They could not be electrons or γ-rays, for these do not produce individual scintillations.

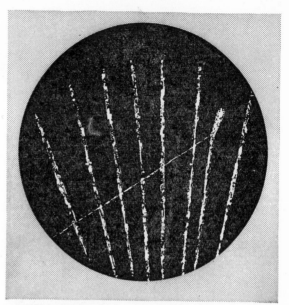

FIGURE **30-3** *Cloud trails showing the transmutation of nitrogen by α-bombardment.*

of fast α-particles in nitrogen. In these photographs (showing more than 400,000 trails) a number of disintegrations were recorded. In every case the trail terminated in a fork. One such fork is diagramed in Figure 30-3. Here the α-particles enter the chamber from the bottom of the figure. One branch of the fork was always a long, lightly ionized trail. The density of the trail indicated that the particle was a proton, and the range gave its velocity. The value of $q/m$, derived from magnetic deflection, verified this conclusion. Notice also that the long trail in this photograph goes *backward* at an angle. Clearly, this is not the simple elastic impact shown in Figure 30-2. The short branch of the fork, in the forward direction and only slightly deviated, is very dense, indicating the passage of a heavy nucleus somewhat like a nitrogen recoil nucleus. But where is the α-particle? No third branch, indicating a rebounding α-particle, was ever observed!

The only interpretation of these experiments is that here is a fundamentally new process. Of the many α-particles entering the cloud chamber, an occasional one (about one in every million) will be headed directly at a nitrogen nucleus (Fig. 30-4a). Enabled by its large KE (7.7 Mev) to overcome the repulsion of the nuclear

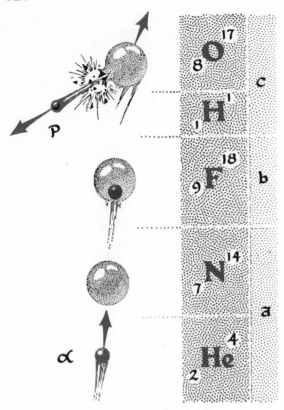

FIGURE **30-4** *Schematic representation of the helium-nitrogen nuclear reaction.*

ments are continuously being transmuted as a result of the spontaneous disintegrations of their unstable nuclei. Here, however, we start with two stable nuclei and transmute them into two different stable nuclei. The process is not dissimilar to a chemical reaction. A helium nucleus and a nitrogen nucleus, when brought into close contact, react to form a hydrogen nucleus and an oxygen nucleus. This **nuclear reaction** may be conveniently written as

$$_2He^4 + {_7}N^{14} \longrightarrow {_1}H^1 + {_8}O^{17} \qquad (30\text{-}1)$$

Notice that the reaction balances in two ways: first, the sum of the nuclear charges (+9) is the same on both sides of the reaction; second, the sum of the mass numbers (18) is also the same on both sides. Since the intermediate compound nucleus ($_9F^{18}$) immediately disappears, it is often omitted from the written reaction.

Rutherford's discovery of the nuclear transmutation of nitrogen by $\alpha$-particle bombardment initiated a systematic search for other transmutations. With the exception of oxygen, carbon, and the first four elements of the periodic table, all the elements up to and including potassium were found to undergo similar disintegration when bombarded by $\alpha$-particles. It is easy to understand why heavier elements do not show the effect. The nuclear charge of these elements is so large (and the coulombic repulsion is therefore so great) that even the fastest naturally produced $\alpha$-particle (7.7 Mev) is deflected before it gets sufficiently close to the nucleus to enter into a reaction. Modern accelerators furnish particles with many times the energy of naturally produced $\alpha$-particles, and by the use of these high-speed projectiles many proton-producing reactions with heavy elements have been observed.

So many disintegrations in which protons are knocked out of a nucleus have been observed that there is no longer any doubt that one of the building blocks of all nuclei is the proton. For a time, indeed, it was thought that Prout's original surmise must be correct. For instance, fourteen hydrogen atoms would supply fourteen protons and fourteen electrons; the protons and seven of the electrons would combine to produce a nitrogen nucleus of mass 14 and charge

charges, the $\alpha$-particle penetrates the nitrogen nucleus and forms a *compound nucleus,* in this case a rare isotope of fluorine (b), which, being very unstable, immediately disintegrates explosively (c). The disintegration products are a proton, which is ejected with high KE, and the stable nucleus of a rare isotope of oxygen† (§ 18-11). The compound nucleus, endowed with high energy by the $\alpha$-particle, disintegrates so quickly that it does not produce a cloud trail and is not observed. The ejected proton produces the long, lightly ionized trail, and the recoiling oxygen nucleus produces the short, densely ionized trail. The absence of any other trail proves conclusively that the $\alpha$-particle has been absorbed in the nucleus.

This great discovery was the first instance of an artificially produced transmutation. As we saw in Chapter 27, the naturally radioactive ele-

---

† At the time (1925) the existence of $_8O^{17}$ in ordinary oxygen was unknown, but the conclusion that it was formed in this process was inescapable.

+7; the remaining seven electrons would be just the number required to form the electronic structure of the nitrogen atom. Similarly, any other atom might be formed from an appropriate number of hydrogen atoms. Putting electrons in the nucleus, however, raised a number of difficulties that could be explained only if the nuclear electrons had properties very different from those of ordinary electrons. In the 1920's, nevertheless, since protons and electrons were the only known fundamental particles, the proton-electron theory of the nucleus persisted. Then, in 1932, a new particle, which resolved the difficulties, was discovered.

## 30-3. *The Nucleus Contains Neutrons*

In the last section it was pointed out that beryllium is one of the few light elements that do not produce protons when bombarded by α-particles. In 1930, however, a very penetrating radiation was found to emanate from beryllium while under such bombardment. The radiation was detected with a Geiger counter, which is one of the electronic counting devices that depend on the ionization of gas in the sensing tube. Investigators studied the penetration of the rays by placing sheets of various substances in front of the counter tube. It soon became evident that these *beryllium rays* were more penetrating than any other radiation known at

the time. As much as 2.0 cm of lead absorbed little—that is, reduced the counts of the Geiger tube only slightly.

In 1932 Irène Curie (daughter of Pierre and Marie Curie) and her husband, Frédéric Joliot (who adopted the name Joliot-Curie), were comparing the absorption of beryllium rays by various substances when they discovered a remarkable property of the rays. They set up the arrangement shown schematically in Figure 30-5. The α-particles from a radioactive substance, *S*, were allowed to bombard a sheet of beryllium metal (Be). The penetrating radiation emitted was detected by the ionization produced in *I*. When sheets of varying thickness of substances such as aluminum, silver, and lead were placed at *A*, only a slight decrease in the ionization was observed; that is, the radiation passed through these heavy metals with very little loss of energy. When a block of paraffin was at *A*, the ionization current was observed to *increase*. A similar effect was observed with water and with cellophane. In other words, the beryllium rays had the property of ejecting highly ionizing rays from target materials at *A*, as shown by the increase in the counting rate. The Joliot-Curies soon proved that the ejected rays were high-speed protons. The absorption characteristics of the rays, plus the fact that they were ejected only from substances containing hydrogen, made this conclusion reasonably certain.

What, then, is the nature of the highly penetrating beryllium rays that knock recoil protons

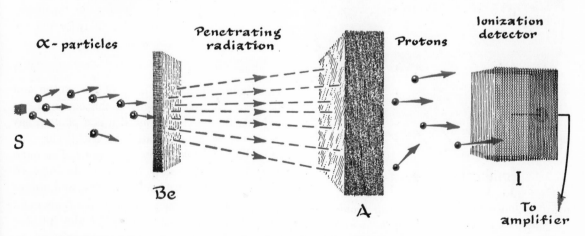

FIGURE **30-5** *Experimental arrangement for the study of beryllium rays.*

out of hydrogenous substances? At the time, the most penetrating radiations known were the high-energy photons of γ-rays. The Joliot-Curies made the plausible assumption that the beryllium rays were photons of sufficiently high energy to eject the recoil protons by a Compton process, just as the less energetic X-ray photons ejected free electrons in the Compton effect (§ 26-5). The hydrogen atoms, to be sure, are bound in the molecules of the paraffin, but the strength of the chemical bond (the energy needed to break the bond and remove the hydrogen atom from the molecule) is only a few electron volts. The high KE of the recoil protons indicated, however, that the beryllium rays, if they are photons, have energies of many millions of electron volts. For such photons, therefore, the hydrogen nuclei in the molecule would be free protons. Reasonable as this assumption was in the light of current knowledge, it was soon found to raise serious difficulties and to contain an intrinsic contradiction.

In the same year (1932) James Chadwick extended the study of recoil nuclei produced by beryllium rays. Allowing the rays to enter a cloud chamber filled with methane, he photo-

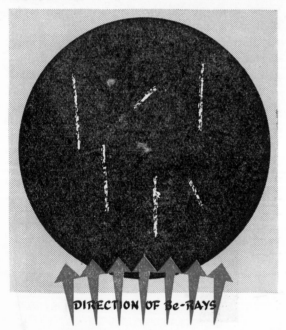

FIGURE **30-6** *Cloud trails of recoil protons produced by bombardment of methane with beryllium rays.*

graphed the trails produced by the recoil protons. He obtained pictures similar to Figure 30-6. Here the beryllium radiation enters from the bottom of the picture. Trails were observed to originate at random points throughout the body of the gas. Beryllium rays themselves leave no trails, for, because of their great penetrating power, they produce very little ionization. The observed trails, due to the recoil protons, originate at the points of impact between beryllium rays and protons. Some of the impacts are glancing and therefore produce shorter trails, at an angle with the direction of the beryllium rays. There is a noticeable frequency of head-on collisions, shown by the longer, forward trails. All this is consistent with the view that beryllium rays are high-energy photons. The range, density, and curvature of the trails in a magnetic field proved that they were proton trails and yielded the velocity of recoil. The velocity for the head-on collisions was found to be $3.3 \times 10^7$ m/sec.

We have already worked out the theory for a head-on collision between a photon and a particle. We applied it, in describing the Compton effect, to collisions with electrons, but nothing in the theory prevents us from applying it to collisions with protons. We may, then, start with equations 26-7 and 26-8. Here, however, we are interested, not in the recoil photon (since it is not observed), but in the recoil proton, which *is* observed. Hence we combine the equations to eliminate $h\nu'$ and solve for $h\nu$, the energy of the incident photon. This operation yields $h\nu = mv(v + 2c)/4$, and, since the recoil velocity, $v$, is small compared with twice the velocity of light, we may write

$$h\nu = mvc/2 \qquad (30\text{-}2)$$

Substituting the known mass of the proton and the observed recoil velocity in this equation, we find that the beryllium ray, if it is a photon, has an energy of approximately 52 Mev! This was a startling and puzzlingly large value. The most energetic γ-ray photon known at the time of these experiments was only 2.6 Mev; and, moreover, the bombarding α-particles that generated the beryllium rays carried only 7.7 Mev into the process. How could this enormous photon be accounted for in the light of these energies?

Chadwick studied the recoil nuclei produced when the cloud chamber contained other light substances besides methane. With nitrogen in the chamber he obtained photographs similar to Figure 30-6. Analysis of the trails showed them to be due to recoil nitrogen nuclei with a velocity (forward) of $4.7 \times 10^6$ m/sec. This velocity is somewhat less than that of protons, as might be expected of the heavier nitrogen nucleus. When the values were inserted in equation 30-2, however, the necessary incident photon came out to have an energy of about 102 Mev! Even if these great energies could in some way be accounted for, how could the same photon have an energy of 52 Mev when colliding with hydrogen nuclei and almost twice as much energy when colliding with nitrogen nuclei? Clearly, the beryllium rays could not be photons.

Chadwick resolved the difficulties by proposing a different assumption. He assumed that the beryllium ray was a stream of particles each approximately equal to a proton in mass but, unlike the proton, carrying no charge. These massive, electrically neutral particles were called **neutrons.** As we have seen, charged particles ($\alpha$-particles, electrons, protons, and other nuclei), by their electric attractions or repulsions of the electrons in the atoms, produce many ionizations as they move through matter. These ionizations consume the KE of the particles, which therefore have a limited range. A neutron, on the other hand, since it carries no charge, is not affected by atomic electrons and is slowed down or stopped only by a rare collision with a nucleus. Hence a beam of neutrons can penetrate thick layers of material with very little diminution in intensity. This, of course, is the effect observed by the Joliot-Curies in their absorption experiments.

The assumption that beryllium radiation is a stream of neutrons also resolves the discrepancies in energy. A neutron, colliding with a proton, is stopped, and the proton moves off with the same velocity. This is the simple elastic impact between two bodies of equal mass (the case $m_1 = m_2$ in § 11-9). The neutron, in other words, hands over all its KE to the recoil proton. This energy, easily calculated from the

known mass and observed recoil velocity of the protons, comes out to be approximately 6 Mev. Hence the impinging neutron need have only 6 Mev of energy instead of the 50 or 100 Mev required by the photon theory. This is a very reasonable amount of energy when compared with the energies involved in the production of beryllium rays. A neutron of 6 Mev would, moreover, according to the laws of elastic impact, produce a nitrogen recoil with approximately the observed velocity.

Working on this assumption, then, Chadwick was able to calculate the mass and velocity of the neutrons that comprised the beryllium rays. The problem was to determine the mass and velocity of a particle from the observed velocities produced by elastic impact on two different particles of known mass (hydrogen and nitrogen nuclei). We have already solved this problem in our study of elastic collisions (§ 11-9). Using the recoil velocities derived from his cloud-chamber measurements ($3.3 \times 10^7$ m/sec for $_1H^1$ and $0.47 \times 10^7$ m/sec for $_7N^{14}$) and the known relative atomic masses, Chadwick found the mass of a neutron to be 1.16 on the atomic weight scale and the velocity to be $3.1 \times 10^7$ m/sec, which corresponds to an energy of approximately 6 Mev. These results, with an estimated error of about 10 percent, were sufficiently precise to remove satisfactorily the contradiction involved in the photon assumption and to prove that beryllium radiation consists of neutral particles. This, then, was the discovery of the neutron, a discovery that required a subtler argument than any we have encountered so far. The argument involved the theory of the Compton effect, the application to atoms of the mechanical laws of collisions, and the interpretation of cloud-chamber measurements. Subsequent developments have amply proved the profound significance of Chadwick's discovery of the neutron, which, with the proton and the electron, is a fundamental building block of matter.

The next question, obviously, concerns the *source* of the neutrons. That can only be a transmutation of beryllium nuciei by high-energy $\alpha$-particles (Fig. 30-5), similar to the transmutation of nitrogen: an $\alpha$-particle enters a beryllium nucleus, a neutron is ejected, and a stable carbon nucleus is formed. This reaction may be written as

$$_2\mathrm{He}^4 + {}_4\mathrm{Be}^9 \longrightarrow {}_6\mathrm{C}^{12} + {}_0n^1 \qquad (30\text{-}3)$$

The zero subscript on the symbol $n$ indicates that the neutron carries no charge, and the superscript indicates that the mass of the neutron is approximately the same as that of a proton— that is, one mass unit. The reaction balances both in charge and in mass number. The many other neutron-producing reactions that were found and studied after Chadwick's discovery led to the precise determination of the mass of the neutron (such a reaction will be discussed later). This mass, now known to a high degree of precision, is 1.008982 on the atomic-weight scale. This, compared with the mass of the proton, shows that Chadwick's original surmise was indeed correct. The two masses are not exactly equal, but they differ only in the fourth figure.

Neutrons, it was found, like protons, could be knocked out of atoms throughout the whole periodic table by particles from modern accelerators. Such neutrons are very useful atomic projectiles. The fact that they are electrically neutral, as we have seen, permits them to travel easily through matter, and neutron beams are therefore often used instead of X-rays when a highly penetrating radiation is desired; even a slow neutron, moreover, since it is not repelled by the nuclear charge, may approach a nucleus close enough to enter into a nuclear reaction. For the present discussion, however, the important result of the experiments just described is that they give conclusive evidence of the existence of neutrons in all atomic nuclei. Here, then, is a second building block of the atomic nucleus.

## 30-4. Nuclear Structure

With the discovery of neutrons it was no longer necessary to assume that the nucleus contains electrons, and the difficulties mentioned earlier disappeared. There are still many problems, to be sure, in the theory of nuclear structure, but these are of a different sort. The evidence that all nuclei are composed only of protons and neutrons is so overwhelming that this may be considered a basic tenet of nuclear theory.† With these particles as building blocks, we can easily construct any known nucleus. The atomic number, $Z$, which, as we have seen, is equal to the number of positive electronic charges on the nucleus, is clearly equal to the number of protons in the nucleus. The mass number, $A$, is equal to the total number of protons plus neutrons. This follows from the whole-number rule for isotopic masses (§ 18-10) and from the fact that the proton and the neutron each have an atomic weight very nearly equal to unity. The term **nucleon** is often used to refer to either a proton or a neutron. The composition of a nucleus may be summarized, then, as follows:

$$A = \text{number of nucleons}$$
$$Z = \text{number of protons}$$
$$A - Z = \text{number of neutrons}$$

For instance, nitrogen ($Z = 7$, $A = 14$) contains seven protons and seven neutrons in the nucleus—equal numbers of each. Iodine ($Z = 53$, $A = 127$) contains fifty-three protons and seventy-four neutrons; there are twenty-one more neutrons than protons. The number of neutrons and the number of protons are approximately equal for light elements (exactly for some), but the number of neutrons increases to about 1.5 times the number of protons for heavy elements.

The helium nucleus (two neutrons and two protons) appears to be a particularly stable "subassembly." It is this group (the $\alpha$-particle) that is ejected as a unit by many of the radioactive elements. A number of the lighter nuclei are seen to consist of an even number of these assemblies, C, O, Ne, and $_{12}\mathrm{Mg}^{24}$ consisting of three, four, five, and six $\alpha$-particles respectively. The expected $_4\mathrm{Be}^8$ has been formed, but it is unstable and breaks up into two $\alpha$-particles. The stable beryllium, $_4\mathrm{Be}^9$, on the other hand, is two $\alpha$-particles plus an extra neutron. When another $\alpha$-particle enters this nucleus, however, the extra neutron is ejected, and carbon remains (equation 30-3). The nitrogen nucleus can be regarded as three $\alpha$-particles plus an extra proton and an extra

---

† The attentive reader will detect an apparent contradiction here. The $\beta$-rays of radioactivity are certainly electrons. This nuclear emission finds another explanation, however, which we shall consider in a later section.

neutron. In this case, however, when an $\alpha$-particle enters the nucleus (equation 30-1), the proton is ejected, leaving four $\alpha$-particles plus a neutron for the $O^{17}$ nucleus.

These are only a few examples of the nuclear structures that the reader can work out by reference to the periodic table. The system has no meaning, of course, for atomic weights that are not integral (we cannot have a fraction of a neutron). But we have already seen that such atomic weights have meaning only as statistical averages of isotopes with integral masses. Chlorine, for instance, consists of two nuclear species (or **nuclides**) that contain the same number of protons but one of which has two more neutrons than the other. Other examples will occur to the reader. If the number of protons in a nuclide is changed by bombardment, the resulting nucleus will assemble electron shells (as outlined in Chap. 29) corresponding to the new nuclear charge, and this structure will have the properties of the new element.

In two transmutations that we have already discussed, $\alpha$-particles from a naturally radioactive material were the projectiles used. Many other reactions have been discovered and studied by means of such $\alpha$-particles. For a wider study of nuclear reactions, however, more varied and controllable projectiles were needed. Rutherford suggested, for instance, that protons (ionized hydrogen) accelerated through known potential differences might lead to new discoveries. This method would have the advantage of using not only a different particle but also a particle whose energy could be controlled by variations of the voltage. An accelerator, furthermore, could produce an intense beam of particles. The number of $\alpha$-particles emitted per second by a radioactive substance is determined by the size of the sample (of necessity small) and by the probability of disintegration (which cannot be affected by the experimenter). If, however, helium gas were doubly ionized and the stripped nuclei were accelerated, many $\alpha$-particles per second would be made available, and the intense beam would greatly enhance the chance of a reaction. Most of the particles in any beam are slowed down by ionizing encounters with the electrons of the atoms, and only a few particles hit the small tar-get (the nucleus) with sufficient energy to activate a reaction. The chance of such a hit is increased by the use of an intense beam in much the same way that one's chance of hitting a small object is increased if one throws at it a handful of gravel instead of three or four pebbles. Considerations such as these stimulated the development of various particle accelerators (the "atom smashers" of popular usage) capable of producing intense beams of controllably high-energy particles. This development has been such an important feature of nuclear research that some of the techniques will be described.

## 30-5. *Particle Accelerators*

We have already formed some idea of the order of magnitude of the energies of particles involved in nuclear processes. These energies range from several thousand to several million electron volts. Since the useful bombarding particles (electrons, protons, $\alpha$-particles, etc.) carry only one or two electronic charges, voltages of the same order of magnitude would be required if the energies were to be produced by simple acceleration through a potential difference. For certain experiments involving the artificial production of sub-atomic particles, however, the energies required run from hundreds of millions up to billions of electron volts (Bev). Voltages of these magnitudes are technically impossible, and the production of energies in the Bev range necessitated other developments. About 1930 machines for producing high-energy particles began to be developed.

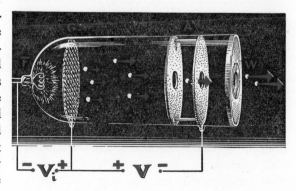

FIGURE **30-7** *Cockcroft-Walton "proton gun."*

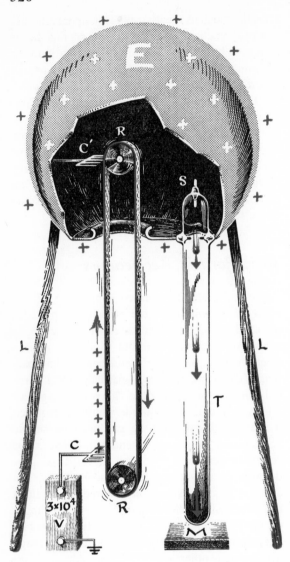

FIGURE **30-8** *Van de Graaff accelerator.*

row stream of high-speed protons, not unlike a stream of bullets from a machine gun. The energy of the protons may be changed by adjustments in the value of $V$. This "proton gun" may be pointed at a target material and the products of the reaction studied by the methods already described. The potential difference $V$, obtained from standard transformers and allied circuits, approaches a million volts. Since a good many transmutations can be carried out with energies ranging up to one Mev, many Cockcroft-Walton accelerators are still in use.

Technical difficulties (of insulation, for example) rule out transformer-produced voltages above a million. In 1931, in America, R. J. Van de Graaff developed a generator that can attain, in its recent models, a potential difference of about 8 million volts. The instrument, shown schematically in Figure 30-8, employs the principle of the electrostatic generator. A large, hollow, metallic sphere, $E$, is mounted on insulating legs, $L$. A continuous belt of insulating fabric is carried over rollers, $R$, the lower of which is connected to a motor that keeps the belt in continuous motion. A source of potential difference of about $3 \times 10^4$ volts is connected between ground and an electrode, $C$, which has a row of sharp points extending the width of the belt. The electric field in the neighborhood of these points is intense enough to set up, in the air, a brush discharge that sprays positive charges onto the moving belt. These charges are carried up by the belt to the inside of $E$, where electrons leap off a second electrode, $C'$, thus leaving $E$ with a positive charge. This process continues as the belt rotates, the motor supplying the energy that lifts the positive charges against the electrostatic repulsion of the charges on $E$. In this way the charge accumulated on $E$ (and hence its potential) increases until leakage through the insulators or into the surrounding air equals the rate at which the charge is carried up by the belt. Positive ions produced at $S$ are repelled down a long evacuated tube, $T$. They fall through the full potential difference from $E$ to ground, emerge from $T$ with high KE, and bombard the target material, $M$. Particles accelerated to energies of 8 Mev can be produced with this type of accelerator. This is somewhat more than the energy

The first accelerator, devised by John Cockcroft and Ernest Walton at the Cavendish Laboratory, is shown schematically in Figure 30-7. Electrons from a hot filament, $F$, accelerated by the potential difference $V_i$, ionize hydrogen atoms in the neighborhood of $G$. These protons are accelerated toward $A$ by the large potential difference $V$. Those headed along the line joining the two holes in $A$ will coast on through and emerge from the apparatus through a thin window, $W$. This window prevents the escape of gas atoms from the apparatus but has little effect on the high-speed protons. The device ejects a nar-

of the fastest α-particle from radioactive materials. The Van de Graaff generator has the added advantage that the voltage (and thus the particle energy) can be easily adjusted and maintained at constant values.

Voltages higher than those attained by a Van de Graaff machine are technically impossible. The important quantity, however, is not the voltage but the final KE of the particle. If a particle could be given a number of successive accelerations, it might attain a very great KE even though the voltage for each acceleration was low. About the same time that Van de Graaff developed his machine, two machines employing successive accelerations, the linear accelerator and the cyclotron, began to come into use. Modern versions of these produce particles of the highest energies.

## 30-6. *Linear Accelerator*

The linear accelerator, as its name implies, drives a particle along a straight line and periodically gives it a push to increase its speed. Consider the following mechanical analogy: A cart free to roll along a level surface is so massive that a person pushing it can produce only a moderate increase of kinetic energy. Ten persons standing in a line, however, could, with a little teamwork, get the cart up to a sizable speed. The first person would push the cart and get it started. It would coast with this low speed till it arrived at the second person, who would give it another push and send it along at a higher speed. The cart would continue in this way, coasting at an increased constant speed between the persons and being accelerated as it passed each person. After passing the tenth person it would have ten times the kinetic energy that any one person alone could have given it.

The apparatus diagramed in Figure 30-9 does exactly the same thing for a charged particle. A long, highly evacuated tank has a series of metal tubes mounted along its axis. These tubes, called *drift tubes,* are insulated electrically and mounted with small gaps between them. The first, third, fifth, . . . tubes are connected to terminal 1 of a generator, $G$; and the second, fourth, sixth, . . . tubes are connected to terminal 2 of the generator. The generator is an oscillator; that is, it reverses the polarity of the terminals at regular intervals. Such generators had been developed particularly for the generation of the high-frequency voltages used in radio broadcasting. Consider now the instant when terminal 1 is negative and 2 is positive. A positive ion, produced in the ion source, $S$, is accelerated into the first drift tube. As soon as it enters the tube, however, the electric force disappears, for there is no electric field inside a hollow charged conductor. The ion, then, coasts along at constant speed while inside the tube. It will require time $t = L/v$ to traverse the tube if $L$ is the length of the tube and $v$ is the speed of the ion. But $L$ is such that $t$ equals the time required for the generator to reverse polarity. Hence, when the ion arrives at the first gap, the first tube becomes positive and the second one negative; the ion is jerked across the gap and enters the second tube with increased speed. The length of the second tube is enough longer than the first

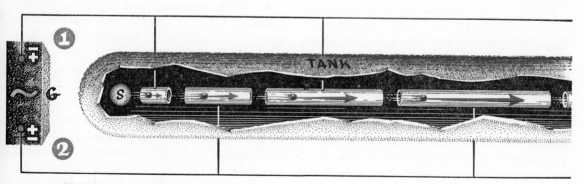

FIGURE **30-9** *Linear accelerator.*

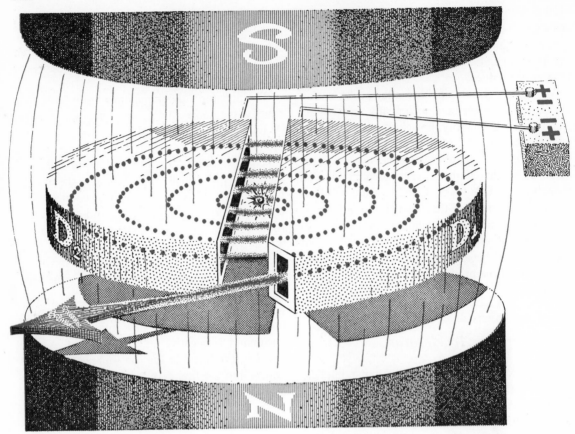

FIGURE **30-10** *Cyclotron*.

so that the time of flight is the same as in the first one. Hence, when the ion arrives at the second gap, the polarity is reversed again, and once more the ion is accelerated across the gap. This continues along the tank, the ion arriving at each gap when the polarity is just right to accelerate it. Hence the ion shoots out of the tank with a KE many times that given it at any one acceleration.

In 1931 E. O. Lawrence and D. H. Sloan produced ions of $2 \times 10^5$ volts with a generator potential difference of only $10^4$ volts. For higher energies, however, the apparatus became cumbersomely long. If an oscillator of higher frequency became available, the time for the polarity to reverse would be shorter, and each drift tube could therefore be shorter. During World War II, techniques of generating and controlling voltages of very high frequency were devised for use in radar. Accelerators using oscillators with reversal times of the order of $10^{-9}$ sec have been

developed. One, with a total length of forty feet, produces 40 Mev protons. At this rate (about 1 Mev per foot of length), an accelerator that produced protons with energies of several Bev would have to be several thousand feet long.

## 30-7. Cyclotron

In 1932, Lawrence and M. S. Livingston overcame the linear accelerator's inherent difficulty of excessive length by coiling the path of the ions into an expanding spiral. The essential parts of their machine, called a cyclotron, are shown schematically in Figure 30-10. Two hollow, semi-circular metallic electrodes are connected to the terminals of an oscillator. These electrodes (called "dees" because of their resemblance to the letter D), mounted with a small gap between their straight sides, enclose a flat cylindrical space in which the ions may move.

The dees, which are enclosed in a highly evacuated box (not shown), are placed between the poles of a powerful electromagnet. When $D_1$ is negative and $D_2$ positive, the ions (formed by a source at the center of the gap between the dees) are accelerated into the space inside $D_1$. There the electric field disappears, just as it does inside a drift tube. But the magnetic field remains unchanged because the dees are made of a nonmagnetic metal. Inside $D_1$, then, the magnetic field guides the ions along a semi-circular path. During this flight the oscillator reverses polarity; so, when the ions emerge from $D_1$, they are again accelerated across the gap and enter $D_2$ with increased speed. In $D_2$ the ions traverse a larger semi-circle while the oscillator again reverses polarity. This process continues, the ions always arriving at the gap when the polarity is such as to produce an acceleration. After many revolutions, the ions (moving in a circle almost as large as the dees) are deflected from their circular path by a negatively charged plate (not shown) and shoot out through a thin window toward the target.

The pertinent quantities involved in these circular paths are related by equation 17-11. From this we find the speed of the ions, which, divided into the distance ($\pi r$), gives the time of flight along a semi-circular path. The results are

$$v = B \frac{q}{m} r \qquad (30\text{-}4)$$

$$t = \frac{\pi}{B} \frac{m}{q} \qquad (30\text{-}5)$$

Since, in practice, the magnetic induction, $B$, is held constant, and $q/m$ is a constant that is characteristic of the accelerated ion, equation 30-4 shows that the speed is directly proportional to the radius of the path. The ions move in larger and larger semi-circles as they speed up. But the time taken to traverse a semi-circle is the same for all; in other words, in a semi-circle of twice the radius of another the ion travels twice as far but also twice as fast and thus gets round in the same time. This fact is expressed by equation 30-5 for the time of flight, which is seen not to depend on either $v$ or $r$. Hence the reversal time, $t$, for the oscillator is a constant of the apparatus. The generator, then, may be a simple fixed-frequency oscillator, changing polarity at regular intervals determined by $B$ and the value of $q/m$ for the ion.

The final kinetic energy ($\frac{1}{2}mv^2$) is determined by the speed of the ion in the last semi-circle. This is given by equation 30-4, with $r$ almost as large as the radius of the dees. Now $q/m$ is not very different for the various ions used (for example, only twice as large for protons as for $\alpha$-particles), and there is a practical upper limit on the attainable values of $B$ (approximately 1.5 newtons/amp m). Hence the maximum energy of the ions is mostly determined by the radius of the dees. A considerable number of cyclotrons have been built with a dee diameter of approximately one meter, and these produce ion beams of 15–20 Mev. The conspicuous part of these machines is the electromagnet, which must be very large in order to produce an intense and uniform magnetic field over the whole area of the dees. The magnets of the cyclotrons just mentioned weigh about a hundred tons.

For still higher energies (hundreds instead of tens of Mev) the dees and magnets must be made still larger. But here we run into a difficulty. In our discussion of the values of $e/m$ for fast $\beta$-particles (§ 27-2) we found that, as the speed of any body approaches that of light, the mass of the body increases appreciably. In a large cyclotron the ions soon attain such speeds that this increase of mass becomes sizable. Then, according to equation 30-5, the time taken to traverse the successive semi-circles becomes progressively longer. Hence the ions get out of step with the oscillator, and acceleration ceases. For a time it was thought that this effect would limit the energies that could be attained with a cyclotron. In the 1940's, however, the application of *frequency modulation* overcame the difficulty. The oscillator, instead of operating at a constant frequency, was designed so that the frequency gradually decreased. Hence, as the ions revolved at greater speeds, the reversal time for the generator became longer so that the ions always found an accelerating potential when they arrived at the gap between the dees. Such a machine, in which the generator is synchronized with the frequency of revolution of the ions, is called a *synchrocyclotron*. One at the University of Cali-

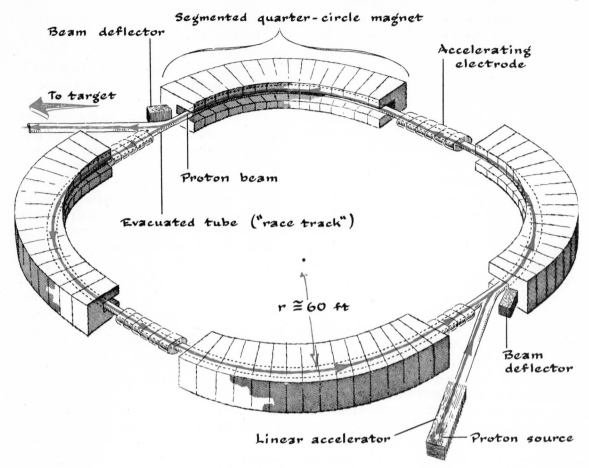

fornia generates a proton beam of almost 400 Mev.† The poles of the magnet (which weighs 4,000 tons) have a diameter of 184 inches. The ions make 10,000 revolutions in about 0.001 second, and this process is repeated about a hundred times per second. Thus every second the target is bombarded with a hundred pulses of high-energy particles.

The only limit on the size of a synchrocyclotron (and therefore on the energy it produces) is cost. The magnet for a synchrocyclotron that would accelerate particles to billions of electron volts would be impossibly expensive. But, as pointed out above, the final energy of the particle is its KE in the largest circle of the dees. If a charged particle could be fired into a machine that would hold it in a circle of fixed radius

(sufficiently large for the desired energy), the magnetic field would be necessary only along the circumference of this circle. Building the magnet in the form of a ring would result in a great saving of materials.

Several such machines have been built to accelerate particles to energies of several Bev. Figure 30-11 shows a very schematic sketch of the arrangement. The magnets are wedge-shaped so that they fit together in the arc of a circle of radius $r$. Four such quarter-circle magnets are connected by straight sections that contain accelerating electrodes but no magnetic field. Inside the whole apparatus is a roughly circular, highly evacuated tube, which forms a "race track" for the ions. These, fired into the machine by a linear accelerator, are deflected into the race track by a momentary field. The value of $B$ in the first quarter circle is just right to deflect the

---

†This is 50–100 times the energy of natural α-particles.

ions along a path of radius *r*. Accelerated in the first straight section, they enter the second quarter circle with increased speed. Here, as required by equation 30-4, the magnetic field is sufficiently greater to deflect the ions along a circle of the same radius as the first quarter circle. As the ions enter each successive quarter circle with increased speed, the magnetic field is increased (by an increase of current in the coils) at the proper rate to keep the radius of curvature of the path constant. The oscillator supplying the accelerating electrodes gradually decreases in frequency (as in the synchrocyclotron) to compensate for the relativistic increase in mass as the ions approach the speed of light. When, after a large number of trips round the track, the ions have acquired a very large energy, a momentary field deflects them out of the orbit and onto a target. At the Brookhaven National Laboratory on Long Island, New York, such an accelerator (called a *cosmotron*) produces a beam of protons with energies of 2–3 Bev. A similar machine at the University of California (called a *bevatron*) is designed to produce a proton beam of 6 Bev. The straight sections of this one are twenty feet long, and *r* is about sixty feet, the over-all width being about 140 feet. The protons, injected with an energy of 10 Mev, attain their maximum energy in about two seconds. During this time they have made approximately four million trips round the "race track"—a distance of about 300,000 miles. The design for a similar accelerator, to produce ions of about 25 Bev, is nearing completion at the Brookhaven Laboratory. Other accelerators are designed for special purposes— the *betatron,* for example, which accelerates electrons to energies of hundreds of Mev.

These, then, are the accelerators required for modern nuclear research. They provide much more intense beams than naturally radioactive sources, and the energies are controllable. The need for energies much greater than those of radioactive particles stems from a firm belief among scientists that new and fundamental discoveries can be made with projectiles of higher and higher energies. The results so far have amply justified this belief. The particles accelerated are mostly hydrogen and helium nuclei (that is, protons and α-particles) and **deuterons.**

A deuteron is the nucleus of the heavy isotope of hydrogen, deuterium, $_1H^2$. This particle, consisting of a proton and a neutron, has twice the energy of a proton at the same speed; but, since it has the same charge as a proton, it is not repelled by the target nucleus with any greater force. This electric repulsion of the target nucleus increases, of course, with the atomic number of the projectile. For this reason nuclei heavier than that of helium are rarely used as atomic projectiles. Neutrons, on the other hand, are very useful particles, for they are not repelled by the target nucleus. Intense beams of neutrons are produced when appropriate substances are bombarded with charged particles from accelerators; Equation 30-3 describes one example. Finally, for certain reactions, high-energy photons are useful "particles." These are produced, just as X-rays are, by high-energy electrons striking a suitable target. With electrons from either a betatron or a linear accelerator, photons with energies of several hundred Mev are obtained.

The experiments consist of bombarding atoms of various types with particles from an accelerator and studying the particles produced in the reaction. The measurements, which determine the energies and nature of the particles, are made by means of counters, cloud chambers, and deflecting magnetic fields. Extremely complicated and precise measurements are made by elaborate combinations of these techniques. None of the operations is performed manually; all are operated from a control panel placed at some distance from the accelerator. During operation no one is allowed near the accelerator, for the high-energy beams produce harmful radiations of vicious intensity. The experimenters are protected from most of these rays by thick concrete walls. For neutrons, however, a tank of water several feet thick is useful. We now consider some of the results of these experiments.

## 30-8. Mass-energy Balance in Nuclear Reactions

The first transmutation with artificially accelerated particles was produced by Cockcroft and Walton. Their "proton gun" (Fig. 30-7), at the time of this experiment, could not produce a beam of protons with energies greater than half a Mev. Such protons could not easily approach the nucleus of a heavy atom, and, since protons have no effect on helium nuclei, they chose the next lightest element, lithium, as a target. With a 0.3 Mev proton they got a reaction that produced two high-speed helium nuclei. The lithium target was in the form of a thin film, and the pair of helium nuclei, like the fragments in any explosion, were observed to fly away from the film in opposite directions. The observed range of the helium nuclei was 8.4 cm, which indicated a KE of 8.6 Mev for each nucleus. In this reaction the proton entering the lithium nucleus forms a very unstable beryllium isotope, which immediately disintegrates explosively into two helium nuclei. The reaction is

$$0.3 \text{ Mev} + {}_1H^1 + {}_3Li^7 \longrightarrow$$
$${}_2He^4 + {}_2He^4 + 17.2 \text{ Mev} \qquad (30\text{-}6)$$

Here, for reasons to be discussed presently, we include the energies of the reaction also. Notice that the energy of the incoming proton triggered the release of more than fifty times as much energy.

The nuclear charges balance; and, since all nuclear charges are integral, the balance is exact. The mass *numbers* also balance; but do the *masses* balance? When this reaction was discovered, the masses of the three atoms involved were known to good precision from mass-spectrographic measurements. Using these values, let us try to strike a *mass* balance for the reaction.

REACTANTS:                   PRODUCTS:
  ${}_1H^1$ = 1.0081            ${}_2He^4$ = 4.0039
  ${}_3Li^7$ = 7.0182           ${}_2He^4$ = 4.0039
  ———————                      ———————
  Sum = 8.0263                 Sum = 8.0078

We find that the masses do *not* balance! During the reaction, some mass must have disappeared, for the products are less massive than the reactants. The difference is small, to be sure, but it is many times the experimental error of the mass measurements. Associated with this decrease of mass, however, is an *increase* of energy. Perhaps we have here a direct observation of the inter-

change of mass and energy that Einstein had predicted more than twenty-five years earlier (1905). This principle of the equivalence of mass and energy we have already encountered. It played a fruitful and central role in the theory of the Compton effect (§ 26-5) and gave a consistent explanation of the observed decrease in $e/m$ for very fast $\beta$-particles (§ 25-2). To test this hypothesis, we should have to convert the masses to equivalent energies, or vice versa, by applying the equation $\mathcal{E} = mc^2$ and seeing whether equation 30-6 balances in total "mass-energy."

These calculations become tedious if we go each time from relative atomic weights to kilograms, then to joules (by $mc^2$), and then to electron volts. We can, however, do this once for an arbitrary unit of mass and obtain a convenient transformation factor. All isotopic atomic weights are expressed on the physical scale (§ 18-11). It is important to adhere to this scale in these calculations because the changes in atomic weight are very small. On this scale the abundant isotope of oxygen is assigned an atomic weight of exactly 16.0000, and one sixteenth of this is the unit of mass. This unit is called the **atomic mass unit** and is abbreviated as *amu*. Now Avogadro's number of $O^{16}$ atoms has a mass of 16 grams or 0.016 kgm. *One* $O^{16}$ atom has, then, a mass of 0.016 kgm/$N_0$, and one amu has a mass of $10^{-3}$ kgm/$N_0$. This multiplied by $c^2$ gives the equivalent energy in joules, which by equation 18-7 may be converted to electron volts. Using the precise values of the constants, we find that one amu is equivalent to $9.3115 \times 10^8$ ev. Except for very precise calculations, however, the first three figures are sufficient:

$$\text{amu} = 931 \text{ Mev} \qquad (30\text{-}7)$$

With this we can easily express atomic weights as energies or energies as atomic weights.

Let us now consider the balance of equation 30-6 again but include, this time, the mass equivalents of the energies; that is, let us strike a *mass-energy* balance. Dividing the 0.3 Mev of the incoming proton by 931 Mev, we find that this energy has an equivalent mass of 0.0003 amu. Similarly, 17.2 Mev is equivalent to 0.0185 amu. The balance sheet in amu, then, is as follows:

| REACTANTS: | | PRODUCTS: | |
|---|---|---|---|
| $_1H^1$ | = 1.0081 | $_2He^4$ | = 4.0039 |
| $_3Li^7$ | = 7.0182 | $_2He^4$ | = 4.0039 |
| 0.3 Mev | = 0.0003 | 17.2 Mev | = 0.0185 |
| Sum | = 8.0266 | Sum | = 8.0263 |

Here the balance is perfect, for the variation in the last figure is within the precision of the measurements. This experiment on the disintegration of lithium was the first direct quantitative verification of Einstein's famous equation for the equivalence of mass and energy. It was also the first experimental verification of the concept of conservation of mass-energy. From a practical standpoint, it was also the first experimental indication of the possibility of releasing the tremendous energies of atomic nuclei—that is, atomic energy. Since then, as the techniques of measuring energy and mass have been developed, the mass-energy equivalence has been amply verified to a high degree of precision (in some cases to seven or eight significant figures).

In writing the equations of the many nuclear reactions that have been studied, we generally express only the *net* mass-energy exchange and do not include the energy on both sides of the equation as we did in equation 30-6. In this reaction there was a net *increase* of energy of $17.2 - 0.3 = 16.9$ or approximately 17 Mev. This energy is represented by the letter $Q$ and, since energy is released, is assigned a positive value; or, more succinctly, $Q = +17$ Mev. This energy was released at the expense of some mass; in other words, the two helium atoms have less mass than the hydrogen and lithium atoms by an amount equal to 17 Mev. $Q$ values are not always positive. In the reaction of Rutherford's first artificial transmutation, for instance (equation 30-1), the products add up to *more* mass than the reactants; in other words, some of the 7.7 Mev of KE of the bombarding $\alpha$-particle is stored in the increased mass of the products of the reaction. Measurements show that this is about 1.1 Mev, which leaves about 6.6 Mev for the KE of the products. For this reaction, then, we write that $Q = -1.1$ Mev.

A few other examples follow:

(A) $_1H^2 + _4Be^9 \longrightarrow _5B^{10} + _0n^1$
$$Q = 4.4 \text{ Mev}$$
(B) $_1H^1 + _5B^{11} \longrightarrow _6C^{12} + h\nu \text{ ($\gamma$-ray)}$
$$Q = 15.8 \text{ Mev}$$
(C) $_0n^1 + _6C^{12} \longrightarrow _4Be^9 + _2He^4$
$$Q = -5.7 \text{ Mev}$$
(D) $_0n^1 + _5B^{10} \longrightarrow _3Li^7 + _2He^4$
$$Q = 2.8 \text{ Mev}$$

(30-8)

The $Q$ values represent changes in the masses of the *nuclei* involved, but in the calculations the masses of the whole atoms (nuclei plus orbital electrons) are used. This results from the fact that in any reaction the nuclear charges balance exactly. Hence there are always the same number of electrons on both sides of the equation, and their masses cancel out in calculations of mass *differences*.

Reaction A of equations 30-8 is often used to produce a beam of high-energy neutrons. For instance, a beam of 10 Mev deuterons from a cyclotron is directed at a beryllium target. In addition to the 10 Mev carried in by the deuteron, the reaction supplies 4.4 Mev, making a total of 14.4 Mev available for the KE of the products. This is divided in approximate inverse proportion to the masses, the neutron receiving about 13 Mev and the boron recoiling with about 1.4 Mev. These 13 Mev neutrons may be directed at other targets for the study of possible reactions. One may vary the energy of the neutrons, of course, by varying the energy of the bombarding deuterons from the accelerator.

Reaction B is an example of a type that is sometimes produced by either proton or neutron bombardment and in which the compound nucleus does not disintegrate but radiates its excess mass as a high-energy photon. In B the proton enters the boron nucleus and forms an unstable, "excited" carbon nucleus, which immediately radiates a $\gamma$-ray photon and stabilizes as ordinary carbon. The mass imbalance is exactly equivalent to the observed quantum of 15.8 Mev.

Reaction C is another with a negative $Q$ value. This is the reverse of the reaction that led to the discovery of the neutron (30-3), which, of course, has a positive $Q$ value.

Reaction D is often used to detect and count

neutrons. A Geiger-Müller tube may be lined with a layer of boron or filled with the gas boron trifluoride ($BF_3$). In either case the boron should be enriched with the 10 isotope.[†] A neutron entering such a counter produces no ionization because, being electrically neutral, it does not disturb the electrons as it passes through the atoms. On striking a boron nucleus, however, the neutron enters into reaction D, which produces a high-speed helium nucleus; this is highly ionizing and activates the counter.

These are only a few of the hundreds of nuclear reactions that are now known. In all of them the mass-energy balance, as computed from Einstein's mass-energy equivalence, is found to be exact. In principle, ordinary chemical reactions should also balance in this way. But, as we have seen, the energy exchanges in these reactions amount, at most, to tens of electron volts. The mass equivalents of such energies are so small that they are not detectable by even the most precise measurement.[‡] Hence the conservation of mass was (and still is) the basic principle in the balancing of chemical reactions. In both chemical and nuclear reactions the electric charge is strictly conserved.

## 30-9. Mass of the Neutron

In chemical reactions, once the principle of the conservation of mass had been firmly established, it became unnecessary to observe the mass of every component of a reaction. For instance, to determine the percentage composition of a mercury oxide, only *two* weighings are required. The mass of the sample of oxide is observed, the oxide is decomposed by heating, and the mass of the remaining mercury is observed. The mass of oxygen in the compound is the difference between the two observed masses. Similarly, in nuclear reactions, once the principle of the conservation of mass-energy had been firmly established, one component of a reaction (either a mass or an energy) could be found

as the difference between the observed quantities. In this way the mass of a large number of nuclei that do not occur in nature have been determined. An important example is the precise determination of the mass of the neutron. Since it carries no charge, the neutron cannot be weighed by the precise methods of magnetic deflection. It is observed, however, that the high-energy photon of a $\gamma$-ray will dissociate a deuteron into a neutron and a proton by a nuclear photoelectric effect. Here part of the energy of the photon is used to dissociate the deuteron and is stored as mass in the products; and the remainder of the photon appears as KE of the products. When, for instance, 2.65 Mev $\gamma$-rays fall on deuterium in a cloud chamber, protons with 0.213 Mev energy are observed. The recoiling neutron leaves no trail, of course, but, since its mass is approximately the same as that of a proton, the laws of mechanics demand that it acquire the same energy as the proton. Thus the KE of the products is 0.426 Mev, and the remainder of the incident photon (equal to 2.224 Mev) is stored as mass in the free proton and neutron. This reaction, then, is

$$h\nu + {}_1H^2 \longrightarrow {}_1H^1 + {}_0n^1 \qquad Q = 2.224 \text{ Mev}$$

This $Q$ value converts to 0.00239 amu. Since the masses of both deuterium and hydrogen are known from mass-spectrograph measurements, the only unknown is the mass of the neutron. When we apply the conservation of mass-energy, this comes out to be 1.00899 amu as the atomic weight of the neutron. Other reactions involving neutrons and measurable nuclei give results that are very close to this value. The average of these precise measurements is the accepted value (stated in § 30-3). Since neutrons are constituents of all nuclei, the importance of this value is obvious.

Since the mass of the neutron is found to be greater than the sum of the masses of a proton and an electron (that is, greater than the mass of a hydrogen atom),[†] one would ex-

---

[†] That is, the sample of boron should be prepared with a higher percentage of $B^{10}$ than appears in nature.

[‡] Conversely, if we could involve even a small fraction of a mole in a nuclear reaction, an enormous energy would become available. We shall return to this topic in a later section.

[†] The sum of the masses of a proton and an electron should, of course, as in the dissociation of the deuterium nucleus, be larger than that of ${}_1H^1$ by an amount equal to the dissociation energy. This energy (the ionization energy for ${}_1H^1$), however, is only 13.6 ev, the mass of which is completely unnoticeable.

pect a free neutron to be unstable and to disintegrate according to the reaction

$$_0n^1 \longrightarrow p + _{-1}e^0$$

This balances, since the proton ($p$) has positive
charge 1 and mass number 1. The mass-energy
balance gives $Q \approx 0.8$ Mev, most of which
would go into the KE of the electron. In other
words, we should expect a *free* neutron to be
radioactive and to emit a $\beta$-particle. There is
good experimental evidence of this reaction. The
half-life of a *free* neutron is about fifteen minutes.

In a nucleus, however, a neutron is not free,
and in most nuclei it is stable. In certain nuclei,
however, the energy state is such that a neutron
is unstable and disintegrates according to the
reaction above. The electron is ejected with
high energy, and the proton remains, thereby increasing the atomic number of the daughter
atom by 1. This is the process referred to in the
footnote of § 30-4.

## 30-10.  *Positron*

In 1932, the same year that Chadwick discovered the neutron, C. D. Anderson discovered
another new elementary particle, which was
given the name **positron.** The positron has the
same mass as an electron but carries a *positive*
electronic charge instead of a negative one. Such
a particle had been predicted theoretically, four
years earlier, by P. A. M. Dirac, who had developed a theory of the electron that accurately
predicted the electron spin—a hypothesis that
was eminently successful, as we have seen, in
developing the electronic structures of the atoms.
The theory, which is much too mathematical for
discussion here, definitely predicted that a particle of equal mass with the electron but of opposite charge would be discovered.

Anderson was studying cosmic rays† by the

―――――――――――

† Cosmic rays are very high-energy rays, of unknown
origin, that travel through the cosmos. On striking the
atoms of the atmosphere and heavier substances, they
effect nuclear reactions that produce a variety of particles.

FIGURE **30-12** *Cloud-chamber trail of a positron.*

cloud-chamber technique. Figure 30-12 is a
sketch of a famous photograph that he obtained.
At the time the photograph was taken the cloud
chamber was in a uniform magnetic field at
right angles to the plane of the paper. The lead
plate was about half a centimeter thick. The
density of the track and the power to penetrate
a sizable thickness of lead were the same as for
very fast electrons. The only effect of the lead
was to slow the particle down. Since the path
is more curved above the plate than below, the
particle was moving more slowly in the upper
half of the picture. Hence the direction of flight
was from the bottom of the chamber to the top.
From the direction of the magnetic field (into the
plane of the drawing), the charge on the particle,
then, must be positive. This rather simple photograph was the first definite evidence of the positron. Since then positrons have been produced
copiously in a variety of reactions. One source,
the artificially produced radioactive isotopes, will
be considered in the next section. The positron
of Figure 30-12 was undoubtedly produced by
cosmic rays bombarding the walls of the cloud
chamber.

The emission of a positron from a radioactive
nucleus means, not that positrons are constituents of nuclear structure, but, rather, that the

excess energy of the unstable nucleus activates the reaction†

$$p \longrightarrow {}_0n^1 + {}_{+1}e^0$$

This disintegration of a proton into a neutron and an ejected positron transmutes the nucleus into an element whose atomic number is 1 *lower* than that of the parent atom. This is very similar to the disintegration of neutrons to produce $\beta$-rays. Which reaction takes place in a radioactive nucleus depends on its particular energy instability. In either case the transition is toward the more stable situation of smaller energy for the nucleus.

Once produced, a positron does not exist for long. As it travels through matter, it ionizes, like an electron, and, losing KE, slows down. At a low velocity it may combine with an electron, the two revolving about each other momentarily and then colliding, the result being the annihilation of both. The total mass of the two is converted into energy, which is carried away by high-energy photons. There is much experimental evidence to verify this picture.

## 30-11. Artificial Radioactivity

In 1934 the Joliot-Curies discovered artificial radioactivity: the production, by a nuclear reaction, of a radioactive nucleus that is not found in nature. Such artificially produced nuclei decay with a definite half-life according to the same law that governs the disintegration of naturally radioactive substances (§ 27-4). Specifically, the Joliot-Curies observed that neutrons were ejected from aluminum bombarded by $\alpha$-particles from polonium according to the reaction

$$_2\text{He}^4 + {}_{13}\text{Al}^{27} \longrightarrow {}_{15}\text{P}^{30} + {}_0n^1 \qquad (30\text{-}9)$$

They noticed, however, that the sheet of aluminum continued to give off radiations even after the polonium was removed. The rays were soon

identified as positrons whose activity decayed with a half-life of 2.5 minutes. The source of the activity was determined in the following way. According to equation 30-9, the $\alpha$-particle was consumed in the reaction, the neutron was ejected, and the phosphorus produced remained as an impurity in the aluminum. After considerable bombardment the aluminum was quickly dissolved in acid, and a chemical separation of aluminum and phosphorus was performed. The aluminum fraction showed no activity, but the phosphorus fraction did. This showed that the phosphorus produced by the reaction of equation 30-9 was radioactive and decayed by the reaction

$$_{15}\text{P}^{30} \longrightarrow {}_{14}\text{Si}^{30} + {}_{+1}e^0 \quad (T = 2.5 \text{ min}) \quad (30\text{-}10)$$

In the reaction of equation 30-9 the phosphorus nucleus was left with an excess of energy; so, after an appropriate half-life, a proton disintegrated into a neutron. The excess mass-energy was carried away by the ejected positron, and the remaining nucleus, with one less proton, became the stable 30 isotope of silicon.

The Joliot-Curies produced other radioactive isotopes by $\alpha$-bombardment of light elements and suggested that bombardment by artificially accelerated particles would produce others. After the development of high-energy accelerators, many reactions using protons, deuterons, $\alpha$-particles, and neutrons as the bombarding agents were studied. Radioactive isotopes of *all* the elements have been produced. At present more than 900 species have been produced and identified.

Examples of deuteron and proton bombardment are

$$(\text{A}) \quad _1\text{H}^2 + {}_6\text{C}^{12} \longrightarrow {}_7\text{N}^{13} + {}_0n^1$$
$$\xrightarrow{\text{10 min}} {}_6\text{C}^{13} + {}_{+1}e^0$$
$$(\text{B}) \quad _1\text{H}^1 + {}_{52}\text{Te}^{130} \longrightarrow {}_{53}\text{I}^{130} + {}_0n^1 \quad \Big\} (30\text{-}11)$$
$$\xrightarrow{\text{12.6 hr}} {}_{54}\text{Xe}^{130} + {}_{-1}e^0$$

In A the deuteron transmutes the abundant stable isotope of carbon into a new isotope of nitrogen. The nitrogen 13 decays radioactively

---

† The symbol ${}_{+1}e^0$ represents the positron just as ${}_{-1}e^0$ represents the equally massive electron. Note that this reaction absorbs energy, the combined mass of the neutron and the positron being greater than that of the proton. Any energy supplied to the reaction in excess of this appears as KE of the ejected positron.

by positron emission, with a half-life of ten minutes, into the stable carbon 13 isotope, which is found in nature in low abundance (about 1%). In B the proton transmutes one of the stable isotopes of tellurium into a new isotope of iodine. Here the radioactive iodine is an electron emitter.

Although many reactions have been achieved with charged particles accelerated to high energies, by far the most effective projectile is the neutron. Since the neutron carries no charge, it can approach the target nucleus with ease even at low speeds. (A slow charged particle, of course, is repelled by the target nucleus and does not approach near enough to enter a reaction.) Examples of neutron reactions are

(A) $_0n^1 + {}_{13}Al^{27} \longrightarrow {}_{11}Na^{24} + {}_2He^4$

$\qquad$ $\overset{15 \text{ hr}}{\underset{\longrightarrow}{\big|}}$ $_{12}Mg^{24} + {}_{-1}e^0$

(B) $_0n^1 + {}_7N^{14} \longrightarrow {}_6C^{14} + {}_1H^1$

$\qquad$ $\overset{5,400 \text{ yr}}{\underset{\longrightarrow}{\big|}}$ $_7N^{14} + {}_{-1}e^0$ $\qquad$ (30-12)

(C) $_0n^1 + {}_{27}Co^{59} \longrightarrow {}_{27}Co^{60} + \gamma\text{-ray}$

$\qquad$ $\overset{5.3 \text{ yr}}{\underset{\longrightarrow}{\big|}}$ $_{28}Ni^{60} + {}_{-1}e^0$
$\qquad\qquad\qquad + \gamma\text{-ray}$

These reactions also transmute abundant stable isotopes into new radioactive isotopes that decay into stable isotopes found in nature. Reaction A is an example of the neutron-alpha ($n$-$\alpha$) type of reaction; an $\alpha$-particle is produced by neutron bombardment. Another class, called neutron-proton ($n$-$p$), is illustrated by B. The last reaction ($n$-$\gamma$) is an example of an important class called *neutron capture*. Here the neutron enters the nucleus (is "captured" by it) and forms a heavier isotope of the same element, which stabilizes by radiating a $\gamma$-ray photon. In some cases the new nucleus is completely stable, but in many it is radioactive, as in this example.†

---

† An interesting example of neutron capture is the formation of potassium 40 from the abundant potassium 39. Potassium 40 is an electron emitter with a very long half-life ($\sim 10^9$ years) and appears in nature in very low abundance ($\sim 0.01\%$). Perhaps it was produced by neutron capture in pre-terrestrial times and a trace still exists because of its long half-life.

For neutron capture *slow* neutrons are most effective. In passing through matter, neutrons may be slowed down by repeated impacts until they are moving with the average KE associated with the temperature of the material. These slow "thermal neutrons" may still approach a nucleus closely, however, and their chance of capture is greatly enhanced by their low speed. One very important use of neutron capture is the removal of thermal neutrons from a system. Cadmium is an exceptionally efficient trap for thermal neutrons.

The uses of radioactive isotopes are numerous and enter many fields, but only a few of them can be mentioned here. One important application of such isotopes is in their use as *tracers*. For instance, the radioactive iodine formed in reaction 30-11(B) has electronic structures, and therefore chemical properties, identical with those of ordinary, stable iodine. Hence, in any chemical reaction, the radioactive isotope behaves like the common, stable isotope. Since the radioactive property, however, as a nuclear process, is completely unaffected by chemical combination, the presence of the radio-isotope is easily detected in all circumstances by a Geiger counter or a similar device. Such devices are so sensitive that they record the disintegration of a single atom. Hence we need to add only minute amounts of a radio-isotope in order to trace the history of a particular element. We have already considered one example: a small amount of radioactive iodine permitted a direct verification of the dynamic character of equilibrium reactions (§ 23-3). Similarly, the motion of atoms in many physical experiments and in many commercial processes may be followed by the introduction of these "tagged" atoms.

The tracer-isotope technique is frequently used in medical and biological research. A simple example: we may measure the rate at which the blood stream carries sodium through the human body by feeding a person some table salt containing a trace of radioactive sodium (equation 30-12A) and measuring the time until a counter held in his hand begins to register. Similarly, the dispositions and concentrations of various elements in living organisms may be determined. A plant may be fed with a solution containing radio-phosphorus[†] and the assimilation traced with a counter. A still more informative method is to place a leaf or section of some other part of the plant on a photographic plate; the radiation from the radio-isotope will produce a "self-photograph" of the part. These radio-autographs clearly show the distribution and relative concentrations of the radio-isotope.

In many hospitals elaborate high-voltage X-ray equipment is being replaced by the radioactive cobalt 60 (equation 30-12c). For the treatment of deep-seated tumors the $\gamma$-rays emitted are as effective as X-rays produced by several million volts. In organic chemistry the use of the radioactive $C^{11}$ and $C^{14}$ isotopes is of the greatest importance in tracing the fate of carbon atoms.

An unexpected use of $C^{14}$ is the dating of archaeological findings. The carbon dioxide in the atmosphere has a small but constant concentration of $C^{14}$. This is steadily disintegrating, to be sure, with a half-life of 5,400 years. Presumably, however, neutrons resulting from cosmic-ray bombardment combine with the nitrogen of the atmosphere (equation 30-12B) to form $C^{14}$ at the proper rate to maintain the constant concentration. By photosynthesis this radioactive carbon is incorporated into the structure of all living plants and hence into all animals feeding on plants and into all animals feeding on those animals. When the plant or animal dies, this process stops, and further generation of $C^{14}$ in the organism is negligible for two reasons: (1) the organism is not as accessible to cosmic rays as the upper atmosphere; (2) the concentration of nitrogen in the organism is much lower than in the atmosphere. Hence, when the organism dies, the $C^{14}$ content disintegrates without replacement. Here, then, is a clock that runs for thousands of years and with which it is possible to determine archaeological dates by the measurement of $C^{14}$ radioactivity. This radio-carbon dating has become a powerful tool in many investigations.

---

[†] Here the radio-isotope $P^{32}$, made from ordinary $P^{31}$ by deuteron-proton reaction, is more useful than the $P^{30}$ of equation 30-10 because the half-life of $P^{32}$ is about fourteen days.

## 30-12. Missing Elements; Trans-uranium Elements

In Chapter 8 we saw that in the periodic listing of the elements it was necessary to leave a number of gaps, which indicated the existence of yet undiscovered elements (§ 8-7). Some of these predicted elements were soon discovered, and, as we have seen (§ 27-1), the radioactive polonium (No. 84) was later isolated by the Curies. Technetium (No. 43), however, evaded detection, although its existence was again predicted by Moseley (§ 25-9).

In 1937 technetium was produced artificially. By neutron capture the stable 98 isotope of molybdenum was converted to the radioactive isotope $_{42}Mo^{99}$, which, by electron emission, becomes $_{43}Tc^{99}$. This technetium isotope, however, is also radioactive and has a half-life of $2 \times 10^5$ years. Other isotopes of technetium, ranging in mass number from 92 to 102, have also been produced, but all are radioactive, with half-lives no longer than that of the 99 isotope. Geologically, $10^5$ years is a short time; if any of these isotopes existed during the formation of the earth, they have long since disappeared. It is not impossible that the 98 isotope (which has not been produced) might have a long enough half-life to exist in nature; but it is quite certain that no stable isotope of technetium can exist. Similarly, a number of isotopes of promethium ($Z = 61$), astatine ($Z = 85$), and francium ($Z = 87$) have been produced artificially, and all have been found to be radioactive, with short half-lives. These "missing elements" are no longer missing, but it is not expected that they will be found in nature. Thus a final and complete justification of the periodic classification and of the predictions made in 1870 by Mendeleev on the basis of this classification has been achieved.

Since 1939 another group of elements not found in nature, with atomic numbers greater than 92, have been produced. The first two of these trans-uranium elements are produced when a *slow* neutron is captured by the nucleus of $_{92}U^{238}$, the abundant isotope of uranium. The reactions are as follows:

$$_0n^1 + {}_{92}U^{238} \longrightarrow {}_{92}U^{239} + \gamma\text{-ray}$$
$$\left.\begin{array}{ll} {}_{92}U^{239} \longrightarrow {}_{93}Np^{239} + {}_{-1}e^0 & T = 23 \text{ min} \\ {}_{93}Np^{239} \longrightarrow {}_{94}Pu^{239} + {}_{-1}e^0 & T = 2.3 \text{ days} \\ {}_{94}Pu^{239} \longrightarrow {}_{92}U^{235} + {}_2He^4 & T = 24{,}100 \text{ years} \end{array}\right\} (30\text{-}13)$$

Here the short-lived uranium 239 emits an electron and becomes neptunium (atomic number 93). This in turn emits an electron to form plutonium (94). Plutonium emits $\alpha$-particles and forms the rare ($\sim 0.7\%$ abundant) 235 isotope of naturally occurring uranium. As we shall see, plutonium is a very useful source of nuclear energy.

By bombardment of plutonium 239 with 40 Mev helium nuclei from a cyclotron, two isotopes (240 and 242) of element 96 were produced in 1944. These are $\alpha$-emitters with half-lives of one month and five months. By similar methods a number of isotopes for all atomic numbers up to and including 102 have been synthesized and identified. All are radioactive, and all have short half-lives. They are very similar chemically, and, since they have a metallic character, their names end with *ium* (p. 96). Starting with atomic number 95, they are americium (Am, 95), curium (Cm, 96), berkelium (Bk, 97), californium (Cf, 98), einsteinium (E, 99), fermium (Fm, 100), mendelevium (Md, 101), and nobelium (No, 102).

The naming of these elements is of interest. Uranium had been named for Uranus, which, for many years, was the outermost known planet of the solar system. Then Neptune was discovered beyond Uranus, and still later Pluto was discovered beyond Neptune. This provided a neatly logical way of naming the first two trans-uranium elements (93 and 94). The rest, however, had to be named by more conventional methods. Several elements (scandium, gallium, and germanium) had been named for the countries in which they were discovered, and americium is in line with this custom. Much of the work of synthesizing new elements was done at the University of *California* at *Berkeley,* which accounts for elements 98 and 97. Marie Curie, Einstein, Enrico Fermi, and Mendeleev all made important contributions to our understanding of the elements; Nobel is honored for establishing the prizes that bear his name.

## 30-13. Nuclear Energy

We have already seen, in our study of nuclear reactions, that enormous amounts of energy are potentially available as a result of these reactions. As a comparison we may consider the heat derived from burning coal, one very common source of energy. Coal is mostly carbon, and the reaction $C + O_2 \rightarrow CO_2$ releases about $10^5$ calories per mole of carbon. This would change about a third of a pint of water into steam for driving electric generators in a power plant. If we divide these calories by Avogadro's number and convert to electron volts, however, we find that the reaction releases only about 4 ev per carbon *atom*. The hydrogen-lithium nuclear reaction (equation 30-6) releases about 17 Mev per lithium atom, which is more than four million times as great as the energy derived from the oxidation of carbon. Hence, if it could be brought about, the nuclear reaction of a mole of lithium with hydrogen would produce enough calories to convert more than a million pints of water into steam. The "lithium pile" for such a generating plant could be very small indeed compared with the usual coal piles of power plants. Unfortunately, a mixture of hydrogen and lithium will not react spontaneously and release this store of energy. But neither will a mixture of oxygen and carbon under ordinary conditions. What is needed in each case is that at least one of the reactants move with sufficient KE to overcome the forces of mutual repulsion and approach near enough for the reaction to take place. In the oxidation of carbon, which involves the outer valence electrons, this energy is small (less than 1 ev); heating the mixture is enough to make a large number of atoms react. When enough atoms react, the heat evolved maintains the temperature, and the mixture reacts completely. In the hydrogen-lithium reaction we have a similar situation but a greater order of magnitude. As the reaction was reported in equation 30-6, the hydrogen nuclei have a KE of 0.3 Mev. Repetitions of the experiment show, however, that the reaction can occur with protons of about 0.1 Mev (slower ones cannot approach the lithium nucleus close enough to react). Protons of this or greater energy are easily produced, of course, by the accelerator. But most of the protons so produced quickly lose KE by ionizing the lithium and begin to move too slowly to produce a reaction. Only rarely does a proton hit the exceedingly small target presented by the lithium nucleus with sufficient energy to react. This situation could be treated, in principle, in the same way as the oxidation of carbon. A mixture of hydrogen and lithium could be heated so that a large number of hydrogen atoms would have sufficient energy to react. This would release enough energy to maintain the temperature until the whole mixture had reacted. But an average thermal energy of 0.1 Mev requires a formidable temperature. To have even a small fraction of the atoms (sufficient to start the gross reaction) moving with this energy would require a temperature of many millions of degrees. The interiors of the sun and other stars are undoubtedly that hot, but such temperatures are not produced in the laboratory.

This discussion has illustrated the general principle that, although a system may be potentially capable of delivering a large amount of energy, a certain amount of energy must be supplied to start the process. A simple example is the large boulder resting in a small depression high on the side of a mountain. If we do the work that will lift the boulder over the edge of the depression, it will roll down the mountain and release a large amount of energy. The energy required to start a process is usually called its *activation energy*. For most chemical reactions the activation energy is small. For the type of nuclear reactions that we have considered so far the activation energy is very large. Such reactions promise enormous energy and, as we shall see later, account for the prodigious quantities of energy radiated by the stars. We have not yet been able to tap this store of energy for useful purposes, but doing so is not beyond the realm of possibility.

Another aspect of nuclear energies is that they furnish a measure of the stability of atoms. As we have seen, any atom is composed of $Z$ protons, $A - Z$ neutrons, and $Z$ orbital electrons. These particles are held together in a

stable isotope by appropriate forces. The orbital electrons are bound to the atom by the familiar electric forces. The protons and the neutrons are held together in the nucleus by the *specifically nuclear forces*. The nature of these nuclear forces is not well understood, and a great deal of contemporary research is directed toward discovering their character. Suppose now that all the particles of a neutral atom are separated to such an extent that the forces between them are negligible. Since this would require a definite amount of work, the group of particles would have more energy when dissociated than when assembled in the neutral atom. The difference between the total energy of the separated particles and the total energy of the particles in the neutral atom is called the *binding energy of the atom*. Though we cannot calculate the binding energy in terms of force times distance (for we do not know the nature of the nuclear forces), we expect, according to the principle of equivalence between mass and energy, that the particles, as they are assembled, will lose energy and that this energy will be supplied by a decrease in the masses of the particles. Hence we expect the mass of a neutral atom to be somewhat less than the sum of the masses of its constituent particles in a free state. This is always found to be so. The masses of the atoms are accurately determined by the mass spectrograph, and, as we have seen, the masses of free electrons, protons, and neutrons are also accurately known. The binding energies, then, are known to high precision although the forces responsible for these energies are not completely understood.

As a simple example of binding energy, let us consider the deuterium atom ($_1H^2$). This is composed of one proton, one neutron, and one electron. The sum of the masses of these particles in the free state is 2.01712, but the mass of $_1H^2$ is 2.01473, or 0.00239 amu less. This is equivalent to 2.224 Mev, which is the binding energy of the deuterium atom. Since removing the electron requires only about 14 ev (the ionization energy), practically all the binding energy is due to the coalesced proton and neutron.† To dissociate the deuteron into a proton

---

† This is generally so. Even for the heaviest ele-

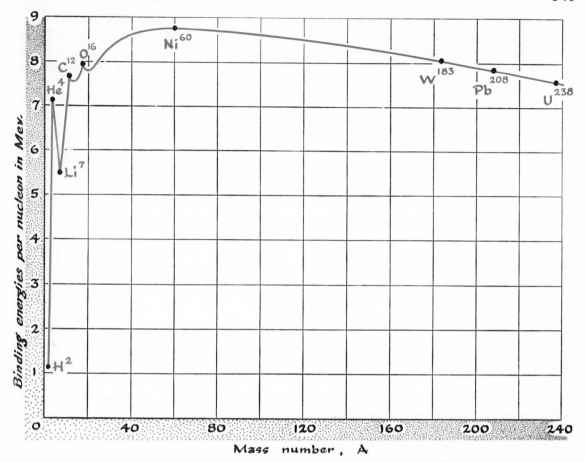

FIGURE **30-13** *Graph of binding energy per nucleon against atomic mass number.*

and a neutron should, then, require 2.224 Mev. This is found to be so (§ 30-9). In a similar way, the reader can easily show that the binding energy of $He^4$ is 28.3 Mev, of $C^{12}$ is 92.1 Mev, and of $O^{16}$ is 127.3 Mev. As we go up the periodic table, the arithmetic becomes more tedious, but no more complicated. For $Ni^{60}$ we find 528 Mev and for $U^{238}$ 1,802 Mev as the binding energies of the atoms.

The calculation of the binding energies of all the atoms yields an interesting regularity, which is best seen if we consider the binding energy per nucleon, a quantity that we arrive at by dividing the binding energy of the atom by the mass number. For $Ni^{60}$, for instance, we get 528 Mev/60, or 8.8 Mev per nucleon. In the forma-

tion of this nucleus, in other words, *each* proton and neutron, on the average, lost a mass equivalent to 8.8 Mev. The result of similar calculations for all the atoms is shown by Figure 30-13. The first striking feature of this graph is that, with the exception of a few light elements, the binding energy per nucleon is approximately constant throughout a very wide range of mass number. This unexpected result tells us that the specifically nuclear forces, whatever their detailed nature, must act over such extremely small distances that any particular nucleon is appreciably attracted only by its immediate neighbor. If this were not so, it would require much more energy to remove a nucleon from tungsten ($W^{183}$), say, with 182 others to attract it, than to remove a nucleon from magnesium ($A = 24$), with only 23 others to attract it. The data, however, show that the bind-

---

ments, with few exceptions, the binding energies of the orbital electrons are negligibly small compared with those of the nucleons (that is, protons and neutrons).

ing energy per nucleon for these two widely separated nuclei is the same, 8.0 Mev.

Of more interest for the present discussion, however, is the small variation that we do find in the binding energy per nucleon. After the lighter elements the curve rises slowly to a maximum of about 8.8 Mev, remains practically unchanged to about $A = 100$, and then gradually decreases to about 7.6 Mev for $U^{238}$. This tells us that the most stable nuclei are those in the *middle* of the periodic table, since here the binding energy per nucleon is greatest. The peaks at $He^4$, $C^{12}$, and $O^{16}$ show that among the lighter elements these three have particularly stable nuclei.† In general, any process that reassembles the nucleons in nuclei nearer the center of the periodic table should release energy, since in this region the nucleons have the smallest mass—that is, the greatest binding energy. This applies especially to the lighter elements, for in general the curve rises most steeply at low mass number. Reaction 30-8(B) is one example; the activation energies of such reactions are, however, rather high. Another example is the uranium-radium radioactive series (§ 27-4), in which each $\alpha$-emission leaves the daughter nucleus with a smaller mass number and—in this part of the periodic table—a larger binding energy per nucleon. Thus the KE of the emitted $\alpha$-particles is supplied by this decrease in the mass-energy of the remaining nucleons.

## 30-14. Fission

Since all the reactions we have considered so far have involved the absorption or emission of light particles, such as protons, neutrons, and $\alpha$-particles, only small displacements along the graph of Figure 30-13 have occurred. A new type of process, called **nuclear fission,** was discovered in 1939. Neutron bombardment of uranium produced a substance that resembled the alkaline-earth metals. Since, as we have pointed out, all previous reactions had produced only small changes in atomic number, it was first thought that this product was radium;

---

† These are the ones that resisted transmutation in the early experiments with $\alpha$-bombardment.

but chemical analysis soon indicated an isotope of barium, and the indication was verified when the product was found to be radioactive with the same half-life as $_{56}Ba^{139}$. If barium ($Z = 56$) is obtained from uranium ($Z = 92$), the other product must be krypton ($Z = 36$). Here is a completely new type of reaction. The neutron entering the uranium nucleus gives up its binding energy and makes the composite nucleus so unstable that it splits ("*fissions*") into two approximately equal parts. The interpretation was soon verified with a cloud chamber. A thin film of uranium in the chamber was bombarded by neutrons. Two very densely ionized trails of approximately equal length were observed to leave the film in opposite directions. Further study of the partially separated isotopes of uranium showed that it was the rare $_{92}U^{235}$ that split.

The fission of $U^{235}$ does not always produce barium and krypton. A variety of other pairs of nuclei may be produced, but in all cases the fragments are of approximately equal size and are therefore atoms near the center of the periodic table. One such reaction is

$$_{0}n^1 + {}_{92}U^{235} \longrightarrow {}_{51}Sb^{133} + {}_{41}Nb^{99} + 4{}_{0}n^1$$
$$Q \approx 200 \text{ Mev!} \qquad (30\text{-}14)$$

This illustrates several characteristic features of fission reactions. First, the products (in this case antimony and niobium) are near the middle of the table but have mass numbers that are much larger than those of their stable isotopes. This means that they have an excess of neutrons and are radioactive. Products of fission usually stabilize by several successive $\beta$-emissions, and they also emit many $\gamma$-rays. Second, the products of fission appear near the middle of the binding-energy curve of Figure 30-13, and the reactant (uranium) is on the extreme right of the curve. Here, in one process, is an increase in the binding energy per nucleon that results in an enormous release of energy. Calculations and experiment show this energy to be about 200 Mev per fission. Third, neutrons are among the products of fission. This is to be expected. The ratio of neutrons to protons [that is, $(A - Z)/Z$] is larger for the heaviest elements than for elements near the middle of the periodic table. The uranium nucleus therefore has more neutrons than the lighter fission products need. Many experiments show that two or three neutrons are emitted immediately upon fission. After an appreciable time, a few more are emitted by the fission products before they start stabilizing by $\beta$-emission. The importance of neutrons among the fission products is that they are available for further fission processes and thus make possible a self-sustaining "chain reaction" that releases an enormous amount of energy. The 200 Mev of equation 30-14 represents about 0.1 percent of the mass of the uranium atom. The complete fission of a kilogram of uranium would convert one gram of mass to almost $10^{14}$ joules. It would take almost a week for a large power plant to generate so much energy.

It is now known that many of the heavy elements will split (undergo fission) if bombarded with particles of high enough energy; a large KE, in addition to the binding energy of the particle, is needed to make the nucleus unstable enough for fission. For $U^{235}$, however, the binding energy of the captured neutron is sufficient; so neutrons of any energy will cause fission. And, since the chance of capture increases as the speed of the neutron decreases, slow neutrons are much more effective than fast ones. In fact, thermal neutrons ($\approx 0.04$ ev) are the most effective for producing fission of $U^{235}$. The plutonium isotope $Pu^{239}$, which is produced from the abundant $U^{238}$ (equation 30-13), and the uranium isotope $U^{233}$ are also fissionable by slow neutrons. This last isotope is produced from the thorium isotope $_{90}Th^{232}$. By neutron capture $Th^{233}$ is formed, and this, after two successive $\beta$-emissions, yields $_{92}U^{233}$.

In summary, then, we find that the curve of the binding energies of atoms reveals two possible methods of releasing nuclear energy. Both the *fusion* of light elements into heavier ones, and the *fission* of heavy elements into lighter ones, produce large amounts of energy. The fact that most of these reactions require high-energy particles for activation makes it difficult to maintain them in gross samples of the substances. Three substances, however (one found with low abundance in nature and two man-made ones), are fissionable by neutrons of any speed and es-pecially by slow neutrons. This, combined with the fact that neutrons are among the fission products, makes possible a self-sustaining chain reaction and the continuous release of nuclear energy.

## 30-15. *Bombs*

Any bomb is simply a rapid and uncontrolled reaction that suddenly releases a large amount of energy and thereby produces a high temperature and a violent expansion. After the discovery of uranium fission, it was soon realized that the possibility of a chain reaction made feasible the construction of a military bomb of unprecedented destructiveness. Calculations showed that, if a mass of reasonable size of pure uranium 235 were assembled, a sudden release of an enormous energy would result. The technical details are complicated, but the principles are simple.

Consider a mass of pure uranium 235. Starting the reaction is no problem, for it requires only one neutron, and there are always a few neutrons available, either as the result of a rare spontaneous fission or as components of the ever-present cosmic rays. One of these neutrons will activate the fission of a uranium atom, which, as we have seen, will produce two or three "prompt" neutrons—that is, neutrons produced simultaneously with fission. These neutrons, if they are not "lost," are available for activating further fissions. There are two major causes of the "loss" of neutrons. The first is the presence of impurities. We have already seen that neutrons may enter into nuclear reactions with almost any nucleus, but very few of these reactions have neutrons among the products. Hence a neutron entering such a reaction is effectively "lost" so far as further fission is concerned. The first requirement of a self-sustaining chain reaction of fission is, therefore, that the uranium 235 be extremely pure. (Impurities as slight as a few parts per million can be serious.) The second cause of the loss of neutrons is that the high energy (about 1 Mev, on the average) with which the fission neutrons are produced makes it possible for them to escape through the surface of the uranium mass before they have had a chance to produce further fission. Such loss is reduced if the size of the assembled mass of uranium is increased. This is a matter of simple geometry. Suppose the mass to be spherical. The area of a sphere is proportional to the square of the diameter, but the volume is proportional to the cube of the diameter. Hence, if we took a sphere of uranium of twice the diameter of another sphere, the area (and thus the chance of escape) would be four times as large. But the volume (and thus the number of atoms and hence the chance of capture) would be *eight* times as large. The chance of maintaining a chain reaction therefore increases with the mass of uranium assembled. Clearly, then (assuming no neutron loss to impurities), the maintenance of a chain reaction depends on the mass of the sample of uranium. If the mass is too small, more neutrons will escape than are produced, and the reaction will quickly die out. At a particular *critical mass* the reaction will be just self-sustaining. For simplicity assume that two neutrons are produced by each fission. If only one of these is lost from the mass, the other is available for another fission, and so on. Thus, for this critical mass, the reaction will just continue—neither dying out nor growing. If the critical mass is exceeded, however, the rate of reaction increases rapidly to catastrophic proportions. Assume now—again for simplicity—that neither of the two neutrons from each fission is lost. Then the fission of one atom will cause the fission of two more, which, supplying four neutrons, will cause the fission of four more atoms; the neutrons from these four fissions will cause the fission of eight other atoms, and so on. In an extremely short time this process will have split most of the atoms, and an enormous energy will have been released.

The critical size is not large. The data necessary for an exact calculation are not available to the public, but a sphere 10 cm in diameter is probably not far from the precise value. A bomb, then, consists of several pieces of uranium 235, each less than the critical size, arranged in such a way that they may be assembled quickly into one supercritical mass. The assembly must be very rapid, for otherwise the reaction, starting as the critical mass was reached, would blow off the pieces arriving later, before they had a chance to react. This rapid assembly may be accomplished by shooting the pieces together with an ordinary explosive.

The bomb is enclosed in an envelope, which serves two purposes. First, this envelope, sometimes called the "tamper," consists of a material that reflects back into the bomb many of the neutrons that might otherwise escape from the reacting mass; since the tamper material has a low probability of neutron capture, most of the neutrons rebound elastically. Beryllium oxide and carbon are good neutron reflectors. The second purpose of the envelope is to hold the reacting mass together long enough for most of the uranium to undergo fission. This, to be sure, is a very short time, perhaps of the order of $10^{-4}$ sec. But in a fraction of this time sufficient energy is released to vaporize the materials. Hence, if not contained, the system would expand and the reaction stop as a result of neutron loss. The inertia of the envelope is great enough to retard the expansion sufficiently to give the explosion time to develop. Under these conditions an enormous temperature (comparable to that at the interior of the sun) and a devastating blast are produced. It is customary to gauge the strength of these "atomic" bombs by the amount of TNT (a common chemical high explosive) that would produce an equivalent blast. The first atomic bombs were equivalent to about 20,000 tons of TNT.

We have already pointed out that the artificially produced plutonium 239 is fissionable in much the same way as uranium 235. The first task in the construction of the atomic bomb, then, was the accumulation of enough of these fissionable materials to make possible the assembly of a supercritical mass; and it was this task that constituted the major effort during the war. Plutonium is produced from the abundant 238 isotope of uranium according to the reactions of equation 30-13. But production in quantity presented formidable engineering problems, some of which we shall discuss in the next section. Once produced, however, plutonium has a distinct advantage: it can be separated and purified by chemical methods. Uranium 235, however, cannot be separated from naturally occurring uranium by chemical methods; although it is readily available, its separation in quantity from the abundant 238 presented difficult problems.

In order to separate the uranium isotopes, we have to rely on their slightly different masses. In one method, using the mass spectrograph, the same magnetic force bends the lighter 235 along a more curved path; the separated beams, instead of falling on a photographic plate (Fig. 18-10), pass through slits, and the atoms are collected in suitable containers. Since the ordinary mass spectrograph, designed for precise mass determinations, uses an extremely small ion current, the separation of gross amounts of material would require a fantastically long time. One project of the war effort was to design a mass spectrograph that operated with large ion currents. This was accomplished by Lawrence and his collaborators at Berkeley and resulted in the construction of an enormous magnetic separator called a *calutron*. Many such units were put into operation at Oak Ridge, Tennessee, and appreciable amounts of uranium 235 were gradually accumulated.

A second method of separating isotopes depends upon the rate of gaseous diffusion. In our study of the kinetic theory we found that the rates of diffusion of two gases are inversely proportional to the square root of their masses (p. 182). Hence, if a mixture of the gases is allowed to diffuse through a porous barrier, the lighter diffuses more rapidly, and a partial separation is achieved; that is, the gases that diffuse through the barrier form a mixture with a higher concentration of the lighter gas, while the remaining gases form a mixture with a higher concentration of the heavier gas, than the original mixture. Repeated fractionations of this kind eventually effect an almost complete separation. Uranium hexafluoride is a gas, and, since there is only one stable fluorine isotope ($A = 19$), it is a mixture of $U^{238}F_6$ and $U^{235}F_6$. Since these gases have molecular weights of 392 and 389 respectively, the square root of the ratio of the heavier to the lighter is only about 1.0003. Hence, if uranium hexafluoride made from natural uranium is pumped through a porous barrier, the lighter $U^{235}F_6$ diffuses only slightly more rapidly and

produces a fractional increase in its concentration of only 1.003. Since natural uranium contains only 0.7 percent $U^{235}$, several thousand repeated fractionations are required to produce 99 percent pure $U^{235}F_6$. Several such diffusion plants have been constructed, with thousands of pumps to circulate the gas between diffusion stages and acres of barrier area.

It was possible during the war, then, to separate enough fissionable material to construct atomic bombs and to verify the theoretical calculations for their explosion. The magnitude of the operation can be appreciated if we remember that in every kilogram of natural uranium there is only 0.007 kgm of $U^{235}$, which, separated with great difficulty, is exploded in quantities from 1 to 100 kgm per bomb. The production of $Pu^{239}$ is also a slow and complicated process.

Enormously destructive as the uranium or plutonium bomb is, fusion reactions can produce explosions that are larger by several orders of magnitude. As we have seen, the production of helium by the fusion of light elements results in a large release of energy, but, since the activation energy is high, the only way to start a chain fusion reaction is to raise the temperature of the reactants. Once the reaction is started, the energy released maintains the local temperature, and the chain proceeds until the reactants are consumed. Nuclear reactions that are maintained by the high temperature of the reactants are called **thermonuclear reactions.** We have already seen that the necessary temperatures are enormous but probably not greater than those attained in a fission bomb. A thermonuclear bomb may consist, then, of a mixture of suitable light elements assembled round a fission bomb. Presumably the fission explosion raises the temperature of the mixture sufficiently to activate the thermonuclear reactions, and the whole device explodes with terrifying violence.

It is a matter of common knowledge that such thermonuclear devices have been constructed and exploded. The details are not available to the public, but we may guess at a possible combination. First we look at the various known reactions between the isotopes of hydrogen. We pick hydrogen because, with a single nuclear charge, it offers the minimum repulsion between reacting nuclei. In addition to $_1H^1$ and $_1H^2$, there is a third hydrogen isotope called tritium ($_1H^3$). Tritium, extremely rare in nature, may be produced at great expense according to the reaction

$$_0n^1 + {}_3Li^6 \longrightarrow {}_1H^3 + {}_2He^4$$

It is radioactive, but, since its half-life is 12.5 years, it may be stored for some time. Among the three hydrogen isotopes there are six known reactions. Some have too low a probability and therefore too low a reaction rate to be useful for explosives. The reaction between $H^1$ and $H^2$, which produces $_2He^3$ (a very rare stable isotope of helium), must be excluded because the other product is a $\gamma$-ray; most of the energy released would be radiated out of the system and would not be available for maintaining the necessary temperature. The two most probable reactions are

$$
\begin{aligned}
\text{(A)} \quad {}_1H^3 + {}_1H^3 &\longrightarrow {}_2He^4 + 2{}_0n^1 \\
Q &= 11 \text{ Mev} \\
\text{(B)} \quad {}_1H^2 + {}_1H^3 &\longrightarrow {}_2He^4 + {}_0n^1 \\
Q &= 17.6 \text{ Mev}
\end{aligned}
\quad (30\text{-}15)
$$

Although reaction A is faster, we choose B for our bomb for three reasons: (1) it will almost certainly chain-react at the temperature of a fission explosion; (2) only one of the reactants is the costly tritium; (3) it releases over 50 percent more energy.

We might imagine a small plutonium bomb surrounded by a mixture of deuterium and tritium, which we have liquefied in order to concentrate the reacting nuclei. We might include all this in an envelope of solid lithium hydride. When the plutonium exploded, the high temperature would certainly start the $H^2$-$H^3$ reaction. It is quite possible that the energy released by this reaction would raise the temperature sufficiently to start the hydrogen-lithium reaction between the concentrated nuclei of the solid lithium hydride. This, of course, is only one guess, and other combinations are possible. Whatever their composition may be, thermonuclear bombs releasing an energy equivalent of ten million tons of TNT have been detonated.

As we have seen, a great variety of products are formed by fission, and all of them are radioactive. These products are blown high into the atmosphere by the blast of a nuclear bomb. Caught by the winds of the upper atmosphere, they are carried for many miles and gradually settle to the earth over a wide area. Many of these radioactive products have short half-lives and soon disappear. Some, however, have half-lives of many years, and the *radioactive fall-out* of these substances could be a serious hazard to life.

## 30-16. Nuclear Reactors

A nuclear reactor is a device in which a self-sustaining nuclear reaction is maintained. Although, strictly speaking, the bombs discussed in the previous section are nuclear reactors, the term usually refers to a device in which the chain reaction proceeds at a *controlled* rate and not explosively. As we have seen, the rate at which a fission chain reaction proceeds depends upon the number of neutrons produced in successive generations by the fission process. This is expressed by the **multiplication factor, k,** which is defined as the ratio of the numbers of neutrons in any two successive generations. The significance of this factor can be understood by a comparison with a human population. Some adults may produce no children at all while others may produce several. If, however, *on the average,* one child is born for each adult before he or she dies, then each successive generation will have the same number of people, and the population will be stationary. For this situation $k$ would be unity. Similarly, in a reacting mass of fissionable material, some neutrons may escape or be captured by impurities before striking another fissionable nucleus; others will cause fission that produces several new neutrons. For $k = 1$ these processes average out to maintain a constant population of neutrons, and the chain reaction proceeds at a steady rate. If $k$ becomes less than 1, the reaction dies out; if $k$ becomes more than 1, the reaction rapidly expands.

Clearly, for the steady production of nuclear energy, the critical situation of $k = 1$ must be maintained. We could accomplish this, in principle, by adjusting the size and shape of the assembled materials. But this would be a highly unstable equilibrium. The slightest fluctuation of $k$ from unity would be enhanced by the nature of the process, and the reactor would either stop or explode. A control that will hold $k$ at unity is required, and this is supplied by control rods inserted into the reactor. These rods are made of substances with a high probability for neutron capture (§ 30-11). We have already mentioned cadmium as an exceptionally good neutron absorber. Boron and hafnium are also used in control rods. As these rods are inserted into the reactor to greater or lesser depths, more or fewer neutrons are absorbed, and fluctuations of the neutron population are controlled.

We can imagine the construction of a reactor to be somewhat as follows: A core of fissionable material is assembled in such a way that, when no control rods are inserted, the value of $k$ is slightly greater than 1, perhaps 1.001, and, when control rods are inserted to the maximum depth, enough neutrons are absorbed to reduce $k$ to a value somewhat less than 1, at which point the assembly is sub-critical and the core is inactive. The core is surrounded by a reflecting blanket (carbon or beryllium oxide) to reduce neutron loss. The whole assembly must be enclosed in a shield to protect the operating personnel from the γ-rays emitted by the fission products and from neutrons escaping from the reactor. Such a shield might consist of a layer of cadmium to absorb the neutrons and a layer of lead to absorb the γ-rays, but it would be very expensive, and therefore, unless size is extremely important, a thick wall of concrete is used to reduce the radiation intensities to safe values.

When, to start the reactor, one withdraws the control rods, the neutron density begins to increase. The number of neutrons may be monitored by a $BF_3$ counter (§ 30-8) placed inside the core. When the neutron density reaches the desired value, the rods are set for $k = 1$, and the activity of the reactor levels off to a constant rate. If the multiplication factor starts to fluctuate, it is brought back to unity by either withdrawal or insertion of the rods by the appropriate amount. This, of course, is not done manually. The motion of the rods is controlled automatically by mechanisms that are capable of holding the variation in the reaction rate to about one part in ten thousand.

Rapid as the mechanical adjustment of the control rods is, it would still be much too slow if there were no *delayed* neutrons in the fission process. Most of the neutrons are emitted immediately upon fission, but about 0.75 percent of them are emitted by some of the fission products as much as a minute after fission occurs. In a fission bomb only the prompt neutrons are used, a fact that accounts for its almost instantaneous explosion. In a reactor, however, the materials are arranged so that $k$ would be slightly less than 1 (0.998, say) if there were only prompt neutrons. The contribution to $k$ of the delayed neutrons (not more than 0.0075) is sufficient to make the total $k$ greater than one. It is therefore only the delayed neutrons that the rods need to control. Because the emission process delays these neutrons by almost a minute, the control rods have ample time to operate.

The energy released in the reactor appears as kinetic energy of the fission products. Since this energy is rapidly shared by impact with other atoms, the whole reactor would soon become very hot if there were no cooling mechanism. A coolant is circulated through the reactor to carry away the heat as fast as it is generated. Air is the simplest coolant, but, because of its low thermal capacity, great quantities would have to be circulated at enormous speeds to keep the reactor at a tolerable temperature. Ordinary water has good thermal properties, but appreciable numbers of neutrons are captured by the hydrogen to form deuterium; heavy water (deuterium oxide) does not have this difficulty but is expensive. In either case, if the reactor is to operate at a high temperature, the water must be under very high pressure to keep the boiling point above the temperature of the reactor. A liquid-metal alloy of sodium and potassium can operate at lower pressures, but the technology of such liquids presents other problems. All these substances, each with its advantages and disadvantages, have been used as coolants in various reactors. Much work is still to be done in this area.

The heat carried away by the coolant, transferred to ordinary water in a "heat exchanger," will generate steam. This steam can be made to run a turbine, which may drive an electric generator or propel a ship. Everyone has heard of the submarine *Nautilus,* which has traveled more than "20,000 leagues under the sea" on its original charge of nuclear fuel. The fuel for the type of reactor we have described could be $Pu^{239}$, $U^{233}$, or uranium greatly enriched in $U^{235}$. As we have seen, $U^{235}$ occurs in nature in small amounts, but the first two must be made from non-fissionable materials.

The first reactors built during the war were designed primarily for the production of $Pu^{239}$, which is produced from $U^{238}$ by an *n-γ* reaction (§ 30-12). Such a reactor presents more difficult problems than the type which we have described, mainly because of the peculiarities of the two important reactions involved. The fission of $U^{235}$ can be effected by neutrons of any speed, but the chance of fission increases as the neutron speed decreases, the greatest probability being for thermal neutrons ($\approx 1/40$ ev). In pure $U^{235}$ (as in a bomb) this is not important, for the high concentration increases the chance of reaction, and the chain can be maintained by fast neutrons. In natural uranium, however, the concentration of $U^{235}$ is only one part in 140; so this low concentration must be counterbalanced by a high probability of fission reaction; that is, the neutrons must be *thermalized*. This might be possible if it were not for a property (called resonance) of the *n-γ* reaction of $U^{238}$. For neutrons of about 11 ev energy the probability of this reaction increases several thousand times. We can picture the fate of the neutrons in a mass of natural uranium somewhat as follows: A $U^{235}$ fission throws out several high-energy neutrons, which, by elastic collision (mostly with $U^{238}$), start losing energy. As they acquire an energy of about 11 ev, they are mostly swallowed up by $U^{238}$ to form $U^{239}$, which leads to the production of $Pu^{239}$. This, of course, is what is desired. So many neutrons are captured, however, that those that remain and slow down further to the thermal-energy range are not enough to cause sufficient fissions of $U^{235}$ to maintain the chain.

The problem, then, was to slow down the neutrons rapidly and carry a sufficient number past the resonance energy to maintain the chain. This was accomplished by mixing the uranium with a material called a **moderator.** A moderator must have two properties: (1) it must be an element light enough to absorb, on elastic impact, a large fraction of a neutron's energy and thus to slow the neutrons rapidly; (2) it must have a very low probability for a neutron reaction (otherwise neutrons would be lost by reaction rather than merely slowed down). The hydrogen of ordinary water would satisfy the first requirement to the greatest degree since hydrogen is the lightest element, but the reaction of hydrogen with thermal neutrons has a high enough probability to produce a serious absorption of neutrons. The deuterium of heavy water (deuterium oxide) is a good moderator since deuterium and thermal neutrons do not react. Helium is a gas and forms no solid compounds. Lithium and boron are highly reactive with thermal neutrons, but beryllium and carbon have very low probabilities of reaction. Of the six lightest elements, therefore, deuterium, beryllium, and carbon are the ones most suitable as moderators. Deuterium is ideal according to both criteria, but deuterium was not available during the war. (Reactors moderated by heavy water are now being built.) Carbon, although heavier than desired, has a much lower probability of neutron capture than beryllium. Pure carbon (graphite) was the moderator used in the first reactors.

A uranium-graphite reactor, then, is essentially a large block of graphite with rods of pure uranium inserted in it at regular intervals. The uranium rods, about an inch in diameter, are jacketed with aluminum, which prevents corrosion of the hot uranium and escape of radioactive fission products. The graphite also contains channels for control rods and for the circulation of a coolant. The whole assembly is carefully designed to minimize the loss of neutrons. The pile of graphite is made large to reduce loss through the surface, and use of only the purest graphite reduces neutron capture by impurities. The spacing of the uranium rods in the graphite is of great importance. If they are too far apart (that is, if too much moderator is used), most of the neutrons are slowed to thermal energies before encountering another uranium rod, and only fission occurs. This keeps the chain reaction going (in fact, almost too well), but little if any $Pu^{239}$ is produced. If the rods are too close, not enough neutrons are slowed below the resonance energy before encountering another rod; neutron capture by $U^{238}$ occurs, giving rise to $Pu^{239}$, but not enough fissions occur to maintain the chain. A proper balance between these two extremes is required and was achieved. To summarize: The neutrons emitted with high energy by fission fly into the moderator and are slowed by elastic impacts. Some, as they reach the resonance energy, enter a rod and are captured by $U^{238}$. Others pass the critical energy and slow down to thermal speed. These, on entering a rod, cause further fission. The control rods balance the delayed neutrons and hold $k$ at unity.

The first reactor was built under the stadium of Stagg Field at the University of Chicago in 1942 by a group under the direction of Enrico Fermi. It was assembled slowly out of graphite bricks, in every alternate layer of which the bricks contained uranium cylinders. As the pile grew, the neutron density was carefully measured. On the morning of December 2, after the fifty-sixth layer of uranium-charged bricks was in place, it appeared that only the incorporated cadmium strips prevented a chain reaction. When these strips were partially withdrawn, the neutron intensity rose to a high level, but it stabilized after a few minutes. Then, to quote Fermi's report, "it was with some trepidation that the order was given to remove one more foot and a half of the strip." When this was done, the neutron intensity began to rise, slowly at first and then more and more rapidly—proof that the reaction would actually expand; that is, $k$ was greater than 1. The cadmium was then inserted again, and the reaction died down. This great achievement marked the beginning of a new epoch in the history of man's production of energy. This first reactor was later moved to the Argonne National Laboratory, where it is still used for experimental purposes. It is about thirty feet square and twenty feet high (about the size of a small house) and contains more than fifty tons of uranium.

The great amount of heat produced in such a moderated reactor is, in principle, available for generation of power, but its efficient transforma-tion presents technical problems. The large piles constructed at Hanford, Washington, solely for the production of plutonium, are cooled by water from the Columbia River. Production figures for the Hanford plant are not available to the public, but some idea of the enormous energy released may be had from the fact that the heat carried away (and wasted) produces an appreciable rise in the temperature of the river. In addition to the production of energy and fissionable materials, reactors have two other important uses. As an instrument for research a reactor is as important as the large cyclotrons. Intense beams of neutrons may be led out, for experiments on their properties and interactions, through a channel in the reactor's shield. A reactor also produces radio-isotopes, which, as we have seen, have many important applications. Substances lowered into a reactor are subjected to intense neutron bombardment and are transformed into radioactive materials. These may be separated by the calutron and are then available in usable quantities for many applications in research, medicine, and industry.

Reactors using heavy water as a moderator have been constructed. These need not be so large as graphite-moderated reactors, for the lighter deuterium slows the neutrons more rapidly. In one type the uranium, instead of being in the form of rods, is distributed uniformly in the form of a salt dissolved in the water. In any type, however, after a certain time in operation, the absorption of neutrons by accumulated fission products reduces the activity. The reactor is then shut down, the materials are removed, and the fission products and plutonium are separated from the uranium. This chemical separation, although easier than the difficult isotope separation, is by no means simple. The radioactivity of a reactor is so great that all operations must be performed by remote control, the operating personnel remaining behind appropriate shields. Since both uranium and plutonium, moreover, are in a long transition group in which an inner shell is being filled ($n = 5$, $l = 3$; Fig. 29-1), their separation is very difficult. The working out of the chemistry of these elements was one of the major achievements of the war effort. Many other problems are involved in reactor design. There are stringent limitations, for instance, on the properties of the structural materials used: they must not absorb neutrons, they must resist corrosion at high temperatures and pressures, and they must be little affected by neutron bombardment. This last is a particularly troublesome problem. The atoms of many substances are appreciably shifted from their normal positions in the crystal lattice by the intense neutron bombardment. This often produces undesirable changes in the thermal, electrical, and mechanical properties of the substance.

The most important problem in reactor design is neutron economy. Nature supplies us (sparsely) with one substance that is split by thermal neutrons. The great energies of $U^{238}$ and $Th^{232}$ are surrounded by high barriers and are obtainable only by transmutation of these substances to fissionable $Pu^{239}$ and $U^{233}$. This

may be accomplished in a breeder reactor, one that generates more nuclear fuel than it consumes. The excess, however, is small. On the average, $U^{235}$ fission produces 2.5 neutrons ($Pu^{239}$, 3.0). One of these must be used for further fission to maintain the chain. Another must be used to produce one $Pu^{239}$ as replacement of the fuel consumed. This leaves an average of only 0.5 (1.0 for plutonium) for the production of *extra* fuel. This excess makes breeding a possibility if practical methods can be developed. With such a development will come another problem: the disposal of the enormous radioactive wastes—the ashes of nuclear fires.

Exploitation of the enormous energies contained in the plentiful $U^{238}$ and $Th^{232}$ of the earth's crust will not prevent the energy famine that threatens our industrial civilization, but it will postpone it for many years.

## Concepts and Terms

Cloud Chamber
    nuclear impacts
    trail density
Nuclear Transmutations
    protons as nuclear constituents
    neutrons as nuclear constituents
    conservation of charge and of mass number
    nuclear structure
Particle Accelerators
    Van de Graaff generator
    linear accelerator
    cyclotron
    synchrocyclotron
    constant-radius accelerators
Nuclear Reactions
    mass-energy balance
    $Q$ values
    free neutron
Positron

Artificial Radioactivity
    tracer isotopes
    carbon 14 dating
Synthetic Elements
Nuclear Energy
    activation energy
    binding energy
    fission
Bombs
    fission bomb: critical mass
    fusion: thermonuclear reactions
    hydrogen bomb: probable reactions
    radioactive fall-out
Reactors
    multiplication factor
    delayed neutrons
    moderator
    pile reactor
    breeder reactors

## Problems

See Table 30-1 (p. 552) for isotopic masses.

**30-1.** Describe the composition of the nuclei of sodium, nitrogen, and radon.

**30-2.** Diagram a *complete* $_{17}Cl^{35}$ atom; a *complete* $_6C^{12}$ atom.

**30-3.** Write the isotopic symbols for the intermediate compound nuclei of reactions 30-6 and 30-8.

*Ans.* 30-6: $_4Be^8$

**30-4.** Complete the following nuclear reactions:

(A) $_5B^{10} + _0n^1 \longrightarrow ($ $) + _2He^4$
(B) $_4Be^9 + \alpha$-particle $\longrightarrow _6C^{12} + ($ $)$
(C) $($ $) + _2He^4 \longrightarrow _{15}P^{30} + _0n^1$
(D) $_{29}Cu^{63} + _1H^2 \longrightarrow ($ $) + _1H^1$
(E) $_6C^{13} + _1H^1 \longrightarrow _7N^{14} + ($ $)$
(F) $_{24}Cr^{52} + _1H^2 \longrightarrow _{25}Mn^{52} + ($ $)$

**30-5.** The particles involved in nuclear reactions are protons, deuterons ($_1H^2$ nuclei), alpha particles, neutrons, and photons, which are abbreviated as *p, d, α, n,* and *γ* respectively. Nuclear reactions are often written in an abbreviated form as follows: The particles involved are written in a parenthesis with the bombarding particle first. The bombarded atom is written in front of the parenthesis and the product atom after the parenthesis. Thus reaction 30-1 becomes $_7N^{14}$ $(\alpha,p)_8O^{17}$. Write reactions 30-8 and those of Prob. 30-4 in this abbreviated form.

**30-6.** Calculate the equivalent energy of one atomic mass unit. Use three-figure values of the constants.

**30-7.** Calculate the $Q$ values for reactions A, B, and E of Prob. 30-4.
*Ans.* (A) 2.79 Mev; (E) 7.54 Mev

**30-8.** In many reactions the $Q$ value can be measured independently, and thus the mass of one of the isotopes in the reaction can be calculated. Calculate (A) the mass of $_5B^{10}$ in reaction 30-8A and (B) the mass of the neutron in reaction 30-8C.
*Ans.* (A) 10.0161 amu; (B) 1.00899

**30-9.** The burning of coal is still a major source of energy in our economy. Coal is mostly carbon, and the reaction is

$$C + O_2 \longrightarrow CO_2 + 9.45 \times 10^4 \text{ cal}$$

Calculate the energy released (in ev) per carbon *atom* reacting. Compare this with the energy released per carbon atom in reaction E of Prob. 30-4. (Note: This is one of the reactions of the "carbon cycle" that accounts for much of the radiated energy of the sun and other stars.)
*Ans.* 4.1 ev/atom

**30-10.** Compute the $Q$ value for the disintegration of $U^{238}$ into $Th^{234}$ by $\alpha$-emission. Compare with the KE of the $\alpha$-particle given in Table 27-2. Why does the $\alpha$-particle get practically all the released energy?

**30-11.** Indicate which side of each reaction must have energy added in order to balance:

$$_0n^1 \longrightarrow _{-1}e^0 + _1p^1$$

$$_1p^1 \longrightarrow _{+1}e^0 + _0n^1$$

(A) Which would you expect to be stable, a free neutron or a free proton? Why?
(B) Where would you expect the second reaction to occur? Why?
*Ans.* (B) In "excited" nuclei, since $Q$ is negative

**30-12.** In discussing the two parts of this question, remember the conservation of mass-energy, of electric charge, and of momentum.
(A) The conversion of a photon into an electron is *never* observed, but "pair production"— the conversion of a sufficiently high-energy photon into an electron and a positron—*is* observed frequently. Discuss. (Hint: Write the equation for each possibility, and consider in the light of the conservation principles.) Calculate the minimum energy of a $\gamma$-ray photon that will produce an electron-positron pair.
(B) In the annihilation of an electron and a positron the emission of a single photon is *never* observed. What *is* observed is the emission of *two equal* photons traveling in *opposite* directions. Discuss. What is the energy of each of the photons?
*Ans.* (A) 1.02 Mev
(B) 0.51 Mev

**30-13.** Ordinary carbon ($_6C^{12}$) and deuterium react and produce a neutron. The other product is a radioactive nucleus that emits a positron. Write the complete reaction for this process.
*Ans.* The final stable nucleus is $_6C^{13}$.

**30-14.** The radioactivity from 1 mg of carbon taken from living plants produces twenty counts per minute in a certain $\beta$-ray counter; that from 1 mg of carbon taken from the wood of an archaeological "find" produces five counts per minute in the same counter. What is the age of the find? (See § 30-11.)
*Ans.* 10,800 years

**30-15.**
(A) Calculate the binding energy per nucleon for $He^4$, $Li^7$, and $Cu^{63}$. Compare your answers with Fig. 30-13.
(B) From a consideration of binding energies show that the energy released by the reaction

$$_1H^1 + _3Li^7 \longrightarrow 2 _2He^4$$

is about 17 Mev.

**30-16.**

(A) What is the least energy that would separate $O^{16}$ into four helium atoms?

(B) Consider reaction 30-14 in relation to the data of Fig. 30-13. Verify the $Q$ value for the fission.

*Ans.* (A) 14.4 Mev

**30-17.**

(A) Manganese has only one stable isotope. Compare the number of neutrons with the number of protons in this nucleus.

(B) Two artificially produced radioactive isotopes of manganese have mass numbers 52 and 56. One of these emits $\beta$-rays, and the other emits positrons. Which is the $\beta$-emitter and which the positron emitter? Give reasons for your answer.

(C) The resulting nuclei are stable. What are they?

*Ans.* (A) $(A - Z)/Z = 1.2$

(C) $_{26}Fe^{56}$ and $_{24}Cr^{52}$

**30-18.** Carry out Chadwick's calculation of the mass and the velocity of the neutrons that comprised beryllium rays from the observed recoil velocities of $_1H^1$ and $_7N^{14}$ (§ 30-3).

**30-19.**

(A) Derive equation 30-2. (Hint: Solve equation 26-7 for the product $hv'$. Put this in equation 26-8, solve for $hv$, and simplify.)

(B) Calculate the energy of the photon that would produce the observed recoil velocities of $_1H^1$ and $_7N^{14}$ (§ 30-3). (Remember that a mole of protons is $10^{-3}$ kgm.)

*Ans.* (B) 51.5 Mev for H; 102.5 Mev for N

**30-20.** A certain Van de Graaff accelerator generates a potential difference of $4.0 \times 10^6$ volts. What kinetic energies will (A) protons, (B) deuterons, and (C) $\alpha$-particles have when accelerated by this machine? (D) Compare the speeds attained by the three particles.

*Ans.* (A) 4.0 Mev; (C) 8.0 Mev; (D) speed of deuteron = speed of $\alpha$-particle = $1/\sqrt{2}$ speed of proton

**30-21.**

(A) The generator of a certain linear accelerator develops a potential difference of $5 \times 10^4$ volts. With what speed will a proton enter the first drift tube? For protons $q/m = 9.58 \times 10^7$ coul/kgm.

(B) If the reversal time of the generator is $2 \times 10^{-8}$ sec, how long must the first drift tube be?

(C) How long must the second tube be? (A little thought will save some arithmetic.)

*Ans.* (A) $3.09 \times 10^6$ m/sec

(B) 6.18 cm

(C) 8.75 cm

**30-22.**

(A) The potential difference between the dees of a cyclotron is $6 \times 10^4$ volts. To produce 12 Mev deuterons, how many revolutions must the ions make?

(B) If the magnetic induction is 1.2 newtons/amp m, what is the ions' total time of flight? For deuterons $q/m = 4.8 \times 10^7$ coul/kgm.

(C) What is the diameter of the dees? The mass of a deuteron is $3.34 \times 10^{-27}$ kgm. (Hint: From the energy calculate the speed in the largest semi-circle and then the diameter of the circle.)

*Ans.* (A) 100

(B) approx. 11 microsec

(C) 1.18 m

| TABLE **30-1** | | *Some Isotopic Masses* | *(Physical Scale)* |
|---|---|---|---|
| NAME | $Z$ | SYMBOL | MASS (AMU) |
| Electron | $-1$ | $e^0$ | 0.00055 |
| Positron | $+1$ | $e^0$ | 0.00055 |
| Proton | $+1$ | $p^1$ | 1.00759 |
| Neutron | 0 | $n^1$ | 1.00898 |
| Hydrogen | 1 | $H^1$ | 1.00814 |
| Deuterium | 1 | $H^2$ | 2.01474 |
| Helium | 2 | $He^4$ | 4.00387 |
| Lithium | 3 | $Li^7$ | 7.01822 |
| Beryllium | 4 | $Be^9$ | 9.01504 |
| Boron | 5 | $B^{10}$ | 10.01611 |
| Carbon | 6 | $C^{12}$ | 12.00380 |
| Carbon | 6 | $C^{13}$ | 13.00747 |
| Nitrogen | 7 | $N^{14}$ | 14.00752 |
| Aluminum | 13 | $Al^{27}$ | 26.99014 |
| Copper | 29 | $Cu^{63}$ | 62.94860 |
| Thorium | 90 | $Th^{234}$ | 234.12394 |
| Uranium | 92 | $U^{238}$ | 238.13232 |

# Suggested Readings

1. H. E. White, *Modern College Physics,* 3rd edition (Van Nostrand, 1956), Chaps. 70 (nuclear disintegrations), 72 (atomic accelerators), 73 (transmutation of elements), 75 (atomic energy).
2. R. D. Rusk, *Introduction to Atomic and Nuclear Physics* (Appleton-Century-Crofts, 1958), Chap. 18 (particle accelerators).
3. M. Born, *The Restless Universe,* translated by W. M. Deans (Dover Publications, 1951), pp. 95–105 (counters and cloud chambers) and 231–278 (nuclear physics).
4. S. Hecht, *Explaining the Atom* (Viking Press, 1947), pp. 101–195 (atomic energy and the development of atomic bombs).
5. D. J. Hughes, *The Neutron Story* (Anchor Books, 1959). Read the whole book, 150 pages —an excellent, non-mathematical discussion of the discovery, properties, and uses of neutrons.
6. R. A. Millikan, *Electrons* (+ *and* −), revised edition (University of Chicago Press, 1947), pp. 321–406. An interesting account of the discoveries and early investigations of the positron and the neutron.
7. Sir W. C. Dampier, *A History of Science,* 4th edition (Cambridge University Press, 1949), Chap. 10 (the new era in physics). A historical account of twentieth-century developments.
8. H. D. Smyth, *Atomic Energy for Military Purposes* (Princeton University Press, 1945). Contains the information released at the end of World War II.
9. Many interesting articles may be found in the *Scientific American.* Following is a partial list:

   L. N. Ridenour, "The Hydrogen Bomb," March 1950

   E. S. Deevey, Jr., "Radiocarbon Dating," February 1952

   M. G. Mayer, "The Structure of the Nucleus," March 1951

   J. F. Flagg and E. L. Zebroski, "Atomic Pile Chemistry," July 1952

   L. R. Hafstad, "Reactors," April 1951

   L. P. Smith, "The Bevatron," February 1951

   I. Perlman and G. T. Seaborg, "The Synthetic Elements," April 1950

CHAPTER

31

The Frontiers
of Science:
Macrocosmos
and
Microcosmos

THE UNIVERSE is expanding. This is a statement of a reasonably well-substantiated theory of cosmology, which we shall discuss briefly later in this chapter. But it is also a metaphorical statement of the current status of science. The probing observations of science are constantly extending further into astronomical space and deeper into the structure of the atomic nucleus, and the searching theories of physical science are also constantly extending. What was a smoothly impenetrable object to the Greek atomic theorist has become a micro-universe of unparalleled complexity and beauty of structure, which now poses hundreds of new fundamental problems; what was a closed issue to the astronomers of the nineteenth century, of no further interest for either investigation or speculation, has become a universe of fascinating fluctuations, in which stars can be seen in birth and in death, about whose motions we know much and will certainly know much more, about whose very beginning and possible fate we can now speculate with reason and intelligence. In thirty chapters of this book we have scratched the surface of the structure of physical science. In this last chapter we shall glance down some of the vistas of modern development, which we can now view from the base of what has gone before. Perhaps the most exciting developments are at the extremes of the scientific horizon. We shall therefore look briefly at current study of the sub-atomic universe and then, turning to the opposite end of the scientific frontier, look equally briefly at the recent expansion of our knowledge of the astronomical universe.

## 31-1. Matter Waves

By the end of the nineteenth century the wave nature of light had been firmly established, for it gave consistent explanations of diffraction and interference phenomena (Chap. 25). In the early decades of the twentieth century, however, the interactions between light and matter just as firmly established the quantum, or "particle," nature of light. By the 1920's, as we saw at the end of Chapter 26, scientists had resigned themselves to accepting this dual (and apparently contradictory) nature of radiant energy. This dual nature had, of course, been determined *indirectly*—no one has ever *seen* a light wave or a photon.

Matter, since the time of the Greeks, has been considered to be composed of particles. A handful of sand can be seen to be composed of real particles, which show no properties of waves. But these directly observed particles are composed of molecules and atoms that are made up of electrons, protons, and neutrons, none of which can be seen any more directly than a photon. Perhaps these indirectly observed "particles" have a dual nature also. If light, originally thought of as waves, also displays particle properties, matter, originally thought of as particles, may also display wave properties. Thus the duality shown by light, instead of presenting a dilemma, may reveal two *complementary* aspects that are fundamental in nature. In certain circumstances the particle aspect may be displayed, in other circumstances (such as passing through small openings) the wave aspect.

This, at any rate, seemed reasonable to Louis Victor de Broglie, who in 1924 proposed such a theory. He assumed that any particle has associated with it a group of waves that guide its motion the way light waves guide the motion of a photon. To arrive at an expression for the wavelength of these matter waves (or de Broglie waves), he assumed that the frequency of the wave is such that $h\nu$ is equal to the energy of the particle. Now in our discussion of the Compton effect (§ 26-5) we saw that a photon exhibits a momentum equal to $h\nu/c$. This reduces to $h/\lambda$ (since $c/\nu = \lambda$) and expresses the momentum of the particle in terms of its assumed wave nature. The same momentum expressed in terms of particle mechanics is, of course, equal to $mv$. De Broglie's assumption is that these two are equivalent; we therefore write $h/\lambda = mv$ or

$$\lambda = h/mv \qquad (31\text{-}1)$$

as the wavelength of the associated waves for a particle of mass $m$ moving with speed $v$. This definition of the de Broglie wavelength would have remained an interesting mathematical speculation if no direct relation to observation had been possible. But we shall see immediately that

in certain cases matter does indeed display this wave nature.

First, for gross matter (a billiard ball, an automobile, etc.) the wavelength is so exceedingly small (consider the value of $h$) that, if these waves did exist, there would be no chance at all of observing them. For an atom or an electron moving slowly, however, the wavelength is well within the operational range. An electron with KE = 100 ev, for instance, would have a wavelength of 1.23 angstroms.† As we have seen (pp. 436–438), wavelengths of this order of magnitude show strong diffraction maxima when reflected from crystals.

The wave nature of electrons was discovered quite by accident three years after de Broglie published his theory. C. J. Davisson and L. H. Germer were studying the scattering of electrons from a nickel target. The target was at a high temperature when an accidental inrush of air into the apparatus heavily oxidized the nickel. To reduce the oxide, the target was held at a high temperature for a long time, and then the experiment was continued. The distribution of the scattered electrons was found to be very different from what it had been before the accident. Instead of the diffuse scattering that would be expected of particles, the scattered beams showed definite maxima at certain angles. Investigation showed that the prolonged heating had recrystallized the nickel target into several large crystals. Perhaps the electrons were being reflected off the faces of these crystals. Following this lead, Davisson and Germer prepared a large *single* nickel crystal and directed a well-collimated beam of electrons at its surface. By rotating the crystal they could make the incident beam strike the surface at various angles. Now, if the electrons, acting as particles, were bouncing off the surface (as would ping-pong balls off a table top), reflection should occur at any angle of incidence; if, acting as waves, they were diffracted by the crystal lattice, then (as outlined in our discussion of the Bragg crystal X-ray spectrometer) reflection should occur only at one particular angle of incidence, which would depend upon the wavelength and the

---

† $\frac{1}{2}mv^2 = Ve$; $m^2v^2 = 2mVe$; $mv = \sqrt{2mVe}$. $\therefore \lambda = h/\sqrt{2mVe} = 1.23$ A for $V = 100$ volts.

crystal spacing. The second alternative was found to be true. In one experiment, for instance, when the electrons were accelerated through a potential difference of 54 volts, reflection was observed at an angle of 65°. The de Broglie wavelength for electrons of 54 ev kinetic energy (see the previous footnote) comes out to be 1.66 A. X-ray analysis showed the spacing of the nickel crystal to be 0.91 angstrom. This value and 65°, substituted in Bragg's equation (25-9), yield a wavelength of 1.65 A. This is a surprising experimental agreement with what started out as a mathematical speculation. Furthermore, if the accelerating voltage is increased, the Bragg angle decreases, yielding a shorter wavelength—in good agreement with expectations for these faster electrons.

Since these early experiments, electrons have been diffracted in many ways and their wavelengths measured very precisely. A whole field known as "electron optics" has, in fact, been developed, and from it has come the electron microscope, which has much higher magnification than the ordinary optical microscope. But is this property of "matter waves" unique to electrons? It turns out that it is not, but is displayed by other particles when conditions are suitable for observation—that is, when the sub-microscopic particles are moving slowly enough so that the wavelengths lie in observable ranges.

A particularly interesting case is the "diffraction" of molecules. One may obtain a beam of gaseous molecules by allowing the gas to escape through a small hole from a heated enclosure into an evacuated space. According to Maxwell's distribution, however, such a beam contains molecules of many different speeds and therefore of many different wavelengths. For the observation of diffraction, a single wavelength (a single speed) is desirable. In one experiment the investigators achieved this by mounting two discs, each containing a slit, on a common axis so that they could be rotated rapidly. A beam of molecules passing through the first slit contained many different speeds, but only molecules with the proper speed (determined by the separation of the discs and the

speed of rotation) arrived at the second disc at the proper time to go through its slit. Thus a beam of "monospeed" molecules was obtained. The investigators allowed these to fall on a lithium fluoride crystal and measured the intensity of the reflected beam by allowing it to pass through a small opening into a receptacle, where a very sensitive device measured the rate of increase of gas pressure as the molecules accumulated. The strong diffraction maximum observed with helium indicated a wavelength of 0.60 A. From the dimensions and rate of rotation of the discs the speed of these helium molecules was determined as $1.64 \times 10^3$ m/sec. This, combined with the mass of a helium molecule, gives a de Broglie wavelength of 0.61 A. The excellent agreement in this experiment has the added interest that the speed was measured in a simple and direct mechanical fashion, not indirectly as in the case of electrons and other charged particles.

Many experiments of this kind have firmly established the wave nature of matter and, in a way, resolved the wave-particle dilemma of quantum theory by merely turning it round. In retrospect we realize that the apparent contradiction is due primarily to the concepts and visualizations formed by our experience with the macroscopic world. So long as we retain the idea of a wave as a continuously spreading disturbance whose energy is distributed uniformly, it is very difficult to conceive of a beam of light as a moving stream of photons. Conversely, so long as we think of electrons, protons, etc. simply as particles, it is very difficult to visualize the associated waves that account for the observed "diffraction" of these "particles." We should not be disturbed by our inability to visualize these matter waves. If they are only "mathematical" waves, which permit us to make calculations and predict the results of experiments, they are not therefore different from earlier concepts of physical science. We have, for instance, no exact knowledge of the fundamental nature of a magnetic field or of an electric field; we use the symbols $B$ and $E$ nevertheless; we speak of magnetic and electric lines of force; and we apply the electromagnetic relations with great confidence and fruitfulness.

## 31-2. Wave Mechanics

De Broglie's hypothesis of matter waves was the starting point for a new theory called *wave mechanics,* which resolved the wave-particle discrepancy. De Broglie was able to arrive at Bohr's quantum condition for circular orbits (equation 28-2). He made the plausible assumption that an electron would move only along circles whose circumference could contain a whole number of waves; that is, $2\pi r = n\lambda$ if $n$ is an integer. But the associated wavelength of the electron is $h/(mv)$, which, substituted for $\lambda$, yields the expression $mv2\pi r = nh$. Thus, for the simple theory of circular orbits, the wave hypothesis leads to the results postulated by Bohr.

Starting in 1926, Erwin Schrödinger developed the hypothesis of matter waves into a general and precise theory for the description of particle motion. He put the hypothesis in mathematical form by developing a "wave equation." This complicated differential equation, which is solved by elaborate mathematical techniques, involves space coordinates, time, constants, including Planck's constant, and the mass and energy of the particle. It also includes a quantity, $\psi$ (psi), which corresponds to the amplitude of ordinary waves. In general, the solution of any problem involves solving the wave equation for $\psi$ at the particular place and time.

A question immediately arises: What is the physical significance of the quantity $\psi$? Max Born's interpretation is that the value of $\psi$ at any place determines the *probability* of finding the particle there. If at a certain place the amplitude of the associated wave is large, it is reasonable to expect a large probability of finding the particle there, and vice versa. This means, not that the waves *are* the particle, but only that the wave pattern determines the probability of the particle's motion. For instance, associated electron waves, on passing through a nickel crystal, form the interference maxima (large $\psi$) and minima (small $\psi$) calculated for a wavelength equal to $h/(mv)$. The maxima are the regions through which the electron is most likely to go. If there is only one electron, it may go in any direction. When a beam contains billions of electrons, we expect the diffraction maxima to be regions through which many electrons move and the minima to be regions through which few if any move. This, of course, is exactly the observation. In a similar way, diffracted light waves (no more directly observable than matter waves) determine the probable paths of the photons. Thus the concepts of waves, on the one hand, and of particles or photons, on the other, are not mutually exclusive but are complementary to one another. The waves form the patterns that guide the motion of the particles.

The first spectacular successes of wave mechanics were in the field of atomic structure. Schrödinger considered that the stationary states (see § 28-1) of an atom would be represented by a system of "standing waves" somewhat analogous to the vibrations of a violin string when sounding its fundamental and overtones. In this situation, parts of the string vibrate with large amplitude while other parts vibrate with small amplitude. This wave pattern, persisting in time, seems to "stand," or be stationary, in the string. Similarly, Schrödinger sought solutions of the wave equation that would specify possible patterns of standing matter waves for the electrons surrounding the nucleus. Regions of large $\psi$ would be the most probable positions of the electrons, and vice versa. Solutions of a wave equation giving standing-wave patterns are determined by sets of integers. When the wave equation was solved, the determining integers turned out to be the quantum numbers of the older theory (§ 28-5). The advantage of wave mechanics is that these numbers appear automatically in the solutions instead of, as in the older theory, being introduced somewhat arbitrarily in terms of hypothetical orbits. As in the older theory, a unique set of quantum numbers determines a unique stationary energy state of the atom. Transitions between these states give rise to the observed spectral lines. Wave mechanics accurately describes the spectra of one-electron atoms as well as the older theory; and it also—as the older theory cannot do—describes the spectrum of neutral helium. The fact that our mathematical techniques fail for many-electron atoms (and that solutions must therefore be approximated) does not invalidate the theory. Furthermore, the wave-mechanics solutions giving the distribution of $\psi$ about the nucleus yield the probabilities of transitions and thus accurately specify the *intensities* of spectral lines as well as the frequencies. The older theory could only specify the frequencies. Note that the new theory says nothing about orbits; it merely specifies the regions where the electron is most likely to be found or—what is the same thing— the regions in which the electron spends more time than in others.

Wave mechanics has been successfully applied to many other problems, among them problems in nuclear theory and a description of the covalent bond of the hydrogen molecule. These successes, plus the fact that it presents a unified treatment of both light and matter, indicate that, abstract as the theory may be, it presents a more fundamental description of nature than either the classical theory or the early quantum theory.

## 31-3. Uncertainty Principle

A fundamental aspect of wave mechanics is that it specifies only probabilities for the motions of particles. To be sure, the idea of probability is not new in physical science. We first encountered it in our study of the kinetic theory of matter, where we talked about the most probable and average velocities rather than the velocity of one particular molecule. And the idea of probability is central in our discussions of reaction rates, both chemical and nuclear. Before the advent of wave mechanics, however, this need to talk of probabilities was considered to be due primarily to our deficiencies in observation rather than to a fundamental principle. In accordance with Newtonian mechanics, it was thought that, with sufficiently precise methods, the position and motion of any particle could be observed exactly. Wave mechanics, on the other hand, makes no claim to be able to specify the motion of a single particle. It does, however, specify the statistical distribution of many particles. This, of course, is just what we usually observe in an experiment; we observe

the light from a large number of atoms, not from a single one; we observe the motion of a beam of electrons, never of a single electron, etc.

The theory's lack of exactness in specifying the motion of the lightest particles is not a deficiency that may be rectified. It is, on the other hand, consistent with a fundamental principle enunciated by Werner Heisenberg in 1927 and called the *uncertainty principle*. This principle, which is derivable from wave mechanics, says that, irrespective of technical errors of measurement, it is *fundamentally impossible* to describe the motion of a particle with unlimited precision. We may specify the position of a particle with increasing precision, but in so doing we introduce uncertainty into its motion, in particular into its momentum. Conversely, we may observe the momentum with increasing precision, but then we introduce uncertainties into its position. In general, these quantities are ultimately uncertain to such an extent that the product of the two uncertainties is not less than Planck's constant; that is, the variation in each measurement is such that $(\Delta M)(\Delta x) = h$.

Involved in the argument is a view that has been increasingly accepted by scientists. This is that a statement has scientific meaning only as the quantities involved can be observed either directly or indirectly. Accepting this attitude, let us see how we should locate an electron inside an atom and also determine its momentum precisely. To do this, we should have to distinguish between positions, say, $10^{-11}$ meter apart—that is, about one-tenth of the diameter of the atom. An ordinary microscope would be useless for this purpose because (a well-known principle of optics) points that are closer together than about the wavelength of the light used in the observation cannot be distinguished. As we know, visible light has a wavelength of several thousand angstroms, but the whole diameter of an atom is only a few angstroms. For our purposes, therefore, we should have to use $\gamma$-rays. To be sure, no one has yet invented a $\gamma$-ray microscope, but let us suppose that some "super"-experimentalist has one and lends it to us. Now, if we are to see the electron at all, at least one photon must bounce off it and enter the microscope. But, in so doing, the photon gives the electron a Compton "kick" and abruptly changes its momentum. We may wish to calculate this change of momentum (as in the Compton effect) and correct for it, but this, as we have seen, depends on the angle of recoil of the photon, and the photon may enter the finite aperture of the microscope along any of several directions. We may stop down the aperture of the microscope to a very fine hole so that the photon can enter in only one sharply defined direction. But then the photon diffracts through this small aperture, and the position of the electron becomes indefinite. It does no good to reverse the process and use long wavelengths to reduce the Compton recoil, for then, as pointed out above, the observed position becomes indefinite. A quantitative analysis of this argument shows that beyond any instrumental errors there is, as stated by the uncertainty principle, a residual uncertainty in these observations. Many other situations may be considered, but they always lead to the same result.

The practicing scientist doing experimental research with the most refined tools available must still contend with errors much larger than those determined by the uncertainty principle. But we must not let this *practical* limitation mask the importance of the *fundamental* limitation imposed by the theory. The great success of Newtonian mechanics, based, as we have seen, on observations of gross matter, gave rise to the conviction that there is a strict cause-and-effect relation in natural processes—that, in other words, a certain body placed in a certain situation will move in a certain way. An identical body placed in the same situation will move in identically the same way. But this seems not to work with atomic particles. A stream of electrons, all identical, passing through the same crystal will not all emerge in the same direction. (But there is a most probable direction.) Why is it that one radium atom ejects an $\alpha$-particle now and an identical atom waits 5,000 years to do so? Wave mechanics defines probabilities for these and all other small-scale processes, and these probabilities combine in such a fashion that they ultimately explain all macroscopic ob-

servations—but not necessarily by a law of causality.

A corollary of the causal relations of classical science is determinism: the belief that, if the position and motion of all particles of a system are known, the future of the system will be completely in accord with the laws of science. Such a mechanistic philosophy was given great impetus in the eighteenth century by the successes of Newtonian mechanics in describing and predicting the motions of both terrestrial and celestial objects. The great advances of the nineteenth century only strengthened this view, and it was confidently expected by many that ultimately all responses (including human) would be perfectly described by the laws of science. The uncertainty principle denies that this ultimate goal can ever be reached. The principle does not say that the deterministic view is wrong; but it does say that we are fundamentally unable to fulfill the initial condition. There is no way of exactly observing both the position and the motion of particles.

These arguments do not disprove a causal deterministic philosophy. What they do say is that there is no way for observational science to prove that the philosophy is ultimately true; and proponents of such a philosophy must therefore look elsewhere for proof of their position. The physical scientist recognizes the limitations of his methods and refrains from predicting the individual motions of particles and photons. Instead, he applies the laws of probability incorporated in wave mechanics and accepts the ultimate indefiniteness required by the uncertainty principle.

## 31-4. Nuclear Forces

Although the electronic structures of the atoms have been worked out in detail, the structure of the nucleus is far from completely known. The electronic structures are held together by the electric field of the nucleus in accordance with wave mechanics. But how is the nucleus held together? Since the electrostatic repulsion of the protons tends to make the nucleus fly apart, a new type of force is required to bind the nucleus into a stable structure. The binding energy per nucleon tells us something about the nuclear force. This binding energy is approximately 8 Mev per nucleon in heavy as well as in light nuclei; that is, any nucleon loses about the same energy as it is incorporated into a nucleus. This tells us that the binding force must act over a very small range—about the distance between two adjacent nucleons. If this were not so, a nucleon in a heavy nucleus, attracted by all the other nucleons, would be bound by a stronger force than a nucleon in a lighter nucleus, with fewer attracting nucleons. This would result in a much greater binding energy per nucleon in heavy nuclei (that is, it would require more work to remove a nucleon). But this is not so. The nuclear forces are therefore short-range forces acting between adjacent particles. The nature of these forces is still to be discovered, and a general theory governing them (as Schrödinger's wave equation governs the extranuclear forces) is still to be worked out.

Careful studies of energy exchanges in nuclear reactions have yielded further clues to nuclear structure. It appears that the nucleus has definite energy levels somewhat analogous to the electronic energy levels outside the nucleus. In a way, nuclear theory seems to have reached about the same stage that atomic theory had reached in the early 1920's. Knowledge of these nuclear energy levels has been very important in practical applications of nuclear energy. But how they fit into a general theory of nuclear structure is one of the major problems of current research.

A new field of research, known as *particle physics,* is related to nuclear structure. In 1932 it was thought that the matter of the universe was composed of three elementary particles: the proton, the neutron, and the electron. This picture changed in 1934 with the discovery of the positron and the postulation of the **neutrino.**

Since the parent nucleus, in radioactive decay, undergoes a definite change of energy, it was expected that the emitted particles would have a definite energy. This was found to be true of $\alpha$-particles but not of $\beta$-particles, which are emitted with a continuous range of energies up to the entire energy loss of the parent nucleus. This fact seemed to contradict the laws of conservation of energy and momentum. Scientists, being reluctant to abandon such powerful and general principles, assumed that each $\beta$-emission was accompanied by the emission of another particle, one that could carry away enough energy and momentum to satisfy the conservation laws. Fermi, in 1934, worked out the theoretical details and specified the properties of this mysterious particle. The rest mass must be almost zero (certainly less than 1/100 of the mass of an electron), and the charge must be zero. Many attempts to detect such an elusive particle met with failure. The theorists were sure it existed, but the experimentalists could not find it. Only in 1956 was conclusive evidence of its existence found. Thus the neutrino (little neutron) was added to the roster of elementary particles.

In 1935 Hideki Yukawa proposed a theory of nuclear binding forces. This involved an exchange of particles between nucleons in a manner similar to the sharing of electrons in the covalent bond of the hydrogen molecule. Since the theory required that the mass of these particles be greater than that of an electron and less than that of a proton, Yukawa named his hypothetical particles **mesons.** His theory presents many difficulties and needs further experimental and theoretical development. The interesting point for our discussion, however, is that mesons have been found among the fragments produced by cosmic-ray bombardment. The primary cosmic rays, coming from interstellar space and bombarding the earth with enormous energies, are mostly protons and heavier nuclei.[†] Atoms struck by these cosmic rays explode, producing showers of a variety of elementary particles, among which nine different types of mesons have been identified, with masses ranging from 200 to 1,000 electronic masses. Some are charged with one electronic unit (either positive or negative), and some are neutral. Also four types of **hyperons,** both charged and neutral, have been discovered. Hyperons have masses somewhat larger than that of a proton, but less

† Their origin and the way they acquire their enormous energies are not clearly understood.

than that of a deuteron. Many of these particles can also be produced and studied under more controlled conditions by bombardments in modern high-energy accelerators. Another interesting particle has been produced in these machines: the **antiproton,** a particle with the same mass as a proton but carrying one negative electronic charge. All these elementary particles, except the proton and the electron, are unstable in the free state. They either combine with other particles (as in the positron-electron annihilation) or disintegrate. As we have seen in § 30-9, the neutron disintegrates into a proton and an electron with a half-life of fifteen minutes. The half-lives of mesons and hyperons are all very small fractions of a second.

The number and variety of these particles have robbed the term "elementary" of much of its significance. It is not unlikely that such particles are structures composed of even more subtle entities. It is expected that further study of them and of their interactions with nuclei will point the way to an integrated theory of nuclear structure and processes that will be comparable to existing theories of extra-nuclear atomic structure.

## 31-5. Stellar Magnitudes

In Chapter 5 we saw how increased precision of telescopic observations of the positions and motions of celestial objects, combined with Newtonian mechanics, led to detailed knowledge of the structure of the solar system. In these measurements, the only property of light that was important was its rectilinear propagation through space; in other words, the light was a sighting device that permitted the determination of directions. Much was accomplished with these methods, but by the middle of the nineteenth century astronomy was considered by some to be an "exhausted" science. Then, with the development of spectroscopy and the discovery of its relations to atomic structure, it became clear that the faint light signals reaching us from the enormously distant stars carry a great amount of information that can be deciphered by the methods and theories of physical science.

If we look at the sky on a clear night, the stars appear to be (and the ancients thought they were) not very far away and all at the same distance. They also appear to vary greatly in luminosity, some seeming spectacularly luminous and others barely discernible. Primarily for convenience in identification, Ptolemy divided the visible stars into six groups according to apparent luminosity and assigned each group a number, now called the *apparent magnitude,* that changes inversely with that luminosity. A first-magnitude star appears more luminous than a second-magnitude star, and so on; a sixth-magnitude star is just discernible by the unaided eye.

When, in the nineteenth century, it became clear not only that the stars were very far away but that their distances from the earth were greatly different, the question arose: What is the actual luminosity of a star? It is well known that any source of light appears less luminous as it gets farther away. This relation, in fact, follows the inverse-square law: the same source five times as far away will appear only $1/25$ as luminous. If two stars have the same *apparent* magnitude and one is ten times as far away as the other, that one is actually a hundred times as luminous as the other. It is a simple problem, then, once the distance to a star is known, to calculate its luminosity and its apparent magnitude at some arbitrarily chosen distance. The standard distance chosen is 32.6 light years†—a tremendous distance ($\approx 2 \times 10^{14}$ miles!) by ordinary standards but conveniently small by astronomical standards. When "placed" at this distance, the relative luminosities yield a scale of magnitudes that are called the **absolute magnitudes** of the stars. Some stars are so luminous—so much more luminous than the old first-magnitude stars —that the magnitude scale has had to be extended through zero to negative numbers. Other stars, nearer than the standard distance, have smaller absolute magnitudes. An outstanding example is our sun, which has an apparent

---

† Another astronomical unit of distance is the parsec, which is the distance to a point whose parallax is one second of angle (§ 31-6). The standard distance was originally defined as ten parsecs, which is equal to 32.6 light years.

magnitude of about −27 but an absolute magnitude of about +5; that is, at the standard distance the sun would be a fifth-magnitude star only faintly visible to the unaided eye! The importance of the absolute magnitude is that it gives a measure of the total rate of radiation from the star. In modern measurement the ultraviolet and infrared as well as the visible light are included.

The spectra of the stars may be photographed with a spectrograph in place of the eyepiece of a telescope. An enormous number of very detailed photographs of stellar spectra have been obtained. These are mostly absorption spectra, produced when certain frequencies of the continuous spectrum from the glowing star are absorbed by the gases of the outer layers of the star. The absorption lines, as we have seen, are characteristic of the absorbing gases. Some of the spectra from different stars vary rather widely in character, but many are quite similar. It was found after a study of the spectra of thousands of stars that they could be grouped into several classes, arranged according to regular changes in the character of the spectra, and each class was designated by a letter. A

very interesting relation was found to exist between the magnitudes of the stars and their spectral classes. The main features of this relation are shown in Figure 31-1, where magnitude is plotted against spectral class. Each dot represents a star. Our sun (the cross in the figure) is a star of class G and of the fifth magnitude. In a complete diagram many more stars would be shown, and the spectral classes would be subdivided into more detail.

Most of the stars fall along a diagonal line called the **main sequence,** which is determined by the sequence of spectral classes. Hydrogen lines appear in all classes. Starting with class M, the lines are rather weak, but they grow stronger across the sequence, reaching a maximum at class A and then falling off for B and O. Again starting with classes M and K, the spectra are complex. The lines of a number of metals are very strong, and the characteristics "bands" of simple molecules are clearly evident. At G the molecular bands have disappeared, and the metallic lines predominate. As we go further up the sequence, the metallic lines weaken and disappear so that the spectra at A are almost entirely strong hydrogen lines. From there on hydrogen weakens, and the lines of neutral helium increase to a maximum at about B. At O the lines of *ionized* helium, oxygen, and nitrogen predominate.

Now these spectral regularities determine the sequence of the spectral classes, and it is surprising that such an empirically determined sequence should show a simple linear relation to magnitude. The fact that it does indicates that the change in the spectral patterns is due chiefly to change in one physical condition—temperature. As we progress up the sequence, the stars change color. M stars are red, K orange-red, and so on through yellow and yellowish white to white at A and blue-white at B and O. This is exactly what we should expect with rising temperature, for we know that in the continuous spectrum from a hot body the wavelengths of maximum energy shift toward shorter length with rising temperature (§ 25-4). By applying the radiation laws for hot bodies we find that the temperature rises as we go up the sequence. The reddest stars have temperatures of 2,000–

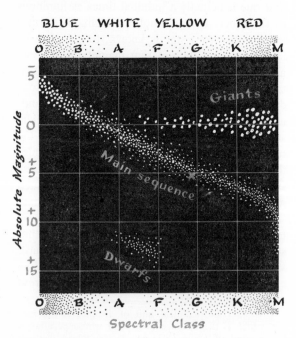

FIGURE **31-1** *Chart of absolute stellar magnitude against spectral class.*

3,000°K, G (our sun) about 6,000°K, and so on to 25,000–30,000°K for the blue stars.

This range of temperature, rather than a varying composition of the stars, accounts for the different absorption spectra of the different classes. The composition of the stars, in fact, is surprisingly uniform. At varying temperatures, however, different substances are variously effective in absorbing radiation. Let us first consider hydrogen, which is so plentiful in the stars that its spectrum appears to some extent in all classes. The Balmer series is observed because, if the stars radiate wavelengths as short as the Lyman series, we cannot see them, for the air is opaque to such waves. Consider the energy-level diagram for hydrogen (Fig. 28-3). The Balmer series terminates on the first *excited* level rather than on the ground state; ordinary hydrogen, therefore, could not absorb the lines. Even at the temperature of M stars, however, enough hydrogen atoms are in the first excited state (as a result of thermal impact) to produce a measurable absorption of Balmer lines. As we go up the sequence to higher temperatures, more and more of the hydrogen is maintained in the first excited state, and the absorption lines become increasingly intense, reaching a maximum at class A. At still higher temperatures, appreciable numbers of hydrogen atoms are ionized as a result of the strong thermal impacts. These, of course, cannot absorb, and the intensity of the hydrogen lines falls off. For helium we have a similar situation but higher up the sequence since the ionization energy of helium is almost twice that of hydrogen. Lines of neutral helium begin to show, and reach a maximum, between A and B. Then helium begins to ionize, and the spectrum of helium ions, along with the spectra of nitrogen ions and oxygen ions, becomes prominent.

The other spectral characteristics are similarly explained. At the low temperatures of M and K stars, simple molecules can exist, and their absorption bands appear. At higher temperatures, however, the molecules are dissociated, and their spectra disappear. Metals such as calcium and sodium have lower ionization energies than the gases, and their principal series (those terminating in the ground state), unlike that of hydrogen, lie in the visible and near ultraviolet ranges. Their absorption lines therefore begin to show in the cool stars and rise to prominence at G. At higher temperatures such metals become ionized, and their spectra disappear.

So far we have been discussing only the main sequence. Since the great majority of stars lie close to the main sequence, this must represent a fairly stable, long-lived part of a star's history. Figure 31-1, however, shows also a sizable number of stars labeled giants. The spectral classes of these stars show that they are cool red stars, but their luminosities are so great that they have magnitudes equal to those of the hot stars of the main sequence. Now luminosity, and therefore magnitude, depend on the total energy radiated per second. Luminosity may be greater, obviously, for two reasons: (1) because the temperature is higher and the radiation per square meter therefore greater (equation 25-4); (2) because the star is bigger (that is, has more square meters of radiating surface) and the total radiation therefore greater. The latter case must be that of the red giants. These stars have a high luminosity because they are enormous. The super-giant red star Betelgeuse, in the right shoulder of Orion, is 500 times as large as the sun in diameter and therefore has a volume 25 million times as great. The diameters of other giants range from 10 to 100 times that of the sun. This estimate was checked by A. A. Michelson for Betelgeuse and some other red and orange giants by an ingenious method involving interference patterns formed by their light. His measurements showed that these stars are indeed giants. The masses of stars, on the other hand, do not vary much. There is good evidence that the masses of most stars range from about one-fifth of the mass to five times the mass of the sun. The giants, it is clear, are stars of low density. Exceptionally large masses (but no more than 100 times that of the sun) are found among the highly luminous stars of class O.

A few stars are labeled as dwarfs in Figure 31-1. Here we have the reverse of the situation of the giants. From their spectral classes we know that these are hot stars that radiate much energy per square meter. But their luminosities are very low. Hence they must have very small areas: they are dwarfs. They must, however, have very high densities. These densities are calculated to be tens of thousands of times the density of water. Such a high compression of matter seemed almost unbelievable at first, but an independent measurement of the density of one such dwarf (Sirius B) verified it. This little star, with a mass equal to the sun's mass but a diameter only four times that of the earth, is found to have a density of 30,000 grams/cm³!

## 31-6. Stellar Distances

The only direct method of measuring the distance of a celestial object is to determine its parallax from a known base line (§ 5-5). Any base line located on the earth is much too short for observation of stellar parallaxes, but the diameter of the earth's orbit is long enough to produce a measurable parallax for near stars. Even with this base line of almost 200 million miles, however, the parallax of even the nearest star is very small. As we saw in Chapter 5, it was not until well into the nineteenth century that stellar parallaxes were observed at all, and then not very precisely. Starting in 1903, the modern photographic method was developed. This consists of taking a photograph of the same region of the sky at six-month intervals. A careful analysis of six such photographs makes it possible to eliminate the real motion of the stars and to measure precisely the apparent parallactic motion. No star has a parallax as great as one second of angle! As might be expected from this result, the distances to even the nearest stars are so tremendous that meters, and even miles, are much too small as units. One convenient unit is the **light year.** This is the distance light travels in one year at its speed of $3 \times 10^8$ m/sec: a distance of $9.46 \times 10^{15}$ meters, or about six million million miles. The star nearest to our sun is 4.24 light years from us! (On this scale the distance from us to the sun is negligible, being only about eight light *minutes*.) The stars are enormously distant from us and from each other.

As the distance gets greater, the parallax gets smaller and soon becomes too small for reliable measurement. As the result of a great deal of concerted effort using the most refined technique, the distances of several thousand stars are now known from direct measurement of parallaxes. The maximum distance so measured is about 300 light years. Distances to the myriad stars that are farther away must be determined by indirect methods, several of which have been found by astronomers. Such methods, depend, in general, on determining the absolute magnitude, which, compared with the apparent magnitude, yields the distance as a result of the inverse-square law.

One method of determining a star's absolute magnitude is to derive it from its spectral class. To be sure, a class K star, say, may be in the main sequence, or it may be among the giants, which have very different magnitudes. As we have seen above, however, the giants are much less dense than the main-sequence stars, and their gases are therefore at a lower pressure. Certain spectral lines are sensitive to pressure; their intensities are conspicuously strengthened or weakened by decreasing pressure even if the temperature remains the same (that is, if the star remains in the same class). By a careful study of the intensities of these lines in the spectra of stars of known magnitude, a simple relation between intensity and magnitude was discovered. Then, by measuring the intensity of these lines in the spectrum of a star of unknown luminosity, one could, with this relation, evaluate the absolute magnitude.

Certain stars pulsate; that is, they alternately expand and contract in regular cycles. Associated with these pulsations are temperature changes that produce cyclic changes in luminosities. There are various types of pulsating stars, and each type has its characteristic cycle. Two types are very useful in determining stellar distances. One type is called *cluster variables* because the pulsating stars are usually found associated with clusters of stars. The second type is called *Cepheid variables* because one of the earliest recognized examples was found in the constellation Cepheus.

Cluster variables display uniform characteristics. They all have slightly irregular periods of about half a day, and all are giants of class A (not shown in Fig. 31-1). A careful study of a number of cluster variables has shown that they all have an absolute *median* magnitude of zero. (The median magnitude is the average of the maximum and minimum magnitudes attained in each cycle.) Whenever, therefore, one of these stars is found and is recognized by its type of fluctuation, its absolute magnitude is known, and its distance is determined by the inverse-square law.

Cepheid variables are important for two reasons: (1) there are many of them scattered throughout the observable universe; (2) they are very luminous, yellow super-giants of classes F and G, with magnitudes ranging to −6, and they can be therefore seen for great distances. Cepheid variables have very regular fluctuations in periods ranging from a day to several weeks. They display a very simple relation between their absolute median magnitudes and their periods of variation: the longer the period, the greater the luminosity. Over a number of years this relation has been worked out in great detail. All that is needed if one wishes to find the distance to a Cepheid variable that one has recognized by its characteristic cycle is to time its variation, get from its period its absolute magnitude, and then, from its apparent magnitude and the inverse-square law, determine its distance.

## 31-7. Stellar Motion

Whenever there is relative motion along the line of sight between the earth and a celestial object, we may detect the motion by observing the Doppler shift of the lines in the object's spectrum (§ 25-7). If the observer and the object are approaching each other, all the lines are shifted slightly toward the violet end of the spectrum (the wavelengths are apparently shorter); if they are separating from each other, the shift is toward the red end of the spectrum. The amount of this shift from the normal wavelengths (those observed in the laboratory with a stationary source) yields the relative speed between the observer and the source.

Several motions may produce Doppler shifts simultaneously. The orbital motion of the earth, for instance, produces, in the spectral lines of a star, shifts that are repeated every year—a violet shift for six months and a red shift for six months.† If the star is also approaching us, however, there is a permanent shift toward the violet, and the oscillations due to our orbital motion occur about a somewhat shorter wavelength than that of the "normal" spectrum. These and other Doppler effects must be sorted out if we wish to determine the relative speeds.

The rates of many types of motion are determined by means of Doppler shifts. We may, for instance, determine the rate of rotation of the sun (and planets) by taking one spectrograph when the telescope is focused on one edge of the sun and a second when the telescope is focused on the opposite edge. One spectrum shows a violet shift and the other a red shift; the difference establishes the rotation, and the amount of shift determines its rate. The expansion and contraction of pulsating stars are also verified by the Doppler effect: during one half of their luminosity cycle the spectra of these stars show a violet shift, and during the other half they show a red shift. These are but a few of many situations that may be inferred from observations of the Doppler effect.

A star is not usually moving directly toward or away from us. Its motion must then be determined in two components, which are combined vectorially for the total velocity. Consider the situation shown in Figure 31-2. A star moving with velocity $v$ will, in a certain time, move from position $A$ to position $B$. As the star is observed from the earth, $E$, its velocity will have rectangular components, $v_r$ along the line of sight and $v_t$ at right angles to the line of sight. The radial component, $v_r$, is given directly by the Doppler shift. The component $v_t$ produces, of course, no Doppler shift. The star will, moreover, *appear* to move across the dome of the heavens from $A$ to $B'$. We meas-

---

† These shifts further verify the revolution of the earth and check the computed orbital speed. Or, conversely, with the speed given by the Doppler shift our mean distance from the sun may be computed. Such "cross checks" occur frequently in astronomy and produce confidence in some of the most indirect methods of measurement.

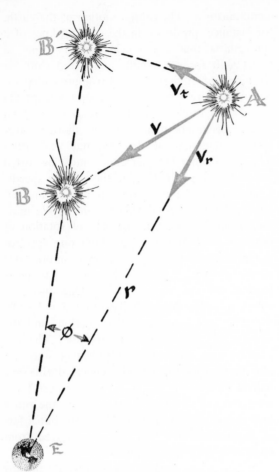

FIGURE **31-2** *Measurement of stellar velocities with reference to the earth.*

The calculations outlined above give, of course, only the velocity of a star with reference to the earth. Our sun may also be moving in space. A complicated analysis, involving statistical methods, of a large number of relative velocities shows that the sun (and with it the solar system) is moving through space at about 170 miles/sec toward the constellation Cygnus.

## 31-8. *Galactic System*

Our sun is one of many thousand million stars that form the **galactic system,** the system of the Milky Way, or our Galaxy. Shortly after nightfall of a day late in summer this spectacular feature of the sky arches overhead in a general north-south direction. Viewed through a telescope, the milky path is seen to be composed of countless stars. If we look south toward Sagittarius, the stars pile up in great "clouds." If we look east or west of the Milky Way, the stars thin out. These casual observations suggest that the galactic system is contained in a flattened space (somewhat like two saucers placed face to face) and that the solar system is far from the center. As we look toward Sagittarius, we are looking through the system the long way, and therefore, though the stars are widely separated, we seem to see them close together. This accounts for the apparently continuous path of the Milky Way. At right angles to this direction the stars extend to much smaller distances and are therefore seen to be widely separated.

The accumulation and analysis of a great number of measurements of distance verify this picture of the galactic structure. The distribution of the stars, if the system were viewed edgewise, would appear as shown schematically in Figure 31-3. Each little dot represents a star (many more should be drawn). The clusters of dots represent globular clusters of stars, which are groups of thousands of stars so closely spaced that they give the appearance of a globule. About a hundred of these clusters are known, and they are distributed through a spherical space round the galactic center. The solar system is in the galactic plane at about 33,000 light years from the center. The full diameter of the "disc"-

ure the rate of this angular displacement by measuring the position of the star (with reference to much more distant "fixed" stars) on a series of photographs taken at known intervals of time. These measurements give the rate at which angle $\phi$ is increasing. This angular velocity is called the **proper motion** of the star. If the distance, $r$, to the star is known, the component $v_t$ is easily calculated from the distance and the proper motion. Although many stars are moving at tremendous speeds, the distances, $r$, are so enormous that the proper motion, $\mu$ ($=\Delta\phi/\Delta t$), is very small. For good values of $\mu$ photographs taken over a period of several years must be compared. Figure 31-2 is misleading, for even after many years the distance $B'B$ is very small in comparison with $r$.

shaped Galaxy is about 100,000 light years, as indicated by the scale at the top of the diagram. If we could view the Galaxy from "above," we should see a dense, brilliant core (the bulge in the diagram) surrounded by the less dense arms, which would spiral round the core instead of spreading out uniformly to the edges.

This spiraling of the arms is deduced from the observed motions of many stars on the same side of the galactic center as the sun. As a group, the stars nearer the galactic center than the sun are moving in one direction while the stars farther from the center than the sun *appear* to be moving in the opposite direction. This is with reference to the sun, but when the motions are referred to the galactic center, all the stars are seen to be moving in the *same* direction. An analogy will help to understand this. Suppose that you are driving along a three-lane highway in the middle lane, where the traffic is moving at 50 miles per hour, that the traffic in the lane to your right is moving at 60 miles per hour, and that the traffic in the lane to your left is moving at 40 miles per hour. From *your* point of view your lane is not moving, the right-hand lane is streaming past you in the forward direction, and the left-hand lane is streaming past you in the opposite direction. An observer standing at the side of the highway, however, sees all three lanes moving forward at different speeds. The stars, then, are moving about the center of the Galaxy with different speeds, which, as we should expect according to the law of gravity, decrease as the distance from the center increases. The problem is not so simple as that of the solar system, for the center, instead of being a single massive object, is a large cluster of many stars. But the motions are consistent with Newton's laws. The rate at which the sun is moving should carry the solar system once round the Galaxy in something more than 200 million years. As long a time as this is, there has been time in geologic history for a number of circuits round the Galaxy.

Though the stars, as we have seen, are widely separated, the interstellar space is not empty. Large clouds of dust and gases are in the galaxy. When close to stars of high luminosity, these clouds, called galactic nebulae, are excited to luminescence and shine with a diffuse light. Other clouds are dark and obscure large areas of the heavens. The galactic center, in fact, is not observable from the earth but was located by the symmetrical distribution of the globular clusters. Even the regions that are apparently transparent contain some matter. Though this tenuous material is of extremely low density, it scatters some of the light from distant stars and complicates the measurement of their magnitudes. Certain lines in the spectra of distant stars do not undergo the Doppler shift that is due to the stars' motion. The absorption of their frequencies by atoms and molecules in interstellar space has revealed the presence there of sodium, potassium, calcium, iron, cyanogen, hydrocarbon molecules, and a great deal of hydrogen. By laboratory standards these spaces are "empty"; that is, the number of atoms per cubic meter is very much smaller than in the most highly evacuated laboratory apparatus. Nevertheless, the total mass scattered through the enormous regions of interstellar space is tremendous.

Certain faint patches of light in the sky were thought for a long time to be other galactic nebulae. In the present century, however, with the development of large telescopes of great mag-

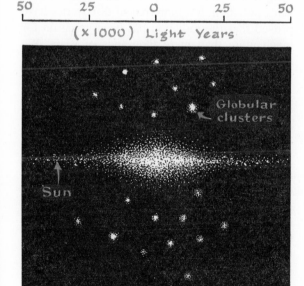

FIGURE **31-3** *Our Galaxy, or the Milky Way, viewed edgewise.*

nification, these patches were found to be other stellar systems—that is, other galaxies of stars. And, since some of the stars are Cepheid variables, it was possible to measure their distances. One of these exterior galaxies, found in the direction of the constellation Andromeda, is at a distance from us of $1.5 \times 10^6$ light years! That is, it is fifteen times as far away as the whole diameter of our galaxy. Since the plane of the Andromeda galaxy is turned toward us (though not at right angles to the line of sight), its features may be studied. It has a dense, highly luminous core, round which spiral less dense arms. Its diameter (determined from its angular size and distance) is about the same as that of our Galaxy. Here, seen as a whole from a great distance, is a stellar system whose architecture, plainly observable, is the same as that *deduced* for our system, seen from the inside looking out! The rotation of the Andromeda galaxy about the core is readily determined by the Doppler shift in the spectral lines.

The total number of observed exterior galaxies is about 100 million. Not all are spiral galaxies, but they all fall into several well-defined types, which indicate a galactic evolution. Some are too distant for individual stars to be distinguished, but on the very plausible assumption that all galaxies of the same type have approximately the same luminosity, the distances of the faintest ones can be calculated. These distances put a severe strain on our ideas of space. The observed galaxies are scattered through space to a distance of a billion ($10^9$) light years! It is expected that this distance will be doubled when the photographs taken with the new 200-inch Hale telescope are analyzed.

## 31-9. *Stellar Energy*

The source of the enormous energy that is continuously radiated from the sun (and other stars) has long been a major mystery of science. The present rate of radiation from the sun is easily determined from the radiation laws for hot bodies (p. 428). The observed wavelength of maximum energy, according to equation 25-5, gives about 6,000°K as the surface temperature

of the sun. This value, substituted in equation 25-4, indicates that more than sixty million joules is radiated from each square meter of the sun's surface per second. This figure, multiplied by the area of the sun, yields the enormous energy that leaves the surface of the sun every second.

Such a prodigious release of energy cannot be accounted for by supposing that the sun is merely cooling. This, in a few years, would produce a noticeable drop in temperature, and no such drop is observed. Chemical reactions cannot be responsible, for most molecules, at the temperature of the sun's surface, would be dissociated by thermal impacts. It was thought for a while that gravitational contraction would account for the sun's radiation. The sun, a gaseous body, would have contracted under the mutual gravitational attraction of its parts. The loss of gravitational potential energy would have increased the temperature and thus the pressure. An equilibrium between these opposing tendencies would finally have been established, and further contraction would only have compensated for the loss of energy by radiation. A moderate rate of contraction would therefore have maintained the sun at its present temperature for many thousands of years. Gravitational contraction undoubtedly did contribute to the sun's radiation, but more recent discoveries have proved that the radiation has been going on for much more than mere thousands of years. We have already seen that radioactive dating of rocks gives the age of the earth as billions of years. The sun is certainly as old as the earth, although it has not necessarily been at its present temperature for all of that time. From the field of biology, however, we learn that the sun must have had a fairly constant rate of radiation for at least the last half billion years. This is the estimated time required for the evolution of organic life on the earth. Since life requires a rather uniform temperature, the energy coming from the sun must have been arriving at about the present rate for hundreds of millions of years rather than thousands.

The discovery of nuclear transmutations and the release of nuclear energy made it possible to explain solar radiation. A relatively small decrease in mass could easily account for the observed rate of production of energy. Hydrogen was the obvious choice for the solar fuel not only because of its low nuclear charge but also because of its great abundance in the sun (and other stars). The "ash" is helium, also for two reasons: (1) among the lightest few elements, it has the highest binding energy (see Fig. 30-13) and is therefore the most stable; (2) it is found, in fact, in the sun and stars. The direct combination of four hydrogens, however, to produce a helium and two positrons, is highly improbable, for its requires the simultaneous collision of four high-energy particles. Since, as we pointed out in Chapter 23, even third-order reactions are very improbable, any over-all reaction involving several particles is usually the result of a series of simpler reactions.

In 1938 H. A. Bethe made a systematic study of known reactions and worked out in detail two sets of reactions for the production of stellar energy. One is the proton chain, and the other is the carbon cycle (the latter also proposed independently by C. F. von Weizsäcker). The equations for the proton chain are

| REACTION | MEAN REACTION TIME |
|---|---|
| (A) $_1H^1 + _1H^1 \longrightarrow _1H^2 + _{+1}e^0$ | $7 \times 10^9$ years |
| (B) $_1H^1 + _1H^2 \longrightarrow _2He^3 + \gamma$ | 10 sec |
| (C) $_2He^3 + _2He^3 \longrightarrow _2He^4 + 2_1H^1$ | $3 \times 10^5$ sec |

Elements of low $Z$, whose nuclear repulsions are low, are preferred for other helium-producing proton reactions. Helium is excluded because it does not react. Lithium, beryllium, and boron react so readily that, if they were present in the early history of stars, they have long since been consumed. The next plausible element for reaction with fast protons is therefore carbon. If we start with this, the following cycle is obtained:

| REACTION | MEAN REACTION TIME |
|---|---|
| (A) $_1H^1 + _6C^{12} \longrightarrow _7N^{13} + \gamma$ | $10^6$ years |
| (B) $_7N^{13} \longrightarrow _6C^{13} + _{+1}e^0$ | 10 min (half-life) |
| (C) $_1H^1 + _6C^{13} \longrightarrow _7N^{14} + \gamma$ | $2 \times 10^5$ years |
| (D) $_1H^1 + _7N^{14} \longrightarrow _8O^{15} + \gamma$ | $2 \times 10^7$ years |
| (E) $_8O^{15} \longrightarrow _7N^{15} + _{+1}e^0$ | 2 min (half-life) |
| (F) $_1H^1 + _7N^{15} \longrightarrow _6C^{12} + _2He^4$ | $10^4$ years |

The first thing we notice about these reactions

is that in each of the two sets four hydrogens are consumed and one helium, two positrons, and γ-rays are produced. (Note that, in the proton chain, A and B must happen *twice* to produce the two light heliums for C.) Each reaction produces energy and the reactant for the next step. The net effect of converting four protons into a helium nucleus releases about 25 Mev of energy. Also notice that the last reaction of the carbon cycle (F) produces carbon 12, which is a reacting substance of the first reaction (A). Thus the carbon is not consumed but emerges from the reactions unchanged; that is, it plays the role of a catalyst. The cycle could be started, furthermore, by any other nucleus, such as the common nitrogen 14. Hence, for the maintenance of both sets of reactions, all we need is a copious supply of hydrogen, some carbon or nitrogen, and a high temperature. All these conditions exist in most stars.

All these reactions have been studied in the cyclotron, and their rates are known with good precision. (The proton-proton reaction has not been studied in the laboratory, but its rate can be calculated with fair accuracy.) These rates lead to the mean reaction times listed opposite the reactions when conditions at the center of the sun are considered.† The center of the sun, with a density of 150 grams/cm³, is at a temperature of about $15 \times 10^{6\circ}$K. Even at this prodigious temperature the nuclei are moving rather slowly compared with cyclotron speeds. The mean kinetic energy $(= \frac{3}{2}kT)$ at the center of the sun is about 2,000 ev; in the laboratory experiments the protons were accelerated to 50 or 100 times as much KE. According to Maxwell's distribution of velocities, however, a few nuclei have many times the mean KE. This distribution, combined with the known reaction rates, leads to the mean reaction times listed.

The processes, we see, are very slow and not explosive. Even these slow reactions release enormous energies steadily, however, because of the tremendous mass of material in a star. The rate of energy production varies, it is clear, with

† The two exceptions are, of course, B and E of the carbon cycle. These nuclei with excess protons stabilize by positron emission. This is a property of the nucleus and is independent of the environment.

the temperature of the materials. The variation is less rapid for the proton chain, because of the low nuclear charges involved, than for the carbon cycle, in which the nuclei are of higher $Z$. For the cooler, less luminous stars of the "main sequence" the proton chain is the main contributor to the stellar radiation. For brilliant hot stars the carbon cycle predominates. For the sun, a rather average star, both processes contribute to the radiation, the proton chain somewhat more than the carbon cycle. The calculated rate of energy production, inevitably involving some approximations, is in good agreement with the observed radiation from the sun. The sun, then, is consuming hydrogen at the rate of many tons per second. But it is still mostly hydrogen and has an enormous mass. It can continue shining at the present rate for billions of years to come and could easily have supplied, over the past half billion years, the unfailing energy that was required for the evolution of life.

## 31-10. Stellar Evolution

It is now thought that stars are being created continuously from the cosmic dust in the galaxies. Perhaps pushed together by radiation pressure from hot stars, a region of higher than average density is formed in the interstellar matter. More matter is drawn to this center by gravitational attraction, and the mass grows. Certain dark "globules" that have been observed, from a hundredth to a tenth of a light year in diameter, may well be examples of these early "protostars." A globule contracts under gravitational attraction, grows hotter, and begins to shine. This is an unstable process, and, since it happens quickly (cosmically speaking), we do not expect to find many stars at this stage.

As the interior of the star becomes hotter, nuclear reactions begin, and the stable situation discussed in the previous section is attained. This is a star of the main sequence. If the condensing mass is small, the star stabilizes at the lower temperature of the K and M stars (refer to Fig. 31-1). If the mass is large, the star stabilizes at a higher temperature in order to create

sufficient pressure to support the larger mass. This is one of the hotter stars of the main sequence. This stable situation, as we have seen, can last a long time; hence the great majority of stars are found in the main sequence.

One might think that, once the nuclear reactions have begun, the star will shine at a constant rate until all the hydrogen is consumed. But this would require enormous "stirring" of the stellar material to carry the hydrogen continuously into the hot core. It is thought, rather, that the following process takes place. When the hydrogen in the core (about 12 percent of the mass of the star) has been converted into helium, the nuclear reactions stop, and the core begins to contract as a result of gravitational attraction. This raises the temperature of the core sufficiently to start nuclear reactions in the overlying layers of hydrogen. As this process continues, the region of nuclear reactions moves toward the outer surface of the star, and the overlying regions become less and less massive. Thus the pressure due to the released nuclear energy expands the star, and it becomes more luminous. It leaves the main sequence and becomes a giant. The hot stars that consume their hydrogen rapidly in order to maintain the high temperature leave the main sequence sooner than the cooler yellow and red stars. It is estimated that our sun, a yellow G star, will remain in the main sequence for six billion years.

When its supply of fuel is almost exhausted, a star can no longer release enough energy to keep itself inflated, and it collapses under gravitational attraction. This is often a highly unstable process, and the star may re-expand explosively several times. During these explosions it throws large amounts of material back into the cosmic dust and temporarily becomes extremely luminous. Certain stars, called novae, have been observed to rise from very faint luminosities to very great ones and then to recede again within a few days. After repeated explosions, the star settles down as a hot white dwarf and shines feebly for the rest of its life. In this stage, without the nuclear energy to support the star, the compression is enormous. Though ordinary matter will withstand very high pressure without appreciable shrinking because the exclusion principle prevents the overlapping of the electronic structures, the pressure inside these dwarfs breaks down the electronic structures, and the nuclei approach each other. This results, as we have seen, in astoundingly high densities.

## 31-11. *Galactic Red Shift*

The spectra of the exterior galaxies all show a shift toward the red end of the spectrum—that is, a shift toward longer wavelength. This shift is greater for the more distant galaxies; a survey of the known galaxies, in fact, yields a very simple relation: the amount of "red shift" is directly proportional to the distance of the galaxy. Now, if this red shift is a Doppler effect (and it is now generally regarded as such), the universe is expanding at a prodigious rate. The calculated speed of recession of the most distant galaxies is one-fifth of the speed of light. That this speed of recession would be observed from any other galaxy as well as from ours can be seen from this analogy: The seats in a lecture room are uniformly distributed over the area of the floor. Now suppose that the floor is expanding its area at a constant rate. A person sitting in any seat would see all other seats receding from him, and the more distant seats would be receding more rapidly than the neighboring ones.

The theory of an expanding universe has raised many questions about the nature of the universe—for example, whether its extent in space and time is finite or infinite. Such questions are fascinating and stimulating, but we need more information before we try to choose among the various speculations. One interesting conclusion can be drawn from our interpretation of the red shift. If, taking the observed speeds and distances, we calculate backward in time, we find that all the observable material of the universe would have been in a very small space about five billion years ago. This, as we have seen, is about the age of the earth and of meteoric material, as determined by radioactive dating. Using this result, George Gamow and associates developed an interesting theory of the formation of the elements. The composition of the mass of the present universe is fairly well established as about 76 percent hydrogen, 23 percent helium, and 1 percent heavier elements, the last in about the same proportions as in the earth.[†] They imagined all the matter of the universe, largely in the form of neutrons, to be contained in an immensely hot and immensely compressed ball about five billion years ago. This ball expanded and threw off pieces, which are the galaxies. During the expansion many neutrons decayed into protons and electrons. Protons and neutrons reacted to form heavier nuclei, which by neutron capture became still heavier. When excess neutrons in these nuclei were reduced by electron emission, nuclei of higher atomic number were formed. The whole process occurred during the first half hour of expansion, after which a fairly stable distribution was achieved. The fascinating aspect of Gamow's theory is that, by assuming a moderate temperature during expansion and by using the reaction rates and probabilities determined in cyclotron experiments, he calculated a relative abundance of the elements that is in good agreement with present observations.

A serious difficulty of the theory, however, is the absence of stable nuclei with mass numbers 5 and 8. Since $He^5$ and $Be^8$ decay into $He^4$ with half-lives of about $10^{-21}$ sec and $10^{-15}$ sec respectively, they would constitute a bottleneck in the formation of heavier nuclei by successive neutron capture. Another theory, proposed by W. A. Fowler and associates, supposes that the elements have been, and still are being, formed in the interiors of stars. As a star leaves the main sequence and becomes a giant, the core, now mostly helium, becomes enormously compressed and hot. For the more massive blue stars, these central temperatures may rise to a billion degrees. Under these extreme conditions of temperature and pressure, a third-order reaction between helium nuclei becomes probable; three heliums combine to make carbon.[‡] Carbon may combine with helium to form oxygen, oxygen

---

[†] The scarcity of hydrogen and helium on the earth and on some other planets is due to the "escape" of these gases. See § 12-4.

[‡] The synthesis of three heliums into carbon was achieved in an accelerator in 1959. The process releases 7.6 Mev of energy.

may form neon, neon may form magnesium, and so on up to iron. To form iron requires a temperature of five billion degrees, at which temperature a star is likely to explode as a supernova. Heavier elements may be formed, however, by neutron capture, as in the Gamow theory. In our discussion of missing elements (§ 30-12) we saw that technetium, with a half-life of the order of $10^5$ years, is not expected to be found among the naturally occurring elements of the earth. Strong technetium lines have been found, however, in the spectra of certain giant stars. This seems to indicate that technetium has been recently formed in these stars and supports the idea that other heavy elements are also being synthesized.

Stars, in their evolution, return much of their material to the cosmic dust of interstellar space. It is estimated that a star has blown off into the cosmic clouds half of its original mass by the time it becomes a white dwarf. Now, if an old, first-generation star, condensed from cosmic gas that was mostly hydrogen, built up heavier elements in its interior and returned much of this material to the cosmic clouds, a younger, second-generation star, condensing from this enriched cosmic dust, would contain a percentage of metals from the start. And a third-generation star, such as our sun, would start with a still higher percentage of metals. This idea seems to be supported by studies of stellar spectra. The percentage of metals ranges from less than 1 percent in old stars to about 3 percent in very young stars.

It should be obvious from this brief review of the current status of astronomy that many problems are yet to be solved. Much is known of the nature of our universe, but even more is yet to be known. Is it finite or infinite? How are galaxies evolved? Are we reasonably certain of the pattern of evolution of a star? What is the origin of the solar system? What is the ultimate fate of the solar system? And what is to become of the earth, which is still the emotional center of the universe? Will it end by exhaustion of energy as the sun slowly cools? Or will it be destroyed by a stellar collision? Or will it be consumed in a puff by the explosion of the sun? Here are plenty of questions worth answering—more than enough to ensure that astronomy will continue as an exciting, living science.

To the practical person it may seem that physical science has become so esoteric with its concern over the problems of the remotely small atomic nucleus and the remotely large cosmos as to have lost touch with mundane affairs. Equally irksome to the practical skeptic are the abstract theories that science uses to deal with these remote problems: particles and waves that seem whimsically interchangeable; structures that can be described only by an equation; uncertainty elevated to the status of a fundamental principle; a universe finite but without limit, expanding at incredible speeds yet stable. Science has two answers to the practical skeptic. To practicality it offers the pragmatic answer: "It works." Physical science has documented by experiment and theory the structure and interactions of matter from the atomic nucleus to the edge of the universe. It has done this well enough to have created a totally new source of unlimited energy and to have thrust a man-made satellite out among the celestial objects. These are truly magnificent accomplishments, and their implications of practical usefulness are tremendous. For the skeptical mind, science's answer is even more satisfying. These theories of science are not dogma, pronounced by the high practitioners of theoretical physics and established for all time. They represent the obviously and admittedly imperfect thinking of men. In spite of their great effectiveness, they are only introductions to even more remarkable, more strange, and more wonderful theories to come. As we pointed out in the introductory chapter of this text, the current developments in science are the beginning stages of a new scientific revolution, which will probably dwarf the magnificent synthesis created by Galileo and Newton in the seventeenth century. To be a participant in this twentieth-century scientific revolution demands an intellectual stamina that few among us have. But even to be an informed and interested spectator is an exciting and rewarding experience. The present is *indeed* a wonderful time to be a student of physical science.

# Concepts and Terms

Matter Waves
  de Broglie wavelength
Wave Mechanics
  Bohr's quantum condition
  wave equation
  significance of $\psi$
  standing waves and quantum numbers; stationary
    states
Uncertainty Principle
Nuclear Structure
  short-range nuclear forces
  nuclear energy levels
  fundamental particles
Magnitude and Spectral Class
  stellar magnitudes; absolute magnitude
  spectral class
  main sequence
  giants and dwarfs
Stellar Distances
  parallax
  distance by magnitudes and inverse-square law
  magnitudes from spectral class
  magnitudes for cluster variables and Cepheid
    variables

Stellar Motions
  Doppler effect
  proper motion
  tangential component
  radial component
Galaxies
  Milky Way
  galactic center
  globular clusters
  galactic rotation
  interstellar dust; galactic nebulae
  exterior galaxies
Stellar Energy
  contraction theory
  proton chain
  carbon cycle
Stellar Evolution
  condensation of cosmic dust
  stable main-sequence phase
  evolution to giant phase
  collapse to dwarf phase
Galactic Red Shift
  expanding universe
Origin of the Elements
  Gamow's theory of primordial formation
  Fowler's theory of continuous formation

# Suggested Readings

1. A. Einstein and L. Infeld, *The Evolution of Physics* (Simon and Schuster, 1938), pp. 280–313. A descriptive account of matter waves.
2. H. E. White, *Modern College Physics,* 3rd edition (Van Nostrand, 1956), pp. 708–713. A short discussion of matter waves and atomic structure.
3. M. Born, *The Restless Universe,* translated by W. M. Deans (Dover Publications, 1951), pp. 133–165, 186–210. An interesting, mostly qualitative, and authoritative account of wave mechanics and the hydrogen atom.
4. R. A. Millikan, *Electrons (+ and −),* revised edition (University of Chicago Press, 1947), pp. 301–319 (discovery of cosmic rays).
5. R. D. Rusk, *Introduction to Atomic and Nuclear Physics* (Appleton-Century-Crofts, 1958), pp. 325–331 ($\beta$-particles and the neutrino) and 431–461 (cosmic rays, mesons, and hyperons).
6. W. T. Skilling and R. S. Richardson, *A Brief Text in Astronomy,* revised edition (Henry Holt, 1959), pp. 205–296. A very readable account of the motions, distribution, and characteristics of stars and galaxies.
7. T. G. Mehlin, *Astronomy* (John Wiley, 1959), Chap. 2, "The Life Story of a Star." An excellent presentation.
8. R. H. Baker, *Astronomy,* 7th edition (Van Nostrand, 1959), pp. 467–475 (stellar evolution) and 526–533 (galactic red shift).
9. G. Gamow, *Matter, Earth and Sky* (Prentice-Hall, 1958), pp. 498–534 (stars and stellar systems) and 535–558 (general relativity and cosmology). A descriptive and authoritative account.
10. *Scientific American:*
    M. Gell-Mann and E. P. Rosenbaum, "Elementary Particles" (July 1957)
    R. E. Marshak, "The Multiplicity of Particles" (January 1952) and "The Energy of Stars" (January 1950)

# I

# Mathematical Operations

## A. Use of Algebra

In Chapter 1, and frequently throughout the rest of the book, the quantitative aspect of science is emphasized. Again and again, throughout the growth of science, precise quantitative observations determined the decision between rival theories or uncovered new properties that required new interpretations. Thus, from the very first, we deal with quantitative observations and statements. Of still more importance are the relations that are found to exist between different measurements of the same quantities. These general relations (the laws, principles, and definitions of science) are expressed in algebraic terms. It is found experimentally, for instance, that, if a sample of a gas is maintained at a constant temperature but is subjected to a number of different pressures, the volume takes on values such that the product of the pressure and the volume always has the same numerical value. This long and somewhat unwieldy statement is summarized by the expression $PV = k$, in which $P$ represents the pressure, $V$ the volume, and $k$ the constant value of the product. Algebra is useful also in stating definitions. Consider, as an example, the idea of density. This quantity, which expresses the compactness of a substance, is measured by the mass contained in one unit of volume. To arrive at this value, we measure the mass and the volume of a sample and divide the former by the latter. This whole idea is expressed by the equation $d = m/V$, in which $d$, $m$, and $V$ represent the density, mass, and volume of the sample.

Beginning students of science tend to memorize, somewhat by rote, the various formulas encountered. This, of course, is useless, for the various laws and definitions then become meaningless groups of letters, and confusion is the result. If the student will form the habit of reading the formulas in words and relating them to the ideas and discoveries they represent, algebra will become a convenient and logically precise language and will soon be seen to be a powerful tool for the expression and derivation of scientific ideas. A second warning: The validity of most laws has limitations that are not expressed by the formula and that must be kept in mind when the formula is used. The formula $PV = k$, for instance, does not include explicitly the experimental fact that the temperature of the gas was maintained at a constant value. To use this formula for a situation in which the temperature is not constant would, of course, lead to an incorrect result. This danger is automatically averted, however, by the habit of understanding the development of a formula (the "story" behind it).

The reader will be gratified to learn that, once the ideas are understood and formulated, the mathematical techniques required by this book are very simple. A surprisingly large amount of science can be expressed with the simplest kind of algebra. Except, possibly, for some topics included in this appendix, we do not use any mathematics with which the reader is not already familiar as a result of high-school training. If the high-school course was taken some years ago, however, it might be wise to review the fundamental rules of algebraic operations.

Remember that both sides of any equation may be multiplied by the same quantity or divided by the same quantity, and the result is still an equality. Similarly, the same quantity may be added to or subtracted from both sides of an equation. And, finally, if a quantity is involved in two different equations, its value as determined from one equation may be substituted in the other equation, and the result is still an equality. The following example will illustrate these useful operations. We are given the two equations

$$\frac{s}{t} = \frac{v}{2} \quad \text{and} \quad a = \frac{v}{t}$$

and are required to find $s$ if $a$ and $t$ are known but not $v$. Since we want $s$, we start by multiplying both sides of the first equation by $t$:

$$\frac{st}{t} = \frac{vt}{2} \quad \text{or} \quad s = \frac{1}{2}vt$$

Similarly, the second given equation yields $at = v$. If for $v$ we substitute $at$, we get

$$s = \frac{1}{2}(at)t \quad \text{or} \quad s = \frac{1}{2}at^2$$

Since both $a$ and $t$ are known, $s$ is determined.

## B. Units

Every scientific quantity has at least two parts. One part is a number that gives the size of the quantity compared with the size of a standard unit of measurement, and the other part is the name of the standard unit. One person, for instance, measuring the length of a lecture desk, might find that a meter stick could be laid along it three times, and another person might find that a foot rule could be laid along it ten times. If these observations of the length of the desk were reported as three and ten, nothing but confusion and argument would result. If they were reported as *three meters* and *ten feet,* however, we should know that the measurements were consistent, for there are three and a third feet in one meter. There is a tendency to give only the number. Form the habit of reporting *both*. It

might seem that a large number of standard units would be needed to express all the various quantities encountered in science. We shall see, however, that only a few fundamental units are required. Other units, called *derived units,* are combinations of the fundamental units.

When we substitute quantities in formulas, we insert both the number and the unit, and in subsequent operations we treat the units exactly like algebraic quantities. The solution of the equation will then yield not only a number for the required quantity but also the appropriate unit. If the proper unit is not obtained, there is an error in the computation. *Any algebraic statement in science is always consistent in units.* The following examples will illustrate some of these ideas.

Suppose that we wish to determine the density of a rectangular sample of a certain substance. Its dimensions are measured as 2 cm, 3 cm, and 4 cm. The volume of the sample is, then,

$$V = 2 \text{ cm} \times 3 \text{ cm} \times 4 \text{ cm}$$

or

$$V = 2 \times 3 \times 4 \times \text{cm} \times \text{cm} \times \text{cm} = 24 \text{ cm}^3$$

The derived unit cm$^3$ (read "cubic centimeter") is correct for volume. The sample is then weighed and is found to have a mass of 120 grams. Substituting in the definition of density, we get

$$d = \frac{m}{V} = \frac{120 \text{ grams}}{24 \text{ cm}^3} = 5 \text{ grams/cm}^3$$

The unit grams/cm$^3$ (read "grams per cubic centimeter") expresses the property of this substance that each cubic centimeter has a mass of five grams.

Suppose that we wish to determine the volume of a sample of mercury. The density of mercury is known to be 13.6 grams/cm$^3$. The sample is weighed and is found to have a mass of 40.8 grams. By definition $d = m/V$. We multiply both sides by $V$ and divide both sides of this result by $d$, and we have

$$V = \frac{m}{d} = \frac{40.8 \text{ grams}}{13.6 \text{ grams/cm}^3} = 3.0 \text{ grams} \frac{\text{cm}^3}{\text{grams}}$$
$$= 3.0 \text{ cm}^3$$

Since the volume comes out in cubic centimeters, we know that our operations have been correct.

## C. Exponents

You will remember from your high-school algebra that $Q^3$ is a short way of indicating the product of three $Q$'s: $Q^3 = QQQ$. We say that $Q$ has been raised to the third power. We may, similarly, indicate that $Q$ has been raised to the fifth power $(Q^5)$, to the one hundred and seventy-first power $(Q^{171})$, etc.

Such quantities may also be multiplied by each other:

$$Q^3Q^2 = QQQ \times QQ = Q^5 = Q^{(3+2)}$$

By repeated trials we can show that in multiplying exponential quantities we always *add* the exponents:

$$Q^aQ^b = Q^{(a+b)} \tag{I-1}$$

Exponential quantities may themselves be raised to a power:

$$(Q^2)^4 = QQ \times QQ \times QQ \times QQ = Q^8 = Q^{(2\times4)}$$

In general,

$$(Q^a)^b = Q^{ab} \tag{I-2}$$

We may also divide one exponential quantity by another:

$$\frac{Q^5}{Q^2} = \frac{QQQQQ}{QQ} = Q^3 = Q^{(5-2)}$$

In general,

$$\frac{Q^a}{Q^b} = Q^{(a-b)} \tag{I-3}$$

A useful extension of this exponential notation is made to quantities having negative exponents. The extension comes from equation I-3. Consider

$$\frac{Q^3}{Q^7} = Q^{(3-7)} = Q^{-4}$$

This expression seems to mean the product of minus four $Q$'s, but that meaning is certainly not clear. (Note that it does *not* mean $-Q^4$!) But by using our method of analysis we see that

$$\frac{Q^3}{Q^7} = \frac{QQQ}{QQQQQQQ} = \frac{1}{Q^4}$$

That is,

$$Q^{-4} = \frac{1}{Q^4}$$

With this definition of a negative power you should try a sufficient number of possibilities to satisfy yourself that equations I-1, I-2, and I-3 will always work whether the $a$'s and $b$'s are plus or minus numbers.

By definition the square root of $Q$ is such that $\sqrt{Q}\sqrt{Q} = Q$. But, according to equation I-1, $Q^{\frac{1}{2}}Q^{\frac{1}{2}} = Q$. Therefore $\sqrt{Q} = Q^{\frac{1}{2}}$. For example, find $\sqrt{1.36\times10^5}$. Rewrite so as to have an even power of 10. Then $\sqrt{13.6\times10^4} = \sqrt{13.6} \times \sqrt{10^4} = \sqrt{13.6} \times (10^4)^{\frac{1}{2}}$. According to equation I-2, $(10^4)^{\frac{1}{2}} = 10^2$. Therefore $\sqrt{13.6\times10^4} = 3.7\times10^2$.

One further quality of exponential numbers that will be of use to us is the fact that any number raised to the zero power is equal to 1. This fact becomes obvious when we apply our method of analysis to the quotient of a quantity raised to a power divided by the same quantity raised to the same power, which, of course, is equal to 1:

$$\frac{Q^4}{Q^4} = Q^{(4-4)} = Q^0 = 1$$

## D. Scientific Notation

Most of the important constants of the physical world are either many times as large or many times as small as our fundamental units of measurement. The speed of light, for example, is 300,000,000 m/sec. The significant figure in this number is the 3, and the long string of zeros simply locates the decimal point. The clue to a convenient way to handle such large numbers (and also extremely small ones) is given by the decimal nature of our number system, where a digit in any place in a number represents ten times as much as the same digit in the next place to the right:

$$66.6 = 60 + 6 + 6/10$$

If we divide each term of this equation by 10, we get

$$6.66 = 6 + 6/10 + 6/100$$

That is, by dividing by 10, we have moved the decimal point one place to the left. Conversely, multiplying by ten moves the decimal point one place to the right.

If we divide the speed of light by 10 eight times, we move the decimal point to the position just to the right of the three, and then, in order to keep the value of the number the same, we must also multiply by 10 eight times. Multiplying by 10 eight times is represented in exponential notation by "$\times 10^8$." The speed of light can therefore be written as $3 \times 10^8$ m/sec.

Another example: The diameter of a red blood corpuscle is about 0.00008 cm. By the same method this becomes $8 \times 10^{-5}$ cm. One more example: The distance between the center of the earth and the center of the sun is 92,900,000, or $9.29 \times 10^7$, miles. This number could be written, of course, as $929 \times 10^5$ miles or in other ways. Usually, unless there is a particular reason for doing otherwise, numbers are written with the decimal point after the first digit.

This method of using powers of ten to express decimal multiples or fractions of a quantity is implied by the standard prefixes in scientific terminology. It is worth while to examine these prefixes and their decimal and exponential equivalents:

kilo- $= \times 1,000 = \times 10^3$
meg- $= \times 1,000,000 = \times 10^6$
deci- $= \times 1/10 = \times 10^{-1}$
centi- $= \times 1/100 = \times 10^{-2}$
milli- $= \times 1/1,000 = \times 10^{-3}$
micro- $= \times 1/1,000,000 = \times 10^{-6}$

According to this system, 1.6 megohms $= 1.6 \times 10^6$ ohms, and 3.4 millimeters $= 3.4 \times 10^{-3}$ meter.

## E. Computation

Often we do not observe directly the quantity we are interested in; instead, we compute it by combining two or more observed quantities (for example, density and the ratio of combining masses). Our arithmetic often ends with more figures than are meaningful. To clarify this idea, consider an example: Suppose that we wish to determine the mass of a sample of mercury but have no balance. Suppose further that we know the density of mercury very precisely to be 13.6

grams/cm³. To get the mass of this sample, we have to measure its volume with a graduated cylinder. Suppose that the reading is 23 cm³. There is uncertainty, however, about the 3 in this number; that is, as far as we can tell, the volume may be 22.9 or 23.1 cm³. Let us italicize the 3 to indicate that it is uncertain—*23* cm³. Then, admitting that a certain number multiplied by an uncertain number gives an uncertain product (and the same applies to sums), let us do the arithmetic. (The product will, of course, be grams.) We see that the uncertainty of the 3 has influenced the 1, the 2, and the 8 of the product, and that, although it is valid to retain the 1 (the first uncertain figure), it is meaningless to report the 2 and the 8. We therefore round off the number by discarding the meaningless figures and report the mass of the sample of mercury as 310 grams. Notice that we have to add a zero to keep the decimal point in the right place even though the product has only two significant figures. This is misleading.

$$
\begin{array}{r}
13.6 \\
\underline{23} \\
408 \\
272\phantom{.} \\
\hline
372.8
\end{array}
$$

Let us now do the problem with the power-of-ten notation. We have

$$\text{mass} = (1.36 \times 10^1 \text{ grams/cm}^3)(2.3 \times 10^1 \text{ cm}^3)$$

or, rewriting,

$$\text{mass} = 1.36 \times 2.3 \times 10^1 \times 10^1 \text{ grams}$$

The first two terms, multiplied and rounded off, give 3.1, and, since $10^1 \times 10^1 = 10^2$, the mass is $3.1 \times 10^2$ grams. Notice that the proper number of significant figures (two) is given by the 3.1 and that the decimal point is determined by the $10^2$. This method not only reports numbers in a more informative way but also saves arithmetic by dropping off figures that are not significant.

To illustrate these ideas further, let us solve one more example: Find the speed of the moon in its circular orbit about the earth; compute to three significant figures. Given: $\pi = 3.14159 \ldots$, the distance from the earth to the moon (that is, the radius of the moon's approximately circular orbit) is 387,000,000 meters, and the time, $P$, needed to go round once is 27.33 days. The speed is the distance traveled (the circumference of the orbit) divided by the time: $v = 2\pi R/P$.

We first have to put $P$ into seconds, and, since we want our result only to three significant figures, we use 27.3 days for $P$:

$$P = 27.3 \text{ days} \times 24 \frac{\text{hours}}{\text{day}} \times 3{,}600 \frac{\text{sec}}{\text{hour}}$$

$$= 2.73 \times 10^1 \times 2.4 \times 10^1 \times 3.6 \times 10^3 \text{ sec}$$

Multiply 2.73 by 2.4, round off to three figures, and multiply by 3.6, getting 23.6. Therefore

$$P = 23.6 \times 10^5 \text{ sec} = 2.36 \times 10^6 \text{ sec}$$

Then

$$v = \frac{2 \times 3.14 \times 3.87 \times 10^8 \text{ m}}{2.36 \times 10^6 \text{ sec}} = 10.3 \times 10^2 \text{ m/sec}$$

or

$$v = 1.03 \times 10^3 \text{ m/sec}$$

Note that in evaluating the product

$$\frac{2 \times 3.14 \times 3.87}{2.36}$$

we round off the result to three figures after each multiplication and division, thus saving a good deal of arithmetic. It is very easy to locate the decimal point in this computation; mere inspection makes it clear that the result is about 10, not 1 or 100. Then our discussion of the manipulation of exponentials shows that $10^8/10^6 = 10^2$, and the final result is found.

If the argument above has not convinced you that the exponential notation is a great worksaver, try doing the same problem with decimal notation, carrying all the zeros and keeping all the figures that come out of the multiplying and dividing. If you do it carefully, you will, of course, end with the same answer (to three significant figures). But you will have used a great deal more pencil, paper, and time, and the chances are quite good that you will have at least misplaced the decimal point, if not completely lost it, somewhere along the way.

## F. Some Notes on Graphs

A graph, as pointed out in the text (§ 3-2), may be used to represent a series of measurements of any pair of related quantities. We start by drawing two lines, called *axes,* perpendicular to each other: one is the *vertical axis* and the other the *horizontal axis.* The point of intersection is called the origin. Regular intervals laid off along the axes from the origin represent increasing amounts of the two quantities being graphed. Values of the quantity plotted along the vertical axis are called *ordinates,* those along the horizontal axis *abscissae.* A scale is chosen for ordinates and for abscissae (generally the scales are different), and the axes are numbered to show how much of each quantity is represented by one interval. The axes are labeled with the quantity being plotted and the unit in which it is measured. A pair of measurements is represented by a point so placed that its distance to the right gives the abscissa (read on the horizontal axis) and its distance up gives the ordinate (read on the vertical axis). The ordinate and abscissa of a point are called its *co-ordinates.* The graph of Figure 3-1, for instance, shows distances measured in meters as ordinates, with one interval representing 6 m, and time of travel in seconds as abscissae, with one interval representing 1 sec. The point $B$ represents the observation that the body traveled 24 m during the first 4 sec.

The choice of scale is quite arbitrary, but a few considerations will increase the usefulness of the graph. (1) The scale should be chosen so that the arithmetic of conversion is simple— that is, involves division or multiplication by simple numbers. (2) The scale should be large enough to be read with the same precision with which the data were observed. If, for instance, a measurement gives 2.63 but the scale for plotting can be read only to tenths, the observed 3 is lost in the graph. (3) The scales should be chosen so that the full range of ordinates covers approximately the same space as the full range of abscissae. Not all three of these criteria can always be realized exactly, but an intelligent balance among them will lead to an informative and useful graph.

When drawing the curve, use a well-sharpened pencil, and draw a fine line. The line should be smooth; that is, it should be a straight line or such a smoothly curving line as that in Figure 3-2. Generally, experimental points, instead of falling exactly on such a smooth curve, will "stagger," but experience shows that this stagger is almost always due to experimental errors and that more refined measurements will bring the points more nearly on a smooth curve. The line is therefore always drawn smooth. A straight line is drawn with a straight edge in such a way that the points that miss are distributed symmetrically about the line. There are two ways of achieving symmetry: (1) if the points miss the line by approximately equal amounts, the line is drawn so that as many lie above it as below; (2) if the points miss unequally, one point that is far from one side of the line may balance two that are close to the other side. A smooth line drawn in this way represents the best average relations of the plotted data. (The same method holds for curved lines, but the mechanics of drawing are somewhat more troublesome.) There are more precise methods of determining the best smooth curve for experimental points, but they are complicated and tedious. For the purposes of this course the method outlined above, if used with care and judgment, will give very satisfactory results.

Once the graph is constructed, information may be obtained from it. Other values of the related quantities plotted (the *variables*) may be read from the graph. From the graph in Figure 3-1, for instance, the distance traveled in 3.5 sec is found to be 21 m; if the graph is extended, a distance of 55.8 m is found for 9.3 sec. The first reading is an example of *interpolation* (between the points); the second is an example of *extrapolation* (outside the points). Interpolation is generally more reliable than extrapolation; that is, more confidence can be placed in the assumption that the relation between the variables (that is, the law) remains the same in regions bracketed by experimental points than in the assumption that it continues unchanged beyond those points. We arrived at the reading of 55.8 m by assuming that the body continued to move at a speed of 6 m/sec.

If the curve is a straight line through the origin, we can evaluate the slope (§ 3-2) by reading the coordinates of some point and computing the ratio of ordinate to abscissa. In theory, any point on the graph would do; in practice, a point (not necessarily an experimental

point) well up the graph and lying *on the graph* is chosen: well up the graph because the inherent error of reading the scales is a smaller fraction of larger than of smaller coordinates; on the *graph* because such a point gives the best average slope for all the data.

## G. *Direct and Inverse Proportion*

If two quantities are so related that an increase in one produces an increase in the other, we say that there is a direct relation between them; if one quantity doubles when the other doubles, triples when the other triples, etc., the direct relation is called a *direct proportion*. (The distances and times of Table 3-1 are in direct proportion.) If we use the terminology of algebra and call one quantity $x$ and the other $y$,

$$y \propto x \quad \text{and} \quad y/x = K$$

or

$$y = Kx \tag{I-4}$$

in which expressions $K$ is a *proportionality constant*. The quantities $y$ and $x$ are not necessarily equal, but their ratio is always the same. A direct proportion, clearly, is represented by a straight line through the origin. The slope of the line is the proportionality constant.

If two quantities are so related that an increase in one produces a decrease in the other, we say that there is an inverse relation between

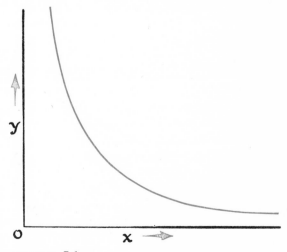

FIGURE **I-1**

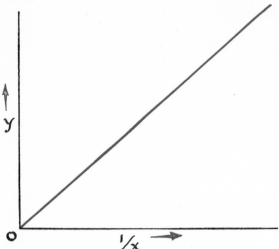

FIGURE **I-2**

them; if doubling one quantity reduces the other to one-half, tripling one reduces the other to one-third, etc., the inverse relation is called an *inverse proportion*. For such a proportion

$$v \propto \frac{1}{x} \quad \text{or} \quad yx = C \tag{I-5}$$

in which expression $C$ is a proportionality constant.

An inverse relation leads to a graph similar to Figure I-1. Whether the relation is an inverse proportion is not easily determined by inspection of the graph; but, if it is, the graph of one quantity plotted against the *reciprocal* of the other quantity shows a straight line through the origin, as in Figure I-2. This follows from the definitions of the two types of proportion and also from equation I-5, which may be rewritten as

$$y = C(1/x) \tag{I-6}$$

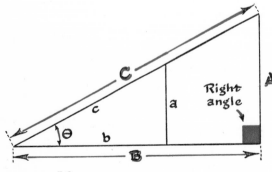

FIGURE **I-3**

By comparison with equation I-4 it is seen that equation I-6 is a direct proportion between $y$ and $1/x$. Thus an inverse proportion between two quantities is established if the plotting of observed values of one against the *reciprocals* of the observed values of the other leads to a straight line through the origin, and the slope of the reciprocal graph gives the value of the proportionality constant.

## H. Sine, Cosine, and Tangent of an Angle

Two superimposed right triangles are shown in Figure I-3. One triangle has sides $a$, $b$, and $c$; the other has sides $A$, $B$, and $C$. The angle $\theta$ is an acute angle in each triangle. The triangles are similar, and the ratios of corresponding sides are therefore equal although the sides are much longer in one triangle than in the other; that is,

$$a/c = A/C$$
$$b/c = B/C$$
$$a/b = A/B$$

Clearly, the only way to change the value of these ratios is to change $\theta$; changing the size of the triangle does not affect them. If, for instance, $\theta$ is made larger, $a$ and $c$ become longer (but *not* in direct proportion), and the ratios change value. Values of the ratios may therefore be computed for various values of $\theta$ and listed in a table. Such tables are very useful in dealing with right triangles. The ratios have been named and defined as follows:

sine $\theta$ (abbreviated as sin $\theta$) $= a/c$
cosine $\theta$ (abbreviated as cos $\theta$) $= b/c$
tangent $\theta$ (abbreviated as tan $\theta$) $= a/b$

Notice that $a$ is the side of the right triangle opposite $\theta$, $b$ is the side adjacent to $\theta$, and $c$ is the hypotenuse.

It is found, for example, that, if $\theta = 30°$, the opposite side is exactly half of the hypotenuse; that is, sin 30° = 0.50, which is read as "the sine of 30° is equal to 0.50." The usefulness of these relations lies in the fact that we can determine all the quantities of a right triangle by measuring any two sides or one side and either acute angle. If we desire, for example, to know the length of side $A$ of the triangle of Figure I-3, we can determine this length by measuring two of the other quantities of the triangle, sides $B$ and $C$ or side $B$ or $C$ and angle $\theta$. If we know $\theta$ and side $B$, we can determine side $A$ from the definition of $\tan \theta$ and the value given for this function in a table of tangents:

$$\tan \theta = A/B$$
$$A = B \tan \theta$$

If sides $B$ and $C$ are both known, $\theta$ can be calculated from these values and the definition of the cosine of $\theta$.

These relations, plus the proportionality of the quantities of similar triangles, make it possible to measure by indirect methods many quantities that are not accessible to direct measurement.

## Problems

**I-1.** Express the following quantities in scientific notation: (A) the electronic charge is 0.000000-0000000000001602 coul; (B) the number of hydrogen molecules in 1 cm$^3$ of the gas under standard conditions of temperature and pressure is 26,900,000,000,000,000,000,000; (C) the wavelength of sodium yellow light is 0.0000005896 m.

**I-2.** Express the following in decimal notation: (A) the mass of one hydrogen molecule is $3.34 \times 10^{-24}$ gram; (B) the radius of the earth is $6.45 \times 10^6$ m.

**I-3.** Evaluate the following expressions. Calculate to two significant figures, and use exponential notation.

| | |
|---|---|
| $(561)0.015$ | *Ans.* 8.4 |
| $\dfrac{8.2 \times 10^5}{4,130}$ | *Ans.* $2.0 \times 10^2$ |
| $\dfrac{(13)6.3 \times 10^{-3}}{0.0000478}$ | *Ans.* $1.7 \times 10^3$ |
| $\sqrt{250,000}$ | *Ans.* $5.0 \times 10^2$ |
| $\sqrt{64,000}$ | *Ans.* $2.5 \times 10^2$ |

**I-4.** Express the following in the fundamental units meter, kilogram, and second:

| | |
|---|---|
| 37 kilometers | *Ans.* $3.7 \times 10^4$ m |
| 18.3 microseconds | *Ans.* $1.83 \times 10^{-5}$ sec |
| 43 centimeters | *Ans.* 0.43 m |
| 73 grams | *Ans.* $7.3 \times 10^{-2}$ kgm |

**I-5.** By solving equations, substituting given values, and deriving the proper units for the result, determine each of the quantities specified in the following answers. In these and *all future* problems make computations to *no more than three* significant figures.

(A) $F = ma$; $m = 6.4$ kgm; $a = 4.2$ m/sec$^2$

$$Ans. \ F = 26.8 \text{ kgm} \frac{m}{sec^2}$$

(B) $V/I = R_1 + R_2$; $R_1 = 3.6$ ohms; $R_2 = 10.78$ ohms; $I = 2.38$ amp

*Ans.* $V = 34.3$ ohm amp

(C) $F = G \dfrac{m_1 m_2}{r^2}$; $F = 7.88 \times 10^{-8}$ newton; $m_1 = 23.5$ kgm; $m_2 = 113$ kgm; $r = 1.5$ m

$$Ans. \ G = 6.67 \times 10^{-11} \frac{\text{newton m}^2}{\text{kgm}^2}$$

(D) $\frac{1}{2}mv^2 = mgh$; $g = 9.8 \dfrac{m}{sec^2}$; $h = 12$ kilometers

*Ans.* $v = 4.85 \times 10^2$ m/sec

(E) $F = K \dfrac{Qq}{r^2}$; also $E = \dfrac{F}{q}$; $r = 0.013$ m; $Q = 3.72 \times 10^{-13}$ coul; $K = 9 \times 10^9 \dfrac{\text{newton m}^2}{\text{coul}^2}$

*Ans.* $E = 19.8$ newtons/coul

**I-6.**

(A) What is the density of hydrogen gas under standard conditions? (See Probs. I-1B and I-2A for data.)

*Ans.* $8.99 \times 10^{-5}$ gram/cm$^3$

(B) What is the volume of 1 gram of hydrogen under standard conditions?

*Ans.* $1.12 \times 10^4$ cm$^3$

**I-7.** The density of lead is 11.3 grams/cm$^3$. A cylinder of lead has a mass of 1.87 kgm. If the area of the base of the cylinder is 23 cm$^2$, what is its height?

*Ans.* 7.20 cm

**I-8.** Three sets of related values† of $y$ and $x$ are

† The numbers in Probs. I-8, I-9, and I-10 are purposely simple, so that, when you work back from the answers, you can see the relations intuitively. It is recommended that these problems be solved graphically as practice in the general method. Probs. I-9 and I-10 are examples of reducing a relation to a simple proportion by appropriate choice of variables. This device is used frequently throughout this course.

| (A) | | (B) | | (C) | |
|---|---|---|---|---|---|
| $y$ | $x$ | $y$ | $x$ | $y$ | $x$ |
| 3 | 1 | 16.0 | 1 | 16.0 | 1 |
| 6 | 2 | 4.0 | 2 | 8.0 | 2 |
| 9 | 3 | 1.8 | 3 | 5.3 | 3 |
| 12 | 4 | 1.0 | 4 | 4.0 | 4 |

Show by graphical analysis that one set is a direct proportion between $y$ and $x$, that one is an inverse proportion, and that one is neither. From your graphs determine the proportionality constants. Write an equation for each proportionality, and verify it by substituting appropriate values from the tables.

*Ans.* The constants are 16 and 3.

**I-9.** Two sets of related values of $y$ and $x$ are

| (A) | | (B) | |
|---|---|---|---|
| $y$ | $x$ | $y$ | $x$ |
| 5 | 1 | 3 | 0 |
| 20 | 2 | 10 | 1 |
| 45 | 3 | 17 | 2 |
| 80 | 4 | 24 | 3 |

Graph these sets, and note that neither yields a straight line through the origin. Regraph relation A, but plot $y$ against corresponding values of $x^2$; for example, 45 and 9 would be the third point. Is this graph a straight line through the origin? Write an equation derived from this graph for relation A. Check by inserting values.

*Ans.* $y = 5x^2$

**I-10.** Inspect graph B of Prob. I-9, and notice that, if each point is dropped three units, the line goes through the origin and is still a straight line. Plot this graph; that is, plot $(y - 3)$ against appropriate values of $x$. For instance, 14 and 2 would be the third point. From this graph derive an equation for relation B, and verify.

*Ans.* $y - 3 = 7x$

**I-11.** Show by graphical analysis that relation B of Prob. I-8 is expressed by $y = 16/x^2$.

| TABLE I-1 | | TABLE I-2 | |
|---|---|---|---|
| $m$ | $t$ | $L$ | $t$ |
| (grams) | (°C) | (cal/gram) | (°C) |
| 54 | 0 | 557 | 70 |
| 64 | 20 | 546 | 85 |
| 74 | 40 | 536 | 100 |
| 84 | 60 | 526 | 115 |
| 94 | 80 | 515 | 130 |

**I-12.** Table I-1 gives the experimentally determined number of grams ($m$) of potassium bromide that will dissolve in 100 cm³ of water at various temperatures ($t$). Graph these data, using $m$ as ordinate. Determine the slope of the graph (both value and units), and interpret its significance. Write the law expressing these experimental results. How many grams will dissolve at 17°? at 100°?

*Ans.* $m - 54$ grams $= 0.5t$ gram/°C; 62.5 grams; 104 grams

**I-13.** Table I-2 gives the experimentally determined heat of vaporization of water ($L$) in calories per gram at various temperatures ($t$). Write the law describing these observations. Does this formula agree exactly with all the data? Discuss. Find the value of $L$ for 93.7°. Read from the graph, compute from the law, and compare.

*Ans.* $L = 606 \dfrac{\text{cal}}{\text{gram}} - 0.7t \dfrac{\text{cal}}{\text{gram °C}}$

# II

# Chemical Calculations

## A. Formulas

If we know the valences and the symbols (available from the periodic table) of any set of elements, we can readily write the formula of the compound composed of those elements. Conversely, if we know the formula of a compound and the valence of some of the elements, we can determine the valence of the other element. We must keep two rules in mind: (1) the sum of the valences of all the atoms in a compound must add up to zero; (2) the most positive element is usually written first in the formula (exceptions are several compounds of hydrogen with more negative elements, in the formulas of which the hydrogen is written second).

### EXAMPLE 1

From their positions in the periodic table, the valences of carbon and oxygen are seen to be $+4$ and $-2$. If two atoms of oxygen $[2(-2) = -4]$ combine with one atom of carbon $(+4)$ the total of the valences is zero. The formula of a compound of carbon and oxygen is, then, $CO_2$ (carbon dioxide).

### EXAMPLE 2

Nitrogen has a valence of $-3$; hydrogen has a valence of $+1$. The formula of a compound of these two elements therefore is $NH_3$ $[-3 + 3(+1) = -3 + 3 = 0]$. This is one of the formulas that violate the rule that the positive element comes first. The name of this compound is ammonia.

### EXAMPLE 3

In sulfuric acid, $H_2SO_4$, the valence of sulfur is calculated as follows: Since H is $+1$ and O is $-2$, the total of valences of these atoms in the compound is $2(+1) + 4(-2) = +2 - 8 = -6$. The one sulfur atom must, then, have a valence of $+6$ in order that the total valence of all the atoms in the compound add up to zero.

### EXAMPLE 4

Calculate the valence of the chromium atom in potassium dichromate, $K_2Cr_2O_7$.

$K_2 \longrightarrow 2(+1) = +2;$   $O_7 \longrightarrow 7(-2) = -14;$ the sum of these is $+2 - 14 = -12$; the sum of the valence of the two Cr atoms must, then, be $+12$; this can be only if the two atoms are each $+6$. The valence of chromium in this compound is therefore $+6$.

## B. Molecular Weights and Compositions

The molecular weight of a substance is the sum of the atomic weights of the atoms that make up the molecule. By a combination of the atomic weights (from the periodic table) and the formula of the molecule, we can calculate the molecular weight. Examples:

$Br_2$: $80 + 80 = 160$
$HBr$: $1 + 80 = 81$
$H_2SO_4$: $2 \times 1 + 32 + 4 \times 16 = 2 + 32 + 64 = 98$
$Na_2HPO_4$: $2 \times 23 + 1 + 31 + 4 \times 16 = 46 + 1 + 31 + 64 = 142$

From these relations we can calculate compositions. Examples: (1) HBr is composed of 1 part of H to 80 parts of Br (by mass, of course); another way of expressing the composition would be: H makes up 1/81, or $1/81 \times 100\%$ = 1.2%, of the mass of HBr. (2) $H_2SO_4$ is 2/98 H, 32/98 S, and 64/98 O, or 2.0% H, 32.7% S, and 65.3% O. (3) $Na_2HPO_4$ is 46/142 Na, 1/142 H, 31/142 P, and 64/142 O, or 32.4% Na, 0.7% H, 21.8% P, and 45.1% O.

Conversely, if the composition is known, we can find the formula of the compound. Again the atomic weights from the table are used.

### EXAMPLE 5

If a compound contains 1 part of H to 16 parts of S, what is its formula?

|   | Parts | Atomic Weight | Relative number of atoms |
|---|---|---|---|
| H | 1 | 1 | 1/1 = 1 |
| S | 16 | 32 | 16/32 = 1/2 |

Ratio: $\dfrac{\text{atoms of H}}{\text{atoms of S}} = \dfrac{1}{1/2} = 2$. Therefore the simplest possible formula for the compound (hydrogen sulfide) is $H_2S$.

### EXAMPLE 6

If a compound is composed of 43.7% P and 56.3% O, what is its formula?

|   | Parts per 100 | Atomic Weight | Relative number of atoms |
|---|---|---|---|
| P | 43.7 | 31 | 43.7/31 = 1.41 |
| O | 56.3 | 16 | 56.3/16 = 3.52 |

Ratio: $\dfrac{\text{atoms of P}}{\text{atoms of O}} = \dfrac{1.41}{3.52} = 0.4 = 4/10 = 2/5$ (simplest integral ratio). Therefore the simplest possible formula for this compound (phosphorus pentoxide) is $P_2O_5$.

These examples were calculated to the simplest possible formula, which is called the **empirical formula.** We should need more evidence to prove that the true formulas are these and not some multiples of these, such as $H_4S_2$ and $P_4O_{10}$. In order to distinguish which multiple of the empirical formula is the true formula, we need experimental evidence of the molecular weight of the compound (see part E of this appendix).

## C. Equations

We have dealt with several examples of the transformation of substances into other substances, such as the combination of copper and sulfur to form copper sulfide, or the combination of magnesium and oxygen to form magnesium oxide, or the decomposition of water into hydrogen and oxygen. The statement of these experimental facts can be expressed most succinctly by chemical equations. Examples:

$$2Cu + S \longrightarrow Cu_2S$$
$$Mg + O \longrightarrow MgO$$
$$2H_2O \longrightarrow 2H_2 + O_2$$

Here we have made use of our symbols, of molecular formulas, and of the law of conservation of matter. This law states that all atoms that are present among the reactants must also be present among the products; that is, the equation must have the same number of each atom on both sides of the arrow. The satisfaction of this requirement is what we refer to when we say that chemical equations must be *balanced*.

Only experience will tell us whether a particular reaction will, in fact, take place or what the products of a particular reaction will be. In a few cases, however, we can make intelligent predictions, and, if we are told what the products of a reaction are, we have the information we need to balance the equation.

### EXAMPLE 7

We know that water is formed by the reaction (burning in this case) of hydrogen with oxygen. We also know the formulas of the three molecules. This information is stated by the unbalanced equation

$$H_2 + O_2 \longrightarrow H_2O$$

in which we have two O atoms on the left and only one O atom on the right. The oxygen of the reactants (on the left) is provided *only* by oxygen gas, which is a *diatomic* molecule, $O_2$. We can therefore provide oxygen atoms only in pairs. We must therefore indicate two molecules of $H_2O$ on the right. But since, in balancing the O atoms, we have required four H atoms on the right, we must supply them on the left by doubling the number of $H_2$ molecules:

$$2H_2 + O_2 \longrightarrow 2H_2O$$

This equation now has four H atoms and two O atoms on each side and is therefore balanced.

## EXAMPLE 8

If water is added to phosphorus pentoxide, $P_2O_5$, phosphoric acid, $H_3PO_4$, is produced. The unbalanced equation is

$$P_2O_5 + H_2O \longrightarrow H_3PO_4$$

Since two P atoms are on the left, we double the $H_3PO_4$:

$$P_2O_5 + H_2O \longrightarrow 2H_3PO_4$$

We now need six H atoms, and therefore three molecules of $H_2O$, on the left:

$$P_2O_5 + 3H_2O \longrightarrow 2H_3PO_4$$

The equation is now entirely balanced, including the O atoms; all atoms, H, P, and O, are equal in number on the two sides of the equation.

Consider all the information that is conveyed by a balanced equation:

1. A statement of the reaction—for example, "Phosphorus pentoxide reacts with water to produce phosphoric acid."
2. The formulas of the reactants and products (and thereby the valences of the elements).
3. The composition of all the reactants and products.
4. The number of molecules of each reactant and each product—for example, "One molecule of phosphorus pentoxide reacts with three molecules of water to produce two molecules of phosphoric acid."
5. The relative masses of the reactants and products. These relative amounts are expressed in moles ("One mole of $P_2O_5$ reacts with three moles of $H_2O$ to produce two moles of $H_3PO_4$"), but by the use of molecular weights we can readily calculate the relative numbers of grams of the reactants and products.

## D. *Reacting Masses*

A balanced equation tells us immediately the number of moles of the reactants and the number of moles of the products. These numbers are, of course, relative. If an equation says that two moles of A react with one mole of B, it is clear that four moles of A will react with two of B, and one of A with one-half of B—that, in general, the ratio of moles of A to moles of B in this reaction is 2/1. We can then use the equation

$$\text{mass} = n \times \text{mol wt}$$

which relates the mass of a substance to the number of moles and the molecular weight, to determine the relative masses of the reactants and products.

## EXAMPLE 9

How many grams of hydrogen and how many grams of oxygen would be produced by the decomposition of 100 grams of water? The balanced equation,

$$2H_2O \longrightarrow 2H_2 + O_2$$

tells us that two moles of water produce two moles of hydrogen and one mole of oxygen; and 100 grams of $H_2O$ is $100/18 = 5.55$ moles of $H_2O$. This amount of water would, then, produce $5.55 \times 2 = 11.1$ grams of $H_2$; and, since any number of moles of $H_2O$ would produce half that number of moles of $O_2$, the 100 grams of $H_2O$ would produce $5.55/2$ moles, or $5.55/2 \times 32 = 88.9$ grams of $O_2$.

## EXAMPLE 10

How many grams of $P_2O_5$ are needed to produce 250 grams of $H_3PO_4$? How many grams of water would be needed?

Equation:

$$P_2O_5 + 3H_2O \longrightarrow 2H_3PO_4$$

Molecular weights:

$$
\begin{aligned}
2P &= 2 \times 31 = 62 \\
5O &= 5 \times 16 = \underline{80} \\
P_2O_5 & \quad\quad\quad = 142
\end{aligned}
$$

$$
\begin{aligned}
2H &= 2 \\
O &= \underline{16} \\
H_2O &= 18
\end{aligned}
$$

$$
\begin{aligned}
3H &= 3 \times 1 = 3 \\
1P &= \quad\quad\quad 31 \\
4O &= 4 \times 16 = \underline{64} \\
H_3PO_4 & \quad\quad\quad = 98
\end{aligned}
$$

$$\text{moles of } H_3PO_4 = \frac{250 \text{ grams}}{98 \text{ grams/mole}} = 2.55 \text{ moles}$$

From the equation: 1 mole $P_2O_5 \longrightarrow 2$ moles $H_3PO_4$, or 1/2 mole $P_2O_5 \longrightarrow$ 1 mole $H_3PO_4$, or 2.55/2 moles $P_2O_5 \longrightarrow$ 2.55 moles $H_3PO_4$ = 250 grams $H_3PO_4$.

2.55/2 moles $\times$ 142 grams/mole = 181 grams $P_2O_5$ needed

From the equation:
3 moles $H_2O \longrightarrow$ 2 moles $H_3PO_4$.
$3 \times 2.55/2$ moles = $3 \times 2.55/2 \times 18$ grams = 69 grams $H_2O$ needed.

# E. General Gas Equation

Our study of the behavior of gases led to the derivation of a general gas equation, applicable to all gases, which relates four variables, amount, volume, pressure, and temperature, of confined gases. If we specify any three of these variables, we can use this equation to calculate the fourth. This equation (10-10) is

$$PV = nRT$$

if $P$ = pressure, $V$ = volume, $n$ = number of moles, $R$ = universal gas constant, and $T$ = absolute temperature. $R$ can be evaluated by any corresponding set of values of the four variables (equation 10-11):

$$R = \frac{PV}{nT}$$

We carry out this evaluation of $R$ in the laboratory by measuring the pressure, temperature, and volume of a known mass of a gas of known molecular weight. From the mass of the sample and its molecular weight we can calculate the number of moles in the sample by using the relation

$$n = \frac{mass}{mol\ wt}$$

The best experimental value of the gas constant, the value we shall use in all calculations, is

$$R = 6.23 \times 10^3\ cm^4/mole°$$

When this constant is used, pressures must be expressed in cm Hg, volumes in $cm^3$, and temperatures in °K (absolute).

Calculations using the general gas equation (10-10) are best considered in two classes: (1) those involving changes in $P$, $V$, and $T$ for a fixed amount of a gas; (2) those involving the

calculation of the amount of a gas from given values of $P$, $V$, and $T$ or of the volume from a given amount at given values of $P$ and $T$.

The first class of calculations are most easily accomplished if we consider the gas equation in the form

$$PV/T = nR$$

If the amount is fixed, the entire right side of the equation is constant. We may therefore write

$$P_1V_1/T_1 = P_2V_2/T_2$$

in which expression the subscripts 1 and 2 denote particular corresponding values of the three variables.

## EXAMPLE 11

If a sample of a gas occupies 100 $cm^3$ at 0°C and 76 cm pressure, what volume will it occupy at 200°C and 50 cm pressure?

$P_1 = 76$ cm
$P_2 = 50$ cm
$T_1 = t_1° + 273° = 0° + 273° = 273°$
$T_2 = 200° + 273° = 473°$
$V_1 = 100\ cm^3$
$V_2 = ?$

Substitute all the known values in the equation, and solve for $V_2$:

$$\frac{76\ cm\ 100\ cm^3}{273°} = \frac{50\ cm\ V_2}{473°}$$

$$V_2 = \frac{473 \times 76 \times 100}{273 \times 50}\ cm^3 = 263\ cm^3$$

## EXAMPLE 12

If a sample of a gas confined at 100°C exerts a pressure of 80 cm, what pressure would it exert if confined to the same volume at 0°C?

$P_1 = 80$ cm
$T_1 = 100° + 273° = 373°$
$T_2 = 0° + 273° = 273°$
$V_1 = V_2$
$P_2 = ?$

Substitute in the equation, and solve for $P_2$:

$$\frac{80\ cm\ V_1\ cm^3}{373°} = \frac{P_2V_1\ cm^3}{273°}$$

$$P_2 = \frac{80 \times 273}{373}\ cm = 58.5\ cm$$

In the second class of calculations, involving the amount of a gas, the entire gas equation

(10-10) is used. A frequent requirement in this class is the calculation of molecular weight, in which case the value for $n$ given above $[n = m/(\text{mol wt})]$ is used. Equation 10-10 then becomes

$$PV = \frac{m}{\text{mol wt}} RT$$

or

$$\text{mol wt} = mRT/PV$$

## EXAMPLE 13

What volume would 1 mole of any gas occupy at 0°C and 76 cm pressure (standard temperature and pressure, abbreviated STP)? This is the **molar volume** of a gas.

For this calculation we solve equation 10-10 for $V$:

$V = nRT/P$
$n = 1$ mole
$R = 6.23 \times 10^3$ cm$^4$/mole°
$T = 0° + 273° = 273°$
$P = 76$ cm

Substitute these values in the equation:

$$V = \frac{1 \text{ mole} \times 6.23 \times 10^3 \text{ cm}^4/\text{mole}° \times 273°}{76 \text{ cm}}$$
$$= 22.4 \times 10^3 \text{ cm}^3 = 2.24 \times 10^4 \text{ cm}^3$$

## EXAMPLE 14

A sample of hydrogen sulfide has a mass of 0.32 gram and occupies 232 cm$^3$ at 25°C and 75.5 cm pressure. Calculate the molecular weight of hydrogen sulfide.

We substitute the following values in the new form of equation 10-10:

$T = 25° + 273° = 298°$
$P = 75.5$ cm
$V = 232$ cm$^3$
$m = 0.32$ gram
mol wt
$\quad = mRT/PV$
$\quad = \dfrac{0.32 \text{ gram} \times 6.23 \times 10^3 \text{ cm}^4/\text{mole}° \times 298°}{75.5 \text{ cm} \times 232 \text{ cm}^3}$
$\quad = 0.034 \times 10^3$
$\quad = 34$ grams/mole

## EXAMPLE 15

What volume would 2.5 moles of carbon dioxide occupy at −15°C and 78.4 cm pressure?

$V = nRT/P$
$n = 2.5$ moles
$P = 78.4$ cm
$T = -15° + 273° = 258°$
$V = ?$
$V = \dfrac{2.5 \text{ moles} \times 6.23 \times 10^3 \text{ cm}^4/\text{mole}° \times 258°}{78.4 \text{ cm}}$
$\quad = 51.3 \times 10^3 \text{ cm}^3 = 5.13 \times 10^4 \text{ cm}^3$

# III Solutions

In Chapters 13 and 14 a number of ideas that involve problem-solving situations were introduced. This appendix summarizes the methods and techniques and offers several examples of the solving of problems related to the behavior of solutions.

## A. Empirical Rules of Solubility

Chapter 13 contains many references to solubilities of solutes in various solvents and some theoretical discussion of solubility relations. The discussion of solubility here is strictly a listing of rules of solubility without theoretical comment. These rules are useful for predicting how a particular solvent-solute pair will behave.

### GENERAL RULES

(1) Substances that are chemically similar are generally soluble in each other. Organic solvents will generally dissolve organic solutes; inorganic solutes are generally soluble in water. Substances are thus divided into two classes by their polarity—organic solutes and solvents being non-polar, water and inorganic solutes being polar. Deviations from this rule are almost always related to some other chemical similarity.

(2) Interaction of solvent and solute enhances solubility. Actual chemical reaction between the solute and the solvent, producing a new molecular species, is the extreme of solute-solvent interaction. A number of gases, includ-

ing ammonia ($NH_3$), sulfur trioxide ($SO_3$), carbon dioxide ($CO_2$), and nitrogen dioxide ($NO_2$), show this behavior in water solution. A much weaker interaction between solute and solvent is solvation, the loose, temporary combination of several solvent molecules with each solute particle. Water's great effectiveness in solvation accounts, in part, for its great effectiveness as a solvent. Solvation in which water is the solvent is called hydration.

(3) The effect of temperature on solubility is best described by solubility curves of the type shown in Figure 13-1. In general, the solubility of solids and liquids increases, but the solubility of most gases decreases, with rising temperature.

(4) Pressure does not affect the solubility of solids or liquids appreciably, but does have strong effects on the solubility of gases. The influence of pressure on the solubility of gases is described by Henry's law (equation 13-5), $p = kc$, which is oftenest used in the form of equation 13-6,

$$p_1/p_2 = c_1/c_2$$

in which $p$ is the partial pressure of the gas, $c$ is the concentration, and the subscripts refer to two sets of conditions of pressure and concentration.

### EXAMPLE 1

At 76 cm pressure and 20°C 1.45 grams of $CO_2$ will dissolve in 1,000 grams of water.

Calculate the concentration at three times this pressure, 228 cm, by the use of equation 13-6. Use subscript 1 for the conditions given and subscript 2 for the conditions asked.

$$\frac{76 \text{ cm}}{228 \text{ cm}} = \frac{1.45 \text{ grams}/1,000 \text{ grams}}{c_2}$$

$$c_2 = \frac{228 \times 1.45}{76} \text{ grams}/1,000 \text{ grams}$$

$$= 3 \times 1.45 = 4.35 \text{ grams}/1,000 \text{ grams of water}$$

(5) The law of partition, which describes the distribution of a solute between two immiscible solvents that are in competition for it, is stated by equation 13-4,

$$c_1/c_2 = s_1/s_2$$

in which $c$ refers to concentration, $s$ to solubility, and the subscripts to the two solvents. The ratio of the two solubilities is usually referred to as the distribution coefficient of the particular solute between the two solvents.

## EXAMPLE 2

The distribution coefficient of succinic acid between water and ether is 6.0. This means that the solubility of succinic acid in water is 6.0 times as great as it is in ether. The solubility of succinic acid in water at room temperature is 84 grams per 1,000 grams of water; the solubility in ether is therefore $84/6 = 14$ grams per 1,000 grams of ether. It might be of interest to calculate how much of the succinic acid in a saturated solution in ether would be extracted into an equal mass of water.

The ratio of the concentrations in the two solvents is given by the law of partition: $c_1/c_2 = k = 6$. These are the concentrations of the solute in the two solvents after we have established equilibrium by shaking the ether solution with water. According to this equation, the concentration in the water phase is then six times the concentration in the ether phase. If we start with 14 grams of succinic acid dissolved in 1,000 grams of ether and shake this solution with 1,000 grams of water, the 14 grams will then be distributed in this ratio of concentrations. This can happen only if 12 grams of the original 14 grams go into the water phase, giving a concentration of 12 grams per 1,000 grams of water and leaving 2 of the 14 grams in the ether phase for a concentration of 2 grams per 1,000 grams of ether. Thus 12/14 of the succinic acid is extracted into the equal mass of water. This fraction can be expressed as a percentage; $12/14 \times 100\% = 85\%$ of the solute is extracted.

It might also be of interest to calculate how many extractions, using equal masses of water each time, it would take to remove 99.9% of the succinic acid. We have seen that 85% is extracted each time, leaving 15% in the ether phase. A second extraction leaves 15% of the 2 grams left by the first extraction; that is, the amount remaining after two extractions is 15% of 15%, or 2.25%. A third extraction reduces this to $0.15 \times 2.25\% = 0.34\%$. A fourth extraction leaves 15% of this, or 0.051%. Thus four extractions with equal masses of water remove 99.95% of the succinic acid from the ether phase.

Obviously, equal masses of water in each extraction mean the use of a huge quantity of water, 4,000 grams in the above case. If a smaller amount is used each time, the same result can be achieved in only a few more extractions and with much less solvent.

## SPECIFIC RULES OF SOLUBILITY IN WATER

Most of the substances we have encountered in this text are soluble in water. There are, however, degrees of solubility. A substance is called *soluble* if at least 10 grams dissolves, *sparingly soluble* if 1–10 grams dissolves, *insoluble* if less than 1 gram dissolves, in 1,000 grams of water.

(1) With very few exceptions all simple compounds of hydrogen, lithium, sodium, potassium, and the ammonium radical with negative elements and negative radicals are soluble. Such compounds of hydrogen are called acids; the compounds of the metals (and ammonium) with negative elements and radicals are called salts.

(2) Most compounds of metals with the nitrate or acetate radical or with chlorine, bromine, or iodine are soluble. The major exceptions to this rule are the compounds of silver and lead with chlorine, bromine, and iodine. Lead chloride is sparingly soluble in cold water but moderately soluble in hot water.

(3) All hydroxides and sulfides except those of the alkali metals, alkaline-earth metals, and ammonium are insoluble.

(4) All carbonates and phosphates except those of the alkali metals and ammonium are insoluble.

## B. Calculation of Concentration

Four methods of expressing concentrations of solutions are used in this text. All of these take the form of a statement of the amount of solute in a certain amount of solvent (or in a certain amount of solution), and any of them may be the most convenient for dealing with a particular situation. The four expressions are: (1) grams of solute per 1,000 grams of solvent; (2) moles of solute per 1,000 grams of solvent; (3) mole fraction; (4) moles of solute per liter of solution. The first three depend entirely on quantities expressed as *masses*. The first is generally used in specifications of solubility but has only a limited usefulness if one is interested in either the number of chemical equivalents or the number of particles in a given quantity of solution. In such cases the second and third expressions are much more useful. The second expression, called **molal**, emphasizes the number of particles of solute and states the amount of solvent in mass units rather than in moles. The third expression, the **mole fraction,** emphasizes the number of moles of each component compared with the total number of moles of all components. We calculate the mole fraction by dividing the number of moles of the particular component by the sum of the number of moles of all components. The fourth expression, called **molar,** states the number of moles in a given volume of *solution*. Its usefulness is most apparent when it is desired to mix chemically equivalent quantities of substances in solution.

The calculations relating the first three of these expressions of concentration are straightforward. It is only necessary to express the quantities of the various components in appropriate mass units, grams or moles. One further step is required to calculate from any of these three to the fourth. It is necessary to know the density of the solution because this quantity is expressed by volume in molar concentration and must be converted to mass units to be related to the other three.

Consider a solution made by mixing 10 grams of alcohol and 80 grams of water. The concentration of this solution can be expressed,

with fairly simple calculations, by any of the four methods of stating concentration.

## EXAMPLE 3

We have stated the concentration as 10 grams of alcohol per 80 grams of water. This, of course, is a ratio of two quantities; as long as the *ratio* has the same value, it states the same concentration and therefore describes the same solution. We therefore calculate the mass of alcohol per 1,000 grams of water by finding what mass stands in the same ratio to 1,000 grams of water as 10 grams stands to 80 grams; that is, the two ratios must be equal, and the way to calculate this concentration is by means of a proportion:

$$\frac{10 \text{ grams alcohol}}{80 \text{ grams water}} = \frac{x \text{ grams alcohol}}{1,000 \text{ grams water}}$$

We solve this equation for $x$:

$$x = \frac{10 \text{ grams alcohol} \times 1,000 \text{ grams water}}{80 \text{ grams water}}$$

$$= 125 \text{ grams alcohol}$$

The concentration of this solution can therefore be stated as 125 grams of alcohol per 1,000 grams of water—the conventional way of expressing concentrations in terms of mass of solute and mass of solvent.

## EXAMPLE 4

To state the same concentration as molality, we must express the amount of solute (alcohol) in moles rather than in grams. The molecular weight of alcohol is 46; the 125 grams of alcohol is therefore $125/46 = 2.72$ moles. The molal concentration of this solution is therefore 2.72 moles per 1,000 grams of solvent, or 2.72 molal.

## EXAMPLE 5

To express the concentration of the same solution as a mole fraction, we must express the amounts of both components in moles. From the calculation above we know that 2.72 moles of alcohol per 1,000 grams of water is the ratio of the components. The next step is to calculate the number of moles of water equal to 1,000 grams of water. Since the molecular weight of water is 18, the number of moles is $1,000/18 = 55.55$. The solution is composed, then, of 2.72 moles of alcohol and 55.55 moles of water, and the total number of moles is the sum of these: $2.72 + 55.55 = 58.27$. The mole fraction of any component in a solution is the ratio of the number of moles of that component to the total number of moles of all components. The mole fraction of alcohol is therefore

2.72/58.27 = 0.047, and the mole fraction of water is 55.55/58.27 = 0.953.

We could also calculate from the original statement of the quantities of the two components: 10 grams of alcohol and 80 grams of water are 10/46 = 0.218 mole of alcohol and 80/18 = 4.444 moles of water. The total number of moles is 0.218 + 4.444 = 4.662, and the mole fractions of the two components are 0.218/4.662 = 0.047, the mole fraction of alcohol, and 4.444/4.662 = 0.953, the mole fraction of water.

### EXAMPLE 6

If we assume a density (which in practice has to be determined experimentally) for the solution under discussion, we can calculate the *molar* concentration. The density is about 0.9 gram/cm³. The solution, made up of 125 grams of alcohol and 1,000 grams of water, has a total mass of 1,125 grams. Using the assumed density, we can calculate the volume of this amount:

$$\frac{1,125 \text{ grams}}{0.9 \text{ gram/cm}^3} = 1,250 \text{ cm}^3$$

We have already calculated that this amount of solution contains 2.72 moles of alcohol. The concentration of alcohol is therefore 2.72 moles per 1,250 cm³ = 2.17 moles per 1,000 cm³, or 2.17 moles per liter.

## C. Colligative Properties

The four properties of solutions that depend on the number of particles of solute in a given quantity of solvent are called colligative properties; they are (1) lowering of the vapor pressure, (2) elevation of the boiling point, (3) depression of the freezing point, and (4) osmotic pressure. The second, third, and fourth can be theoretically related to the first, and all can be explained by the kinetic-molecular theory. For experimental use, however, and for use in solving problems, the empirical laws that simply state the experimental facts of the relation of these properties to concentration are sufficient. This discussion will therefore be limited to the use of these empirical laws in solving problems.

The four equations (14-1, 14-2, 14-3, 14-7) used in calculations related to colligative properties are

$$p = X_{\text{solvent}} \times p_0$$

in which $p$ = vapor pressure of solution, $p_0$ = vapor pressure of pure solvent, and $X$ = mole fraction of *solvent,*

$$\Delta t_B = (k_B)c$$

in which $\Delta t_B$ = boiling-point elevation, $k_B$ = molal-boiling-point constant for solvent, and $c$ = molal concentration of solute,

$$\Delta t_F = (k_F)c$$

in which $\Delta t_F$ = freezing-point depression, $k_F$ = molal-freezing-point constant for solvent, and $c$ = molal concentration of solute, and

$$\pi V = nRT$$

in which $\pi$ = osmotic pressure of solution, $n/V$ = molar concentration of solute, $R$ = universal gas constant, and $T$ = absolute temperature.

### EXAMPLE 7

Calculate the vapor pressure at 30°C of a 10% solution of naphthalene ($C_{10}H_8$) in carbon tetrachloride ($CCl_4$).

Figure 14-2 shows that the vapor pressure of pure carbon tetrachloride at 30° is 14.3 cm. The other quantity needed is the mole fraction of the solvent. It will be simplest to consider some mass —for example, 1,000 grams—of the solution. This quantity contains 900 grams of $CCl_4$ and 100 grams of $C_{10}H_8$. We calculate these masses to moles. The molecular weight of $CCl_4$ is 154; there are, therefore, 900/154 = 5.85 moles of $CCl_4$. The molecular weight of $C_{10}H_8$ is 128; there are, therefore, 100/128 = 0.78 mole of $C_{10}H_8$. The total number of moles is 5.85 + 0.78 = 6.63 moles, and the mole fraction of $CCl_4$ is 5.85/6.63 = 0.883. We now calculate the vapor pressure of the solution by the use of equation 14-1:

$$p = Xp_0 = 0.883 \times 14.3 \text{ cm} = 12.6 \text{ cm}$$

### EXAMPLE 8

The boiling point of this solution can be calculated by the use of equation 14-2 and the boiling point of the pure solvent, obtained from Figure 14-2.

In the calculation above it was determined that the solution in question contains 0.78 mole of solute ($C_{10}H_8$) in 900 grams of solvent. The molality is calculated by proportion:

$$\frac{x \text{ moles}}{1{,}000 \text{ grams}} = \frac{0.78 \text{ mole}}{900 \text{ grams}}$$

$$x = 0.78 \frac{1{,}000}{900} = 0.87$$

The molal concentration of $C_{10}H_8$ in $CCl_4$ is therefore 0.87. Table 14-1 shows the $k_B$ for $CCl_4$ to be 4.85 degrees per mole. These quantities are now substituted into equation 14-2:

$$\Delta t = k_B c = 4.85°/\text{mole} \times 0.87 \text{ mole} = 4.2°$$

Figure 14-2 shows the boiling point of pure $CCl_4$ to be 77°C; the boiling point of the solution is therefore

$$77° + 4.2° = 81.2°C$$

The calculation of freezing points of solutions is exactly analogous to the calculation of a boiling point. The differences are that $k_F$ is used and that the $\Delta t$ values are subtracted from the freezing point of the pure solvent.

Osmotic pressures of solutions can be calculated most directly by the use of equation 14-7 in the form

$$\pi = cRT$$

in which the substitution of $c$ for $n/V$ has been made. The concentration is therefore expressed in moles per liter (or other *volume*) of solution. The calculations are a completely straightforward use of this equation and the only point that requires comment is the need of caution to keep the units straight. If $c$ is expressed as a molar concentration, $R$ must be in liter cm/mole°. In these units $R$ has the numerical value 6.23. Note the magnitude of the osmotic pressure developed between a solvent and a solution. A 1 molar solution at room temperature (27°C) has an osmotic pressure of 1,867 cm, which is almost 25 times atmospheric pressure. This value can be calculated by substitution in equation 14-7:

$$\pi = cRT = 1 \text{ mole/liter} \times 6.23 \text{ liter cm/mole}°$$
$$\times 300°$$
$$= 6.23 \times 300 \text{ cm} = 1{,}867 \text{ cm}$$

# D. Determinations of Molecular Weight

The most common and useful calculation based on the colligative properties of solutions is that connected with determinations of molecular weight. For this purpose the lowering of the freezing point is the property most often used, for the magnitude of the effect is usually large enough to permit precise and easy measurement. Measurements of osmotic pressure are particularly useful when we are dealing with substances of extremely high molecular weight.

The experimental observations necessary for a determination of molecular weight include the observation of $\Delta t$ for a solution of known concentration in a solvent whose $k_F$ is known. We get the molal concentration, by means of equation 14-3, from the observed depression of the freezing point and the known constant. Then, by comparing the two expressions for concentration, one in grams per 1,000 grams of solvent and the other in moles per 1,000 grams of solvent, we calculate the molecular weight of the solute.

EXAMPLE 9

A common method of determining the molecular weights of organic compounds is to find how much the unknown substance, as a solute, lowers the freezing point of camphor. Camphor is chosen because of its very high freezing-point-lowering constant ($k_F = 40°/\text{mole}$). The melting point (or freezing point) of camphor is 175°C. A typical experiment might be as follows:

A solution of 0.21 gram of the unknown substance in 10 grams of camphor has a freezing point of 168.5°. The freezing-point depression, $\Delta t_F$, is therefore $175° - 168.5° = 6.5°$. Since a 1 molal solution would have had a $\Delta t_F$ of 40°, this solution must be $6.5/40 = 0.1625$ molal; that is, it must have a concentration of 0.1625 mole of the unknown solute per 1,000 grams of camphor. But this concentration must be the same as that of the prepared solution, 0.21 gram per 10 grams = 21 grams per 1,000 grams. Since these two concentrations must be equal, 0.1625 mole of the solute must have a mass of 21 grams. The molecular weight is, then, (21 grams)/(0.1625 mole) = 129 grams/mole. This value, which is close to the value of 128 calculated for naphthalene from its formula ($C_{10}H_8$), would be one bit of evidence but would obviously be insufficient by itself to decide the identity of the unknown substance.

Calculations based on the equations describing the four colligative properties are precise only if the solutions are dilute. At high concentrations interaction between solute particles becomes noticeable, and the behavior deviates markedly from "ideality"; that is, the four equations do not describe accurately the colligative properties of such solutions.

· If, moreover, the solute dissociates into sub-molecular particles, the equations must be modified to indicate the number of *particles,* not the number of molecules. One can, in fact, by measuring the colligative properties, determine the degree of dissociation of solutes.

# INDEX

Page references to important concepts and definitions are printed in **boldface** type. The letter "n" refers to a footnote.

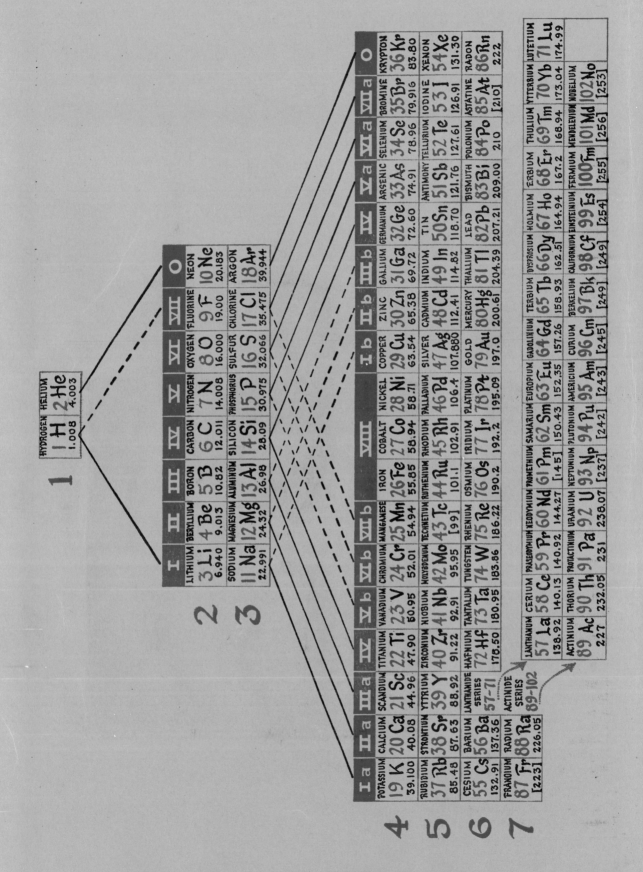